Glencoe Science Level Green
Contents in Brief

S0-AJB-528

Teacher Wraparound Edition

Correlations and Standards

Program Resources

WITHDRAWN

Support for All Learners

Classroom Activities and Materials

Student Edition

SAFETY SYMBOLS

SAFETY SYMBOLS	HAZARD	EXAMPLES	PRECAUTION	REMEDY
DISPOSAL	Special disposal procedures need to be followed.	certain chemicals, living organisms	Do not dispose of these materials in the sink or trash can.	Dispose of wastes as directed by your teacher.
BIOLOGICAL	Organisms or other biological materials that might be harmful to humans	bacteria, fungi, blood, unpreserved tissues, plant materials	Avoid skin contact with these materials. Wear mask or gloves.	Notify your teacher if you suspect contact with material. Wash hands thoroughly.
EXTREME TEMPERATURE	Objects that can burn skin by being too cold or too hot	boiling liquids, hot plates, dry ice, liquid nitrogen	Use proper protection when handling.	Go to your teacher for first aid.
SHARP OBJECT	Use of tools or glassware that can easily puncture or slice skin	razor blades, pins, scalpels, pointed tools, dissecting probes, broken glass	Practice common-sense behavior and follow guidelines for use of the tool.	Go to your teacher for first aid.
FUME	Possible danger to respiratory tract from fumes	ammonia, acetone, nail polish remover, heated sulfur, moth balls	Make sure there is good ventilation. Never smell fumes directly. Wear a mask.	Leave foul area and notify your teacher immediately.
ELECTRICAL	Possible danger from electrical shock or burn	improper grounding, liquid spills, short circuits, exposed wires	Double-check setup with teacher. Check condition of wires and apparatus.	Do not attempt to fix electrical problems. Notify your teacher immediately.
IRRITANT	Substances that can irritate the skin or mucous membranes of the respiratory tract	pollen, moth balls, steel wool, fiberglass, potassium permanganate	Wear dust mask and gloves. Practice extra care when handling these materials.	Go to your teacher for first aid.
CHEMICAL	Chemicals that can react with and destroy tissue and other materials	bleaches such as hydrogen peroxide; acids such as sulfuric acid, hydrochloric acid; bases such as ammonia, sodium hydroxide	Wear goggles, gloves, and an apron.	Immediately flush the affected area with water and notify your teacher.
TOXIC	Substance may be poisonous if touched, inhaled, or swallowed	mercury, many metal compounds, iodine, poinsettia plant parts	Follow your teacher's instructions.	Always wash hands thoroughly after use. Go to your teacher for first aid.
OPEN FLAME	Open flame may ignite flammable chemicals, loose clothing, or hair	alcohol, kerosene, potassium permanganate, hair, clothing	Tie back hair. Avoid wearing loose clothing. Avoid open flames when using flammable chemicals. Be aware of locations of fire safety equipment.	Notify your teacher immediately. Use fire safety equipment if applicable.

Eye Safety Proper eye protection should be worn at all times by anyone performing or observing science activities.

Clothing Protection This symbol appears when substances could stain or burn clothing.

Animal Safety This symbol appears when safety of animals and students must be ensured.

Radioactivity This symbol appears when radioactive materials are used.

Teacher Wraparound Edition

Glencoe
Science

NATIONAL
GEOGRAPHIC
SOCIETY

science.glencoe.com

LEVEL GREEN

Glencoe
McGraw-Hill

New York, New York   Columbus, Ohio   Woodland Hills, California   Peoria, Illinois

GLENCOE SCIENCE LEVEL GREEN

Student Edition
Teacher Wraparound Edition
Interactive Teacher Edition CD-ROM
Interactive Lesson Planner CD-ROM
Lesson Plans
Content Outline for Teaching
Directed Reading for Content Mastery
Foldables: Reading and Study Skills
Assessment
    Chapter Review
    Chapter Tests
    ExamView® Pro Test Bank CD-ROM
    Assessment Transparencies
    Performance Assessment in the Science Classroom
    The Princeton Review Test Practice Booklet
Directed Reading for Content Mastery in Spanish
Spanish Resources
English/Spanish Guided Reading Audio Program
Reinforcement

Enrichment
Activity Worksheets
Section Focus Transparencies
Teaching Transparencies
Laboratory Activities
Science Inquiry Labs
Critical Thinking/Problem Solving
Reading and Writing Skill Activities
Mathematics Skill Activities
Cultural Diversity
Laboratory Management and Safety in the Science Classroom
MindJogger Videoquizzes and Teacher Guide
Interactive CD-ROM with Presentation Builder
Vocabulary PuzzleMaker Software
Cooperative Learning
Environmental Issues in the Science Classroom
Home and Community Involvement
Using the Internet in the Science Classroom
Dinah Zike's Teaching Science with Foldables

Handwritten: CURR Q 161.2 .G53 2003 v.2 Teacher

"Test-Taking Tip," "Study Tip," and "Test Practice" features in this book were written by The Princeton Review, the nation's leader in test preparation. Through its association with McGraw-Hill, The Princeton Review offers the best way to help students excel on standardized assessments.

The Princeton Review is not affiliated with Princeton University or Educational Testing Service.

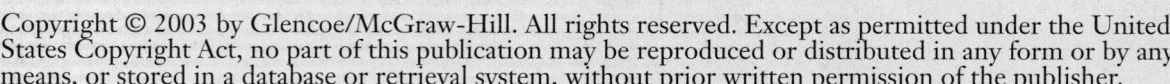

Glencoe/McGraw-Hill

A Division of The McGraw·Hill Companies

Send all inquiries to:
    Glencoe/McGraw-Hill
    8787 Orion Place
    Columbus, OH 43240

ISBN 0-07-828241-1

Printed in the United States of America

3 4 5 6 7 8 9 10 071/055 10 09 08 07 06 05 04 03 02

Authors, Reviewers, and Consultants

for the *Teacher Wraparound Edition*

Authors   082104

National Geographic Society
Education Division
Washington, D.C.

Alton Biggs
Biology Teacher
Allen High School
Allen, Texas

Lucy Daniel, EdD
Teacher/Consultant
Rutherford County Schools
Rutherfordton, North Carolina

Ralph M. Feather Jr., PhD
Science Department Chair
Derry Area School District
Derry, Pennsylvania

Norman G. Lederman, PhD
Professor of Science and Math Education
Oregon State University
Corvallis, Oregon

Edward Ortleb
Science Consultant
St. Louis Public Schools
St. Louis, Missouri

Peter Rillero, PhD
Professor of Science Education
Arizona State University West
Phoenix, Arizona

Susan Leach Snyder
Earth Science Teacher, Consultant
Jones Middle School
Upper Arlington, Ohio

Dinah Zike
Educational Consultant
Dinah-Might Activities, Inc.
San Antonio, Texas

Contributing Authors

Patricia Horton
Mathematics and Science Teacher
Summit Intermediate School
Etiwanda, California

Deborah Lillie
Science Teacher
Sudbury Intermediate School
Sudbury, Massachusetts

Reviewers

Sandra K. Enger, PhD
Coordinator
UAH Institute for Science Education
Huntsville, Alabama

Lee Meadows, PhD
Associate Professor of Science Education
University of Alabama
Birmingham, Alabama

Gilbert Naizer, PhD
Assistant Professor of Elementary Education
Texas A&M University
Commerce, Texas

Kimberly S. Roempler, PhD
Associate Director
Eisenhower National Clearinghouse for
   Math and Science
The Ohio State University
Columbus, Ohio

Cultural Diversity Consultants

Nedaro Bellamy
Associate Director,
   Rice Model Science Laboratory
Lanier Middle School, Houston ISD
Houston, Texas

Joyce Hilliard-Clark, PhD
Director, Imhotep Academy
North Carolina State University
Raleigh, North Carolina

Inclusion Strategies Consultant

Barry Barto
Special Education Teacher
John F. Kennedy Elementary School
Manistee, Michigan

National Science Education Standards

"The National Science Education Standards *are premised on a conviction that all students deserve and must have the opportunity to become scientifically literate. The* Standards *look toward a future in which all Americans, familiar with basic scientific ideas and processes, can have fuller and more productive lives."*

—*National Science Education Standards*

About the Standards

This book, published by the National Research Council, represents the contributions of thousands of educators and scientists, and offers a comprehensive vision of a scientifically literate society. The standards describe what all students should know at the end of grades 4, 8, and 12, and offer guidelines for science teaching and assessment.

How *Glencoe Science Level Green* Aligns with *The National Science Education Standards*

Content Standards

The correlations that follow show the close alignment between *Glencoe Science Level Green* and the grade-appropriate standards. *Glencoe Science Level Green* allows students to discover concepts within each of the content standards and gives students opportunities to make connections among the science disciplines. Hands-on activities and inquiry-based lessons reinforce the science processes emphasized in the standards.

Teaching Standards

Glencoe Science Level Green provides activities and discussions that allow students to discover science concepts through inquiry and to apply the knowledge they've constructed to their own lives. The *Teacher Wraparound Edition* supports this endeavor with an abundance of effective strategies for guiding students of different ability levels and interests as they explore science.

Assessment Standards

Glencoe Science Level Green provides many opportunities in many different formats to assess students' understanding of important concepts. Ideas for portfolios, performance activities, and written assessments accompany every section. Glencoe's Professional Series booklet *Performance Assessment in the Science Classroom* contains rubrics and Performance Task Assessment Lists. This booklet also contains information about evaluating cooperative work. Learning outcomes improve for students of all ability levels in a cooperative learning environment.

Correlation to
National Science Education Standards

The following chart illustrates how *Glencoe Science Level Green* addresses the
National Science Education Standards.

Content Standard	Chapter and Section
(UCP) Unifying Concepts and Processes	
1. Systems, order, and organization	1-1, 1-2, 1-3, 3-1, 3-2, 4-1, 5-1, 5-2, 6-1, 6-2, 10-1, 10-2, 12-1, 12-2, 12-3, 13-1, 13-2, 13-3, 17-3, 18-1, 18-3
2. Evidence, models, and explanation	4-1, 11-1, 11-2, 11-3, 14-1, 14-2, 14-3, 15-1, 15-2, 15-3, 16-2, 17-1, 17-2, 19-1, 19-2, 20-3, 21-1, 21-2, 22-3, 23-1, 23-2, 23-3, 23-4
3. Change, constancy, and measurement	2-1, 2-2, 2-3, 7-1, 7-2, 8-1, 8-2, 8-3, 9-1, 10-2, 14-1, 14-2, 14-3, 16-3, 18-2, 20-2, 22-2
4. Evolution and equilibrium	4-2, 8-2, 8-3, 16-1
5. Form and function	3-1, 3-3, 9-2, 9-3, 10-1, 10-3, 20-1, 22-1
(A) Science as Inquiry	
1. Abilities necessary to do scientific inquiry	1-1, 1-2, 1-3, 2-1, 2-2, 2-3, 3-1, 3-2, 3-3, 4-1, 4-2, 4-3, 5-1, 5-2, 6-1, 6-2, 7-1, 7-2, 8-1, 8-3, 9-1, 9-2, 9-3, 10-2, 10-3, 11-1, 11-2, 11-3, 12-1, 12-2, 12-3, 13-1, 13-2, 13-3, 14-1, 14-2, 14-3, 15-1, 15-2, 15-3, 16-2, 16-3, 17-2, 17-3, 18-1, 18-2, 18-3, 19-1, 19-2, 20-1, 20-2, 20-3, 21-1, 21-2, 22-1, 22-2, 22-3, 23-1, 23-2, 23-4
2. Understandings about scientific inquiry	1-1, 1-2, 1-3, 7-2, 14-1, 14-3
(B) Physical Science	
1. Properties and changes of properties in matter	2-1, 2-2, 2-3, 4-1, 13-2, 13-3, 16-2, 16-3, 18-1, 18-2, 19-1, 19-2, 20-1, 20-3
2. Motion and forces	14-3, 15-3, 17-1
3. Transfer of energy	4-1, 13-3, 16-2, 16-3, 18-3, 20-1, 20-2, 20-3, 21-1, 21-2, 22-1, 22-2, 22-3, 23-1, 23-2, 23-3, 23-4
(C) Life Science	
1. Structure and function in living systems	3-1, 3-2, 3-3, 4-1, 4-2, 4-3, 5-1, 5-2, 6-1, 6-2, 8-1, 8-3, 9-1, 9-2, 9-3, 10-1, 10-2, 10-3, 12-1, 12-2, 12-3, 13-1, 13-2, 13-3, 21-2
2. Reproduction and heredity	3-3, 7-2, 8-2, 8-3, 9-1, 9-2, 9-3, 10-2, 10-3, 11-1, 11-2, 11-3
3. Regulation and behavior	4-2, 5-1, 5-2, 7-1, 7-2, 10-1, 10-2, 10-3
4. Populations and ecosystems	4-3, 12-1, 12-2, 12-3, 13-1, 13-2, 13-3
5. Diversity and adaptations of organisms	7-1, 7-2, 9-2, 9-3
(D) Earth and Space Science	
1. Structure of the Earth system	13-1, 13-2, 13-3, 14-1, 14-2, 14-3, 15-1, 15-2, 15-3, 16-1, 16-2, 16-3
2. Earth's history	14-1, 14-2, 14-3, 16-1
3. Earth in the solar system	16-3, 17-1, 17-2, 17-3, 21-1
(E) Science and Technology	
1. Abilities of technological design	1-3, 11-3, 15-1, 22-1, 22-2, 22-3, 23-2, 23-3, 23-4
2. Understandings about science and technology	1-3, 3-3, 8-3, 9-3, 11-3, 16-3, 22-1, 23-4
(F) Science in Personal and Social Perspectives	
1. Personal Health	3-3, 6-1, 6-2, 10-2, 10-3, 11-2, 21-2, 23-3, 23-4
2. Populations, resources, and environments	13-1, 13-2, 13-3
3. Natural hazards	15-1, 15-2, 15-3, 17-3
4. Risks and benefits	21-2, 22-2
5. Science and technology in society	1-3, 8-3, 9-3, 11-3, 12-3, 15-1, 17-3, 19-2, 21-1, 21-2, 22-2, 22-3
(G) History and Nature of Science	
1. Science as a human endeavor	1-1, 1-2, 3-1, 4-3, 5-2, 7-2, 8-3, 11-3, 12-3, 14-1, 14-2, 14-3, 16-3, 22-3, 23-4
2. Nature of science	1-1, 1-2, 1-3, 16-3, 17-2, 18-3, 19-2, 22-3
3. History of science	3-3, 6-2, 7-1, 11-1, 12-3, 14-1, 14-2, 14-3, 15-3, 22-3, 23-4

National Council of Teachers of Mathematics
Principles and Standards for School Mathematics

Students often make personal, educational, and career choices on their own that can influence the rest of their lives. Throughout their school years, they acquire skills that help them make these decisions. The development of keen mathematical skills can ensure that students have a wide variety of life options.

Principles and Standards for School Mathematics of the National Council of Teachers of Mathematics describes the foundation of mathematical concepts and applications that can provide students with the necessary mathematical skills to help achieve their life goals.

The ten categories of mathematical concepts and applications, as shown in the table below, include a broad range of topics that build on previous knowledge. They also allow students to increase their abilities to visualize, describe, and analyze situations in mathematical terms.

In *Glencoe Science Level Green,* each Math Skill Activity and Problem-Solving Activity provides students with the opportunity to practice and apply some of the mathematical concepts and applications described in the Standards. These activities serve to reinforce mathematical skills in real-life situations, thus preparing students to meet their needs in an ever-changing world.

Correlation of
Glencoe Science Level Green to NCTM Standards Grades 6–8

Standard	Page
1. Number and Operations	14, 44, 76, 104, 139, 166, 193, 221, 258, 271, 305, 339, 364, 440, 460, 499, 531, 558, 651
2. Algebra	14, 104, 139, 258, 271, 305, 339, 364, 440, 460, 558, 591, 651
3. Geometry	76, 531
4. Measurement	44, 76, 104, 139, 166, 193, 271, 305, 339, 364, 440, 460, 531, 558, 651
5. Data Analysis and Probability	14, 193, 166, 193, 271, 305, 339, 364, 499, 591
6. Problem Solving	14, 44, 76, 104, 139, 166, 193, 221, 258, 271, 305, 339, 364, 402, 440, 460, 499, 531, 558, 591, 610, 651, 684
7. Reasoning and Proof	14, 402, 499, 610, 684
8. Communication	14, 44, 76, 104, 139, 166, 193, 221, 258, 271, 305, 339, 402, 440, 460, 499, 531, 558, 591, 610, 651, 684
9. Connections	14, 76, 104, 139, 166, 193, 221, 258, 271, 305, 339, 364, 402, 440, 460, 499, 531, 558, 591, 610, 651, 684
10. Representation	14, 305, 364, 591, 610

Benchmarks for Science Literacy

Benchmarks for Science Literacy is a publication by the American Association for the Advancement of Science that describes how students should progress toward science literacy. People who are science literate are "equipped with knowledge and skills they need to make sense of how the world works, to think critically and independently, and to lead interesting, responsible, and productive lives in a culture increasingly shaped by science and technology."

Benchmarks was the culmination of Project 2061, the work of scientists, mathematicians, engineers, and educators to develop benchmarks, or statements, of what *all* students should know or be able to do in science, mathematics, and technology by the end of grades 2, 5, 8, and 12.

Glencoe Science Level Green is aligned with *Benchmarks* in the following ways:

- Concepts are presented in ways that help students understand the how and why of science, not just requiring them to learn facts that they commit to short-term memory.

- Science concepts are related to students' daily experiences.

- Teachers are provided strategies for encouraging students in independent work and for addressing the needs of students of varied abilities.

- Specific strategies are provided for identifying and addressing student misconceptions.

IDENTIFYING Misconceptions

Educators are becoming increasingly aware of the importance of identifying and addressing misconceptions—prescientific or naïve ideas—that students may hold about science. Students often develop these from their experiences as a way to make sense of the world.

A one-page feature, Identifying Misconceptions, is found on the F interleaf pages preceding selected chapters in the *Teacher Wraparound Edition*. This feature provides specific teaching strategies to find out what students think about a particular concept, to help them understand the concept, and to assess the accuracy of their understanding after learning the concept. These strategies were developed by science education professors with a special interest in the field of student misconceptions. These professors are Norman G. Lederman, Ph.D., Professor of Science and Math Education at Oregon State University, and Peter Rillero, Ph.D., Professor of Science Education at Arizona State University.

Correlation to **Benchmarks**

Glencoe Science Level Green addresses many of the Benchmarks for Science Literacy.

Benchmark	Chapter(s)
4 The Physical Setting	
4A. The Universe	17
4B. The Earth	14, 15, 16
4C. Processes That Shape the Earth	14, 15, 16
4D. Structure of Matter	18, 19, 20, 21
4E. Energy Transformation	12, 13, 20, 21, 22, 23
4F. Motion	14, 15, 16, 17
4G. Forces of Nature	14, 15, 16, 17, 22
5 The Living Environment	
5A. The Diversity of Life	3, 5, 8, 9
5B. Heredity	8, 9, 10, 11
5C. Cells	3, 4, 8
5D. Interdependence of Life	5, 7, 12, 13
5E. Flow of Matter and Energy	4, 5, 12, 13
5F. Evolution of Life	11
6 The Human Organism	
6A. Human Identity	7, 10
6B. Human Development	10, 11
6C. Basic Functions	6, 10, 11
6D. Learning	7, 10
6E. Physical Health	10
6F. Mental Health	7, 10
12 Habits of Mind	
12A. Values and Attitudes	1, 2, All "Oops! Accidents in Science," "Science and History," and "Science and Language Arts" features
12B. Computation and Estimation	All Chapters, 1–23
12D. Communication Skills	All Activities and Skill Builders

Planning Your Course

Glencoe Science Level Green is a flexible program that allows you to decide the pace at which you cover the content and which topics to present, based on the needs of your students and on district requirements. The *Glencoe Interactive Lesson Planner* integrates the *Teacher Classroom Resources* with an electronic lesson planner to make your job easier.

Pacing Options

Two approaches to covering all content are provided in the Planning Guide.

- A **traditional, full-year** course comprises 180 periods of approximately 45 minutes each.
- A **block scheduling** approach involves covering the same information in fewer days but in longer class periods.

Chapter Organizers

A two-page organizer (A–B pages) precedes every chapter in the teacher edition. These organizers include:

- pacing information and objectives.
- correlations to standards.
- lists of activities and the materials needed.
- lists of reproducible resources, assessments, and technologies with page or booklet references.

Interactive Lesson Planner

This easy-to-use CD-ROM allows you to:

- plan daily, weekly, monthly, or yearlong lessons in a versatile calendar format.
- select or customize a built-in plan, or make a new plan.
- print lesson plans.
- access all print components of the *Teacher Classroom Resources* through a convenient pop-up menu.
- print student pages and answer keys from the resource list or from the lesson plan.

Unit	Chapter	Single-Class (180 days*)	Block (90 days*)
1	**The Nature of Science**		
	1 The Nature of Science	7	3.5
	2 Measurement	9	4.5
2	**Life's Building Blocks and Processes**		
	3 Cells	10	5
	4 Cell Processes	10	5
	5 Plant Processes	6	3
	6 Respiration and Excretion	6	3
	7 Animal Behavior	6	3
3	**Reproduction and Heredity**		
	8 Cell Reproduction	8	4
	9 Plant Reproduction	8	4
	10 Regulation and Reproduction	7	3.5
	11 Heredity	7	3.5
4	**Ecology**		
	12 Interactions of Life	8	4
	13 The Non-Living Environment	8	4
5	**Earth and the Solar System**		
	14 Plate Tectonics	8	4
	15 Earthquakes and Volcanoes	8	4
	16 Ocean Motion	8	4
	17 Earth in Space	7	3.5
6	**Building Blocks of Matter**		
	18 Matter	8	4
	19 Properties and Changes of Matter	8	4
7	**Waves, Sound, and Light**		
	20 Waves	7	3.5
	21 Sound	8	4
	22 Electromagnetic Waves	7	3.5
	23 Light, Mirrors, and Lenses	11	5.5

*The suggested number of days is the recommended maximum number of days needed to thoroughly cover a chapter. Individual planning will vary.

Student Edition Features

This table will help you choose from many options that will help you teach the chapter.

Feature	Location and Suggestions For Use
Design Your Own Experiment	• Find near end of chapter where concept is taught. • Promote inquiry learning through open-ended activities. • Reinforce understanding of scientific methods.
Use the Internet	• Find near end of chapter where concept is taught. • Strengthen skills in collecting, organizing, and sharing data. • Integrate the Internet into your class easily.
Model and Invent	• Find near end of chapter where concept is taught. • Reinforce the use of models to represent relationships or abstract ideas, and to predict outcomes. • Strengthen investigative skills.
Other Full-Length Activities	• Find near end of chapter where concept is taught. • Strengthen lab skills. • Reinforce understanding of science process.
Mini LAB **TRY AT HOME** **Mini LAB**	• Find in every chapter. • Do as a demonstration. • Involve parents in the student's learning. • Reinforce that science is not restricted to the classroom.
EXPLORE ACTIVITY	• Find at beginning of each chapter. • Stimulate curiosity for the topic and focus students' attention.
Problem-Solving Skills **Math Skills Activity**	• Find one in every chapter at the point where the concept is taught. • Use after reading or other work to strengthen critical thinking and math skills.
SCIENCE Online	• Find in every chapter. • Focus students' Internet time with predetermined links.

Feature	Location and Suggestions For Use
Skill Builders	• Find at the end of every Section Assessment. • Assign as homework or class work.
FOLDABLES Reading & Study Skills	• Find on every Chapter Opener and Chapter Study Guide. • Provide a purpose for reading with these fun, simple, hands-on activities. • Encourage students to use as a study tool for review of chapter content.
Interdisciplinary Connections **Oops! Accidents in Science** **Science and Language Arts** **Science Stats** **TIME Science & History** **TIME Science & Society**	• Find one of these five features in every chapter. • Stimulate students' interest by studying science-related events that are out of the ordinary. • Advance reading and writing skills through literature connected to science. • Show students the fun side of mathematics and how it is an integral part of science. • Illustrate how scientific phenomena, discoveries, and inventions shape history. • Connect science to people's everyday lives.
NATIONAL GEOGRAPHIC **Visualizing**	• Find in every chapter. • Use the discussion and activities to teach science content.
Career Connection	• Find in every Science & Language Arts feature. • Point out that people of all ages, ethnicities, and training work in science.
Field GUIDE	• Find in the back of the student text. • Promote interest and independent study. • Teach students how to use a classification key.
Science, Technology, and Math Skill Handbooks	• Find at the back of the student and teacher editions. • Use to teach students scientific processes. • Use to teach students how to organize information. • Refer students to handbooks for assistance.

Teacher Wraparound Edition Features

This table will help you locate features of the *Teacher Wraparound Edition* that will help you develop your lesson plans.

Component	Where and How Many	What It Provides
	Every Unit Opener	Teaching tip that relates to teaching unit content or activities.
Chapter Organizer	A and B pages preceding every chapter	• Objectives • Occurrence of activities and other features within each section • List of materials needed for each activity • List of materials from the *Teachers Classroom Resources* box • List of technology resources
Science Content Background	In every chapter on E page and F page where an Identifying Misconceptions feature does not appear	• Helps you prepare for the lesson by giving you more information about each section • Assists you with questions the students might ask
IDENTIFYING **Misconceptions**	F page of some chapters	Strategies to • determine misconceptions students may hold • promote understanding of concept • assess understanding
Key to Teaching Strategies	B page preceding every chapter	Coding to assist in planning for individual needs
Three-Step Teaching Cycle **1 Motivate** **2 Teach** **3 Assess**	Every chapter	• Help for a first-year teacher • Help for experienced teacher in the first year in a new program
Resource Manager	C and D pages of every chapter Every two pages throughout each chapter	**C and D pages:** • List of transparencies • List of chapter teacher resources **Throughout chapter:** • List of reproducible resources • List of technology resources
Activity	Throughout all chapters in side wrap	Reinforces science concepts

Component	Where and How Many	What It Provides
Quick Demo	Throughout all chapters in side wrap	Idea to illustrate a concept; performed in a short amount of time, using available materials
LAB DEMONSTRATION	Throughout all chapters in bottom wrap	Teacher-performed activity, more complex than Quick Demo, often involving students
Extension	Throughout all chapters in side wrap	An activity idea for: • more advanced students • students who finish their work early • students who want to learn more about the topic
Teacher FYI	Throughout all chapters in side wrap	Additional information about a concept
Visual Learning	Throughout all chapters in side and bottom wrap	Idea for discussion or activity related to a graphic
Fun Fact	Throughout all chapters in side and bottom wrap	Interesting science content to share with students
Make a Model	Throughout all chapters in side wrap	Idea for model that students can make to clarify or illustrate abstract concepts
Use an Analogy	Throughout all chapters in side wrap	Way to make abstract concepts more concrete
Curriculum Connection	Throughout all chapters in bottom wrap	Way that science ties in with other curricular areas
Cultural Diversity	Throughout all chapters in bottom wrap	Current or historical background on a custom or belief associated with a science concept
Use Science Words	Throughout all chapters in side wrap	Strategies for students to learn word origins, meanings, and uses
Active Reading Strategies	Throughout all chapters in bottom wrap	Strategies to help students read and understand content
Science Journal	Throughout all chapters in bottom wrap	Writing exercises that promote writing and critical thinking skills
Assessment		
Section Assessment	First page of every section	• Location of Portfolio, Performance, and Content Assessments in the section
Chapter Assessment	Chapter Assessment page	• Ideas for Portfolio and Performance Assessments
Assessment Resources	Chapter Assessment page	• List of Reproducible Masters, CD-ROMs, and other technologies for assessment

The McGraw-Hill
**Learning
Network**
mhln.com

The Interactive E-Textbook that will change the way you teach!

The McGraw-Hill Learning network is an online learning space connecting parents, teachers, and students.

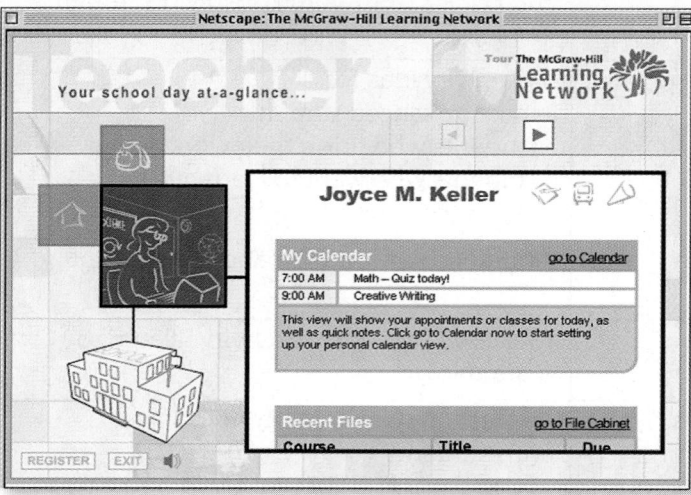

For Teachers

- Online Lesson Planner
- Calendar/Class Organizer
- Assignment Creator (Teachers can create, grade, and send assignments to students.)
- Grade Book/Class Roster
- And much more . . .

There's a ton of helpful tools, such as a Web site builder and thousands of educational Web links.

For Students

- Interactive games
- 24–hour homework help
- Online planner
- Instant feedback with diagnostic assessments
- Unlimited practice
- And much more . . . including movies, animations, sound, Web links, and an online encyclopedia

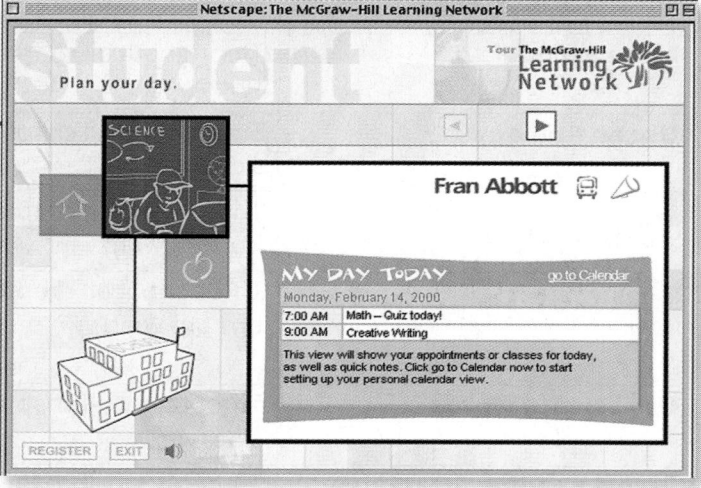

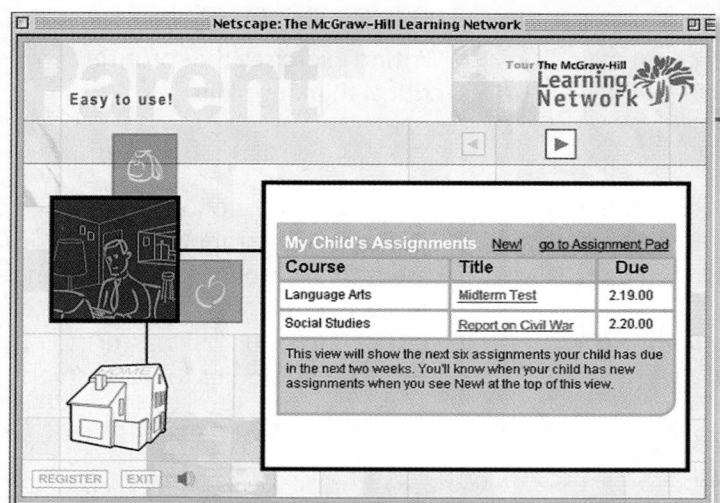

For Parents

- Tips to help their child succeed in school
- Instant access to textbooks, homework assignments, and progress reports

Online Science

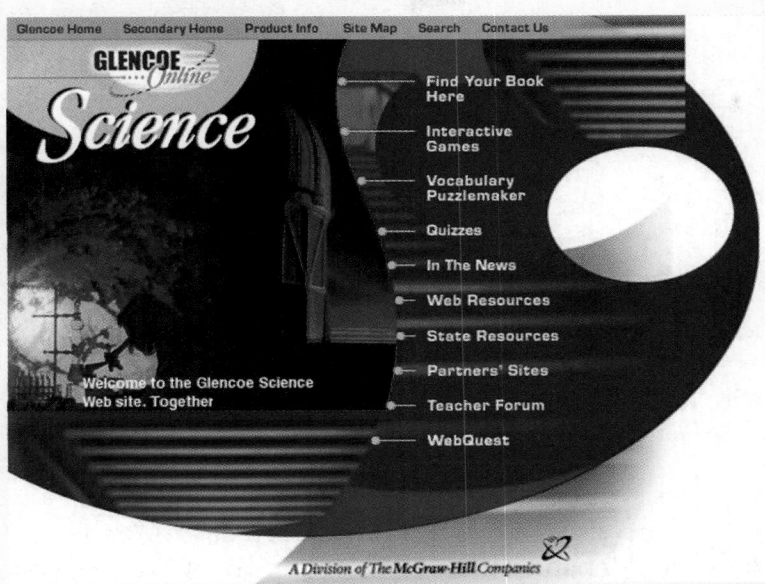

The Glencoe Science Web site **science.glencoe.com** is an invaluable resource for all teachers and students.

Teachers can:
- share ideas on Teacher Bulletin Board.
- access current scientific information on textbook updates.

Students can:
- access the *Student Edition* online.
- access previewed Web links.
- record information on printable Internet log worksheets.
- review chapter content with the Interactive Tutor.
- prepare for tests using Interactive Quizzes.
- share data with students worldwide using our exclusive Internet Activities.

Teaching TODAY

Access *Teaching Today* at **teachingtoday.glencoe.com** for teaching tips, annotated Web resources, educational news, and more. New material is added each week to meet the diverse needs of secondary classroom teachers.

Interactive CD-ROM with Presentation Builder

Provides students the opportunity to:
- develop hypotheses.
- manipulate variables.
- build presentations.
- review content.
- think critically.

ExamView® Pro
Test Bank CD-ROM

You can design and create your own test instruments in minutes, using Glencoe Science ExamView® Pro Test Bank CD-ROM. This versatile program allows you to create paper tests as well as tests that can be used on your school LAN system, or posted on your class Web site.

Interactive **Student Edition**

Give your students the option of carrying home a single CD-ROM instead of a book! With interactive assessments and many more exciting tools, the Interactive Student Editions become powerful learning resources.

Interactive **Lesson Planner**

Need help planning your lessons and organizing your resources? Glencoe's Interactive Lesson Planner is the perfect solution. All you need to do is to identify your length of course and number of class days and the program automatically places all the materials available for each day for each chapter into the calendar. Every page of your Teacher Classroom Resources is available to you at the click of a mouse.

Interactive **Teacher Edition**

Imagine having your entire Teacher Edition and all your Teacher Classroom Resources available to you on one CD-ROM. That is what the Interactive Teacher Edition provides for you. The program allows you to view all teacher material and the student

text on your computer screen. You can export all worksheet masters to your own word processor for editing.

MindJogger Videoquizzes

The interactive quiz-show format of the Glencoe Science MindJogger Videoquizzes provides fun for your students while reviewing key concepts for every chapter. The three levels of increasing difficulty add to the drama and excitement of the game, and help you assess your students' understanding of the concepts.

Guided Reading Audio Program
English/Spanish

Complete chapter text read in English provides another way for students who are auditory learners, or for ELL students, to access chapter content. Students can listen individually in class or at home. They can also choose to read along with their texts to improve reading skills. Tie to the Directed Reading for Content Mastery in the *Chapter Resources* booklets to give students a way to check their understanding of the material. The Guided Reading program is provided in CD format.

Vocabulary PuzzleMaker
Software

This software program allows you to create crossword puzzles, jumble puzzles, or word searches in minutes to review chapter vocabulary. The puzzles can be printed or played on the computer screen.

Teacher Classroom Resources

Chapter Resources

We've organized all of the materials you need for each chapter into chapter-based booklets. The cover of each booklet becomes a file folder to help you stay organized.

Chapter Resources

CHAPTER
11 Heredity

INCLUDES:

Reproducible Student Pages

ASSESSMENT
- Chapter Tests
- Chapter Review

HANDS-ON ACTIVITIES
- Activity Worksheets for each Student Edition Activity
- Two additional Laboratory Activities
- Foldables—Reading and Study Skills activity sheet

MEETING INDIVIDUAL NEEDS

Extension and Intervention
- Directed Reading for Content Mastery
- Directed Reading for Content Mastery in Spanish
- Reinforcement
- Enrichment
- Note-taking Worksheets

TRANSPARENCY ACTIVITIES

Glencoe
Science

Each **Chapter Resources** booklet contains:

Reproducible Student Pages

Assessment
- Chapter Review
- Chapter Test

Hands-On Activities
- Activity Worksheets for each activity in the **Student Edition**
- Two additional laboratory activities
- Foldables: Reading and Study Skills

Meeting Individual Needs
(Extension and Intervention)
- Directed Reading for Content Mastery
- Directed Reading for Content Mastery *in Spanish*
- Reinforcement
- Enrichment
- Note-taking Worksheets

Transparency Activities
- Section Focus Activity
- Teaching Transparency Activity
- Assessment Transparency Activity

Teacher Support and Planning
- Content Outline for Teaching
- Spanish Resources
- Teacher Guide and Answers

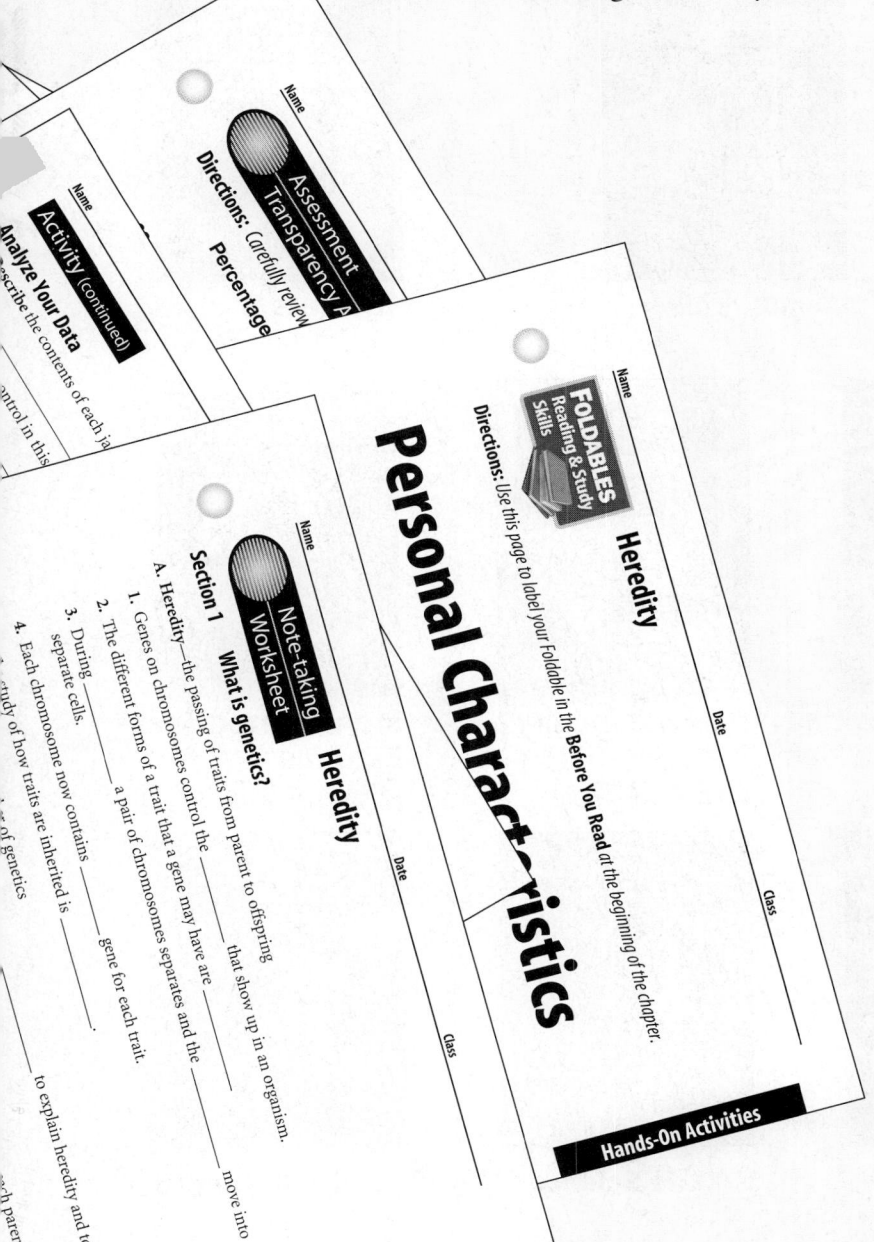

Additional Resources

These resources are available as stand-alone booklets to give you the flexibility to decide when to use them.

Program Resources

Transparencies
Section Focus Transparencies
Teaching Transparencies
Assessment Transparencies

Content Outline for Teaching

Lesson Plans

Laboratory Activities *SE*

Math Skill Activities *(SE and TE)*

Reading and Writing Skill Activities *(SE and TE)*

Science Inquiry Labs *(SE and TE)*

Standardized Test Practice *(SE and TE)*

Critical Thinking/ Problem Solving

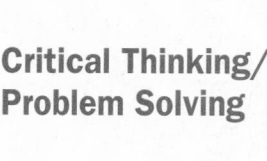

Physical Science

Life Science

Earth Science

Home and
Community
Involvement

Laboratory
Management
and Safety

Dinah Zike's
Teaching
Science
with
Foldables

Guide to
Using the
Internet
in the
Science
Classroom

Cooperative Learning

Cultural Diversity

Performance Assessment
in the Science Classroom

Meeting Individual Needs

Each student brings his or her unique set of abilities, perceptions, and needs into the classroom. *Glencoe Science Level Green Teacher Wraparound Edition* offers you a variety of strategies so that your students can learn science concepts through many different methods.

Strategy	Designation
Ability Levels Activities are provided that accommodate students of all ability levels.	L1 Basic activities that reinforce the concepts for lower-ability students L2 Application activities that give all students an opportunity for practical application of concepts L3 Challenging activities that allow students to expand their perspectives on the basic concepts
English-Language Learners These strategies focus on overcoming a language barrier. It is important not to confuse ability in speaking/reading English with academic ability or "intelligence."	ELL These activities reinforce content and aid in the development of science vocabulary.
Learning Styles A variety of instructional strategies help students to learn science concepts through their preferred learning styles. Students generally display more than one of these styles. You may want to assign activities to students that accommodate their strongest learning styles, but assign other activities that help to develop their weaker styles.	LS Look for these bold-faced designations wherever you see this logo: • **Kinesthetic** learners learn through touch, movement, and manipulating objects. • **Visual-Spatial** learners think in terms of images, illustrations, and models. • **Logical-Mathematical** learners understand numbers easily and have highly-developed reasoning skills. • **Linguistic** learners write clearly and easily understand the written word. • **Auditory-Musical** learners remember spoken words and can create rhythms and melodies. • **Interpersonal** learners understand and work well with other people. • **Intrapersonal** learners can analyze their own strengths and weaknesses and may prefer to work on their own.

Support for All Learners

Strategy	Designation
Inclusion Strategies Inclusion strategies provide you with additional support for helping students with special needs.	Look for these bold-faced designations and strategies wherever you see the **Inclusion** Strategies • **Learning Disabled**—ideas for additional concept review • **Behaviorally Disordered**—activities for helping to keep students on task • **Physically Challenged**—tips for adjusting activities to accommodate students who have less mobility or dexterity than others • **Visually Impaired** or **Hearing Impaired**—ideas for aiding these students in grasping concepts • **Gifted**—challenging activities and research projects that extend chapter concepts
Cooperative Learning In cooperative learning, students work together in small groups to learn content and interpersonal skills. Group members learn that each is responsible for accomplishing an assigned group task as well as for learning the material. Cooperative learning fosters academic, personal, and social success for all students.	COOP LEARN Strategies with this designation are suitable for group work that will help students to: • develop positive attitudes toward science and school; • build respect for others, regardless of race, ethnic origin, or gender; and • increase their sensitivity to and tolerance of diverse perspectives.
Cultural Diversity Classrooms in the United States reflect the rich and diverse cultural heritage of the American people. Students come from different ethnic backgrounds and different cultural experiences into a common classroom that must assist all of them in learning.	**Cultural Diversity** The Cultural Diversity features provide insights into unique ways in which different people have approached science or adapted to their environments. The intent of these features is to build awareness and appreciation for the global community in which we live.
Misconceptions Students have had many experiences outside the science classroom that have shaped their understandings of the natural world. Unfortunately, interpretations based on casual observation are not always accurate. For example, based on their observations, some students might think that the Sun moves around Earth. As a science teacher, you need strategies to help replace these naive conceptions with scientific facts.	IDENTIFYING Misconceptions This one-page feature provides ideas about the types of misconceptions your students may have. It provides you with teaching strategies to uncover misconceptions and to help students understand concepts. You can find these preceding many chapters on the F interleaf pages of the Teacher Wraparound Edition. In addition, you will find several misconceptions stated, followed by the correct information, in the teacher wrap throughout each chapter.

Reading and Writing in the Content Area

Glencoe Science Level Green is designed to increase science literacy through improving reading comprehension and deepening students' understanding of ideas and concepts. The reading strategies are active, constructive, and engaging.

In the Student Edition

Reading Checks throughout each chapter stimulate quick recall to keep students focused on main ideas and important details.

> ☑ **Reading Check**
>
> *Which type of chemical reaction is burning?*

Caption Questions throughout each chapter help students to comprehend what they have read through interpreting the visual. This is especially useful for less proficient readers.

> **Figure 6**
> **After a golf ball is thrown, it follows a curved path toward the ground.** *How does this curved path show that the ball is accelerating?*

Skill Builder Activities in each Section Assessment often include questions that directly address reading and writing skills. Students are referred to the *Science Skill Handbook* for help.

> **Communicating** Watch carefully as you travel home from school or walk down your street. What examples of wave reflection and refraction do you notice? Describe each of these in your Science Journal and explain your reasons. **For more help,** refer to the Science Skill Handbook.

The Before You Read and After You Read Activities in every chapter set a purpose for reading and help students to construct a graphic organizer to use for learning content and as a study aide.

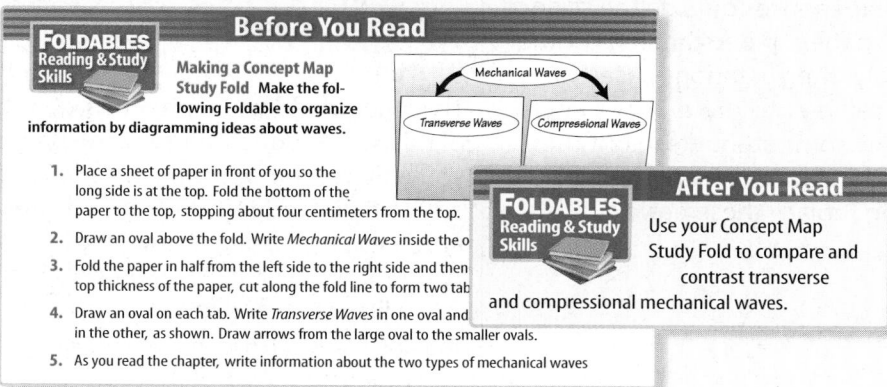

Before You Read

FOLDABLES Reading & Study Skills

Making a Concept Map Study Fold Make the following Foldable to organize information by diagramming ideas about waves.

Mechanical Waves
Transverse Waves   Compressional Waves

1. Place a sheet of paper in front of you so the long side is at the top. Fold the bottom of the paper to the top, stopping about four centimeters from the top.
2. Draw an oval above the fold. Write *Mechanical Waves* inside the o[...]
3. Fold the paper in half from the left side to the right side and then [...] top thickness of the paper, cut along the fold line to form two tab[...]
4. Draw an oval on each tab. Write *Transverse Waves* in one oval and [...] in the other, as shown. Draw arrows from the large oval to the smaller ovals.
5. As you read the chapter, write information about the two types of mechanical waves

After You Read

FOLDABLES Reading & Study Skills

Use your Concept Map Study Fold to compare and contrast transverse and compressional mechanical waves.

Print and Technology Resources to Promote Reading and Writing in the Content Area

Ancillaries

Chapter Resources

- Directed Reading for Content Mastery pages *(in English and Spanish)*
- Foldables: Reading and Study Skills Worksheets
- Note-taking Worksheets

Dinah Zike's Teaching Science with Foldables

Reading and Writing Skill Activities

Technology

Guided Reading Audio Program *(English and Spanish)*

MindJogger VideoQuizzes

Interactive CD-ROM

Vocabulary PuzzleMaker

Glencoe Science Online

Support for All Learners

Foldables: Improving Reading and Study Skills

Students love Foldables because they're fun. Teachers love them because they're effective.

What is a Foldable?

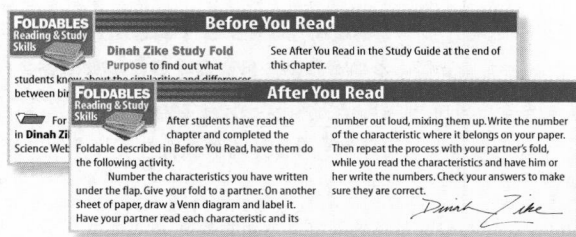

Foldables are three-dimensional, interactive graphic organizers. As students fold paper, cut tabs, write, and manipulate what they have made, they are kinesthetically involved in learning. These unique, hands-on tools for studying and reviewing were created exclusively for Glencoe Science by teaching specialist Dinah Zike.

Foldables are Useful!

Reading in the Content Area

Foldables help students develop ways of organizing information that are fun and creative. These useful activities help students practice basic writing skills, find and report main ideas, organize information, review key vocabulary terms, and much more!

Every chapter begins with a Foldable activity. Students make the physical structure of a Foldable that incorporates one of many prereading strategies. Then, as students read through the chapter and do the activities, students record information as they learn it in the appropriate part of the foldable. In the Chapter Study Guide, the After You Read feature gives students a strategy for using the fold they made to help them review the chapter concepts.

FOLDABLES
Reading & Study Skills

Before You Read	
Dinah Zike Study Fold Purpose to find out what students know about the similarities and differences between birds	See After You Read in the Study Guide at the end of this chapter.

For ... in **Dinah Zi**... Science Web...

FOLDABLES
Reading & Study Skills

After You Read	

After students have read the chapter and completed the Foldable described in Before You Read, have them do the following activity.

Number the characteristics you have written under the flap. Give your fold to a partner. On another sheet of paper, draw a Venn diagram and label it. Have your partner read each characteristic and its number out loud, mixing them up. Write the number of the characteristic where it belongs on your paper. Then repeat the process with your partner's fold, while you read the characteristics and have him or her write the numbers. Check your answers to make sure they are correct.

Dinah Zike

Review One advantage of Foldables is that they result in an organized study guide. The Foldables then can be used not only while preparing for the chapter test, but they can also be used for reviewing for unit tests, end of course exams, and even standardized tests.

Assessment Foldables present an ideal opportunity for you to probe the depth of your students' knowledge. You'll get detailed feedback on exactly what they know and what misconceptions they may have.

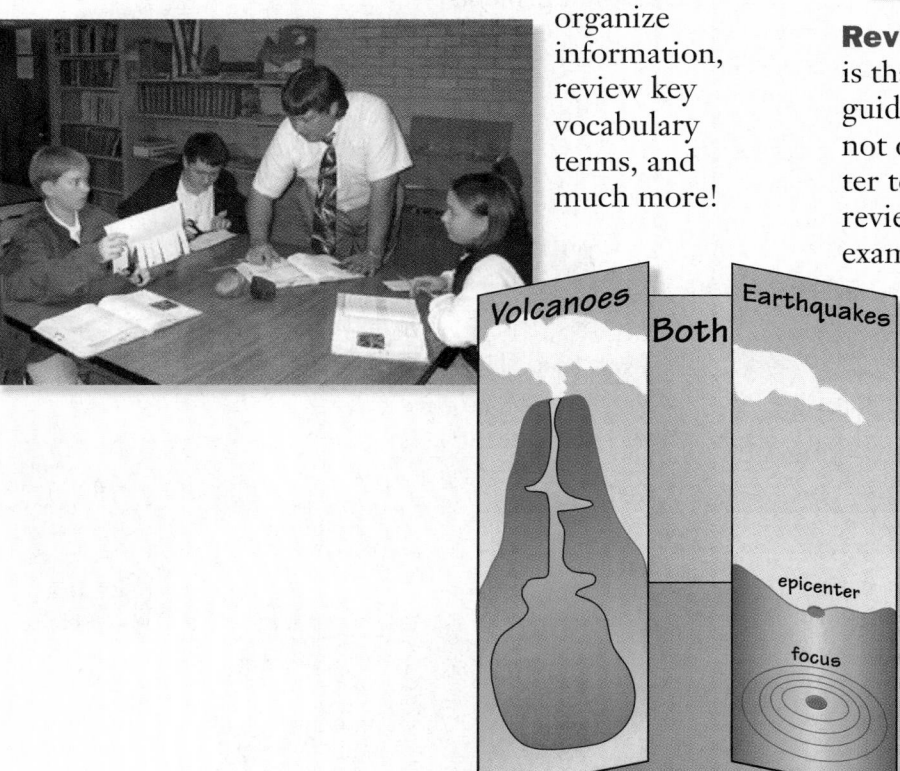

Volcanoes   Both   Earthquakes
epicenter
focus

Foldables are Easy!

Anyone who has paper, scissors, and maybe a stapler or some glue can implement Foldables in the classroom. Glencoe's Foldables have been tested with teachers and middle school students to make sure the directions are easy for both students and teachers. After doing a couple of them, your class will quickly become seasoned experts. Don't be surprised if you find them inventing their own for use in projects and reports in all of their classes!

A message from **the creator of Foldables,** Dinah Zike

You might not know my name or me, but I bet you have seen at least one of my graphic organizers or folds used in supplemental programs or teacher workshops. Today, my graphic organizers and manipulatives are used internationally. I present workshops and keynote presentations to over 50,000 teachers a year, sharing the manipulatives I began inventing, designing, and adapting over thirty years ago. Around the world, students of all ages are using them as daily work, note-taking activities, student-directed projects, forms of alternative assessment, science lab journals, quantitative and qualitative observation books, graphs, tables, and more. But through all my years of teaching, designing, and publishing, my materials had never been featured in a middle school textbook. When Glencoe/McGraw-Hill approached me to share some of my three-dimensional, manipulative graphic organizers with you in this new and innovative science series, I was thrilled.

Working with Glencoe, we all had the vision that Foldables should be an integral part of the curriculum, not simply tacked on. What we ended up with was a strategy that will help students read and learn science concepts. One of the advantages of using the same manipulative repeatedly is that students are immersed in what they are learning. It is not out of sight and out of mind. How long is your average student actively involved with a duplicated activity sheet? Ten minutes? Fifteen? Students will use the Foldable at the beginning of each chapter, before reading the chapter, during reading, and after reading. That's a lot of immersion!

Dinah Zike

Reading and Writing in the Content Area

In the Teacher Edition

Science & Language Arts

Pre-Reading Activity helps students draw upon their personal experience and sets a purpose for reading.

Respond to the Reading provides active reading strategies that provide a variety of ways for students to respond to the feature through listening, speaking, and writing activities. It also provides students with an opportunity to make connections to the theme.

Linking Science and Writing provides options that all students can use to respond in writing to the feature.

Use Science Words

Word Usage The distinction between distance and displacement can be confusing. Have students use each of these words correctly in a sentence. Possible response: When I go to school and then back home, my displacement is zero, even though the distance from home to school is 2 km. **L2** **LS** **Linguistic**

Use Science Words appears throughout each chapter and provides three types of reading strategies. Students structurally analyze root words (Word Origin), develop vocabulary (Word Meaning), or apply their knowledge of science terms (Word Usage).

Science Journal

Cathode-Ray Tube Ask students to pretend that they are coworkers with Crookes at the time of his experiments with a cathode-ray tube. Have students write letters in their Science Journals to a fellow scientist telling about the exciting results they obtained and how they interpreted the results. **L2** **LS** **Linguistic**

Science Journals throughout each chapter provide opportunities for students to write responses to questions that require critical thinking; to conduct research and write about it; or to practice creative writing skills.

Active Reading Strategies

A variety of active reading strategies are provided throughout the *Teacher Wraparound Edition*. These strategies utilize a variety of learning styles, and encourage cooperative learning and intrapersonal reflection on chapter content.

✔ Active Reading

Think-Pair Share This strategy encourages students to think first before discussing their ideas or thoughts about a topic. Ask students to respond to a question by writing a response. After thinking for a few minutes, partners share responses to the question. Finally, ask the students to share responses with the class. Have students become involved in a Think-Pair Share about cathode rays.

Making Concept Maps and Charts

Bubble Map Students brainstorm and organize words in clusters to describe concepts.

Double-Bubble Map Students compare concepts using two bubble maps.

Flow Chart Students logically analyze and draw a sequence of events.

Cause and Effect Chart Students visually represent the causes and effects of an event or process.

Supporting Idea Chart Students make a concept map to analyze the relationship between a whole and its parts.

Using the Science Journal

Double Entry Journal Students read and record ideas, then reflect on the text and respond to the ideas.

Metacognition Students analyze what and how they have learned.

Learning Journal Students write and reflect on notes about content.

Problem-Solution Journal Students analyze problems and suggest workable solutions.

Speculation About Effects/ Prediction Journal Students examine events and speculate about their possible long-term effects.

Synthesis Journal Students reflect on a project, a paper, or a performance task and plan how to apply what they have learned to their own lives.

Reflective Journal Students identify what they learned in an activity and record responses.

Quickwrites Students use spontaneous writing to discover what they already know.

Collaborative Learning Strategies

Pair of Pairs Partners respond to a question and compare their response to that of other pairs and to the class.

Write-Draw-Discuss Students write about and draw a picture of a concept, then share it with the class.

Four-Corner Discussion The class works in four groups to debate a complex issue.

Jigsaw Students work in groups to become experts on a portion of text and share their expertise with their "home" group.

Buddy Interviews Students interview one another to find out what helps them to understand what they are reading.

Reciprocal Teaching Students take turns reading the text and retelling it in their own words, then asking one another questions.

News Summary Students are given several minutes to summarize, retell, or analyze an activity for a "TV" audience.

ReQuest The teacher reads aloud an article or story. Student pairs then construct discussion questions and review the content.

Concept Maps

Helping students understand concepts through visuals

Concept maps are visual representations or graphic organizers of relationships among particular concepts. Concept maps can be generated by individual students, small groups, or an entire class. Four types of concept maps that are most applicable to studying science are developed and reinforced in this program. Students can learn how to construct each of these types of concept maps by referring to the Skill Handbook in the ***Student Edition.***

Concept maps can be used to increase understanding of science concepts, to strengthen reading skills, to promote cooperative learning, and to assess learning. When evaluating concept maps, look for the conceptual strength of student responses, not absolute accuracy.

- **Science Concepts** Concept mapping helps students to understand science concepts through analyzing relationships among ideas and reinforcing those relationships by visualizing them.

- **Reading Skills** Concept maps can help students preview a chapter's content by visually relating the concepts to be learned and aiding students to read with purpose. Students learn key science terms by choosing the terms to use, supplying connecting words, or by placing terms and connecting words when provided by the teacher. To further develop concept mapping skills, the *Chapter Resources* booklet for each chapter contains concept maps in the reproducible student pages Directed Reading for Content Mastery.

- **Cooperative Learning** Construction of concept maps using cooperative learning strategies allows students to practice interpersonal skills as they work together to build the map.

- **Review and Assessment** As a review, constructing concept maps reinforces main ideas and clarifies their relationships. As an assessment tool, concept maps can be constructed by students or students can fill in the terms. Look for concept mapping assessment in the Chapter Assessment section of every chapter.

Network Tree
- Order information from general to specific.
- Show a hierarchy.
- Use branching procedures.
- Explain relationships with connecting terms.

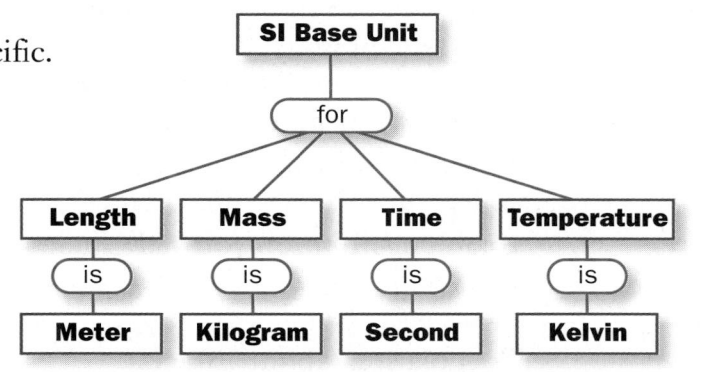

Events Chain

- Describe the stages of a process.
- Order the steps in a linear procedure.
- Show a sequence of events.

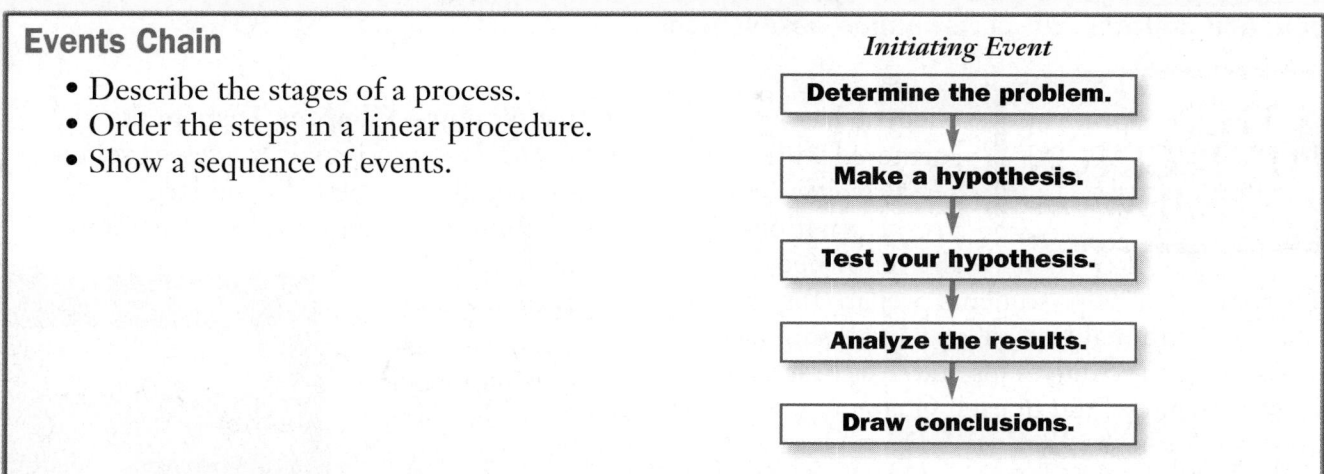

Initiating Event

Determine the problem.

Make a hypothesis.

Test your hypothesis.

Analyze the results.

Draw conclusions.

Cycle Concept Map

- Show how a series of events interact.
- Depict how the last event relates to the initiating event.

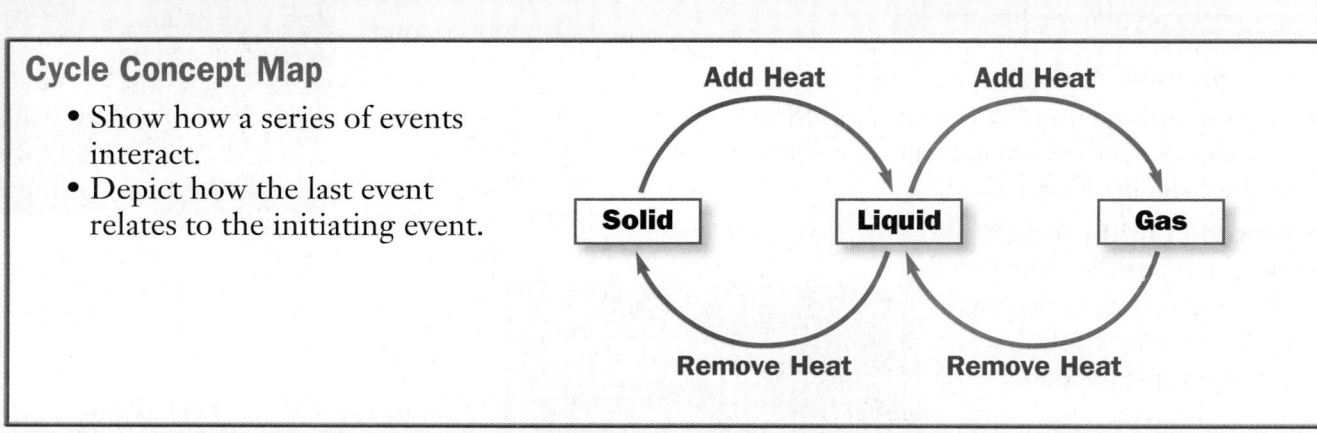

Add Heat

Add Heat

Solid

Liquid

Gas

Remove Heat

Remove Heat

Spider Concept Map

- Use for brainstorming.
- Separate and group unrelated terms.
- Show relationship of nonrelated terms to a central idea.

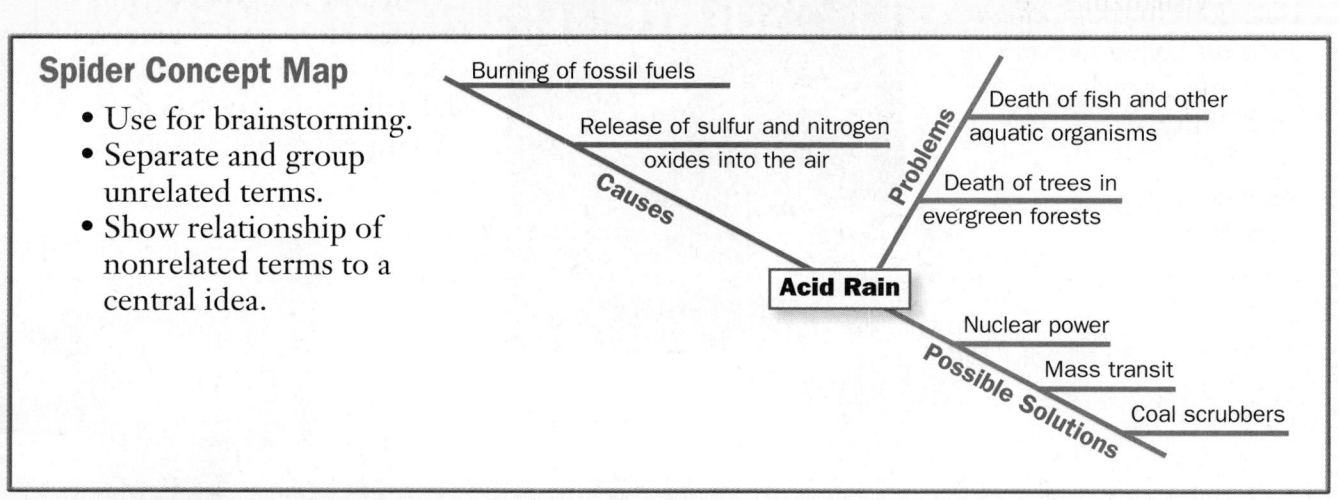

Burning of fossil fuels

Release of sulfur and nitrogen oxides into the air

Causes

Problems

Death of fish and other aquatic organisms

Death of trees in evergreen forests

Acid Rain

Nuclear power

Mass transit

Possible Solutions

Coal scrubbers

Assessment Support

Glencoe Science Level Green offers the Glencoe Assessment Advantage, a system of assessment options designed to give you the flexibility and tools to conduct standardized test preparation, and content and performance assessment.

Glencoe has partnered with *The Princeton Review*, a nationally renowned company that helps students prepare for state and national tests. This partnership has resulted in the Study Tips and Test Practice questions at the end of each Chapter Assessment in the **Student Edition**. Test practice booklets help prepare students for success on standardized tests.

Content Assessment

- **Section Assessment** questions and **Skill Builder Activities** appear in every chapter of the **Student Edition**.

- A **Study Guide** at the end of each chapter in the **Student Edition** allows you to determine whether reteaching is needed.

- The **Chapter Assessment** questions in the **Student Edition** help you evaluate students' knowledge and ability to apply science concepts.

- **Assessment—Chapter Tests** in the *Chapter Resources* booklets assess recognition, recall of vocabulary and facts, and ability to interpret information and relationships.

- **MindJogger Videoquizzes** offer interactive videos that provide a fun way for your students to review chapter concepts.

- The **Interactive CD-ROM** provides quizzes that can be used as a whole-class presentation or as a review for individual students. These materials also are available on the Glencoe Science Web site.

- **ExamView Pro® Test Bank CD-ROM (English/Spanish)** for Macintosh and Windows provides an easy way to make, edit, and print tests. You can add your own questions and graphics.

Performance Assessment

Performance Assessment refers to the strategies used to assess students' level of science literacy. Performance Assessment is based on judging the quality of a student's response to a performance task. A performance task is constructed to require the use of important concepts with supporting information, work habits important to science, and one or more of the elements of scientific literacy.

Performance Task Assessment Lists

Performance Assessments accompany **Activities** and **Chapter Assessments** in the ***Glencoe Science Level Green Student Edition***. Task Assessment Lists are provided in Glencoe's *Performance Assessment in the Science Classroom*. Both the teacher and the student assess the work and assign points based on the well-defined categories and possible points for each category. These task lists were developed for the summative performance tasks included in the booklet.

Assessing Student Work with Rubrics

A rubric is a set of descriptions of the quality of a process and a product. The set of descriptions includes a continuum of quality from excellent to poor. Rubrics for various types of assessment products are provided in the Glencoe Professional Development Series booklet *Performance Assessment in the Science Classroom*. In addition to sample rubrics, blank rubric forms allow teachers to customize assessment methods. The booklet also

provides a step-by step model showing teachers how to use the materials most effectively.

Portfolios

Portfolio suggestions are featured throughout each chapter in the ***Glencoe Science Level Green Teacher Wraparound Edition***. The Portfolio should help the student see the big picture of how he or she is performing in gaining knowledge and skills and how effective his or her work habits are. The performance portfolio is not a complete collection of all worksheets and other assignments but rather a collection that reflects the student's growth in concept attainment and skill development. Writings and drawings from the student's **Science Journal**, featured in the *Student Edition* and the *Teacher Wraparound Edition*, often are suggested to include in portfolios.

Group Assessment

All students benefit from a cooperative learning environment. Research has shown that student-learning outcomes improve for students of all ability levels. An example, along with information about evaluating cooperative work, is provided in the booklet *Performance Assessment in the Science Classroom*.

Lab Safety

The activities in *Glencoe Science Level Green* have been tested in the laboratory and have been reviewed by safety consultants. Even so, there are no guarantees against accidents. For additional help, refer to the *Laboratory Management and Safety* booklet, which contains safety guidelines and masters to test students' lab and safety skills.

General Guidelines

- Post safety guidelines, fire escape routes, and a list of emergency procedures in the classroom. Make sure students understand these procedures. Remind them at the beginning of *every* lab session.

  - Understand and make note of the Safety Symbols used in each activity.

  - Have students fill out a safety contract. Students should pledge to follow the rules, to wear safety attire, and to conduct themselves in a responsible manner.

- Know where emergency equipment is stored and how to use it.

- Supervise students at all times. Check assembly of all setups.

- Perform all activities before you allow students to do so.

- Instruct students to follow directions carefully.

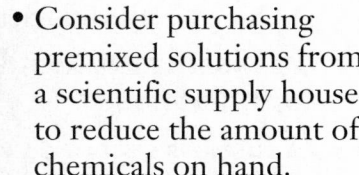
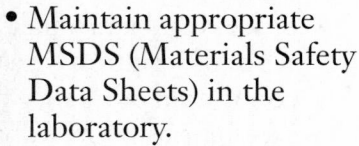

- Make sure that all students are wearing proper safety attire. They should wear safety goggles at all times. They should secure long hair and loose clothing. Do not permit wearing contact lenses, even with safety glasses; splashing chemicals could infuse under a lens and cause eye damage.

Handling Chemicals

- Handle chemicals carefully at all times. Always wear safety goggles, gloves, and an apron when handling chemicals. Treat all chemicals as potentially dangerous.

- Never ingest chemicals. Use proper techniques to smell solutions.

- Use a fume hood when handling chemicals that are poisonous or corrosive or that give off a vapor.

- *Always add acids to water, never the reverse.*

- Prepare solutions by adding the solid to a small amount of distilled water and then diluting with water to the volume listed. If you use a hydrate that is different from the one specified in a particular preparation, you will need to adjust the amount of hydrate to obtain the correct concentration.

- Consider purchasing premixed solutions from a scientific supply house to reduce the amount of chemicals on hand.

- Maintain appropriate MSDS (Materials Safety Data Sheets) in the laboratory.

Chemical Storage and Disposal

The following are some commonly used guidelines for chemical storage and disposal, but your school or local government may have additional requirements for handling chemicals. It is your responsibility to be informed of the rules governing chemical storage and disposal in your area.

- Use wood shelving rather than metal. All shelving should be firmly attached to the wall and have antiroll edges.

- Store only those chemicals you intend to use. Do not store chemicals above eye level.

- Store chemicals in labeled containers that indicate the contents, concentration, source, date purchased (or prepared), safety precautions for handling, and expiration date.

- Separate chemicals by reaction type. Store acids in one place and bases in another. Oxidants should be stored away from easily oxidized materials, for example.

- Dispose of outdated or waste chemicals properly.

- Follow regulations for storing hazardous chemicals.

Disposal of Chemicals

Local, state, and federal laws regulate the disposal of chemicals. Consult these laws before attempting to dispose of any chemicals. The following resource provides some general guidelines for handling and disposing of chemicals: *Prudent Practices in the Laboratory: Handling and Disposal of Chemicals.* Washington, DC: National Academy Press, 1995. Current laws in your area supersede the information in this book.

Disclaimer

Glencoe/McGraw-Hill makes no claims to the completeness of this discussion of laboratory safety and chemical storage. The material presented is not all-inclusive, nor does it address all of the hazards associated with handling, storage, and disposal of chemicals, or with laboratory management.

Classroom Activities and Materials

Activity Materials

Glencoe Science Level Green makes it easy for you to plan and facilitate activities in your classroom.

- You'll find a variety of hands-on activities, from short to long, from directed to open-ended.
- Many activities use common, inexpensive materials.
- Activities are easy to manage, with clearly numbered steps and illustrations.
- All MiniLABS have been teacher tested.

All laboratory activities have been thoroughly reviewed by a safety expert.

All full-length labs were bench tested by Science Kit to ensure quality and safety.

It's Quick and Easy to Order

Glencoe and Science Kit, Inc., have teamed up to make materials for *Glencoe Science Level Green* easier with an activity-materials folder. You can order materials and equipment for the program using the **Activity Materials List** master. Call Science Kit at 1-800-828-7777 to get your folder.

Materials Support Provided by

Science Kit® & Boreal®
  Laboratories
777 East Park Drive
Tonawanda, NY 14151-5003
Phone: 800-828-7777
Fax 800-828-3299
www.sciencekit.com

List of Activity Materials

It is assumed that laboratory aprons, goggles, tap water, metersticks, metric rulers, textbooks, scissors, calculators, paper, pencils, and pens are available.

Non-Consumables

Item	EXPLORE ACTIVITY Page	Mini LAB Page	Activity Chapter and 1-page or 2-page
Baking pan(s)			17-2
Balance	97		1-1, 4-1, 13-2, 16-2, 18-1, 18-2
Bar, metal			19-1
Basin		337, 606	19-1
Basketball	479	488	
Beaker, 250 mL			1-1
Beaker, glass, 1 L	517		
Beaker(s)	97, 451	40, 72, 107, 459, 527	9-2, 18-2
Bicycle pump			6-2
Block, metal			18-2
Block(s), wooden	419		17-2, 18-2, 19-1
Bowl(s)	5, 97	82, 159, 606	5-1, 12-1, 16-2, 19-2
Bricks			17-2
Carpet			19-1
Casserole dish, clear, colorless		405	
Clock or watch	97, 517, 633		7-1
Clock or watch with second hand	153	107, 362	2-2, 16-1, 17-2, 20-2
Clock or watch with second hand that ticks audibly			21-1
Clothing, wool		637	
Coiled spring toy			15-2, 20-1, 20-2
Comb, hard plastic		637	
Computer temperature probe		40	
Container, miscellaneous	545	241, 362	4-1
Convex lens			23-2
Cork	575	463	18-2
Diffraction grating			22-2
Dissecting needle			9-1
Dowels or sticks			18-1

Non-Consumables *continued*

Item	EXPLORE ACTIVITY Page	Mini LAB Page	Activity Chapter and 1-page or 2-page
Dropper	269, 451, 575	18, 107	3-1, 3-2, 9-1
Dropper bottle			4-2
Fan, electric, 3-speed			16-1
Feather			19-1
Film canisters, plastic			15-1
Flashlight		72	7-1, 22-1, 23-1, 23-2
Forceps			3-1, 5-1, 9-1
Funnel		165	
Glass, drinking		82, 107, 241, 459, 588	19-1, 19-2
Glass prism	633		
Globe (not used as reference)			18-1
Gloves, disposable			6-1
Graduated cylinder, 100 mL			18-1
Graduated cylinder, 250 mL			18-2
Graduated cylinder, 50 mL			1-1, 15-1
Graduated cylinder, large			16-2
Graduated cylinder(s)	548		9-2, 13-1
Hand lens	69, 209, 331	82	6-1, 9-1, 12-1, 12-2
Heater, electric		641	
Hot plate	517	403	
Jar, clear glass or plastic, 1 L			5-2
Jars, wide-mouthed			4-1, 13-1
Keys		606	
Lamp, gooseneck			16-1
Lightbulbs and socket			22-2
Magnet			19-1
Marble(s)		158	
Materials to make a scale model			7-2
Measuring cup, clear		40, 48	
Microscope			3-1, 3-2, 5-1, 8-1, 9-1

Non-Consumables *continued*

Item	EXPLORE ACTIVITY Page	Mini LAB Page	ACTIVITY Chapter and 1-page or 2-page
Microscope slides			3-1, 3-2, 5-1, 9-1, 22-1
Mirror, concave		641	
Musical instruments			21-2
Paint brush, artist's			19-2
Pans			18-2
Pennies	663		
Petri dishes, plastic			3-2
Photos of different foods		184	
Photos of different landscapes		184	
Pins		430	
Plane mirror, small			23-1
Plant pots		337	
Plant trays			9-2
Plate (not paper)	269, 575		
Power supply with variable resistor switch			22-2
Prepared slide of human check cells			3-1
Prepared slide of onion root tip			8-1
Protractor			17-2
Reference-globe or world map	359		
Reference-periodic table of the elements		519	
Reference-weather references	359		
Rock/Mineral-obsidian	545		
Rock/Mineral-pumice	545		
Rock/Mineral-quartz			18-2
Rock/Mineral-rock, any kind			18-1, 18-2, 19-1
Rubber ball			19-1
Rubber bands	419	618	
Ruler, wooden		579	
Scalpel			6-1
Screen, wire		165	

Non-Consumables *continued*

Item	EXPLORE ACTIVITY Page	Mini LAB Page	ACTIVITY Chapter and 1-page or 2-page
Seedling warming cables			9-2
Shirt, flannel		637	
Shoe box		618	
Shoe box with lid			7-1
Spatula		394	
Sponge			18-2
Spoon		362, 459, 463, 527, 606	1-1, 4-1
Sports bottle			6-2
Spring scale			19-1
Stereomicroscope			3-2
Stirring rod	97	72	4-2
Stopwatch			2-2, 17-2, 20-1, 20-2
Storage box, clear plastic		459, 463	16-1
Tape measure			10-2, 21-2
Teaspoon		459	15-1, 16-2
Telescope			17-1
Test tube, glass		682	
Test tubes, 150 mm			4-2
Test tubes, 16 mm			4-2
Test-tube rack			4-2
Test-tube stopper(s)		682	4-2
Thermal mitts	517	405	
Thermometer, alcohol		40	
Thermometer, non-mercury			17-2, 18-1
Thermometer(s)	5, 633		9-2
Tuning fork			21-2
Watering can		337	

Consumables

Item	EXPLORE ACTIVITY Page	Mini LAB Page	ACTIVITY Chapter and 1-page or 2-page
Aluminum foil	127		5-2
Bromothymol blue solution			4-2
Buttons		256, 394	
Cardboard	419, 479		17-2
Cardboard boxes/lids			17-2
Cardboard tube		158	6-2, 21-1
Cardboard with white surface, 20 cm square			23-2
Construction paper, black	633	131	23-1
Coverslips			3-1, 3-2, 5-1, 9-1
Crayons		501	
Culture containers and covers			12-2
Culture kit, fruit fly			12-2
Cups, disposable	663	103, 165, 588	9-2, 13-2
Dishwashing liquid		362	
Drawing paper		501	17-1
Elodea sprig or other aquatic plant			4-2
Fertilizer, houseplant		371	
Filter paper	269	165	
Food coloring	451	107, 405, 459	
Food-apple			19-1
Food-apple juice			19-2
Food-baking soda	269		15-1
Food-banana		140	12-2
Food-beans, dried			11-1
Food-bread slice			19-1
Food-carrots	97		
Food-cereal, dry			19-1
Food-corn syrup			4-1
Food-drink mixes			1-1

Consumables *continued*

Item	EXPLORE ACTIVITY Page	Mini LAB Page	ACTIVITY Chapter and 1-page or 2-page
Food-eggs			4-1, 19-1, 19-2
Food-fruit, whole, various kinds		341	
Food-gelatin		72, 103, 430	
Food-grapes, two different kinds	239		
Food-lemon juice, concentrated			19-2
Food-lettuce			5-1, 12-1
Food-liver or meat, raw			12-1
Food-macaroni, dry		394	
Food-orange			12-2
Food-peanuts		394	
Food-pineapple		103	
Food-potato, small, uncooked			16-2
Food-salt	97, 69, 269	459, 527	5-1, 9-2, 16-2
Food-sugar	69	527	
Food-taffy		421	
Food-vegetables, various			19-1
Food-vinegar	269		4-1, 15-1
Glue		215, 256	
Graph paper		278, 284	1-2, 2-2, 10-2
Grass clippings or green leaves			13-1
Gravel, fine		165	
Highlighter		519	
Ice	451	40, 527	
Index cards		682	
Kidney, large animal, or model of kidney			6-1
Knife, plastic	239	341	
Markers		103, 215	5-2, 7-2, 11-2, 13-1
Modeling clay		394	6-2, 18-2, 22-1, 23-1, 23-2

Consumables *continued*

Item	EXPLORE ACTIVITY Page	Mini LAB Page	Activity Chapter and 1-page or 2-page
Newspaper		82	
Paper bags		140	11-1
Paper towels	209, 239	18, 341, 606	5-2, 7-1, 13-2
Paper, colored		215, 665	17-2, 22-2
Pencils, colored		501	7-2
Pencils, drawing			17-1
Perfume or air freshener		189	
Photos from discarded magazines	391		
Plastic bag, self-sealing	127, 209	430	
Plate, paper		555	
Poster board		215	7-2, 11-2, 21-1
Sand	69	527	19-1
Seeds, bean	209		
Seeds, fast-germinating			9-2
Seeds, mustard or bean			5-2
Seeds, radish		337	13-2
Sod	331		
Soil		165, 362	13-1, 19-1
Soil, potting		241, 337	9-2, 13-2
Steel wool, fine		555	
Straw, drinking	575	588	
String		606	15-2, 18-1
Tape	479, 517, 633	131, 463	7-1, 10-2, 20-2, 23-1
Tape, masking		488	23-2
Tape, transparent			17-2, 22-1
Thread		215	
Toothpaste, 2 or 3 different brands			19-2
Toothpick(s)		215	

Consumables *continued*

Item	EXPLORE ACTIVITY Page	Mini LAB Page	Activity Chapter and 1-page or 2-page
Water, carbonated			4-2
Water, distilled			3-2, 4-1, 4-3
Water, pond or stream			12-1
Wax pencil		107	
Weighing paper			1-1
Yarn		215	15-2, 20-1

Live Organisms

Item	Explore Activity Page	Mini Lab Page	Activity Chapter and 1-page or 2-page
Coleus or another houseplant		241	
Earthworms			7-1
Elodea plant or coleus or similar houseplant			3-1
Ferns with gametophytes and sporophytes			9-1
Flower			19-1
Fruit flies			12-2
Guppies			12-1
Live mosses with gametophytes and sporophytes			9-1
Liverworts with gametophytes and sporophytes			9-1
Planarians			12-1
Plant, any kind			19-1
Plant, potted, with leaves	127	131, 337	

Suppliers

Scientific Suppliers

Carolina Biological Supply Company
2700 York Road
Burlington, NC 27215
800-334-5551
www.carolina.com

Fisher Scientific Company
4500 Turnberry Drive
Hanover Park, IL 60103
800-766-7000
www.fishersci.com

Fisher Scientific Educational
485 South Frontage Road
Burr Ridge, IL 60521
800-955-1177
www.fisheredu.com

Flinn Scientific
P.O. Box 219
770 N. Raddant Road
Batavia, IL 60510
800-452-1261
www.flinnsci.com

Frey Scientific
100 Paragon Road
Mansfield, OH 44903
800-225-3739
www.freyscientific.com

Sargent-Welch/Cenco
P.O. Box 5229
911 Commerce Court
Buffalo Grove, IL 60089
800-727-4368
www.sargentwelch.com

Science Kit & Boreal Laboratories
777 East Park Drive
Tonawanda, NY 14150
800-828-7777
www.sciencekit.com

Ward's Natural Science Establishment, Inc.
P.O. Box 92912
5100 Henrietta Road
Rochester, NY 14692
800-962-2660
www.wardsci.com

Software Distributors

(AIT) Agency for Instructional Technology
Box A
Bloomington, IN 47402-0120
800-457-4509
www.ait.net

Educational Activities, Inc.
1937 Grand Avenue
Baldwin, NY 11510
800-645-3739
www.edact.com

IBM Educational Systems
Department PC
4111 Northside Parkway
Atlanta, GA 30327
800-426-4968
www.IBM.com

Microphys
12 Bridal Way
Sparta, NJ 07871
800-832-6591
www.microphys.com

Queue, Inc.
338 Commerce Drive
Fairfield, CT 06432
800-335-0906
www.queueinc.com

School Division of The Learning Company
6160 Summit Drive
Minneapolis, MN 55430
www.learningcompanyschool.com

Ventura Educational Systems
P.O. Box 425
Grover Beach, CA 93483
2782 Sevada
Arroyo, CA 93420
800-336-1022
www.venturaES.com

Audiovisual Distributors

Aims Multimedia
9710 Desoto Avenue
Chatsworth, CA 91311-4409
800-367-2467
www.aimsmultimedia.com

BFA Educational Media
2349 Chaffee Drive
St. Louis, MO 63146
800-221-1274
www.phoenixcoronet.com

CRM Films
2215 Faraday Avenue
Carlsbad, CA 92008
800-421-0833
www.crmfilms.com

Encyclopedia Britannica Educational Corp. (EBEC)
310 S. Michigan Avenue
Chicago, IL 60604
800-554-9862 ext. 7007
www.ebec.com

Hawkill Associates, Inc.
125 E. Gilman Street
Madison, WI 53703
800-422-4295
www.hawkill.com

Lumivision
877 Federal Boulevard
Denver, CO 80204
303-446-0400
www.lumivision.com

National Geographic School Publishing
P.O. Box 10579
Des Moines, IA 50340
17th and "M" Streets, NW
Washington, DC 20009
800-368-2728
www.nationalgeographic.com\education

Time-Life Education
P.O. Box 8502
Richmond, VA 23285
800-449-2010
www.timelifeedu.com

Video Discovery
Suite 600
1700 Westlake Avenue, N
Seattle, WA 98109
800-548-3472
www.videodiscovery.com

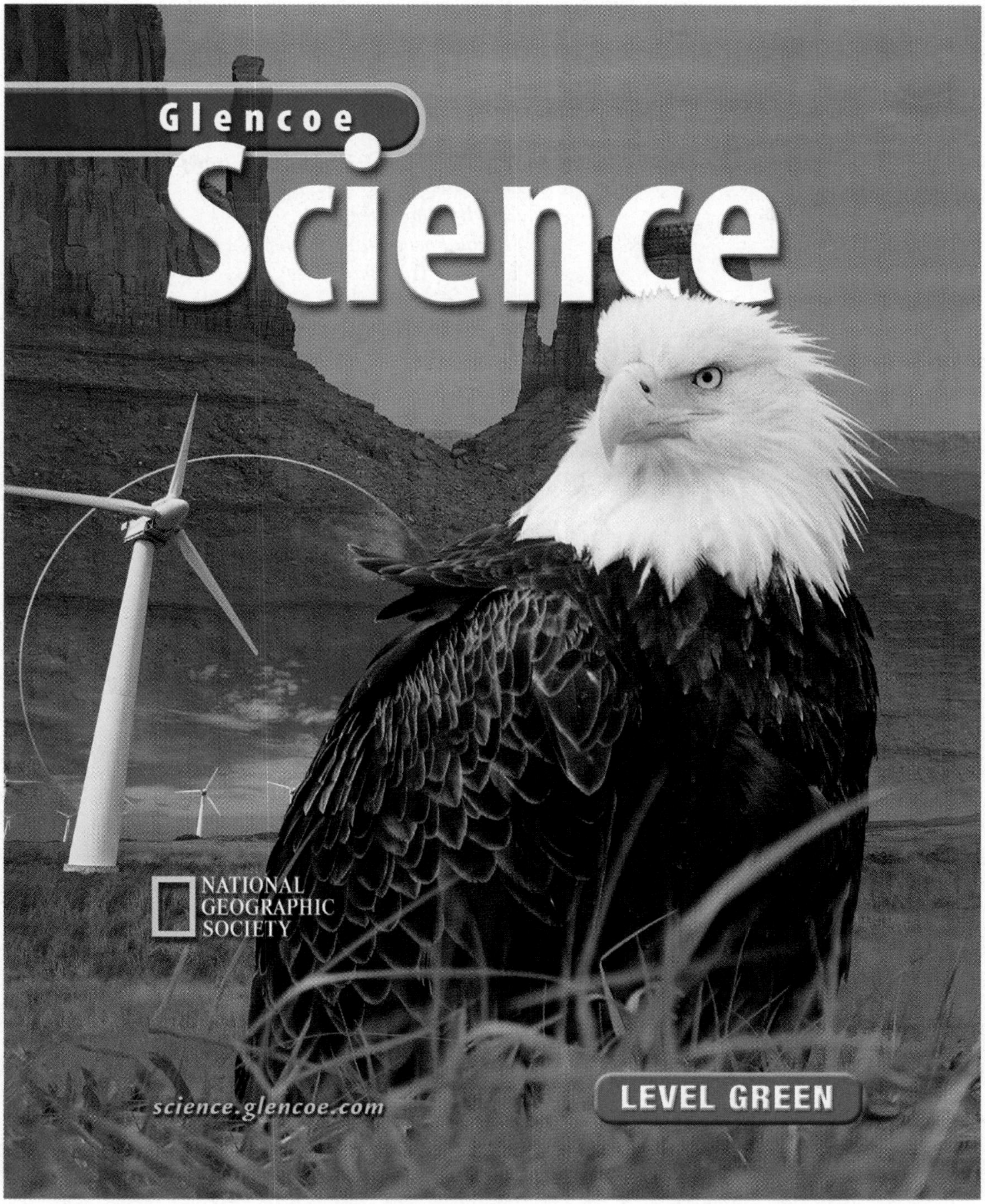

Glencoe
Science

NATIONAL
GEOGRAPHIC
SOCIETY

science.glencoe.com

LEVEL GREEN

Glencoe
McGraw-Hill

New York, New York   Columbus, Ohio   Woodland Hills, California   Peoria, Illinois

Glencoe Science

LEVEL GREEN

Student Edition
Teacher Wraparound Edition
Interactive Teacher Edition CD-ROM
Interactive Lesson Planner CD-ROM
Lesson Plans
Content Outline for Teaching
Dinah Zike's Teaching Science with Foldables
Directed Reading for Content Mastery
Foldables: Reading and Study Skills
Assessment
    Chapter Review
    Chapter Tests
    ExamView Pro Test Bank Software
    Assessment Transparencies
    Performance Assessment in the Science Classroom
    The Princeton Review Standardized Test Practice Booklet
Directed Reading for Content Mastery in Spanish
Spanish Resources
English/Spanish Guided Reading Audio Program

Reinforcement
Enrichment
Activity Worksheets
Section Focus Transparencies
Teaching Transparencies
Laboratory Activities
Science Inquiry Labs
Critical Thinking/Problem Solving
Reading and Writing Skill Activities
Mathematics Skill Activities
Cultural Diversity
Laboratory Management and Safety in the Science Classroom
MindJogger Videoquizzes and Teacher Guide
Interactive CD-ROM with Presentation Builder
Vocabulary PuzzleMaker Software
Cooperative Learning in the Science Classroom
Environmental Issues in the Science Classroom
Home and Community Involvement
Using the Internet in the Science Classroom

"Study Tip," "Test-Taking Tip," and the "Test Practice" features in this book were written by The Princeton Review, the nation's leader in test preparation. Through its association with McGraw-Hill, The Princeton Review offers the best way to help students excel on standardized assessments.

The Princeton Review is not affiliated with Princeton University or Educational Testing Service.

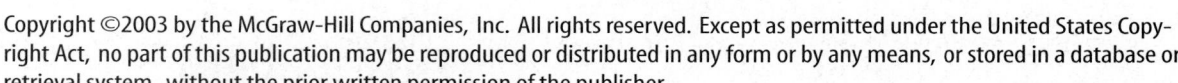

Glencoe/McGraw-Hill

A Division of The **McGraw-Hill** Companies

Cover Images: full moon in the sky over Monument Valley, Arizona; bald eagle; wind turbines

Send all inquiries to:
Glencoe/McGraw-Hill
8787 Orion Place
Columbus, OH 43240

ISBN 0-07-828240-3
Printed in the United States of America.
3 4 5 6 7 8 9 10 071/055 06 05 04 03 02

Authors

National Geographic Society
Education Division
Washington, D.C.

Alton Biggs
Biology Teacher
Allen High School
Allen, Texas

Lucy Daniel, EdD
Teacher/Consultant
Rutherford County Schools
Rutherfordton, North Carolina

Ralph M. Feather Jr., PhD
Science Department Chair
Derry Area School District
Derry, Pennsylvania

Edward Ortleb
Science Consultant
St. Louis Public Schools
St. Louis, Missouri

Peter Rillero, PhD
Professor of Science Education
Arizona State University West
Phoenix, Arizona

Susan Leach Snyder
Earth Science Teacher, Consultant
Jones Middle School
Upper Arlington, Ohio

Dinah Zike
Educational Consultant
Dinah-Might Activities, Inc.
San Antonio, Texas

Contributing Authors

Cathy Ezrailson
Oak Ridge High School
Conroe ISD
Conroe, Texas

Patricia Horton
Mathematics and Science Teacher
Summit Intermediate School
Etiwanda, California

Deborah Lillie
Math and Science Writer
Sudbury, Massachusetts

Series Reading Consultants

Elizabeth Babich
Special Education Teacher
Mashpee Public Schools
Mashpee, Massachusetts

Barry Barto
Special Education Teacher
John F. Kennedy Elementary
Manistee, Michigan

Carol A. Senf, PhD
Associate Professor of English
Georgia Institute of Technology
Atlanta, Georgia

Rachel Swaters
Science Teacher
Rolla Middle Schools
Rolla, Missouri

Nancy Woodson, PhD
Professor of English
Otterbein College
Westerville, Ohio

Series Math Consultants

Michael Hopper, D.Eng
Manager of Aircraft Certification
Raytheon Company
Greenville, Texas

Teri Willard, EdD
Department of Mathematics
Montana State University
Belgrade, Montana

Content Consultants

Michelle Anderson
Community Faculty
Marion Technical College
Marion, Ohio

Jack Cooper
Adjunct Faculty Math and Science
Navarro College
Corsicana, Texas

Sandra K. Enger, PhD
Coordinator
UAH Huntsville Institute for Science Education
Huntsville, Alabama

Leanne Field, PhD
Lecturer Molecular Genetics and Microbiology
University of Texas
Austin, Texas

Michael A. Hoggarth, PhD
Department of Life and Earth Sciences
Otterbein College
Westerville, Ohio

William C. Keel, PhD
Department of Physics and Astronomy
University of Alabama
Tuscaloosa, Alabama

Linda Knight, EdD
Associate Director
Rice Model Science Lab
Houston, Texas

Lisa McGaw
Science Teacher
Hereford High School
Hereford, Texas

Lee Meadows, PhD
UAB Birmingham Education Department
Birmingham, Alabama

Robert Nierste
Science Department Head
Hendrick Middle School
Plano, Texas

Connie Rizzo, MD
Professor of Biology
Pace University
New York, New York

Dominic Salinas, PhD
Middle School Science Supervisor
Caddo Parish Schools
Shreveport, Louisiana

Carl Zorn, PhD
Staff Scientist
Jefferson Laboratory
Newport News, Virginia

Betsy Wrobel-Boerner
Department of Microbiology
Ohio State University
Columbus, Ohio

Series Activity Testers

José Luis Alvarez, PhD
Math and Science Mentor Teacher
El Paso, Texas

Mary Helen Mariscal-Cholka
Science Teacher
William D. Slider Middle School
El Paso, Texas

José Alberto Marquez
TEKS for Leaders Trainer
El Paso, Texas

Nerma Coats Henderson
Teacher
Pickerington Jr. High School
Pickerington, Ohio

Science Kit and Boreal Laboratories
Tonawanda, New York

CONTENTS IN BRIEF

CONTENTS

CONTENTS

CONTENTS

Interdisciplinary Connections

 Unit Openers

NATIONAL GEOGRAPHIC VISUALIZING

Activities

Full Period Labs

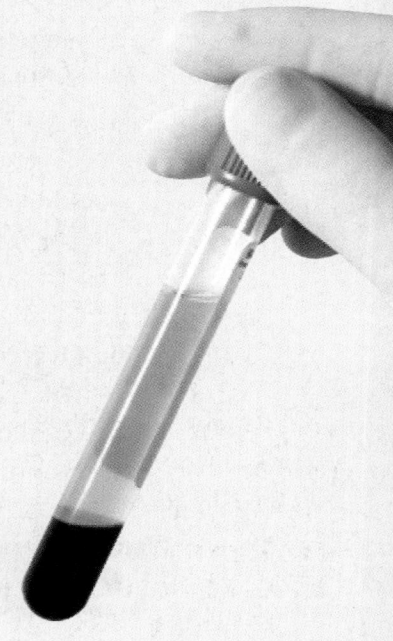

Feature Contents

Mini LAB

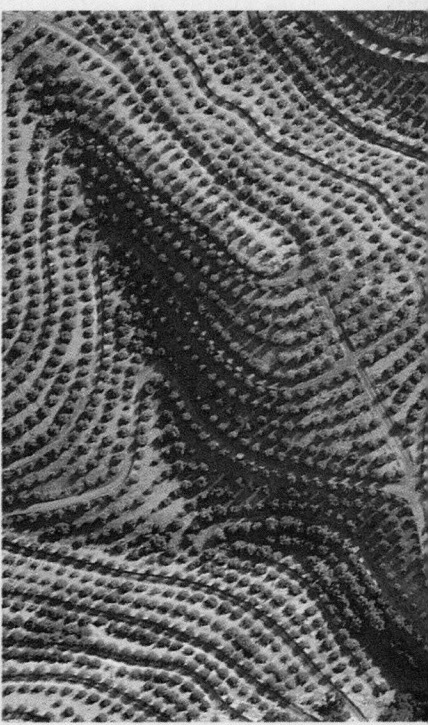

Activities

EXPLORE ACTIVITY

Feature Contents

Problem-Solving Activities

Math Skills Activities

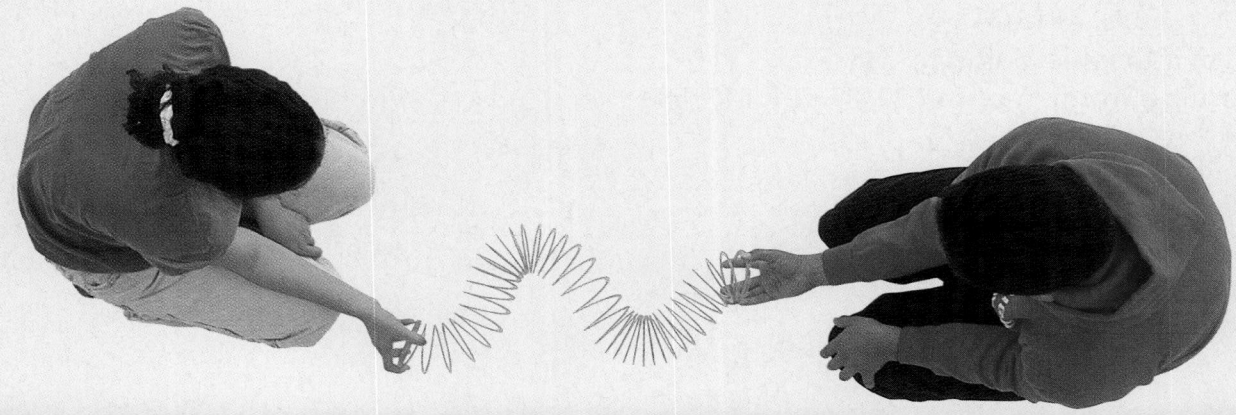

Activities

Skill Builder Activities

Science

Classifying: 377, 535, 561

Communicating: 11, 45, 77, 110, 143, 162, 223, 243, 259, 314, 335, 373, 395, 428, 468, 485, 528, 593, 623, 653, 668, 685

Comparing and Contrasting: 11, 27, 143, 395, 468, 503, 522, 528, 550, 593, 638

Concept Mapping: 83, 87, 110, 168, 229, 247, 279, 317, 398, 455, 580

Drawing Conclusions: 243, 668

Forming Hypotheses: 135, 335, 441, 674

Interpreting Scientific Illustrations: 77, 105

Making and Using Graphs: 55

Making and Using Tables: 223, 343, 428

Making Models: 289, 623

Measuring in SI: 23, 50

Predicting: 274, 306, 314, 409, 434, 461, 485, 585, 680

Recognizing Cause and Effect: 494, 647

Researching Information: 162, 185, 259, 274, 653

Testing a Hypothesis: 194, 216

Math

Calculating Ratios: 503, 638

Converting Units: 50

Identifying and Manipulating Variables and Controls: 117, 348, 366, 373

Solving One-Step Equations: 83, 117, 135, 168, 194, 216, 247, 279, 343, 377, 398, 434, 522, 550, 561, 585, 613, 680, 685

Using Percentages: 23, 306

Using Precision and Significant Digits: 45

Using Proportions: 455

Technology

Using a Database: 647

Using an Electronic Spreadsheet: 55, 105, 185, 289, 366, 409, 441, 461, 494, 613, 674

Using Graphics Software: 348, 535

Using a Word Processor: 27, 87, 229, 317, 580

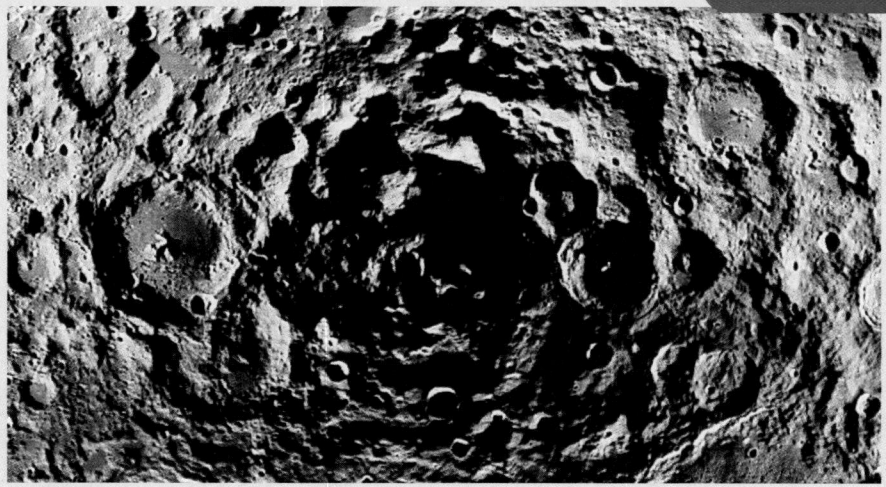

Science
INTEGRATION

SCIENCE *Online*

THE PRINCETON REVIEW

UNIT 1

Unit Contents

Pre-Reading Activity

Have students list as many tools for measuring as they can. Have them identify the ones they have used.

UNIT 1

The Nature of Science

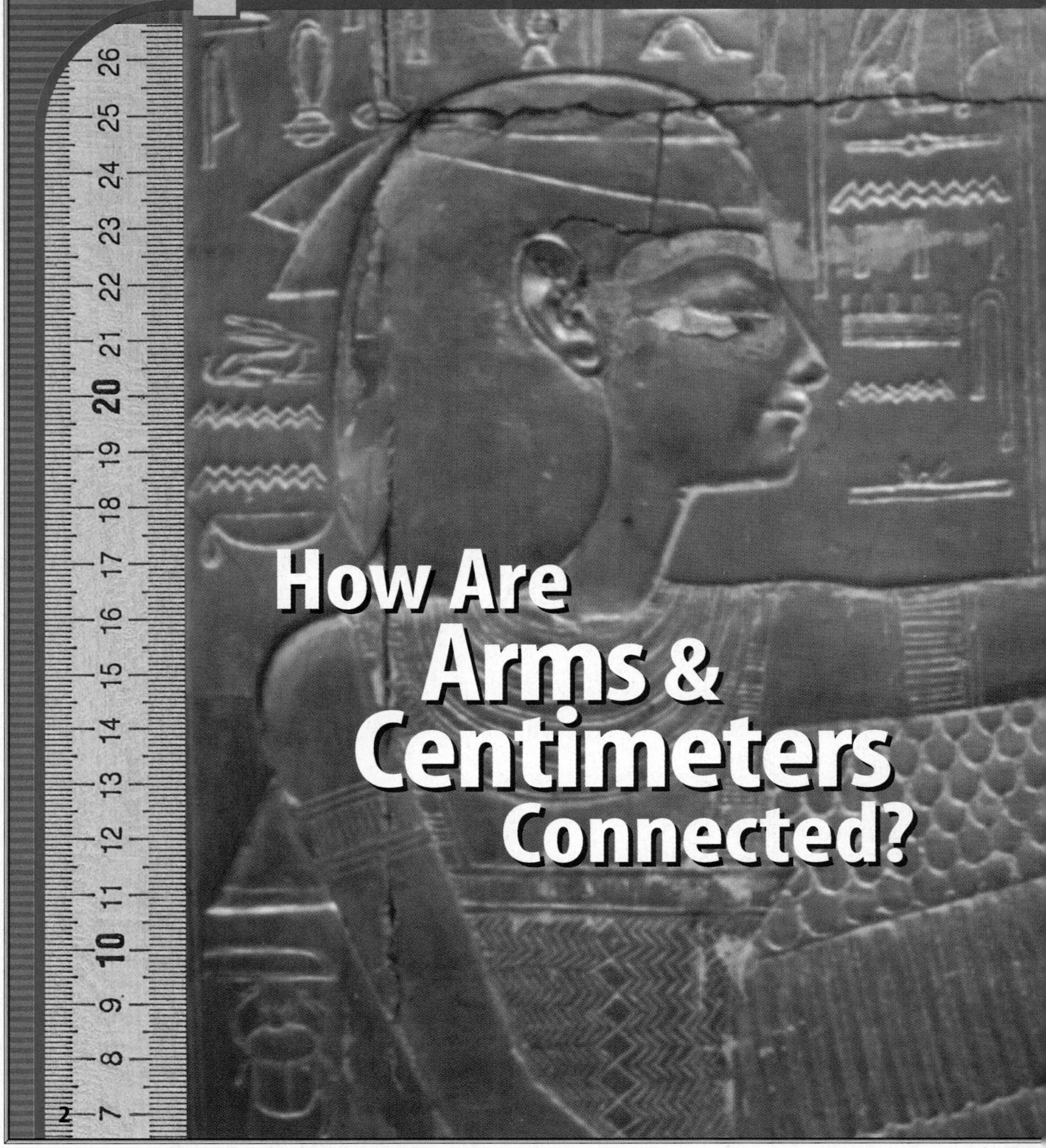

How Are Arms & Centimeters Connected?

Teacher to Teacher

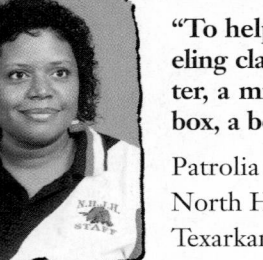

"To help students visualize a variety of concepts, I have them use modeling clay. For example, to better understand the size of a cubic centimeter, a milliliter, and a gram, students can use the clay to make a 1-cm^3 box, a box that has a mass of 1 g, and a box that holds 1 mL of water."

Patrolia Moss, Teacher
North Heights Junior High
Texarkana, AR

A bout 5,000 years ago, the Egyptians developed one of the earliest recorded units of measurement—the cubit, which was based on the length of the arm from elbow to fingertip. The Egyptian measurement system probably influenced later systems, many of which also were based on body parts such as arms and feet. Such systems, however, could be problematic, since arms and feet vary in length from one person to another. Moreover, each country had its own system, which made it hard for people from different countries to share information. The need for a precise, universal measurement system eventually led to the adoption of the meter as the basic international unit of length. A meter is defined as the distance that light travels in a vacuum in a certain fraction of a second—a distance that never varies. Meters are divided into smaller units called centimeters, which are seen on the rulers here.

SCIENCE CONNECTION

MEASUREMENT SYSTEMS Ancient systems of measurement had their flaws, but they paved the way for the more exact and uniform systems used today. Devise your own measurement system based on parts of your body (for example, the length of your hand or the width of your shoulders) or common objects in your classroom or home. Give names to your units of measurement. Then calculate the width and height of a doorway using one or more of your units.

SCIENCE *Online*
Internet Addresses

_____

_____

_____

_____

Explore the Glencoe Science Web site at **science.glencoe.com** to find out more about topics in this unit.

Introducing the Unit

How Are Arms & Centimeters Connected?

As ancient peoples travelled and trade began, a need for accuracy in measuring became necessary. Tell students that early weight units may have been derived from containers or calculations of what a person or animal could haul. Explain that early linear measurements were often based on body parts.

Because of its accuracy, the Egyptian cubit was the standard of linear measurement. The accuracy of the Egyptian cubit stick is attested to by the dimensions of the Great Pyramid of Giza. Its sides vary only slightly even though thousands of people were employed to build it. This is because the cubit was standardized by a royal master cubit of black granite. All cubit sticks used in Egypt were measured against the master at regular intervals.

Today, the only SI or fundamental unit of measurement based on a physical object is the kilogram. Other SI units are defined with physical descriptions based on stable properties in the universe. There are seven basic SI units, one of which is the meter. The centimeter is a subunit of the meter.

SCIENCE CONNECTION
Activity

Have students develop their own systems of measurement, then divide the class into pairs. Each student should use his or her partner's system of measurement to see how measurements vary when two students use the same system. Explain that this is why a standard system of measurement is needed.

Section/Objectives	Standards		Activities/Features
Chapter Opener	National	State/Local	**Explore Activity:** Measuring using tools, p. 5
	See p. 6T for a Key to Standards.		**Before You Read,** p. 5
Section 1 What is science? 🕐 2 sessions 📦 1 block 1. **Identify** how science is a part of your everyday life. 2. **Describe** what skills and tools are used in science.	National Content Standards: UCP1, A1, A2, G1, G2		**Health Integration,** p. 7 **Science Online,** p. 8 **MiniLAB:** Inferring from Pictures, p. 9 **Activity:** Battle of the Drink Mixes, p. 12
Section 2 Doing Science 🕐 2 sessions 📦 1 block 1. **Examine** the steps used to solve a problem in a scientific way. 2. **Explain** how a well-designed investigation is developed.	National Content Standards: UCP1, A1, A2, G1, G2		**Problem-Solving Activity:** Problem-Solving Skills, p. 14 **Environmental Science Integration,** p. 15 **MiniLAB:** Comparing Paper Towels, p. 18 **Visualizing Descriptive and Experimental Research,** p. 20
Section 3 Science and Technology 🕐 3 sessions 📦 1.5 blocks 1. **Determine** how science and technology influence your life. 2. **Analyze** how modern technology allows scientific discoveries to be communicated worldwide.	National Content Standards: UCP1, A1, A2, E1, E2, F5, G1, G2		**Science Online,** p. 25 **Activity:** When is the Internet the busiest? pp. 28–29 **Science and Language Arts:** The Everglades: River of Grass, pp. 30–31

NATIONAL GEOGRAPHIC   Teacher's Corner

PRODUCTS AVAILABLE FROM NATIONAL GEOGRAPHIC SOCIETY
To order call 1-800-368-2728:
Book
Everyday Science Explained

Video
Scientific Method

Activity Materials	Reproducible Resources	Section Assessment	Technology
Explore Activity: 3 bowls; cold, warm, and hot water; thermometer	**Chapter Resources Booklet** Foldables Worksheet, p. 15 Directed Reading Overview, p. 17 Note-taking Worksheets, pp. 31–32	GLENCOE'S ASSESSMENT ADVANTAGE	
MiniLAB: Science Journal **Activity:** weighing paper, 50-mL graduated cylinder, 3–4 powdered drink mixes, triple-beam balance, 250-mL beaker, water, spoon	**Chapter Resources Booklet** Transparency Activity, p. 42 MiniLAB, p. 3 Enrichment, p. 28 Reinforcement, p. 25 Directed Reading, p. 18 Activity Worksheet, pp. 5–6 **Cultural Diversity,** p. 29 **Science Inquiry Labs,** p. 19 **Reading and Writing Skill Activities,** p. 17	Portfolio Science Journal, p. 9 Performance MiniLAB, p. 9 Skill Builder Activities, p. 11 Content Section Assessment, p. 11	🔋 Section Focus Transparency 💿 Interactive CD-ROM 🎧 Guided Reading Audio Program
MiniLAB: 3 brands of paper towels, scissors, water, dropper *Need materials?* Contact Science Kit at 1-800-828-7777 or www.sciencekit.com on the Internet.	**Chapter Resources Booklet** Transparency Activity, p. 43 MiniLAB, p. 4 Enrichment, p. 29 Reinforcement, p. 26 Directed Reading, p. 18 Lab Activities, pp. 9–10, 11–13 Transparency Activity, pp. 45–46 **Home and Community Involvement,** p. 23	Portfolio Curriculum Connection, p. 17 Performance Problem-Solving Activity, p. 14 MiniLAB, p. 18 Skill Builder Activities, p. 23 Content Section Assessment, p. 23	🔋 Section Focus Transparency 🔋 Teaching Transparency 💿 Interactive CD-ROM 🎧 Guided Reading Audio Program
Activity: Internet and other resources on Internet use, graph paper	**Chapter Resources Booklet** Transparency Activity, p. 44 Enrichment, p. 30 Reinforcement, p. 27 Directed Reading, pp. 19, 20 Activity Worksheet, pp. 7–8 **Cultural Diversity,** p. 49 **Lab Management and Safety,** p. 63	Portfolio Extension, p. 25 Performance Skill Builder Activities, p. 27 Content Section Assessment, p. 27	🔋 Section Focus Transparency 💿 Interactive CD-ROM 🎧 Guided Reading Audio Program

End of Chapter Assessment

GLENCOE'S ASSESSMENT ADVANTAGE

Blackline Masters	Technology	Professional Series
Chapter Resources Booklet Chapter Review, pp. 35–36 Chapter Tests, pp. 37–40 **Standardized Test Practice by The Princeton Review,** pp. 9–12	📼 MindJogger Videoquiz 💿 Interactive CD-ROM 💿 Vocabulary PuzzleMakers 💿 ExamView Pro Test Bank 💿 Interactive Lesson Planner 💿 Interactive Teacher Edition	Performance Assessment in the Science Classroom (PASC)

Transparencies

Section Focus

Section Focus Transparency 1 — Where'd it go?

These students are exploring the natural world. By making and recording careful observations, the students can learn about this aquatic ecosystem.

1. How are these students working together as they explore?
2. Do you act like a scientist in your everyday life? How?

L2

Section Focus Transparency 2 — The Nobel Prize for Cookies

Cookies are a tasty treat to bite into. Have you ever changed a recipe to try and make it better? That's what Charlie is doing. He's adding more butter because he thinks the cookies will taste better.

1. How is Charlie's changing the recipe similar to a scientific experiment? What, specifically, did Charlie change?
2. How will Charlie tell if his experiment is a success?

L2

Section Focus Transparency 3 — Yes, but can it walk the dog?

In 1970, Congress passed the Occupational Safety and Health Act (OSHA). This act encouraged the use of automation, a technology that includes robots.

1. What are some advantages of using robots in factories such as the one shown?
2. What are some disadvantages?

L2

This is a representation of key blackline masters available in the Teacher Classroom Resources. See Resource Manager boxes within the chapter for additional information.

Assessment

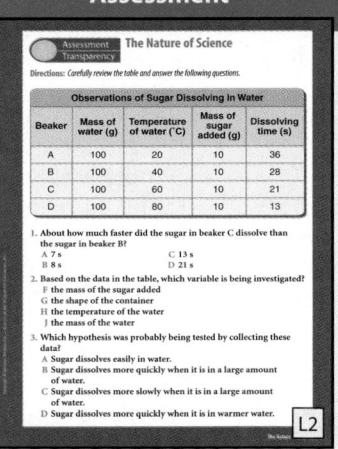

Assessment Transparency — The Nature of Science

Directions: *Carefully review the table and answer the following questions.*

Observations of Sugar Dissolving in Water

Beaker	Mass of water (g)	Temperature of water (°C)	Mass of sugar added (g)	Dissolving time (s)
A	100	20	10	36
B	100	40	10	28
C	100	60	10	21
D	100	80	10	13

1. About how much faster did the sugar in beaker C dissolve than the sugar in beaker B?
   A 7 s C 13 s
   B 8 s D 21 s
2. Based on the data in the table, which variable is being investigated?
   F the mass of the sugar added
   G the shape of the container
   H the temperature of the water
   J the mass of the water
3. Which hypothesis was probably being tested by collecting these data?
   A Sugar dissolves easily in water.
   B Sugar dissolves more quickly when it is in a large amount of water.
   C Sugar dissolves more slowly when it is in a large amount of water.
   D Sugar dissolves more quickly when it is in warmer water.

L2

Teaching

Teaching Transparency 2 — Scientific Method

L2

Key to Teaching Strategies

The following designations will help you decide which activities are appropriate for your students.

L1 Level 1 activities should be appropriate for students with learning difficulties.

L2 Level 2 activities should be within the ability range of all students.

L3 Level 3 activities are designed for above-average students.

ELL ELL activities should be within the ability range of English Language Learners.

COOP LEARN Cooperative Learning activities are designed for small group work.

LS Multiple Learning Styles logos, as described on page 22T, are used throughout to indicate strategies that address different learning styles.

P These strategies represent student products that can be placed into a best-work portfolio.

Hands-on Activities

Activity Worksheets

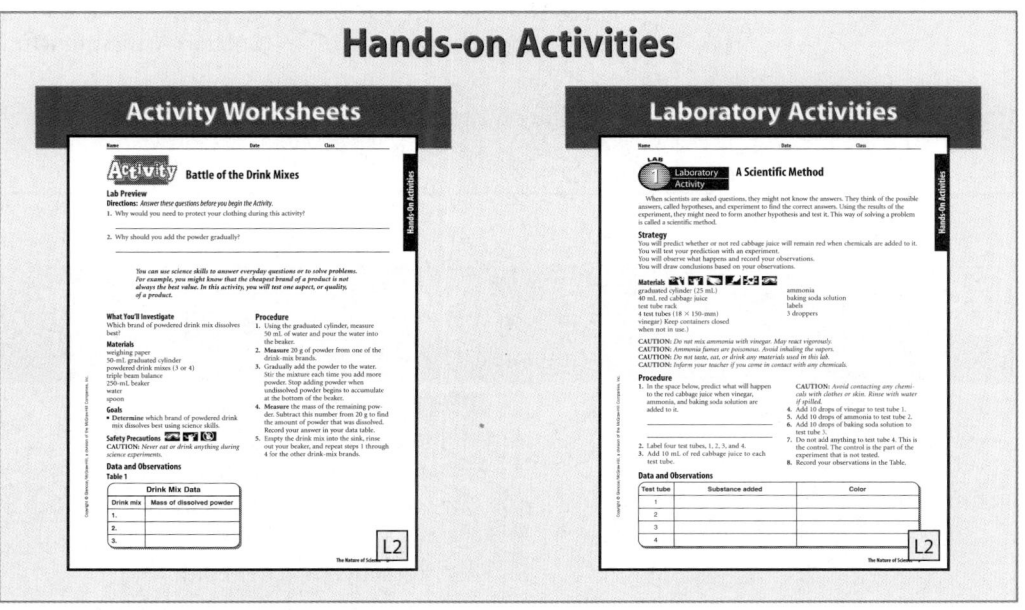

Activity — Battle of the Drink Mixes

Lab Preview
Directions: *Answer these questions before you begin the Activity.*
1. Why would you need to protect your clothing during this activity?

2. Why should you add the powder gradually?

You can use science skills to answer everyday questions or to solve problems. For example, you might know that the cheapest brand of a product is not always the best value. In this activity, you will test one aspect, or quality, of a product.

What You'll Investigate
Which brand of powdered drink mix dissolves best?

Materials
weighing paper
50-mL graduated cylinder
powdered drink mixes (3 or 4)
triple beam balance
250-mL beaker
water
spoon

Goals
• **Determine** which brand of powdered drink mix dissolves best using science skills.

Safety Precautions
CAUTION: *Never eat or drink anything during science experiments.*

Data and Observations
Table 1

Drink Mix Data

Drink mix	Mass of dissolved powder
1.	
2.	
3.	

Procedure
1. Using the graduated cylinder, measure 50 mL of water and pour the water into the beaker.
2. **Measure** 20 g of powder from one of the drink-mix brands.
3. Gradually add the powder to the water. Stir the mixture each time you add more powder. Stop adding powder when undissolved powder begins to accumulate at the bottom of the beaker.
4. **Measure** the mass of the remaining powder. Subtract this number from 20 g to find the amount of powder that was dissolved. Record your answer in your data table.
5. Empty the drink mix into the sink, rinse out your beaker, and repeat steps 1 through 4 for the other drink-mix brands.

L2

Laboratory Activities

Laboratory Activity 1 — A Scientific Method

When scientists are asked questions, they might not know the answers. They think of the possible answers, called hypotheses, and experiment to find the correct answers. Using the results of the experiment, they might need to form another hypothesis and test it. This way of solving a problem is called a scientific method.

Strategy
You will predict whether or not red cabbage juice will remain red when chemicals are added to it.
You will test your prediction with an experiment.
You will observe what happens and record your observations.
You will draw conclusions based on your observations.

Materials
graduated cylinder (25 mL.)   ammonia
40 mL red cabbage juice   baking soda solution
test tube rack   labels
4 test tubes (18 × 150-mm)   3 droppers
(vinegar) Keep containers closed
when not in use.)

CAUTION: *Do not mix ammonia with vinegar. May react vigorously.*
CAUTION: *Ammonia fumes are poisonous. Avoid inhaling the vapors.*
CAUTION: *Do not taste, eat, or drink any materials used in this lab.*
CAUTION: *Inform your teacher if you come in contact with any chemicals.*

Procedure
1. In the space below, predict what will happen to the red cabbage juice when vinegar, ammonia, and baking soda solution are added to it.
2. Label four test tubes, 1, 2, 3, and 4.
3. Add 10 mL of red cabbage juice to each test tube.

CAUTION: *Avoid contacting any chemicals with clothes or skin. Rinse with water if spilled.*
4. Add 10 drops of vinegar to test tube 1.
5. Add 10 drops of ammonia to test tube 2.
6. Add 10 drops of baking soda solution to test tube 3.
7. Do not add anything to test tube 4. This is the control. The control is the part of the experiment that is not tested.
8. Record your observations in the Table.

Data and Observations

Test tube	Substance added	Color
1		
2		
3		
4		

L2

Meeting Different Ability Levels

Content Outline

Note-taking Worksheet — The Nature of Science

L2

Reinforcement

Reinforcement — What is science?

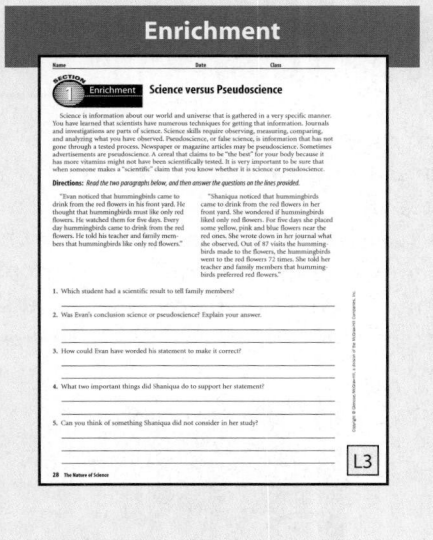

L2

Directed Reading

Directed Reading for Content Mastery — *Overview* The Nature of Science

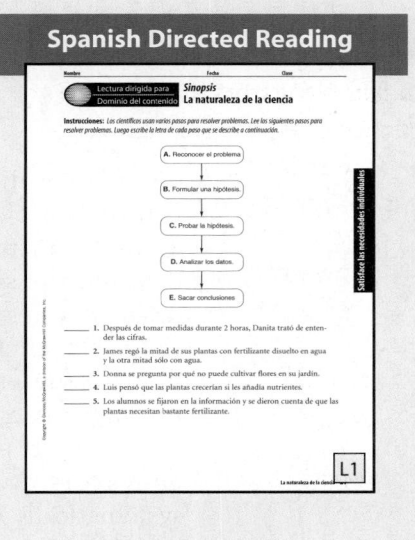

L1

Assessment

Chapter Tests

Chapter Test — The Nature of Science

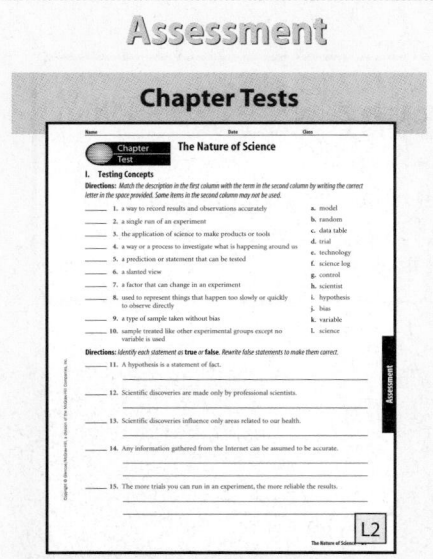

L2

Enrichment

Enrichment — Science versus Pseudoscience

L3

Spanish Directed Reading

Lectura dirigida para Dominio del contenido — *Sinopsis* La naturaleza de la ciencia

L1

Test Practice Workbook

Standardized Test Practice
Teacher Edition

Glencoe
Science

LEVEL GREEN

L2

Chapter Review

Chapter Review — The Nature of Science

L2

Science Content Background

SECTION 1
What is science?
Science in Society

Epidemiologists are medical detectives who look for clues to find the causes and prevention of diseases. They combine medical knowledge with statistics. Epidemiologists at the local, state, and national level look for patterns that might identify outbreaks. They also conduct observational studies in which they look for clues that might explain why some people get certain diseases.

SECTION 2
Doing Science
Scientific Methods and Descriptive Science

The work of many scientists is descriptive in nature and typically does not follow the classic "scientific method." For example, anatomists do their investigations to describe the structural components of various organisms at either the microscopic or macroscopic level. Ecologists investigate in order to describe energy flow through an ecosystem. In neither of the above endeavors do scientists systematically control all variables except an isolated variable of interest for manipulation.

SECTION 3
Science and Technology
Who practices science?

Garrett A. Morgan (1877–1963) is best known for the invention of the automatic traffic light and the gas mask. Flossie Wong-Staal serves on the editorial board of many journals and is currently the Florence Riford Professor in AIDS Research at the University of California at San Diego. Dr. Mae Jemison, a medical doctor, was the first African American in space and is currently working on a satellite-based communication system to improve health care in West Africa.

SCIENCE *Online*

For additional content background on this topic, go to the Glencoe Science Web site at science.glencoe.com.

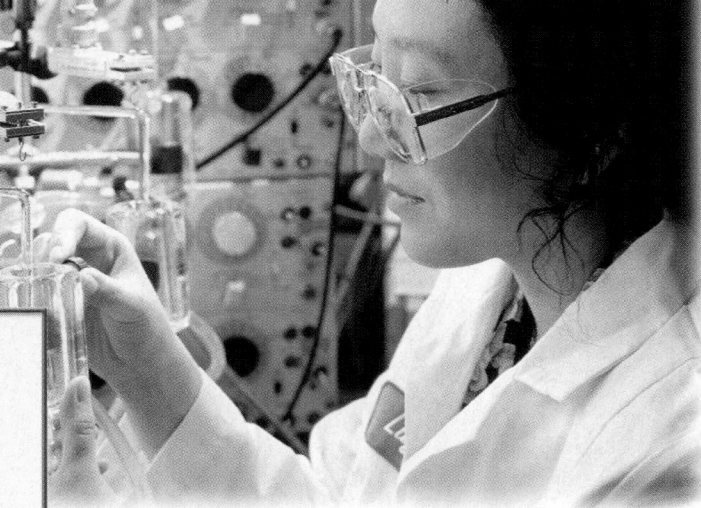

Terry Vine/Stone

Student Misconception

There is a sequence of steps followed in scientific investigations known as the scientific method.

Refer to the facing page for teaching strategies to address this misconception. Refer to pages 13–23 for content related to this topic.

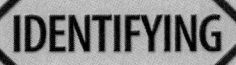

IDENTIFYING Misconceptions

Find Out What Students Think

Students may think that . . .

- **There is a sequence of steps followed in scientific investigations known as the scientific method.**

Students commonly have been taught that there is a single scientific method. Typically, textbooks present a series of sequential steps to characterize scientific investigations. The "scientific method," as presented, is most similar to classic experimental design. While this design is important in science, it is not representative of the varieties of approaches scientists use to answer their questions. Descriptive and correlational designs are just two common examples of investigative techniques that do not follow the classic "scientific method" structure.

Discussion

Ask students to explain what they think scientists do. When answers have been compiled, state that some people think that all scientific investigations must follow the same general set of steps, or method, in order to be considered "science." Others think that there are different methods scientific investigations can follow. **Is there one scientific method that all investigations must follow to be considered science? What do you think?** Do not correct any misconceptions as students respond.

Promote Understanding

Activity

Provide each group of students with an owl pellet and tweezers. Explain that owl pellets are undigested parts of animals that owls have eaten.

- Have students carefully dissect the pellets. Ask them to assemble the bones from the pellets into a skeleton or skeletons. Then have each group report how many and what kinds of animals the owl has eaten.

- After the reports have been given, ask students whether they think people who do this kind of work are "doing science." Point out that descriptive studies such as this are commonly done as scientists study animals and ecosystems.

Michael T. Sedam/Corbis

Assess

After completing the chapter, see *Identifying Misconceptions* in the Study Guide.

The Nature of Science

Chapter Vocabulary

science, p. 6
technology, p. 9
descriptive research, p. 13
experimental research design, p. 13
scientific methods, p. 13
model, p. 16
hypothesis, p. 21
independent variable, p. 21
dependent variable, p. 21
constant, p. 21
control, p. 22

What do you think?

Science Journal This photo is of *vibrio cholerae,* a bacterium that causes cholera when it enters the body through the mouth and causes an infection in the small intestine.

The Nature of Science

Why explore outer space or dive to the depths of the ocean? How can you examine microscopic cells or study animal behavior? In this chapter you will learn about skills and tools that are used to answer scientific questions. You'll also learn about the different methods scientists use to investigate the world. You will discover that you already use many of these skills every day.

What do you think?

Science Journal Look at the picture below with a classmate. Discuss what you think this might be. Here's a hint: *Somebody found this by drawing a map.* Write your answer or best guess in your Science Journal.

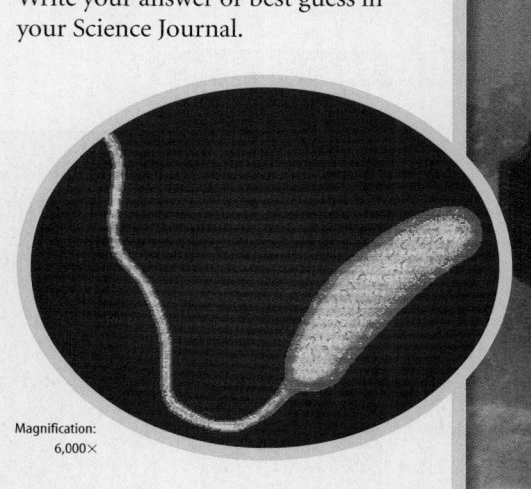

Magnification: 6,000×

4

Systems and Interactions Scientists use technology and science skills to study systems in nature and then interact with one another to find methods and products that improve the quality of life.

O uch! That soup is hot. Your senses tell you a great deal of information about the world around you, but they can't answer every question. Scientists use tools, such as thermometers, to measure accurately. Learn more about the importance of tools in the following activity.

Measure using tools

1. Use three bowls. Fill one with cold water, one with lukewarm water, and the third with hot water. **WARNING:** *Make sure the hot water will not burn you.*

2. Use a thermometer to measure the temperature of the lukewarm water. Record the temperature.

3. Submerse one hand in the cold water and the other in the hot water for 2 min.

4. Put both hands into the bowl of lukewarm water. What do you sense with each hand? Record your response in your Science Journal.

Observe

In your Science Journal, write a paragraph that explains why it is important to use tools to measure information.

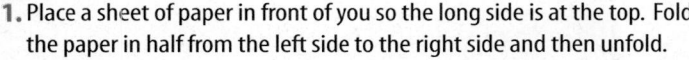

Before You Read

FOLDABLES
Reading & Study
Skills

Making a Question Study Fold **Asking yourself questions helps you stay focused and better understand scientists when you are reading the chapter.**

1. Place a sheet of paper in front of you so the long side is at the top. Fold the paper in half from the left side to the right side and then unfold.

2. Fold each side in to the center line, dividing the paper into fourths.

3. Fold the paper in half from top to bottom and unfold.

4. Through the top thickness of paper, cut along both middle fold lines to form four tabs, as shown. Label each tab *Who, When, What,* and *Why,* as shown.

5. Before you read, select a scientist and write their name on the front of the *Who* tab.

6. As you read the chapter, write answers to *What, When,* and *Why* under the tabs.

5

Purpose Students learn the importance of using tools to measure information. L1 ELL
LS Kinesthetic

Preparation Make sure the hot water is not hot enough to cause burns.

Materials three bowls, hot water, lukewarm water, cold water, thermometer

Teaching Strategies

• Tell students not to say aloud what they feel when they place their hands in the lukewarm water.

• Periodically check the temperatures of the water bowls, and adjust if necessary.

Observe

Answers will vary, but paragraphs should include the ideas that human senses can often be fooled and that using tools is a much more accurate way to collect data.

✓ Assessment

Process Have students compare this experience to the experience of seeing dry ice. Use **Performance Assessment in the Science Classroom,** p. 89.

Before You Read

FOLDABLES
Reading & Study
Skills

Dinah Zike Study Fold
Purpose Have students use a Foldable journal to record ways in which science influences and affects the daily lives of students.

📁 For additional help, see Foldables Worksheet, p. 15 in **Chapter Resources Booklet,** or go to the Glencoe Science Web site at **science.glencoe.com.** See After You Read in the Study Guide at the end of this chapter.

Bellringer Transparency

Display the Section Focus Transparency for Section 1. Use the accompanying Transparency Activity Master. L2 ELL

Tie to Prior Knowledge

Have students discuss what they have read or heard on the news about *E. coli* bacteria. *E. coli* O157:H7 is a strain of *E.coli* that has been responsible in recent years for major outbreaks of the disease colitis, which is characterized by severe abdominal cramping and diarrhea.

What is science?

As You Read

What You'll Learn
- **Identify** how science is a part of your everyday life.
- **Describe** what skills and tools are used in science.

Vocabulary
science
technology

Why It's Important
What and how you learn in science class can be applied to other areas of your life.

Science in Society

When you hear the word *science,* do you think only of your science class, your teacher, and certain terms and facts? Is there any connection between what happens in science class and the rest of your life? You might have problems to solve or questions that need answers, as illustrated in **Figure 1. Science** is a way or a process used to investigate what is happening around you. It can provide possible answers.

Science Is Not New Throughout history, people have tried to find answers to questions about what was happening around them. Early scientists tried to explain things based on their observations. They used their senses of sight, touch, smell, taste, and hearing to make these observations. From the Explore Activity, you know that using only your senses can be misleading. What is cold or hot? How heavy is heavy? How much is a little? How close is nearby? Numbers can be used to describe observations. Tools, such as thermometers and metersticks, are used to give numbers to descriptions. Scientists observe, investigate, and experiment to find answers, and so can you.

Figure 1
You use scientific thinking every day to make decisions.

6 CHAPTER 1

Section ✓Assessment Planner

PORTFOLIO
Science Journal, p. 9
PERFORMANCE ASSESSMENT
MiniLAB, p. 9
Skill Builder Activities, p. 11
See page 34 for more options.

CONTENT ASSESSMENT
Section, p. 11
Challenge, p. 11
Chapter, pp. 34–35

Science as a Tool

As Luis and Midori walked into science class, they still were talking about their new history assignment. Mr. Johnson overheard them and asked what they were excited about.

"We have a special assignment—celebrating the founding of our town 200 years ago," answered Luis. "We need to do a project that demonstrates the similarities of and differences between a past event and something that is happening in our community now."

Mr. Johnson responded. "That sounds like a big undertaking. Have you chosen the two events yet?"

"We read some old newspaper articles and found several stories about a cholera epidemic here that killed ten people and made more than 50 others ill. It happened in 1871—soon after the Civil War. Midori and I think that it's like the *E. coli* outbreak going on now in our town," replied Luis.

"What do you know about an outbreak of cholera and problems caused by *E. coli*, Luis?"

"Well, Mr. Johnson, cholera is a disease caused by a bacterium that is found in contaminated water," Luis replied. "People who eat food from this water or drink this water have bad cases of diarrhea and can become dehydrated quickly. They might even die. *E. coli* is another type of bacterium. Some types of *E. coli* are harmless, but others cause intestinal problems when contaminated food and water are consumed."

"In fact," added Midori, "one of the workers at my dad's store is just getting over being sick from *E. coli*. Anyway, Mr. Johnson, we want to know if you can help us with the project. We want to compare how people tracked down the source of the cholera in 1871 with how they are tracking down the source of the *E. coli* now."

Using Science Every Day

"I'll be glad to help. This sounds like a great way to show how science is a part of everyone's life. In fact, you are acting like scientists right now," Mr. Johnson said proudly.

Luis had a puzzled look on his face, then he asked, "What do you mean? How can we be doing science? This is supposed to be a history project."

Figure 2
Newspapers, magazines, books, and the Internet are all good sources of information.

Health
INTEGRATION

You can't prevent all illnesses. You can, however, take steps to reduce your chances of coming in contact with disease-causing organisms. Antibacterial soaps and cleansers claim to kill such organisms, but how do you know if they work? Read ads for or labels on such products. Do they include data to support their claims? Communicate what you learn to your class.

IDENTIFYING
Misconceptions

Many students think of bacteria as harmful "germs." Explain to students that not all bacteria are harmful. *E. coli* is a type of bacteria that is normally found in the intestines of humans and some other animals. Most strains of *E. coli* do not cause disease.

Teacher FYI

German bacteriologist Robert Koch (1843–1910) and French chemist Louis Pasteur (1822–1895) are widely regarded as the founders of modern bacteriology. Pasteur developed a method to heat foods and beverages at a temperature low enough not to ruin them, but high enough to kill microorganisms—a process known as *pasteurization*. Koch demonstrated that tuberculosis was caused by bacteria, not genes. His methods for isolating microorganisms and his other procedures gave medical investigators valuable insights into the control of bacterial infections.

Resource Manager

Chapter Resources Booklet
  Transparency Activity, p. 42
  Enrichment, p. 28
Reading and Writing Skill Activities, p. 17

Curriculum Connection

Health *E. coli* O157:H7 can be transmitted to humans by eating beef, drinking unpasteurized milk or apple cider, or drinking contaminated water. *E. coli* O157:H7 produces a toxin that can result in a range of symptoms, from mild diarrhea, which is often bloody, to damaged blood vessels and kidneys, which sometimes causes death.

Health
INTEGRATION

Answers will vary but should include the product claims and whatever data the students gather in their research.

Using Prior Knowledge

Use an Analogy

Point out that learning science skills is similar to learning to play a musical instrument. You must practice science skills to get them right, just as you must practice a musical instrument to play it well.

Discussion

Why do scientists need to obtain background information when doing research? By doing background research, scientists can learn what has already been done in the field and what has been successful and what has not. Scientists may also learn about materials, equipment, and specific methods researchers have used in the past.

Caption Answer

Figure 3 Possible answers: use prior knowledge, conduct research; personal observations, newspapers, books, science journals, scientific lectures, the Internet, prior knowledge.

Using Science and Technology

Extension

Have students choose a topic to research. Have them locate five articles from science magazines or the Glencoe Science Web site. Students should write one new fact they learned from each article. L2 IS **Linguistic**

Visual Learning

Figure 4 Why have computers become an important research tool? They can store data, analyze experimental data, play CD-ROMs containing background information, and connect to the Internet. Also, computers greatly reduce the amount of time needed for research.

Research Visit the Glencoe Science Web site at **science.glencoe.com** for more information about disease control. Report two different diseases that the Centers for Disease Control and Prevention (CDC) have tracked down and identified in the past five years. Make a poster that shows what you have learned.

Figure 3
When solving a problem, it is important to discover all background information. Different sources can provide such information. *How would you find information on a specific topic? What sources of information would you use?*

Scientists Use Clues "Well, you're acting like a detective right now. You have a problem to solve. You and Midori are looking for clues that show how the two events are similar and different. As you complete the project, you will use several skills and tools to find the clues." Mr. Johnson continued, "In many ways, scientists do the same thing. People in 1871 followed clues to track the source of the cholera epidemic and solve their problem. Today, scientists are doing the same thing by finding and following clues to track the source of the *E. coli.*"

Using Prior Knowledge

Mr. Johnson asked, "Luis, how do you know what is needed to complete your project?"

Luis thought, then responded, "Our history teacher, Ms. Hernandez, said the report must be at least three pages long and have maps, pictures, or charts and graphs. We have to use information from different sources such as written articles, letters, videotapes, or the Internet. I also know that it must be handed in on time and that correct spelling and grammar count."

"Did Ms. Hernandez actually talk about correct spelling and grammar?" asked Mr. Johnson.

Midori quickly responded, "No, she didn't have to. Everyone knows that Ms. Hernandez takes points away for incorrect spelling or grammar. I forgot to check my spelling in my last report and she took off two points."

"Ah-ha! That's where your project is like science," exclaimed Mr. Johnson. "You know from experience what will happen. When you don't follow her rule, you lose points. You can predict, or make an educated guess, that Ms. Hernandez will react the same way with this report as she has with others."

Mr. Johnson continued, "Scientists also use prior experience to predict what will occur in investigations. Scientists form theories when their predictions have been well tested. A theory is an explanation that is supported by facts. Scientists also form laws, which are rules that describe a pattern in nature, like gravity."

Inclusion Strategies

Learning Disabled Explain how experience is important for solving problems. Suppose you lost a set of keys. You might think about when you last saw the keys and where you've been since. If you sat in a certain chair, you would look there. If you went into the kitchen for a snack, you would try there next. You do not try the same thing again if it did not work the first time. You make a new prediction instead.

Internet Addresses

_____

_____

_____

Explore the Glencoe Science Web site at **science.glencoe.com** to find out more about topics in this section.

Using Science and Technology

"Midori, you said that you want to compare how the two diseases were tracked. Like scientists, you will use skills and tools to find the similarities and differences." Mr. Johnson then pointed to Luis. "You need a variety of resource materials to find information. How will you know which materials will be useful?"

"We can use a computer to find books, magazines, newspapers, videos, and web pages that have information we need," said Luis.

"Exactly," said Mr. Johnson. "That's another way that you are thinking like scientists. The computer is one tool that modern scientists use to find and analyze data. The computer is an example of technology. **Technology** is the application of science to make products or tools that people can use. One of the big differences you will find between the way diseases were tracked in 1871 and how they are tracked now is the result of new technology."

Science Skills Perhaps some of the skills used to track the two diseases will be one of the similarities between the two time periods," continued Mr. Johnson. "Today's doctors and scientists, like those in the late 1800s, use skills such as observing, classifying, and interpreting data. In fact, you might want to review the science skills we've talked about in class. That way, you'll be able to identify how they were used during the cholera outbreak and how they still are used today."

Luis and Midori began reviewing the science skills that Mr. Johnson had mentioned. Some of these skills used by scientists are described in the **Science Skill Handbook** at the back of this book. The more you practice these skills, the better you will become at using them.

Figure 4
Computers are one example of technology. Schools and libraries often provide computers for students to do research and word processing.

Inferring from Pictures
Procedure
1. Study the two pictures to the left. Write your observations in your **Science Journal.**
2. Make and record inferences based on your observations.
3. Share your inferences with others in your class.

Analysis
1. Analyze your inferences. Are there other explanations for what you observed?
2. Why must you be careful when making inferences?

Using Science and Technology, continued

 **Reading Check**

Answer observing, measuring, comparing and contrasting

Use Science Words

Word Meaning In science, an *observation* is what you learn through your senses. An *inference* is how you explain what you observe. Tell students to be careful when making inferences from observations. Remind them that in the Explore Activity they could not tell the temperature of the lukewarm water. They needed further observations, such as measuring with a thermometer, to draw a conclusion. Other instruments, such as balances to measure mass, are used in the laboratory to make accurate observations.

Communication in Science

Quick Demo

Provide students with examples of articles from professional scientific journals, such as *Nature* and *Science*. Show students examples from different sciences.

Teacher FYI

Caution students that just because information is available, it is not necessarily reliable. Point out that anyone can construct a Web site and post information on the Internet. Discuss reliable sources of information, such as government agencies, universities, and professional organizations.

Observation and Measurement Think about the Explore Activity at the beginning of this chapter. Observing, measuring, and comparing and contrasting are three skills you used to complete the activity. Scientists probably use these skills more than other people do. You will learn that sometimes observation alone does not provide a complete picture of what is happening. To ensure that your data are useful, accurate measurements must be taken, in addition to making careful observations.

 **Reading Check** *What are three skills commonly used in science?*

Luis and Midori want to find the similarities and differences between the disease-tracking techniques used in the late 1800s and today. They will use the comparing and contrasting skill. When they look for similarities among available techniques, they compare them. Contrasting the available techniques is looking for differences.

Communication in Science

What do scientists do with their findings? The results of their observations, experiments, and investigations will not be of use to the rest of the world unless they are shared. Scientists use several methods to communicate their observations.

Results and conclusions of experiments often are reported in one of the thousands of scientific journals or magazines that are published each year. Some of these publications are shown in **Figure 5.** Scientists spend a large part of their time reading journal articles. Sometimes, scientists discover information in articles that might lead to new experiments.

Figure 5
Scientific publications allow scientists around the world to learn about the latest research. Papers are submitted to journals. Other scientists review them before they are published.

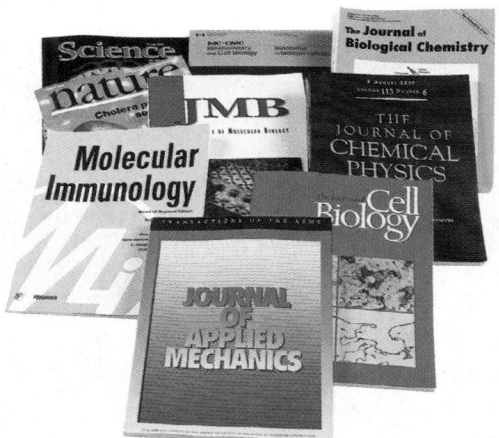

Resource Manager

Chapter Resources Booklet
  Reinforcement, p. 25
Cultural Diversity, p. 29
Life Science Critical Thinking/Problem Solving, p. 1

Cultural Diversity

An Accomplished Scientist Shirley Jackson entered the Massachusetts Institute of Technology (MIT) in 1964. She was one of two African American women in a group of no more than 40 women in the school—a pioneer for both women and African Americans. In 1973, Jackson became the first African American to receive a doctoral degree in physics from MIT. Have students investigate Jackson's many accomplishments.

Science Journal Another method to communicate scientific data and results is to keep a Science Journal. Observations and plans for investigations can be recorded, along with the step-by-step procedures that were followed. Listings of materials and drawings of how equipment was set up should be in a journal, along with the specific results of an investigation. You should record mathematical measurements or formulas that were used to analyze the data. Problems that occurred and questions that came up during the investigation should be noted, as well as any possible solutions. Your data might be summarized in the form of tables, charts, or graphs, or they might be recorded in a paragraph. Remember that it's always important to use correct spelling and grammar in your Science Journal.

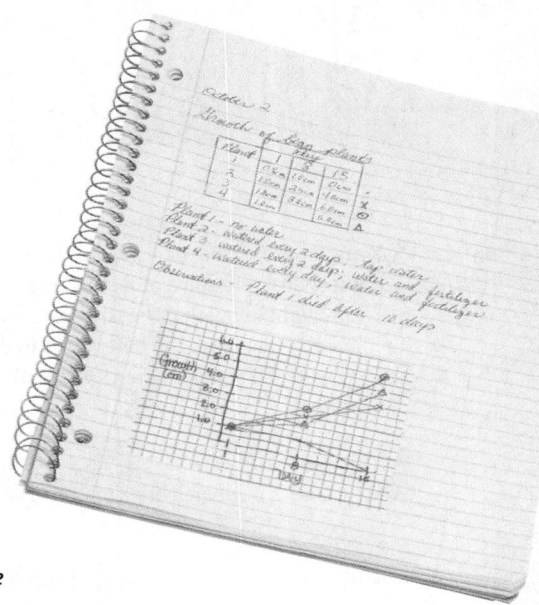

 Reading Check *What are some ways to summarize data from an investigation?*

You will be able to use your Science Journal, as illustrated in **Figure 6,** to communicate your observations, questions, thoughts, and ideas as you work in science class. You will practice many of the science skills and become better at identifying problems. You will learn to plan investigations and experiments that might solve these problems.

Figure 6
Your Science Journal is used to record and communicate your findings. It might include graphs, tables, and illustrations.

Section 1 Assessment

1. Why do scientists use tools, such as thermometers and metersticks, when they make observations?

2. What are some sources for information about problems that you need to solve?

3. What are some skills used in science? Name one science skill that you have used today.

4. Give one example of technology. How is technology different from science?

5. **Think Critically** Why is a Science Journal used to record data? What are three different ways you could record or summarize data in your Science Journal?

Skill Builder Activities

6. **Comparing and Contrasting** Sometimes you use your senses and observations to find the answer to a question. Other times you use tools and measurements to provide answers. Compare and contrast these two methods of answering scientific questions. **For more help, refer to the** Science Skill Handbook.

7. **Communicating** In your Science Journal record five things you observe in or about your classroom. Make sure to include observations based on more than just one of your senses. **For more help, refer to the** Science Skill Handbook.

Answer Tables, graphs, and charts are clear, concise ways of summarizing data from an investigation.

3 Assess

Reteach
Have students list the science skills discussed in this section and give one example of how they use each skill in everyday life. [L2]

Challenge
How might advanced computer technologies benefit societies of the future? Answers will vary. Students may mention an increasing use of robots for such things as surgery, manufacturing, and education. Students may also mention how new computer technologies might be used in space exploration or for cleaning the environment.

✔ Assessment

Process Make a table that compares and contrasts the various sources of information available today with the sources available 100 years ago. Use **Performance Assessment in the Science Classroom,** p. 109.

Answers to Section Assessment

1. Tools quantify observations and make them more accurate.
2. prior experience, books, newspapers, magazines, the Internet
3. Possible answers: observation, measurement, making inferences, comparing and contrasting, graphing, classifying, predicting, and sequencing
4. Answers will vary. Science is a process,

a way of thinking that helps people solve problems and answer questions. Technology is using science to make products or tools people can use.
5. A Science Journal can be used to record investigative data and display results so they can be communicated to others. Data may be summarized in charts, tables, and graphs.

6. Both methods are important. However, sometimes the senses can be tricked. Tools and measurements are more accurate and therefore are more reliable.
7. Answers may include smells, different sounds, colors, and temperature. Accept all reasonable answers.

Activity

Purpose Students will use basic science skills to perform a product evaluation of different brands of drink mix powder.

Process Skills Measuring, observing, identifying, controlling variables, discussing, inferring

Time Requirement 40 minutes

Safety Precautions Caution students never to eat or drink anything in science class without permission.

Teaching Strategy Ask students to dissolve one level spoonful of powder at a time to be certain groups do not fall behind.

Troubleshooting Substituting a small plastic container or beaker for the weighing paper will avoid excess mess.

Answers to Questions

1. Answers will be subjective and based on the students' individual research.
2. Answers will vary, but students will probably infer that the best dissolving drink mix brand with the darkest color will probably taste best.
3. Answers will vary based on the the students' individual research. Science skills should include measuring, observing, recording and analyzing data, drawing conclusions, and communicating results.
4. Answers will vary based on the students' individual research.

✓Assessment

Process Ask each student group to design an experiment to test the primary characteristics of a certain product such as the strength of paper towels or clinging ability of transparent wrap. Use **Performance Assessment in the Science Classroom,** p. 95.

Activity — Battle of the Drink Mixes

You can use science skills to answer everyday questions or to solve problems. For example, you might know that the cheapest brand of a product is not always the best value. In this activity, you will test one aspect, or quality, of a product.

What You'll Investigate
Which brand of powdered drink mix dissolves best?

Materials
weighing paper
50-mL graduated cylinder
powdered drink
  mixes (3 or 4)
triple-beam balance
250-mL beaker
water
spoon

Goals
■ **Determine** which brand of powdered drink mix dissolves best using science skills.

Safety Precautions
WARNING: *Never eat or drink anything during science experiments.*

Procedure

1. Copy the following data table in your Science Journal.

Drink Mix Data	
Drink Mix	**Mass of Dissolved Powder (g)**
1	15
2	12
3	17

2. Using the graduated cylinder, measure 50 mL of water and pour the water into the beaker.
3. **Measure** 20 g of powder from one of the drink-mix brands.

4. Gradually add the powder to the water. Stir the mixture each time you add more powder. Stop adding powder when undissolved powder begins to accumulate at the bottom of the beaker.
5. **Measure** the mass of the remaining powder. Subtract this number from 20 g to find the amount of powder that was dissolved. Record your answer in your data table.
6. Empty the drink mix into the sink, rinse out your beaker, and repeat steps 2 through 5 for the other drink-mix brands.

Conclude and Apply

1. **Identify** the drink-mix powder that dissolved best in the water.
2. Based on the data you collected, infer which drink-mix brand would taste the best. Remember, do not taste any of your samples.
3. Which drink-mix brand would you buy? Identify the science skills you used during this experiment that helped you determine the best drink mix.
4. Review promotional pamphlets for services such as landscaping or pool services. Make a list of inferences about the claims presented.

Communicating Your Data

Write the script for a 15 s advertisement that tells why people should buy your best-dissolving drink-mix brand. Perform your commercial for the class. **For more help, refer to the Science Skill Handbook.**

Communicating Your Data

Have students bring in sample food advertisements from television programs and ask them to evaluate and identify basic components used by advertisers to sell products.

Resource Manager

Chapter Resources Booklet
  Activity Worksheet, pp. 5–6

Earth Science Critical Thinking/Problem Solving, p. 23

Performance Assessment in the Science Classroom, p. 52

Doing Science

Solving Problems

When Luis and Midori did their project, they were answering a question. However, there is more than one way to answer a question or solve a scientific problem. Every day, scientists work to solve scientific problems. Although the investigation of each problem is different, scientists use some steps in all investigations.

Identify the Problem Scientists first make sure that everyone working to solve the problem has a clear understanding of the problem. Sometimes, scientists find that the problem is easy to identify or that several problems need to be solved. For example, before a scientist can find the source of a disease, the disease must be identified correctly.

How can the problem be solved? Scientists know that scientific problems can be solved in different ways. Two of the methods used to answer questions are descriptive research and experimental research design. **Descriptive research** answers scientific questions through observation. When Louis and Midori gathered information to learn about cholera and *E. coli,* they performed descriptive research. **Experimental research design** is used to answer scientific questions by testing a hypothesis through the use of a series of carefully controlled steps. **Scientific methods,** like the one shown in **Figure 7,** are ways, or steps to follow, to try to solve problems. Different problems will require different scientific methods to solve them.

As You Read

What **You'll Learn**
- **Examine** the steps used to solve a problem in a scientific way.
- **Explain** how a well-designed investigation is developed.

Vocabulary
descriptive research
experimental research design
scientific methods
model
hypothesis
independent variable
dependent variable
constant
control

Why **It's Important**
Using scientific methods and carefully thought-out experiments can help you solve problems.

Recognize the problem

Form a Hypothesis!

Test your hypothesis

Analyze your data

Draw conclusions

Figure 7
This poster shows one way to solve problems using scientific methods.

Doing Science

1 Motivate

Bellringer Transparency
 Display the Section Focus Transparency for Section 2. Use the accompanying Transparency Activity Master. L2
ELL

Tie to Prior Knowledge

Have students describe investigations they have done in the past. Students should explain what problem they were trying to solve and the materials and methods they used. Point out that investigations do not have to involve sophisticated equipment. An investigation may be as simple as making observations of an animal.

Section ✓*Assessment* Planner

PORTFOLIO
Curriculum Connection, p. 17
PERFORMANCE ASSESSMENT
Problem-Solving Activities, p. 14
Try at Home MiniLAB, p. 18
Skill Builder Activities, p. 23
See page 34 for more options.

CONTENT ASSESSMENT
Section, p. 23
Challenge, p. 23
Chapter, pp. 34–35

Problem-Solving Activity

National Math Standards

Correlation to Mathematics Objectives

1, 2, 5, 6, 7, 8, 9, 10

Answers
1. Students should observe that the larger states are not always the most populated. Alaska is the least populated state, yet it has the greatest square area of land. The data table doesn't show a correlation between population and area.
2. In order to be conclusive, statistics of several different states should be researched. Additional research on the states' economies and population distributions would also be valuable.

Figure 8
Items can be described by using words and numbers. *How could you describe these objects using both of these methods?*

Descriptive Research

Some scientific problems can be solved, or questions answered, by using descriptive research. Descriptive research is based mostly on observations. What observations can you make about the objects in **Figure 8?** Descriptive research can be used in investigations when experiments would be impossible to perform. For example, a London doctor, Dr. John Snow, tracked the source of a cholera epidemic in the 1800s by using descriptive research. Descriptive research usually involves the following steps.

State the Research Objective This is the first step in solving a problem using descriptive research. A research objective is what you want to find out, or what question you would like to answer. Luis and Midori might have said that their research objective was "to find out how the sources of the cholera epidemic and *E. coli* epidemic were tracked." Dr. John Snow might have stated his research objective as "finding the source of the cholera epidemic in London."

Problem-Solving Activity

Problem-Solving Skills

Drawing Conclusions from a Data Table
During an investigation, data tables often are used to record information. The data can be evaluated to decide whether or not the prediction was supported and then conclusions can be drawn.

A group of students conducted an investigation of the human populations of some states in the United States. They predicted that the states with the highest human population also would have the largest area of land. Do you have a different prediction? Record your prediction in your Science Journal before continuing.

Identifying the Problem

The results of the students' research are shown in this chart. Listed are several states in the United States, their human population, and land area.

State Population and Size		
State	**Human Population**	**Area (km²)**
New York	18,976,457	122,284
New Jersey	8,414,350	19,210
Massachusetts	6,349,097	20,306
Maine	1,274,923	79,932
Montana	902,195	376,978
North Dakota	642,200	178,647
Alaska	626,902	1,481,350

Source: United States Census Bureau, United States Census 2000

1. What can you conclude about your prediction? If your prediction is not supported by the data, can you come up with a new prediction? Explain.
2. What other research could be conducted to support your prediction?

14   CHAPTER 1 The Nature of Science

✔ Active Reading

Reciprocal Teaching This strategy is designed to help construct meaning and apply reading skills. Have pairs of students begin by each partner silently reading a portion of text. After several minutes of reading, one student retells the key points of what was read in his or her own words. The other student asks a question that can be answered directly from the text but could require inferences or evaluation. Continue the reading with each student alternating the questions and summaries. Consciously asking questions and summarizing content will help students to listen to what is being read. Have students do Reciprocal Reading with text about doing science.

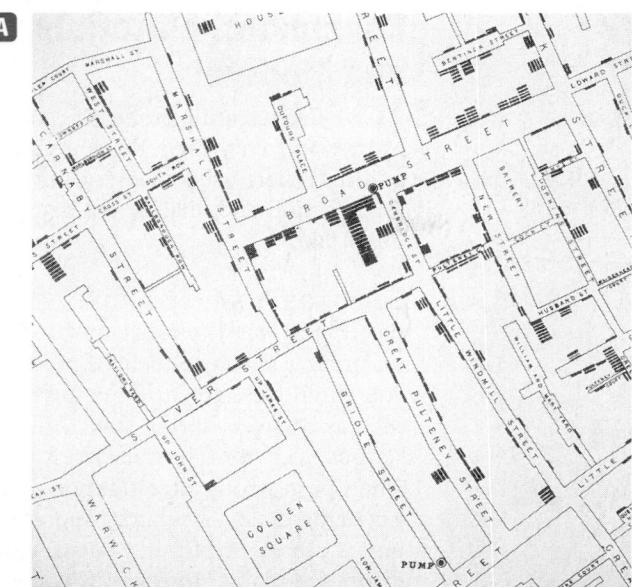

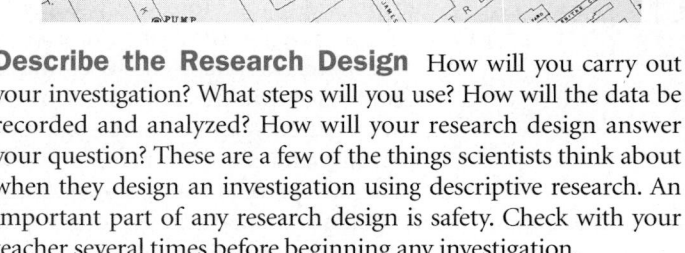

A

B

Describe the Research Design
How will you carry out your investigation? What steps will you use? How will the data be recorded and analyzed? How will your research design answer your question? These are a few of the things scientists think about when they design an investigation using descriptive research. An important part of any research design is safety. Check with your teacher several times before beginning any investigation.

✓ Reading Check *What are some questions to think about when planning an investigation?*

Dr. John Snow's research design included the map in **Figure 9A.** The map shows where people with cholera had lived, and where they obtained their water. He used these data to predict that the water from the Broad Street pump, shown in **Figure 9B,** was the source of the contamination.

Eliminate Bias
It's a Saturday afternoon. You want to see a certain movie, but your friends do not. To persuade them, you tell them about a part of the show that they will find interesting. You give only partial information so they will make the choice you want. Similarly, scientists might expect certain results. This is known as bias. Good investigations avoid bias. One way to avoid bias is to use careful numerical measurements for all data. Another type of bias can occur in surveys or groups that are chosen for investigations. To get an accurate result, you need to use a random sample.

Figure 9
A Each mark on Dr. Snow's map shows where a cholera victim lived. **B** Dr. Snow had the water-pump handle removed, and the cholera epidemic ended.

Environmental Science
INTEGRATION

The U.S. Congress has passed several laws to reduce water pollution. The 1986 Safe Drinking Water Act is a law to ensure that drinking water in the United States is safe. The 1987 Clean Water Act gives money to the states for building sewage- and wastewater-treatment facilities. Find information about a state or local water quality law and share your findings with the class.

Equipment, Materials, and Models

Use Science Words

Word Origin The word *experiment* is related to the Latin root *experiri*, which means "to try." Have students explain how the meaning of the word reflects its root. [L2] [IS] **Linguistic**

Teacher FYI

Making a model is one way to solve a problem or answer a question. A model is an idea, system, or structure that represents whatever you are trying to explain. The model is never exactly like the thing being explained, but it is similar enough to allow comparisons (a good example is a globe). Models are used in many scientific investigations. To find out how airplane shape affects performance, scientists may make model airplanes of different shapes. These models are based on theories that describe how moving air behaves. Scientists then test the different models under various conditions to find out which shape works best. They also may create different computer models.

Make a Model

Explain to students that a model can be as detailed as one wishes. The more detailed a model is, the more useful it is for making predictions. Have students draw maps of the insides of their homes. Tell them to be as detailed with their maps as possible; the maps should be detailed enough so that someone who has never been there could find their way around. [L2] [IS] **Kinesthetic**

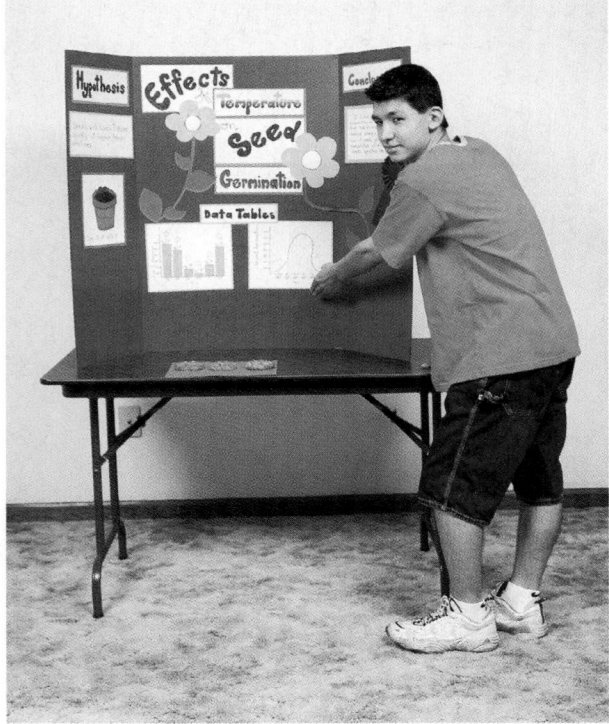

Figure 10
This presentation neatly and clearly shows experimental data.

Equipment, Materials, and Models

When a scientific problem is solved by descriptive research, the equipment and materials used to carry out the investigation and analyze the data are important.

Selecting Your Materials Scientists try to use the most up-to-date materials available to them. If possible, you should use scientific equipment such as balances, spring scales, microscopes, and metric measurements when performing investigations and gathering data. Calculators and computers can be helpful in evaluating or displaying data. However, you don't have to have the latest or most expensive materials and tools to conduct good scientific investigations. Your investigations can be completed successfully and the data displayed with materials found in your home or classroom, like paper, colored pencils, or markers. An organized presentation of data, like the one shown in **Figure 10,** is as effective as a computer graphic or an extravagant display.

Using Models One part of carrying out the investigative plan might include making or using scientific models. In science, a **model** represents things that happen too slowly, too quickly, or are too big or too small to observe directly. Models also are useful in situations in which direct observation would be too dangerous or expensive.

Dr. John Snow's map of the cholera epidemic was a model that allowed him to predict possible sources of the epidemic. Today, people in many professions use models. Many kinds of models are made on computers. Graphs, tables, and spreadsheets are models that display information. Computers can produce three-dimensional models of a microscopic bacterium, a huge asteroid, or an erupting volcano. They are used to design safer airplanes and office buildings. Models save time and money by testing ideas that otherwise are too small, too large, or take too long to build.

Curriculum Connection

Math Have students contact the state health department and ask for a summary of reportable communicable diseases for the past year. Have them rank the diseases from the most commonly reported to the least commonly reported. [L2] [IS] **Logical-Mathematical**

Inclusion Strategies

All Special Needs When doing science activities in the classroom, do not give different objects and materials to students who have disabilities. Try to make sure that all the objects you use can be easily manipulated and are easy to see. Students with visual impairments may need to use a hand lens when reading measurements from laboratory equipment or when they are working with very small objects.

Table 1 Common SI Measurements

Measurement	Unit	Symbol	Equal to
Length	1 millimeter	mm	0.001 (1/1,000) m
	1 centimeter	cm	0.01 (1/100) m
	1 meter	m	100 cm
	1 kilometer	km	1,000 m
Liquid Volume	1 milliliter	mL	0.001 L
	1 liter	L	1,000 mL
Mass	1 milligram	mg	0.001 g
	1 gram	g	1,000 mg
	1 kilogram	kg	1,000 g
	1 tonne	t	1,000 kg = 1 metric ton

Scientific Measurement Scientists around the world use a system of measurements called the International System of Units, or SI, to make observations. This allows them to understand each other's research and compare results. Most of the units you will use in science are shown in **Table 1.** Because SI uses certain metric units that are based on units of ten, multiplication and division are easy to do. Prefixes are used with units to change their names to larger or smaller units. See the Reference Handbook to help you convert English units to SI. **Figure 11** shows equipment you can use to measure in SI.

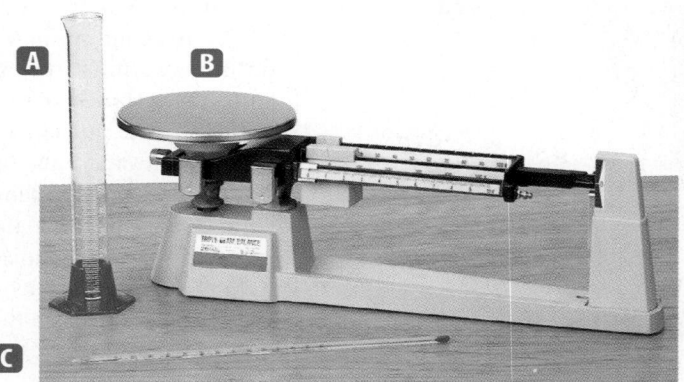

Figure 11
Some of the equipment used by scientists is shown here.
A The amount of space occupied by an object is its volume. A graduated cylinder is used to measure liquid volume. **B** Mass is the amount of matter in an object. Mass is measured with a balance. **C** A scientist would use a thermometer with the Celsius scale to measure temperature. On the Celsius scale, water freezes at 0°C and boils at 100°C.

Resource Manager

Chapter Resources Booklet
  Enrichment, p. 29
Cultural Diversity, p. 55
Home and Community Involvement, p. 23

Equipment, Materials, and Models, continued

Visual Learning

Table 1 Have students examine the organization of this data table. Remind them that a data table is simply a place to record and organize data. Above all, a data table should be functional. It should be easy to use and interpret. Point out that this data table could have been arranged in a different way. Have students study the data table, and then ask them to redesign it. L2 [IS] **Visual-Spatial**

Quick Demo

Tell students you want to measure the circumference of a balloon in centimeters. Take out a metric ruler and try to measure the balloon with it. Show students that you are having difficulty. Ask them to explain why. Students will probably say that you need to use a tape measure. Ask students to explain why the ruler didn't work, even though it measures in the same units. Help students to understand that you need different tools for different measuring tasks.

Curriculum Connection

History Hundreds of people died during London's 1854 cholera epidemic. Ships dumped contaminated water into the Thames River, which supplied drinking water to the city. One company that supplied water to public pumps failed to filter it. Today, international travelers may be at risk of cholera. Have students research and write a report about where most outbreaks occur and how to avoid infection. L2 P

Data

TRY AT HOME

Mini LAB

Purpose Students use scientific methods to evaluate paper towels. **Logical-Mathematical**

Materials three different brands of paper towels, scissors, dropper, water

Teaching Strategies

- Before conducting the experiment, ask students to make a guess and rank the paper towel brands from least to most absorbent. Ask them why guessing is not as reliable as experimentation.
- Remind students to add all drops to the center of the square.

Analysis

1. No; students should use data to support answers.
2. No; the towel may not absorb oil well or may be too expensive.
3. observing, comparing and contrasting

✓Assessment

Portfolio Have students rank the towels from least to most absorbent and from least to most expensive. Have them summarize how absorbency and cost are related. Use **Performance Assessment in the Science Classroom,** p. 115.

TRY AT HOME

Mini LAB

Comparing Paper Towels

Procedure

1. Make a data table similar to the one in **Figure 12.**
2. Cut a 5-cm by 5-cm square from each of **three brands of paper towel.** Lay each piece on a level, smooth, waterproof surface.
3. Add one drop of **water** to each square.
4. Continue to add drops until the piece of paper towel no longer can absorb the water.
5. Tally your observations in a frequency table and graph your results.
6. Repeat steps 2 through 5 three more times.

Analysis

1. Did all the squares of paper towels absorb equal amounts of water?
2. If one brand of paper towel absorbs more water than the others, can you conclude that it is the towel you should buy? Explain.
3. Which scientific methods did you use to compare paper towel absorbency?

Figure 13
Charts and graphs can help you organize and analyze your data.

Figure 12
Data tables help you organize your observations and results.

Paper Towel Absorbency (Drops of Water Per Sheet)			
Trial	Brand A	Brand B	Brand C
1			
2			
3			
4			

Data

In every type of scientific research, data must be collected and organized carefully. When data are well organized, they are easier to interpret and analyze.

Designing Your Data Tables A well-planned investigation includes ways to record results and observations accurately. Data tables, like the one shown in **Figure 12,** are one way to do this. Most tables have a title that tells you at a glance what the table is about. The table is divided into columns and rows. These are usually trials or characteristics to be compared. The first row contains the titles of the columns. The first column identifies what each row represents.

As you complete a data table, you will know that you have the information you need to analyze the results of the investigation accurately. It is wise to make all of your data tables before beginning the experiment. That way, you will have a place for all of your data as soon as they are available.

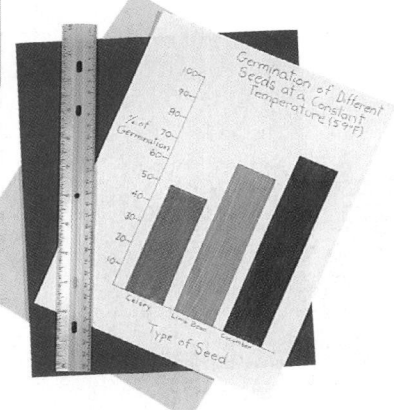

Analyze Your Data
Your investigation is over. You breathe a sigh of relief. Now you have to figure out what your results mean. To do this, you must review all of the recorded observations and measurements. Your data must be organized to analyze them. Charts and graphs are excellent ways to organize data. You can draw the charts and graphs, like the ones in **Figure 13,** or use a computer to make them.

Resource Manager

Chapter Resources Booklet
   MiniLAB, p. 4

Home and Community Involvement, p. 49

Reading and Writing Skill Activities, p. 47

Science Journal

Using Units In their Science Journals, have students list the different units they use every day and what they measure. Possible responses: they measure time in hours or minutes, distance in feet or miles, and the volume of a soda can in ounces. L2

Logical-Mathematical

Draw Conclusions

After you have organized your data, you are ready to draw a conclusion. Do the data answer your question? Was your prediction supported? You might be concerned if your data are not what you expected, but remember, scientists understand that it is important to know when something doesn't work. When looking for an antibiotic to kill a specific bacteria, scientists spend years finding out which antibiotics will work and which won't. Each time scientists find that a particular antibiotic doesn't work, they learn some new information. They use this information to help make other antibiotics that have a better chance of working. A successful investigation is not always the one that comes out the way you originally predicted.

Communicating Your Results Every investigation begins because a problem needs to be solved. Analyzing data and drawing conclusions are the end of the investigation. However, they are not the end of the work a scientist does. Usually, scientists communicate their results to other scientists, government agencies, private industries, or the public. They write reports and presentations that provide details on how experiments were carried out, summaries of the data, and final conclusions. They can include recommendations for further research. Scientists usually publish their most important findings.

✔ **Reading Check** *Why is it important for scientists to communicate their data?*

Just as scientists communicate their findings, you will have the chance to communicate your data and conclusions to other members of your science class, as shown in **Figure 14.** You can give an oral presentation, create a poster, display your results on a bulletin board, prepare computer graphics, or talk with other students or your teacher. You will share with other groups the charts, tables, and graphs that show your data. Your teacher, or other students, might have questions about your investigation or your conclusions. Organized data and careful analysis will allow you to answer most questions and to discuss your work confidently. Analyzing and sharing data are important parts of descriptive and experimental research, as shown in **Figure 15.**

Figure 14
Communicating experimental results is an important part of the laboratory experience.

Discussion

You hypothesize that popcorn stored in the freezer pops better than popcorn stored at room temperature. Name the variables and control for an experiment to test this hypothesis. **Which variable would you change?** Variables are brand name, freshness, amount of corn used, time cooked, amount of heat used, and cooking method. The control is a bag of popcorn stored at room temperature. Your change would be to store one bag of popcorn in the freezer.

Draw Conclusions

✔ **Reading Check**

Answer so other scientists may learn from the information

IDENTIFYING Misconceptions

Students may confuse the everyday use of *theory* with its scientific use. Many people think of theories as unsupported speculation. In science, a theory is based on reasoning and evidence. A theory is a hypothesis that has been confirmed through observations and experiments.

LAB DEMONSTRATION

Purpose to illustrate a controlled experiment

Materials two large beakers, water, antifreeze, thermometer, freezer

Preparation Pour 100 mL of water into each beaker, and label them Beaker 1 and Beaker 2. Pour 50 mL of antifreeze into Beaker 2. Put beakers in a freezer set at 32°F for 2 hours.

Procedure Explain that you have performed an experiment to see if antifreeze lowers the freezing point of water. Show students how you set up the experiment, then display the two beakers.

Expected Outcome Beaker 1: water will be frozen; Beaker 2: contents are liquid

Assessment

Does this experiment prove that antifreeze lowers the freezing point of water? Explain. Yes; the experimental beaker did not freeze at 32°F. **Which was the control and what was its purpose?** beaker with water; showed that pure water will freeze at 32°F

Visualizing Descriptive and Experimental Research

Have students examine the pictures and read the captions. Then ask the following questions.

What are some other settings where both descriptive and experimental research might be used? Possible answer: A hospital, where a patient's condition is assessed both through observation and through testing in a lab setting.

Why might computers and instruments be used to process and analyze data in a wastewater treatment plant? Possible answer: A computer and other instruments might be used due to the large quantity of data that needs to be processed, or the complexity of the calculations that need to be performed.

Activity

Have students contact a local wastewater treatment facility to find out what types of tests are performed there. Have students classify the tests as descriptive or experimental research, and report their findings to the class.

Extension

Provide professional scientific journals or photocopies of journal articles to students. Let the students explore the format of scientific articles, the number and location of authors, and the type of research reported in the articles.

Figure 15

Scientists use a series of steps to solve scientific problems. Depending on the type of problem, they may use descriptive research or experimental research with controlled conditions. Several of the research steps involved in determining water quality at a wastewater treatment plant are shown here.

A Gathering background information is an important first step in descriptive and experimental research.

B Some questions can be answered by descriptive research. Here, the scientists make and record observations about the appearance of a water sample.

C Some questions can be answered by experimentation. These scientists collect a wastewater sample for testing under controlled conditions in the laboratory.

D Careful analysis of data is essential after completing experiments and observations. The technician at right uses computers and other instruments to analyze data.

20 CHAPTER 1

Inclusion Strategies

Gifted Explain that when conducting clinical trials, scientists use samples that represent the population they are studying. Have students plan how they would conduct a survey of 10% of everyone in the school. Offer hints in the form of questions, such as **"How would you categorize and count everyone?"** and **"How would you make sure that 10% of each category was represented?"** L3

Experimental Research Design

Another way to solve scientific problems is through experimentation. Experimental research design answers scientific questions by observation of a controlled situation. Experimental research design includes several steps.

Form a Hypothesis A **hypothesis** (hi PAH thuh sus) is a prediction, or statement, that can be tested. You use your prior knowledge, new information, and any previous observations to form a hypothesis.

Variables In well-planned experiments, one factor, or variable, is changed at a time. This means that the variable is controlled. The variable that is changed is called the **independent variable.** In the experiment shown below, the independent variable is the amount or type of antibiotic applied to the bacteria. A **dependent variable** is the factor being measured. The dependent variable in this experiment is the growth of the bacteria, as shown in **Figure 16.**

To test which of two antibiotics will kill a type of bacterium, you must make sure that every variable remains the same but the type of antibiotic. The variables that stay the same are called **constants.** For example, you cannot run the experiments at two different room temperatures, for different lengths of time, or with different amounts of antibiotics.

Figure 16
In this experiment, the effect of two different antibiotics on bacterial growth was tested. The type of antibiotic is the independent variable.

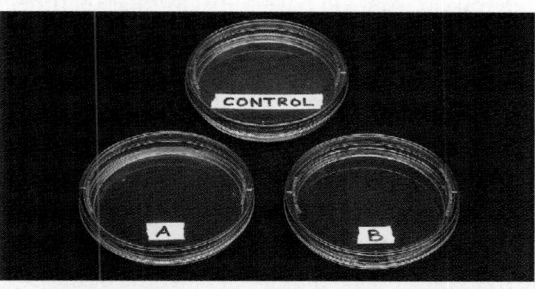

A At the beginning of the experiment, dishes A and B of bacteria were treated with different antibiotics. The control dish did not receive any antibiotic.

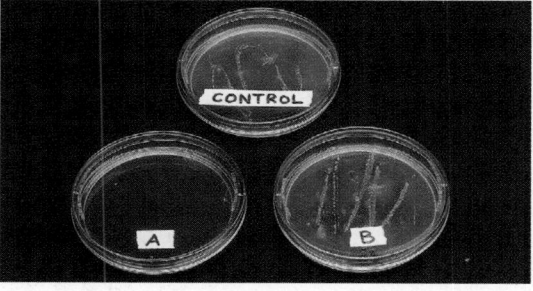

B The results of the experiment are shown. All factors were constant except the type of antibiotic applied. *Based on these photographs, what would you conclude about the effects of these antibiotics on bacteria?*

SECTION 2 Doing Science **21**

Experimental Research Design

Teacher FYI

Students should keep the following guidelines in mind when designing an experiment:

1. You will be more likely to have fun and do a good job if you choose a topic that interests you.
2. Choose a topic within your knowledge level. You will be frustrated and may be unable to complete the experiment if it is too difficult.
3. Make sure you have access to necessary equipment, and have the skills to do the experiment.
4. Design an experiment that will not take too much time to complete.

Activity

Organize the class into groups of four. Give each group an index card on which to write a problem or question for an experiment. Have groups exchange their cards. Each group should generate a hypothesis for the problem or question they now hold and write it on the card. Have them exchange the cards again. One person in each group should read the problem and hypothesis aloud to the class. Have the class discuss whether the hypothesis is appropriate for the problem. L2 ⬛ **Interpersonal**

Caption Answer

Figure 16B The antibiotic in A worked. The antibiotic in B did not work.

Activity

Organize the class into groups of three. Give a rubber ball and a meterstick to each group. Tell students that one person from each group will drop the ball from a height of two meters, one person will count the number of bounces and measure the height of each bounce, and one person will record the results. Groups may perform this procedure as many times as they feel necessary to get a good average.

Have each group design a table to hold their data and report how many times the ball bounced, and the difference in height between the first and last bounce. Ask students if they think their measurements would have been accurate if they had performed the procedure only once. Point out that the more trials conducted in an experiment, the more certain the investigator can be of the results. L2 ELL COOP LEARN
LS Kinesthetic

Figure 17
Check with your teacher several times as you plan your experiment.

Identify Controls Your experiment will not be valid unless a control is used. A **control** is a sample that is treated like the other experimental groups except that the independent variable is not applied to it. In the experiment with antibiotics, your control is a sample of bacteria that is not treated with either antibiotic. The control shows how the bacteria grow when left untreated by either antibiotic.

✔ Reading Check   *What is an experimental control?*

You have formed your hypothesis and planned your experiment. Before you begin, you must give a copy of it to your teacher, who must approve your materials and plans before you begin, as shown in **Figure 17.** This is also a good way to find out whether any problems exist in how you proposed to set up the experiment. Potential problems might include health and safety issues, length of time required to complete the experiment, and the cost and availability of materials.

Once you begin the experiment, make sure to carry it out as planned. Don't skip or change steps in the middle of the process. If you do, you will have to begin the experiment again. Also, you should record your observations and complete your data tables in a timely manner. Incomplete observations and reports result in data that are difficult to analyze and threaten the accuracy of your conclusions.

Number of Trials Experiments done the same way do not always have the same results. To make sure that your results are valid, you need to conduct several trials of your experiment. Multiple trials mean that an unusual outcome of the experiment won't be considered the true result. For example, if another substance is spilled accidentally on one of the containers with an antibiotic, that substance might kill the bacteria. Without results from other trials to use as comparisons, you might think that the antibiotic killed the bacteria. The more trials you do using the same methods, the more likely it is that your results will be reliable and repeatable. The number of trials you choose to do will be based on how much time, space, and material you have to complete the experiment.

Curriculum Connection

Math Have students describe results from investigations that would best be presented in each of the three types of graphs used to display data. Line graphs show trends or how data changes over time. A bar graph is useful for comparing quantities. Circle graphs are used to show how a fixed quantity is broken down into parts. L2
LS Logical-Mathematical

Analyze Your Results After completing your experiment and obtaining all of your data, it is time to analyze your results. Now you can see if your data support your hypothesis. If the data do not support your original hypothesis, you can still learn from the experiment. Experiments that don't work out as you had planned can still provide valuable information. Perhaps your original hypothesis needs to be revised, or your experiment needs to be carried out in a different way. Maybe more background information is available that would help. In any case, remember that professional scientists, like those shown in **Figure 18,** rarely have results that support their hypothesis without completing numerous trials first.

 **Reading Check** *What are some possible reasons that data are different than expected?*

After your results are analyzed, you can communicate them to your teacher and your class. Sharing the results of experiments allows you to hear new ideas from other students that might improve your research. Your results might contain information that will be helpful to other students.

In this section you learned the importance of scientific methods—steps used to solve a problem. Remember that some problems are solved using descriptive research, and others are solved through experimental research. In the next section you will learn more ways that science and technology are parts of your life.

Figure 18
These scientists might work for months or years to find the best experimental design to test a hypothesis.

Section 2 Assessment

1. Why do scientists use models? Give three examples of models.

2. What is a hypothesis?

3. Name the three steps scientists might use when designing an investigation to solve a problem.

4. Why is it important to identify carefully the problem to be solved?

5. **Think Critically** The data that you gathered and recorded during an experiment do not support your original hypothesis. Explain why your experiment is not a failure.

Skill Builder Activities

6. **Measuring in SI** Measurements can communicate experimental results. Use a meterstick to measure the length of your desktop in meters, centimeters, and millimeters. **For more help, refer to the** Science Skill Handbook.

7. **Using Percentages** A town of 1,000 people is divided into five areas, each with the same number of people. Use the data below to make a bar graph showing the number of people ill with cholera in each area. *Area: A—50%; B—5%; C—10%; D—16%; E—35%.* **For more help, refer to the** Math Skill Handbook.

SECTION

Science and Technology

1 Motivate

Bellringer Transparency

Display the Section Focus Transparency for Section 3. Use the accompanying Transparency Activity Master. [L2]

[ELL]

Tie to Prior Knowledge

Initiate a discussion about how people use technology. Ask students to describe some of the technology they use every day.

Visual Learning

Figure 19 Have students list the ways in which the technologies in this figure have affected society.

As You Read

What You'll Learn
- **Determine** how science and technology influence your life.
- **Analyze** how modern technology allows scientific discoveries to be communicated worldwide.

Why It's Important
Modern communication systems allow scientific discoveries and information to be shared with people all over the world.

Science in Your Daily Life

You have learned how science is useful in your daily life. Doing science means more than just completing a science activity, reading a science chapter, memorizing vocabulary words, or following a scientific method to find answers.

Scientific Discoveries

Science is meaningful in other ways in your everyday life. New discoveries constantly lead to new products that influence your lifestyle or standard of living, such as those shown in **Figure 19.** For example, in the last 100 years, technological advances have allowed entertainment to move from live stage shows to large movie screens. Now DVDs allow users to choose a variety of options while viewing a movie. Do you want to hear English dialogue with French subtitles or Spanish dialogue with English subtitles? Do you want to change the ending? You can do it all from your chair by using the remote control.

Figure 19
New technology has changed the way people work and relax.

Section ✓*Assessment* Planner

PORTFOLIO
Extension, p. 25
PERFORMANCE ASSESSMENT
Skill Builder Activities, p. 27
See page 34 for more options.

CONTENT ASSESSMENT
Section, p. 27
Challenge, p. 27
Chapter, pp. 34–35

Technological Advances

Technology also makes your life more convenient. Hand-held computers can be carried in a pocket. Foods can be prepared quickly in microwave ovens, and hydraulic tools make construction work easier and faster. A satellite tracking system in your car can give you verbal and visual directions to a destination in an unfamiliar city.

New discoveries influence other areas of your life as well, including your health. Technological advances, like the ones shown in **Figure 20,** help many people lead healthier lives. A disease might be controlled by a skin patch that releases a constant dose of medicine into your body. Miniature instruments allow doctors to operate on unborn children and save their lives. Bacteria also have been engineered to make important drugs such as insulin for people with diabetes.

Reading Check *What new scientific discoveries have you used?*

Science—The Product of Many

New scientific knowledge can mean that old ways of thinking or doing things are challenged. Aristotle, an ancient Greek philosopher, classified living organisms into plants and animals. This system worked until new tools, such as the microscope, allowed scientists to study organisms in greater detail. The new information changed how scientists viewed the living world. The current classification system will be used only as long as it continues to answer questions scientists have or until a new discovery allows them to look at information in a different way.

Figure 20
Modern medical technology helps people have better health. The physician is studying a series of X rays. New, more complete ways of seeing internal problems helps to solve them.

Research Visit the Glencoe Science Web site at **science.glencoe.com** for news about students who have made a scientific discovery or invented new technology. Communicate to your class what you learn.

Resource Manager

Chapter Resources Booklet
 Transparency Activity, p. 44
 Enrichment, p. 30
Cultural Diversity, p. 49

② Teach

Scientific Discoveries

Discussion

Discuss how technologies such as microprocessors, jumbo jets, lasers, fiber-optic communication, satellites, and genetically engineered products have affected modern society. Be sure to discuss both positive and negative aspects.

Extension

Have students research the kinds of technology used in producing animated movies. Have students make posters of their findings to display to the class. L2 IS **Visual-Spatial** P

Reading Check

Answer Answers will vary but may include hand-held computers, microwave ovens, satellite television, or prescription drugs.

SCIENCE Online
Internet Addresses

_____
_____
_____

Explore the Glencoe Science Web site at **science.glencoe.com** to find out more about topics in this section.

Inclusion Strategies

Learning Disabled Using a bubble map helps students understand the relationships between certain terms and concepts. Words are clustered to describe a topic or idea that is studied. Students can use a bubble map for prewriting, to generate ideas before writing in their Science Journals, or to review for a test. Have students design a bubble map for a concept in this section. L1 IS **Visual-Spatial**

Science—The Product of Many

Activity

Have students bring in examples of packaging that show technological improvements, such as twist-off bottle caps, pull-tab cans, or self-sealing food storage bags. Explain to students that it wasn't too long ago that these types of products didn't exist. If possible, bring in examples (photos or the actual items) of old-style packaging to show to the class. Have them compare the benefits and possible drawbacks of these products. L2

Extension

Encourage interested students to investigate some of the important technological improvements to cars that have been developed over the past 25 years. Possible answers: improved streamlining, tires that prevent hydroplaning, light-weight construction, and halogen headlights L2

Discussion

Discuss with students how new computer technologies have dramatically changed the way science is done. Provide students with examples from videos, magazines, journals, or books that explain how computers are used for particular science applications. Ideas include the use of computers in meteorology, ecosystem modeling, and paleontology.

Figure 21
Science and technology are the results of many people's efforts.

Who practices science? Scientific discoveries have never been limited to people of one race, sex, culture, or time period, or to professional scientists, as shown in **Figure 21**. In fact, students your age have made some important discoveries.

A Sarita M. James was a teenager when she developed a system that allows computers to recognize human speech easily.

B Stephen Hawking, a physicist, studies the universe and black holes.

C Grace Murray Hopper, a mathematician and software developer, helped pioneer the computer field.

D Fred Begay is a physicist who studies ways to produce heat energy without harming the environment.

E Ellen Ochoa is an inventor and an astronaut in NASA's space shuttle program.

F Daniel Hale Williams performed the first open-heart surgery and founded a hospital.

26 CHAPTER 1 The Nature of Science

Resource Manager

Chapter Resources Booklet
Reinforcement, p. 27
Directed Reading For Content Mastery, pp. 19, 20
Reading and Writing Skill Activities, p. 9

Use of Scientific Information The Internet quickly spreads word of new discoveries. New knowledge and technology brought about by these discoveries are shared by people in all countries. Any information gathered from the Internet must be checked carefully for accuracy.

Science provides new information every day that people use to make decisions. A new drug can be found or a new way to produce electricity can be developed. However, science cannot decide whether the new information is good or bad, moral or immoral. People decide whether the new information is used to help or harm the world and its inhabitants.

Looking to the Future

Midori and Luis discovered that technology has changed how modern scientists track the source of a disease. New information about bacteria and modern tools, such as those shown in **Figure 22,** help identify specific types of these organisms. Computers are used to model how the bacteria kill healthy cells or which part of a population the bacteria will infect. Today's scientists use cellular phones and computers to communicate with each other. This information technology has led to the globalization, or worldwide distribution, of information.

Figure 22
Modern laboratories allow scientists to track the source of a disease or solve many other scientific problems.

3 Assess

Reteach
On the chalkboard, list some general reasons why it is important to have scientific literacy. Ask the class to provide examples for each general category. L2 COOP LEARN Interpersonal

Challenge
Have students brainstorm ideas about how familiar machines, such as televisions, computers, telephones, refrigerators, stereos, and microwave ovens will change in the future. Have them suggest new products that will improve on these familiar devices. L2 COOP LEARN Interpersonal

Assessment

Portfolio Have students look through the local paper or recent issues of magazines for one week and identify articles about new scientific discoveries or new products. Have students write a short summary about the article and present it to the class. Use **Performance Assessment in the Science Classroom,** p. 159.

Section 3 Assessment

1. What is one way that science or technology has improved your health?

2. What might cause scientists to change a 100-year-old theory?

3. List five ways that scientists are able to communicate their discoveries.

4. Name an advance in technology that makes your life more enjoyable. What discoveries contributed to this technology?

5. **Think Critically** Explain why modern communications systems are important to scientists worldwide.

Skill Builder Activities

6. **Comparing and Contrasting** Make a drawing showing how a modern scientist and one from the 1800s would communicate their data with other scientists of their time. **For more help, refer to the** Science Skill Handbook.

7. **Using a Word Processor** Research the life of a famous scientist. Find at least two sources for your information. Take notes on ten facts about the scientist and use a word processing program to write a short biography. **For more help, refer to the** Technology Skill Handbook.

SECTION 3 Science and Technology **27**

Answers to Section Assessment

1. New drugs, medicines, and surgical techniques have been developed.
2. New information might prove the theory wrong or allow scientists to look at it differently.
3. published articles, books, the Internet, lectures, computers
4. Answers will vary.
5. They allow scientists to communicate their findings rapidly.
6. Drawings will vary. Scientists in the 1800s would be writing in a journal or a letter. Another possible form of communication would be the telegraph or telephone (after it was invented). Modern scientists could

be writing on a computer, using the World Wide Web or a cell phone, or video conferencing.
7. Check students' work.

Activity

Recognize the Problem

Internet Students will use Internet sites that can be accessed through the Glencoe Science Web site. They will investigate how information travels through the Internet as well as how long it takes for information to travel through the Internet at different times of day.

Non-Internet Sources Collect recent magazine articles that discuss current issues related to Internet use.

Time Required

about three days

Preparation

Internet Access the Glencoe Science Web site to run through the steps that the students will follow.

Non-Internet Have students review magazine articles to find out information about Internet traffic at different times of the day.

Form a Hypothesis

Possible Hypothesis

Students may choose to investigate the times of day when the people in their lives most often use the Internet. This allows them to form an opinion about how long it takes for information to travel. For example, data travels at its slowest rate in the evening hours, from 5:00 P.M. to 8:00 P.M.

Activity — Use the Internet

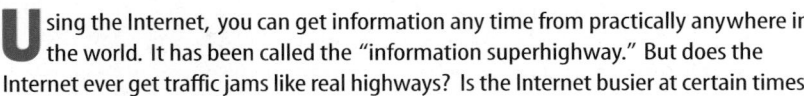

When is the Internet the busiest?

Using the Internet, you can get information any time from practically anywhere in the world. It has been called the "information superhighway." But does the Internet ever get traffic jams like real highways? Is the Internet busier at certain times?

Recognize the Problem

How long does it take data to travel across the Internet at different times of the day?

Form a Hypothesis

Think about using the Internet. When are you online most often? When do most other people use the Internet? Can you measure how busy the Internet is? Form a prediction about what time of day the Internet is the busiest.

Goals
- **Observe** when you, your friends, or your family use the Internet.
- **Research** how to measure the speed of the Internet.
- **Identify** the times of day when the Internet is the busiest in different areas of the country.
- **Graph** your findings and communicate them to other students.

Data Source

SCIENCE *Online* Go to the Glencoe Science Web site at **science.glencoe.com** for more information on how to measure the speed of the Internet, when the Internet is busiest, and data from other students.

Test Your Hypothesis

Possible Procedures

Remind students to consider that people use the internet at different times each day all across the country. They should include time zone differences in their hypotheses about the speed of the Internet.

Resource Manager

Chapter Resources Booklet
   Activity Worksheet, pp. 7–8
Lab Management and Safety, p. 63
Reading and Writing Skill Activities, p. 43

Test Your Prediction

Plan

1. **Observe** when you, your family, and your friends use the Internet. Do you think that everyone in the world uses the Internet during the same times?

2. How are you going to measure the speed of the Internet? Research different factors that might affect the speed of the Internet. What are your variables?

3. How many times are you going to measure the speed of the Internet? What times of day are you going to gather your data?

Do

1. Make sure your teacher approves your plan before you start.

2. Visit the Glencoe Science Web site. Click on the Web Links button to view links that will help you do this activity.

3. Complete your investigation as planned.

4. **Record** all of your data in your Science Journal.

5. **Share** your data by posting it on the Glencoe Science Web site.

Analyze Your Data

1. **Record** in your Science Journal what time of day you found it took the most time to send data over the Internet.

2. **Compare** your results with those of other students around the country. In which areas did data travel the most quickly?

Draw Conclusions

1. **Compare** your findings to those of your classmates and other data that were posted on the Glencoe Science Web site. When is the Internet the busiest in your area? How does that compare to different areas of the country?

2. What factors could cause different results in your class?

3. How do you think your data would be affected if you had performed this experiment during a different time of the year, like the winter holidays?

Communicating Your Data

SCIENCE *Online* Find this *Use the Internet* activity on the Glencoe Science Web site at **science. glencoe.com.** **Post** your data in the table provided. Combine your data with those of other students and plot the combined data on a map to recognize patterns in internet traffic.

ACTIVITY 29

Teaching Strategies

As students decide how to measure the speed of the Internet, remind them that the processing speed of the computer they are using, as well as the speed of other computers along the network, may play a role in the speed at which their information travels.

Analyze Your Data

1. Answers will be based on students' individual research.

2. Students should obtain this information from the Glencoe Science Web site. Answers will vary based on individual research.

Error Analysis

Have students compare their results and their hypotheses and explain why differences occurred.

Draw Conclusions

1. Answers will vary. Students may find that their data show that the Internet is busiest at the same time in their area as in a different area of the country if time zone differences are taken into consideration.

2. Answers will vary. Students may find that different computers and different ways to connect to the Internet may be part of the explanation for the differences in the amount of time taken for data to travel.

3. Answers will vary. Students may conclude that the Internet will be busier because people will be home using their computers.

✓Assessment

Oral Have students use the line graphs they constructed with their Internet speed data to analyze the flow of information during different times of the day. Have them describe Internet traffic during different times of day. Students should compare speeds within a time period and hypothesize why Internet speed is faster or slower during other time periods. Use **PASC,** p. 113.

Communicating Your Data

Have students use a word processing program to define the steps used to measure the speed of the Internet. Have them create a step-by-step plan that describes how they will collect data to determine how fast information traveled during their investigation.

The Everglades: River of Grass
by Marjory Stoneman Douglas

Pre-Reading Activity

Ask students their impressions about Florida. Start by asking students if they have ever been to the state of Florida. **What part of Florida did you visit? Was there water near? From your own experience, is the climate in Florida similar to the state in which you live?** It's not likely all students have visited Florida. In this case allow students who have to lead the discussion.

Respond to the Reading

Active Reading Strategies

Predict At certain points in your reading, take time to wonder what will happen next in the passage. **Is this particular passage a work of fiction?** no

Review Review what you have read. By looking back over several paragraphs, you can see how the information fits together. **Have you learned anything new about bodies of water in Florida?** Answers will vary.

Answers to Questions

1. You could research Florida's history using reliable history books. Also, you could research local newspaper articles from the year in which the dike was built.
2. The words "cutting a long ugly canal straight through the green curving jungle" suggests that she dislikes the project.

Respond to the Reading

1. How would you verify facts contained in this passage such as the construction of the dike and its location?
2. What hints does the author give you about her opinion of the dike-building project?

In this passage, Douglas writes about Lake Okeechobee, the large freshwater lake that lies in the southern part of Florida, north of the Everglades. A dike is an earthen wall usually built to protect against floods.

Something had to be done about the control of Okeechobee waters in storms. . . . A vast dike was constructed from east to south to west of the lake, within its average rim.[1] Canal gates were opened in it. It rises now between the lake itself and all those busy towns. . . .

To see the vast pale water you climb the levee[2] and look out upon its emptiness, hear the limpkins[3] crying among the islands of reeds in the foreground, and watch the wheeling creaking sea gulls flying about a man cutting bait in a boat. . . .

From the lake the control project extended west, cutting a long ugly canal straight through the green curving jungle and the grove-covered banks of Caloosahatchee [River].

[1] "Average rim" refers to the average location of the southern bank of the lake. Before the dike was built, heavy rains routinely caused Lake Okeechobee to overflow, emptying water over its southern banks into the Everglades. The overflowing water would carry silt and soil toward the southern banks of the lake, causing the southern banks to vary in size and location.
[2] dike
[3] waterbirds

Reading Further

Other works by this author include:
A River in Flood and Other Florida Stories, by Marjory Stoneman Douglas, University Press of Florida, 1998.

Other sources on this topic include:
Marjory Stoneman Douglas: Friend of the Everglades (Gateway Green Biography), by Tricia Andryszewski, Millbrook Press, 1994.

Understanding Literature

Nonfiction *The Everglades: River of Grass* is a nonfiction book about the history of the Florida Everglades. Nonfiction stories are about real people, places, and events. Nonfiction includes autobiographies, biographies, and essays, as well as encyclopedias, history and science books, and newspaper and magazine articles. When reading nonfiction, you should ask yourself these questions: What do I know about this subject that will help me judge the accuracy of this information? Do I understand why the writer has included this specific information? Does the writer express an opinion about the subject matter?

Science Connection Because nonfiction is based upon real life, nonfiction writers must research their subjects thoroughly. As you learned in this chapter, scientific investigation involves being a detective. Author Marjory Stoneman Douglas relied upon her own observations as a long-time resident of Florida. She also thoroughly researched the history of the Florida Everglades. Douglas's book is an excellent example of the importance of communication in science. *The Everglades: River of Grass* brought the world's attention to the need to preserve the Everglades because of its unique ecosystems.

Linking Science and Writing

Nonfiction Write a one-page nonfiction account of your favorite outdoor place. You might write a description of the place, or write about an experience that you had there. Afterwards, read through your account and underline or highlight the facts that are in it. What information is factual? What information is based on your opinion?

Career Connection

Anthropologist

Jane Goodall entered the African jungle at the age of 26 to study chimps in the wild. Goodall spent five years observing the chimps, taking extensive notes, and earning their trust. Since then, she has been the world's foremost expert on chimpanzees. She was the first person to discover that chimpanzees use tools to gather food. Today she spends her time traveling and teaching young people about the environment.

SCIENCE*Online* To learn more about careers in anthropology, visit the Glencoe Science Web site at **science.glencoe.com.**

Career Connection

Goodall worked as a secretary and as a film production assistant until she gained passage to Africa. Once there, Goodall began assisting paleontologist and anthropologist Louis Leakey. Her work with Leakey led her to the establishment in June 1960 of a camp in the Gombe Stream Game Reserve so that she could observe the behavior of chimpanzees.

SCIENCE *Online*
Internet Addresses
_____
_____
_____

Explore the Glencoe Science Web site at **science.glencoe.com** to find out more about topics in this feature.

Understanding Literature

Answers to Questions

- Answers will vary depending on each student's experience and on how well each student understands the passage.
- The author does imply that she is unhappy about the "long ugly canal straight through the green curving jungle." Saying something is ugly reveals an opinion.

Science Connection

The Everglades is a subtropical sawgrass marsh covering about 10,000 square km (4,000 square miles) of the southern region of Florida. Water moves slowly through it from the mouth of Lake Okeechobee to mangrove swamps bordering the Gulf of Mexico and the Florida Bay on the west-side. On the east side, the marsh reaches near the thin, sandy belt that includes the Greater Miami metropolitan area, while on the south end it borders Florida Bay at the bottom of the peninsula.

Linking Science and Writing

Writing Strategies

Remind the students that in writing nonfiction it is important to include factual information. But, as Douglas has illustrated, it gives the passage character and individuality to include some opinion on the place about which you are reporting.

Reviewing Main Ideas

Preview

Students can answer the questions in their Science Journals. Discuss the answers as you go through the chapter. **IS Linguistic**

Review

Students can write their answers, then compare them with those of other students. **IS Interpersonal**

Reteach

Students can look at the illustrations and describe details that support the main ideas of the chapter. **IS Visual-Spatial**

Answers to Chapter Review

SECTION 1

2. The senses can often be fooled. A thermometer can accurately determine the temperature of water.

SECTION 2

3. Answers will vary. Accept all reasonable responses.

SECTION 3

4. Possible answers: scientists in South America could communicate data via email or telephone, or by using video-conferencing technology; they could post data on a Web site.

Reviewing Main Ideas

Section 1 What is science?

1. Science is a process that can be used to solve problems or answer questions. Everyone uses science every day.

2. Scientists use tools to measure. *Why should this student use a thermometer to measure the temperature of the water?*

3. Technology is the application of science to make tools and products you use each day. Computers are a valuable technological tool.

4. Communication is an important part of all aspects of science.

Section 2 Doing Science

1. No one scientific method is used to solve all problems. Organization and careful planning are important when trying to solve any problem.

2. Scientific questions can be answered by descriptive research or experimental research.

3. Models save time and money by testing ideas that are too difficult to build or carry out. Computer models cannot completely replace experimentation. *Why might this scientist use a computer model to design aircraft?*

4. A hypothesis is an idea that can be tested. Sometimes experiments don't support the original hypothesis, and a new hypothesis must be formed.

5. In a well-planned experiment, there is a control and only one variable is changed at a time. All other factors are kept constant.

Section 3 Science and Technology

1. Science is part of everyone's life. New discoveries lead to new technology and products.

2. Science continues to challenge old knowledge and ways of doing things. Old ideas are kept until new discoveries prove them wrong.

3. People of all races, ages, sexes, cultures, and professions practice science.

4. Modern communication assures that scientific information is spread around the world. *When a new discovery is made in a South American rain forest, how can a scientist in Chicago find out about the data?*

FOLDABLES
Reading & Study Skills

After You Read

Exchange your Question Study Fold with another classmate to learn more about other scientists. Write down the information your classmates collected on their scientists.

FOLDABLES
Reading & Study Skills

After You Read

After students have read the chapter and completed the Foldable described in Before You Read, have them do the activity on the student page.

Dinah Zike

Visualizing Main Ideas

Complete the following concept map with steps to solving a problem.

Identify a Problem → to learn more → Gather background information → how can the problem be solved?

make observations to → Descriptive research

perform an experiment to → Experimental research

Gather data → Analyze data to → Form conclusions

Visualizing Main Ideas

See student page.

Vocabulary Review

Using Vocabulary

1. C
2. F
3. K
4. B
5. J
6. A
7. G

Vocabulary Review

Vocabulary Words

a. constant
b. control
c. dependent variable
d. descriptive research
e. experimental research design
f. hypothesis
g. independent variable
h. model
i. science
j. scientific methods
k. technology

Study Tip

Practice reading tables. Devise a graph that shows the same information as a table does.

Using Vocabulary

Match each phrase with the correct vocabulary word from the list.

1. the factor being measured in an experiment

2. a statement that can be tested

3. use of knowledge to make products

4. sample treated like other experimental groups except variable is not applied

5. steps to follow to solve a problem

6. a variable that stays the same during every trial of an experiment

7. the variable that is changed in an experiment

CHAPTER STUDY GUIDE 33

IDENTIFYING Misconceptions

Assess

After doing the activity on page 4F and completing the chapter, have students perform this activity.

Materials map of town, felt-tip highlighter

Procedure Explain that the first step in scientific method isn't always recognizing the problem. Sometimes you don't know a problem exists until you analyze the data. Have them study the map a few minutes and use the highlighter pen to trace the route they generally take to get to school. As an alternative, they could trace the route to the grocery store or some other place. Have them see if there is a better or a shorter route than the one they are accustomed to taking.

Expected Outcome Students will realize that sometimes a problem isn't recognized until accumulated data are analyzed. This is one example of the "steps" being done out of order.

Checking Concepts

1. A
2. D
3. D
4. A
5. B
6. D
7. B
8. A
9. C
10. C

Thinking Critically

11. It is a way of recording results so they can be communicated to others and so experiments can be repeated.

12. You won't forget and have incomplete or inaccurate data; your conclusions will be more accurate.

13. Analyzing data is reviewing and organizing it in an orderly way so you can understand it. You then use this information as a basis for your conclusions about whether the hypothesis is supported.

14. Experimental results are more reliable when bias is eliminated.

15. Listing what they already know gives scientists a starting point for their investigations. They won't waste time learning something that has already been discovered. They also will learn what does not work.

Chapter ① Assessment

Checking Concepts

Choose the word or phrase that best answers the question.

1. To make sure experimental results are valid, which of these procedures must be followed?
   - A) conduct multiple trials
   - B) pick two hypotheses
   - C) add bias
   - D) communicate uncertain results

2. In an experiment on bacteria, using different amounts of antibiotics is an example of which of the following?
   - A) control
   - C) bias
   - B) hypothesis
   - D) variable

3. Computers are used in science to do which of the following processes?
   - A) analyze data
   - B) make models
   - C) communicate with other scientists
   - D) all of the above

4. If you use a computer to make a three-dimensional picture of a building, it is an example of which of the following?
   - A) model
   - C) control
   - B) hypothesis
   - D) variable

5. Predictions about what will happen can be based on which of the following?
   - A) controls
   - C) technology
   - B) prior knowledge
   - D) number of trials

6. Which of the following is the greatest concern for scientists using the Internet?
   - A) speed
   - C) language
   - B) availability
   - D) accuracy

7. Which of the following can be used to record information?
   - A) conclusion
   - C) observation
   - B) data table
   - D) hypothesis

8. When scientists make a prediction that can be tested, what skill is being used?
   - A) hypothesizing
   - B) inferring
   - C) taking measurements
   - D) making models

9. Which of the following is the first step toward finding a solution?
   - A) analyze data
   - B) draw a conclusion
   - C) identify the problem
   - D) test the hypothesis

10. Which of the following terms describes a variable that does not change in an experiment?
    - A) hypothesis
    - C) constant
    - B) dependent
    - D) independent

Thinking Critically

11. How is a Science Journal a valuable tool for scientists?

12. Why is it important to record data as they are collected?

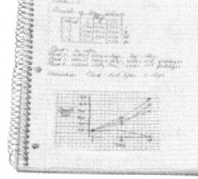

13. What is the difference between analyzing data and drawing conclusions?

14. What is the advantage of eliminating bias in experiments?

15. When trying to solve a problem, why do scientists collect information about what is already known?

Developing Skills

16. **Recognizing Cause and Effect** If three variables were changed at one time, what would happen to the accuracy of the conclusions made for an experiment?

Chapter ✓Assessment Planner

Portfolio Encourage students to place in their portfolios one or two items of what they consider to be their best work. Examples include:
- Science Journal, p. 9
- Curriculum Connection, p. 17
- Extension, p. 25

Performance Additional performance assessments, Performance Task Assessment Lists, and rubrics for evaluating these activities can be found in Glencoe's **Performance Assessment in the Science Classroom.**

17. Communicating Prepare a report for a kindergarten class about the result of a science experiment. How would this be different than a report prepared for a group of adults?

18. Interpreting Data You applied three different antibiotics to three bacteria samples. The control bacteria sample did not receive any antibiotics. All four of the bacteria samples grew at the same rate. How could you interpret your data?

19. Making and Using Graphs Prepare a bar graph of the data in this table. Which age group seems most likely to get the disease?

Disease Victims	
Age Group (years)	Number of People
0–5	37
6–10	20
11–15	2
16–20	1
over 20	0

20. Form Hypotheses More books were checked out of the school library during April than at any other time of the year. Form a hypothesis about why this occurred. How can the hypothesis be tested?

Performance Assessment

21. Poster Create a poster showing steps in a scientific method. Use creative images to show the steps to solving a scientific problem.

TECHNOLOGY

Go to the Glencoe Science Web site at **science.glencoe.com** or use the **Glencoe Science CD-ROM** for additional chapter assessment.

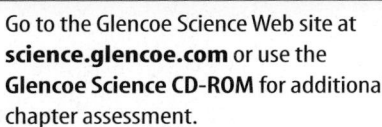

Test Practice

Anita heated four beakers of water to boiling. Each beaker contained 100 mL of water with a certain amount of salt dissolved in it. The results of her experiment are listed in the table below.

Boiling Temperatures of Salt Solutions		
Beaker	Mass of Salt Dissolved (g)	Boiling Temperature (°C)
A	0	99
B	3	102
C	6	105
D	9	?

Study the table and answer the following questions.

1. If everything remains the same, what will be the boiling temperature of the solution in beaker D?
- **A)** 102°C
- **B)** 106°C
- **C)** 108°C
- **D)** 110°C

2. Which hypothesis probably was being tested by this experiment?
- **F)** The boiling temperature of water increases as the mass of water increases.
- **G)** When salt is dissolved in water, the water takes longer to boil.
- **H)** The boiling temperature of salt depends on the mass of the salt.
- **J)** The boiling temperature of a saltwater solution increases as the mass of dissolved salt increases.

Test Practice

The Test-Taking Tip was written by The Princeton Review, the nation's leader in test preparation.
1. C
2. J

Developing Skills

16. It would be in doubt; you wouldn't know whether one variable had caused the reaction or whether it was caused by a combination of variables.

17. The report for the kindergartners would have more graphics and would explain things very simply.

18. One might conclude that applying antibiotics to these species of bacteria had no effect, that quantities of antibiotics were insufficient to slow growth, or that bacteria were resistant to antibiotics.

19. Bar graphs should reflect chart information. Those most likely to get the disease are zero to five years old.

20. Possible hypothesis: teachers assign more reports and projects during that month. It could be tested by asking students in school when their teachers assigned projects. Data could be compiled and analyzed.

Performance Assessment

21. Posters will vary. Use **PASC**, p. 145.

✓Assessment Resources

📁 **Reproducible Masters**

Chapter Resources Booklet
Chapter Review, pp. 35–36
Chapter Tests, pp. 37–40
Assessment Transparency Activity, p. 47

Glencoe Science Web site
Interactive Tutor
Chapter Quizzes

Glencoe Technology
- Assessment Transparency
- Interactive CD-ROM Chapter Quizzes
- ExamView Pro Test Bank
- Vocabulary PuzzleMaker Software
- MindJogger Videoquiz

CHAPTER 2 MEASUREMENT

Section/Objectives	Standards		Activities/Features
Chapter Opener	**National**	**State/Local**	**Explore Activity:** Measure length, p. 37
	See p. 7T for a Key to Standards.		**Before You Read,** p. 37
Section 1 Description and Measurement 🕐 3 sessions 📦 1.5 blocks 1. **Determine** how reasonable a measurement is by estimating. 2. **Identify** and use the rules for rounding a number. 3. **Distinguish** between precision and accuracy in measurements.	National Content Standards: UCP3, A1, B1		**Chemistry Integration,** p. 39 **MiniLAB:** Measuring Accurately, p. 40 **Visualizing Precision and Accuracy,** p. 42 **Science Online,** p. 43 **Math Skills Activity:** Rounding, p. 44
Section 2 SI Units 🕐 2 sessions 📦 1 block 1. **Identify** the purpose of SI. 2. **Identify** the SI units of length, volume, mass, temperature, time, and rate.	National Content Standards: UCP3, A1, B1		**Astronomy Integration,** p. 47 **MiniLAB:** Measuring Volume, p. 48 **Activity:** Scale Drawing, p. 51
Section 3 Drawings, Tables, and Graphs 🕐 4 sessions 📦 2 blocks 1. **Describe** how to use pictures and tables to give information. 2. **Identify** and use three types of graphs. 3. **Distinguish** the correct use of each type of graph.	National Content Standards: UCP3, A1, B1		**Science Online,** p. 54 **Activity:** Pace Yourself, p. 56 **Science Stats:** Biggest, Tallest, Loudest, p. 58

Activity Materials	Reproducible Resources	Section Assessment	Technology
Explore Activity: items of various sizes to measure in hand-widths	**Chapter Resources Booklet** Foldables Worksheet, p. 13 Directed Reading Overview, p. 15 Note-taking Worksheets, pp. 29–31	GLENCOE'S **ASSESSMENT** ADVANTAGE	
MiniLAB: 400 mL beaker, crushed ice, water, computer temperature probe, alcohol thermometer	**Chapter Resources Booklet** Transparency Activity, p. 40 MiniLAB, p. 3 Enrichment, p. 26 Reinforcement, p. 23 Directed Reading, p. 16 **Cultural Diversity,** p. 29 **Physical Science Critical Thinking/Problem Solving,** p. 11	**Portfolio** Science Journal, p. 41 **Performance** MiniLAB, p. 40 Math Skills Activity, p. 44 Skill Builder Activities, p. 45 **Content** Section Assessment, p. 45	Section Focus Transparency Interactive CD-ROM Guided Reading Audio Program
MiniLAB: transparent measuring cup, water, solid object that will fit in cup, pencil **Activity:** 1-cm graph paper, pencil, metric ruler, meterstick	**Chapter Resources Booklet** Transparency Activity, p. 41 MiniLAB, p. 4 Enrichment, p. 27 Reinforcement, p. 24 Directed Reading, pp. 16, 17 Activity Worksheet, pp. 5–6 Lab Activity, pp. 9–10, 11–12 Transparency Activity, pp. 43–44 **Reading and Writing Critical Thinking/Problem Solving,** p. 13	**Portfolio** Performance Assessment, p. 45 **Performance** MiniLAB, p. 48 Skill Builder Activities, p. 50 **Content** Section Assessment, p. 50	Section Focus Transparency Teaching Transparency Interactive CD-ROM Guided Reading Audio Program
Activity: meterstick, stopwatch or watch with a second hand *Need materials?* Contact Science Kit at 1-800-828-7777 or www.sciencekit.com on the Internet.	**Chapter Resources Booklet** Transparency Activity, p. 42 Enrichment, p. 28 Reinforcement, p. 25 Directed Reading, pp. 17, 18 Activity Worksheet, pp. 7–8 **Lab Management and Safety,** pp. 70, 71	**Portfolio** Make a Model, p. 51 **Performance** Skill Builder Activities, p. 55 **Content** Section Assessment, p. 55	Section Focus Transparency Interactive CD-ROM Guided Reading Audio Program

End of Chapter Assessment

GLENCOE'S **ASSESSMENT** ADVANTAGE

Blackline Masters	Technology	Professional Series
Chapter Resources Booklet Chapter Review, pp. 33–34 Chapter Tests, pp. 35–38 **Standardized Test Practice by The Princeton Review,** pp. 13–16	MindJogger Videoquiz Interactive CD-ROM Vocabulary PuzzleMakers ExamView Pro Test Bank Interactive Lesson Planner Interactive Teacher Edition	Performance Assessment in the Science Classroom (PASC)

Transparencies

Section Focus

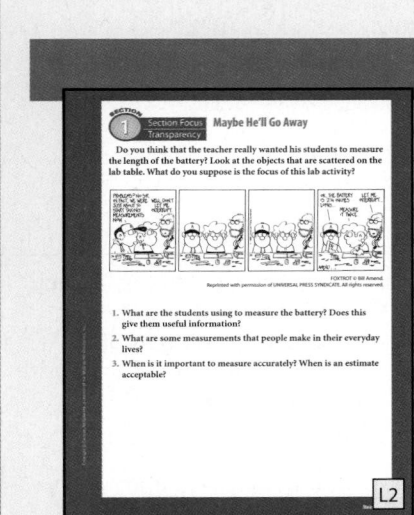

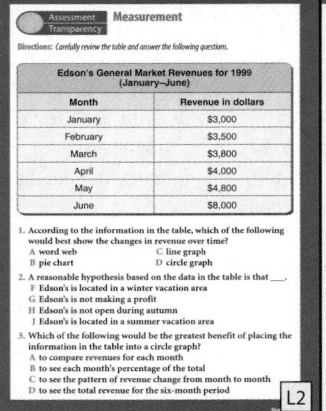

This is a representation of key blackline masters available in the Teacher Classroom Resources. See Resource Manager boxes within the chapter for additional information.

Assessment

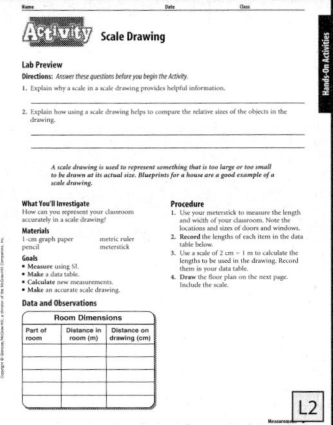

Teaching

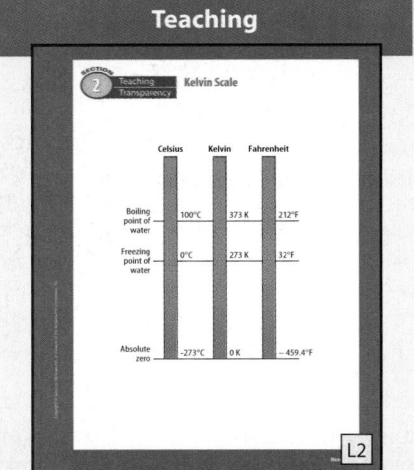

Key to Teaching Strategies

The following designations will help you decide which activities are appropriate for your students.

L1 Level 1 activities should be appropriate for students with learning difficulties.

L2 Level 2 activities should be within the ability range of all students.

L3 Level 3 activities are designed for above-average students.

ELL ELL activities should be within the ability range of English Language Learners.

COOP LEARN Cooperative Learning activities are designed for small group work.

LS Multiple Learning Styles logos, as described on page 22T, are used throughout to indicate strategies that address different learning styles.

P These strategies represent student products that can be placed into a best-work portfolio.

Hands-on Activities

Activity Worksheets

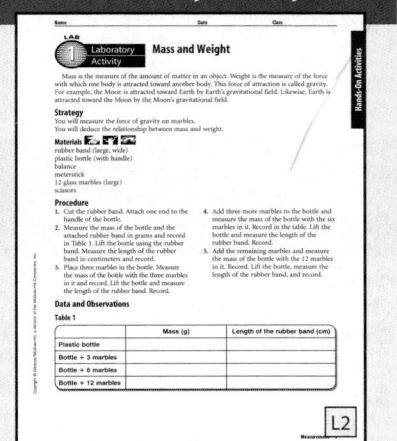

Laboratory Activity

Meeting Different Ability Levels

Content Outline

Note-taking Worksheet — Measurement

Section 1 Description and Measurement

A. _____—describes world using numbers
  1. Types of measurement—distance, time, _____, volume, mass
  2. Measurement can also describe _____.
B. Approximated measurement based on previous experience is _____.
  1. Estimation is useful when actual measurements are _____ made.
  2. Estimation can check that an answer is _____.
  3. When you estimate, you often use the word _____.
C. Precision and accuracy
  1. _____—a description of how close measurements are to each other
    a. Used to discuss number of _____ a measuring device can measure
    b. Degrees of Precision—today's measuring devices are more _____
  2. _____—comparison of measurement to actual value
  3. Precision and accuracy are important in many _____ procedures.
  4. Measurements can be _____ when precision is not needed.
  5. _____—reflect true precision of a calculation
    a. Multiplication or division—measurement with the fewest _____ digits determines the number of significant digits.
    b. Addition or subtraction—significance determined to the place value of the _____ precise measurement

Section 2 SI Units

A. The International System—_____ units, in multiples of _____, provide a standard of consistent measurement for global science, business, and industry.
B. Length—the distance between two points; SI unit—_____
  1. Measure pencil—use _____
  2. Measure distance from New York to Chicago—use _____

L2

Reinforcement

Reinforcement 1 — Description and Measurement

Directions: *For each object below, list four questions that can be answered by making measurements.*

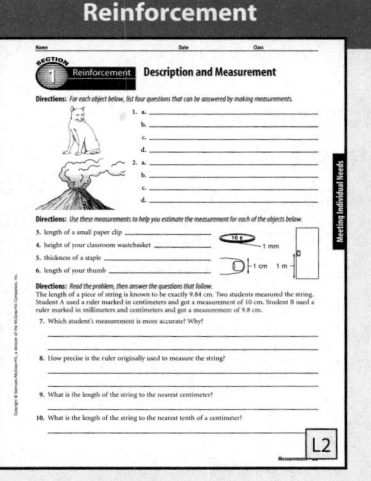

1. a. _____
    b. _____
    c. _____
    d. _____

2. a. _____
    b. _____
    c. _____
    d. _____

Directions: *Use these measurements to help you estimate the measurement for each of the objects below.*

3. length of a small paper clip _____
4. height of your classroom wastebasket _____
5. thickness of a staple _____
6. length of your thumb _____

Directions: *Read the problem, then answer the questions that follow.*

The length of a piece of string is known to be exactly 9.84 cm. Two students measured the string. Student A used a ruler marked in centimeters and got a measurement of 10 cm. Student B used a ruler marked in millimeters and centimeters and got a measurement of 9.8 cm.

7. Which student's measurement is more accurate? Why?
8. How precise is the ruler originally used to measure the string?
9. What is the length of the string to the nearest centimeter?
10. What is the length of the string to the nearest tenth of a centimeter?

L2

Directed Reading

Directed Reading for Content Mastery — *Overview* Measurement

Directions: *Complete the concept map using the terms below.*

volume   mass   weight   temperature   length

[concept map diagram]

Measuring Physical Properties
1. _____ measures → hot and cold
2. _____ measures → distance between points
3. _____ measures → space an object occupies
4. _____ measures → action of gravity on an object
5. _____ measures → amount of matter in an object

Directions: *Complete the following sentences using the terms below.*

tenth   giga   kilo
hundred   liter   million

6. A prefix that means thousand (1000) is _____.
7. The prefix *deci-* means _____.
8. One thousand milliliters is one _____.
9. There are one _____ centimeters in one meter.
10. The prefix *mega-* stands for _____.
11. The multiplier billion has the prefix _____.

L1

Enrichment

Enrichment 1 — Weather Instrument Precision

The symbol ± is used to show precision in measuring devices. For example, ±3°C means that the actual temperature may be 3°C greater or 3°C less than the temperature shown on the instrument.

Max/Min Thermohygrometer
• Digitally displays relative humidity and temperature
• Measures relative humidity (RH) from 25% to 95% with precision ±5%RH
• Measures temperature 0°C to 50°C with precision ±2°C

Battery Operated Hygrothermograph
• Measures relative humidity and temperature and records them on a chart
• Measures relative humidity from 5% to 99% with ±3% RH precision
• Measures temperature from −10°C to 50°C with ±1°C precision

1. Describe ways these two instruments are alike.
2. Describe the differences between these two instruments.
3. How precise are the measurements for each instrument?
4. If the display on the thermohygrometer shows 15°C, between what temperatures might the actual temperature fall? How do you know?
5. Suppose the thermohygrometer shows 52% relative humidity and at the same time the hygrothermograph shows 55% relative humidity. What would you expect to be the actual relative humidity?

26 Measurement

L3

Spanish Directed Reading

Lectura dirigida para Dominio del contenido — *Sinopsis* La medición

Instrucciones: *Completa el mapa conceptual usando los siguientes términos.*

el volumen   la masa   el peso   la temperatura   la longitud

[concept map diagram]

Cómo medir propiedades físicas
1. _____ mide → el grado de calor o de frío de un cuerpo
2. _____ mide → distancia entre puntos
3. _____ mide → el espacio que ocupa un cuerpo
4. _____ mide → la acción de la gravedad sobre un cuerpo
5. _____ mide → la cantidad de materia en un cuerpo

Instrucciones: *Completa las oraciones usando los siguientes términos.*

decenas   giga   kilo
centena   litro   millón

6. Un prefijo que significa millar (1000) es _____.
7. El prefijo *deci-* significa _____.
8. Mil mililitros equivalen a un _____.
9. Hay un(a) _____ de centímetros en un metro.
10. El prefijo *mega-* significa _____.
11. El multiplicador de billón tiene el prefijo _____.

L1

Assessment

Chapter Tests

Chapter Test — Measurement

I. Testing Concepts

Directions: *In the blank at the left, write the letter of the term that best completes each statement or answers the question.*

____ 1. A pitcher holds 1.725 L. What is the capacity of the pitcher to the nearest liter?
  a. 1 L.   b. 1.73 L.   c. 1.7 L.   d. 2 L.

____ 2. Which unit would you use to measure the length of a mailbox?
  a. nanometer   b. centimeter   c. meter   d. kilometer

____ 3. The temperature on a spring day is 18°C. To the nearest whole number, what is the temperature in kelvins?
  a. 291K   b. 255K   c. −229K   d. −255K

____ 4. A scale is marked in tenths of a kilogram. To what precision can the mass of a bag of apples be measured?
  a. the nearest tenth of a kilogram   c. the nearest kilogram
  b. the nearest one-half kilogram   d. the nearest ten kilograms

____ 5. Which of the following is NOT a measurement?
  a. age   b. shoe size   c. weight   d. eye color

____ 6. Which multiplier would you use to convert 1.9 km to meters?
  a. 1000   b. 10   c. 1/100   d. 1/1000

____ 7. Which unit would you use to measure the distance from Dallas, Texas, to Memphis, Tennessee?
  a. light years   b. kilometer   c. meter   d. centimeter

____ 8. Suppose you traveled to Mars. Compare your weight and your mass on Mars to your weight and mass on Earth.
  a. Both your weight and mass would remain the same.
  b. Your weight would remain the same, your mass would change.
  c. Your weight would change, your mass would remain the same.
  d. Both your weight and your mass would change.

____ 9. A digital thermometer shows the temperature as 21.2°C. The thermometer is precise to the nearest _____.
  a. 10°   b. 1°   c. 0.1°   d. 0.01°

____ 10. A baseball is pitched at 148 km per hour. Which term describes this measurement?
  a. scale   b. base unit   c. volume   d. rate

____ 11. What property of an object is measured in grams?
  a. volume   b. capacity   c. mass   d. weight

____ 12. A section of a circle graph measures 180°. What percent of a circle graph is this section?
  a. 18%   b. 50%   c. 80%   d. 100%

____ 13. What unit would you use to measure the area of a carpet?
  a. meters   b. square meters   c. cubic centimeters   d. square kilograms

L2

Test Practice Workbook

Standardized Test Practice
Teacher Edition
Glencoe **Science**

LEVEL GREEN

L2

Chapter Review

Chapter Review — Measurement

Part A. Vocabulary Review

Directions: *Use the clues to complete the puzzle.*

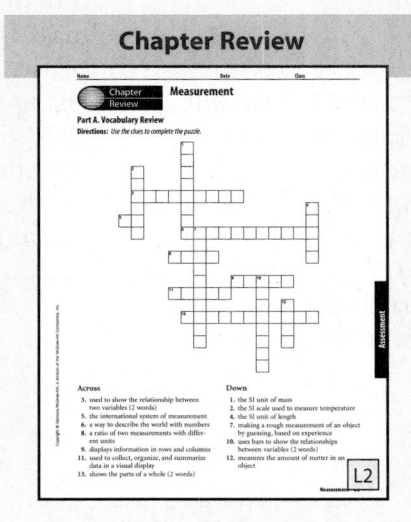

Across
3. used to show the relationship between two variables (2 words)
5. the international system of measurement
6. a way to describe the world with numbers
8. a ratio of two measurements with different units
9. displays information in rows and columns
11. used to collect, organize, and summarize data in a visual display
13. shows the parts of a whole (2 words)

Down
1. the SI unit of mass
2. the SI scale used to measure temperature
4. the SI unit of length
7. making a rough measurement of an object by guessing, based on experience
10. uses bars to show the relationships between variables (2 words)
12. measures the amount of matter in an object

L2

Science Content Background

SECTION 1

Description and Measurement

Degrees of Precision

Scientists use physical and chemical properties to describe matter. Measurement describes properties with numbers, which is known as quantifying. It describes features such as how long, how far, and how many.

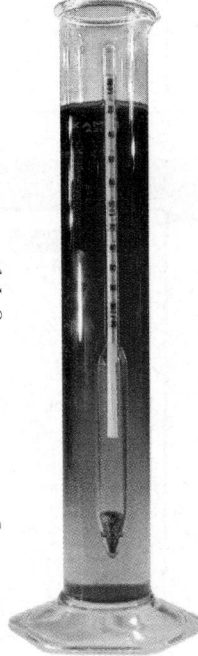

Precision and Accuracy

Precision is related to the degree of exactness that is used to measure an item. A measurer can make adjustments by using tools or methods that refine the results of measuring. Precision can improve with more sophisticated tools. Although measurements of 4.2 and 4.20 may seem to be the same, the 4.20 measurement shows that it is a more precise measurement. When numbers are rounded off in calculations, they are rounded to show the precision of the measuring instruments.

SECTION 2

SI Units

The International System

The initials SI stand for *Système International d'Unités*—the International System of Units for measurement. These units are used all over the world for science, commerce, and communication. The U.S. Bureau of Standards determines standards for measurements in the United States.

SI standards are based on key measurement units such as meter, liter, and kilogram. These units are further defined by the prefixes, of which the most commonly used are *kilo-*, *centi-*, and *milli-*. All units differ by factors of ten, so to convert the same unit with different prefixes simply requires the sliding of the decimal point to the left or right. To convert between units, use dimensional analysis, also called unit analysis. Cancel units the same way you cancel numbers.

- 3 km × (1,000m/1 km) = 3,000 m
- 45 cm (1 m/100 cm) = 0.45 m

In the classroom, SI length is measured with a metric ruler or a meterstick. A meterstick or a graduated cylinder is used to measure volume.

Length

Old units of length students might have heard of include the cubit and the roman mile. Accurate length measurement was important for ancient engineering projects such as the Nazca lines, pyramids in Central America and Africa, and the great public buildings found in many cultures.

Mass

Mass and weight are often confused. When moving an object to different locations, the mass is constant while the weight—a measure of the amount of gravity on an object—can change. Because the force of gravity is nearly constant on Earth's surface, mass and weight are often used interchangeably. The weight on Earth is found by multiplying the mass by the acceleration due to gravity, which averages 9.8 m/s^2.

Drawings, Tables, and Graphs

Scientific Illustrations

Each science develops a visual language, a standard way to illustrate and communicate important information. A geologist, for example, will learn to "read," or interpret, illustrations of geological strata as part of his or her training. Meteorologists learn to interpret images captured by satellites.

Tables and Graphs

A line graph is used to show the relationship between two numerical variables. As a rule, the independent variable is on the horizontal axis and the dependent variable is on the vertical axis. For example, distance traveled depends on time. While it is common to use the left and bottom sides of a grid as axes, the top or right side can also be used. Bar graphs and circle graphs often are used to present the results of opinion polls.

SCIENCE Online

For additional content background on this topic, go to the Glencoe Science Web site at science.glencoe.com.

Warren Faidley/International Stock

Chapter Vocabulary

What do you think?

Science Journal The photograph shows a stopwatch. When the large dial goes around one time or 30 s, the small dial advances one mark. For example, if the large dial goes around two times, or 60 s, the small dial moves two marks to the "1" mark. Ask students why they think this small dial is necessary.

D oes the expression "winning by a nose" mean anything to you? If you have ever "won by a nose," that means the race was close. Sometimes horse races, such as this one, are so close the winner has to be determined by a photograph. But there is more to measure than just how close the race was. How fast did the horse run? Did he break a record? In this chapter, you will learn how scientists measure things like distance, time, volume, and temperature. You also will learn how to use illustrations, pictures, and graphs to communicate measurements.

What do you think?

Science Journal Look at the picture below with a classmate. Discuss what you think this might be. Here's a hint: *How fast did you come up with an answer?* Write your answer or best guess in your Science Journal.

Theme Connection

Systems and Interactions The SI system is used throughout the world. Because it is based on powers of 10, it is easy to convert between units and do calculations.

EXPLORE ACTIVITY

You make measurements every day. If you want to communicate those measurements to others, how can you be sure that they will understand exactly what you mean? Using vague words without units won't work. Do the Explore Activity below to see the confusion that can result from using measurements that aren't standard.

Measure length

1. As a class, choose six objects to measure in your classroom.
2. Measure each object using the width of your hand and write your measurements in your Science Journal.
3. Compare your measurements to those of your classmates.

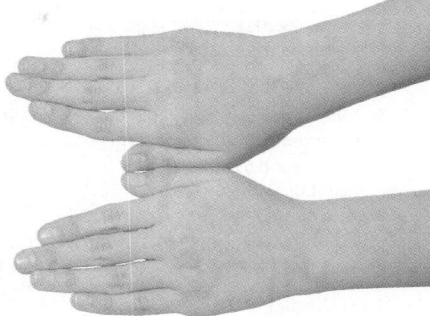

Observe

Is your hand the same width as your classmates' hands? Discuss in your Science Journal why it is better to switch from using hands to using units of measurement that are the same all the time.

Before You Read

FOLDABLES Reading & Study Skills

Making an Organizational Study Fold When information is grouped into clear categories, it is easier to understand what you are learning. Before you begin reading, make the following Foldable to help you organize your thoughts about measurements.

1. Place a sheet of paper in front of you so the short side is at the top. Fold the paper in half from the left side to the right side two times. Unfold all the folds.
2. Fold the paper from top to bottom in equal thirds and then in half. Unfold all the folds.
3. Trace over all the fold lines and label the table you created. Label the columns: *Estimate It, Measure It,* and *Round It,* as shown. Label the rows: *Length of _____, Volume of _____, Mass of _____, Temperature of _____,* and *Rate of _____,* as shown.
4. Before you read the chapter, select objects to measure and estimate their measurements. As you read the chapter, complete the *Measure It* column.

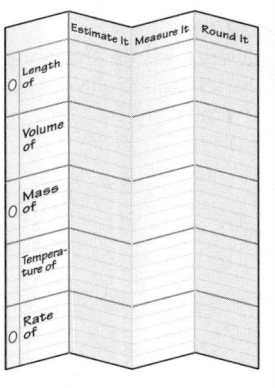

37

Purpose Students discover what happens when measurements aren't standardized. [L1] [ELL] [COOP LEARN] [IS] **Kinesthetic**

Preparation Before doing this activity, practice using your hand as a unit of length and measure the length of several objects.

Materials something to measure, such as a tabletop, a bookshelf, and a door, in addition to smaller objects

Teaching Strategy Model for the students by measuring your arm or desk with your hand.

Observe

No; because hands vary in size, a more standard unit of measurement is needed.

✓ *Assessment*

Process Have students work in pairs. Each pair should choose a limb of the body, then use it to measure the length of something. Have each student of the pair do the measurement using his or her own limb, then have students compare their measurements with one another. Use **Performance Assessment in the Science Classroom,** p. 169.

Before You Read

FOLDABLES Reading & Study Skills

Dinah Zike Study Fold

Purpose Students make and use a Foldable table to practice measuring the length, volume, mass, temperature and rates of different objects. The Foldable table will also provide practice in estimating measurements, recording exact measurements, and rounding measurements.

For additional help, see Foldables Worksheet, p. 13 in **Chapter Resources Booklet,** or go to the Glencoe Science Web site at **science.glencoe.com.** See After You Read in the Study Guide at the end of this chapter.

Description and Measurement

① Motivate

Bellringer Transparency

Display the Section Focus Transparency for Section 1. Use the accompanying Transparency Activity Master. L2
ELL

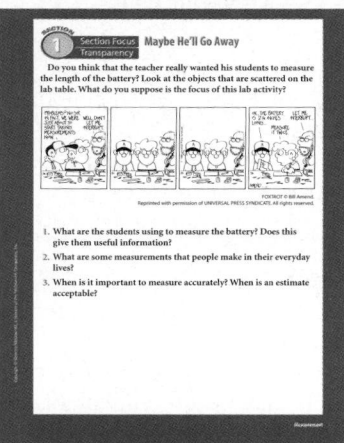

Tie to Prior Knowledge

Discuss with students times when they have used measuring tools such as rulers or scales.

Description and Measurement

As You Read

What You'll Learn
- **Determine** how reasonable a measurement is by estimating.
- **Identify** and use the rules for rounding a number.
- **Distinguish** between precision and accuracy in measurements.

Vocabulary
measurement   precision
estimation   accuracy

Why It's Important
Measurement helps you communicate information and ideas.

Measurement

How would you describe what you are wearing today? You might start with the colors of your outfit, and perhaps you would even describe the style. Then you might mention sizes—size 7 shoes, size 14 shirt. Every day you are surrounded by numbers. **Measurement** is a way to describe the world with numbers. It answers questions such as how much, how long, or how far. Measurement can describe the amount of milk in a carton, the cost of a new compact disc, or the distance between your home and your school. It also can describe the volume of water in a swimming pool, the mass of an atom, or how fast a penguin's heart pumps blood.

The circular device in **Figure 1** is designed to measure the performance of an automobile in a crash test. Engineers use this information to design safer vehicles. In scientific endeavors, it is important that scientists rely on measurements instead of the opinions of individuals. You would not know how safe the automobile is if this researcher turned in a report that said, "Vehicle did fairly well in head-on collision when traveling at a moderate speed." What does "fairly well" mean? What is a "moderate speed?"

Figure 1
This device measures the range of motion of a seat-belted mannequin in a simulated accident.

Section ✓*Assessment* Planner

PORTFOLIO
Science Journal, p. 41
Performance Assessment, p. 45

PERFORMANCE ASSESSMENT
MiniLAB, p. 40
Math Skills Activity, p. 44
Skill Builder Activities, p. 45

See page 62 for more options.

CONTENT ASSESSMENT
Section, p. 45
Challenge, p. 45
Chapter, pp. 62–63

Figure 2
Accurate measurement of distance and time is important for competitive sports like track and field. *Why wouldn't a clock that measured in minutes be precise enough for this race?*

Describing Events Measurement also can describe events such as the one shown in **Figure 2.** In the 1956 summer Olympics, sprinter Betty Cuthbert of Australia came in first in the women's 200-m dash. She ran the race in 23.4 s. In the 2000 summer Olympics, Marion Jones of the United States won the 100-m dash in a time of 10.75 s. In this example, measurements convey information about the year of the race, its length, the finishing order, and the time. Information about who competed and in what event are not measurements but help describe the event completely.

Estimation

What happens when you want to know the size of an object but you can't measure it? Perhaps it is too large to measure or you don't have a ruler handy. **Estimation** can help you make a rough measurement of an object. When you estimate, you can use your knowledge of the size of something familiar to estimate the size of a new object. Estimation is a skill based on previous experience and is useful when you are in a hurry and exact numbers are not required. Estimation is a valuable skill that improves with experience, practice, and understanding.

 Reading Check *When should you not estimate a value?*

How practical is the skill of estimation? In many instances, estimation is used on a daily basis. A caterer prepares for each night's crowd based on an estimation of how many will order each entree. A chef makes her prize-winning chili. She doesn't measure the cumin; she adds "just that much." Firefighters estimate how much hose to pull off the truck when they arrive at a burning building.

Chemistry INTEGRATION

A description of matter that does not involve measurement is *qualitative.* For example, water is composed of hydrogen and oxygen. A *quantitative* description uses numbers to describe. For example, one water molecule is composed of one oxygen atom and two hydrogen atoms. Research another compound containing hydrogen and oxygen—hydrogen peroxide. Infer a qualitative and quantitative description of hydrogen peroxide in your Science Journal.

SECTION 1 Description and Measurement **39**

Curriculum Connection

History Length was once measured using units such as the width of the palm or the length of the foot. A cubit is the distance from the elbow to the tip of the middle finger. A pace is the length of a walking step from one heel to another. Have students measure a distance of ten paces, and compare their results. L2 ELL
 Kinesthetic

② Teach

Measurement

Activity

Have students measure a common item to the nearest 0.1 cm using a ruler. Ask them to share the measurements and to discuss possible reasons for variations. differences in the rulers, differences in the way students align the ruler with the object, differences in the angle at which they look at the ruler L1 ELL
 Kinesthetic

Caption Answer

Figure 2 Olympic runners often win by fractions of a second.

Chemistry INTEGRATION

Possible answers: quantitative: two hydrogen and two oxygen atoms, it has more oxygen atoms than water has; qualitative: hydrogen peroxide is made up of hydrogen atoms and oxygen atoms.

Estimation

Make a Model

Collect commonly used containers such as one- and two-liter bottles. Pour given amounts of water into each bottle. Use a permanent ink marker to draw a line at the water level and to mark metric amounts on the outside of the bottle. For example, pour 100mL of water into a two-liter bottle, draw a line around the container at the water level, and write 100 mL above the line. Have students estimate where the 200-mL mark would be on each bottle. L2 ELL **Visual-Spatial**

 Reading Check

Answer when you need to know the exact measurement

Caption Answer

Figure 3 About 4.5 meters (15 feet); accept all reasonable estimates.

Mini LAB

Purpose Students will practice measurement skills with computer temperature probes and thermometers.

Materials 400-mL beaker, crushed ice, cold water, computer temperature probe, alcohol thermometer.

Teaching Strategies

- Demonstrate how to make accurate temperature measurements by not letting the thermometer touch the sides or bottom of the beaker.
- Show students how to read an alcohol thermometer.
- Make sure that the beaker is mostly ice for each measurement.

Analysis

1. Review the process for calculating an average.

2. Possible answers: The most precise instrument will give the set of measurements that are closest together. The computer probe tends to be more precise. To determine the accuracy of the measurements, the actual temperature needs to be known. If the students know that the water should be 0°C, then they can determine which device is more accurate by seeing which average is closest to 0°C.

✓Assessment

Oral Have students work in small groups to define measurement and show how it is done. Have students demonstrate and present their results to the class. Use **PASC,** p. 143.

Mini LAB

Measuring Accurately

Procedure 🥽 🧤

1. Fill a **400-mL beaker** with **crushed ice**. Add enough **cold water** to fill the beaker.
2. Make three measurements of the temperature of the ice water using a **computer temperature probe.** Remove the computer probe and allow it to warm to room temperature between each measurement. Record the measurements in your **Science Journal.**
3. Repeat step two using an **alcohol thermometer.**

Analysis

1. Average each set of measurements.
2. Which measuring device is more precise? Explain. Can you determine which is more accurate? How?

40   CHAPTER 2 Measurement

Figure 3
This student is about 1.5 m tall. *Estimate the height of the tree in the photo.*

Using Estimation You can use comparisons to estimate measurements. For example, the tree in **Figure 3** is too tall to measure easily, but because you know the height of the student next to the tree, you can estimate the height of the tree. When you estimate, you often use the word *about.* For example, doorknobs are about 1 m above the floor, a sack of flour has a mass of about 2 kg, and you can walk about 5 km in an hour.

Estimation also is used to check that an answer is reasonable. Suppose you calculate your friend's running speed as 47 m/s. You are familiar with how long a second is and how long a meter is. Think about it. Can your friend really run a 50-m dash in 1 s? Estimation tells you that 47 m/s is unrealistically fast and you need to check your work.

Precision and Accuracy

One way to evaluate measurements is to determine whether they are precise. **Precision** is a description of how close measurements are to each other. Suppose you measure the distance between your home and your school five times with an odometer. Each time, you determine the distance to be 2.7 km. Suppose a friend repeated the measurements and measured 2.7 km on two days, 2.8 km on two days, and 2.6 km on the fifth day. Because your measurements were closer to each other than your friend's measurements, yours were more precise. The term *precision* also is used when discussing the number of decimal places a measuring device can measure. A clock with a second hand is considered more precise than one with only an hour hand.

Inclusion Strategies

Learning Disabled Make sure that learning disabled students handle measuring equipment and make measurements, rather than just reading and observing. Check that they are using the correct scale and starting their measurement at the zero position.

Resource Manager

Chapter Resources Booklet
   MiniLAB, p. 3
   Note-taking Worksheets, pp. 29–31

Earth Science Critical Thinking/Problem Solving, p. 11

Degrees of Precision The timing for Olympic events has become more precise over the years. Events that were measured in tenths of a second 100 years ago are measured to the hundredth of a second today. Today's measuring devices are more precise. **Figure 4** shows an example of measurements of time with varying degrees of precision.

Accuracy When you compare a measurement to the real, actual, or accepted value, you are describing **accuracy.** A watch with a second hand is more precise than one with only an hour hand, but if it is not properly set, the readings could be off by an hour or more. Therefore, the watch is not accurate. On the other hand, measurements of 1.03m, 1.04m and 1.06m compared to an actual value of 1.05 m is accurate, but not precise. **Figure 5** illustrates the difference between precision and accuracy.

> **✔ Reading Check** *What is the difference between precision and accuracy?*

Figure 4
Each of these clocks provides a different level of precision. *Which of the three could you use to be sure to make the 3:35 bus?*

A Before the invention of clocks, as they are known today, a sundial was used. As the Sun passes through the sky, a shadow moves around the dial.

B For centuries, analog clocks—the kind with a face—were the standard.

C Digital clocks are now as common as analog ones.

SECTION 1 Description and Measurement **41**

Precision and Accuracy

Discussion

Discuss with students time-keeping tools used at school and at home. These include a stopwatch, clock, kitchen timer, alarm clock, and timer on a microwave oven. **What are some of the limitations of these tools for timing an event?** Possible answers: Many timers read only to the second and sometimes it is necessary to measure tenths or hundredths of seconds. The time it takes a timekeeper to start and stop a stopwatch affects its precision. [L2] [LS] **Linguistic**

> **✔ Reading Check**

Answer Precision describes the exactness of a measure. Accuracy compares a measurement to the actual or accepted value.

Caption Answer
Figure 4 the analog or digital clock

Visual Learning

Figure 4 Have small groups discuss ways each of the clocks could be used. Possible answers: sundial to see if it is before or after noon; analog clock to make it on time for school or for after-school activities; The digital clock could be used to determine if exactly three minutes has elapsed. [L2] [ELL] [COOP LEARN] [LS] **Interpersonal**

Science Journal

Using Measurements In their Science Journals, have students describe a situation in which both accuracy and precision in measurement are necessary. Have students share examples in a small group. Sample answers: Shooting a basketball into a hoop. Landing on a balance beam after doing a flip. Throwing a strike in bowling. [L2] [LS]
Linguistic [P]

Teacher FYI
The cesium atomic clock uses the radiation generated by the transition between two states of cesium-133 atoms to operate a clock that is both precise and accurate. The clock is used for the basic unit of time in the International System of Units. It has an error of plus or minus one second in one million years.

Visualizing Precision and Accuracy

Have students examine the pictures and read the captions. Then ask the following questions.

- **How would you describe the accuracy and the precision of a basketball player who makes 97 out of 100 free throws?** good accuracy and good precision

- **How would you describe the accuracy and precision of a basketball player who has 99 out of 100 free throws hit the front rim of the basket and bounce off?** good precision, poor accuracy

- **How would you describe the accuracy and precision of a basketball player who makes 33 out of 100 free throws, while the others miss the basket completely?** poor precision, poor accuracy

Activity

Have small groups of students select another sport and make a similar display that illustrates precision and accuracy. Have each group present its display to the class. `L2` `ELL` `COOP LEARN` **LS Visual-Spatial and Interpersonal**

Extension

Ask students to write paragraphs explaining whether they think it is possible for experimental data to have good accuracy but poor precision. Encourage them to explain their reasoning. `L2` `ELL` `COOP LEARN` **LS Linguistic and Logical-Mathematical**

Figure 5

From golf to gymnastics, many sports require precision and accuracy. Archery—a sport that involves shooting arrows into a target—clearly shows the relationship between these two factors. An archer must be accurate enough to hit the bull's-eye and precise enough to do it repeatedly.

A The archer who shot these arrows is neither accurate nor precise—the arrows are scattered all around the target.

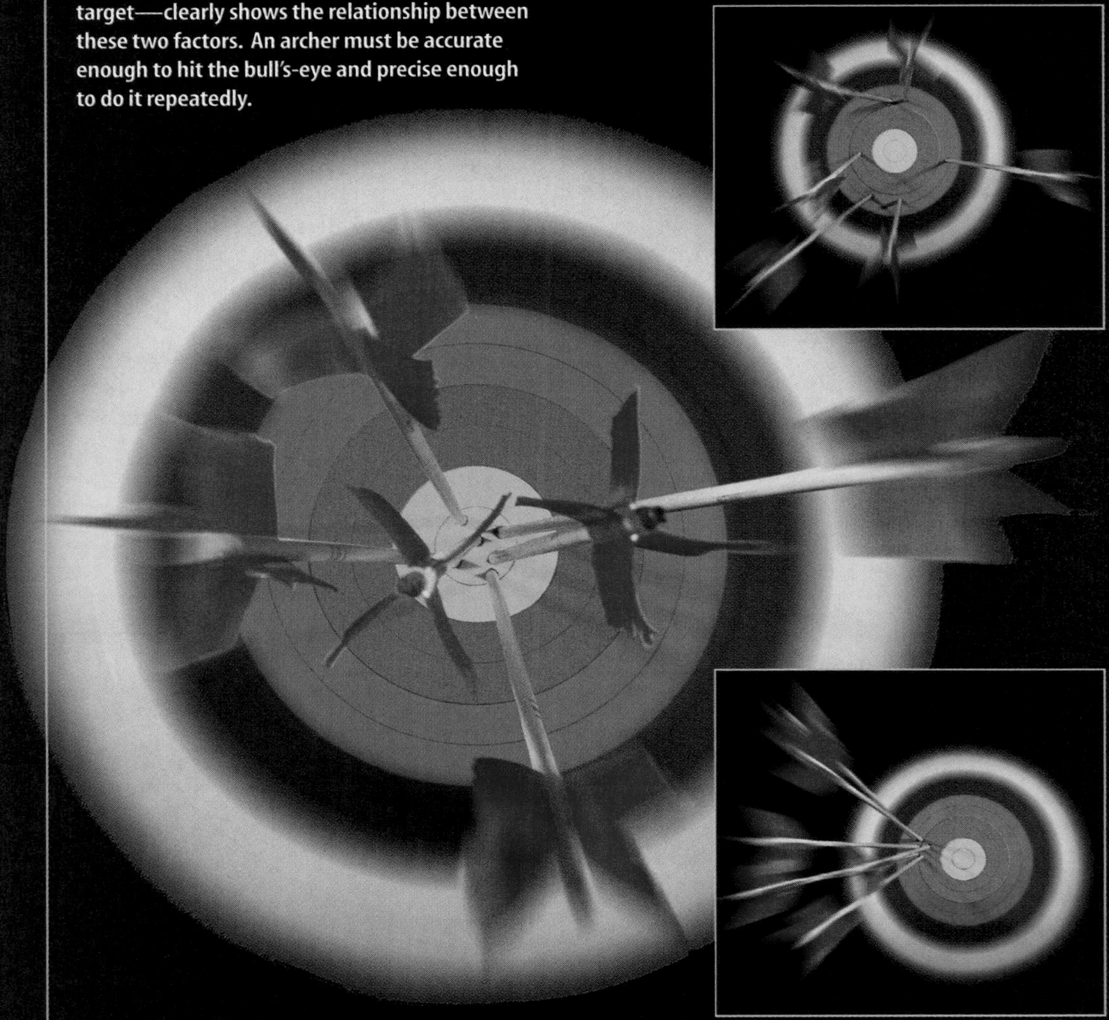

C Here we have a winner! All of the arrows have hit the bull's-eye, a result that is both precise and accurate.

B This archer's attempt demonstrates precision but not accuracy—the arrows were shot consistently to the left of the target's center.

Resource Manager

Chapter Resources Booklet
  Enrichment, p. 26
Cultural Diversity, p. 29

Health
INTEGRATION

Precision and accuracy are important in many medical procedures. One of these procedures is the delivery of radiation in the treatment of cancerous tumors. Because radiation damages cells, it is important to limit the radiation to only the cancerous cells that are to be destroyed. A technique called Stereotactic Radiotherapy (SRT) allows doctors to be accurate and precise in delivering radiation to areas of the brain. The patient makes an impression of his or her teeth on a bite plate that is then attached to the radiation machine. This same bite plate is used for every treatment to position the patient precisely the same way each time. A CAT scan locates the tumor in relation to the bite plate, and the doctors can pinpoint with accuracy and precision where the radiation should go.

Rounding a Measurement Not all measurements have to be made with instruments that measure with great precision like the scale in **Figure 6.** Suppose you need to measure the length of the sidewalk outside your school. You could measure it to the nearest millimeter. However, you probably would need to know the length only to the nearest meter or tenth of a meter. So, if you found that the length was 135.841 m, you could round off that number to the nearest tenth of a meter and still be considered accurate. How would you round this number? To round a given value, follow these steps:

1. Look at the digit to the right of the place being rounded to.
    • If the digit to the right is 0, 1, 2, 3, or 4, the digit being rounded to remains the same.
    • If the digit to the right is 5, 6, 7, 8, or 9, the digit being rounded to increases by one.

2. The digits to the right of the digit being rounded to are deleted if they are also to the right of a decimal. If they are to the left of a decimal, they are changed to zeros.

Look back at the sidewalk example. If you want to round the sidewalk length of 135.841 to the tenths place, you look at the digit to the right of the 8. Because that digit is a 4, you keep the 8 and round it off to 135.8 m. If you want to round to the ones place, you look at the digit to the right of the 5. In this case you have an 8, so you round up, changing the 5 to a 6, and your answer is 136 m.

SCIENCE *Online*

Research Visit the Glencoe Science Web site at **science.glencoe.com** for more information about measurement. Communicate to your class what you learn.

Figure 6
This laboratory scale measures to the nearest hundredth of a gram.

Precision and Accuracy, continued

Teacher FYI

Twenty-four Global Positioning System (GPS) satellites orbit Earth. Each satellite measures time precisely and accurately using four atomic clocks, and continuously broadcasts toward Earth a coded signal telling the time, the satellite's location, and other data. The signals are picked up by GPS receivers that can measure their distance from any GPS satellite based on the time the signal took to arrive. The receiver compares data from four different satellites to calculate its own latitude, longitude, and elevation, as well as the correct time. If the receiver is moving, it can also determine its own velocity.

Health
INTEGRATION

Ask students to identify which parts of the procedure make the measurement precise and which make it accurate. Precise: the instruments and the techniques used make measurements with a high degree of exactness; also, the bite plate positions the patient exactly the same way each time. Accurate: the CAT scan locates the tumor accurately.

Curriculum Connection

History The first chemists were the alchemists of ancient Egypt, China, Greece, and Rome, and of medieval Arabia and Europe. Have students find out what alchemists did and what kinds of systems they used for measurement. Alchemists tried to change metals into gold and helped develop perfumes, cosmetics and the gilding of metals. They did not have precise tools or a standard measuring system.

SCIENCE *Online*
Internet Addresses

_____
_____
_____

Explore the Glencoe Science Web site at **science.glencoe.com** to find out more about topics in this section.

Precision and Accuracy, continued

Extension

Discuss this example with your students. The mass of a substance is determined to be 0.0045 kilograms. **How many significant digits are in this measurement?** There are two significant digits. The zeros in 0.0045 are used to show only the place value of the decimal and are not counted as significant digits.

Precision and Number of Digits When might you need to round a number? Suppose you want to divide a 2-L bottle of soft drink equally among seven people. When you divide 2 by 7, your calculator display reads as shown in **Figure 7.** Will you measure exactly 0.285 714 285 L for each person? No. All you need to know is that each person gets about 0.3 L of soft drink.

Using Precision and Significant Digits The number of digits that truly reflect the precision of a number are called the significant digits or significant figures. They are figured as follows:

- Digits other than zero are always significant.
- Final zeros after a decimal point (6.54600 g) are significant.
- Zeros between any other digits (507.0301 g) are significant.
- Zeros before any other digits (0.0002030 g) are NOT significant.
- Zeros in a whole number (1650) may or may not be significant.
- An exact number, such as the number of people in a room or the number of meters in a kilometer, has infinite significant digits.

Math Skills Activity

Rounding

Example Problem

The mass of one object is 6.941 g. The mass of a second object is 20.180 g. You need to know these values only to the nearest whole number to solve a problem. What are the rounded values?

Solution

1 *This is what you know:*   mass of first object = 6.941 g
     mass of second object = 20.180 g

2 *This is what you need to know:*   the number to the right of the one's place

     first object: 9, second object: 1

3 *This is what you need to use:*   digits 0, 1, 2, 3, 4 remain the same
     for digits 5, 6, 7, 8, 9, round up

4 *Solution:*   first object: 9 makes the 6 round up = 7
     second object: 1 makes the 0 remain the same = 20

Practice Problem

What are the rounded masses of the objects to the nearest tenth of a unit?

For more help, refer to the Math Skill Handbook.

Cultural Diversity

Social Time While time's passage can be accurately measured, its perceived importance, or social time, varies from culture to culture. In the U.S., people call and apologize if they expect to be late. In Latin American and Arab countries, people may arrive an hour late with no apology expected or given. One study of social time rated Japan highest and the U.S. second in accuracy of bank clocks and pace of life.

Resource Manager

Chapter Resources Booklet
   Reinforcement, p. 23

Physical Science Critical Thinking/Problem Solving, p. 11

Following the Rules In the soda example you have an exact number, seven, for the number of people. This number has infinite significant digits. You also have the number two, for how many liters of soda you have. This has only one significant digit.

There are also rules to follow when deciding the number of significant digits in the answer to a calculation. They depend on what kind of calculation you are doing.

- For multiplication and division, you determine the number of significant digits in each number in your problem. The significant digits of your answer are determined by the number with fewer digits.

$$6.14 \times 5.6 = \boxed{34}.384$$
3 digits   2 digits   2 digits

- For addition and subtraction, you determine the place value of each number in your problem. The significant digits of the answer is determined by the number that is least precise.

$$
\begin{array}{ll}
6.14 & \text{to the hundredths} \\
+\ 5.6 & \text{to the tenths} \\
\hline
\boxed{11.7}4 & \text{to the tenths}
\end{array}
$$

Therefore, in the soda example you are dividing and the limiting number of digits is determined by the amount of soda, 2 L. There is one significant digit there; therefore, your answer has one.

 **Reading Check** *What determines the number of significant digits in the answer to an addition problem?*

Figure 7
Sometimes considering the size of each digit will help you realize they are unneeded. In this calculation, the seven ten-thousandths of a liter represents just a few drops of soda.

Section ① Assessment

1. Estimate the distance between your desk and your teacher's desk. Explain the method you used.

2. Measure the height of your desk to the nearest half centimeter.

3. Sarah's garden is 11.72 m long. Round to the nearest tenth of a meter.

4. John's puppy has chewed on his ruler. Will John's measurements be accurate or precise?

5. **Think Critically** Would the sum of 5.7 and 6.2 need to be rounded? Why or why not? Would the sum of 3.28 and 4.1 need to be rounded? Why or why not?

Skill Builder Activities

6. **Using Precision and Significant Digits** Perform the following calculations and express the answer using the correct number of significant digits: 42.35 + 214; 225/12. **For more help, refer to the** Math Skill Handbook.

7. **Communicating** Describe your backpack in your Science Journal. Include in your description one set of qualities that have no measurements, such as color and texture, and one set of measured quantities, such as width and mass. **For more help, refer to the** Science Skill Handbook.

Reading Check

Answer the number that is least precise

③ Assess

Reteach

Obtain measuring tools and items to measure. Have students describe how they can use the tools to collect data that are accurate and precise. [L2] **Ⅰ\ Visual-Spatial**

Challenge

Use a math textbook or other reference book to locate information about estimation. **Are there specific rules given? Will the method give accurate results?** Example: Front-end estimation is done by retaining the number in the largest place and rewriting all other digits as 0. Thus 7899 becomes 7000. The result is precise according to this method, but the result is not accurate; it is 899 smaller than the original number. [L3] **Ⅰ\ Logical-Mathematical**

✔ Assessment

Performance Have each student make a poster that shows the difference between estimation and precise measurement. Students should present their posters to a small group of students or to the class. Use **Performance Assessment in the Science Classroom**, p. 145. [P]

Answers to Section Assessment

1. Possible answer: about 3 m; it looks like two students could almost lie down head to toe in the space.
2. Check students' work.
3. 11.7 m
4. John's measurements will not be precise in the area in which measuring lines have been destroyed by the dog. They may still be accurate, depending on what he's measuring and what the dog destroyed.
5. The sum of 5.7 and 6.2 does not need to be rounded because both are measured to the same place value. 3.28 and 4.1 would need to be rounded to the place of the least precise measurement—the tenth place.
6. 256; 19
7. Answers will vary. Qualities might include color, fabric, or design. Measurements might include dimensions, mass, or number of pockets.

SECTION

2 SI Units

1 Motivate

1 Motivate

Bellringer Transparency

Display the Section Focus Transparency for Section 2. Use the accompanying Transparency Activity Master. L2 ELL

Section Focus Transparency — **Fresh, not Frozen**

These people are shopping in a market in Grenada. Grenada uses a unit of currency called the East Caribbean dollar. How do tourists from the United States know how many U.S. dollars to use when buying something in Grenada? They need to convert their American money into Grenadian money.

1. Would it be easier if all countries used one type of money? Explain.
2. What would happen if each country had its own way of measuring length or time?
3. What units of measurement do you know that are used everywhere?

Tie to Prior Knowledge

Recall from the previous section the importance of using precise tools. In this section, students will learn about the tools and units used for scientific measurement.

✔ Reading Check

Answer to provide a worldwide standard of physical measurement for science, industry, and commerce

As You Read

What You'll Learn

- **Identify** the purpose of SI.
- **Identify** the SI units of length, volume, mass, temperature, time, and rate.

Vocabulary

SI	kilogram
meter	kelvin
mass	rate

Why It's Important

The SI system is used throughout the world, allowing you to measure quantities in the exact same way as other students around the world.

The International System

Can you imagine how confusing it would be if people in every country used different measuring systems? Sharing data and ideas would be complicated. To avoid confusion, scientists established the International System of Units, or **SI,** in 1960 as the accepted system for measurement. It was designed to provide a worldwide standard of physical measurement for science, industry, and commerce. SI units are shown in **Table 1.**

✔ Reading Check *Why was SI established?*

The SI units are related by multiples of ten. Any SI unit can be converted to a smaller or larger SI unit by multiplying by a power of 10. For example, to rewrite a kilogram measurement in grams, you multiply by 1,000. The new unit is renamed by changing the prefix, as shown in **Table 2.** For example, one millionth of a meter is one *micro*-meter. One thousand grams is one *kilo*gram. **Table 3** shows some common objects and their measurements in SI units.

Table 1 SI Base Units

Quantity	Unit	Symbol
length	meter	m
mass	kilogram	kg
temperature	kelvin	K
time	second	s
electric current	ampere	A
amount of substance	mole	mol
intensity of light	candela	cd

Table 2 SI Prefixes

Prefix	Multiplier
giga-	1,000,000,000
mega-	1,000,000
kilo-	1,000
hecto-	100
deka-	10
[unit]	1
deci-	0.1
centi-	0.01
milli-	0.001
micro-	0.000 001
nano-	0.000 000 001

Section ✔*Assessment* Planner

PORTFOLIO
Astronomy Integration, p. 47
Activity Assessment, p. 51
PERFORMANCE ASSESSMENT
Try at Home MiniLAB, p. 48
Skill Builder Activities, p. 50
See page 62 for more options.

CONTENT ASSESSMENT
Section, p. 50
Challenge, p. 50
Chapter, pp. 62–63

Length

Length is defined as the distance between two points. Lengths measured with different tools can describe a range of things from the distance from Earth to Mars to the thickness of a human hair. In your laboratory activities, you usually will measure length with a metric ruler or meterstick.

The **meter** (m) is the SI unit of length. One meter is about the length of a baseball bat. The size of a room or the dimensions of a building would be measured in meters. For example, the height of the Washington Monument in Washington, D.C. is 169 m.

Smaller objects can be measured in centimeters (cm) or millimeters (mm). The length of your textbook or pencil would be measured in centimeters. A twenty-dollar bill is 15.5 cm long. You would use millimeters to measure the width of the words on this page. To measure the length of small things such as blood cells, bacteria, or viruses, scientists use micrometers (millionths of a meter) and nanometers (billionths of a meter).

A Long Way Sometimes people need to measure long distances, such as the distance a migrating bird travels or the distance from Earth to the Moon. To measure such lengths, you use kilometers. Kilometers might be most familiar to you as the distance traveled in a car or the measure of a long-distance race, as shown in **Figure 8.** The course of a marathon is measured carefully so that the competitors run 42.2 km. When you drive from New York to Los Angeles, you cover 4,501 km.

Figure 8
These runners have just completed a 10-kilometer race—known as a 10K. *About how many kilometers is the distance between your home and your school?*

Astronomy
INTEGRATION

How important are accurate measurements? In 1999, the *Mars Climate Orbiter* disappeared as it was to begin orbiting Mars. NASA later discovered that a unit system error caused the flight path to be incorrect and the orbiter to be lost. Research the error and determine what systems of units were involved. How can using two different systems of units cause errors?

Table 3 Common Objects in SI Measurements

Object	Type of Measurement	Measurement
can of soda	volume	355 cm³
bag of potatoes	mass	4.5 kg
fluorescent tube	length	1.2 m
refrigerator	temperature	276 K

Visual Learning

Tables 1 and 2 Have students use the information in the tables to determine the meaning of the following units: kilogram—1,000 grams; centimeter—1/100 meter; millimeter—1/1,000 meter. Have pairs take turns using the prefixes to make their own units and identifying their meanings. sample answer: gigagram (1 billion grams) and megameter (1 million meters) L2 ELL IS **Logical-Mathematical**

The International System

Fun Fact

SI stands for Système International d'Unités, which is the French term for International System of units.

Caption Answer

Figure 8 Answers will vary. Have students explain how they arrived at their answers.

Use Science Words

Word Origin The prefix *centi-*, the word *percent*, and the American unit of money called cent all derive from the same French and Latin root, which means 100. **Can you think of other ways we use the root word *cent?*** centimeter, century, centigrade, centipede L2 IS **Linguistic**

Astronomy
INTEGRATION

The error occurred because the common unit pound • seconds was used instead of the SI unit Newton • seconds in the computer program that determined trajectories of the orbiter.

Length

Activity

Have students use rulers to measure the length of a small item on their desks while sitting with their backs against the backs of their chairs. Then have them remeasure the item while looking directly at it from above. Discuss which measurement is more accurate. The measurement made while looking directly at it from above is more accurate. L2 ELL IS **Kinesthetic**

Volume

Figure 9
A cubic meter equals the volume of a cube 1 m by 1 m by 1 m. *How many cubic centimeters are in a cubic meter?*

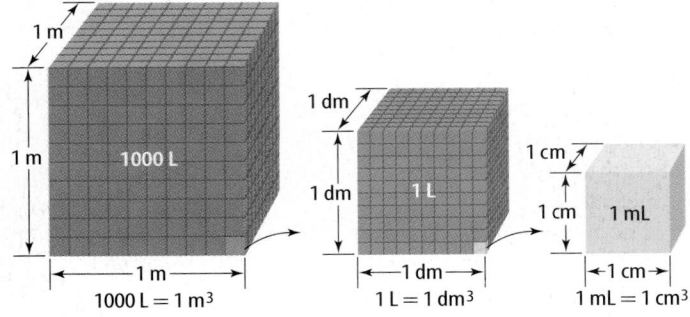

TRY AT HOME
Mini LAB

Measuring Volume

Procedure

1. Fill a plastic or glass **liquid measuring cup** until half full with **water.** Measure the volume.
2. Find an **object,** such as a rock, that will fit in your measuring cup.
3. Carefully lower the object into the water. If it floats, push it just under the surface with a **pencil.**
4. Record in your **Science Journal** the new volume of the water.

Analysis

1. How much space does the object occupy?
2. If 1 mL of water occupies exactly 1 cm³ of space, what is the volume of the object in cm³?

Volume

The amount of space an object occupies is its volume. The cubic meter (m³), shown in **Figure 9,** is the SI unit of volume. You can measure smaller volumes with the cubic centimeter (cm³ or cc). To find the volume of a square or rectangular object, such as a brick or your textbook, measure its length, width, and height and multiply them together. What is the volume of a compact disc case?

You are probably familiar with a 2-L bottle. A liter is a measurement of liquid volume. A cube 10 cm by 10 cm by 10 cm holds 1 L (1,000 cm³) of water. A cube 1 cm on a side holds 1 mL (1 cm³) of water.

Volume by Immersion Not all objects have an even, regular shape. How can you find the volume of something irregular like a rock or a piece of metal?

Have you ever added ice cubes to a nearly full glass of water only to have the water overflow? Why did the water overflow? Did you suddenly have more water? The volume of water did not increase at all, but the water was displaced when the ice cubes were added. Each ice cube takes up space or has volume. The difference in the volume of water before and after the addition of the ice cubes equals the volume of the ice cubes that are under the surface of the water.

The ice cubes took up space and caused the total volume in the glass to increase. When you measure the volume of an irregular object, you do the same thing. You start with a known volume of water and drop in, or immerse, the object. The increase in the volume of water is equal to the volume of the object.

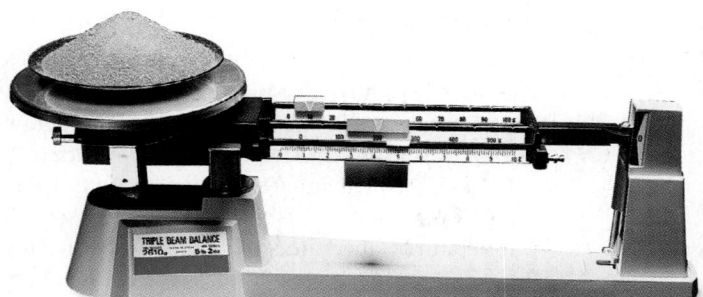

Figure 10
A triple beam balance compares an unknown mass to known masses.

Mass

The **mass** of an object measures the amount of matter in the object. The **kilogram** (kg) is the SI unit for mass. One liter of water has a mass of about 1 kg. Smaller masses are measured in grams (g). One gram is about the mass of a large paper clip.

You can determine mass with a triple beam balance, shown in **Figure 10.** The balance compares an object to a known mass. It is balanced when the known mass of the slides on the balance is equal to the mass of the object on the pan.

Why use the word *mass* instead of *weight*? Weight and mass are not the same. Mass depends only on the amount of matter in an object. If you ride in an elevator in the morning and then ride in the space shuttle later that afternoon, your mass is the same. Mass does not change when only your location changes.

Weight Weight is a measurement of force. The SI unit for weight is the newton (N). Weight depends on gravity, which can change depending on where the object is located. A spring scale measures how a planet's gravitational force pulls on objects. Several spring scales are shown in **Figure 11.**

If you were to travel to other planets, your weight would change, even though you would still be the same size and have the same mass. This is because gravitational force is different on each planet. If you could take your bathroom scale, which uses a spring, to each of the planets in this solar system, you would find that you weigh much less on Mars and much more on Jupiter. A mass of 75 pounds, or 34 kg, on Earth is a weight of 332 N. On Mars, the same mass is 126 N, and on Jupiter it is 782 N.

 **Reading Check** *What does weight measure?*

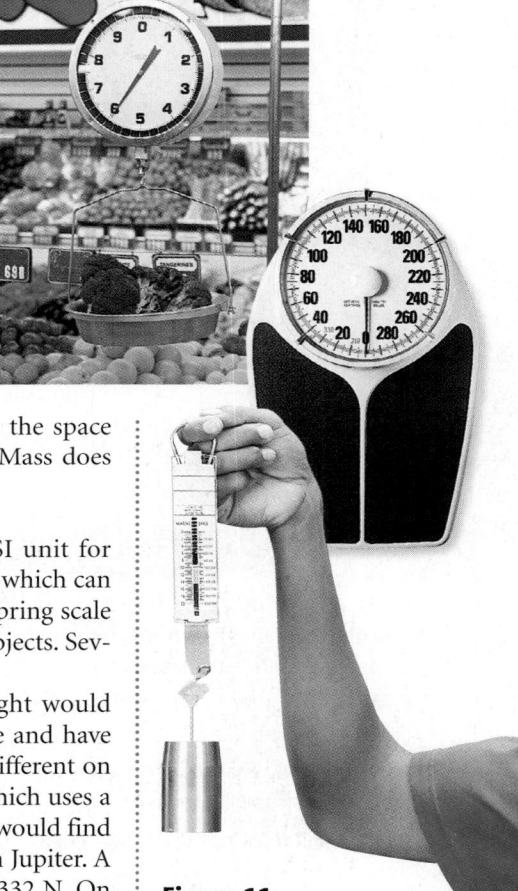

Figure 11
A spring scale measures an object's weight by how much it stretches a spring.

SECTION 2 SI Units **49**

Mass

Discussion

Have students discuss what would happen to their mass and weight if they visited the Moon. What might happen if they tried jumping while on the Moon? They would have the same mass but less weight, so they would be able to jump higher and farther. L2
IS Logical-Mathematical

Use Science Words

Word Usage Have students use the words mass and weight in sentences describing how the concepts are different. Possible answer: Mass is the amount of matter in an object; it is not affected by gravity. Weight is a measure of the force of gravity; it changes with the force of gravity. L2 ELL **IS** Linguistic

Use an Analogy

A pan balance is like a seesaw. When the weights on each side are equal, it is balanced.

✔ Reading Check

Answer the force of gravity on an object

Challenge

Have students suspend two 2–packs of fig cookies from a spring scale calibrated in newtons and record the weight. Have them determine the weight of a single cookie by dividing by 4. Then have them weigh a single cookie on the spring scale to check their answers.

Resource Manager

Chapter Resources Booklet
    MiniLAB, p. 4
    Enrichment, p. 27

Reading and Writing Critical Thinking/ Problem Solving, p. 13

Science Journal

Rates Have students use the information in the student text to write several rates. Possible answers: kilometers per hour, kilometers per liter of gas. Ask them to explain how these rates are used.

Temperature

3 Assess

Reteach

Collect a set of measurement tools. Display each tool and have a student volunteer tell the class its name, what it measures, and the unit(s) it uses. L1 ELL
LS Visual-Spatial

Challenge

Have each student make a chart to organize the information he or she learned in this section. The chart should include a title with International System in it. It should also include pictures and information about measuring length, volume, mass, temperature, and time. L2 ELL LS
Visual-Spatial

Assessment

Process Ask each student to make an illustration of a spring scale, showing how it works. Use **Performance Assessment in the Science Classroom,** p. 127.

Figure 12
The kelvin scale starts at 0 K. In theory, 0 K is the coldest temperature possible in nature.

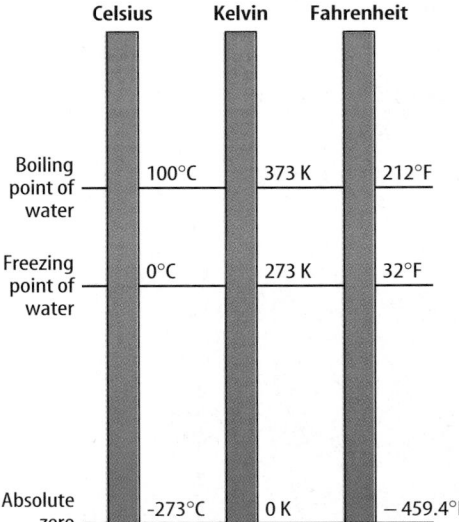

Temperature

The physical property of temperature is related to how hot or cold an object is. Temperature is a measure of the kinetic energy, or energy of motion, of the particles that make up matter.

The Fahrenheit and Celsius temperature scales are two common scales used on thermometers. Temperature is measured in SI with the **kelvin (K)** scale. A 1-K difference in temperature is the same as a 1°C difference in temperature, as shown in **Figure 12.** However, the two scales do not start at zero.

Time and Rates

Time is the interval between two events. The SI unit of time is the second (s). Time also is measured in hours (h). Although the hour is not an SI unit, it is easier to use for long periods of time. Can you imagine hearing that a marathon was run in 7,620 s instead of 2 h and 7 min?

A **rate** is the amount of change of one measurement in a given amount of time. One rate you are familiar with is speed, which is the distance traveled in a given time. Speeds often are measured in kilometers per hour (km/h).

The unit that is changing does not necessarily have to be an SI unit. For example, you can measure the number of cars that pass through an intersection per hour in cars/h. The annual rate of inflation can be measured in percent/year.

Section 2 Assessment

1. Describe a situation in which different units of measure could cause confusion.

2. What type of quantity does the cubic meter measure?

3. How would you change a measurement in centimeters to kilometers?

4. What SI unit replaces the pound? What does this measure?

5. **Think Critically** You are told to find the mass of a metal cube. How will you do it?

Skill Builder Activities

6. **Measuring in SI** Measure the length, volume, and mass of your textbook in SI units. Describe any tools or calculations you use. **For more help, refer to the** Science Skill Handbook.

7. **Converting Units** A block of wood is 0.2 m by 0.1 m by 0.5 m. Find its dimensions in centimeters. Use these to find its volume in cubic centimeters. Show your work. **For more help, refer to the** Math Skill Handbook.

Answers to Section Assessment

1. Possible answer: Someone thinks a temperature is given in Fahrenheit degrees, but it is actually in Celsius degrees.
2. volume
3. divide by 100,000
4. newton; the force of gravity on an object

5. Use a pan balance or scale. The description should provide step-by-step instructions for using the instrument.
6. Answers will vary, but length should be measured in centimeters, volume in cubic centimeters, and mass in grams.

7. 20 cm × 10 cm × 50 cm = 10,000 cm^3

Scale Drawing

A scale drawing is used to represent something that is too large or too small to be drawn at its actual size. Blueprints for a house are a good example of a scale drawing.

What You'll Investigate
How can you represent your classroom accurately in a scale drawing?

Materials
1-cm graph paper   metric ruler
pencil   meterstick

Goals
- **Measure** using SI.
- **Make** a data table.
- **Calculate** new measurements.
- **Make** an accurate scale drawing.

Procedure

1. Use your meterstick to measure the length and width of your classroom. Note the locations and sizes of doors and windows.
2. **Record** the lengths of each item in a data table similar to the one below.
3. Use a scale of 2 cm = 1 m to calculate the lengths to be used in the drawing. Record them in your data table.
4. **Draw** the floor plan. Include the scale.

Room Dimensions		
Part of Room	Distance in Room (m)	Distance on Drawing (cm)
Front right corner to door	1.5	3
Across door	1.0	2

Conclude and Apply

1. How did you calculate the lengths to be used on your drawing? Did you put a scale on your drawing?
2. What would your scale drawing look like if you chose a different scale?
3. **Sketch** your room at home, estimating the distances. Compare this sketch to your scale drawing of the classroom. When would you use each type of illustration?
4. What measuring tool simplifies this task?

*C*ommunicating
Your Data

Measure your room at home and compare it to the estimates on your sketch. Explain to someone at home what you did and how well you estimated the measurements. **For more help, refer to the** Science Skill Handbook.

Resource Manager

Chapter Resources Booklet
Reinforcement, p. 24
Lab Activity, pp. 11–12
Activity Worksheet, pp. 5–6

*C*ommunicating
Your Data

Have students use a drawing to discuss scale and features with a small group or the class, in addition to explaining these things to someone at home.

BENCH TESTED

Purpose To learn how to make and use a scale drawing [L2] ELL COOP LEARN [S] **Visual-Spatial**

Process Skills comparing and contrasting, interpreting data, making and using tables, using numbers, making models

Time Required one 45-minute period to measure the classroom, one 30-minute period to draw the room to scale (could be homework)

Teaching Strategies
- Discuss where to start measuring, and whether to measure from the inner or outer edge of doors and window frames.
- Demonstrate how to draw the length of a wall to scale.

Answers to Questions
1. Length was measured with a meterstick. The scale of 2 cm/1 m should be noted on the drawing.
2. The shape of the drawing would remain the same, but it would be larger or smaller, depending on the new scale chosen.
3. Check students' work. A rough sketch might be used to give an idea of how to design a room. A scale drawing might be used to determine if the furniture will actually fit in the space available.
4. Possible tools to use: meterstick, tape measure, retractable metal tape measure, measuring wheel

✓*Assessment*

Portfolio Have students add to their work a detailed explanation of how to make and use a scale drawing. Use **PASC**, p. 177. P

SECTION

3

Drawings, Tables, and Graphs

Bellringer Transparency

Display the Section Focus Transparency for Section 3. Use the accompanying Transparency Activity Master. L2
ELL

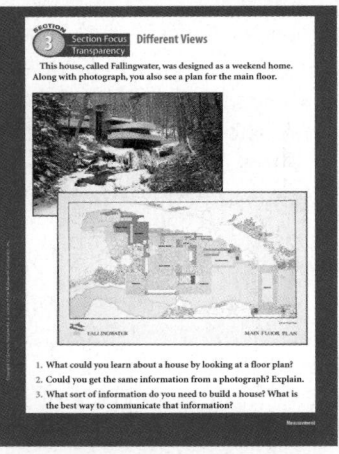

As You Read

What You'll Learn
- **Describe** how to use pictures and tables to give information.
- **Identify** and use three types of graphs.
- **Distinguish** the correct use of each type of graph.

Vocabulary

table	bar graph
graph	circle graph
line graph	

Why It's Important

Illustrations, tables, and graphs help you communicate data about the world around you in an organized and efficient way.

Scientific Illustrations

Most science books include pictures. Photographs and drawings model and illustrate ideas and sometimes make new information more clear than written text can. For example, a drawing of an airplane engine shows how all the parts fit together much better than several pages of text could describe it.

Drawings A drawing is sometimes the best choice to show details. For example, a canyon cut through red rock reveals many rock layers. If the layers are all shades of red, a drawing can show exactly where the lines between the layers are. The drawing can emphasize only the things that are necessary to show.

A drawing also can show things you can't see. You can't see the entire solar system, but drawings show you what it looks like. Also, you can make quick sketches to help model problems. For example, you could draw the outline of two continents to show how they might have fit together at one time.

A drawing can show hidden things, as well. A drawing can show the details of the water cycle, as in **Figure 13.** Architects use drawings to show what the inside of a building will look like. Biologists use drawings to show where the nerves in your arm are found.

Figure 13
This drawing shows details of the water cycle that can't be seen in a photograph.

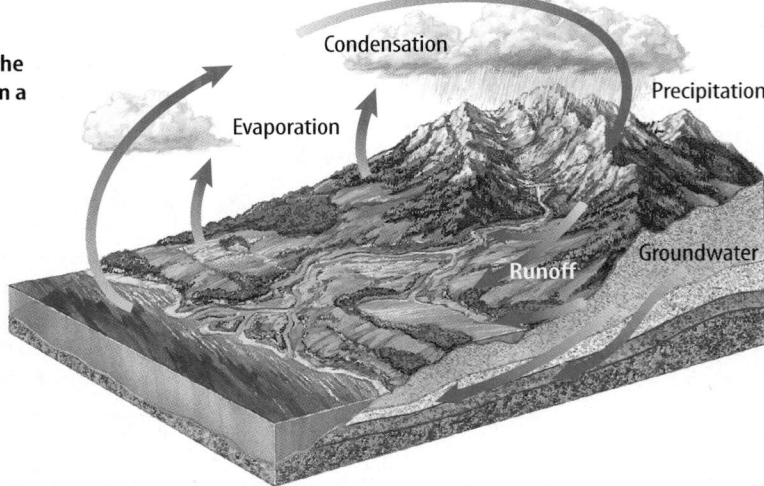

Condensation

Precipitation

Evaporation

Runoff

Groundwater

Tie to Prior Knowledge

Ask students to recall publications other than science books in which they have seen graphs and charts. Newspapers and news magazines are good sources of examples.

52   CHAPTER 2 Measurement

Section ✓ *Assessment* Planner

PORTFOLIO
Make a Model, p. 53
PERFORMANCE ASSESSMENT
Skill Builder Activities, p. 55
See page 62 for more options.

CONTENT ASSESSMENT
Section, p. 55
Challenge, p. 55
Chapter, pp. 62–63

Photographs A still photograph shows an object exactly as it is at a single moment in time. Movies show how an object moves and can be slowed down or sped up to show interesting features. In your schoolwork, you might use photographs in a report. For example, you could show the different types of trees in your neighborhood for a report on ecology.

Tables and Graphs

Everyone who deals with numbers and compares measurements needs an organized way to collect and display data. A **table** displays information in rows and columns so that it is easier to read and understand, as seen in **Table 4.** The data in the table could be presented in a paragraph, but it would be harder to pick out the facts or make comparisons.

A **graph** is used to collect, organize, and summarize data in a visual way. The relationships between the data often are seen more clearly when shown in a graph. Three common types of graphs are line, bar, and circle graphs.

Line Graph A **line graph** shows the relationship between two variables. A variable is something that can change, or vary, such as the temperature of a liquid or the number of people in a race. Both variables in a line graph must be numbers. An example of a line graph is shown in **Figure 14.** One variable is shown on the horizontal axis, or *x*-axis, of the graph. The other variable is placed along the vertical axis, or *y*-axis. A line on the graph shows the relationship between the two variables.

Table 4 Endangered Animal Species in the United States

Year	Number of Endangered Animal Species
1980	174
1982	179
1984	192
1986	213
1988	245
1990	263
1992	284
1994	321
1996	324
1998	357

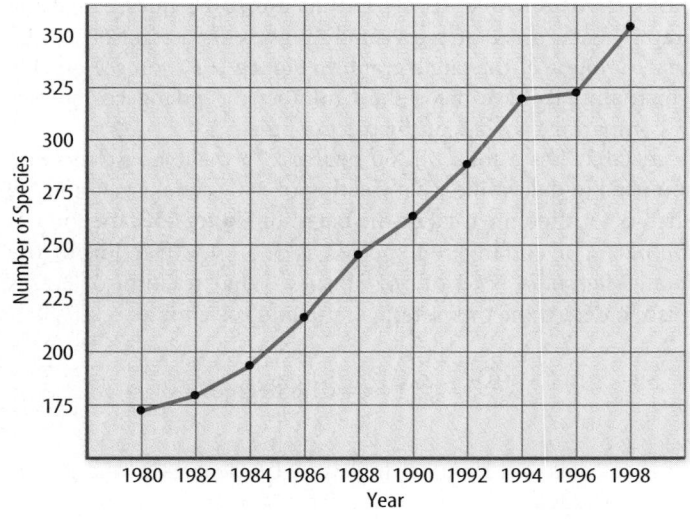

U.S. Endangered Animal Species per Calendar Year

(y-axis: Number of Species; x-axis: Year)

Figure 14
To find the number of endangered animal species in 1988, find that year on the *x*-axis and see what number corresponds to it on the *y*-axis.

LAB DEMONSTRATION

Purpose to show how to collect information and organize it as a table and a line graph

Materials graph paper, ten books (some thick, some thin), centimeter ruler, meterstick

Preparation Set up a table on the board for data collected in this demonstration.

Procedure Measure and record the height of one book placed on a table. Add books one at a time, and measure and record the height of the stack after each addition. Finally, demonstrate how to use the data to make a line graph.

Expected Outcome The graph shows that the height of the stack of books increases.

✓ Assessment

What does the graph tell about the relationship between the number of books and the height of the stack? The height of the stack increases with each additional book, but the rate of increase is not even.

Tables and Graphs

Quick Demo

On the board draw two line graphs of the same data using two different scales for the *y*-axis. Point out to students that one of the lines looks much steeper than the other. Have students study the units on the axes of the graphs to see that the information in both graphs is the same. L2 **IS** **Visual-Spatial**

SCIENCE *Online*

Internet Addresses

_____

_____

_____

_____

Explore the Glencoe Science Web site at **science.glencoe.com** to find out more about topics in this section.

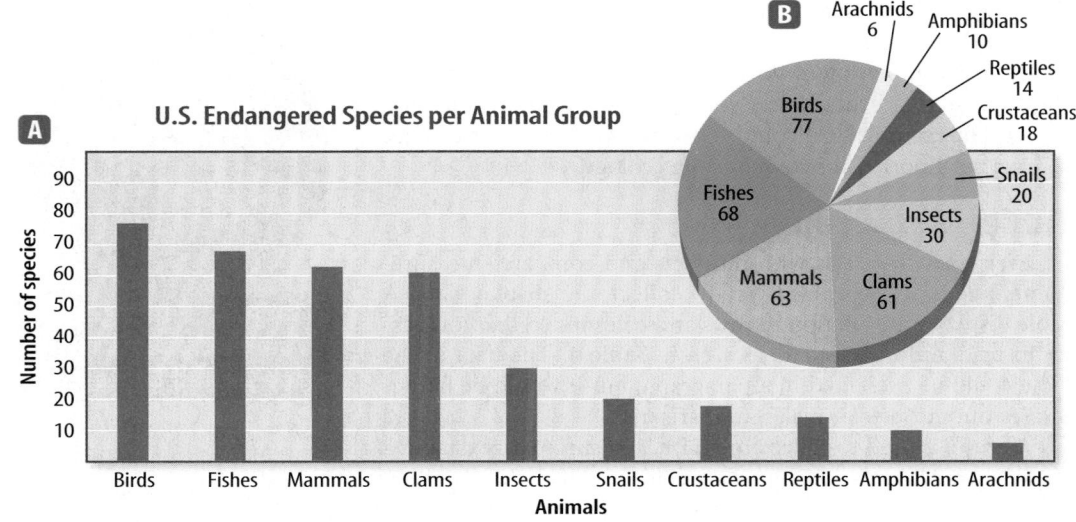

U.S. Endangered Species per Animal Group

A (bar graph, *y*-axis: Number of species 10–90, *x*-axis: Animals — Birds, Fishes, Mammals, Clams, Insects, Snails, Crustaceans, Reptiles, Amphibians, Arachnids)

B (circle graph) Arachnids 6, Amphibians 10, Reptiles 14, Crustaceans 18, Snails 20, Insects 30, Clams 61, Mammals 63, Fishes 68, Birds 77

Figure 15

A Bar graphs allow you to picture the results easily. *Which category of animals has the most endangered species?* **B** On this circle graph, you can see what part of the whole each animal represents.

SCIENCE *Online*

Research Visit the Glencoe Science Web site at **science.glencoe.com** for more information about scientific illustrations. Communicate to your class what you learn.

Bar Graph A **bar graph** uses rectangular blocks, or bars, of varying sizes to show the relationships among variables. One variable is divided into parts. It can be numbers, such as the time of day, or a category, such as an animal. The second variable must be a number. The bars show the size of the second variable. For example, if you made a bar graph of the endangered species data from **Figure 14,** the bar for 1990 would represent 263 species. An example of a bar graph is shown in **Figure 15A.**

Circle Graph Suppose you want to show the relationship among the types of endangered species. A **circle graph** shows the parts of a whole. Circle graphs are sometimes called pie graphs. Each piece of pie visually represents a fraction of the total. Looking at the circle graph in **Figure 15B,** you see quickly which animals have the highest number of endangered species by comparing the sizes of the pieces of pie.

A circle has a total of 360 degrees. To make a circle graph, you need to determine what fraction of 360 each part should be. First, determine the total of the parts. In **Figure 15B,** the total of the parts, or endangered species, is 367. One fraction of the total, *Mammals,* is 63 of 367 species. What fraction of 360 is this? To determine this, set up a ratio and solve for *x*:

$$\frac{63}{367} = \frac{x}{360} \quad x = 61.8 \text{ degrees}$$

Mammals will have an angle of 61.8 degrees in the graph. The other angles in the circle are determined the same way.

✓ Guided Reading

Metacognition Journal In this strategy, each student analyzes his or her own thought processes. Have students divide the paper in half. On the left, have them record what they have learned about a topic. On the right, have them record the reason they learned it. Have students write a Metacognition Journal about graphs.

Resource Manager

Chapter Resources Booklet
   Reinforcement, p. 25
   Activity Worksheet, pp. 7–8
Lab Management and Safety, pp. 70, 71

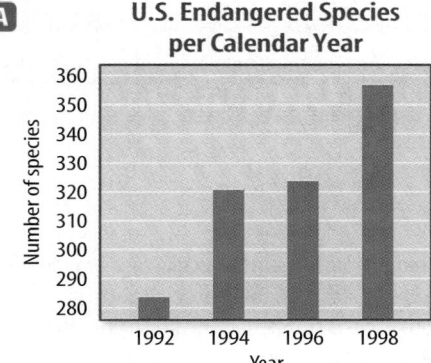

A U.S. Endangered Species per Calendar Year

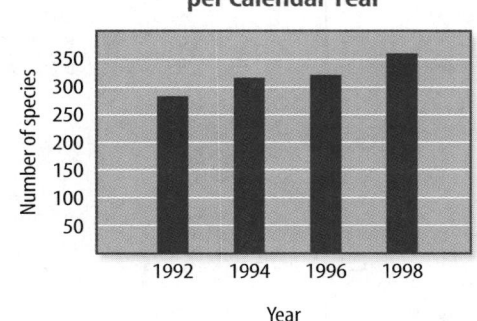

B U.S. Endangered Species per Calendar Year

Reading Graphs When you are using or making graphs to display data, be careful—the scale of a graph can be misleading. The way the scale on a graph is marked can create the wrong impression, as seen in **Figure 16A.** Until you see that the *y*-axis doesn't start at zero, it appears that the number of endangered species has quadrupled in just six years.

This is called a broken scale and is used to highlight small but significant changes, just as an inset on a map draws attention to a small area of a larger map. **Figure 16B** shows the same data on a graph that does not have a broken scale. The number of species has only increased 22 percent from 1980 to 1986. Both graphs have correct data, but must be read carefully. Always analyze the measurements and graphs that you come across. If there is a surprising result, look closer at the scale.

Figure 16
Careful reading of graphs is important. **A** This graph does not start at zero, which makes it appear that the number of species has more than quadrupled from 1980 to 1986. **B** The actual increase is about 22 percent as you can see from this full graph. The broken scale must be noted in order to interpret the results correctly.

Section **3** Assessment

1. Describe a time when an illustration would be helpful in everyday activities.

2. Explain how to use **Figure 16** to find the number of endangered species in 1998.

3. Explain the difference between tables and graphs.

4. Suppose your class surveys students about after-school activities. What type of graph would you use to display your data? Explain.

5. **Think Critically** How are line, bar, and circle graphs the same? How are they different?

Skill Builder Activities

6. **Making and Using Graphs** Record the amount of time you spend reading each day for the next week. Then make a graph to display the data. What type of graph will you use? Could more than one kind of graph be used? **For more help, refer to the** Science Skill Handbook.

7. **Using an Electronic Spreadsheet** Use a spreadsheet to display how the total mass of a 500-kg elevator changes as 50-kg passengers are added one at a time. **For more help, refer to the** Technology Skill Handbook.

SECTION 3 Drawings, Tables, and Graphs **55**

Activity

Recognize the Problem

Purpose

to apply the concepts of precision, measurement, and graphing to a specific problem L2 ELL **LS Kinesthetic**

Process Skills

designing an experiment, forming a hypothesis, communicating, observing and inferring, making and using tables, interpreting data

Time Required

45 minutes each to plan and do the experiment

Materials

meterstick, stopwatch

Alternate Materials

clock with a second hand

Safety Precautions

Work in an area where it is safe to run. If this is not possible, measure walking speed only. Check that students do not have health problems that could prevent them from exercising. Allow students to decline running if it is physically uncomfortable or embarrassing for them.

Form a Hypothesis

Possible Hypotheses

A course on a flat, straight surface will be the most accurately measurable with the given tools. Accuracy will be better if more than one group member times each walker or runner.

Activity — Design Your Own Experiment

Pace Yourself

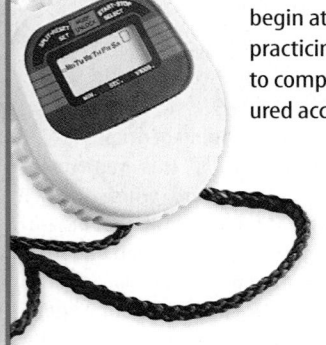

Track meets and other competitions require participants to walk, run, or wheel a distance that has been precisely measured. Officials make sure all participants begin at the same time, and each person's time is stopped at the finish line. If you are practicing for a marathon or 10K race, you need to know your speed or pace in order to compare it with those of other participants. How can your performance be measured accurately?

Recognize the Problem

How will you measure the speed of each person in your group? How will you display these data?

Form a Hypothesis

Think about the information you have learned about precision, measurement, and graphing. In your group, make a hypothesis about a technique that will provide you with the most precise measurement of each person's pace.

Goals

■ **Design** an experiment that allows you to measure speed for each member of your group accurately.
■ **Display** data in a table and a graph.

Possible Materials

meterstick
stopwatch
*watch with a second hand
*Alternate materials

Safety Precautions

Work in an area where it is safe to run. Participate only if you are physically able to exercise safely. As you design your plan, make a list of all the specific safety and health precautions you will take as you perform the investigation. Get your teacher's approval of the list before you begin.

56 CHAPTER 2 Measurement

Test Your Hypothesis

Possible Procedures

Measure the distance to be walked. Mark the starting and ending points for the walk. For each student, use a stopwatch to measure walking time to the nearest tenth of a second. Record each student's time on a data table. Graph the results. Repeat these steps, replacing the walk with a run.

Time to walk and run 18 m				
Student	Walking time	Running time	Walking speed	Running speed
Carlos	21.3 s	10.6 s	0.845 m/s	1.70 m/s
Brianna	19.6 s	10.9 s	0.918 m/s	1.65 m/s

Test Your Hypothesis

Plan

1. As a group, decide what materials you will need.

2. How far will you travel? How will you measure that distance? How precise can you be?

3. How will you measure time? How precise can you be?

4. List the steps and materials you will use to test your hypothesis. Be specific. Will you try any part of your test more than once?

5. Before you begin, create a data table. Your group must decide on its design. Be sure to leave enough room to record the results for each person's time. If more than one trial is to be run for each measurement, include room for the additional data.

Do

1. Make sure that your teacher approves your plan before you start.

2. Carry out the experiment as planned and approved.

3. Be sure to record your data in the data table as you proceed with the measurements.

Analyze Your Data

1. **Graph** your data. What type of graph would be best?

2. Are your data table and graph easy to understand? Explain.

3. How do you know that your measurements are precise?

4. Do any of your data appear to be out of line with the rest?

Draw Conclusions

1. How is it possible for different members of a group to find different times while measuring the same event?

2. What tools would help you collect more precise data?

3. What other data displays could you use? What are the advantages and disadvantages of each?

*C*ommunicating Your Data

Make a larger version of your graph to display in your classroom with the graphs of other groups. **For more help, refer to the** Science Skill Handbook.

Teaching Strategy

Demonstrate to students how to use the meterstick to measure walking/running distance and how to stop, start, and reset the stopwatch.

Expected Outcome

Most results will show students moving at different speeds from each other. Often, two students recording the same event will measure different times.

Analyze Your Data

1. bar graph
2. Check students' work. A person unfamiliar with the experiment should be able to quickly grasp the results.
3. Students should explain their efforts to measure precisely.
4. Students should use their bar graphs to answer this question.

Error Analysis

Have students compare their results and their hypotheses and explain why differences occurred.

Draw Conclusions

1. People's reaction times with the stopwatch may be different, people watching the race from different angles may see the runner pass the finish line at slightly different times, and the stopwatches may vary.
2. Sample response: global positioning data, a timer that used infrared or laser light to determine start and stop times
3. Sample response: graph with a different scale, bar graph or data table comparing average time for male students versus average time for female students; each arranges the information in different ways, so more relationships can be seen

Assessment

Performance Ask students to design a method to measure another speed, such as the speed of a person swimming two laps in a pool. Use **Performance Assessment in the Science Classroom,** p. 95.

*C*ommunicating Your Data

Have each group use its graph to explain its data to the class.

Science Stats

Biggest, Tallest, Loudest

Did you know...

Content Background

The rafflesia is a parasitic plant that grows in the mountains of Malaysia. This plant has adapted to feed off of the roots of large vines that are in the grape family. The large, fleshy flower remains open for five to seven days. The flower emits a very strong offensive odor that attracts carrion-feeding flies. It is thought that the flies are the source of pollination.

The eruption of Krakatau in 1883 was so loud that the explosion was heard 3,500 km (2,175 mi) away. A series of eruptions discharged so much ash and dust into the air that the area surrounding the volcano was plunged into darkness for days. The massive eruption set off a series of tsunamis and tidal waves that killed thousands of people in the nearby islands.

Discussion

Students may not have a good grasp of the magnitude of these features. Make the conversion calculations to English units on the board as a class to give students a better idea of how large these items are. Useful conversion factors (numbers are rounded off): 1 kg = 2.2 lbs; 1 m = 3.3 ft. Converted Numbers: 11 kg = 24.2 lbs; 1 m = 39.37 in; 1,800 m = 5,940 ft; 110 m = 363 ft; 452 m = 1,492 ft; 442 m = 1,459 ft; 33.5 m = 110.6 ft; 1.65 m = 5.45 ft.

Extension

Have students find out more about the blue whale, including its diet and habitat. Suggest that students record their findings in their Science Journals.

... The world's most massive flower belongs to a species called *Rafflesia* (ruh FLEE zhee uh) and has a mass of up to 11 kg. The diameter, or the distance across the flower's petals, can measure up to 1 m.

... The Grand Canyon is so deep— as much as 1,800 m—that it can hold more than four Empire State Buildings stacked on top of one another.

... The world's tallest building is the Petronus Towers in Kuala Lumpur, Malaysia. It is 452 m tall. The tallest building in the United States is Chicago's Sears Tower, shown here, which measures 442 m.

... The world's tallest tree is a coast redwood in the Montgomery Woods State Park in California. The tree stands 112.1 m high.

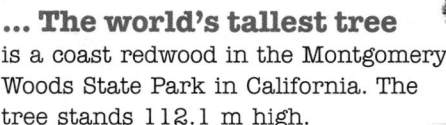

SCIENCE *Online*
Internet Addresses
_____
_____
_____

Explore the Glencoe Science Web site at **science.glencoe.com** to find out more about topics in this feature.

...The largest animal on Earth

is the blue whale. It can grow to be 33.5 m long. If 20 people who are each 1.65 m tall were lying head to toe, it would almost equal this length.

How do they measure up?

...One of the loudest explosions on Earth

was the 1883 eruption of Krakatau (krah kuh TAHEW), an Indonesian volcano. It was heard from more than 3,500 km away.

Do the Math

1. How many of the largest rafflesia petals would you have to place side by side to equal the length of a blue whale?
2. When Krakatau erupted, it ejected 18,000 km^3 of ash and rock. Other large eruptions released the following: Mount Pinatubo—7,000 km^3, Mount Katmai—13,000 km^3, Tambora—30,000 km^3, Vesuvius—5,000 km^3. Make a bar graph to compare the sizes of these eruptions.
3. Use the information provided about the Grand Canyon to calculate how many Sears Towers would have to stand end on end to equal the depth of the canyon.

Go Further

Do research on the Internet at **science.glencoe.com** to find facts that describe some of the shortest, smallest, or fastest things on Earth. Create a class bulletin board with the facts you and your classmates find.

Do the Math

Teaching Strategies

- Discuss which units should be used to mark the y-axis on the bar graph for the second question in the Do the Math.
- Provide graph paper to assist the students with question 2 in the Do the Math.

Answers

1. 33.5 or 34
2. Check student's graph.
3. About four

Go Further

A good source of information for this may be *The Guinness Book of World Records.*

Visual Learning

How do they measure up? Approximately how tall is the Great Pyramid? 200 m **How tall is the Great Pyramid in feet?** about 660 feet **What is the difference in height of The Large Sahara Desert Sand Dune and the Great Pyramid?** about 300 m

Reviewing Main Ideas

Preview

Students can answer the questions in their Science Journals. Discuss the answers as you go through the chapter. **IS Linguistic**

Review

Students can write their answers, then compare them with those of other students. **IS Interpersonal**

Reteach

Students can look at the illustrations and describe details that support the main ideas of the chapter. **IS Visual-Spatial**

Answers to Chapter Review

SECTION 1

4. neither

SECTION 2

2. length

SECTION 3

2. San Francisco, CA

Reviewing Main Ideas

Section 1 Description and Measurement

1. Measurements such as length, volume, mass, temperature, and rates are used to describe objects and events.

2. Estimation is used to make an educated guess at a measurement.

3. Accuracy describes how close a measurement is to the true value.

4. Precision describes how close measurements are to each other. *Are the shots accurate or precise on the basketball hoop shown?*

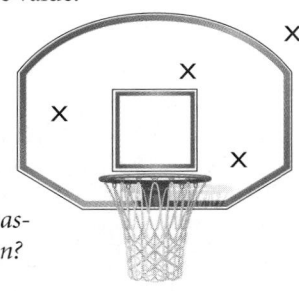

Section 2 SI Units

1. The international system of measurement is called SI. It is used throughout the world for communicating data.

2. The SI unit of length is the meter. Volume—the amount of space an object occupies—can be measured in cubic meters. The mass of an object is measured in kilograms. The SI unit of temperature is the kelvin. *What type of measurement is being made according to the sign shown?*

NEXT 96 km

Section 3 Drawings, Tables, and Graphs

1. Tables, photographs, drawings, and graphs can sometimes present data more clearly than explaining everything in words. Scientists use these tools to collect, organize, summarize, and display data in a way that is easy to use and understand.

2. The three common types of graphs are line graphs, bar graphs, and circle graphs. *Which city on the line graph shown is the coldest in the fifth month?*

Average Normal Temperature

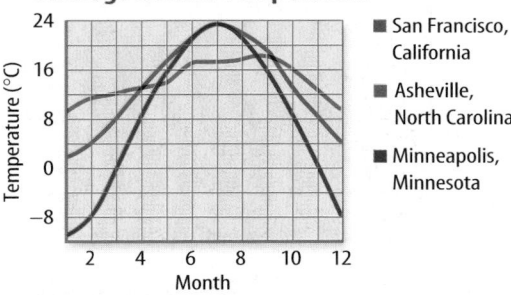

- San Francisco, California
- Asheville, North Carolina
- Minneapolis, Minnesota

3. Line graphs show the relationship between two variables that are numbers on an *x*-axis and a *y*-axis. Bar graphs divide a variable into parts to show a relationship. Circle graphs show the parts of a whole like pieces of a pie.

FOLDABLES Reading & Study Skills

After You Read

Fill in the *Round It* column on your Foldable. Explain when it is acceptable and appropriate for scientists to round measurements.

FOLDABLES Reading & Study Skills

After You Read

After students have read the chapter and completed the Foldable described in Before You Read, have them do the activity on the student page.

Visualizing Main Ideas

Complete the following concept map.

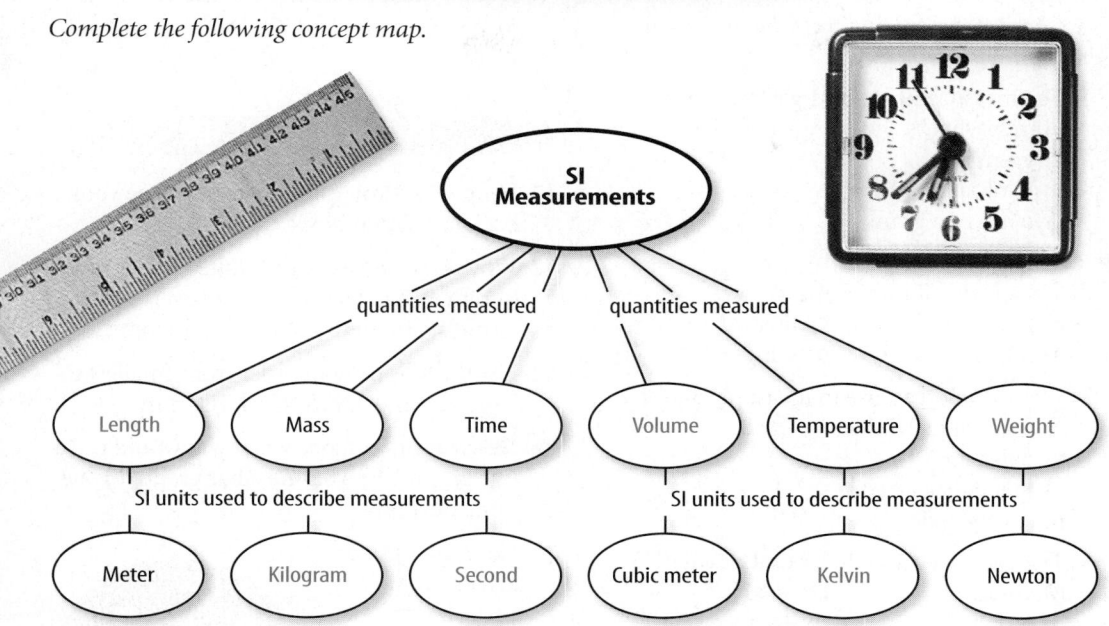

Visualizing Main Ideas

See student page.

Vocabulary Review

Using Vocabulary

1. meter
2. measurement
3. estimation
4. mass
5. circle graph
6. precision
7. Kelvin
8. SI

Vocabulary Review

Vocabulary Words

a. accuracy
b. bar graph
c. circle graph
d. estimation
e. graph
f. kelvin
g. kilogram
h. line graph
i. mass
j. measurement
k. meter
l. precision
m. rate
n. SI
o. table

THE PRINCETON REVIEW — Study Tip

When you encounter new vocabulary, write it down in your Science Journal. This will help you understand and remember them.

Using Vocabulary

Each phrase below describes a vocabulary word. Write the word that matches the phrase describing it.

1. the SI unit for length

2. a description with numbers

3. a method of making a rough measurement

4. the amount of matter in an object

5. a graph that shows parts of a whole

6. a description of how close measurements are to each other

7. the SI unit for temperature

8. an international system of units

Chapter 2 Assessment

Checking Concepts

1. D
2. D
3. C
4. A
5. D
6. C
7. A
8. C
9. D
10. B

Thinking Critically

11. Multiply its length times its width times its height.

12. The SI system of measurement is understood internationally, while the English system is understood in only a limited number of countries.

13. 1 mm, 100 mm, 1 m, 10 km

14. Accept any reasonable answer. Sample answer: to show distance traveled versus time of travel; no, you cannot use a bar graph for this.

15. Sample response: to allow for precision and reproducibility in design and printing; for example, ads for a given product all use exactly the same colors.

Checking Concepts

Choose the word or phrase that best answers the question.

1. The measurement 25.81 g is precise to the nearest what?
 A) gram
 B) kilogram
 C) tenth of a gram
 D) hundredth of a gram

2. What is the SI unit of mass?
 A) kilometer   **C)** liter
 B) meter   **D)** kilogram

3. What would you use to measure length?
 A) graduated cylinder
 B) balance
 C) meterstick
 D) spring scale

4. The cubic meter is the SI unit of what?
 A) volume   **C)** mass
 B) weight   **D)** distance

5. Which term describes how close measurements are to each other?
 A) significant digits   **C)** accuracy
 B) estimation   **D)** precision

6. Which is a temperature scale?
 A) volume   **C)** Celsius
 B) mass   **D)** mercury

7. Which is used to organize data?
 A) table   **C)** precision
 B) rate   **D)** meterstick

8. To show the number of wins for each football team in your district, which of the following would you use?
 A) photograph   **C)** bar graph
 B) line graph   **D)** SI

9. What organizes data in rows and columns?
 A) bar graph   **C)** line graph
 B) circle graph   **D)** table

---

10. To show 25 percent on a circle graph, the section must measure what angle?
 A) 25°   **C)** 180°
 B) 90°   **D)** 360°

Thinking Critically

11. How would you estimate the volume your backpack could hold?

12. Why do scientists in the United States use SI rather than the English system (feet, pounds, pints, etc.) of measurement?

13. List the following in order from smallest to largest: 1 m, 1 mm, 10 km, 100 mm.

14. Describe an instance when you would use a line graph. Can you use a bar graph for the same purpose?

15. Computer graphics artists can specify the color of a point on a monitor by using characters for the intensities of three colors of light. Why was this method of describing color invented?

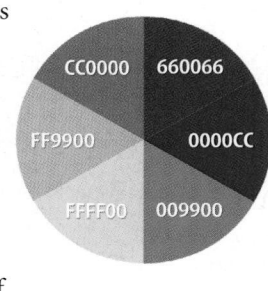

Developing Skills

16. Measuring in SI Make a fist. Use a centimeter ruler to measure the height, width, and depth of your fist.

17. Comparing and Contrasting How are volume, length, and mass similar? How are they different? Give several examples of units that are used to measure each quantity. Which units are SI?

Chapter ✓Assessment Planner

Portfolio Encourage students to place in their portfolios one or two items of what they consider to be their best work. Examples include:
- Science Journal, p. 41
- Performance Assessment, p. 45
- Activity Assessment, p. 51
- Make a Model, p. 51

Performance Additional performance assessments, Performance Task Assessment Lists, and rubrics for evaluating these activities can be found in Glencoe's **Performance Assessment in the Science Classroom.**

18. Making and Using Graphs The table shows the area of several bodies of water. Make a bar graph of the data.

Areas of Bodies of Water	
Body of Water	**Area (km²)**
Currituck Sound (North Carolina)	301
Pocomoke Sound (Maryland/Virginia)	286
Chincoteague Bay (Maryland/Virginia)	272
Core Sound (North Carolina)	229

19. Interpreting Scientific Illustrations What does the figure show? How has this drawing been simplified?

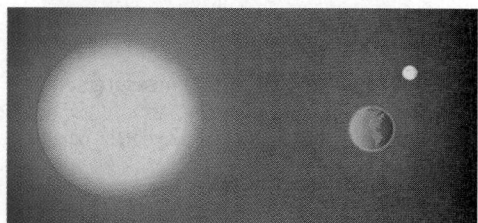

Performance Assessment

20. Poster Make a poster to alert the public about the benefits of using SI units.

21. Newspaper Search Look through a week's worth of newspapers and evaluate any graphs or tables that you find.

TECHNOLOGY

Go to the Glencoe Science Web site at **science.glencoe.com** or use the **Glencoe Science CD-ROM** for additional chapter assessment.

THE PRINCETON REVIEW — Test Practice

Some students in Mrs. Olsen's science class measured their masses during three consecutive months. They placed their results in the following table. Study the table and answer the following questions.

Student Masses: Sept. – Nov. 1999			
Student	**September**	**October**	**November**
Domingo	41.13 kg	40.92 kg	42.27 kg
Latoya	35.21 kg	35.56 kg	36.07 kg
Benjamin	45,330 g	45,680 g	45,530 g
Poloma	31.78 kg	31.55 kg	31.51 kg
Frederick	50,870 g	51,880 g	51,030 g
Fiona	37.62 kg	37.71 kg	37.85 kg

1. According to the table, which shows Frederick's weight in kilograms for the three months?
  A) 5.087, 5.118, 5.103
  B) 50.87, 51.88, 51.03
  C) 508.7, 511.8, 510.3
  D) 5,087, 5,118, 5,103

2. According to this information, which lists the students from lightest to heaviest during November?
  F) Poloma, Benjamin, Domingo, Frederick
  G) Domingo, Latoya, Frederick, Benjamin
  H) Fiona, Domingo, Benjamin, Frederick
  J) Frederick, Benjamin, Domingo, Poloma

THE PRINCETON REVIEW — Test Practice

The Test-Taking Tip was written by The Princeton Review, the nation's leader in test preparation.
1. B
2. H

Developing Skills

16. Answers will vary. Check students' work.
17. Volume, length, and mass are all properties that can be measured. Volume is the amount of space an object occupies; length is the distance between two points; mass is the amount of matter in an object. Sample units: cubic meter (volume); meter (length); kilogram (mass). These are all SI units.
18. Check students' graphs.
19. It shows Earth, the Moon, and the Sun. Size and distance are not to scale, and the inner planets are missing.

Performance Assessment

20. Use **Performance Assessment in the Science Classroom**, p. 145.
21. Use **Performance Assessment in the Science Classroom**, p. 99.

✓Assessment Resources

 Reproducible Masters

Chapter Resources Booklet
  Chapter Review, pp. 33–34
  Chapter Tests, pp. 35–38
  Assessment Transparency Activity, p. 45

Glencoe Science Web site
  Interactive Tutor
  Chapter Quizzes

Glencoe Technology
  🔊 Assessment Transparency
  💿 Interactive CD-ROM Chapter Quizzes
  💿 ExamView Pro Test Bank
  💿 Vocabulary PuzzleMaker Software
  📼 MindJogger Videoquiz

Reading Comprehension

QUESTION 1: B

Students must use information in the passage in order to identify the best supported conclusion.

- **Choice A** No; this is not supported by the passage.
- **Choice B** Yes; this is supported by the passage.
- **Choice C** No; this is not supported by the passage.
- **Choice D** No; this is not supported by the passage.

QUESTION 2: H

Students must determine, based on the reading passage, which of the answer choices is appropriate in describing ancient measurements.

- **Choice F** No; they were not precise.
- **Choice G** No; they were correct for those who used them.
- **Choice H** Yes; they were reasonable estimates.
- **Choice J** No; this term is judgmental.

THE PRINCETON REVIEW — All questions written and validated by The Princeton Review.

Reading Comprehension

Read the passage carefully. Then read each question that follows the passage. Decide which is the best answer to each question.

History of Measurement Units

In modern society, units of measurement that have been defined and agreed upon by international scientists are used. In ancient times, people were just beginning to invent and use units of measurement. For example, thousands of years ago, a cabinetmaker would build one cabinet at a time and measure the pieces of wood needed relative to the size of the other pieces of that cabinet. Today, factories manufacture many of the same products. Ancient cabinetmakers rarely made two cabinets that were exactly the same. Eventually, it became obvious that units of measurement had to mean the same thing to everybody.

Measurements, such as the inch, foot, and yard, began many years ago as fairly crude units. For example, the modern-day inch began as "the width of one's thumb." The foot originally was defined as "the length of one's foot." The yard was defined as "the distance from the tip of one's nose to the end of one's arm."

Although using these units of measurement was easier than not using any units of measurement, these ancient units were confusing. Human beings come in many different sizes and shapes, and one person's foot can be much larger than another person's foot. So, whose foot defines a foot? Who's thumb width defines an inch? Ancient civilizations used these kinds of measurements for thousands of years. Over time, these units were redefined and standardized, eventually becoming the exact units of measurement that you know today.

Test-Taking Tip After you read and think about the passage, write one or two sentences that summarize the most important points. Read your sentences out loud.

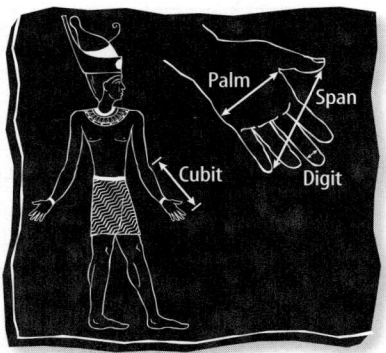

Ancient people created units of measurement.

1. Based on the passage, the reader can conclude that _____.
   A) ancient cultures had no concept of measurement
   B) standards of measurement developed over a long period of time
   C) ancient people were probably good at communicating exacts units of measurement
   D) units of measurement are needed only in modern and technologically advanced societies

2. According to the passage, which of these best describes ancient units of measurement?
   F) precise
   G) incorrect
   H) approximate
   J) irresponsible

Reasoning and Skills

Read each question and choose the best answer.

1. All of these are things that can be measured accurately EXCEPT _____.
   A) the temperature of a human body
   B) the space that a couch takes up in a living room
   C) the beauty in a piece of artwork
   D) the mass of a rock from the Moon

Test-Taking Tip   Think about the reasons why people use measurement and the kinds of things that can and cannot be measured.

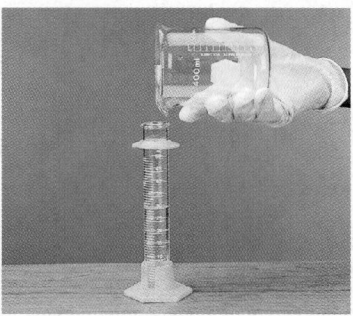

2. Jodie and William are using the graduated cylinder pictured above to measure the volume of liquid in milliliters. What multiple of a liter is a milliliter?
   F) 1,000
   G) 0.01
   H) 0.001
   J) 0.000 001

Test-Taking Tip   Consider the prefixes used in SI units, as well as the amount of liquid shown.

Group S
- How does this medication work to reduce a fever?
- Why do tides occur?
- What is the melting point of iron?
- What was Earth's climate like in the past?

Group T
- Who would make the best class president?
- Is it right to compliment a friend's new shirt if you don't like the shirt?
- Shouldn't everyone like cauliflower, broccoli, turnips, and spinach?
- Why is a sunset beautiful?

3. The questions in Group S are different from the questions in Group T because only the questions in Group S _____.
   A) cannot be answered by science
   B) will have answers that are solely opinions
   C) can be answered with absolute certainty
   D) can be answered by science

Test-Taking Tip   Think about the kinds of questions that scientists try to and are able to answer.

Consider this question carefully before writing your answer on a separate sheet of paper.

4. Suppose you decide to investigate this problem: Which brand of fertilizer produces the most tomatoes per plant? Identify the independent and dependent variables. List the constants in your investigation.

Test-Taking Tip   Think about the procedures that scientists must go through in order to discover and explain.

QUESTION 4: Answers will vary.
Students should design a controlled experiment with the brand of fertilizer as the independent (tested) variable. All other factors, including kind of plant, soil, water, temperature, and light, would have to be kept constant to insure valid results.

Standardized Test Practice

Reasoning and Skills

QUESTION 1: C
Students must understand the difference between objective and subjective measurements (also known as fact and opinion).
- **Choice A** Yes; this can be measured.
- **Choice B** Yes; this can be measured.
- **Choice C** No; this can not be measured. It is an opinion.
- **Choice D** Yes; this can be measured.

QUESTION 2: H
Students must know that the prefix *milli-* means one-thousandth.

QUESTION 3: D
Students must consider the information in the two groups.
- **Choice A** No; the questions in Group T, not Group S, cannot be answered by science.
- **Choice B** No; the questions in Group T, not Group S, will have answers that are opinions.
- **Choice C** No; although the questions in Group S are fact-based and can be answered by science, they may only be answered by scientific hypothesis, which are not absolute certainties.
- **Choice D** Yes; the questions in Group S are looking for facts and, therefore, can be answered by science.

Teaching Tip
Have students review SI prefixes and their meanings.

Life's Building Blocks and Processes

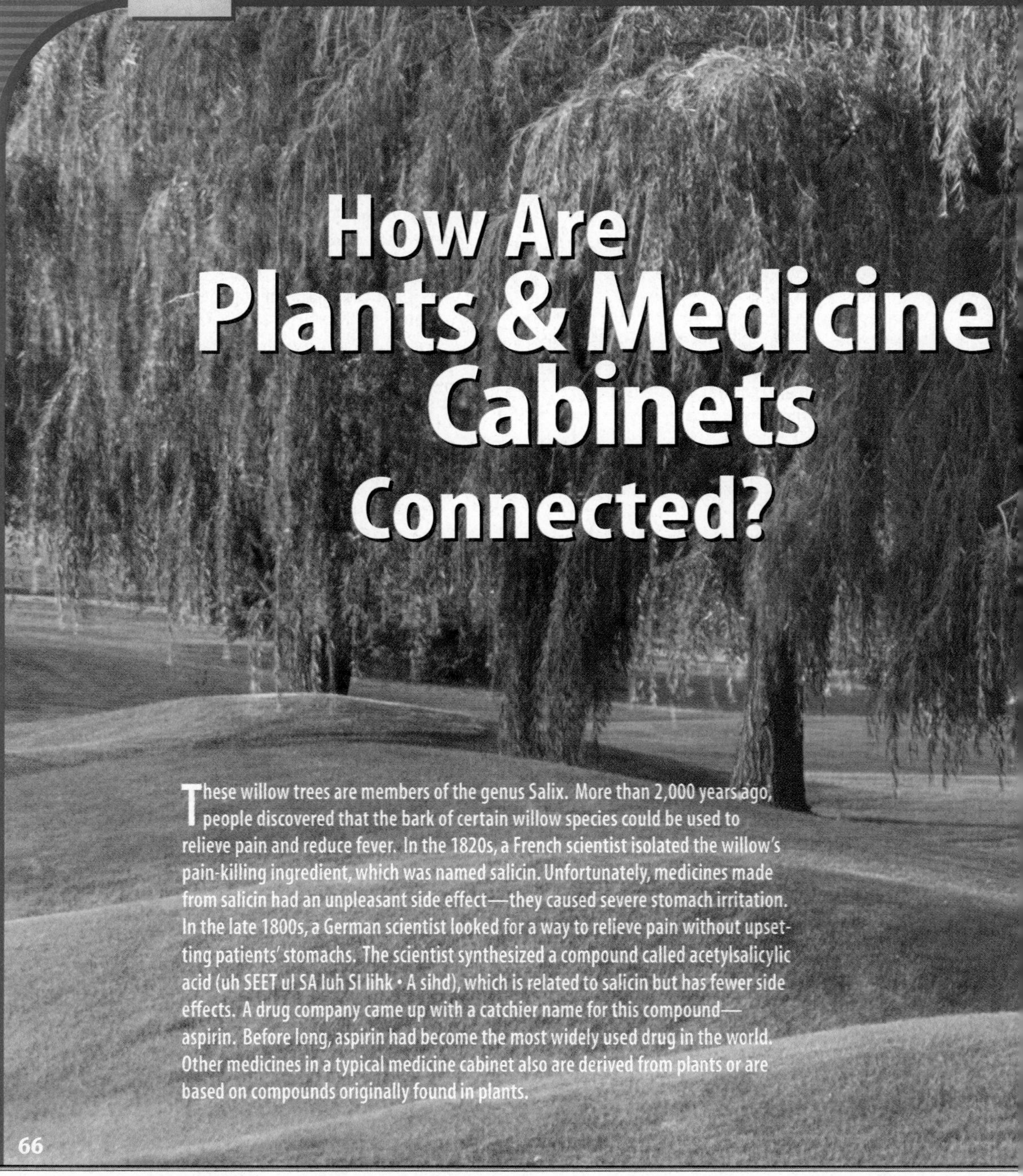

Unit Contents

✔ Pre-Reading Activity

Ask students to skim the chapter for names of one-celled and many-celled organisms. Then ask them to name different types of cells within the human body.

How Are Plants & Medicine Cabinets Connected?

These willow trees are members of the genus Salix. More than 2,000 years ago, people discovered that the bark of certain willow species could be used to relieve pain and reduce fever. In the 1820s, a French scientist isolated the willow's pain-killing ingredient, which was named salicin. Unfortunately, medicines made from salicin had an unpleasant side effect—they caused severe stomach irritation. In the late 1800s, a German scientist looked for a way to relieve pain without upsetting patients' stomachs. The scientist synthesized a compound called acetylsalicylic acid (uh SEET ul SA luh SI lihk • A sihd), which is related to salicin but has fewer side effects. A drug company came up with a catchier name for this compound—aspirin. Before long, aspirin had become the most widely used drug in the world. Other medicines in a typical medicine cabinet also are derived from plants or are based on compounds originally found in plants.

66

Teacher to Teacher

"To demonstrate osmosis, I put liquid starch in a plastic sandwich bag and close it with a twist tie. I then place the plastic bag into a beaker filled with a mixture of water and iodine. As the iodine moves through the plastic bag membrane, the starch begins to turn purple."

Patricia M. Horton, Mentor Teacher
Summit Intermediate School
Etiwanda, CA

Introducing the Unit

How Are Plants and Medicine Cabinets Connected?

Plants have been used as a source of curative compounds since prehistoric times. Ancient cultures usually had individuals who understood the healing properties of plants.

The development of modern chemistry in the 1800s allowed the isolation of the active compounds in medicinal plant products. Eventually it became possible to recreate the active ingredients chemically. Many drugs in use today that were originally plant derived are now only produced synthetically. Aspirin and quinine are two such drugs.

The modern reliance on synthetic compounds has brought about a decrease in formal research into the medicinal properties of plants. Only about 90 of the 250,000 known plant species are used to produce the 119 plant-derived drugs currently on the market. Outside the industrialized world, the vast majority of people still are treated with medicines produced directly from plants.

The native healers in Southeast Asia use more than 5,000 different plants to treat a wide range of diseases. Many governments have recently allocated funds to assist in surveying and cataloging the uses of their countries' native plant species.

SCIENCE CONNECTION

PLANT COMPOUNDS Some modern medicines contain compounds extracted directly from plants. Others contain synthetic versions of plant compounds. Among the drugs with plant origins are digitalis, vincristine, and quinine. Investigate one of these three drugs to discover what plant it comes from, how it helps people, and how its medicinal properties were first discovered. Then write a newspaper article in which you relate your findings.

SCIENCE CONNECTION
Activity
Have students use a world map to plot the places of origin for the naturally derived medicines they research. Are there any obvious concentrations of these plants? What might these concentrations indicate?

SCIENCE *Online*
Internet Addresses
_____
_____
_____

Explore the Glencoe Science Web site at **science.glencoe.com** to find out more about topics in this unit.

Section/Objectives	Standards		Activities/Features
Chapter Opener	**National**	**State/Local**	**Explore Activity:** Measure a small object, p. 69 **Before You Read,** p. 69
	See p. 5T for a Key to Standards.		
Section 1 Cell Structure 🕐 2 sessions 📦 1 block 1. **Identify** names and functions of each part of a cell. 2. **Explain** how important a nucleus is in a cell. 3. **Compare** tissues, organs, and organ systems.	National Content Standards: UCP1, UCP5, A1, C1		**MiniLAB:** Modeling Cytoplasm, p. 72 **Environmental Science Integration,** p. 76 **Math Skills Activity:** Calculate the Ratio of Surface Area to Volume of Cells, p. 76 **Activity:** Comparing Cells, p. 78
Section 2 Viewing Cells 🕐 2 sessions 📦 1 block 1. **Compare** the differences between the compound light microscope and the electron microscope. 2. **Summarize** the discoveries that led to the development of the cell theory. 3. **Relate** the cell theory to modern biology.	National Content Standards: UCP1, A1, C1		**Visualizing Microscopes,** pp. 80–81 **MiniLAB:** Observing Magnified Objects, p. 82 **Physics Integration,** p. 82
Section 3 Viruses 🕐 3 sessions 📦 1.5 blocks 1. **Explain** how a virus makes copies of itself. 2. **Identify** the benefits of vaccines. 3. **Investigate** some uses of viruses.	National Content Standards: UCP5, A1, C1, C2, E2, F1, G3		**Science Online,** p. 85 **Science Online,** p. 86 **Activity:** Comparing Light Microscopes, pp. 88–89 **Science and History:** Cobb Against Cancer, pp. 90–91

NATIONAL GEOGRAPHIC

Teacher's Corner

PRODUCTS AVAILABLE FROM GLENCOE
To order call 1-800-334-7344:
CD-ROM
NGS PictureShow: The Cell

Curriculm Kit
GeoKit: Cells and Microorganisms
Transparency Set
NGS PicturePack: The Cell

PRODUCTS AVAILABLE FROM NATIONAL GEOGRAPHIC SOCIETY
To order call 1-800-368-2728:
Videos
Discovering the Cell
Virus!

Activity Materials	Reproducible Resources	Section Assessment	Technology
Explore Activity: hand lens, metric ruler	**Chapter Resources Booklet** Foldables Worksheet, p. 17 Directed Reading Overview, p. 19 Note-taking Worksheets, pp. 33–35	GLENCOE'S ASSESSMENT ADVANTAGE	
MiniLAB: water, clear container, unflavored gelatin, flashlight, stirring rod **Activity:** microscope, microscope slide, coverslip, forceps, tap water, dropper, *Elodea* plant, prepared slide of human cheek cells	**Chapter Resources Booklet** Transparency Activity, p. 44 MiniLAB, p. 3 Enrichment, p. 30 Reinforcement, p. 27 Directed Reading, p. 20 Transparency Activity, pp. 47–48 Activity Worksheet, pp. 5–6 **Mathematics Skill Activities,** p. 5	**Portfolio** Visual Learning, p. 73 **Performance** MiniLAB, p. 72 Skill Builder Activities, p. 77 **Content** Section Assessment, p. 77	♪ Section Focus Transparency ♪ Teaching Transparency ⊙ Interactive CD-ROM ∩ Guided Reading Audio Program
MiniLAB: newspaper, clear empty glass, clear empty glass bowl, water, hand lens *Need materials?* Contact Science Kit at 1-800-828-7777 or www.sciencekit.com on the Internet.	**Chapter Resources Booklet** Transparency Activity, p. 45 MiniLAB, p. 4 Enrichment, p. 31 Reinforcement, p. 28 Directed Reading, p. 20 Lab Activity, pp. 9–12, 13–16 **Science Inquiry Labs,** p. 3	**Portfolio** Assessment, p. 83 **Performance** MiniLAB, p. 82 Skill Builder Activities, p. 83 **Content** Section Assessment, p. 83	♪ Section Focus Transparency ⊙ Interactive CD-ROM ∩ Guided Reading Audio Program
Activity: compound light microscope, stereomicroscope, 8 classroom items to view, microscope slides and coverslips, plastic petri dishes, distilled water, dropper	**Chapter Resources Booklet** Transparency Activity, p. 46 Enrichment, p. 32 Reinforcement, p. 29 Directed Reading, pp. 21, 22 Activity Worksheet, pp. 7–8 **Lab Management and Safety,** p. 58 **Reading and Writing Skill Activities,** p. 31	**Portfolio** Extension, p. 86 **Performance** Skill Builder Activities, p. 87 **Content** Section Assessment, p. 87	♪ Section Focus Transparency ⊙ Interactive CD-ROM ∩ Guided Reading Audio Program

End of Chapter Assessment

Blackline Masters	Technology	Professional Series
Chapter Resources Booklet Chapter Review, pp. 37–38 Chapter Tests, pp. 39–42 **Standardized Test Practice by The Princeton Review,** pp. 15–18	MindJogger Videoquiz Interactive CD-ROM Vocabulary PuzzleMakers ExamView Pro Test Bank Interactive Lesson Planner Interactive Teacher Edition	Performance Assessment in the Science Classroom (PASC)

Transparencies

Section Focus

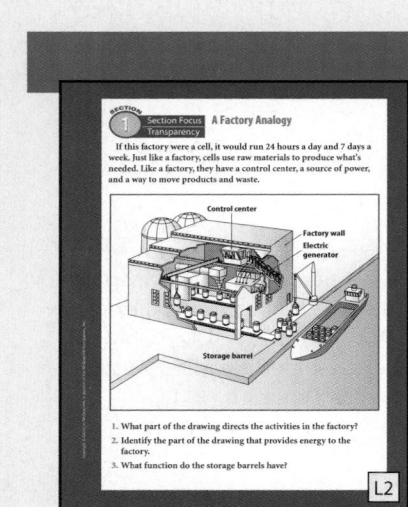

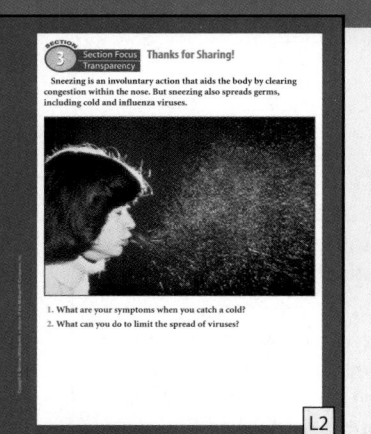

This is a representation of key blackline masters available in the Teacher Classroom Resources. See Resource Manager boxes within the chapter for additional information.

Assessment

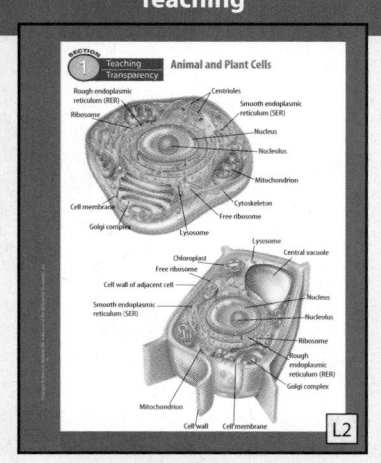

Teaching

Key to Teaching Strategies

The following designations will help you decide which activities are appropriate for your students.

L1 Level 1 activities should be appropriate for students with learning difficulties.

L2 Level 2 activities should be within the ability range of all students.

L3 Level 3 activities are designed for above-average students.

ELL ELL activities should be within the ability range of English Language Learners.

COOP LEARN Cooperative Learning activities are designed for small group work.

LS Multiple Learning Styles logos, as described on page 22T, are used throughout to indicate strategies that address different learning styles.

P These strategies represent student products that can be placed into a best-work portfolio.

Hands-on Activities

Activity Worksheets

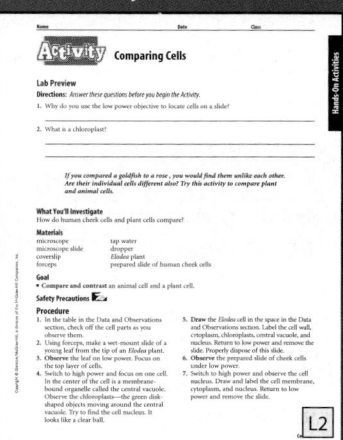

Laboratory Activities

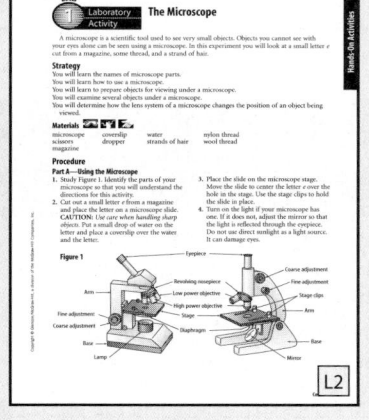

Meeting Different Ability Levels

Content Outline
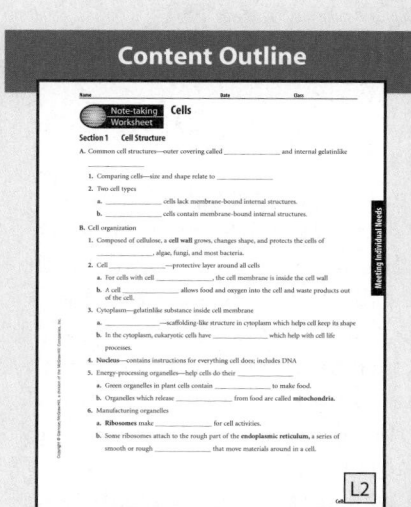
L2

Reinforcement
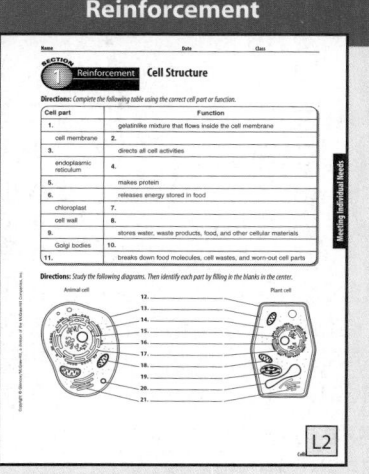
L2

Directed Reading
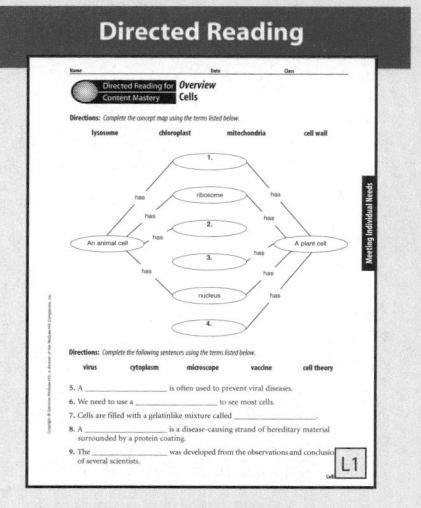
L1

Assessment

Chapter Tests

L2

Enrichment
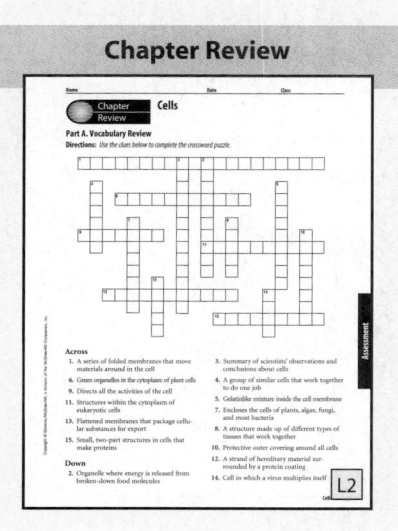
L3

Spanish Directed Reading
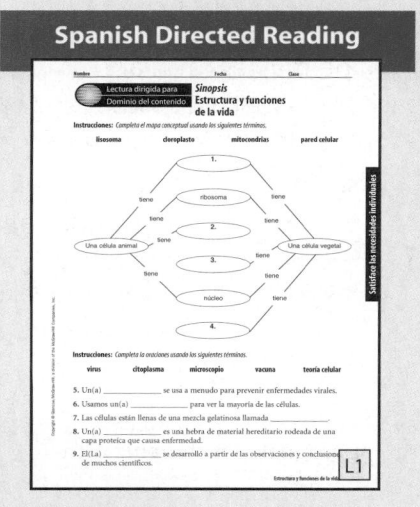
L1

Test Practice Workbook

Chapter Review
L2

Science Content Background

SECTION 1

Cell Structure
Common Cell Traits

The two kinds of cells are prokaryotes and eukaryotes. Each type is surrounded by a cell membrane and contains cytoplasm, DNA, and ribosomes. Prokaryotes have a relatively uniform cytoplasm that is not divided into separate compartments by interior membranes. The ribosomes of prokaryotes are different from those of eukaryotes. Prokaryotic DNA is a single molecule and is found floating freely in the cell's cytoplasm. The nucleus is the organelle that contains the eukaryotic cell's many molecules of DNA. All prokaryotic cells are one-celled organisms. Eukaryotic cells make up all many-celled organisms and some one-celled organisms.

> ### Fun Fact
> Scientists have found small sporelike cells in mammal tissues that are involved in tissue repair. They have been used to repair breaks in the spinal cords of rats.

Cell Wall

Although structurally they resemble plant cell walls, the walls of fungi cells are chemically quite different. Some contain cellulose, but most fungal cell walls are made up of chitin, a polysaccharide that also is found in the exoskeletons of insects. Just like cellulose in plants, the chitin is laid down in bundles of fibers that make the fungal cell walls tough and able to support the fungal body.

Bacterial cell walls are different from those found in either plants or fungi. Bacterial cell walls are composed in large part of a compound called peptidoglycan. Various other substances coat and bind to the cell wall. Other bacteria have an outer membrane that surrounds the peptidoglycan cell wall.

Cell Organization

The cytoskeleton, found only in eukaryotic cells, anchors cell organelles. This "scaffolding" cannot be seen with a normal light microscope but stands out clearly when special fluorescent

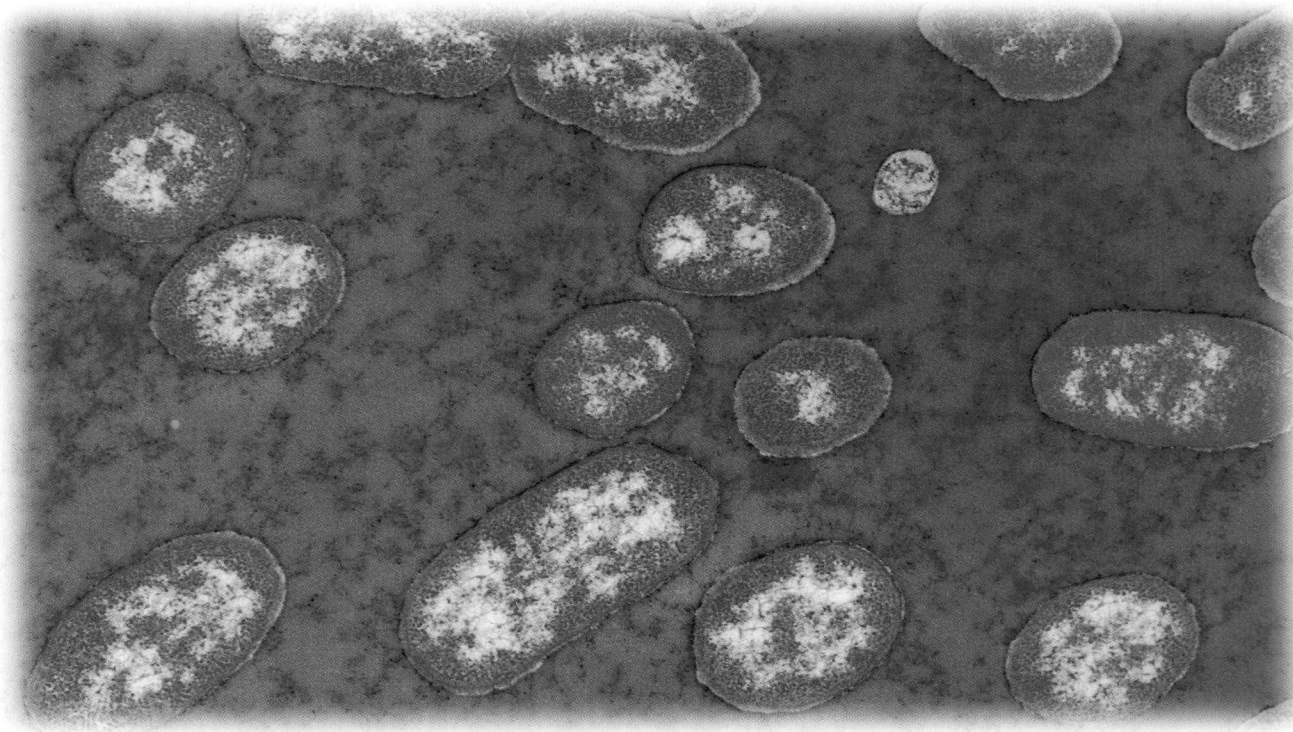

Dwight R. Kuhn/DRK Photo

dyes are used on the cell. Three different kinds of protein fibers—microfilaments, micro-tubules, and intermediate fibers—make up the cytoskeleton.

SECTION 2

Viewing Cells

Magnifying Cells

Microscopes enlarge the image of an object and show its details. The change of an object's apparent size is magnification. The power to show details is resolution. The resolution power of light microscopes is limited by the wavelengths of visible light. Unless the wavelength of light can pass between two objects, the objects are seen as one unit, not two. The electron microscope allows for greater resolution because it uses a beam of electrons to generate an image of the specimen. Because they move in waves that have extremely short wavelengths, electron waves can easily pass through microscopic spaces that visible light cannot enter.

Fun Fact

Creatures 20–150 nanometers in length were found living in sandstone from the Australian seabed. They are smaller than any other known living organism. They contain DNA and distinct cell membranes.

Development of the Cell Theory

The cell theory is sometimes called the cell doctrine. Those scientists who use the term *cell doctrine* want to make it clear that extensive data support the cell theory and that it is universally accepted by biologists.

SECTION 3

Viruses

Living or Not?

To a biologist, living organisms are cellular and are able to grow and reproduce independently. The smallest organisms that satisfy these criteria are bacteria. Viruses do not meet most criteria for being a living organism.

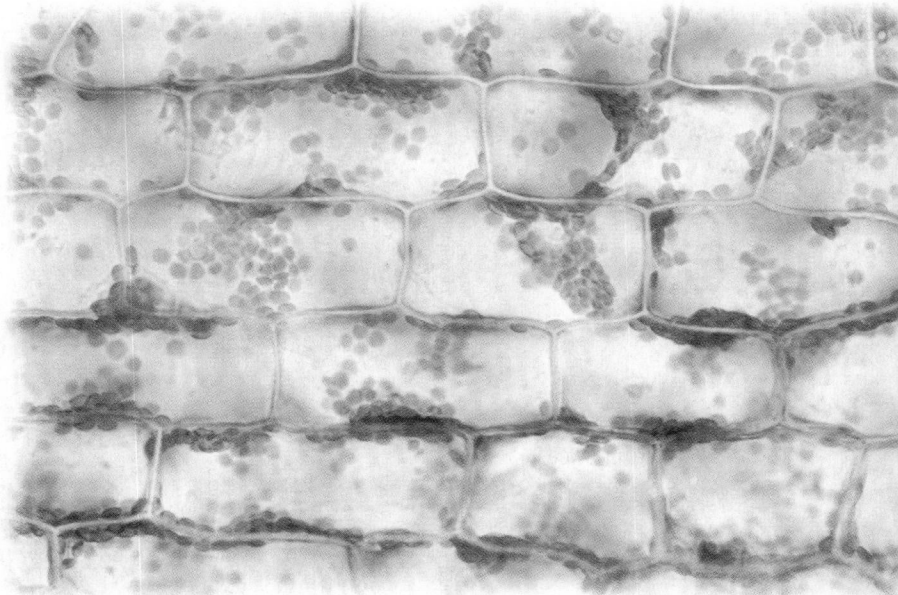

Telegraph Colour Library/FPG International

Viruses are segments of DNA or RNA wrapped in a protein coat. A membranous envelope surrounds many animal viruses. The lipids of the envelope are taken from the host cell, but the proteins are coded by the virus's genetic material. Viruses cannot reproduce on their own but multiply only within host cells using the cellular machinery of the host cell. The host cells often are destroyed when viruses multiply. For the host organism, infection by a virus may have a minor effect like a cold or may be devastating like AIDS. Several types of cancer, including some skin and cervical cancers, are now known to be caused by viruses. Viruses continue to have a major impact on the living world.

SCIENCE *Online*

For additional content background on this topic, go to the Glencoe Science Web site at science.glencoe.com.

Cells

Chapter Vocabulary

What do you think?

Science Journal The photograph is of a virus attacking a bacterium.

Cells

The world around you is filled with organisms that you could overlook, or even be unable to see. Some of these organisms are one-celled and some are many-celled. The monster in this photograph is a louse crawling across human skin. It can be seen in great detail with a microscope that is found in many classrooms. You can study the cells of smaller organisms with other kinds of microscopes.

What do you think?

Science Journal Look at the picture below with a classmate. Discuss what you think is happening. Here's a hint: *Not every battlefield is found on land or at sea.* Write your answer or best guess in your Science Journal.

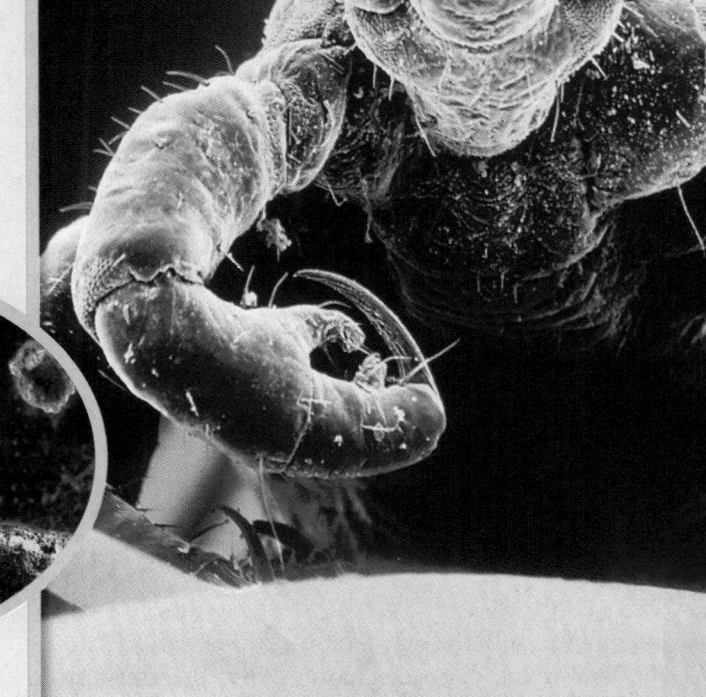

Theme Connection

Scale and Structure The scale and structure of cells and viruses are compared and the parts of which they are composed are described.

If you look around your classroom, you can see many things of all sizes. With the aid of a hand lens, you can see more details. You might examine a speck of dust and discover that it is a living or dead insect. In the following activity, use a hand lens to search for the smallest thing you can find in the classroom.

Measure a small object

1. Obtain a hand lens from your teacher. Note its power (the number followed by ×, shown somewhere on the lens frame or handle).

2. Using the hand lens, look around the room for the smallest object you can find.

3. Measure the size of the image as you see it with the hand lens. To estimate the real size of the object, divide that number by the power. For example, if it looks 2 cm long and the power is 10×, the real length is about 0.2 cm.

Observe
In your Science Journal, describe what you observe. Did the details become clearer? Explain.

Purpose Students will use a hand lens to study very small objects. Students will calculate the actual size of the object from a measured size seen through the hand lens.

Preparation Obtain hand lenses and make sure the power is clearly visible on each one.

Materials hand lenses, rulers

Teaching Strategy Have some very small objects, such as grains of sand, salt, sugar, etc., available for students to study with their hand lenses.

Observe
Details of small objects will become larger and clearer when seen through a hand lens.

Assessment

Oral Have students describe aloud additional features of small objects, such as sand, salt, sugar, dust particles, etc., that they can observe through a hand lens. Use **Performance Assessment in the Science Classroom,** p. 89.

Before You Read

FOLDABLES
Reading & Study
Skills

Making a Main Ideas Study Fold   Make the following Foldable to help you identify the main ideas or major topics on cells.

1. Place a sheet of paper in front of you so the long side is at the top. Fold the paper in half from the left side to the right side. Then unfold.

2. Label the left side of the paper *Plant Cell*. Label the right side of the paper *Animal Cell,* as shown.

3. Before you read the chapter, draw a plant cell on the left side of the paper and an animal cell on the right side of the paper.

4. As you read the chapter, change and add to your drawings.

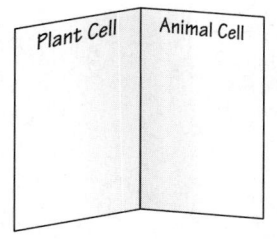

69

Before You Read

FOLDABLES
Reading & Study
Skills

Dinah Zike Study Fold

Purpose Students make and use a Foldable to diagram and collect information on plant and animal cells. Students use this information to compare and contrast these two types of cells and explain how the structure of each relates to its function.

📁 For additional help, see Foldables Worksheet, p. 17 in **Chapter Resources Booklet,** or go to the Glencoe Science Web site at **science.glencoe.com.** See After You Read in the Study Guide at the end of this chapter.

1 Motivate

Bellringer Transparency

Display the Section Focus Transparency for Section 1. Use the accompanying Transparency Activity Master. L2
ELL

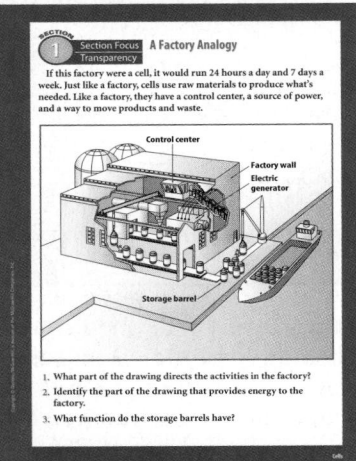

Tie to Prior Knowledge

Ask students what body systems they need to live. Write their responses on the board or overhead projector. Use this list to help students understand that the functions of life are carried out in the cell.

Cell Structure

As You Read

What You'll Learn
- **Identify** names and functions of each part of a cell.
- **Explain** how important a nucleus is in a cell.
- **Compare** tissues, organs, and organ systems.

Vocabulary

cell membrane	ribosome
cytoplasm	endoplasmic
cell wall	reticulum
organelle	Golgi body
nucleus	tissue
chloroplast	organ
mitochondrion	

Why It's Important
If you know how organelles function, it's easier to understand how cells survive.

Common Cell Traits

Living cells are dynamic and have several things in common. A cell is the smallest unit that is capable of performing life functions. All cells have an outer covering called a **cell membrane.** Inside every cell is a gelatinlike material called **cytoplasm** (SI toh plaz uhm). In the cytoplasm of every cell is hereditary material that controls the life of the cell.

Comparing Cells Cells come in many sizes. A nerve cell in your leg could be a meter long. A human egg cell is no bigger than the dot on this **i.** A human red blood cell is about one-tenth the size of a human egg cell. A bacterium is even smaller—8,000 of the smallest bacteria can fit inside one of your red blood cells.

A cell's shape might tell you something about its function. The nerve cell in **Figure 1** has many fine extensions that send and receive impulses to and from other cells. Though a nerve cell cannot change shape, muscle cells and some blood cells can. In plant stems, some cells are long and hollow and have openings at their ends. These cells carry food and water throughout the plant.

Figure 1
The shape of the cell can tell you something about its function. These cells are drawn 700 times their actual size.

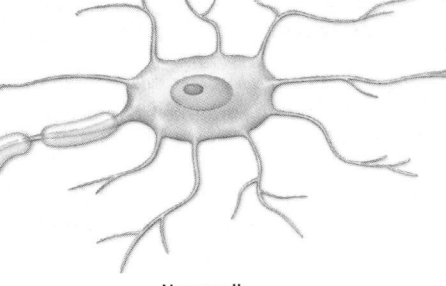

Bacterium

Nerve cell

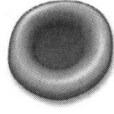

Red blood cell

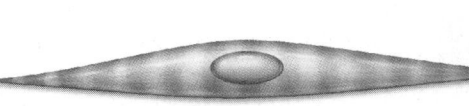

Muscle cell

Section ✓*Assessment* Planner

PORTFOLIO
Visual Learning, p. 73

PERFORMANCE ASSESSMENT
MiniLAB, p. 72
Skill Builder Activities, p. 77
See page 94 for more options.

CONTENT ASSESSMENT
Section, p. 77
Challenge, p. 77
Chapter, pp. 94–95

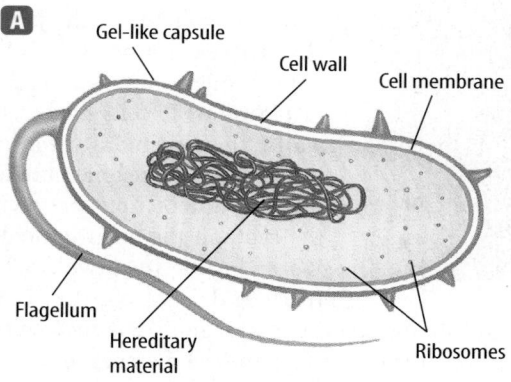

A
Gel-like capsule
Cell wall
Cell membrane
Flagellum
Hereditary material
Ribosomes

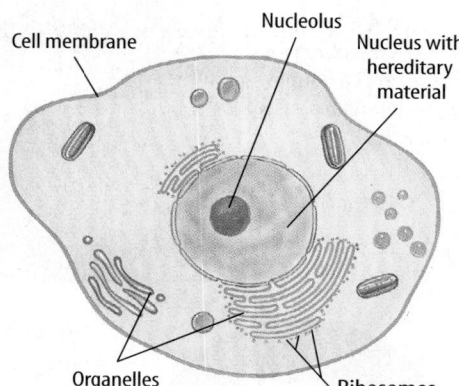

B
Cell membrane
Nucleolus
Nucleus with hereditary material
Organelles
Ribosomes

Cell Types Scientists have found that cells can be separated into two groups. One group has no membrane-bound structures inside the cell and the other group does, as shown in **Figure 2.** Cells without membrane-bound structures are called prokaryotic (proh KAYR ee yah tihk) cells. Cells with membrane-bound structures are called eukaryotic (yew KAYR ee yah tihk) cells.

> ✔ **Reading Check** *Into what two groups can cells be separated?*

Cell Organization

Each cell in your body has a specific function. You might compare a cell to a busy delicatessen that is open 24 hours every day. Raw materials for the sandwiches are brought in often. Some food is eaten in the store, and some customers take their food with them. Sometimes food is prepared ahead of time for quick sale. Wastes are put into trash bags for removal or recycling. Similarly, your cells are taking in nutrients, secreting and storing chemicals, and breaking down substances 24 hours every day.

Cell Wall Just like a deli that is located inside the walls of a building, some cells are enclosed in a cell wall. The cells of plants, algae, fungi, and most bacteria are enclosed in a cell wall. **Cell walls** are tough, rigid outer coverings that protect the cell and give it shape.

A plant cell wall, as shown in **Figure 3,** mostly is made up of a carbohydrate called cellulose. The long, threadlike fibers of cellulose form a thick mesh that allows water and dissolved materials to pass through it. Cell walls also can contain pectin, which is used in jam and jelly, and lignin, which is a compound that makes cell walls rigid. Plant cells responsible for support have a lot of lignin in their walls.

Figure 2
Examine these drawings of cells.
A Prokaryotic cells are only found in one-celled organisms, such as bacteria. **B** Protists, fungi, plants and animals are made of eukaryotic cells. *What differences do you see between them?*

Figure 3
The protective cell wall of a plant cell is outside the cell membrane.

Magnification: 9,000×

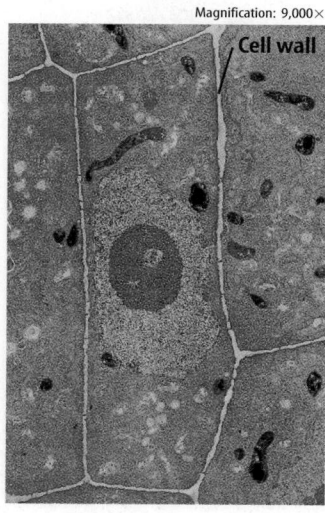

Cell wall

Common Cell Traits

Quick Demo

Use a microprojector to show prepared slides of plant, animal, and bacterial cells. Have students identify the characteristics of each cell shown. L2
LS Visual-Spatial

Caption Answer

Figure 2 The prokaryotic cell has no membrane-bound structures inside; the eukaryotic cell does have membrane-bound structures.

> ✔ **Reading Check**

Answer prokaryotic and eukaryotic

Cell Organization

Use an Analogy

To show how a plant cell wall provides strength, inflate a balloon and place it inside a small cardboard box. The balloon represents the cell membrane and the box represents the cell wall.

Activity

Make a bulletin board showing unlabeled parts of an animal and plant cell. As each cell part is studied, have a student place its label beside it on the bulletin board. L1 **LS Visual-Spatial**

Discussion

How are prokaryotic and eukaryotic cells similar? Both have cell membranes, cytoplasm, and DNA as their genetic material.

Curriculum Connection

Health Cellulose, found in all plant cell walls, is not digestible by humans. However, it provides fiber, which is important because it helps in the elimination of wastes. Have students make a list of foods that contain fiber. Lists should include fruits, grains, and leafy vegetables. L2

Cell Organization, continued

Discussion

What would happen if the nucleus of a cell were damaged? The cell would no longer function correctly because the nucleus controls all the cell's activities. L2

Purpose Students model cytoplasm. L1 ELL IS **Kinesthetic**

Materials 250 mL beaker, unflavored gelatin (one package per student group), water, flashlight, stirring rod

Teaching Strategy Be certain students stir the gelatin well before shining the light on the beaker.

Analysis

1. particles suspended in the gelatin, which represent organelles suspended in the cytoplasm
2. A model is a representation of an abstract object that is used to help visualize and better understand it.

✓ Assessment

Oral Have students infer how the chemical composition of cytoplasm compares to that of gelatin. Both are water-based suspensions. Cytoplasm is 80% water. Use **PASC**, p. 89.

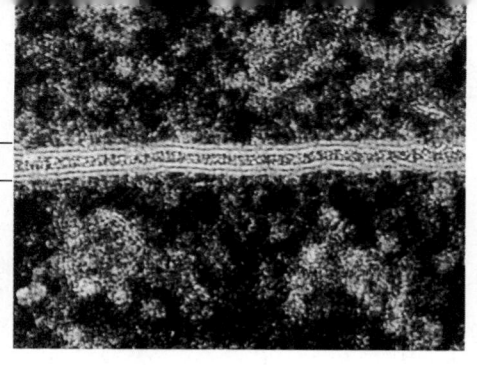

Figure 4
The cell membrane is made up of a double layer of fatlike molecules.

Cell membrane

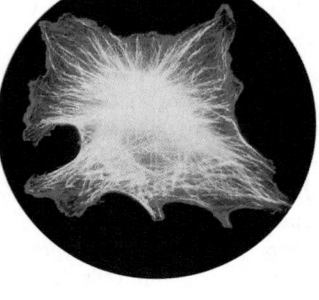

Figure 5
Cytoskeleton, a network of fibers in the cytoplasm, gives cells structure and helps them maintain shape.

Mini LAB

Modeling Cytoplasm

Procedure
1. Add 100 mL of **water** to a **clear container.**
2. Add **unflavored gelatin** and stir.
3. Shine a **flashlight** through the solution.

Analysis
1. Describe what you see.
2. How does a model help you understand what cytoplasm might be like?

Cell Membrane The protective layer around all cells is the cell membrane, as shown in **Figure 4.** If cells have cell walls, the cell membrane is inside of it. The cell membrane regulates interactions between the cell and the environment. Water is able to move freely into and out of the cell through the cell membrane. Food particles and some molecules enter and waste products leave through the cell membrane.

Cytoplasm Cells are filled with a gelatinlike substance called cytoplasm that constantly flows inside the cell membrane. Many important chemical reactions occur within the cytoplasm.

Throughout the cytoplasm is a framework called the cytoskeleton, which helps the cell maintain or change its shape. Cytoskeletons enable some cells to move. An amoeba, for example, moves by stretching and contracting its cytoskeleton. The cytoskeleton is made up of thin, hollow tubes of protein and thin, solid protein fibers, as shown in **Figure 5.** Proteins are organic molecules made up of amino acids.

✓ **Reading Check** *What is the function of the cytoskeleton?*

Most of a cell's life processes occur in the cytoplasm. Within the cytoplasm of eukaryotic cells are structures called **organelles.** Some organelles process energy and others manufacture substances needed by the cell or other cells. Certain organelles move materials, while others act as storage sites. Most organelles are surrounded by membranes. The nucleus is usually the largest organelle in a cell.

Nucleus The nucleus is like the deli manager who directs the store's daily operations and passes on information to employees. The **nucleus,** shown in **Figure 6,** directs all cell activities and is separated from the cytoplasm by a membrane. Materials enter and leave the nucleus through openings in the membrane. The nucleus contains the instructions for everything the cell does. These instructions are found on long, threadlike, hereditary material made of DNA. DNA is the chemical that contains the code for the cell's structure and activities. During cell division, the hereditary material coils tightly around proteins to form structures called chromosomes. A structure called a nucleolus also is found in the nucleus.

Teacher FYI

Before electron microscopes, scientists could only theorize about many cell structures and their makeups. Even the best compound microscope cannot reveal what can be seen with electron microscopes.

Curriculum Connection

Health Students may think that any cholesterol in the body presents a health risk. Cholesterol is an important component of the cell membrane. It creates a health risk only when it is present in high levels in the blood, where it builds up in arteries and obstructs blood flow. Ask students to investigate cholesterol to differentiate between blood cholesterol and dietary cholesterol. L3

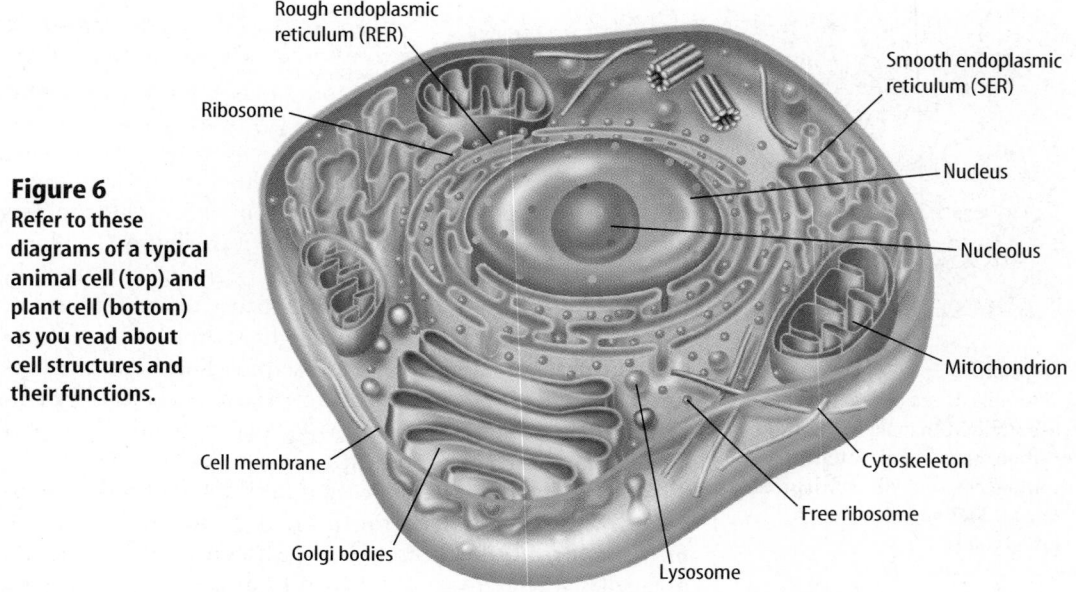

Figure 6
Refer to these diagrams of a typical animal cell (top) and plant cell (bottom) as you read about cell structures and their functions.

Rough endoplasmic reticulum (RER)

Ribosome

Smooth endoplasmic reticulum (SER)

Nucleus

Nucleolus

Mitochondrion

Cell membrane

Cytoskeleton

Golgi bodies

Free ribosome

Lysosome

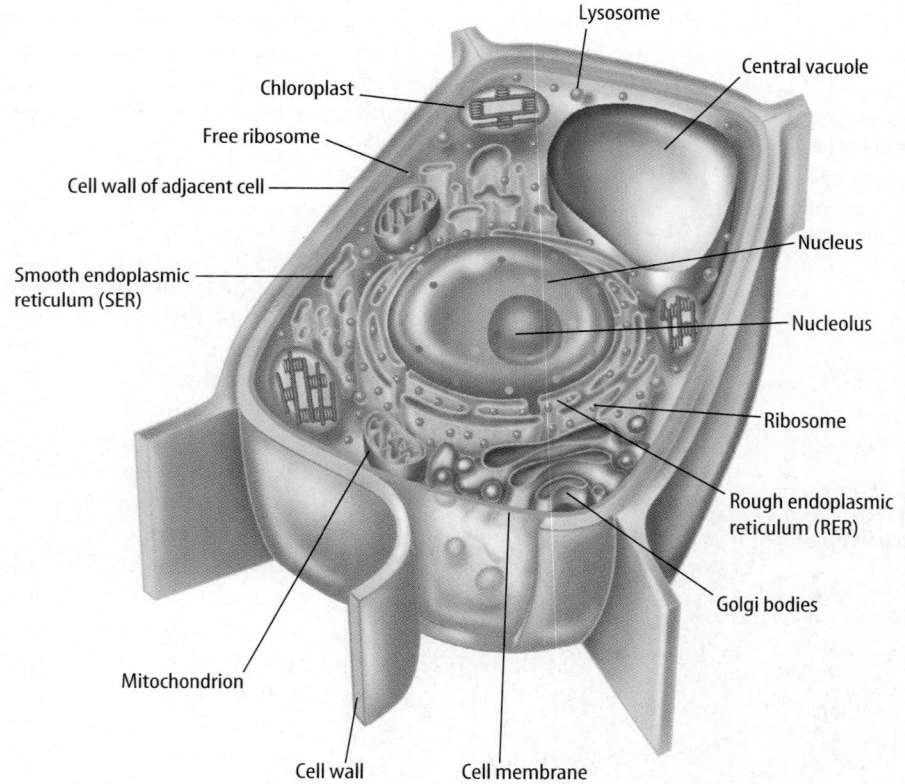

Lysosome

Central vacuole

Chloroplast

Free ribosome

Cell wall of adjacent cell

Smooth endoplasmic reticulum (SER)

Nucleus

Nucleolus

Ribosome

Rough endoplasmic reticulum (RER)

Golgi bodies

Mitochondrion

Cell wall

Cell membrane

SECTION 1 Cell Structure   **73**

Use an Analogy

Point out that just as each part of a machine performs a different function to enable the machine to work, each organelle performs a different function in the cell.

Use Science Words

Word Origin Greek and Latin words are used in naming cell parts. Have students make a list of cell parts and use a dictionary to find the origins of the words and their meanings. ⌊L2⌋
IS Linguistic

Visual Learning

Figure 6 Have students create a network tree concept map comparing and contrasting plant and animal cells. Diagrams should make clear which organelles appear in both cells, and which are specific to only one type of cell. ⌊L2⌋ **IS Visual-Spatial** ⌊P⌋

IDENTIFYING Misconceptions

Students may think that cells are solid. Explain that almost 80% of a cell is water. The water is enclosed in a membrane that allows certain materials to enter and leave.

Resource Manager

Chapter Resources Booklet
  MiniLAB, p. 3
  Enrichment, p. 30

IDENTIFYING Misconceptions

Students may think that because plant cells carry out photosynthesis, they do not have mitochondria. Explain that plants also carry out cellular respiration.

Discussion

What color are most cells? Most cells are colorless. Photographs of cells are usually color-enhanced; prepared slides of cells are usually stained so cell parts are visible.

Text Question Answer

Mitochondria provide energy, and active cells would be more in need of energy than inactive cells.

Caption Answer

Figure 8 Possible answer: muscle cells

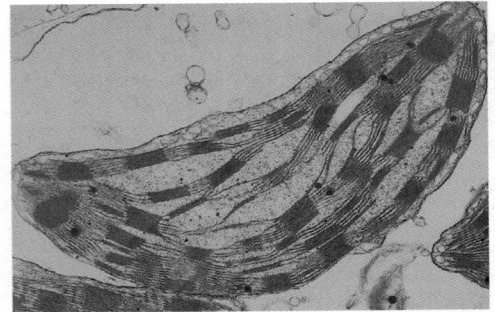

Magnification: 37,000×

Figure 7
Chloroplasts are organelles that use sunlight to make sugar from carbon dioxide and water. They contain chlorophyll, which gives most leaves and stems their green color.

Figure 8
Mitochondria are known as the powerhouses of the cell because they release energy that is needed by the cell from food.
What types of cells might contain many mitochondria?

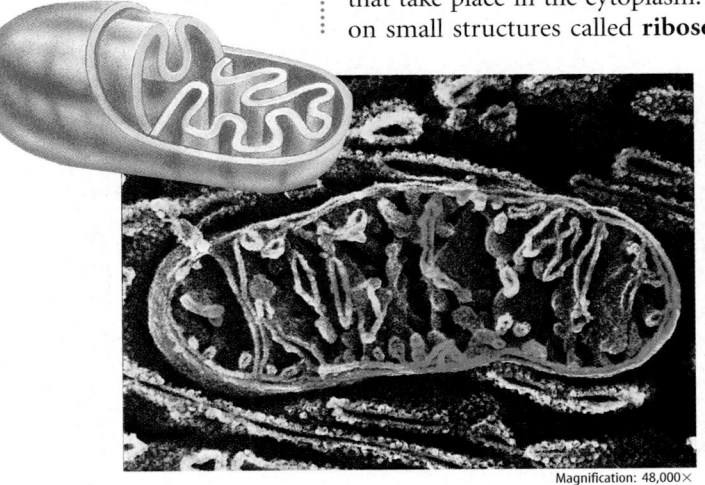

Magnification: 48,000×

Physics INTEGRATION

Energy-Processing Organelles Cells require a continuous supply of energy to process food, make new substances, eliminate wastes, and communicate with each other. In plant cells, food is made in green organelles in the cytoplasm called **chloroplasts** (KLOR uh plasts), as shown in **Figure 7.** Chloroplasts contain the green pigment chlorophyll, which gives leaves and stems their green color. Chlorophyll captures light energy that is used to make a sugar called glucose. Glucose molecules store the captured light energy as chemical energy. Many cells, including animal cells, do not have chloroplasts for making food. They must get food from their environment.

The energy in food is stored until it is released by the mitochondria. **Mitochondria** (mi tuh KAHN dree uh) (singular, *mitochondrion*), such as the one shown in **Figure 8,** are organelles where energy is released from breaking down food into carbon dioxide and water. Just as the gas or electric company supplies fuel for the deli, a mitochondrion releases energy for use by the cell. Some types of cells, such as muscle cells, are more active than other cells. These cells have large numbers of mitochondria. Why would active cells have more or larger mitochondria?

Manufacturing Organelles One substance that takes part in nearly every cell activity is protein. Proteins are part of cell membranes. Other proteins are needed for chemical reactions that take place in the cytoplasm. Cells make their own proteins on small structures called **ribosomes.** Even though ribosomes are considered organelles, they are not membrane bound. Some ribosomes float freely in the cytoplasm; and others are attached to the endoplasmic reticulum. Ribosomes are made in the nucleolus and move out into the cytoplasm. Ribosomes receive directions from the hereditary material in the nucleus on how, when, and in what order to make specific proteins.

Cultural Diversity

Ernest Everett Just, an African American biologist in the early 1900s, studied cells and how they function. His research showed that all parts of the cell influence its activities, not just the nucleus, as scientists then believed. This idea changed scientific opinion concerning the basis of life. Discuss how Just's research is important to the study of cells today.

Inclusion Strategies

Learning Disabled Provide pairs of students with an unlabeled drawing of an animal cell. Have students print small stick-on labels and place them appropriately on the drawing. The labels can be folded to conceal the words and removed as the students learn the cell structures, then replaced for review. L1

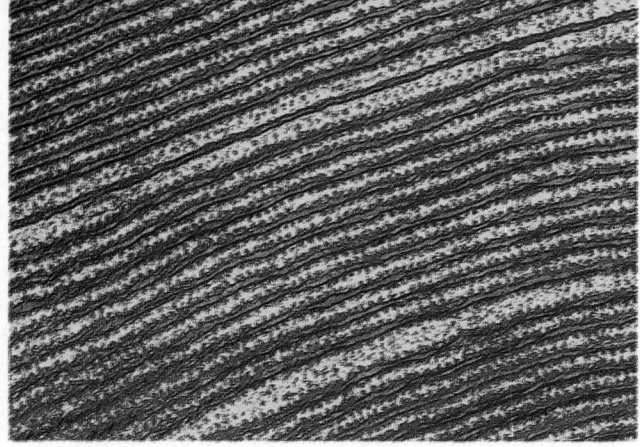

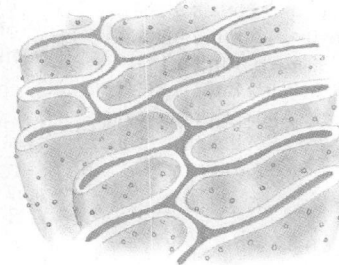

Figure 9
Endoplasmic reticulum (ER) is a complex series of membranes in the cytoplasm of the cell. *What would smooth ER look like?*

Processing, Transporting, and Storing Organelles

The **endoplasmic reticulum** (en duh PLAZ mihk • rih TIHK yuh lum) or ER, as shown in **Figure 9,** extends from the nucleus to the cell membrane. It is a series of folded membranes in which materials can be processed and moved around inside of the cell. The ER takes up a lot of space in some cells.

The endoplasmic reticulum may be "rough" or "smooth." ER that has no attached ribosomes is called smooth endoplasmic reticulum. This type of ER processes other cellular substances such as lipids that store energy. Ribsomes are attached to areas on the rough ER. There they carry out their job of making proteins that are moved out of the cell or used within the cell.

✓ Reading Check *What is the difference between rough ER and smooth ER?*

After proteins are made in a cell, they are transferred to another type of cell organelle called the Golgi (GAWL jee) bodies. The **Golgi bodies**, as shown in **Figure 10,** are stacked, flattened membranes. The Golgi bodies sort proteins and other cellular substances and package them into membrane-bound structures called vesicles. The vesicles deliver cellular substances to areas inside the cell. They also carry cellular substances to the cell membrane where they are released to the outside of the cell.

Just as a deli has refrigerators for temporary storage of some its foods and ingredients, cells have membrane-bound spaces called vacuoles for the temporary storage of materials. A vacuole can store water, waste products, food, and other cellular materials. In plant cells, the vacuole may make up most of the cell's volume.

Figure 10
The Golgi body packages materials and moves them to the outside of the cell. *Why are materials removed from the cell?*

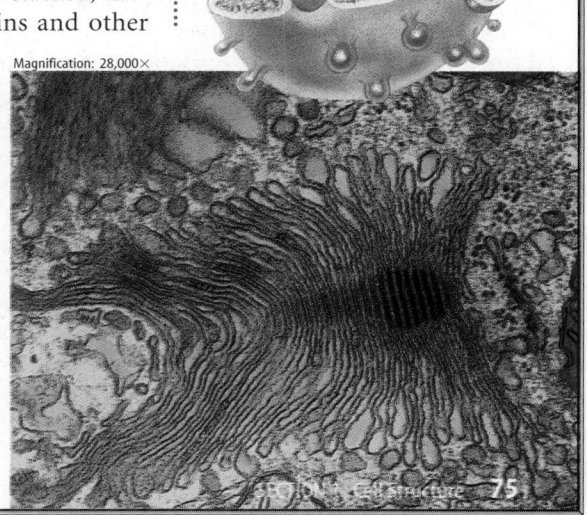

Magnification: 28,000×

SECTION 1 Cell Structure **75**

Cell Organization, continued

Environmental Science
INTEGRATION

Posters will vary.

☑ **Reading Check**

Answer to prevent digestive chemicals from leaking into the cytoplasm and destroying the cell

---

IDENTIFYING
Misconceptions

Students may assume that the larger an organism is, the larger its cells. Explain that while cells vary in shape and size, most are only about 0.0025 cm in diameter. The number of cells, not how large they are, determines an organism's size.

Math Skills Activity

National Math Standards
Correlation to Mathematics Objectives
1, 2, 3, 4, 6, 8, 9

Answers to Practice Problems

1. $A = 2\,cm \times 2\,cm \times 6 = 24\,cm^2$
$V = 2\,cm \times 2\,cm \times 2\,cm = 8\,cm^3$
$R = 24\,cm^2 / 8\,cm^3 = 3\,cm^2/cm^3$
As the size of the cube decreases, the ratio increases.

2. $A = 2(4\,cm \times 4\,cm) + 4(4\,cm \times 8\,cm) = 160\,cm^2$
$V = 4\,cm \times 4\,cm \times 8\,cm = 128\,cm^3$
$R = 160\,cm^2 / 128\,cm^3 = 1.25\,cm^2/cm^3$

Environmental Science
INTEGRATION

Just like a cell, you can recycle materials. Paper, plastics, aluminum, and glass are materials that can be recycled into usable items. Make a promotional poster to encourage others to recycle.

Recycling Organelles Active cells break down and recycle substances. Organelles called lysosomes (LI suh sohmz) contain digestive chemicals that help break down food molecules, cell wastes, and worn-out cell parts. In a healthy cell, chemicals are released into vacuoles only when needed. The lysosome's membrane prevents the digestive chemicals inside from leaking into the cytoplasm and destroying the cell. When a cell dies, a lysosome's membrane disintegrates. This releases digestive chemicals that allow the quick breakdown of the cell's contents.

☑ **Reading Check** *What is the function of the lysosome's membrane?*

Math Skills Activity

Calculate the Ratio of Surface Area to Volume of Cells

Example Problem
Assume that a cell is like a cube with six equal sides. Find the ratio of surface area to volume for a cube that is 4 cm high.

4 cm
4 cm   4 cm

Solution

1 *This is what you know:*   A cube has 6 equal sides of 4 cm × 4 cm.

2 *This is what you want to find:*   the ratio (R) of surface area to volume for each cube

3 *These are the equations you use:*   surface area (A) = width × length × 6
volume (V) = length × width × height
$R = A/V$

4 *Solve for surface area and volume, then solve for the ratio:*
$A = 4\,cm \times 4\,cm \times 6 = 96\,cm^2$
$V = 4\,cm \times 4\,cm \times 4\,cm = 64\,cm^3$
$R = 96\,cm^2/64\,cm^3 = 1.5\,cm^2/cm^3$

Check your answer by multiplying the ratio by the volume. Do you calculate the surface area?

Practice Problems

1. Calculate the ratio of surface area to volume for a cube that is 2 cm high. What happens to this ratio as the size of the cube decreases?

2. If a 4-cm cube doubled just one of its dimensions—length, width, or height—what would happen to the ratio of surface area to volume?

For more help, refer to the Math Skills Handbook.

Resource Manager

Chapter Resources Booklet
Activity Worksheet, pp. 5–6
Reinforcement, p. 27
Mathematics Skill Activities, p. 5

☑ **Active Reading**

ReQuest To improve listening skills, have students listen carefully as you read an interesting article or story aloud. After the reading, have students construct discussion questions. Have students participate in a ReQuest with the chapter feature or another interesting article related to cell structure or function.

From Cell to Organism

Many one-celled organisms perform all their life functions by themselves. Cells in a many-celled organism, however, do not work alone. Each cell carries on its own life functions while depending in some way on other cells in the organism.

In **Figure 11,** you can see cardiac muscle cells grouped together to form a tissue. A **tissue** is a group of similar cells that work together to do one job. Each cell in a tissue does its part to keep the tissue alive.

Tissues are organized into organs. An **organ** is a structure made up of two or more different types of tissues that work together. Your heart is an organ made up of cardiac muscle tissue, nerve tissue, and blood tissues. The cardiac muscle tissue contracts, making the heart pump. The nerve tissue brings messages that tell the heart how fast to beat. The blood tissue is carried from the heart to other organs of the body.

 **Reading Check** *What type of tissues make up your heart?*

A group of organs working together to perform a certain function is an organ system. Your heart, arteries, veins, and capillaries make up your cardiovascular system. In a many-celled organism, several systems work together in order to perform life functions efficiently. Your nervous, circulatory, respiratory, muscular, and other systems work together to keep you alive.

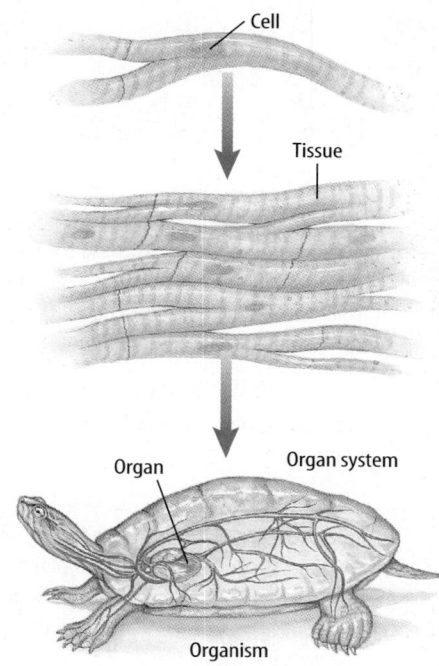

Figure 11
In a many-celled organism, cells are organized into tissues, tissues into organs, organs into systems, and systems into an organism.

Section 1 Assessment

1. Explain the important role of the nucleus in the life of a cell.

2. Compare and contrast the energy processing organelles.

3. Why are digestive enzymes in a cell enclosed in a membrane-bound organelle?

4. How are cells, tissues, organs, and organ systems related?

5. **Think Critically** How is the cell of a one-celled organism different from the cells in many-celled organisms?

Skill Builder Activities

6. **Interpreting Scientific Illustrations** Examine the illustrations of the animal cell and the plant cell in **Figure 6** and make a list of differences and similarities between them. **For more help, refer to the** Science Skill Handbook.

7. **Communicating** Your textbook compared some cell functions to that of a deli. In your Science Journal, write an essay that explains how a cell is like your school or town. **For more help, refer to the** Science Skill Handbook.

From Cell to Organism

 **Reading Check**

Answer cardiac muscle tissue, nerve tissue, and blood tissue

3 Assess

Reteach

What are the differences between plant and animal cells? Most plant cells contain chloroplasts and cell walls; animal cells do not. **What is the difference between a prokaryotic and eukaryotic cell?** Eukaryotic cells have membrane-bound structures; prokaryotic cells do not.

Challenge

How do the cell walls, chloroplasts, and vacuoles of plant cells illustrate that cell structure is related to cell function? Cell walls, chloroplasts, and vacuoles provide the cell with protection, photosynthesis, and storage.

Assessment

Process To further assess students' abilities to compare and contrast different cell types, have them write statements in their Science Journals comparing animal and plant cells. Use **PASC,** p. 175.

Answers to Section Assessment

1. It directs the activities of the cell and stores hereditary information.

2. The chlorophyll in chloroplasts captures light energy and stores it as chemical energy in sugar molecules. Mitochondria release the energy stored in food.

3. It prevents the digestive chemicals inside from destroying the cell.

4. Organ systems are made of organs, which are made of tissues. Tissues are made of cells.

5. one-celled—performs all life functions; many-celled—cells depend on each other

6. Plant cells have chloroplasts and cell walls which animal cells do not have. Unlike plant cells, animal cells have centrioles.

7. A town or school has many parts. Different people supply services. Each person has a job. Each building has a function. All these things working together make the town or school function properly. A cell has many parts. The different parts of a cell have jobs, and each part helps the cell carry out its life processes.

Activity

BENCH TESTED

Purpose Students identify and compare the parts of a plant and animal cell. [L2] [ELL]

LS Visual-Spatial

Process Skills observing, identifying, inferring, diagramming, comparing and contrasting, classifying

Time Required 45 minutes

Alternate Materials If *Elodea* is unavailable, cell parts can be seen in the thin, newest leaves of a coleus plant or similar houseplant.

Safety Precautions Caution students to use extreme care when working with a microscope and microscope slides.

Teaching Strategies

- Have students work in pairs. One student obtains and sets up the microscope while the other prepares the wet mount and obtains the cheek-cell slide. Both observe the slides and record data.

- Have students clean slides and coverslips after use.

Troubleshooting To see movement of cytoplasm, use only leaves from the tips of *Elodea*. Help students focus so they will see cell layers. Students may not be able to see the nucleus because most cell parts need to be stained to be visible. Many students may mistake the chloroplast for the cells, not realizing that the chloroplasts are *inside* the larger structure.

Answers to Questions

1. The *Elodea* cell is rectangular; the cheek cell is oval.
2. Only plant cells have a cell wall and chloroplasts.

Activity

Comparing Cells

If you compared a goldfish to a rose, you would find them unlike each other. Are their individual cells different also? Try this activity to compare plant and animal cells.

What You'll Investigate
How do human cheek cells and plant cells compare?

Materials
microscope	dropper
microscope slide	*Elodea* plant
coverslip	prepared slide of human
forceps	cheek cells
tap water	

Goal
■ **Compare and contrast** an animal cell and a plant cell.

Safety Precautions

Procedure

1. Copy the data table in your Science Journal. Check off the cell parts as you observe them.

Cell Observations		
Cell Part	**Cheek**	**Elodea**
Cytoplasm	✔	✔
Nucleus	✔	✔
Chloroplasts		✔
Cell Wall		✔
Cell Membrane	✔	✔

2. Using forceps, make a wet-mount slide of a young leaf from the tip of an *Elodea* plant.

3. **Observe** the leaf on low power. Focus on the top layer of cells.

4. Switch to high power and focus on one cell. In the center of the cell is a membrane-bound organelle called the central vacuole. Observe the chloroplasts—the green, disk-shaped objects moving around the central vacuole. Try to find the cell nucleus. It looks like a clear ball.

5. **Draw** the *Elodea* cell. Label the cell wall, cytoplasm, chloroplasts, central vacuole, and nucleus. Return to low power and remove the slide. Properly dispose of the slide.

6. **Observe** the prepared slide of cheek cells under low power.

7. Switch to high power and observe the cell nucleus. Draw and label the cell membrane, cytoplasm, and nucleus. Return to low power and remove the slide.

Conclude and Apply

1. **Compare and contrast** the shapes of the cheek cell and the *Elodea* cell.

2. What can you conclude about the differences between plant and animal cells?

Communicating Your Data

Draw the two kinds of cells on one sheet of paper. Use a green pencil to label the organelles found only in plants, a red pencil to label the organelles found only in animals, and a blue pencil to label the organelles found in both. **For more help, refer to the Science Skill Handbook.**

✓ Assessment

Performance To further assess students' abilities to compare plant and animal cells, have them examine cells from lettuce leaves and other types of animal cells on prepared slides. Use **Performance Assessment in the Science Classroom,** p. 97.

Communicating Your Data

Chloroplasts and cell walls should be labeled in green on the plant cell. No organelles are labeled red. Cytoplasm, nuclei, and cell membranes should be labeled in blue, on plant and animal cells.

Viewing Cells

Magnifying Cells

The number of living things in your environment that you can't see is much greater than the number that you can see. Many of the things that you cannot see are only one cell in size. To see most cells, you need to use a microscope.

Trying to see separate cells in a leaf, like the ones in **Figure 12,** is like trying to see individual photos in a photo mosaic picture that is on the wall across the room. As you walk toward the wall, it becomes easier to see the individual photos. When you get right up to the wall, you can see details of each small photo. A microscope has one or more lenses that enlarge the image of an object as though you are walking closer to it. Seen through these lenses, the leaf appears much closer to you, and you can see the individual cells that carry on life processes.

Early Microscopes In the late 1500s, the first microscope was made by a Dutch maker of reading glasses. He put two magnifying glasses together in a tube and got an image that was larger than the image that was made by either lens alone.

In the mid 1600s, Antonie van Leeuwenhoek, a Dutch fabric merchant, made a simple microscope with a tiny glass bead for a lens, as shown in **Figure 13.** With it, he reported seeing things in pond water that no one had ever imagined. His microscope could magnify up to 270 times. Another way to say this is that his microscope could make the image of an object 270 times larger than its actual size. Today you would say his lens had a power of 270×. Early compound microscopes were crude by today's standards. The lenses would make an image larger, but it wasn't always sharp or clear.

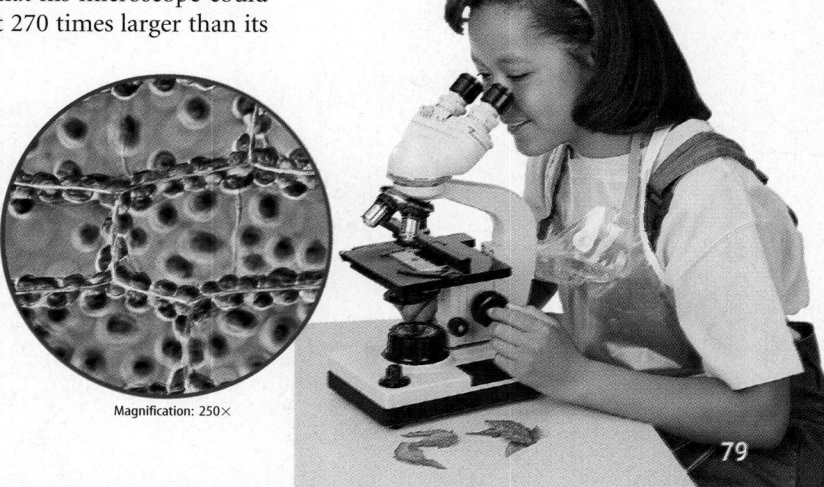

Magnification: 250×

As You Read

What You'll Learn
- **Compare** the differences between the compound light microscope and the electron microscope.
- **Summarize** the discoveries that led to the development of the cell theory.
- **Relate** the cell theory to modern biology.

Vocabulary
cell theory

Why It's Important
Humans are like other living things because they are made of cells.

Figure 12
Individual cells become visible when a plant leaf is viewed using a microscope with enough magnifying power.

SECTION

Viewing Cells

1 Motivate

Bellringer Transparency

Display the Section Focus Transparency for Section 2. Use the accompanying Transparency Activity Master. L2
ELL

Tie to Prior Knowledge

Students may have used magnifying glasses and binoculars. Explain that a microscope magnifies in the same way.

Section ✓Assessment Planner

PORTFOLIO
Assessment, p. 83
PERFORMANCE ASSESSMENT
Try at Home MiniLAB, p. 82
Skill Builder Activities, p. 83
See page 94 for more options.

CONTENT ASSESSMENT
Section, p. 83
Challenge, p. 83
Chapter, pp. 94–95

Resource Manager

Chapter Resources Booklet
Transparency Activities, p. 45
Directed Reading for Content Mastery, p. 20

Visualizing Microscopes

Have students examine the pictures and read the captions. Then ask the following questions.

What are the similarities and differences between a fluorescence microscope and a phase-contrast microscope? Possible answers: Both microscopes magnify up to 1500x. With the fluorescence microscope, the specimen must be stained and can be viewed through the scope directly. With the phase-contrast microscope, the specimen is not stained and can only be viewed on a monitor or in a photograph. Phase-contrast microscopes are good for viewing living things.

Compare and contrast the features of a TEM and an SEM. Possible answers: Both microscope use electrons to help produce the magnified image. Also, with both microscopes the specimen can only be viewed on a monitor or in a photograph. In a TEM the electrons go through the specimen and the magnification is up to 1,000,000×. With an SEM, the electrons sweep over the surface of the specimen and a three-dimensional image is produced. The magnification of an SEM is only up to 200,000×.

Activity

Have students identify the type of microscope(s) they use in science class. Then have students view different slides under the microscope (e.g. onion slices, hair, sliver from a grass blade, comics color section of the newspaper). Have students draw what they observe. If possible, use several types of microscopes and a magnifying glass and have students compare how the same slide looks under each one. Ask students to list the similarities and differences between them, and hypothesize what accounts for these differences.

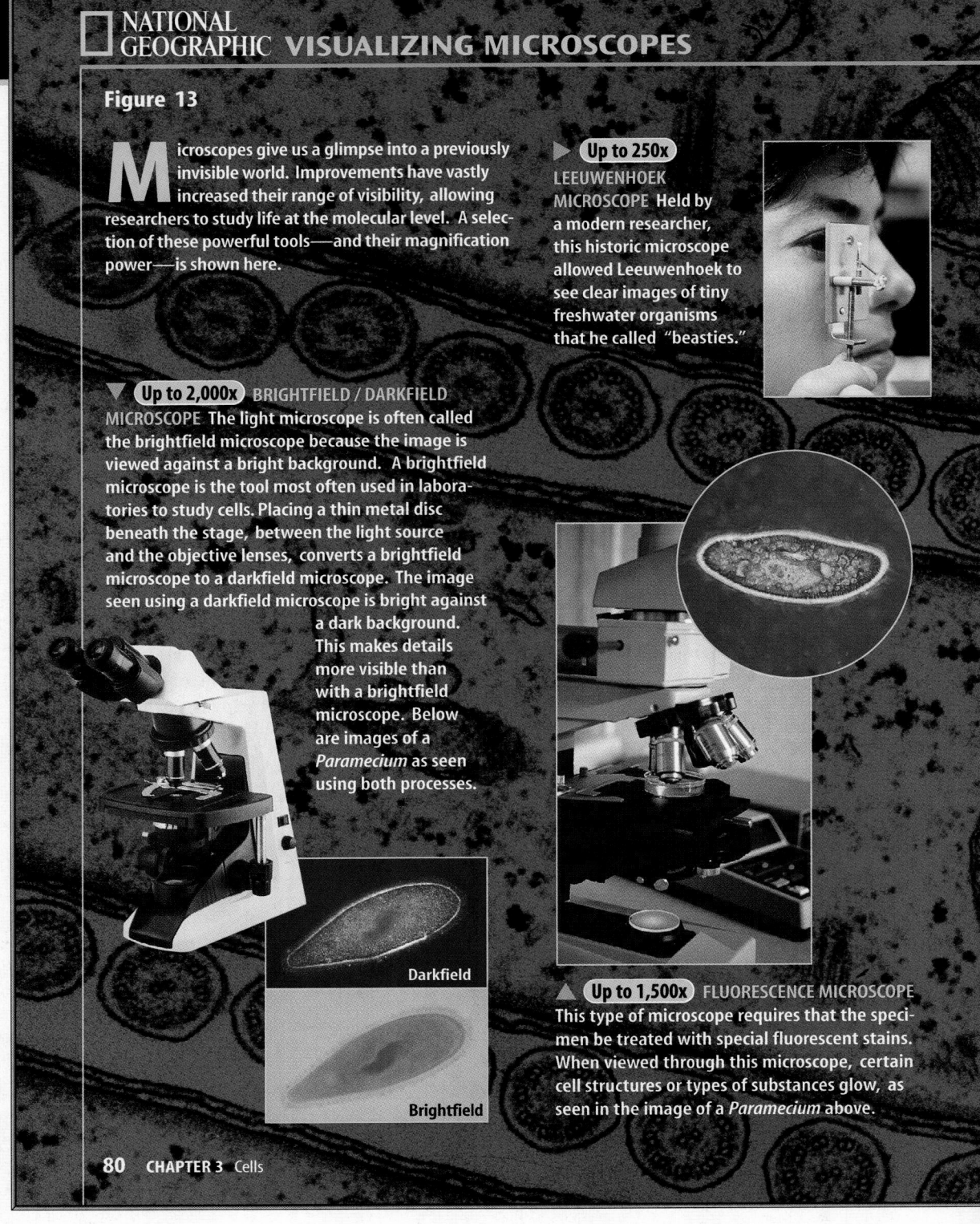

Figure 13

Microscopes give us a glimpse into a previously invisible world. Improvements have vastly increased their range of visibility, allowing researchers to study life at the molecular level. A selection of these powerful tools—and their magnification power—is shown here.

Up to 250x
LEEUWENHOEK MICROSCOPE Held by a modern researcher, this historic microscope allowed Leeuwenhoek to see clear images of tiny freshwater organisms that he called "beasties."

Up to 2,000x **BRIGHTFIELD / DARKFIELD MICROSCOPE** The light microscope is often called the brightfield microscope because the image is viewed against a bright background. A brightfield microscope is the tool most often used in laboratories to study cells. Placing a thin metal disc beneath the stage, between the light source and the objective lenses, converts a brightfield microscope to a darkfield microscope. The image seen using a darkfield microscope is bright against a dark background. This makes details more visible than with a brightfield microscope. Below are images of a *Paramecium* as seen using both processes.

Darkfield

Brightfield

Up to 1,500x **FLUORESCENCE MICROSCOPE** This type of microscope requires that the specimen be treated with special fluorescent stains. When viewed through this microscope, certain cell structures or types of substances glow, as seen in the image of a *Paramecium* above.

80 CHAPTER 3 Cells

Science Journal

Magnification Have students make a time line showing discoveries made with the light microscope, beginning with Robert Hooke (1665) identifying and drawing cells. [L2]

Teacher FYI

Any phenomena that occurs as a result of the fixing or staining procedure used to prepare a specimen to be viewed on a slide is called an artifact. An artifact is not a feature of the living organism. Sometimes an artifact can be a simple air bubble, other times the procedure can change the shape of a particular feature.

Up to 1,000,000x TRANSMIS-SION ELECTRON MICROSCOPE A TEM aims a beam of electrons through a specimen. Denser portions of the specimen allow fewer electrons to pass through and appear darker in the image. Organisms, such as the *Paramecium* at right, can only be seen when the image is photographed or shown on a monitor. A TEM can magnify hundreds of thousands of times.

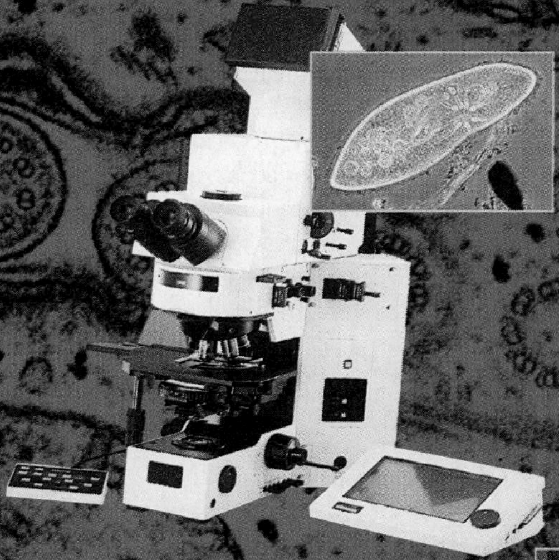

Up to 1,500x PHASE-CONTRAST MICROSCOPE A phase-contrast microscope emphasizes slight differences in a specimen's capacity to bend light waves, thereby enhancing light and dark regions without the use of stains. This type of microscope is especially good for viewing living cells, like the *Paramecium* above left. The images from a phase-contrast microscope can only be seen when the specimen is photographed or shown on a monitor.

Up to 200,000x SCANNING ELECTRON MICROSCOPE An SEM sweeps a beam of electrons over a specimen's surface, causing other electrons to be emitted from the specimen. SEMs produce realistic, three-dimensional images, which can only be viewed as photographs or on a monitor, as in the image of the *Paramecium* at right. Here a researcher compares an SEM picture to a computer monitor showing an enhanced image.

SECTION 2 Viewing Cells **81**

Resource Manager

Chapter Resources Booklet
  Enrichment, p. 31
  Lab Activity, pp. 9–12, 13–16
Science Inquiry Labs, p. 3

Visual Learning

Figure 13 Have students make a chart comparing and contrasting the different types of microscopes in this figure. They should include information on lenses and the uses of each. L2
IS Visual-Spatial

Visualizing Microscopes

Extension

Have students do a simple experiment involving refraction. Pour a quarter cup of water into a clear glass jar or beaker. Place a ruler in the beaker so that it is leaning against the top rim. Gently pour in a quarter cup each of cooking oil and rubbing alcohol successively. Do not stir. Have students record their observations regarding the appearance of the ruler. Students should see refraction of light as it passes through the different mediums as evidenced by the ruler appearing as though it is misshapen. Have students look up the definition of refraction and relate it to what they are seeing.

Content Background

Microscopes are used by many different types of scientists including, biologists, microbiologists, botanists, geologists, and epidemiologists. In 1665, Robert Hooke was the first person to see cells through a microscope of his creation. The idea of cell theory-that all living things are made of cells- was borne from his discovery. Although Hooke could see the individual cells clearly, he did not stain any of his specimens, therefore, he would not have been able to see other single-celled organisms such as bacteria. It was Antoni van Leeuwenhoek who first examined living organisms through a simple microscope in the late seventeenth century. He found organisms in the rain water he collected, as well as in the scrapings he took from the surface of his teeth.

Magnifying Cells

Purpose Students discover objects that can be used to magnify. L2 ELL IS **Kinesthetic**

Materials clear drinking glass, clear glass bowl, water, magnifying glass, newspaper pages

Teaching Strategy Try this activity with the glasses students will use. Determine beforehand the amount of water that will be needed.

Analysis
Each of the objects magnifies the newsprint.

Performance Cover newsprint with clear plastic wrap. Place a drop of water on the plastic wrap. Have students explain what they see and why. The words appear magnified because the water drop acts like a convex lens. Use **Performance Assessment in the Science Classroom,** p. 97.

Physics
INTEGRATION

A convex lens is thicker in the middle than at the edges. This causes the light rays to bend inward and meet at a point. Placing the object to be viewed a certain distance from the convex lens produces an enlarged image.

Observing Magnified Objects

Procedure
1. Look at a **newspaper** through the curved side and through the flat bottom of an **empty, clear glass.**
2. Look at the newspaper through a **clear glass bowl** filled with **water** and then with a **magnifying glass.**

Analysis
In your Science Journal, compare how well you can see the newspaper through each of the objects.

Physics
INTEGRATION

A magnifying glass is a convex lens. All microscopes use one or more convex lenses. In your Science Journal, diagram a convex lens and describe its shape.

Modern Microscopes Scientists use a variety of microscopes to study organisms, cells, and cell parts that are too small to be seen with the human eye. Depending on how many lenses a microscope contains, it is called simple or compound. A simple microscope is similar to a magnifying glass. It has only one lens. A microscope's lens makes an enlarged image of an object and directs light toward your eye. The change in apparent size produced by a microscope is called magnification. Microscopes vary in powers of magnification. Some microscopes can make images of individual atoms.

The microscope you probably will use to study life science is a compound light microscope, similar to the one in the Reference Handbook at the back of this book. The compound light microscope has two sets of lenses—eyepiece lenses and objective lenses. The eyepiece lenses are mounted in one or two tubelike structures. Images of objects viewed through two eyepieces, or stereomicroscopes, are three-dimensional. Images of objects viewed through one eyepiece are not. Compound light microscopes usually have two to four movable objective lenses.

Magnification The powers of the eyepiece and objective lenses determine the total magnifications of a microscope. If the eyepiece lens has a power of 10× and the objective lens has a power of 43×, then the total magnification is 430× (10× times 43×). Some compound microscopes, like those in **Figure 13,** have more powerful lenses that can magnify an object up to 2,000 times its original size.

Electron Microscopes Things that are too small to be seen with other microscopes can be viewed with an electron microscope. Instead of using lenses to direct beams of light, an electron microscope uses a magnetic field in a vacuum to direct beams of electrons. Some electron microscopes can magnify images up to one million times. Electron microscope images must be photographed or electronically produced.

Several kinds of electron microscopes have been invented, as shown in **Figure 13.** Scanning electron microscopes (SEM) produce a realistic, three-dimensional image. Only the surface of the specimen can be observed using an SEM. Transmission electron microscopes (TEM) produce a two-dimensional image of a thinly-sliced specimen. Details of cell parts can be examined using a TEM. Scanning tunneling microscopes (STM) are able to show the arrangement of atoms on the surface of a molecule. A metal probe is placed near the surface of the specimen and electrons flow from the tip. The hills and valleys of the specimen's surface are mapped.

Curriculum Connection

Art Discuss the use of art in science before the camera was invented. Photocopy a picture of Hooke's drawing of cells for each student. Ask them to compare it with the photographs of cells throughout the chapter and write in their Science Journals their opinions of the advantages and disadvantages of using artwork and photography. L2 IS **Linguistic and Visual-Spatial**

Resource Manager

Chapter Resources Booklet
MiniLAB, p. 4
Reinforcement, p. 28

Development of the Cell Theory

During the seventeenth century, scientists used their new invention, the microscope, to explore the newly discovered microscopic world. They examined drops of blood, scrapings from their own teeth, and other small things. Cells weren't discovered until the microscope was improved. In 1665, Robert Hooke cut a thin slice of cork and looked at it under his microscope. To Hooke, the cork seemed to be made up of empty little boxes, which he named cells.

In the 1830s, Matthias Schleiden used a microscope to study plant parts. He concluded that all plants are made of cells. Theodor Schwann, after observing many different animal cells, concluded that all animals also are made up of cells. Eventually, they combined their ideas and became convinced that all living things are made of cells.

Several years later, Rudolf Virchow hypothesized that cells divide to form new cells. Virchow proposed that every cell came from a cell that already existed. His observations and conclusions and those of others are summarized in the **cell theory**, as described in **Table 1**.

✓ Reading Check *Who made the conclusion that all animals are made of cells?*

Table 1 The Cell Theory	
All organisms are made up of one or more cells.	An organism can be one cell or many cells like most plants and animals.
The cell is the basic unit of organization in organisms.	Even in complex organisms, the cell is the basic unit of structure and function.
All cells come from cells.	Most cells can divide to form two new, identical cells.

Section 2 Assessment

1. Explain why the invention of the microscope was important in the study of cells.
2. What is stated in the cell theory?
3. What is the difference between a simple and a compound light microscope?
4. What was Virchow's contribution to the cell theory?
5. **Think Critically** Why would it be better to look at living cells than at dead cells?

Skill Builder Activities

6. **Concept Mapping** Using a network tree concept map, compare a compound light microscope to an electron microscope. **For more help, refer to the** Science Skill Handbook.
7. **Solving One-Step Equations** Calculate the magnifications of a microscope that has an 8× eyepiece, and 10× and 40× objectives. **For more help, refer to the** Math Skill Handbook.

Teacher FYI

Hooke saw only cell walls. When plant cells die, the cell wall remains. Tree bark is dead tissue. The cork that Hooke examined comes from the bark of an oak tree.

✓ Reading Check

Answer Theodor Schwann

3 Assess

Reteach

Place a large drawing of a compound microscope on the bulletin board. Write the functions of each part on a 3 x 5 card. Have students select a card, name the part, and find it on the drawing. L1
COOP LEARN Ⓘ **Visual-Spatial**

Challenge

How does the cell theory contradict the theory that living things come from non-living things? It shows that cells are the basic units of life, all organisms are made of one or more cells, and all cells come from existing cells.

✓ Assessment

Portfolio Have students write a paragraph describing the limitations as they understand them of each microscope presented in this section. Use **PASC,** p. 157. P

Answers to Section Assessment

1. Microscopes made cells visible, which established them as a scientific fact. This led to the understanding that all living things are made of cells.
2. All organisms are made of one or more cells. The cell is the basic unit of organization in organisms. All cells come from other cells.
3. A simple light microscope has one lens. A compound light microscope has two or more lenses.
4. Virchow proposed that every cell came from a cell that already existed.
5. Possible answer: some cell parts disintegrate when the cell dies.
6. Map should include the following
information: compound light microscopes—use light, magnify up to 2000×; electron microscopes—use electrons, magnify up to 1,000,000×.
7. The low-power magnification is 80× = (8 × 10) and the high-power magnification is 320× = (8 × 40).

SECTION

3 Viruses

1 Motivate

Bellringer Transparency

Display the Section Focus Transparency for Section 3. Use the accompanying Transparency Activity Master. L2 ELL

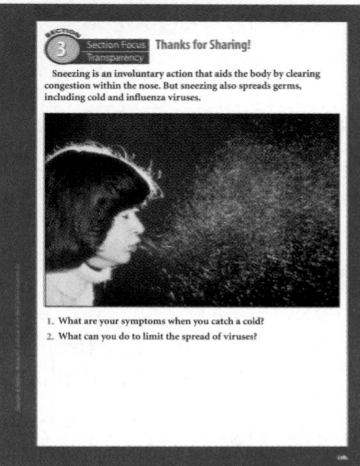

Tie to Prior Knowledge

Most students will be familiar with at least one viral disease (chicken pox, cold sores, the common cold). Have them list its symptoms on the board.

As You Read

What You'll Learn
- **Explain** how a virus makes copies of itself.
- **Identify** the benefits of vaccines.
- **Investigate** some uses of viruses.

Vocabulary
virus
host cell

Why It's Important
Viruses infect nearly all organisms, usually affecting them negatively yet sometimes affecting them positively.

Figure 14
Viruses come in a variety of shapes.

What are viruses?

Cold sores, measles, chicken pox, colds, the flu, and AIDS are diseases caused by nonliving particles called viruses. A **virus** is a strand of hereditary material surrounded by a protein coating. Viruses don't have a nucleus or other organelles. They also lack a cell membrane. Viruses, as shown in **Figure 14,** have a variety of shapes. Because they are too small to be seen with a light microscope, they were discovered only after the electron microscope was invented. Before that time, scientists only hypothesized about viruses.

How do viruses multiply?

All viruses can do is make copies of themselves. However, they can't do that without the help of a living cell called a **host cell.** Crystalized forms of some viruses can be stored for years. Then, if they enter an organism, they can multiply quickly.

Once a virus is inside of a host cell, the virus can act in two ways. It can either be active or it can become latent, which is an inactive stage.

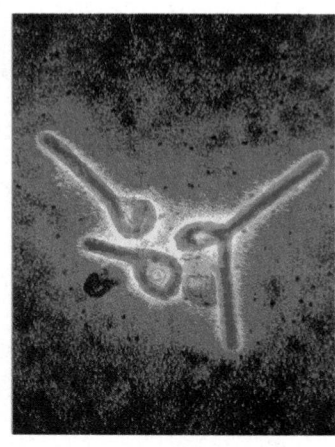

A Filoviruses do not have uniform shapes. Some of these *Ebola* viruses have a loop at one end.

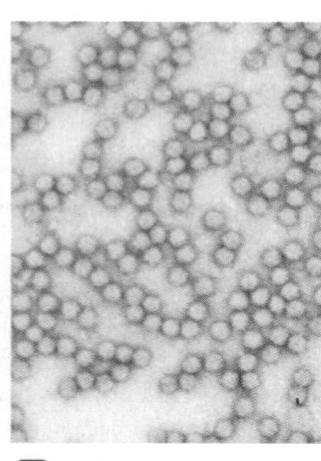

B The potato leafroll virus, *Polervirus,* damages potato crops worldwide.

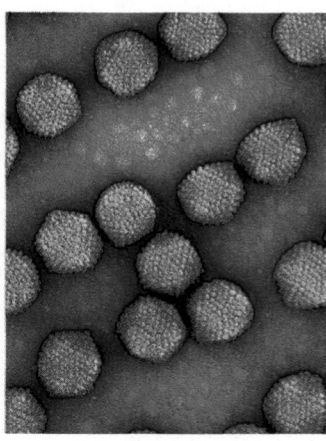

C This is just one of the many adenoviruses that can cause the common cold.

84 CHAPTER 3 Cells

Section ✓ *Assessment* Planner

PORTFOLIO
Extension, p. 86

PERFORMANCE ASSESSMENT
Skill Builder Activities, p. 87
See page 94 for more options.

CONTENT ASSESSMENT
Section, p. 87
Challenge, p. 87
Chapter, pp. 94–95

Figure 15

An active virus multiplies and destroys the host cell.
A The virus attaches to a specific host cell. **B** The virus's hereditary material enters the host cell. **C** The hereditary material of the virus causes the cell to make viral hereditary material and proteins. **D** New viruses form inside of the host cell. **E** New viruses are released as the host cell bursts open and is destroyed.

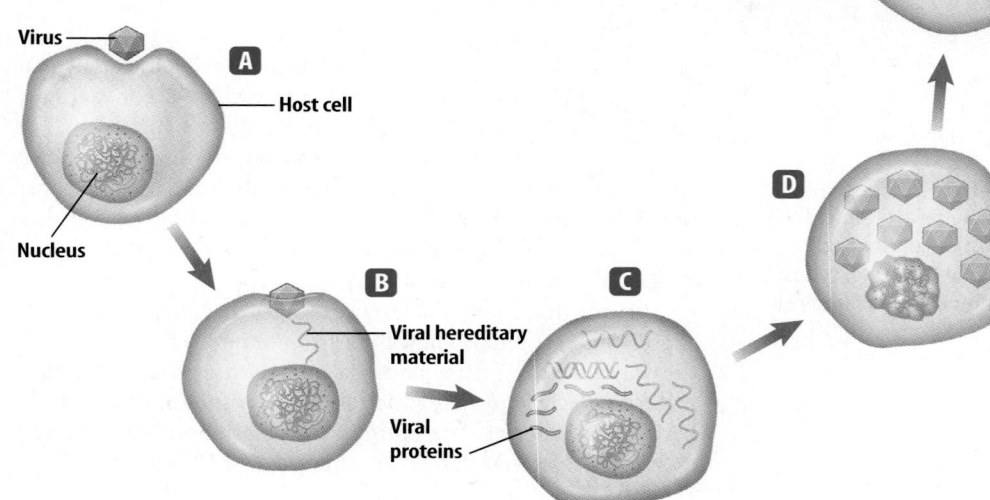

Virus
Host cell
Nucleus
A
B Viral hereditary material
Viral proteins
C
D
E

Active Viruses When a virus enters a cell and is active, it causes the host cell to make new viruses. This process destroys the host cell. Follow the steps in **Figure 15** to see one way that an active virus functions inside a cell.

Latent Viruses Some viruses can be latent. That means that after the virus enters a cell, its hereditary material can become part of the cell's hereditary material. It does not immediately make new viruses or destroy the cell. As the host cell reproduces, the viral DNA is copied. A virus can be latent for many years. Then, at any time, certain conditions, either inside or outside your body, can activate the virus.

If you have had a cold sore on your lip, a latent virus in your body has become active. The cold sore is a sign that the virus is active and destroying cells in your lip. When the cold sore disappears, the virus has become latent again. The virus is still in your body's cells, but it is hiding and doing no apparent harm.

SCIENCE *Online*

Research Visit the Glencoe Science Web site at **science.glencoe.com** for information on viruses. What environmental stimuli might activate a latent virus? Record your answer in your Science Journal.

How do viruses affect organisms?

Extension

Have students report on a specific virus. The report should give the shape of the virus, the organism infected, and symptoms of the infection. Possible viruses: hog cholera, wilt disease, HIV, Ebola, smallpox, and ringspot disease

L3 **LS** **Linguistic** P

Fighting Viruses

Use Science Words

Word Usage Have students use the word *vaccine* in a sentence describing its characteristics.

L2 **LS** **Linguistic**

Extension

Have students research the use of viruses in genetic engineering to insert genes into people with genetic disorders. L3

SCIENCE Online
Internet Addresses

_____
_____
_____
_____

Explore the Glencoe Science Web site at **science.glencoe.com** to find out more about topics in this section.

Reading Check

Answer a preparation of weakened virus particles that helps prevent disease

---

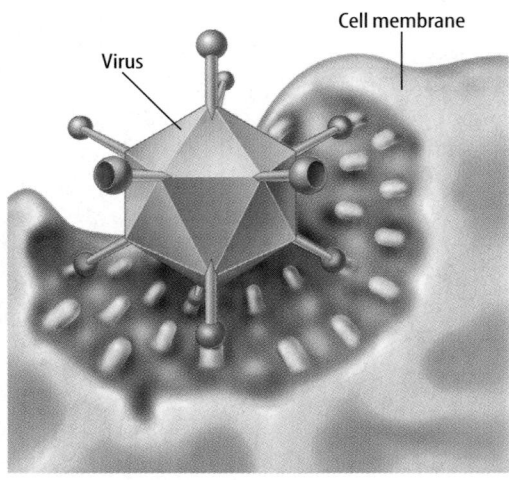
Cell membrane
Virus

Figure 16
Viruses and the attachment sites of the host cell must match exactly. That's why most viruses infect only one kind of host cell.

SCIENCE Online

Data Update Scientists have determined that *Marburg* virus, *Ebola zaire*, and *Ebola reston* belong to the virus family Filoviridae. Visit the Glencoe Science Web site at **science.glencoe.com** for the latest information about these viruses. Share your results with your class.

How do viruses affect organisms?

Viruses attack animals, plants, fungi, protists, and all prokaryotes. Some viruses can infect only specific kinds of cells. For instance, many viruses, such as the potato leafroll virus, are limited to one host species or to one type of tissue within that species. A few viruses affect a broad range of hosts. An example of this is the rabies virus. Rabies can infect humans and many other animal hosts.

A virus cannot move by itself, but it can reach a host's body in several ways. For example, it can be carried onto a plant's surface by the wind or it can be inhaled by an animal. In a viral infection, the virus first attaches to the surface of the host cell. The virus and the place where it attaches must fit together exactly, as shown in **Figure 16.** Because of this, most viruses attack only one kind of host cell.

Viruses that infect bacteria are called bacteriophages (bak TIHR ee uh fay juhz). They differ from other kinds of viruses in the way that they enter bacteria and release their hereditary material. Bacteriophages attach to a bacterium and inject their hereditary material. The entire cycle takes about 20 min, and each virus-infected cell releases an average of 100 viruses.

Fighting Viruses

Vaccines are used to prevent disease. A vaccine is made from weakened virus particles that can't cause disease anymore. Vaccines have been made to prevent many diseases, including measles, mumps, smallpox, chicken pox, polio, and rabies.

✓ Reading Check *What is a vaccine?*

The First Vaccine Edward Jenner is credited with developing the first vaccine in 1796. He developed a vaccine for smallpox, a disease that was still feared in the early twentieth century. Jenner noticed that people who got a disease called cowpox didn't get smallpox. He prepared a vaccine from the sores of people who had cowpox. When injected into healthy people, the cowpox vaccine protected them from smallpox. Jenner didn't know he was fighting a virus. At that time, no one understood what caused disease or how the body fought disease.

Curriculum Connection

Math A common unit of measure for viruses is the nanometer (nm), which is 1,000 times smaller than a micrometer (μm) and 1 million times smaller than a millimeter. A typical virus is 20 nm in size. What part of a millimeter is that? 0.000 02 mm A virus of 0.3 micrometers is how many nanometers? 300 nm

L2 **LS** **Logical-Mathematical**

Resource Manager

Chapter Resources Booklet
Reinforcement, p. 29
Reading and Writing Skill Activities, p. 31

Treating and Preventing Viral Diseases Antibiotics are used to treat bacterial infections. They are ineffective against any viral disease. One way your body can stop viral infections is by making interferons. Interferons are proteins that protect cells from viruses. These proteins are produced rapidly by infected cells and move to noninfected cells in the host. They cause the noninfected cells to produce protective substances.

Antiviral drugs can be given to infected patients to help fight a virus. A few drugs show some effectiveness against viruses but some have limited use because of their adverse side effects.

Public health measures for preventing viral diseases include vaccinating people, improving sanitary conditions, quarantining patients, and controlling animals that spread the disease. Yellow fever was wiped out completely in the United States through mosquito-control programs. Annual rabies vaccinations protect humans by keeping pets and farm animals free from infection. To control the spread of rabies in wild animals such as coyotes and wolves, wildlife workers place bait containing an oral rabies vaccine, as shown in **Figure 17,** where wild animals will find it.

Research with Viruses

You might think viruses are always harmful. However, through research, scientists are discovering helpful uses for some viruses. One use, called gene therapy, is being tried on cells with defective genes. Normal hereditary material is substituted for a cell's defective hereditary material. The normal material is enclosed in viruses. The viruses then "infect" targeted cells, taking the new hereditary material into the cells to replace the defective hereditary material. Using gene therapy, scientists hope to help people with genetic disorders and find a cure for cancer.

Figure 17
This oral rabies bait is being prepared for an aerial drop by the Texas Department of Health as part of their Oral Rabies Vaccination Program. This five-year program has prevented the expansion of rabies into Texas.

Section 3 Assessment

1. Describe the structure of viruses and explain how viruses multiply.
2. How are vaccines beneficial?
3. How might some viruses be helpful?
4. How might viral diseases be prevented?
5. **Think Critically** Explain why a doctor might not give you any medication if you have a viral disease.

Skill Builder Activities

6. **Concept Mapping** Make an events chain concept map to show what happens when a latent virus becomes active. **For more help, refer to the** Science Skill Handbook.
7. **Using a Word Processor** Make an outline of the cycle of an active virus. **For more help, refer to the** Technology Skill Handbook.

Answers to Section Assessment

1. A virus is a particle of hereditary material surrounded by protein. Viruses are reproduced only in a host cell. The host cell is destroyed when the viruses are released.
2. Vaccines, when properly administered, help prevent many viral infections.
3. They may be used to transfer normal DNA into a cell.
4. vaccinating people, improving sanitary conditions, quarantining patients, and controlling animals that spread disease
5. No medications cure a viral disease.
6. Maps should show the following: latent virus enters cell; virus becomes part of cell's DNA; cell divides; virus reproduces as part of cell division; virus becomes active; virus forms new virus particles; cell is destroyed.
7. Outline should be similar to Figure 15.

Teacher FYI

Even though bacteriophages typically inject their DNA into the host cell, not all viruses invade a host cell in this way. Many animal viruses enter the host cell through endocytosis, the binding of the virus to the cell membrane. Once inside the host cell, the virus sheds its protein coat and either undergoes replication or becomes part of the host's DNA.

Research with Viruses

Use Science Words

Word Meaning Have students look up the terms *lysis*, *virion*, and *virology*. Have them write a paragraph about the relevance of each to the study of viruses. L2 IS **Linguistic**

3 Assess

Reteach

Have students write a paragraph that describes the differences between active and latent viruses. L1 IS **Linguistic**

Challenge

Some advertisements imply that their medicine will cure a cold even though it can't. **How would a real cure for the common cold work?** A cure must disrupt the replication cycle. It could prevent the virus from entering the cell or replicating.

Assessment

Oral How does a virus invade a cell? The virus's hereditary material enters the cell, which becomes infected and eventually replicates the virus. Use **PASC**, p. 143.

ACTIVITY

Recognize the Problem

Purpose
Students will design an experiment to compare uses of stereomicroscopes and compound light microscopes. L2
COOP LEARN
Logical-Mathematical

Process Skills
observing, identifying, recognizing and using spatial relationships, classifying, communicating

Time Required
15 minutes to plan the experiment and 45 minutes to do the experiment

Safety Precautions
Caution students to use care when working with microscope slides and coverslips. Remind them to carry microscopes with both hands. Have students wash the slides and coverslips when finished.

Form a Hypothesis

Possible Hypothesis
Students may hypothesize that large items can be viewed with the stereomicroscope and small objects can be viewed with the compound light microscope.

Test Your Hypothesis

Possible Procedures
Separate items into two groups: those that can be viewed with the stereomicroscope, and those that can be viewed with the light microscope.

Teaching Strategies
• Demonstrate how to make a wet-mount.
• If microscopes have mirrors, explain how to use them.

ACTIVITY — *Design Your Own Experiment*

Comparing Light Microscopes

You're a technician in a police forensic laboratory. You use a stereomicroscope and a compound light microscope in the laboratory. A detective just returned from a crime scene with bags of evidence. You must examine each piece of evidence under a microscope. How do you decide which microscope is the best tool to use?

Recognize the Problem
Will all of the evidence that you've collected be viewable through both microscopes?

Form a Hypothesis
Compare the items to be examined under the microscopes. Which microscope will be used for each item?

Possible Materials
compound light microscope
stereomicroscope
items from the classroom—include
    some living or once-living items (8)
microscope slides and coverslips
plastic petri dishes
distilled water
dropper

Goals
■ **Learn** how to correctly use a stereomicroscope and a compound light microscope.
■ **Compare** the uses of the stereomicroscope and compound light microscope.

Safety Precautions

Thoroughly wash your hands when you have completed this experiment.

88

Resource Manager

Chapter Resources Booklet
    Activity Worksheet, pp. 7–8
Home and Community Involvement, p. 26
Lab Management and Safety, p. 58

Test Your Hypothesis

Plan

1. As a group, decide how you will test your hypothesis.

2. **Describe** how you will carry out this experiment using a series of specific steps. Make sure the steps are in a logical order. Remember that you must place an item in the bottom of a plastic petri dish to examine it under the stereomicroscope and you must make a wet mount of any item to be examined under the compound light microscope. For more help, see the Reference Handbook.

3. If you need a data table or an observation table, design one in your Science Journal.

Do

1. Make sure your teacher approves the objects you'll examine, your plan, and your data table before you start.

2. Carry out the experiment.

3. While doing the experiment, record your observations and complete the data table.

Analyze Your Data

1. **Compare** the items you examined with those of your classmates.

2. Based on this experiment, classify the eight items you observed.

Draw Conclusions

1. **Infer** which microscope a scientist might use to examine a blood sample, fibers, and live snails.

2. **List** five careers that require people to use a stereomicroscope. List five careers that require people to use a compound light microscope. Enter the lists in your Science Journal.

3. If you examined an item under a compound light microscope and a stereomicroscope, how would the images differ?

4. Which microscope was better for looking at large, or possibly live items?

*C*ommunicating Your Data

In your Science Journal, **write** a short description of an imaginary crime scene and the evidence found there. **Sort** the evidence into two lists—items to be examined under a stereomicroscope and items to be examined under a compound light microscope. **For more help, refer to the Science Skill Handbook.**

*C*ommunicating Your Data

Items small enough to fit under a coverslip should be examined with a compound light microscope; larger items should be examined with a stereomicroscope.

✓ *Assessment*

Performance To further assess students' understanding of the differences in microscopes, provide other items and have students demonstrate how to use the appropriate microscope to view each item. Use **Performance Assessment in the Science Classroom,** p. 169.

Troubleshooting Place slides and coverslips for each group in a plastic petri dish to prevent breakage.

Expected Outcome

The stereomicroscope is used for items that are too large to fit under a coverslip on a slide. The compound light microscope reveals greater detail. Students should note that the image produced by the compound light microscope is upside down and reversed left to right.

Analyze Your Data

1. Answers will vary.

2. Large items should be classified together, and items small enough to fit on a slide should be grouped together.

Error Analysis

Have students compare their results and their hypotheses and explain why differences occurred.

Draw Conclusions

1. A scientist might use a stereomicroscope to examine live snails and a compound light microscope to examine blood and fibers.

2. Answers will vary, but may include lab technicians, forensic scientists, and cell biologists for the compound light microscope and surgeons, botanists, entomologists, geologists, and gemologists for the stereomicroscope.

3. The image under the compound light microscope will be magnified more, show greater detail, be upside down, and reversed left to right.

4. stereomicroscope

Content Background

As a control, Cobb exposed cells from non-cancerous tissues to chemotherapy drugs. She hoped to discover if there was a particular drug or combination of drugs which would be effective in destroying specific types of cancer. She would also need to determine whether these drugs would also destroy healthy tissues.

Her results demonstrated that some drugs could stop the uncontrolled growth of certain types of cancer cells, but normal cells also were harmed. There were differences, however, as normal cells never showed the dramatic destruction produced in some cancer cells.

This suggested that chemotherapy was a viable approach to treatment of cancer.

Levy's research is one example of attempts to find ways to deliver high doses of cancer-killing drugs directly to a tumor while reducing the risk of damage to healthy cells.

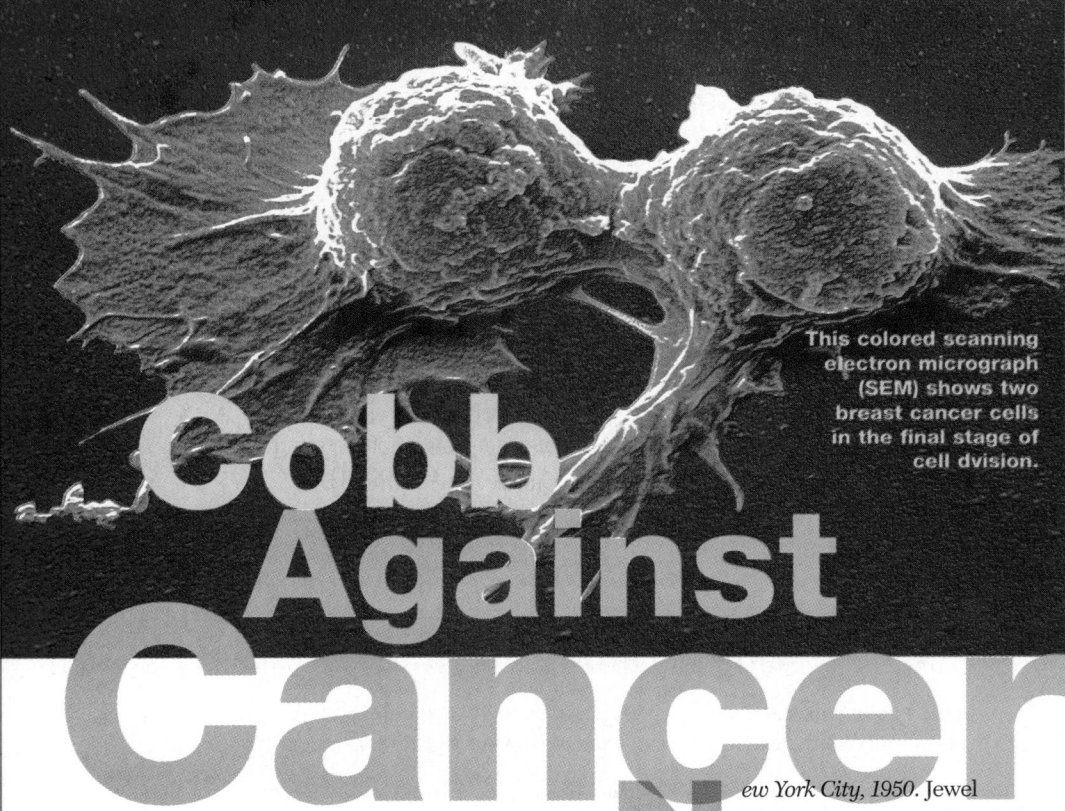

Magnification: 2,000×

This colored scanning electron micrograph (SEM) shows two breast cancer cells in the final stage of cell dvision.

Cobb Against Cancer

90

ew York City, 1950. Jewel Plummer put yet another slide onto the stage of her microscope and clipped it into place. She switched to the high power objective, looked through the eyepiece, and turned the fine adjustment a tiny bit to bring her subject—cells from a cancerous tumor—into focus. She switched back to low power and removed the slide. She had found no change in the tumor cells. The drug that doctors had used wasn't killing or slowing the growth rate of those cancer cells. Sighing, she reached for the next slide. Maybe the slightly different drug they had used on that batch of cells would be the answer....

Resources for Teachers and Students

The National Cancer Institute
Public Inquiries Office
Building 31, Room 10A31
31 Center Drive
MSC 2580
Bethesda, MD 20892-2580 USA,
(301) 435-3848

Advancing Current Treatments for Cancer, by Samuel Hellman and Everett E. Vokes, Scientific American, September 1996.

How Cancer Arises, by Robert A. Weinberg, Scientific American, September 1996.

Jewel Plummer Cobb is a cell biologist who did important background research on the use of drugs against cancer. She removed cells from cancerous tumors and cultured them in the lab. Then, in a controlled study, she tried a series of different drugs against batches of the same cells. Her goal was to find the right drug to cure each patient's particular cancer. Cobb never met that goal, but her research laid the groundwork for modern chemotherapy—the use of chemicals to treat people with cancer.

Role Model

Jewel Cobb also influenced the course of science in a different way. She served as dean or president of several universities, retiring as president of the University of California at Fullerton. In her role as a college official, she was able to promote equal opportunity for students of all backgrounds, especially in the sciences.

Light Up a Cure

Vancouver, British Columbia, 2000. While Cobb herself was only able to infer what was going on inside a cell from its reactions to various drugs, her work has helped others go further. Building on Cobb's work, Professor Julia Levy and her research team at the University of British Columbia actually go inside cells and even inside organelles to work against cancer. One technique they are pioneering is the use of light to guide cancer drugs to the right cells. First, the patient is given a chemotherapy drug that reacts to light. Next, a fiber optic tube is inserted into the tumor. Finally, laser light is passed through the tube. The light activates the light-sensitive drug—but only in the tumor itself. This technique keeps healthy cells healthy but kills sick cells on the spot.

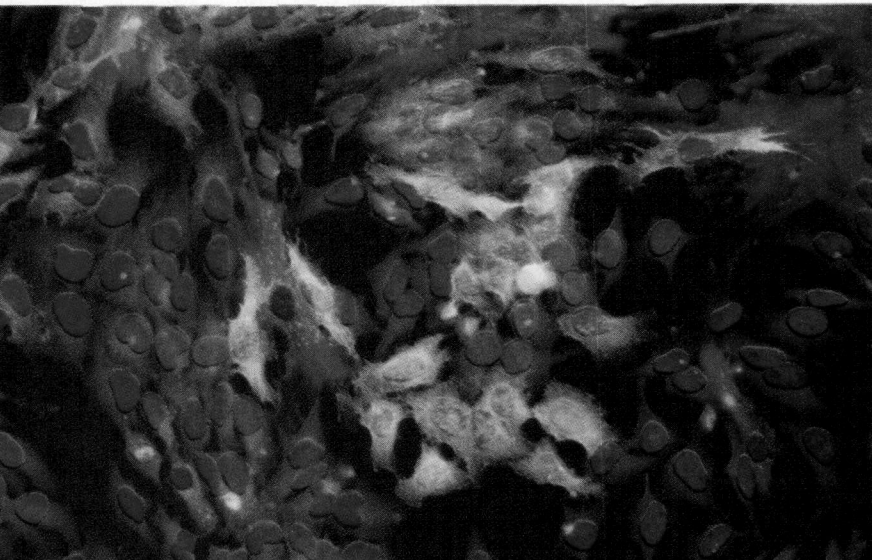

The image to the left shows human cervical cells magnified 125 times that have been attacked by cancer. The light blue areas at the center are keratin, a kind of protein. The cell nuclei are stained blue, and the red areas are fibroblasts, a kind of connective-tissue cell. These are the first human cells used to research cancer. This type of cell grows well in a lab, and is used in research worldwide.

CONNECTIONS Write Report on Cobb's experiments on cancer cells. What were her dependent and independent variables? What would she have used as a control? What sources of error did she have to guard against? Answer the same questions about Levy's work.

SCIENCE *Online*

For more information, visit science.glencoe.com

Discussion

Using Cobb's research as an example, discuss the value of experiments even if the results do not meet the researcher's specific goals. Possible answer: Science is a continuing process of discovery. Cobb's work is a necessary first step to new approaches to treatment like Levy's. **Chemotherapy treatments often result in discomfort and risk for cancer patients. Discuss why this is so.** Possible answer: All cells share the same genetic mechanisms. Treatments that affect DNA in one cell type will do so in others as well.

Historic Significance

The structure and function of DNA were not discovered until 1953. Cobb's research began shortly thereafter, long before the role of genes in the development of cancer was understood. Research like Cobb's leads to questions about how certain drugs can stop the unchecked growth of tumors. In combination with an increasing understanding of how genes work, these results allow scientists to refine the methods of administering treatments and to target the development of drugs specifically aimed at preventing the replication of DNA, a process that all cells require.

CONNECTIONS In Cobb's study the control group consisted of normal human cells that were exposed to the chemotherapeutic drugs. The independent variable was the specific drug administered to the cells. The dependent variable was the response of the cells to the treatment. Differences in these responses would allow conclusions about the effects of specific drugs, alone and in combination, on both cancerous and healthy cells.

SCIENCE *Online*

Internet Addresses

_____
_____
_____

Explore the Glencoe Science Web site at **science.glencoe.com** to find out more about topics in this feature.

Reviewing Main Ideas

Preview

Students can answer the questions in their Science Journals. Discuss the answers as you go through the chapter. **LS Linguistic**

Review

Students can write their answers, then compare them with those of other students. **LS Interpersonal**

Reteach

Students can look at the illustrations and describe details that support the main ideas of the chapter. **LS Visual-Spatial**

Answers to Chapter Review

SECTION 1

6. temporarily stores cellular material

SECTION 2

4. The ant is dead because specimens are placed in a vacuum to be examined with an electron microscope.

SECTION 3

3. They can multiply only within living cells. They do not have the cell components associated with living organisms.

Reviewing Main Ideas

Section 1 Cell Structure

1. There are two basic cell types. Cells without membrane-bound structures are called prokaryotic cells. Cells with membrane-bound structures are called eukaryotic cells.

2. Most of the life processes of a cell occur within the cytoplasm.

3. Cell functions are performed by organelles under the control of DNA in the nucleus.

4. Organelles such as mitochondria and chloroplasts process energy.

5. Proteins take part in nearly every cell activity.

6. Golgi bodies and vacuoles transport substances, rid the cell of wastes, and store cellular materials. *What does this organelle do?*

7. Most many-celled organisms are organized into tissues, organs, and organ systems that perform specific functions to keep an organism alive.

Section 2 Viewing Cells

1. A simple microscope has just one lens. A compound light microscope has eyepiece lenses and objective lenses.

2. To calculate the magnification of a microscope, multiply the power of the eyepiece by the power of the objective lens.

3. An electron microscope uses a beam of electrons instead of light to produce an image of an object.

4. Things that are too small to be viewed with a light microscope can be viewed with an electron microscope. This is an SEM of an ant. *How do you know if the ant is alive or dead?*

5. According to the cell theory, the cell is the basic unit of life. Organisms are made of one or more cells, and all cells come from other cells.

Section 3 Viruses

1. A virus is a structure containing hereditary material surrounded by a protein coating.

2. A virus can make copies of itself only when it is inside a living host cell.

3. Viruses cause diseases in animals, plants, fungi, and bacteria. *Why don't scientists consider viruses like these in the photo to be living organisms?*

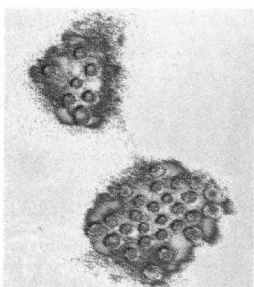

FOLDABLES
Reading & Study Skills

After You Read

On the inside of the Main Ideas Study Fold you made at the beginning of the chapter describe the characteristics of each type of cell.

FOLDABLES
Reading & Study Skills

After You Read

After students have read the chapter and completed the Foldable described in Before You Read, have them do the activity on the student page.

Dinah Zike

Visualizing Main Ideas

Complete the following concept map of the basic units of life.

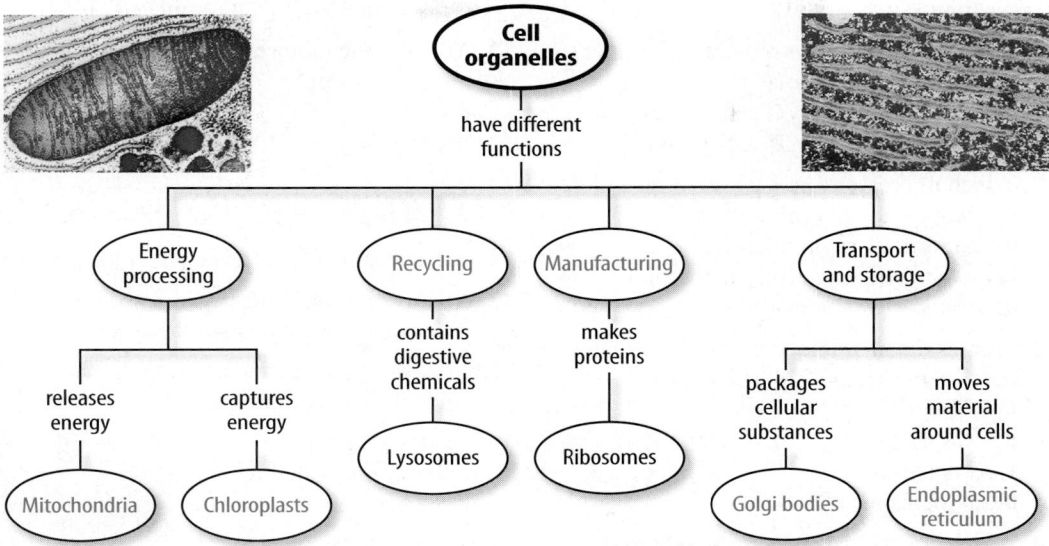

Vocabulary Review

Vocabulary Words

a. cell membrane
b. cell theory
c. cell wall
d. chloroplast
e. cytoplasm
f. endoplasmic reticulum
g. Golgi body
h. host cell
i. mitochondrion
j. nucleus
k. organ
l. organelle
m. ribosome
n. tissue
o. virus

THE PRINCETON REVIEW

Study Tip

In order to understand the information that a graph is trying to communicate, write out a sentence that talks about the relationship between the x-axis and y-axis in the graph.

Using Vocabulary

Using the vocabulary words, give an example of each of the following.

1. found in every organ

2. smaller than one cell

3. a plant-cell organelle

4. part of every cell

5. powerhouse of a cell

6. used by biologists

7. contains hereditary material

8. a structure that surrounds the cell

9. can be damaged by a virus

10. made up of cells

Visualizing Main Ideas

See student page.

Vocabulary Review

Using Vocabulary

1. n
2. d, f, g, i, j, l, m, o
3. d, f, g, j, m
4. a, e
5. i
6. b
7. e, j, o
8. a, c
9. h
10. k, n

Chapter 3 Assessment

Checking Concepts

1. B
2. A
3. D
4. A
5. C
6. C
7. B
8. C
9. A
10. A

Thinking Critically

11. Once a virus infects a cell, it uses the cell to produce more viruses. The immune system has to work to get rid of viruses because no drugs will kill them.

12. Answers may vary, but a stereomicroscope would enable you to view a large specimen as well as to look closely at the mold.

13. The plant cell would die or become dependent on other cells to provide its food.

14. No proteins could be made, and the animal cell would die.

15. If there is a cell wall and chloroplasts, it is a plant cell. A cell with no chloroplasts or cell wall is an animal cell. If no membrane-bound organelles are present, it is a bacterial cell.

Checking Concepts

Choose the word or phrase that best answers the question.

1. What structure allows only certain things to pass in and out of the cell?
   A) cytoplasm
   C) ribosomes
   B) cell membrane
   D) Golgi body

2. Which microscope uses lenses to magnify?
   A) compound light microscope
   B) scanning electron microscope
   C) transmission electron microscope
   D) atomic force microscope

3. What is made of folded membranes that move materials around inside the cell?
   A) nucleus
   B) cytoplasm
   C) Golgi body
   D) endoplasmic reticulum

4. Which scientist gave the name *cells* to structures he viewed?
   A) Hooke
   C) Schleiden
   B) Schwann
   D) Virchow

5. What organelle helps recycle old cell parts?
   A) chloroplast
   C) lysosome
   B) centriole
   D) cell wall

6. Which of the following is a viral disease?
   A) tuberculosis
   C) smallpox
   B) anthrax
   D) tetanus

7. What are structures in the cytoplasm of a eukaryotic cell called?
   A) organs
   C) organ systems
   B) organelles
   D) tissues

8. Which microscope can magnify up to a million times?
   A) compound light microscope
   B) stereomicroscope
   C) transmission electron microscope
   D) atomic force microscope

9. Which of the following is part of a bacterial cell?
   A) a cell wall
   C) mitochondria
   B) lysosomes
   D) a nucleus

10. Which of the following do groups of different tissues form?
   A) organ
   C) organ system
   B) organelle
   D) organism

Thinking Critically

11. Why is it difficult to treat a viral disease?

12. What type of microscope would be best to view a piece of moldy bread? Explain.

13. What would happen to a plant cell that suddenly lost its chloroplasts?

14. What would happen to this animal cell if it didn't have ribosomes?

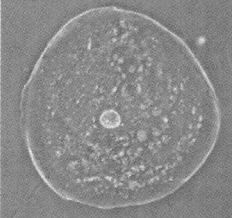

15. How would you decide whether an unknown cell was an animal cell, a plant cell, or a bacterial cell?

Developing Skills

16. **Concept Mapping** Make an events-chain concept map of the following from simple to complex: *small intestine, circular muscle cell, human,* and *digestive system.*

17. **Interpreting Scientific Illustrations** Use the illustrations in **Figure 1** to describe how the shape of a cell is related to its function.

18. **Making and Using Graphs** Use a computer to make a line graph of the following data. At 37°C there are 1.0 million viruses; at, 37.5°C, 0.5 million; at 37.8°C, 0.25 million; at 38.3°C, 0.1 million; and at 38.9°C, 0.05 million.

Chapter ✓Assessment Planner

Portfolio Encourage students to place in their portfolios one or two items of what they consider to be their best work. Examples include:
- Visual Learning, p. 73
- Assessment, p. 83
- Extension, p. 86

Performance Additional performance assessments, Performance Task Assessment Lists, and rubrics for evaluating these activities can be found in Glencoe's **Performance Assessment in the Science Classroom.**

19. Comparing and Contrasting Complete the following table to compare and contrast the structures of a prokaryotic cell to those of a eukaryotic cell.

Cell Structures		
Structure	**Prokaryotic Cell**	**Eukaryotic Cell**
Cell Membrane	Yes	Yes
Cytoplasm	Yes	Yes
Nucleus	No	Yes
Endoplasmic Reticulum	No	Yes
Golgi Bodies	No	Yes

20. Making a Model Make and illustrate a time line to show the development of the cell theory. Begin with the development of the microscope and end with Virchow. Include the contributions of Leeuwenhoek, Hooke, Schleiden, and Schwann.

Performance Assessment

21. Model Use materials that resemble cell parts or that represent their functions to make a model of a plant cell or an animal cell. Make a key to the cell parts to explain your model.

22. Poster Research the history of vaccinations. Contact your local Health Department for current information. Display your results on a poster.

TECHNOLOGY

 Go to the Glencoe Science Web site at **science.glencoe.com** or use the **Glencoe Science CD-ROM** for additional chapter assessment.

 **Test Practice**

A scientist is studying living cells. Below is an image of one of the cells that is being studied. This image represents what a scientist sees when he or she uses a tool in the laboratory.

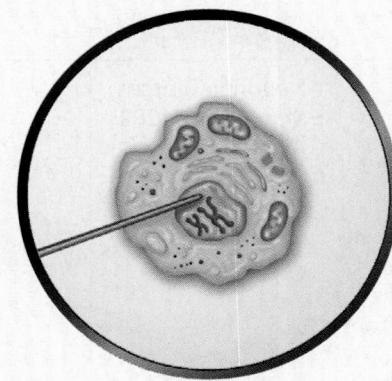

Closely examine the image above then answer the following questions.

1. If the pointer shown above with the cell is 10 micrometers in length, then about how wide is this cell?
A) 20 micrometers
B) 10 micrometers
C) 5 micrometers
D) 0.1 micrometers

2. Which of the following tools is the scientist probably using to view the living cell?
F) telescope
G) endoplasmic reticulum
H) compound light microscope
J) kaleidoscope

CHAPTER ASSESSMENT 95

THE PRINCETON REVIEW **Test Practice**

The Test-Taking Tip was written by The Princeton Review, the nation's leader in test preparation.
1. B
2. H

Developing Skills

16. circular muscle cell, small intestine, digestive system, human
17. Answers will vary but should relate each shape to a function of the cell, such as the elongated shape of the nerve cell and its function in transmitting impulses.
18. Line graphs should show that, as temperature increases, the number of viruses decrease.
19. See student page.
20. The time line should have equal divisions of time and cover from the late 1500s to the late 1800s. Include these dates: late 1500s, microscope invented; late 1600s, Leeuwenhoek improves microscope; 1665, Hooke uses the word *cell;* 1830s, Schleiden discovers plants are made of cells; mid 1800s, Schwann discovers animals are made of cells; late 1800s, Virchow concludes that all cells come from cells.

Performance Assessment

21. Model should include cell parts and a key to identify them. Use **PASC**, p. 123.
22. Posters should correctly show the history of vaccinations. Use **PASC**, p. 145.

✓Assessment Resources

📁 **Reproducible Masters**
Chapter Resources Booklet
Chapter Review, pp. 37–38
Chapter Tests, pp. 39–42
Assessment Transparency Activity, p. 49
Glencoe Science Web site
Interactive Tutor
Chapter Quizzes

Glencoe Technology
🖱 Assessment Transparency
💿 Interactive CD-ROM Chapter Quizzes
💿 ExamView Pro Test Bank
💿 Vocabulary PuzzleMaker Software
📼 MindJogger Videoquiz

Section/Objectives	Standards		Activities/Features
Chapter Opener	**National**	**State/Local**	**Explore Activity:** Demonstrate why water leaves plant cells, p. 97 **Before You Read,** p. 97
	See p. 5T for a Key to Standards.		
Section 1 Chemistry of Life 🕐 2 sessions 📦 1 block 1. **List** the differences among atoms, elements, molecules, and compounds. 2. **Explain** the relationship between chemistry and life science. 3. **Discuss** how organic compounds are different from inorganic compounds.	National Content Standards: UCP2, A1, B1, C1		**Science Online,** p. 102 **MiniLAB:** Determining How Enzymes Work, p. 103 **Math Skills Activity:** Calculating the Importance of Water, p. 104
Section 2 Moving Cellular Materials 🕐 2 sessions 📦 1 block 1. **Describe** the function of a selectively permeable membrane. 2. **Explain** how the processes of diffusion and osmosis move molecules in living cells. 3. **Explain** how passive transport and active transport differ	National Content Standards: UCP4, A1, C1, C3		**MiniLAB:** Observing Diffusion, p. 107 **Health Integration,** p. 109 **Visualizing Cell Membrane Transport,** p. 111 **Activity:** Observing Osmosis, p. 112
Section 3 Energy for Life 🕐 3 sessions 📦 1.5 blocks 1. **List** the differences between producers and consumers. 2. **Explain** how the processes of photosynthesis and respiration store and release energy. 3. **Describe** how cells get energy from glucose through fermentation.	National Content Standards: UCP1, A1, B3, C1, C4, G1		**Chemistry Integration,** p. 115 **Science Online,** p. 116 **Activity:** Photosynthesis and Respiration, pp. 118–119 **Science and Language Arts:** Tulip, pp. 120–121

NATIONAL GEOGRAPHIC

Teacher's Corner

PRODUCTS AVAILABLE FROM GLENCOE
To order call 1-800-334-7344:
CD-ROM's
NGS PictureShow: Looking at Living Things
Curriculum Kit
GeoKit: Cells and Microorganisms

Transparency Sets
NGS PicturePack: The Cell
NGS PicturePack: Looking At Living Things
PRODUCTS AVAILABLE FROM NATIONAL GEOGRAPHIC SOCIETY
To order call 1-800-368-2728:

Videos
Photosynthesis: Life Energy

INDEX TO NATIONAL GEOGRAPHIC SOCIETY
The following articles may be used for research relating to this chapter: "The Awesome Worlds Within a Cell," by Rick Gore, September 1976.

Activity Materials	Reproducible Resources	Section Assessment	Technology
Explore Activity: bowl, label, water (500 mL), salt (15 g), carrot sticks (6), watch or clock, beaker (250ml), balance, stirrer	**Chapter Resources Booklet** Foldables Worksheet, p. 15 Directed Reading Overview, p. 17 Note-taking Worksheets, pp. 31–33	**GLENCOE'S ASSESSMENT ADVANTAGE**	
MiniLAB: prepared gelatin, small cups, fresh pineapple pieces *Need materials?* Contact Science Kit at 1-800-828-7777 or www.sciencekit.com on the Internet.	**Chapter Resources Booklet** Transparency Activity, p. 42 MiniLAB, p. 3 Enrichment, p. 28 Reinforcement, p. 25 Directed Reading, p. 18 Transparency Activity, pp. 45–46 **Cultural Diversity,** p. 65	**Portfolio** Science Journal, p. 102 **Performance** MiniLAB, p. 103 Math Skills Activity, p. 104 Skill Builder Activities, p. 105 **Content** Section Assessment, p. 105	Section Focus Transparency Teaching Transparency Interactive CD-ROM Guided Reading Audio Program
MiniLAB: clean glasses (2 of equal size), labels, very warm water, cold water, food coloring, dropper, clock, marker or wax pencil **Activity:** unshelled egg, balance, spoon, distilled water (250 mL), light corn syrup (250 mL), 500-mL container	**Chapter Resources Booklet** Transparency Activity, p. 43 MiniLAB, p. 4 Enrichment, p. 29 Reinforcement, p. 26 Directed Reading, p. 18 Lab Activity, pp. 9–10 Activity Worksheet, pp. 5–6 **Home and Community Involvement,** p. 47	**Portfolio** Visual Learning, p. 111 **Performance** MiniLAB, p. 107 Skill Builder Activities, p. 110 **Content** Section Assessment, p. 110	Section Focus Transparency Interactive CD-ROM Guided Reading Audio Program
Activity: 16-mm test tubes (3), 150-mm test tubes with stoppers (4), test-tube rack, stirring rod, scissors, carbonated water (5 mL), bromothymol blue solution in dropper bottle, aged tap water (20 mL), sprig of *Elodea*	**Chapter Resources Booklet** Transparency Activity, p. 44 Enrichment, p. 30 Reinforcement, p. 27 Directed Reading, pp. 19, 20 Lab Activity, pp. 11–14 Activity Worksheet, pp. 7–8 **Lab Management and Safety,** p. 63	**Portfolio** Visual Learning, p. 117 **Performance** Skill Builder Activities, p. 117 **Content** Section Assessment, p. 117	Section Focus Transparency Interactive CD-ROM Guided Reading Audio Program

End of Chapter Assessment

GLENCOE'S ASSESSMENT ADVANTAGE

Blackline Masters	Technology	Professional Series
Chapter Resources Booklet Chapter Review, pp. 35–36 Chapter Tests, pp. 37–40 **Standardized Test Practice by The Princeton Review,** pp. 19–22	MindJogger Videoquiz Interactive CD-ROM Vocabulary PuzzleMakers ExamView Pro Test Bank Interactive Lesson Planner Interactive Teacher Edition	Performance Assessment in the Science Classroom (PASC)

Transparencies

Section Focus

Section Focus Transparency 1 — Chemicals for Life (Chapter 3)

Every living thing is made of compounds containing carbon and hydrogen. We consume many of these compounds for energy. However, some compounds that we consume do not contain the elements carbon and hydrogen. These compounds are also necessary for life.

1. Of the objects above, which come from living things?
2. Which objects do not contain substances that were once alive?
3. Name three substances that your body needs to survive that do not come from living things.

L2

Section Focus Transparency 2 — Skin Deep (Chapter 3)

Misting with water helps keep supermarket produce fresh. Not all the water stays on the skin of these fruits and vegetables; most of it seems to disappear. The trick is finding out where it went.

1. When the water on the fruits and vegetables disappears, where does it go?
2. Create a simple test to explain what happens to the water when it disappears.
3. How do you think the water keeps the produce fresh?

L2

Section Focus Transparency 3 — What's for dinner? (Chapter 3)

Some organisms don't need anyone to survive, but others need help to get by. In this picture, some of the living things shown can make their own food. They are called producers. Other living things, called consumers, depend on these producers for their survival.

1. Which things in the picture are producers? Consumers?
2. Explain whether you are a producer or consumer.
3. If all the plants died, what effect would it have on the animals?

L2

This is a representation of key blackline masters available in the Teacher Classroom Resources. See Resource Manager boxes within the chapter for additional information.

Key to Teaching Strategies

The following designations will help you decide which activities are appropriate for your students.

L1 Level 1 activities should be appropriate for students with learning difficulties.

L2 Level 2 activities should be within the ability range of all students.

L3 Level 3 activities are designed for above-average students.

ELL ELL activities should be within the ability range of English Language Learners.

COOP LEARN Cooperative Learning activities are designed for small group work.

LS Multiple Learning Styles logos, as described on page 22T, are used throughout to indicate strategies that address different learning styles.

P These strategies represent student products that can be placed into a best-work portfolio.

Assessment

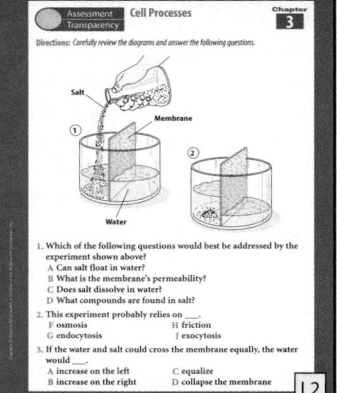

Assessment Transparency — Cell Processes (Chapter 3)

Directions: Carefully review the diagrams and answer the following questions.

1. Which of the following questions would best be addressed by the experiment shown above?
   A Can salt float in water?
   B What is the membrane's permeability?
   C Does salt dissolve in water?
   D What compounds are found in salt?
2. This experiment probably relies on ___.
   F osmosis   H friction
   G endocytosis   J exocytosis
3. If the water and salt could cross the membrane equally, the water would ___.
   A increase on the left   C equalize
   B increase on the right   D collapse the membrane

L2

Teaching

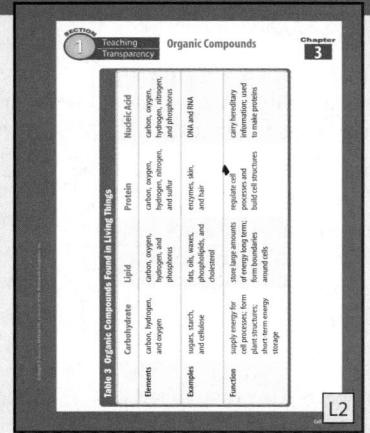

Teaching Transparency 1 — Organic Compounds (Chapter 3)

L2

Hands-on Activities

Activity Worksheets

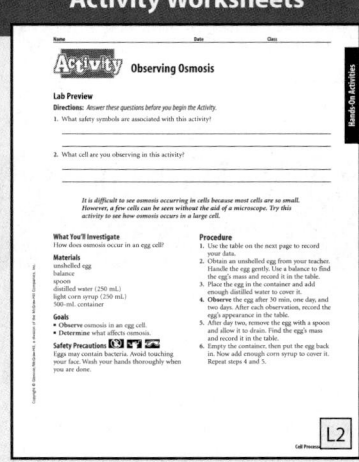

Activity — Observing Osmosis

L2

Laboratory Activities

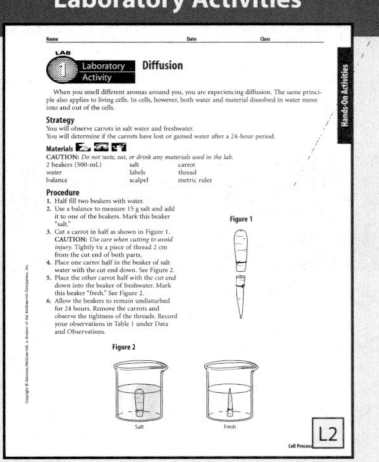

Laboratory Activity 1 — Diffusion

L2

Meeting Different Ability Levels

Content Outline

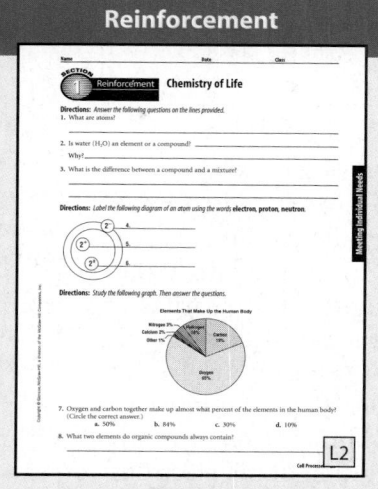

Reinforcement

Directed Reading

Assessment

Chapter Tests

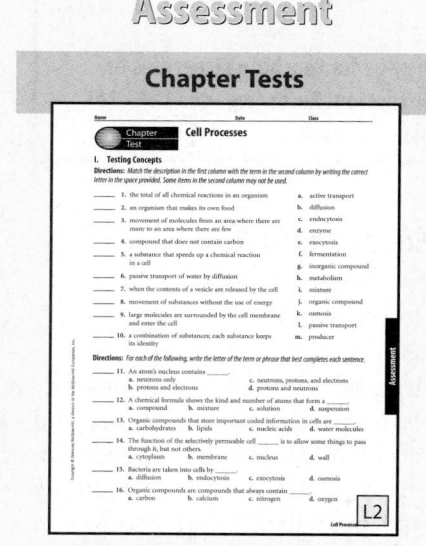

Enrichment

Spanish Directed Reading

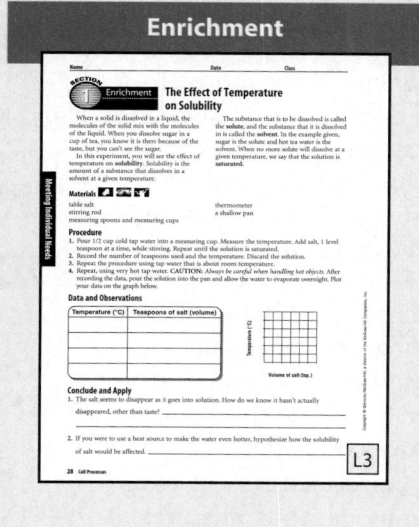

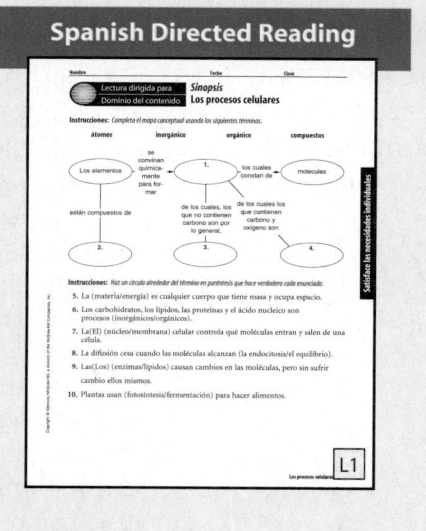

Test Practice Workbook

Chapter Review

Science Content Background

SECTION 1

Chemistry of Life
The Nature of Matter

Democritus, an ancient Greek philosopher, proposed that atoms were small, solid spheres. From the late 1800s until recently, it was thought that negatively-charged electrons orbited the positively-charged nucleus in specific paths. Quantum mechanics provide us with the current model of a positively-charged nucleus surrounded by a region in which the electrons move. The location of the electrons depends on each electron's energy level.

Compounds and Mixtures

Compounds are formed when two or more elements combine by a chemical reaction. Molecular components form when atoms share electrons. Ionic compounds form when negative and positive ions join. Organic compounds all contain carbon atoms. Most organic compounds are produced within living organisms. However, organic compounds such as plastics and synthetic fibers are constructed from organic substances such as petroleum. Inorganic compounds usually are made from elements other than carbon. Water is the most important inorganic compound.

Most things in nature are mixtures of elements. Components of homogeneous mixtures, such as solutions, cannot be distinguished from one another. The components of a heterogeneous mixture are generally visibly identifiable.

SECTION 2

Moving Cellular Materials
Maintaining Balance

The cell membrane regulates what enters and leaves a cell. The sizes, shapes, and electrical charges of molecules determine the permeability of the cell membrane. It is important for a cell to maintain its internal concentrations of substances such as water, glucose, and other nutrients while allowing elimination of waste products.

Transport

Passive transport—transport without the input of energy—depends on temperature. One form of passive transport, called diffusion, occurs when molecules move from an area where their concentration is greater into an area where they are less concentrated. Osmosis is the diffusion of water into or out of a cell. Active transport, transport with energy input, requires transport proteins.

Student Misconception

Plants do not use oxygen and do not release carbon dioxide.

Refer to the facing page for teaching strategies to address this misconception. Refer to pages 114–117 for content related to this topic.

SECTION 3

Energy for Life
Photosynthesis, Respiration, and Fermentation

During photosynthesis, plants and other producers convert light energy to chemical energy and make carbohydrates (food). During respiration, the food is broken down and the released energy can be used by the producer, other producers, and consumers. When there is a shortage of oxygen, fermentation is a process some cells can use to release energy from glucose.

SCIENCE *Online*

For additional content background on this topic, go to the Glencoe Science Web site at science.glencoe.com.

IDENTIFYING Misconceptions

Find Out What Students Think

Students may think that . . .

• **Plants do not use oxygen and do not release carbon dioxide.**

Students may not completely understand the complementary nature of photosynthesis and respiration, especially with respect to exchange of gases.

Demonstration

Ask students to give the relationship between producers, consumers, oxygen, and carbon dioxide. Summarize students' responses on the board. If students do not explicitly respond that plants also give off carbon dioxide, don't point it out at this time. Let that understanding come from the activities below.

Promote Understanding

Activity 1

WARNING: Remind students not to suck on the straw.

Prepare a 0.1% solution of bromthymol blue.

• Have students blow through a straw into the bromthymol blue solution. The solution should turn yellow as the carbon dioxide from respiration dissolves in the solution (forming carbonic acid).

• Have students add drops of dilute ammonium hydroxide so that the solution again turns blue. Explain that the bromthymol blue is an indicator that turns yellow in an acidic solution and blue in a neutral or alkaline solution.

• Ask students what gas is given off in the process of respiration. (carbon dioxide) Explain that the carbon dioxide blown into the solution dissolves and makes the solution slightly acidic. Point out that adding the ammonium hydroxide made the solution slightly basic.

Activity 2

Acidify a large test tube of bromthymol blue by adding carbonated water to the solution. Add a sprig of *Elodea* to the tube.

• Put the test tube in sunlight or under a bright light. The solution should begin to turn blue in 30 to 45 minutes. Have students record results.

• At the same time, have students put a sprig of *Elodea* in a test tube of bromthymol blue solution that is just very slightly alkaline and thus blue and place the tube in a dark area. Within 24 hours the color of the solution should change to a pale yellow as the plant respires and releases carbon dioxide. Again have students record their results.

Discussion

• Ask why the bromthymol blue solution turned blue in the light. Ask students what evidence supports their answer. Explicitly reinforce the fact the carbon dioxide was absorbed by the plant and used in the process of photosynthesis.

• Ask students whether they think carbon dioxide was given off by the *Elodea* kept in the dark. Light-independent photosynthesis and respiration occur in the dark, so carbon dioxide is used and released. Stress that their results indicate that plants give off carbon dioxide during respiration. Point out that all living things must carry out some form of respiration.

Assess

After completing the chapter, see *Identifying Misconceptions* in the Study Guide.

Cell Processes

Chapter Vocabulary

What do you think?

Science Journal The object in the picture is a mitochondrion, the place in a eukaryotic cell in which energy is released from food molecules.

Cell Processes

The Sun is hot. Your back aches and your hands are sore. Weeding a garden is hard work. You are sweaty, tired, thirsty, and hungry. Are the weeds having the same reactions? You may know that plants don't sweat or get tired, but they do need water and food, just like you. How do plants take in and use water and food? In this chapter you'll find the answer to this question. You'll also find out how living things get the energy that they need to survive.

What do you think?

Science Journal Look at the picture below with a classmate. Discuss what this might be or what is happening. Here's a hint: *It's sometimes called the powerhouse of the cell.* Write your answer or best guess in your Science Journal.

96

Theme Connection

Stability and Change Living things function as a result of chemical reactions in cells. The equilibrium maintained by cells results from their selectively permeable membranes. This is critical to the life of cells and the organism as a whole.

I f you forget to water a plant, it will wilt. After you water the plant, it probably will straighten up and look healthier. Why does the plant straighten? In the following activity, find out about water entering and leaving plant cells.

Demonstrate why water leaves plant cells

1. Label a small bowl "salt water." Pour 250 mL of water into the bowl. Then add 15 g of salt to the water and stir.

2. Pour 250 mL of water into another small bowl.

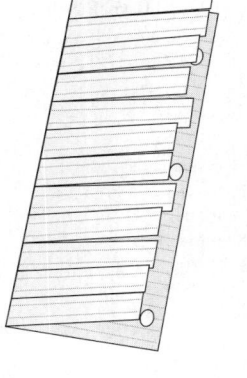

3. Place two carrot sticks into each bowl. Also, place two carrot sticks on the lab table.

4. After 30 min, remove the carrot sticks from the bowls and keep them next to the bowl they came from. Examine all six carrot sticks, then describe them in your Science Journal.

Observe

Predict what would happen if you moved the carrot sticks from the plain water to the lab table, the ones from the salt water into the plain water, and the ones from the lab table into the salt water. Now try it. Write your predictions and your results in your Science Journal.

Before You Read

FOLDABLES
Reading & Study Skills

Making a Vocabulary Study Fold To help you study cell processes, make the following vocabulary Foldable. Knowing the definition of vocabulary words in a chapter is a good way to ensure that you have understood the content.

1. Place a sheet of notebook paper in front of you so the short side is at the top. Fold the paper in half from the left to the right side.

2. Through the top thickness of paper, cut along every third line from the outside edge to the center fold, forming ten tabs as shown.

3. On the front of each tab, write a vocabulary word listed on the first page of each section in this chapter. On the back of each tab, define the word.

97

Before You Read

FOLDABLES
Reading & Study Skills

Dinah Zike Study Fold

Purpose Use this activity to expose students to the chapter's content and vocabulary before they read, and to encourage a search for terms and definitions as they read. The resulting Foldable can be used as an assessment tool and study guide before, during and after reading.

📁 For additional help, see Foldables Worksheet, p. 15 in **Chapter Resources Booklet,** or go to the Glencoe Science Web site at **science.glencoe.com.** See After You Read in the Study Guide at the end of this chapter.

Purpose Use the Explore Activity to show students that water moves into and out of carrot cells. Explain that the materials moving into and out of cells are atoms, molecules, and compounds. L1 **LS** Visual-Spatial

Preparation Purchase carrots for the activity. Peel and cut the carrots into sticks.

Materials salt, 250-mL beaker, balance, 2 bowls, stirrer, 6 carrot sticks, water, label, watch or clock

Teaching Strategy Provide students with water at room temperature so the salt will dissolve more readily.

Observe

The carrot sticks in salt water and on the lab table were limp because water moved out of them. The carrot sticks in plain water were crisp because water moved into the cells that had less water. Students should predict that these conditions are reversible, depending on the relative amount of water inside and outside the carrot's cells.

✓ *Assessment*

Oral Why does a wilted plant become rigid again after it has been watered? The water diffuses into the plant's cells. Use **Performance Assessment in the Science Classroom,** p. 89.

1 Motivate

Bellringer Transparency

Display the Section Focus Transparency for Section 1. Use the accompanying Transparency Activity Master. L2

ELL

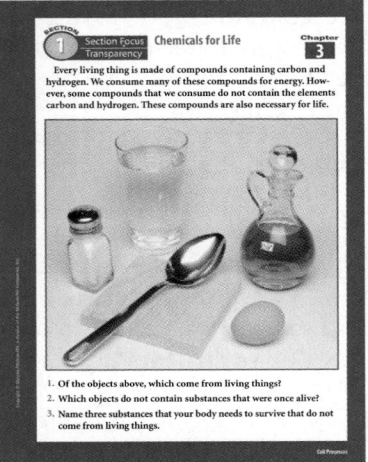

Tie to Prior Knowledge

Bring in labels from foods and cleaning products. Have students use the periodic table at the back of the book to determine what elements are in the compounds contained in these products.

SECTION

1 Chemistry of Life

As You Read

What You'll Learn

- **List** the differences among atoms, elements, molecules, and compounds.
- **Explain** the relationship between chemistry and life science.
- **Discuss** how organic compounds are different from inorganic compounds.

Vocabulary
mixture
organic compound
enzyme
inorganic compound

Why It's Important
You grow because of chemical reactions in your body.

Figure 1
An oxygen atom model shows the placement of electrons, protons, and neutrons.

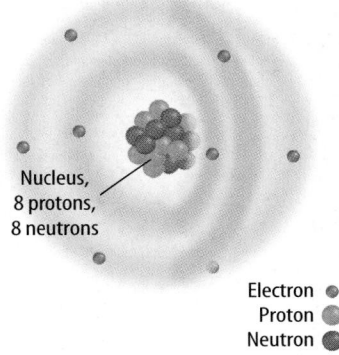

Oxygen atom

Nucleus,
8 protons,
8 neutrons

Electron
Proton
Neutron

The Nature of Matter

Think about everything that surrounds you—chairs, books, clothing, other students, and air. What are all these things made up of? You're right if you answer "matter and energy." Matter is anything that has mass and takes up space. Energy is anything that brings about change. Everything in your environment, including you, is made of matter. Energy can hold matter together or break it apart. For example, the food you eat is matter that is held together by chemical energy. When food is cooked, energy in the form of heat can break some of the bonds holding the matter in food together. **Table 1** compares matter and energy and gives some examples of each.

Atoms Whether it is solid, liquid, or gas, matter is made of atoms. **Figure 1** shows a model of an oxygen atom. At the center of an atom is a nucleus that contains protons and neutrons. Although they have nearly equal masses, a proton has a positive charge and a neutron has no charge. Outside the nucleus are electrons, each of which has a negative charge. It takes about 1,837 electrons to equal the mass of one proton. Electrons are important because they are the part of the atom that is involved in chemical reactions. Look at **Figure 1** again and you will see that an atom is mostly empty space. Energy holds the parts of an atom together.

Table 1 Matter and Energy	Definition	Examples
Matter	anything that has mass and takes up space	atoms, electrons, protons, and neutrons, living things, rocks, soil, and air
Energy	ability to cause change	sunlight, electricity, heat, chemical energy

98 CHAPTER 4 Cell Processes

Section ✓Assessment Planner

PORTFOLIO
Science Journal, p. 102
PERFORMANCE ASSESSMENT
MiniLAB, p. 103
Math Skills Activity, p. 104
Skill Builder Activities, p. 105
See page 124 for more options.

CONTENT ASSESSMENT
Section, p. 105
Challenge, p. 105
Chapter, pp. 124–125

Table 2 Elements That Make Up the Human Body		
Symbol	Element	Percent
O	Oxygen	65.0
C	Carbon	18.5
H	Hydrogen	9.5
N	Nitrogen	3.2
Ca	Calcium	1.5
P	Phosphorus	1.0
K	Potassium	0.4
S	Sulfur	0.3
Na	Sodium	0.2
Cl	Chlorine	0.2
Mg	Magnesium	0.1
	Other elements	0.1

Oxygen 65.0%

Carbon 18.5%

Hydrogen 9.5%

Nitrogen 3.2%

Calcium 1.5%

Phosphorus 1.0%
Other elements 1.3%

Elements When something is made up of only one kind of atom, it is called an element. An element can't be broken down into a simpler form by chemical reactions. The element oxygen is made up of only oxygen atoms, and hydrogen is made up of only hydrogen atoms. Scientists have given each element its own one- or two-letter symbol.

All elements are arranged in a chart known as the periodic table of elements. You can find this table at the back of this book. The table provides information about each element including its mass, how many protons it has, and its symbol.

Everything is made up of elements. Most things, including all living things, are made up of a combination of elements. Few things exist as pure elements. **Table 2** lists elements that are in the human body. What two elements make up most of your body?

 Reading Check *What types of things are made up of elements?*

Six of the elements listed in the table are important because they make up about 99 percent of living matter. The symbols for these elements are S, P, O, N, C, and H. Use **Table 2** to find the names of these elements.

Resource Manager

Chapter Resources Booklet
Transparency Activity, p. 42
Directed Reading for Content Mastery, pp. 17, 18
Note-taking Worksheets, pp. 31–33

Inclusion Strategies

Visually Impaired To help visually impaired students understand the structure of an atom, make a model of an atom. Outline the nucleus and energy levels by gluing yarn to cardboard. Use marshmallows for protons, gumdrops for neutrons, and red hots for electrons. Have students feel the model to compare the sizes of the different parts. **IS Kinesthetic**

2 Teach

The Nature of Matter

Teacher FYI

Elements are often given names by their discoverers. An element's name may reflect a property of the element. For example, chlorine, a greenish gas, comes from the Greek word *chloros*, which means "green." Some elements, such as ytterbium—discovered in Ytterby, Sweden—are named for the place where they were discovered. Other elements are named to honor someone. Einsteinium is named in honor of Albert Einstein, fermium for Enrico Fermi, and curium for Marie and Pierre Curie.

Activity

Play Tom Lehrer's *Elements Song*, which lists the elements. Have students listen to see how many elements they recognize.

Fun Fact

The symbols of many elements are derived from the first one or two letters of the Greek, Latin, or English name of the elements. Scientists worldwide use these symbols.

Text Question Answer

oxygen and carbon

Reading Check

Answer Everything is made up of elements or a combination of elements.

The Nature of Matter, continued

Caption Answer

Figure 2 A molecule, the smallest part of a molecular compound, is a group of atoms held together by chemical bonds.

Quick Demo

To demonstrate attraction between opposite charges, run a comb through your hair. Then bring the comb close to your hair without touching it. The hair is attracted to the comb because the negative charges on the comb are attracted to the positive charges of the hair.

Discussion

Have students predict what might happen when a negatively charged ion comes in contact with a positively charged ion. The two ions may bond to form an electrically neutral compound.

Figure 2
The words *atoms, molecules,* and *compounds* are used to describe substances. *How are they related to each other?*

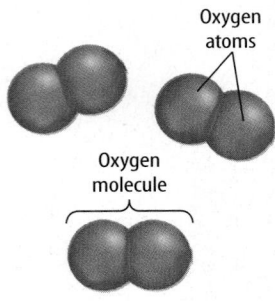

Oxygen atoms

Oxygen molecule

A Some elements, like oxygen, occur as molecules. These molecules contain atoms of the same element bonded together.

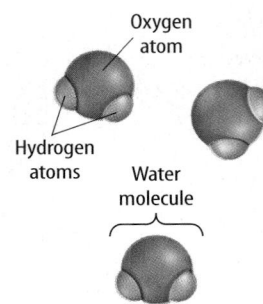

Oxygen atom

Hydrogen atoms

Water molecule

B Compounds also are composed of molecules. Molecules of compounds contain atoms of two or more different elements bonded together, as shown by these water molecules.

Compounds and Molecules

Suppose you make a pitcher of lemonade using a powdered mix and water. The water and the lemonade mix, which is mostly sugar, contain the elements oxygen and hydrogen. Yet, in one, they are part of a nearly tasteless liquid—water. In the other they are part of a sweet solid—sugar. How can the same elements be part of two materials that are so different? Water and sugar are compounds. Compounds are made up of two or more elements in exact proportions. For example, pure water, whether one milliliter of it or one million liters, is always made up of hydrogen atoms bonded to oxygen atoms in a ratio of two hydrogen atoms to one oxygen atom. Compounds have properties different from the elements they are made of. There are two types of compounds—molecular compounds and ionic compounds.

Molecular Compounds The smallest part of a molecular compound is a molecule. A molecule is a group of atoms held together by the energy of chemical bonds, as shown in **Figure 2.** When chemical reactions occur, chemical bonds break, atoms are rearranged, and new bonds form. The molecules produced are different from those that began the chemical reaction.

Molecular compounds form when different atoms share their outermost electrons. For example, two atoms of hydrogen each can share one electron on one atom of oxygen to form one molecule of water, as shown in **Figure 2B.** Water does not have the same properties as oxygen and hydrogen. Under normal conditions on Earth, oxygen and hydrogen are gases. Yet, water can be a liquid, a solid, or a gas. When hydrogen and oxygen combine, changes occur and a new substance forms.

Ions Atoms also combine because they've become positively or negatively charged. Atoms are usually neutral—they have no overall electric charge. When an atom loses an electron, it has more protons than electrons, so it becomes positively charged. When an atom gains an electron, it has more electrons than protons, so it becomes negatively charged. Electrically charged atoms—positive or negative—are called ions.

Inclusion Strategies

Hearing Impaired Provide discussion questions to hearing-impaired students before discussion. Assign another student to record the answers to the questions when they are given. L2
LS Auditory-Musical

Curriculum Connection

History Have students research alchemy. During the Middle Ages, alchemists searched for a way to turn common metals into gold. Though unsuccessful, they were precursors to modern chemists. Much of alchemy was based on Aristotle's idea that matter tries to reach perfection. Alchemists concluded that there must be a way to turn other metals into gold, since it was the "perfect" metal. L3 **LS** Linguistic

Ionic Compounds Ions of opposite charges attract one another to form electrically neutral compounds called ionic compounds. Table salt is made of sodium (Na^+) and chlorine (Cl^-) ions, as shown in **Figure 3B.** When they combine, a chlorine atom gains an electron from a sodium atom. The chlorine atom becomes a negatively charged ion, and the sodium atom becomes a positively charged ion. These oppositely charged ions then are attracted to each other and form the ionic compound sodium chloride, NaCl.

Ions are important in many life processes that take place in your body and in other organisms. For example, messages are sent along your nerves as potassium and sodium ions move in and out of nerve cells. Calcium ions are important in causing your muscles to contract. Ions also are involved in the transport of oxygen by your blood. The movement of some substances into and out of a cell would not be possible without ions.

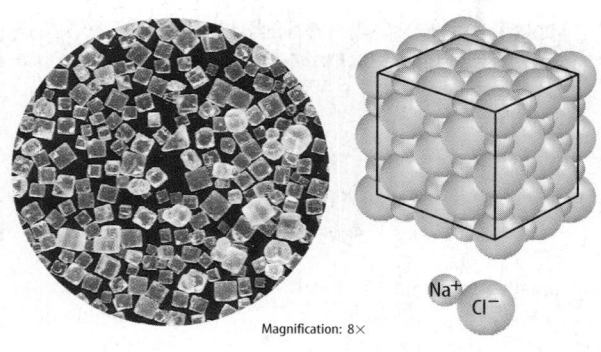

Magnification: 8×

A Magnified crystals of salt look like this.

B The salt crystal is held together by the attraction between sodium ions and chlorine ions.

Figure 3
Table salt, or sodium chloride (NaCl), is a crystal composed of sodium ions and chlorine ions held together by ionic bonds.

Mixtures

Some substances, such as a combination of sugar and salt, can't change each other or combine chemically. A **mixture** is a combination of substances in which individual substances retain their own properties. Mixtures can be solids, liquids, gases, or any combination of them.

✔ **Reading Check** *Why is a combination of sugar and salt said to be a mixture?*

Most chemical reactions in living organisms take place in mixtures called solutions. You've probably noticed the taste of salt when you perspire. Sweat is a solution of salt and water. In a solution, two or more substances are mixed evenly. A cell's cytoplasm is a solution of dissolved molecules and ions.

Living things also contain mixtures called suspensions. A suspension is formed when a liquid or a gas has another substance evenly spread throughout it. Unlike solutions, the substances in a suspension eventually sink to the bottom. If blood, shown in **Figure 4,** is left undisturbed, the red blood cells and white blood cells will sink gradually to the bottom. However, the pumping action of your heart constantly moves your blood and the blood cells remain suspended.

Figure 4
When a test tube of whole blood is left standing, the blood cells sink in the watery plasma.

SECTION 1 Chemistry of Life **101**

Resource Manager

Chapter Resources Booklet
Enrichment, p. 28

Inclusion Strategies

Gifted Mark lines on a glass jar with a glass-marking pen, indicating the one-cup and two-cup levels. Pour 1 cup of hot water into the jar. Add 1 cup of sugar. Stir until the sugar dissolves. Ask why there are not two cups of solution. The sugar takes up the spaces between the particles of water. L3 **IS** **Logical-Mathematical**

Teacher FYI

The two most common bonds in compounds are covalent and ionic. In covalent bonds, atoms share outermost electrons. In ionic bonds, oppositely charged ions are attracted to one another.

Mixtures

Quick Demo

Demonstrate mixtures and compounds. Mix baking soda with darker sand. Point out the different, distinct parts of the mixture. Then mix baking soda with vinegar in a clear container. The bubbles indicate that a new compound—carbon dioxide—has formed. **NOTE:** Make sure students understand that formation of bubbles does not *always* indicate that a chemical reaction has taken place. For example, the bubbles in soda indicate carbon dioxide is coming out of the mixture, not that a new substance is being formed.

✔ **Reading Check**

Answer It is a combination of two substances, each of which retains its own properties when combined with the other.

Visual Learning

Figure 4 Have students identify the visibly separate parts in the test tube. **What is the transparent substance in the tube?** plasma **What is the concentrated substance at the bottom of the tube?** red and white blood cells **Describe what would happen if the tube was shaken.** The blood cells and plasma would mix, forming a suspension. This suspension is blood.

Organic Compounds

Activity

Display a Food Guide Pyramid and discuss the types of organic compounds represented by foods in each group. Ask students to use this information to create a bulletin board display of foods rich in carbohydrates, lipids, and proteins. Have students illustrate the display with pictures of the foods.

Fun Fact

A paste made of meat tenderizer and water is often used to treat bee and jellyfish stings. An enzyme in the meat tenderizer helps to break down the proteins in the venom, making the area less painful.

Table 3 Organic Compounds Found in Living Things

	Carbohydrates	Lipids	Proteins	Nucleic Acids
Elements	carbon, hydrogen, and oxygen	carbon, oxygen, hydrogen, and phosphorus	carbon, oxygen, hydrogen, nitrogen, and sulfur	carbon, oxygen, hydrogen, nitrogen, and phosphorus
Examples	sugars, starch, and cellulose	fats, oils, waxes, phospholipids, and cholesterol	enzymes, skin, and hair	DNA and RNA
Function	supply energy for cell processes; form plant structures; short-term energy storage	store large amounts of energy long term; form boundaries around cells	regulate cell processes and build cell structures	carry hereditary information; used to make proteins

SCIENCE Online

Research Air is a mixture of many things. Weather forecasts often include information about air quality. Visit the Glencoe Science Web site at **science.glencoe.com** for more information about air quality. In your Science Journal list some things that may be measured when testing air quality.

Organic Compounds

You and all living things are made up of compounds that are classified as organic or inorganic. Rocks and other nonliving things contain inorganic compounds, but most do not contain large amounts of organic compounds. **Organic compounds** always contain carbon and hydrogen and usually are associated with living things. One exception would be nonliving things that are products of living things. For example, coal contains organic compounds because it was formed from dead and decaying plants. Organic molecules can contain hundreds or even thousands of atoms that can be arranged in many ways. **Table 3** compares the four groups of organic compounds that make up all living things—carbohydrates, lipids, proteins, and nucleic acids.

Carbohydrates Carbohydrates are organic molecules that supply energy for cell processes. Sugars and starches are carbohydrates that cells use for energy. Some carbohydrates also are important parts of cell structures. For example, a carbohydrate called cellulose is an important part of plant cells.

Lipids Another type of organic compound found in living things is a lipid. Lipids do not mix with water. Lipids such as fats and oils store and release even larger amounts of energy than carbohydrates do. One type of lipid, the phospholipid, is a major part of cell membranes.

Science Journal

CFCs Have students research and summarize in their Science Journals the organic compounds known as chlorofluorocarbons (CFCs). Summaries should include a description of the composition of these compounds, their use as refrigerants, and a description of how the use of these substances has impacted the environment. P

SCIENCE Online
Internet Addresses

Explore the Glencoe Science Web site at **science.glencoe.com** to find out more about topics in this section.

Proteins Organic compounds called proteins have many important functions in living organisms. They are made up of smaller molecules called amino acids. Proteins are the building blocks of many structures in organisms. Your muscles contain large amounts of protein. Proteins are scattered throughout cell membranes. Certain proteins called **enzymes** regulate nearly all chemical reactions in cells.

Nucleic Acids Large organic molecules that store important coded information in cells are called nucleic acids. One nucleic acid, deoxyribonucleic acid, or DNA—genetic material—is found in all cells. It carries information that directs each cell's activities. Another nucleic acid, ribonucleic acid, or RNA, is needed to make enzymes and other proteins.

Inorganic Compounds

Most **inorganic compounds** are made from elements other than carbon. Generally, inorganic molecules contain fewer atoms than organic molecules. Inorganic compounds are the source for many elements needed by living things. For example, plants take up inorganic compounds from the soil. These inorganic compounds can contain the elements nitrogen, phosphorus, and sulfur. Many foods that you eat contain inorganic compounds. **Table 4** shows some of the inorganic compounds that are important to you. One of the most important inorganic compounds for living things is water.

Table 4 Some Inorganic Compounds Important in Humans

Compound	Use in Body
Water	makes up most of the blood; most chemical reactions occur in water
Calcium phosphate	gives strength to bones
Hydrochloric acid	breaks down foods in the stomach
Sodium bicarbonate	helps the digestion of food to occur
Salts containing sodium, chlorine, and potassium	important in sending messages along nerves

Mini LAB

Determining How Enzymes Work

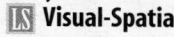

Procedure
1. Get two small cups of **prepared gelatin** from your teacher. Do not eat or drink anything in lab.
2. On the gelatin in one of the cups, place a piece of **fresh pineapple.**
3. Let both cups stand undisturbed during your class period. Wash your hands when you are done.
4. Observe what happens to the gelatin.

Analysis
1. What effect did the piece of fresh pineapple have on the gelatin?
2. What does fresh pineapple contain that caused it to have the effect on the gelatin you observed?
3. Why do the preparation directions on a box of gelatin dessert tell you not to mix it with fresh pineapple?

Mini LAB

Purpose to observe how enzymes affect gelatin L1

LS Visual-Spatial

Materials two small cups of prepared gelatin, 1 slice of fresh pineapple

Teaching Strategies
- To prepare gelatin, add only half the amount of water indicated on the gelatin package.
- After students add pineapple to one cup, allow both cups of gelatin to sit overnight.

Analysis
1. The gelatin under the fresh pineapple turned to a liquid.
2. an enzyme
3. The gelatin would not solidify if in contact with fresh pineapple.

Assessment

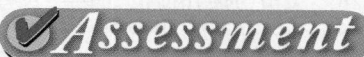

Performance Have students design an experiment to show conclusively that fresh pineapple contains enzymes that keep gelatin from becoming solid. They can repeat the experiment using canned pineapple. Use **PASC,** p. 95.

Inorganic Compounds

Teacher FYI

Life on Earth could not have evolved without water. Wherever life is found, water is found. Life is found in water at all temperatures. Bacteria can live under snow and in the near-boiling water of hot springs.

Resource Manager

Chapter Resources Booklet
MiniLAB, p. 3
Reinforcement, p. 25

Curriculum Connection

Health Provide students with copies of the periodic table. Ask them to research which elements are important for good health. They can find this information on food labels, in reference books, and on the Internet. Ask students to shade each element they discover on the table and to share their results with the class. L2

 **Interpersonal**

Inorganic Compounds, continued

Quick Demo

Display different liquids, such as a glass of fruit juice, a jar of paint, a bottle of oil, a beaker of alcohol, and a glass of water. Ask which substance is unique. Explain that water is unique, as it contains chemical and physical properties seen in no other substance. It is liquid at temperatures found on most of Earth's surface. Unlike most other substances, water expands when it freezes. In addition, water is the most common solvent in the world. **IS Visual-Spatial**

Make a Model

Have students make a model of a water molecule. They may use foam balls or colored marshmallows to represent the atoms, and toothpicks to hold them together. L2 **IS Kinesthetic**

Math Skills Activity

National Math Standards

Correlation to Mathematics Objectives
1, 2, 4, 6, 8, 9

Answer to Practice Problem

Calculate the infant's water weight and the adult's water weight, then subtract to find the difference.

Infant: $78/100 = x \div 3.2$ kg
$x = (78 \times 3.2) \div 100$
$x = 2.496$ kg of water;
Adult: $60 \div 100 = x \div 95$ kg
$x = (60 \times 95) \div 100$
$x = 57$ kg of water;
Difference: 57 kg $- 2.496$ kg
$= 54.504$ kg

Importance of Water Some scientists hypothesize that life began in the water of Earth's ancient oceans. Chemical reactions might have occurred that produced organic molecules. Similar chemical reactions can take place in cells in your body.

Living things are composed of more than 50 percent water and depend on water to survive. You can live for weeks without food but only for a few days without water. **Figure 5** shows where water is found in your body. Although seeds and spores of plants, fungi, and bacteria can exist without water, they must have water if they are to grow and reproduce. All the chemical reactions in living things take place in water solutions, and most organisms use water to transport materials through their bodies. For example, many animals have blood that is mostly water and moves materials. Plants use water to move minerals and sugars between the roots and leaves.

Math Skills Activity

Calculating the Importance of Water

All life on Earth depends on water for survival. Water is the most vital part of humans and other animals. It is required for all of the chemical processes that keep us alive.

Example Problem

At least 60% of an adult human body consists of water. If an adult man weighs 90 kg, how many kilograms of water does his body contain?

Solution

1 *This is what you know:*   adult human body = 60% water
   man = 90 kg

2 *This is what you want to find:*   60% of 90 kg

3 *This is the equation you need to use:* $60/100 = x/90$

4 *Solve the equation for* x: $x = (60 \times 90)/100$
   $x = 54$ kg

Check your answer by dividing your answer by 90, then multiplying by 100. Do you get 60%?

Practice Problem

A human body at birth consists of 78% water. This percent gradually decreases to 60% in an adult. Assume a baby weighed 3.2 kg at birth, and grew into an adult weighing 95 kg. Calculate the approximate number of kilograms of water the human gained.

For more help, refer to the Math Skill Handbook.

104 **CHAPTER 4** Cell Processes

Resource Manager

Chapter Resources Booklet
   Transparency Activity, pp. 45–46
Mathematics Skill Activities, p. 5
Science Inquiry Labs, pp. 43, 47

Curriculum Connection

Art Have students cut out pictures from magazines that illustrate water use by organisms, in industry, and in the environment. Then, have each student make a water collage using the pictures they chose. Display collages in the classroom. L1 **IS Visual-Spatial**

Characteristics of Water

The atoms of a water molecule are arranged in such a way that the molecule has areas with different charges. Water molecules are like magnets. The negative part of a water molecule is attracted to the positive part of another water molecule just like the north pole of a magnet is attracted to the south pole of another magnet. This attraction, or force, between water molecules is why a film forms on the surface of water. The film is strong enough to support small insects because the forces between water molecules are stronger than the force of gravity on the insect.

When heat is added to any substance, its molecules begin to move faster. Because water molecules are so strongly attracted to each other, the temperature of water changes slowly. The large percentage of water in living things acts like an insulator. The water in a cell helps keep its temperature constant, which allows life-sustaining chemical reactions to take place.

You've seen ice floating on water. When water freezes, ice crystals form. In the crystals, each water molecule is spaced at a certain distance from all the others. Because this distance is greater in frozen water than in liquid water, ice floats on water. Bodies of water freeze from the top down. The floating ice provides insulation from extremely cold temperatures and allows living things to survive in the cold water under the ice.

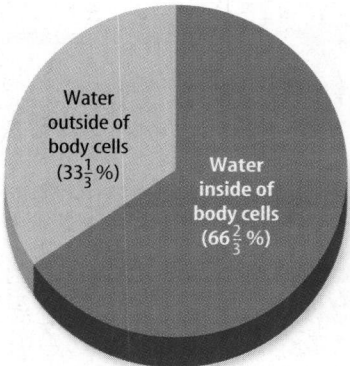

Water outside of body cells ($33\frac{1}{3}$ %)

Water inside of body cells ($66\frac{2}{3}$ %)

Figure 5
About two thirds of your body's water is located within your body's cells. Water helps maintain the cells' shapes and sizes. One third of your body's water is outside of your body's cells.

③ Assess

Reteach

Display carbon compounds such as starch, soap, vinegar, and alcohol. Ask students to explain why these are considered to be organic compounds. They all contain carbon and hydrogen.
LS **Logical-Mathematical**

Challenge

If you were on a space mission looking for signs of life on another planet, what elements would you search for and why? Possible response: carbon, hydrogen, oxygen, nitrogen, sulfur, and phosphorus; these elements make up about 99% of all living things.

✔ Assessment

Portfolio Have students write an essay to explain why water is important to them. Ask them to think about their family's use of water each day and what would happen if they were asked to cut their water usage. Use **Performance Assessment in the Science Classroom,** p. 157.

Section Assessment

1. What are the similarities and differences between atoms and molecules?

2. What is the difference between organic and inorganic compounds? Give an example of each type of compound.

3. What are the four types of organic compounds found in all living things?

4. Why does life as we know it depend on water?

5. **Think Critically** If you mix salt, sand, and sugar with water in a small jar, will the resulting mixture be a suspension, a solution, or both?

Skill Builder Activities

6. **Interpreting Scientific Illustrations**
Carefully observe **Figure 1** and determine how many protons, neutrons, and electrons an atom of oxygen has. **For more help, refer to the** Science Skill Handbook.

7. **Using an Electronic Spreadsheet**
Research to find the percentage of elements that make up Earth's crust. Make a spreadsheet that includes this information and the information in **Table 2.** Create a circle graph for each set of percentages. **For more help, refer to the** Technology Skill Handbook.

Answers to Section Assessment

1. Possible answer: similarities=both are made of smaller units. Atoms consist of protons, neutrons, and electrons, and molecules consist of two or more atoms; differences= molecules are larger than atoms. Molecules can be formed or broken down in a chemical reaction but atoms cannot.

2. Organic compounds, such as lipids, contain carbon; most inorganic compounds, such as water, do not.

3. lipids, carbohydrates, proteins, and nucleic acids

4. Most life processes can occur only in water solutions.

5. Salt and sugar dissolve in water forming a solution; if shaken, sand will spread throughout the solution and form a suspension.

6. 8 protons, 8 neutrons, and 8 electrons

7. Human body graph: 65% oxygen, 18.5% carbon, 9.5% hydrogen, 3.2% nitrogen, 1.5% calcium, and 2.3% other elements; Earth's crust graph: 46.6% oxygen, 27.7% silicon, 8.1% aluminum, 5.0% iron, 3.6% calcium, 2.8% sodium, 2.6% potassium, 2.1% magnesium, 1.5% other elements

Bellringer Transparency

Display the Section Focus
Transparency for Section 2.
Use the accompanying Trans-
parency Activity Master. L2
ELL

Tie to Prior Knowledge

Use an overhead transparency
to review the parts of a cell.
Point out that the cell membrane helps a cell maintain a
balance between the cell and
materials, such as water, salt,
and sugars, in its environment.

SECTION 2 Moving Cellular Materials

As You Read

What You'll Learn

- **Describe** the function of a selectively permeable membrane.
- **Explain** how the processes of
diffusion and osmosis move
molecules in living cells.
- **Explain** how passive transport and
active transport differ.

Vocabulary

passive transport   active transport
diffusion   endocytosis
equilibrium   exocytosis
osmosis

Why It's Important

Cell membranes control the substances that enter and leave the cells
in your body.

Passive Transport

"Close that window. Do you want to let in all the bugs and
leaves?" How do you prevent unwanted things from coming
through the window? As seen in **Figure 6,** a window screen provides the protection needed to keep unwanted things outside. It
also allows some things to pass into or out of the room like air,
unpleasant odors, or smoke.

Cells take in food, oxygen, and other substances from their
environments. They also release waste materials into their environments. A cell has a membrane around it that works for a cell
like a window screen does for a room. A cell's membrane is selectively permeable (PUR mee uh bul). It allows some things to
enter or leave the cell while keeping other things outside or
inside the cell. The window screen also is selectively permeable
based on the size of its openings.

Things can move through a cell membrane in several ways.
Which way things move depends on the size of the molecules or
particles, the path taken through the membrane, and whether or
not energy is used. The movement of substances through the
cell membrane without the input of energy is called **passive
transport.** Three types of passive transport can occur. The type
depends on what is moving through the cell membrane.

Figure 6
A cell membrane, like a screen,
will let some things through
more easily than others. Air gets
through a screen, but insects are
kept out.

106 CHAPTER 4 Cell Processes

Section ✔*Assessment* Planner

PORTFOLIO
Visual Learning, p. 111
PERFORMANCE ASSESSMENT
Try at Home MiniLAB, p. 107
Skill Builder Activities, p. 110
See page 124 for more options.

CONTENT ASSESSMENT
Section, p. 110
Challenge, p. 110
Chapter, pp. 124–125

Figure 7
Like all other cells in your body, cells in your toes need oxygen.

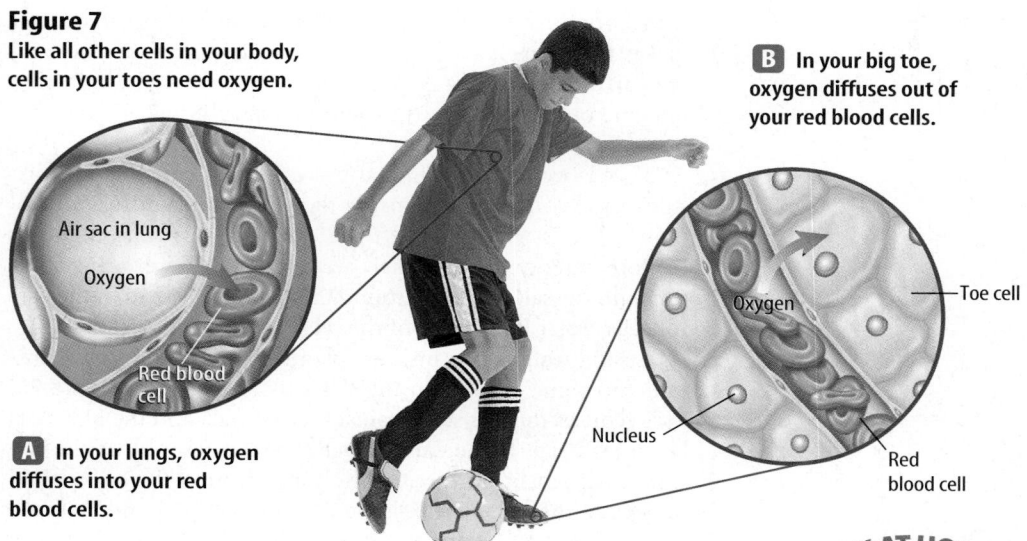

B In your big toe, oxygen diffuses out of your red blood cells.

Air sac in lung

Oxygen

Red blood cell

A In your lungs, oxygen diffuses into your red blood cells.

Oxygen

Toe cell

Nucleus

Red blood cell

Diffusion Molecules in solids, liquids, and gases move constantly and randomly. You might smell perfume when you sit near or as you walk past someone who is wearing it. This is because perfume molecules randomly move throughout the air. This random movement of molecules from an area where there is relatively more of them into an area where there is relatively fewer of them is called **diffusion**. Diffusion is one type of cellular passive transport. Molecules of a substance will continue to move from one area into another until the relative number of these molecules is equal in the two areas. When this occurs, **equilibrium** is reached and diffusion stops. After equilibrium occurs, it is maintained because molecules continue to move.

✔ **Reading Check** *What is equilibrium?*

Every cell in your body uses oxygen. When you breathe, how does oxygen get from your lungs to cells in your big toe? Oxygen is carried throughout your body in your blood by the red blood cells. When your blood is pumped from your heart to your lungs, your red blood cells do not contain much oxygen. However, your lungs have more oxygen molecules than your red blood cells do, so the oxygen molecules diffuse into your red blood cells from your lungs, as shown in **Figure 7A.** When the blood reaches your big toe, there are more oxygen molecules in your red blood cells than in your big toe cells. The oxygen diffuses from your red blood cells and into your big toe cells, as shown in **Figure 7B.**

Observing Diffusion

Procedure 🥽 🧪 👕
1. Use **two clean glasses** of equal size. Label one "hot," then fill it until half full with **very warm water.** Label the other "cold," then fill it until half full with **cold water. WARNING:** *Do not use boiling hot water.*
2. Add one drop of **food coloring** to each glass. Carefully release the drop just at the water's surface to avoid splashing the water.
3. Observe the glasses. Record your observations immediately and again after 15 min.

Analysis
1. Describe what happens when food coloring is added to each glass.
2. How does temperature affect the rate of diffusion?

---

2 Teach

Passive Transport

Purpose to investigate the effect of temperature on diffusion rate L1 ELL COOP LEARN
LS Logical-Mathematical
Materials 2 clean glasses, hot water, cold water, food coloring, dropper, marker or wax pencil, clock, labels

Teaching Strategies
- Have students record how long it takes the food coloring to diffuse evenly throughout each beaker.
- Caution students not to move the water-filled beakers.

Analysis
1. The food coloring spreads throughout the water; it spreads faster in the hot water.
2. Heat increases the rate of diffusion.

✔ *Assessment*

Performance To further assess understanding of the effect of temperature on diffusion, have students repeat the activity using ice water instead of hot water. Use **PASC**, p. 105.

✔ **Reading Check**

Answer when the relative number of molecules of a substance is equal in the two areas

---

Resource Manager

Chapter Resources Booklet
Transparency Activity, p. 43
Directed Reading for Content Mastery, p. 18
MiniLAB, p. 4

Teacher FYI

A permeable membrane allows all molecules to pass through. An impermeable membrane doesn't allow any to pass. Only some molecules can pass through a semipermeable membrane—usually only small molecules that can pass through quickly.

Passive Transport,
continued

Quick Demo

To demonstrate a selectively permeable membrane, pour different substances (i.e. sand, salt, marbles, water) through a kitchen strainer. Select some substances that will pass through the strainer, and some that will not. **LS Visual-Spatial**

Discussion

Why do salty foods make you thirsty? The salt present in the food causes water to leave your cells; therefore, your body needs water to replace what your cells have lost.

Extension

Fertilizers contain chemical salts. If fertilizers are placed on plants and it doesn't rain soon after, the plants may die. Have students investigate and report on the use of fertilizers by interviewing farmers or lawn-maintenance workers. **L2 LS Interpersonal**

✔ Reading Check

Answer Because there are relatively fewer water molecules in the salt solution around the carrot cells than inside the carrot cells, water leaves the carrot and moves into the salt solution.

Osmosis—The Diffusion of Water Remember that water makes up a large part of living matter. Cells contain water and are surrounded by water. Water molecules move by diffusion into and out of cells. The diffusion of water through a cell membrane is called **osmosis.**

If cells weren't surrounded by water that contains few dissolved substances, water inside the cells would diffuse out of them. This is why water left the carrot cells in this chapter's Explore Activity. Because there were relatively fewer water molecules in the salt solution around the carrot cells than in the carrot cells, water moved out of the cells and into the salt solution.

Losing water from inside a plant cell causes the cell membrane to come away from the cell wall, as shown in **Figure 8A.** This reduces the pressure against the cell wall, and the plant cell becomes limp. If the carrot sticks were taken out of the salt water and put in pure water, the water around the cells would move into the cells. The cells would fill with water and their cell membranes would press against their cell walls, as shown in **Figure 8B.** Pressure would increase and the plant cells would become firm. That is why the carrot sticks would be crisp again.

✔ Reading Check   *Why do carrots in salt water become limp?*

Osmosis also takes place in animal cells. If animal cells were placed in pure water, they too would swell up. However, animal cells are different from plant cells. Just like an overfilled water balloon, animal cells will burst if too much water enters the cell.

Figure 8
Cells respond to differences between the amount of water inside and outside the cell.

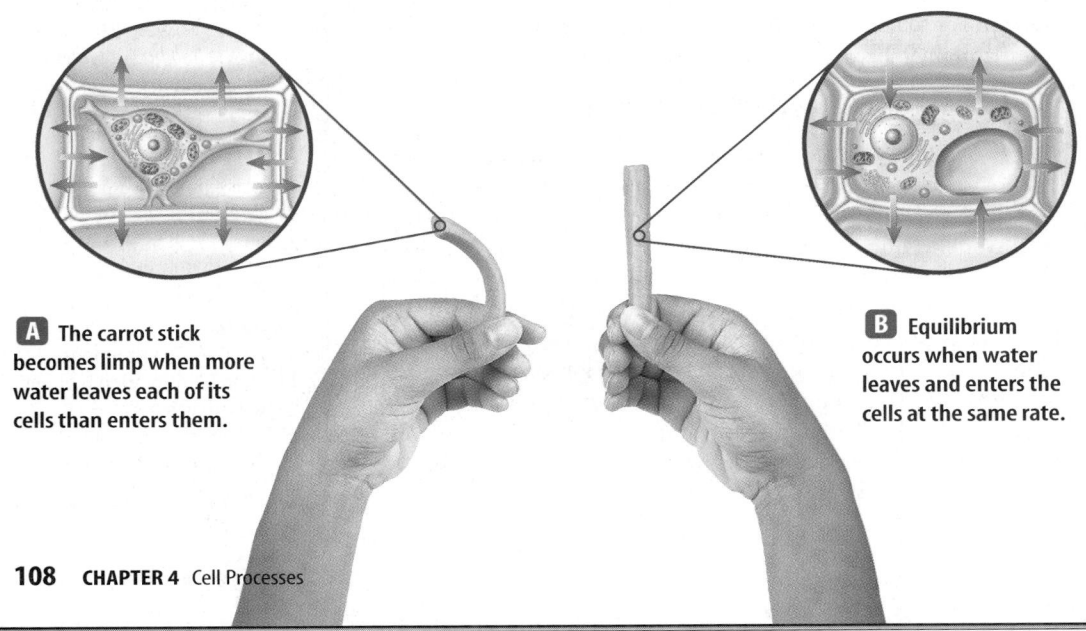

A The carrot stick becomes limp when more water leaves each of its cells than enters them.

B Equilibrium occurs when water leaves and enters the cells at the same rate.

LAB DEMONSTRATION

Purpose to observe diffusion

Materials self-sealing plastic sandwich bag, cooked rice, tincture of iodine, 8-oz. clear plastic cups, tablespoon

Preparation Half-fill the plastic cups with water and add 6 drops of tincture of iodine. Cook rice.

Procedure Seal a sandwich bag containing 2 tablespoons of rice, and place it into the water that contains iodine. Observe after 10 minutes.

Expected Outcome Iodine molecules will move through the plastic bag, turning the rice blue-black. Iodine always turns blue-black in the presence of starch.

✔ Assessment

What did you observe? The rice inside the plastic bag turned blue-black. **Explain what occurred.** Iodine molecules diffused from an area where there was a large number of iodine molecules (outside the bag) to an area where there were few iodine molecules (inside the bag).

Facilitated Diffusion

Cells take in many substances. Some substances pass easily through the cell membrane by diffusion. Other substances, such as glucose molecules, are so large that they can enter the cell only with the help of molecules in the cell membrane called transport proteins. This process, a type of passive transport, is known as facilitated diffusion. Have you ever used the drive through at a fast-food restaurant to get your meal? The transport proteins in the cell membrane are like the drive-through window at the restaurant. The window lets you get food out of the restaurant and put money into the restaurant. Similarly, transport proteins are used to move substances into and out of the cell.

Active Transport

Imagine that a football game is over and you leave the stadium. As soon as you get outside of the stadium, you remember that you left your jacket on your seat. Now you have to move against the crowd coming out of the stadium to get back in to get your jacket. Which required more energy—leaving the stadium with the crowd or going back to get your jacket? Something similar to this happens in cells.

Sometimes, a substance is needed inside a cell even though the amount of that substance inside the cell is already greater than the amount outside the cell. For example, root cells require minerals from the soil. The roots of the plant in **Figure 9** already might contain more of those mineral molecules than the surrounding soil does. The tendency is for mineral molecules to move out of the root by diffusion or facilitated diffusion. But they need to move back across the cell membrane and into the cell just like you had to move back into the stadium. When an input of energy is required to move materials through a cell membrane, **active transport** takes place.

Active transport involves transport proteins, just as facilitated diffusion does. In active transport, a transport protein binds with the needed particle and cellular energy is used to move it through the cell membrane. When the particle is released, the transport protein can move another needed particle through the membrane.

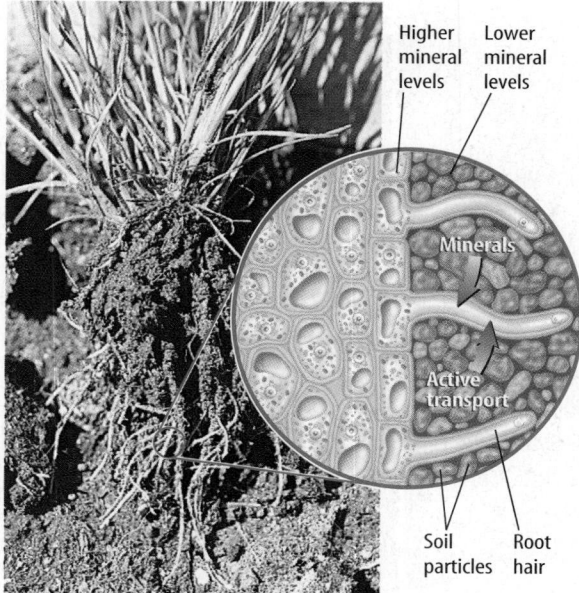

Higher mineral levels
Lower mineral levels
Minerals
Active transport
Soil particles
Root hair

Figure 9
Some root cells have extensions called root hairs that may be 5 mm to 8 mm long. Minerals are taken in by active transport through the cell membranes of root hairs.

Health
INTEGRATION

Transport proteins are important to your health. Sometimes transport proteins are missing or do not function correctly. What would happen if proteins that transport cholesterol across membranes were missing? Cholesterol is an important lipid used by your cells. Write your ideas in your Science Journal.

Active Transport

Use an Analogy

Have students compare active and passive transport with the energy they must exert to get a bicycle to the top of a hill and then ride it back down. Students must exert energy to get the bicycle up the hill. In the same way, the cell uses energy to move substances from areas of low concentration to areas of high concentration. Students do not need to exert energy to ride the bicycle down the hill. In passive transport, cells do not have to use energy to move substances from areas of high concentration to areas of low concentration.
LS Logical-Mathematical

Text Question Answer

going back for the jacket

Teacher FYI

Cell membranes contain spaces through which some substances (water molecules, mineral ions, sugar molecules) can easily pass. The spaces are too small for most proteins and other large molecules to pass through. Some ions cannot pass through membranes due to their charge. These move into a cell via channels or active transport.

Health
INTEGRATION

Cholesterol would not be transported to different areas of the body. Without cholesterol, the body could not synthesize bile acids, steroid hormones, or Vitamin D.

Cultural Diversity

Preserving Foods A practical use of osmosis is the drying and salting of food. Have students report on the processes and uses of dried and salted foods in Native American and other cultures. For example, the French developed a vegetable dehydrator in 1795. Both processes remove water from cells in order to preserve the food. In drying, water evaporates. In salting, a salt solution is used to remove water from cells.

Resource Manager

Chapter Resources Booklet
Enrichment, p. 29
Reinforcement, p. 26
Lab Activity, pp. 9–10

Endocytosis and Exocytosis

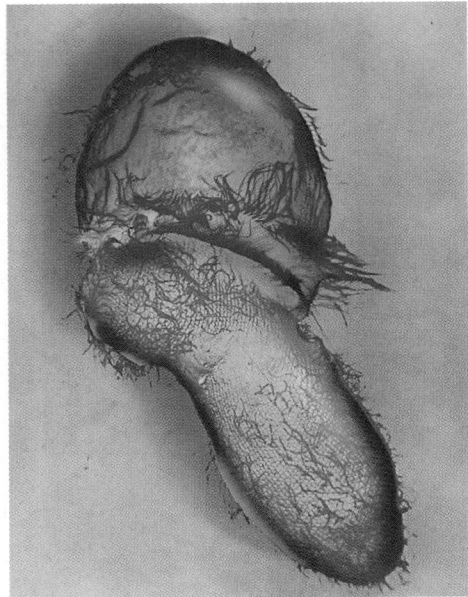

Magnification: 1400×

Figure 10
One-celled organisms like this egg-shaped one can take in other one-celled organisms using endocytosis.

Endocytosis and Exocytosis

Some molecules and particles are too large to move by diffusion or to use the cell membrane's transport proteins. Large protein molecules and bacteria, for example, can enter a cell when they are surrounded by the cell membrane. The cell membrane folds in on itself, enclosing the item in a sphere called a vesicle. Vesicles are transport and storage structures in a cell's cytoplasm. The sphere pinches off, and the resulting vesicle enters the cytoplasm. A similar thing happens when you poke your finger into a partially inflated balloon. Your finger is surrounded by the balloon in much the same way that the protein molecule is surrounded by the cell membrane. This process of taking substances into a cell by surrounding it with the cell membrane is called **endocytosis** (en duh si TOH sus). Some one-celled organisms, as shown in **Figure 10,** take in food this way.

The contents of a vesicle may be released by the cell using a process called **exocytosis** (ek soh si TOH sus). Exocytosis occurs in the opposite way that endocytosis does. The membrane of the vesicle fuses with the cell's membrane, and the vesicle's contents are released. Cells in your stomach use this process to release chemicals that help digest food. The different ways that materials may enter or leave a cell are summarized in **Figure 11.**

Section ② Assessment

1. Explain how cell membranes are selectively permeable.
2. Compare and contrast the processes of osmosis and diffusion.
3. Identify the molecules that help substances move through the cell membrane during active transport and facilitated diffusion.
4. Why are endocytosis and exocytosis important processes to cells?
5. **Think Critically** Why are fresh fruits and vegetables sprinkled with water at produce markets?

Skill Builder Activities

6. **Concept Mapping** Make a network tree concept map to use as a study guide to help you tell the difference between passive transport and active transport. Begin with the phrase "Transport through membranes." **For more help, refer to the** Science Skill Handbook.
7. **Communicating** Seawater is saltier than tap water. In your Science Journal, explain why drinking large amounts of seawater would be dangerous to humans. **For more help, refer to the** Science Skill Handbook.

Figure 11

A flexible yet strong layer, the cell membrane is built of two layers of lipids (gold) pierced by protein "passageways" (purple). Molecules can enter or exit the cell by slipping between the lipids or through the protein passageways. Substances that cannot enter or exit the cell in these ways may be surrounded by the membrane and drawn into or expelled from the cell.

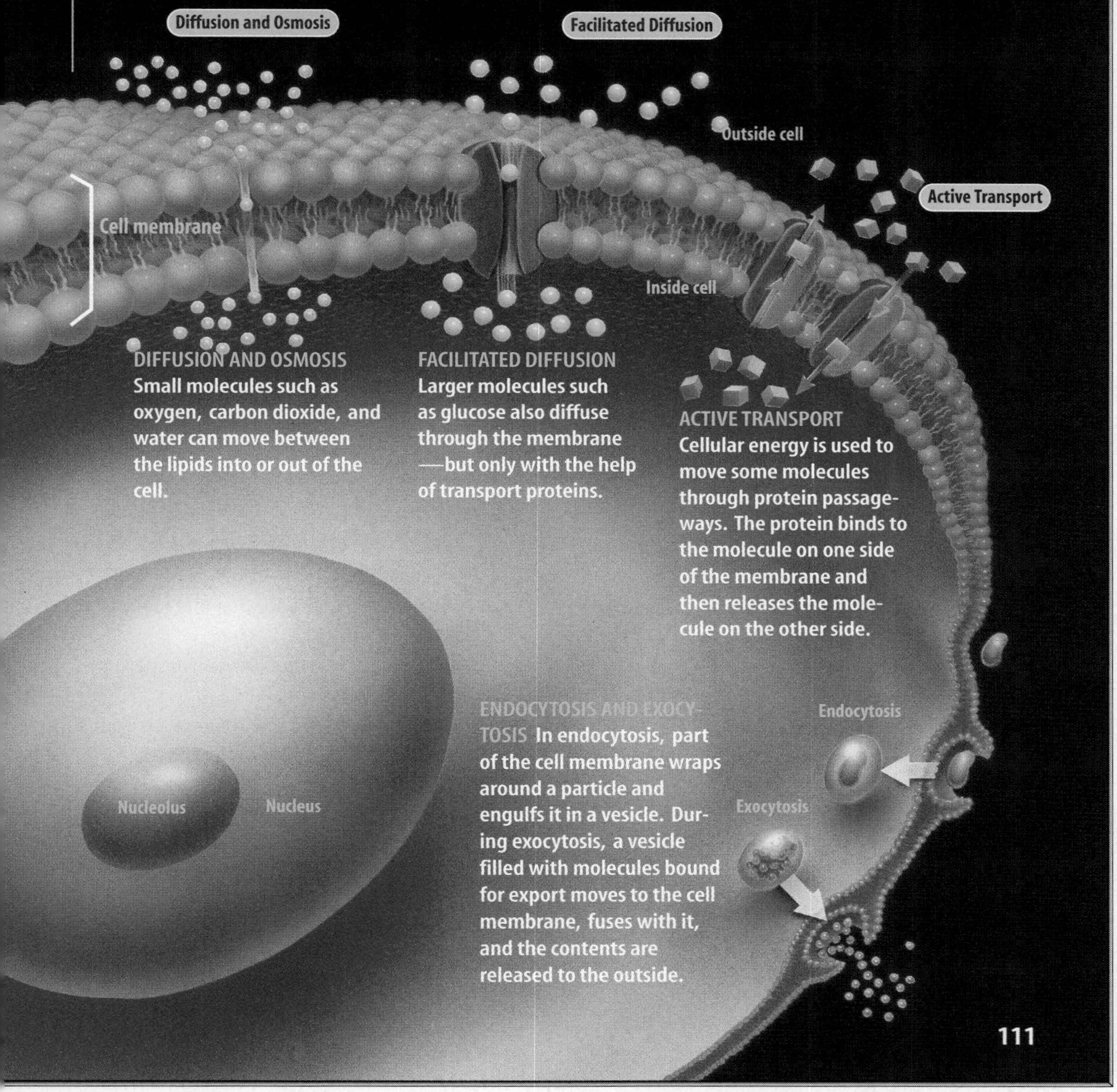

Diffusion and Osmosis

Facilitated Diffusion

Outside cell

Active Transport

Inside cell

Cell membrane

DIFFUSION AND OSMOSIS
Small molecules such as oxygen, carbon dioxide, and water can move between the lipids into or out of the cell.

FACILITATED DIFFUSION
Larger molecules such as glucose also diffuse through the membrane —but only with the help of transport proteins.

ACTIVE TRANSPORT
Cellular energy is used to move some molecules through protein passageways. The protein binds to the molecule on one side of the membrane and then releases the molecule on the other side.

ENDOCYTOSIS AND EXOCYTOSIS In endocytosis, part of the cell membrane wraps around a particle and engulfs it in a vesicle. During exocytosis, a vesicle filled with molecules bound for export moves to the cell membrane, fuses with it, and the contents are released to the outside.

Nucleolus Nucleus

Endocytosis

Exocytosis

111

Visual Learning

Figure 11 Have students make an outline from this figure of the steps a transport protein goes through to move substances into and out of cells. L2 IS **Visual-Spatial** P

Resource Manager

Life Science Critical Thinking/Problem Solving, p. 15

Visualizing Cell Membrane Transport

Have students examine the pictures and read the captions. Then ask the following questions.

Why do some substances move through the cell membrane through exocytosis and endocytosis instead of one of the other transport methods? These substances, which include proteins and nucleic acids, are too large to use the other methods. For example, cholesterol enters by endocytosis; neurotransmitters exit by exocytosis.

Which transport method(s) is like floating downstream? Which is like paddling upstream? Why? In diffusion (osmosis and facilitated diffusion), a substance moves from an area of higher concentration to an area of lower concentration. This does not require energy because it goes with the flow, like floating downstream. In active transport, the substance must go against the concentration gradient which, like paddling upstream, requires energy.

Activity

Have students make a model of a cell that illustrates one type of cell membrane transport. IS **Kinesthetic**

Extension

Challenge students to investigate transport proteins and the substances each transports. Have students make a card game to teach other students what they learned. IS **Logical-Mathematical**

Activity

Activity

BENCH TESTED

Purpose to observe and measure the amount of water diffusing through an egg membrane [L2]

LS **Logical-Mathematical**

Process Skills observing and inferring, measuring, communicating, recognizing cause and effect, forming operational definitions

Time Required 50 minutes to set up, 5 minutes each day to observe, 15 minutes to summarize

Alternate Materials Clean, empty food containers with lids may be used to hold the unshelled egg.

Teaching Strategy Cover raw eggs with vinegar. Leave undisturbed for two or three days until the shells dissolve.

Troubleshooting

• Remind students to handle unshelled eggs carefully to avoid breaking membranes.
• Thick syrup works better than thin syrup.
• Make sure students replace lids on containers when not in use.

Answers to Questions

1. water— increased in size; corn syrup—decreased in size
2. about 30 mL of water entered; about 40 mL of water left
3. The eggshell is not permeable to water and syrup.
4. cell membrane

✓ Assessment

Performance Have students place ten dried beans in water and let them remain overnight. Direct them to explain their observations. Use **PASC**, p. 97.

Observing Osmosis

It is difficult to see osmosis occurring in cells because most cells are so small. However, a few cells can be seen without the aid of a microscope. Try this activity to see how osmosis occurs in a large cell.

What You'll Investigate
How does osmosis occur in an egg cell?

Materials
unshelled egg*	distilled water (250 mL)
balance	light corn syrup (250 mL)
spoon	500-mL container

Goals
■ **Observe** osmosis in an egg cell.
■ **Determine** what affects osmosis.

Safety Precautions

Eggs may contain bacteria. Avoid touching your face. Wash your hands thoroughly when you are done.

*an egg whose shell has been dissolved by vinegar

Procedure

1. Copy the table below into your Science Journal and use it to record your data.

Egg Mass Data

	Beginning Egg Mass	Egg Mass After Two Days
Distilled water	Answers may vary.	Answers may vary.
Corn syrup	Answers may vary.	Answers may vary.

2. Obtain an unshelled egg from your teacher. Handle the egg gently. Use a balance to find the egg's mass and record it in the table.

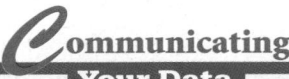

3. Place the egg in the container and add enough distilled water to cover it.

4. **Observe** the egg after 30 min, one day, and two days. After each observation, record the egg's appearance in your Science Journal.

5. After day two, remove the egg with a spoon and allow it to drain. Find the egg's mass and record it in the table.

6. Empty the container, then put the egg back in. Now add enough corn syrup to cover it. Repeat steps 4 and 5.

Conclude and Apply

1. **Explain** the difference between what happened to the egg in water and in corn syrup.

2. **Calculate** the mass of water that moved into and out of the egg.

3. **Hypothesize** why you used an unshelled egg for this investigation.

4. **Infer** what part of the egg controlled water's movement into and out of the egg.

Communicating Your Data

Compare your conclusions with those of other students in your class. **For more help, refer to the Science Skill Handbook.**

Resource Manager

Chapter Resources Booklet
  Activity Worksheet, pp. 5–6

Communicating Your Data

Students should discuss why their conclusions did or did not agree with those of other students.

SECTION 3

Energy for Life

Trapping and Using Energy

Think of all the energy that players use in a basketball game. Where does the energy come from? The simplest answer is "from the food they eat." The chemical energy stored in food is changed in cells into forms needed to perform all the activities necessary for life. In every cell, these changes involve chemical reactions. All of the activities of an organism involve chemical reactions in some way. The total of all chemical reactions in an organism is called **metabolism.**

The chemical reactions of metabolism need enzymes. What do enzymes do? Suppose you are hungry and decide to open a can of spaghetti. You use a can opener to open the can. Without a can opener, the spaghetti is unusable. The can of spaghetti changed because of the can opener, but the can opener did not change. The can opener can be used again later to open more cans of spaghetti. Enzymes in cells work something like can openers, as shown in **Figure 12.** The enzyme, like the can opener, causes a change, but the enzyme is not changed and is reusable. Unlike the can opener, which can only break things apart, enzymes also can cause molecules to join. Without the right enzymes, chemical reactions in cells cannot take place.

As You Read

What You'll Learn
- **List** the differences between producers and consumers.
- **Explain** how the processes of photosynthesis and respiration store and release energy.
- **Describe** how cells get energy from glucose through fermentation.

Vocabulary
metabolism   respiration
photosynthesis   fermentation

Why It's Important
Because of photosynthesis and respiration, you use the Sun's energy.

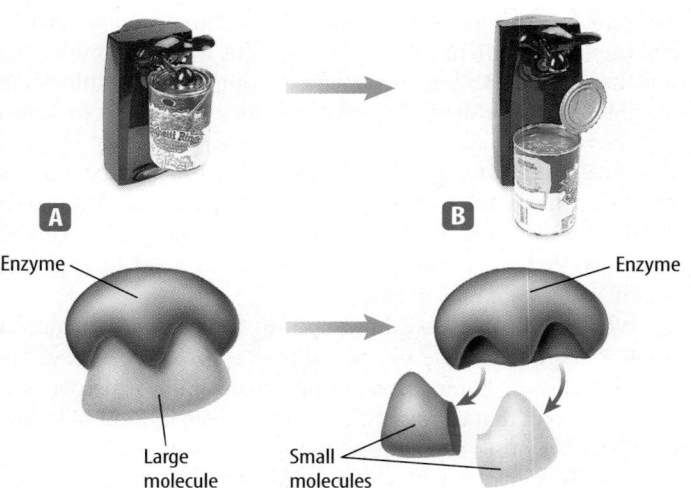

Figure 12
Enzymes are needed for most chemical reactions that take place in cells. **A** The enzyme attaches to the large molecule it will help change. **B** The enzyme causes the larger molecule to break down into two smaller molecules. Like the can opener, the enzyme is not changed and can be used again.

SECTION 3 Energy for Life **113**

SECTION 3

Energy for Life

1 Motivate

Bellringer Transparency

Display the Section Focus Transparency for Section 3. Use the accompanying Transparency Activity Master. L2
ELL

Tie to Prior Knowledge

Display pictures of people using energy—playing sports, gardening, working, and so on. Ask students to identify the source of this energy. chemical bonds in food Then ask where the energy in the food came from. It was derived from plants that captured the Sun's energy.

Section ✓Assessment Planner

PORTFOLIO
Visual Learning, p. 117
PERFORMANCE ASSESSMENT
Skill Builder Activities, p. 117
See page 124 for more options.

CONTENT ASSESSMENT
Section, p. 117
Challenge, p. 117
Chapter, pp. 124–125

Trapping and Using Energy

Activity

Pick a leaf from a plant that has been exposed to sunlight for a few hours. Submerge it in water. Observe the surface of the leaf. **What forms on the leaf? Why?** Bubbles; the leaf is giving off oxygen.

Use an Analogy

Compare the construction of a house to photosynthesis. Building a house is a physical process that requires the putting together of raw materials. Photosynthesis is a chemical process of putting raw materials together. They both require raw materials and result in a usable product. [IS] **Logical-Mathematical**

Caption Answer

Figure 13 carbon dioxide, water, light energy, and chlorophyll

IDENTIFYING Misconceptions

Some students may think that plants obtain food from the soil. Plants take in a variety of minerals and other substances from the soil, but these are not used as food. They are dissolved in water and absorbed through the plant's roots. Once absorbed, they are transported to structures in the plant where they are needed. The food of plants—glucose—is produced by the plant from carbon dioxide, water, and radiant energy in the chloroplasts of their cells.

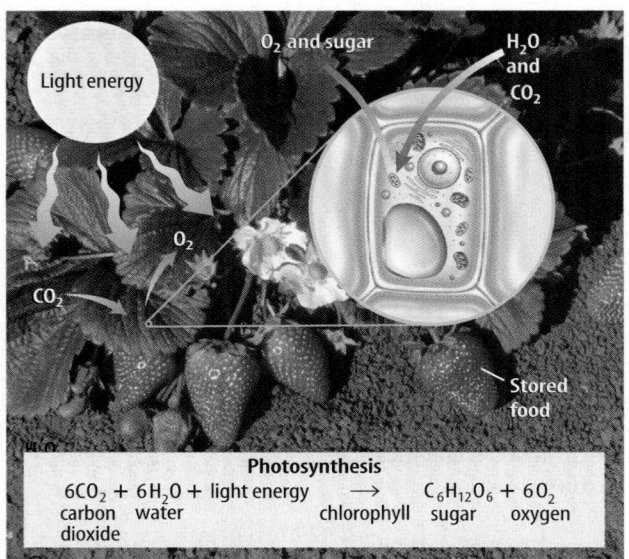

Photosynthesis

$$6CO_2 + 6H_2O + \text{light energy} \longrightarrow C_6H_{12}O_6 + 6O_2$$

carbon dioxide   water   chlorophyll   sugar   oxygen

Figure 13
Plants use photosynthesis to make food. *According to the chemical equation, what raw materials would the plant pictured need for photosynthesis?*

Photosynthesis Living things are divided into two groups—producers and consumers—based on how they obtain their food. Organisms that make their own food, such as plants, are called producers. Organisms that cannot make their own food are called consumers.

If you have ever walked barefoot across a sidewalk on a sunny summer day, you probably moved quickly because the sidewalk was hot. Sunlight energy was converted into thermal energy and heated the sidewalk. Plants and many other producers can convert sunlight energy into another kind of energy—chemical energy. The process they use is called photosynthesis. During **photosynthesis,** producers use light energy to make sugars, which can be used as food.

Producing Carbohydrates Producers that use photosynthesis are usually green because they contain a green pigment called chlorophyll (KLOR uh fihl). Chlorophyll and other pigments are used in photosynthesis to capture sunlight energy. In plant cells, these pigments are found in chloroplasts.

The captured sunlight energy is used to drive chemical reactions during which the raw materials, carbon dioxide and water, are used to produce sugar and oxygen. For plants, the raw materials come from air and soil. Some of the captured sunlight energy is stored in the chemical bonds that hold the sugar molecules together. **Figure 13** shows what happens during photosynthesis in a plant. Enzymes also are needed before these reactions can occur.

Storing Carbohydrates Plants make more sugar during photosynthesis than they need for survival. Excess sugar is changed and stored as starches or used to make other carbohydrates. Plants use these carbohydrates as food for growth, maintenance, and reproduction.

Why is photosynthesis important to consumers? Do you eat apples? Apple trees use photosynthesis to produce apples. Do you like cheese? Some cheese comes from milk, which is produced by cows that eat plants. Consumers take in food by eating producers or other consumers. No matter what you eat, photosynthesis was involved directly or indirectly in its production.

Inclusion Strategies

Gifted There are certain plants such as the Indian pipe (*Monotropa uniflora*) and dodder (*Cuscuta*) that lack chlorophyll. Have students research these plants and report to the class how they obtain food. Indian pipe is a saprophyte; it lives on the remains of dead organisms. Dodder is a parasite; it absorbs nourishment from a host plant. [L3]

Energy and Photosynthesis In their Science Journals, have students list all the foods they eat in one day. Have them to divide the list into two groups: (1) foods formed directly by photosynthesis, (2) foods not formed directly by photosynthesis. Use the lists to help students see that all food energy comes from photosynthesis, whether directly or indirectly.

Respiration Imagine that you get up late for school. You dress quickly, then run three blocks to school. When you get to school, you feel hot and are breathing fast. Why? Your muscle cells use a lot of energy when you run. To get this energy, muscle cells break down food. Some of the energy from the food is used when you move and some of it becomes thermal energy, which is why you feel warm or hot. Most cells also need oxygen to break down food. You were breathing fast because your body was working to get oxygen to your muscles. Your muscle cells were using the oxygen for the process of respiration. During **respiration,** chemical reactions occur that break down food molecules into simpler substances and release their stored energy. Just as in photosynthesis, enzymes are needed for the chemical reactions of respiration.

✓ Reading Check *What must happen to food molecules for respiration to take place?*

Breaking Down Carbohydrates The type of food that is most easily broken down by cells is carbohydrates. Respiration of carbohydrates begins in the cytoplasm of the cell. The carbohydrates are broken down into glucose molecules. Each glucose molecule is broken down further into two simpler molecules. As the glucose molecules are broken down, energy is released.

The two simpler molecules are broken down again. This breakdown occurs in the mitochondria of the cells of plants, animals, fungi, and many other organisms. This process uses oxygen, releases much more energy, and produces carbon dioxide and water as wastes. When you exhale, you breathe out carbon dioxide and some of the water.

Respiration occurs in the cells of all living things. **Figure 14** shows how respiration occurs in one consumer. As you are reading this section of the chapter, millions of cells in your body are breaking down glucose, releasing energy, and producing carbon dioxide and water.

Compounds often are represented by a chemical formula. The chemical formula shows how many and what type of atoms are found in one molecule of the compound. For example, the sugar glucose has the chemical formula $C_6H_{12}O_6$. What is the total number of atoms in one glucose molecule?

Figure 14
Producers and consumers carry on respiration that releases energy from foods.

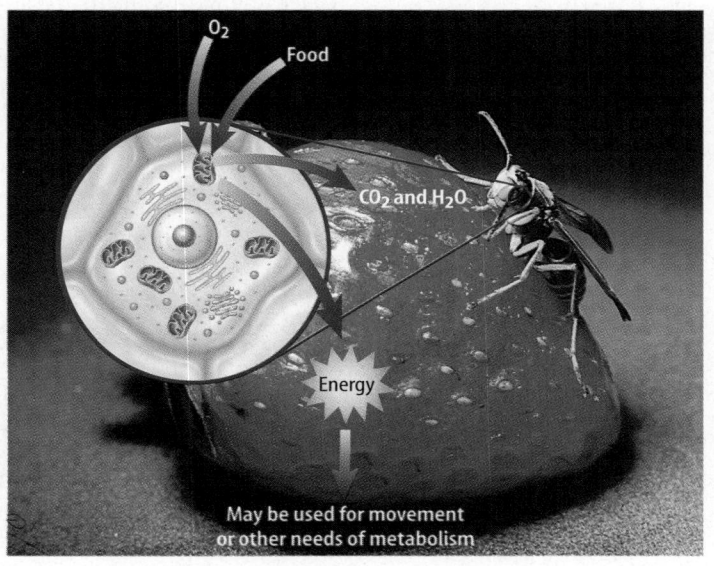

O₂
Food
CO₂ and H₂O
Energy
May be used for movement or other needs of metabolism

Chemistry
INTEGRATION

There are 24 atoms in one glucose molecule.

Use Science Words

Word Origin Have students study the parts of the word *photosynthesis*. It comes from the Greek *photo*, *syn-*, and *thesis*. Have them find the meaning of these words and word parts and describe how the word is defined. Photo: "light;" syn-: "together;" thesis: "to place;" photosynthesis uses light to place compounds together.

✓ Reading Check

Answer They are broken down into simpler substances and their stored energy is released.

IDENTIFYING
Misconceptions

Students often think that plants do not use oxygen, only that they produce oxygen and use carbon dioxide during photosynthesis. See page 96F for teaching strategies that address this misconception.

Resource Manager

Chapter Resources Booklet
Transparency Activity, p. 44
Directed Reading for Content Mastery, pp. 19, 20
Lab Activity, pp. 11–14

✓ Active Reading

Buddy Interviews This strategy helps students understand and clarify the reading. Have students interview one another to find out what helps them to understand what they are reading, how they find answers, and how they assimilate new vocabulary terms. Have students use Buddy Interviews to help them master photosynthesis and respiration. L2

Explore the Glencoe Science Web site at **science.glencoe.com** to find out more about topics in this section.

✔ **Reading Check**

Answer cytoplasm

Teacher FYI

The body of an average person running a 100-yard dash in 12 seconds would require 6 L (1.6 gal.) of air. The person's lungs could supply only about 1.2 L of air. As a result, oxygen debt would occur, and the muscles would produce lactic acid. Most athletes take in at least 10 percent more oxygen than the average person; trained marathon runners take in up to 45 percent more oxygen. They have more efficient respiratory and circulatory systems and can exert greater effort without incurring oxygen debt.

Discussion

Why do bakers use yeast for breadmaking? Yeast carry out processes that release energy in the absence of oxygen and produce carbon dioxide, which causes bread to rise.

SCIENCE Online

Collect Data Visit the Glencoe Science Web site at **science.glencoe.com** for more information about how microorganisms are used to produce many useful products. In your Science Journal list three products produced by microorganisms.

Figure 15
Organisms that use fermentation produce several different wastes.

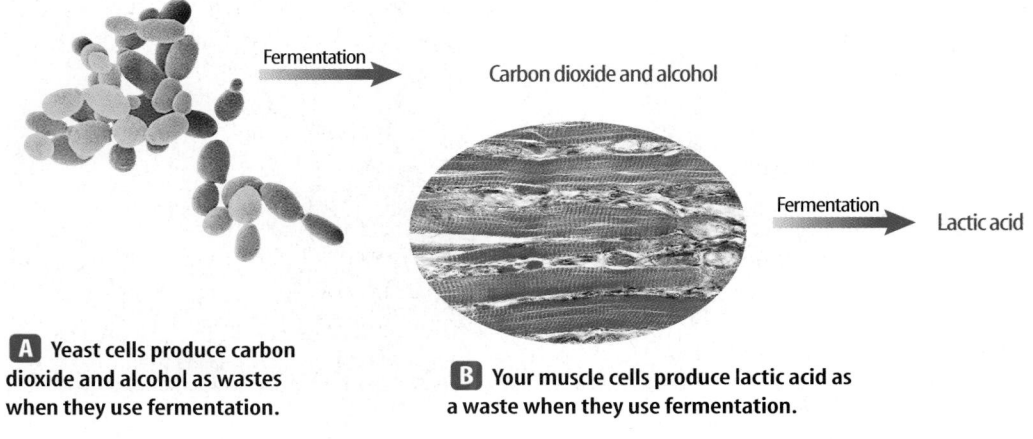

Fermentation → Carbon dioxide and alcohol

Fermentation → Lactic acid

A Yeast cells produce carbon dioxide and alcohol as wastes when they use fermentation.

B Your muscle cells produce lactic acid as a waste when they use fermentation.

116   CHAPTER 4 Cell Processes

Fermentation Remember imagining you were late and had to run to school? During your run, your muscle cells might not have received enough oxygen, even though you were breathing rapidly. When cells do not have enough oxygen for respiration, they use a process called **fermentation** to release some of the energy stored in glucose molecules.

Like respiration, fermentation begins in the cytoplasm. Again, as the glucose molecules are broken down, energy is released. But the simple molecules from the breakdown of glucose do not move into the mitochondria. Instead, more chemical reactions occur in the cytoplasm. These reactions release some energy and produce wastes. Depending on the type of cell, the wastes may be lactic acid, alcohol, and carbon dioxide, as shown in **Figure 15.** Your muscle cells can use fermentation to change the simple molecules into lactic acid while releasing energy. The presence of lactic acid is why your muscle cells might feel stiff and sore after you run to school.

✔ **Reading Check**   *Where in a cell does fermentation take place?*

Some microscopic organisms, such as bacteria, carry out fermentation and make lactic acid. Some of these organisms are used to produce yogurt and some cheeses. These organisms break down a sugar in milk to release energy. The lactic acid produced causes the milk to become more solid and gives these foods some of their flavor.

Have you ever used yeast to make bread? Yeasts are one-celled living organisms. Yeast cells use fermentation to break down sugar in bread dough. They produce alcohol and carbon dioxide as wastes. The carbon dioxide waste is a gas that makes bread dough rise before it is baked. The alcohol is lost as the bread bakes.

Resource Manager

Chapter Resources Booklet
   Enrichment, p. 30
   Reinforcement, p. 27
Life Science Critical Thinking/Problem Solving, p. 5

Cultural Diversity

Fermenting Food Lactic acid fermentation by bacteria is responsible for a number of foods from different cultures. Have students research these foods and report their findings to the class in oral reports. Possible topics: Hawaiian *poi*, Japanese soy sauce, Korean *kimchi*, German sauerkraut, yogurt. L2

CO₂, H₂O

Sugars, O₂

Photosynthesis (producers)

Respiration (all living things)

Figure 16
The chemical reactions of photosynthesis and respiration could not take place without each other.

Related Processes How are photosynthesis, respiration, and fermentation related? Some producers use photosynthesis to make food. All living things use respiration or fermentation to release energy stored in food. If you think carefully about what happens during photosynthesis and respiration, you will see that what is produced in one is used in the other, as shown in **Figure 16.** These two processes are almost the opposite of each other. Photosynthesis produces sugars and oxygen, and respiration uses these products. The carbon dioxide and water produced during respiration are used during photosynthesis. Most life would not be possible without these important chemical reactions.

Section 3 Assessment

1. Explain the difference between producers and consumers and give three examples of each.

2. Explain how the energy used by many living things on Earth can be traced back to sunlight.

3. Compare and contrast respiration and fermentation.

4. What condition must exist in cells for fermentation to occur?

5. **Think Critically** How can some indoor plants help improve the quality of air in a room?

Skill Builder Activities

6. **Identifying and Manipulating Variables and Controls** Design an experiment to show what happens to a plant when you limit sunlight or one of the raw materials for photosynthesis. Identify the control. **For more help, refer to the** Science Skill Handbook.

7. **Solving One-Step Equations** Refer to the chemical equation for photosynthesis. Calculate then compare the number of carbon, hydrogen, and oxygen atoms before and after photosynthesis. **For more help, refer to the** Math Skill Handbook.

Quick Demo

Prepare a sugar solution by mixing 1 tablespoon of sugar with 1 cup of warm water in a jar. Add some yeast to the solution a few hours before class and cover it. Have students note the odor of alcohol and the bubbles of carbon dioxide. Point out that these products result from alcoholic fermentation. L1
LS **Logical-Mathematical**

Visual Learning

Figure 16 Have students create an events chain concept map to illustrate what is occurring in each of these pictures. Producer takes in carbon dioxide and water, goes through the process of photosynthesis, and produces oxygen and sugars; other living organisms take in oxygen and sugars, go through the process of respiration, and give off carbon dioxide and water. LS **Visual-Spatial** P

3 Assess

Reteach

Have students identify organisms that photosynthesize and those that respire. Only organisms with chlorophyll photosynthesize; all organisms respire.

Challenge

Have students compare photosynthesis and respiration in regard to energy. Photosynthesis stores energy; respiration releases energy.

Assessment

Content Have students make a table to compare and contrast photosynthesis and respiration. Use **Performance Assessment in the Science Classroom,** p. 109.

Activity

What You'll Investigate

Purpose

Students observe photosynthesis and respiration in plants and infer whether the processes occur in light or darkness. L2
ELL COOP LEARN IS **Visual-Spatial**

Process Skills

measuring, observing, inferring, communicating, comparing and contrasting, recognizing cause and effect, separating and controlling variables, interpreting data

Time Required

50 minutes (leave overnight if using artificial light)

Safety Precautions

Students should use care when working with chemicals.

Procedure

Teaching Strategy

Tie to Prior Knowledge Most students are aware that plants use light energy to make food and that photosynthesis will occur in the tube placed near the light.

Activity

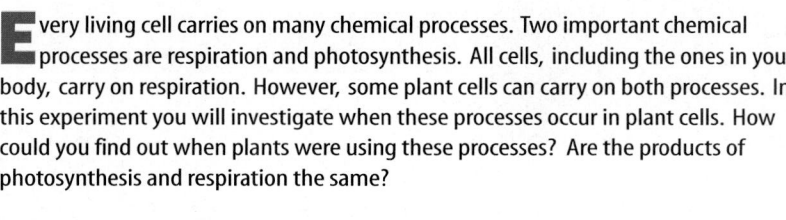

Photosynthesis and Respiration

Every living cell carries on many chemical processes. Two important chemical processes are respiration and photosynthesis. All cells, including the ones in your body, carry on respiration. However, some plant cells can carry on both processes. In this experiment you will investigate when these processes occur in plant cells. How could you find out when plants were using these processes? Are the products of photosynthesis and respiration the same?

What You'll Investigate

When do plants carry on photosynthesis and respiration?

Materials

16-mm test tubes (3)
150-mm test tubes with stoppers (4)
small, clear-glass baby food jars with lids (4)
test-tube rack
stirring rod
scissors
carbonated water (5 mL)
bromothymol blue solution in dropper bottle
aged tap water (20 mL)
distilled water (20 mL)
sprig of *Elodea* (2)
other water plants
Alternate materials

Goals

- **Observe** green water plants in the light and dark.
- **Determine** whether plants carry on photosynthesis and respiration.

Safety Precautions

Wear splash-proof safety goggles to protect eyes from hazardous chemicals. Wash hands thoroughly after the activity.

Inclusion Strategies

Visually Impaired Pair students who are visually impaired with those who can describe to them the colors in the test tubes, both before and after the experiment. L2

Resource Manager

Chapter Resources Booklet
  Activity Worksheet, pp. 7–8
Lab Management and Safety, p. 63

Procedure

1. Label each test tube using the numbers 1, 2, 3, and 4. Pour 5 mL of aged tap water into each test tube.

2. Add 10 drops of carbonated water to test tubes 1 and 2.

3. Add 10 drops of bromothymol blue to all of the test tubes. Bromothymol blue turns green to yellow in the presence of an acid.

4. Cut two 10-cm sprigs of *Elodea*. Place one sprig in test tube 1 and one sprig in test tube 3. Stopper all test tubes.

5. In your Science Journal, copy and complete the test-tube data table.

6. Place test tubes 1 and 2 in bright light. Place tubes 3 and 4 in the dark. Observe the test tubes for 30 min or until the color changes. Record the color of each of the four test tubes.

Test Tube Data		
Test Tube	**Color at Start**	**Color After 30 Minutes**
1	yellow	blue
2	yellow	yellow
3	blue	yellow
4	blue	blue

Conclude and Apply

1. What is indicated by the color of the water in all four test tubes at the start of the activity?

2. **Infer** what process occurred in the test tube or tubes that changed color after 30 min.

3. **Describe** the purpose of test tubes 2 and 4 in this experiment.

4. Do the results of this experiment show that photosynthesis and respiration occur in plants? Explain.

*C*ommunicating
Your Data

Choose one of the following activities to **communicate** your data. Prepare an oral presentation that explains how the experiment showed the differences between products of photosynthesis and respiration. Draw a cartoon strip to **explain** what you did in this experiment. Use each panel to show a different step. **For more help, refer to the Science Skill Handbook.**

ACTIVITY 119

Troubleshooting

Elodea should be kept in the dark for two days before the activity. Use sharp scissors to make a clean diagonal cut at the bottom of each stem.

Expected Outcome

Most results will reflect that plants used carbon dioxide in the light and gave off carbon dioxide in the dark.

Conclude and Apply

1. Test tubes 1 and 2 contain carbon dioxide. Tubes 3 and 4 do not.

2. They underwent photosynthesis or respiration.

3. Tubes 2 and 4 were controls.

4. Yes, the experimental results showed that both processes happen in plant cells. In test tube 1, the green plant used carbon dioxide for photosynthesis. In test tube 3, the green plant gave off carbon dioxide as a result of respiration.

Error Analysis

Have students compare their results and explain why any differences occurred.

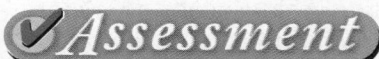

Oral How are fermentation and respiration similar? Both processes release energy through the breakdown of other substances. Use **Performance Assessment in the Science Classroom,** p. 99.

*C*ommunicating
Your Data

Students should use data from the experiment for the presentation or cartoon.

Science (and) Language Arts

Pre-Reading Activity

This activity should help students think about the power of nature. Collect photographs that show both the beauty and the harshness of nature. Photographs by Edward Weston and Ansel Adams are good sources of these types of images. Have students work in small groups to discuss one photograph and consider what they learn about the natural world from the image.

Respond to the Reading

Active Reading Strategies

Predict At certain points in the poem, stop and have students consider what the flower might look like as it grows and whether or not they think the plant will survive. **What gives the flower the strength to break through the rubble?**

Visualize Suggest that students keep the tulip and construction site in their minds' eye as they read. Encourage them to form a mental image of the tulip as it first sprouts, and then to imagine its growth as it fights the debris. **How do you picture the contrast between the flower and the rubble?**

Answers to Questions

1. Possible answers: The tulip bulb is buried deep in the ground; the tulip is a hardy plant.
2. Possible answer: The tulip represents the rebirth of spring. The narrator herself may be experiencing a rebirth or renewal.
3. the yellow color at the base of each petal

from "Tulip"
by Penny Harter

Respond to the Reading

1. Why do you suppose the tulip survived the builders' abuse?
2. The poet chooses to write about a tulip rather than another kind of flower. Why do you think that is?
3. What is the yellow throat that the narrator is staring into?

I watched its first green push
through bare dirt, where the builders
had dropped boards, shingles,
  plaster—
killing everything.
I could not recall what grew
  there,
what returned each spring,
but the leaves looked tulip,
and one morning it arrived,
a scarlet slash against the
  aluminum siding.

Mornings, on the way to
  my car,
I bow to the still bell
of its closed petals; evenings,
it greets me, light ringing
at the end of my driveway.

Sometimes I kneel
to stare into the yellow
  throat . . . .
It opens and closes my days.
It has made me weak with
  love . . . .

120   CHAPTER 4 Cell Processes

Reading Further

Other sources on this topic include:

Tulipa: A Photographer's Botanical, by Christopher Baker (Photographer), Willem Lemmers, Emma Sweeny, and Michael Pollan, Artisan, 1999.

Methods in Plant Cell Biology, by Editors David W. Galbreth, Hans J. Bohnert, and Leslie Wilson, Academic Press, 1995.

Photosynthesis, by Krishna Rao and David O. Hall, Cambridge University Press, 1999.

Plant Identification Terminology: An Illustrated Glossary, by James G. Harris and Melinda Woolf Harris, Spring Lake Publishers, 2001.

Guide to Flowering Plant Families, by Wendy B. Zomlefer, University of North Carolina, 1995.

American Society for Microbiology, Office of Education, 1325 Massachusetts Avenue, NW, Washington, DC 20005-4171.

Understanding Literature

Personification Using human traits or emotions to describe an idea, animal, or inanimate object is called personification. When the poet writes that the tulip has a "yellow throat," she uses personification. This can make the reader think of the tulip as more than just a plant. The poet also uses personification when she states that the tulip inspires love.

Science Connection Living things are made of more than 50 percent water and depend on it for their survival. Because most chemical reactions in plants take place in water, plants must have water in order to grow. In the poem, the tulip only pushes up through the ground in the spring when the tulip's underground bulb and roots absorb enough water. The water carries nutrients and minerals from the soil into the plant.

The process of active transport allows needed nutrients to enter the roots. The cell membranes of root cells contain proteins that bind with the needed nutrients. Cellular energy is used to move these nutrients through the cell membrane.

You also learned about photosynthesis in this chapter. From reading the poem, how would you know that photosynthesis had taken place?

Linking Science and Writing

Gardener's Journal Select a plant to observe. It could be a plant that you, your family, or one of your classmates grows. Depending on the season, it could be a plant growing on the grounds of your school or in a public park. Keep a gardener's observation journal of the plant for a month. Write weekly entries in your journal, describing the plant's condition, size, health, color, and other physical qualities.

Career Connection

Microbiologist

Dr. Harold Amos is a microbiologist who has studied cell processes in bacteria and mammals over the course of his career. He studied the way that sugar is transported in normal cells and cancer cells. Dr. Amos has a medical degree and a doctorate in bacteriology and immunology, which deals with the immune system and its interaction with diseases. He also has received many awards for his scientific work and his contributions to the careers of other scientists.

SCIENCE *Online* Visit the Glencoe Science Web site at **science.glencoe.com** to learn more about careers in microbiology.

Understanding Literature

Science Connection

Plant stems play a part in the transport of materials from roots to leaves. Stems vary greatly in size and shape from one plant species to another. Some grow entirely underground and other stems can store water and nutrients. Plants often store food in their stems during their growth period. When a plant's growth stops, this stored food enables them to survive dormancy. Dormancy occurs during a cold winter or a long dry period. The dormant plant uses the stored food to begin growing when conditions again become favorable.

Linking Science and Writing

Writing Strategies

Divide the class into groups. Have each group choose a flower from those provided to study. Make study guides and plant books available for use in identification and research. Students should draw a picture of it in their Science Journals. Then by carefully pulling the flower apart, they can identify, sketch and label the petals, stamens, sepals, and carpal. As they study the flower, the group should discuss and record the role each part plays in the plant's reproduction.

Career Connection

Students interested in a career in biology should study sciences, math and Latin. Taking courses that require laboratory and field work is also advisable. A bachelor's degree is required to work in this field. For the highest professional status, a doctorate is necessary. Microbiologists study organisms of microscopic or submicroscopic size. Other scientists work to diagnose, treat, and prevent diseases.

SCIENCE *Online*
Internet Addresses

_____
_____
_____

Explore the Glencoe Science Web site at **science.glencoe.com** to find out more about topics in this feature.

Chapter 4 Study Guide

Reviewing Main Ideas

Preview

Students can answer the questions in their Science Journals. Discuss the answers as you go through the chapter. **LS Linguistic**

Review

Students can write their answers, then compare them with those of other students. **LS Interpersonal**

Reteach

Students can look at the illustrations and describe details that support the main ideas of the chapter. **LS Visual-Spatial**

Answers to Chapter Review

SECTION 1

4. lipds, proteins, carbohydrates, and nucleic acids

SECTION 2

2. Osmosis moves water into the plant's cells where it is used.

SECTION 3

1. Their cells do not have chlorophyll.

Reviewing Main Ideas

Section 1 Chemistry of Life

1. Matter is anything that has mass and takes up space.

2. Energy in matter is in the chemical bonds that hold matter together.

3. All organic compounds contain the elements hydrogen and carbon. The organic compounds in living things are carbohydrates, lipids, proteins, and nucleic acids.

4. Organic and inorganic compounds are important to living things. *What organic compounds could be found in an elephant and a pumpkin?*

Section 2 Moving Cellular Materials

1. The selectively permeable cell membrane controls which molecules can pass into and out of the cell.

2. In diffusion, molecules move from areas where there are relatively more of them into areas where there are relatively fewer of them. Osmosis is the diffusion of water through a cell membrane. *Why might these plants use osmosis?*

3. Cells use energy to move molecules by active transport but do not use energy for passive transport.

4. Cells move large particles through cell membranes by endocytosis and exocytosis.

Section 3 Energy for Life

1. Photosynthesis is the process by which some producers change light energy into chemical energy. *Why can't cells in these humans use sunlight to make food?*

2. Respiration that uses oxygen releases the energy in food molecules and produces waste carbon dioxide and water.

3. Some one-celled organisms and cells that lack oxygen use fermentation to release small amounts of energy from glucose. Wastes such as alcohol, carbon dioxide, and lactic acid are produced.

FOLDABLES Reading & Study Skills

After You Read

Under each tab of your Vocabulary Study Fold, write a sentence about one of the cell processes using the vocabulary word on the tab.

FOLDABLES Reading & Study Skills

After You Read

After students have read the chapter and completed the Foldable described in Before You Read, have them do the activity on the student page.

Dinah Zike

Visualizing Main Ideas

Complete the following table on energy processes.

Energy Processes	Photosynthesis	Respiration	Fermentation
Energy Source	Sun	food (glucose)	food (glucose)
In plant and animal cells, occurs in	chloroplast	mitochondria	cytoplasm
Reactants are	water, carbon dioxide	glucose, oxygen	glucose, oxygen
Products are	glucose, oxygen	water, carbon dioxide	lactic acid, alcohol, carbon dioxide

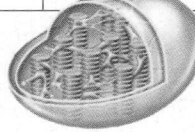 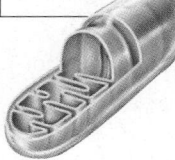 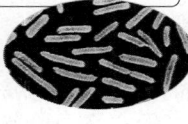

Vocabulary Review

Vocabulary Words

a. active transport
b. diffusion
c. endocytosis
d. enzyme
e. equilibrium
f. exocytosis
g. fermentation
h. inorganic compound
i. metabolism
j. mixture
k. organic compound
l. osmosis
m. passive transport
n. photosynthesis
o. respiration

Using Vocabulary

Use what you know about the vocabulary words to answer the following questions.

1. What is the diffusion of water called?

2. What type of protein regulates nearly all chemical reactions in cells?

3. How do large food particles enter an amoeba?

4. What type of compound is water?

5. What process is used by some producers to convert light energy into chemical energy?

6. What type of compounds always contain carbon and hydrogen?

7. What process uses oxygen to break down glucose?

8. What is the total of all chemical reactions in an organism called?

Study Tip

Make a note of anything you don't understand so that you'll remember to ask your teacher about it.

Chapter **4** Study Guide

Visualizing Main Ideas

See student page.

Vocabulary Review

Using Vocabulary

1. The diffusion of water is called osmosis.
2. The proteins that regulate nearly all chemical reactions in cells are enzymes.
3. Large food particles enter the amoeba by endocytosis.
4. Water is an inorganic compound.
5. Some producers convert sunlight into chemical energy by photosynthesis.
6. An organic compound always contains carbon and hydrogen.
7. Respiration uses oxygen to break down glucose.
8. The total of all chemical reactions in an organism is metabolism.

IDENTIFYING Misconceptions

Assess

Use the assessment as follow-up to page 96F after students have completed the chapter.

Discussion Do animals ever give off oxygen as a product of their metabolic activities? No **Explain.** Oxygen is given off as a product of photosynthesis, thus only organisms that can carry out photosynthesis produce this gas. Animals are not photosynthetic organisms. **What products do plants release during their metabolic processes?** both oxygen and carbon dioxide Specifically reinforce the idea that plants carry out both photosynthesis and respiration.

Expected Outcome At this point students should understand and be able to explain the complementary processes of photosynthesis and respiration in plants and animals.

Checking Concepts

1. C
2. B
3. A
4. B
5. D
6. C
7. A
8. C
9. D
10. D

Thinking Critically

11. The red blood cell would burst because water molecules would move into the cell. The water would move from an area of greater concentration (outside the cell) to an area of lesser concentration (inside the cell) in an effort to reach equilibrium.

12. Plants die as water molecules move out of the cells into the salty soil.

13. The molecules in hot water move faster than those in cold. These faster-moving molecules bump into the sugar molecules more often and more vigorously, dissolving the sugar faster.

14. Consumers would also die; they depend on producers for food.

15. The enzymes increase the rate at which protein bonds are broken; this makes the meat more tender.

Chapter 4 Assessment

Checking Concepts

Choose the word or phrase that best answers the question.

1. What is it called when cells use energy to move molecules?
   A) diffusion
   C) active transport
   B) osmosis
   D) passive transport

2. How might a cell take in a bacterium?
   A) osmosis
   C) exocytosis
   B) endocytosis
   D) diffusion

3. What occurs when the number of molecules of a substance is equal in two areas?
   A) equilibrium
   C) fermentation
   B) metabolism
   D) cellular respiration

4. Which of the following substances is an example of a carbohydrate?
   A) enzymes
   C) waxes
   B) sugars
   D) proteins

5. What is RNA an example of?
   A) carbon dioxide
   C) lipid
   B) water
   D) nucleic acid

6. What organic molecule stores the greatest amount of energy?
   A) carbohydrate
   C) lipid
   B) water
   D) nucleic acid

7. Which of these formulas is an example of an organic compound?
   A) $C_6H_{12}O_6$
   C) H_2O
   B) NO_2
   D) O_2

8. What are organisms that cannot make their own food called?
   A) biodegradables
   C) consumers
   B) producers
   D) enzymes

9. Which one of these cellular processes requires the presence of chlorophyll?
   A) fermentation
   C) respiration
   B) endocytosis
   D) photosynthesis

10. What kind of molecule is water?
    A) organic
    C) carbohydrate
    B) lipid
    D) inorganic

Thinking Critically

11. If you could place one red blood cell in distilled water, what would you see happen to the cell? Explain.

12. In snowy places, salt is used to melt ice on the roads. Explain what could happen to many roadside plants as a result.

13. Why does sugar dissolve faster in hot tea than in iced tea?

14. What would happen to the consumers in a lake if all the producers died?

15. Meat tenderizers contain protein enzymes. How do these enzymes affect meat?

Developing Skills

16. **Concept Mapping** Complete the events-chain concept map to sequence the following parts of matter from smallest to largest: *atom*, *electron*, and *compound*.

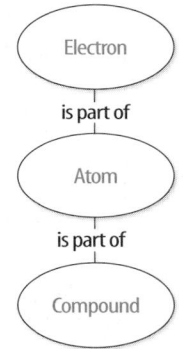

Electron

is part of

Atom

is part of

Compound

17. **Forming Hypotheses** Make a hypothesis about what will happen to wilted celery when placed in a glass of plain water.

Chapter ✓Assessment Planner

Portfolio Encourage students to place in their portfolios one or two items of what they consider to be their best work. Examples include:
- Science Journal, p. 102
- Visual Learning, p. 111
- Visual Learning, p. 117

Performance Additional performance assessments, Performance Task Assessment Lists, and rubrics for evaluating these activities can be found in Glencoe's **Performance Assessment in the Science Classroom.**

18. Interpreting Data Water plants were placed at different distances from a light source. Bubbles coming from the plants were counted to measure the rate of photosynthesis. What can you say about how the distance from the light affected the rate?

Photosynthesis in Water Plants

Beaker Number	Distance from Light (cm)	Bubbles per Minute
1	10	45
2	30	30
3	50	19
4	70	6
5	100	1

19. Making and Using Graphs Using the data from question 18, make a line graph that shows the relationship between the rate of photosynthesis and the distance from light.

Performance Assessment

20. Puzzle Make a crossword puzzle with words describing ways substances are transported across cell membranes. Use the following words in your puzzle: *diffusion, osmosis, facilitated diffusion, active transport, endocytosis,* and *exocytosis.* Make sure your clues give good descriptions of each transport method.

TECHNOLOGY

Go to the Glencoe Science Web site at **science.glencoe.com** or use the **Glencoe Science CD-ROM** for additional chapter assessment.

THE PRINCETON REVIEW Test Practice

Organic compounds called carbohydrates and proteins form many parts of a cell and also help connect cells to each other. Several organic compounds, along with their characteristics and where they are found, are listed below.

Cell Substances

Organic Compound	Flexibility	Found In
Keratin	Not very flexible	Hair and skin of mammals
Collagen	Not very flexible	Skin, bones, and tendons of mammals
Chitin	Very rigid	Tough outer shell of insects, crabs
Cellulose	Very flexible	Trees and flowers

Study the chart and answer the following questions.

1. According to this information, which organic compound is the least flexible?
   A) keratin
   B) collagen
   C) chitin
   D) cellulose

2. According to the chart, cellulose might be found in _____.
   F) mammals
   G) bones
   H) insects
   J) trees

THE PRINCETON REVIEW Test Practice

The Test-Taking Tip was written by The Princeton Review, the nation's leader in test preparation.
1. C
2. J

Developing Skills

16. See student page.
17. Wilted celery will become crisp as water molecules move by osmosis into its cells to reach equilibrium.
18. The closer a plant is to light, the faster its rate of photosynthesis.
19.

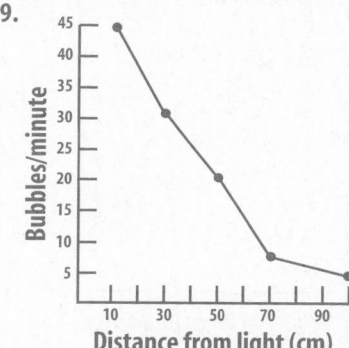

Performance Assessment

20. Definitions in the chapter for these terms can be used. Use **PASC**, p. 91.

✓Assessment Resources

Reproducible Masters
Chapter Resources Booklet
   Chapter Review, pp. 35–36
   Chapter Tests, pp. 37–40
   Assessment Transparency Activity, p. 47

Glencoe Science Web site
   Interactive Tutor
   Chapter Quizzes

Glencoe Technology
   Assessment Transparency
   Interactive CD-ROM Chapter Quizzes
   ExamView Pro Test Bank
   Vocabulary PuzzleMaker Software
   MindJogger Videoquiz

Section/Objectives	Standards		Activities/Features
	National	State/Local	
Chapter Opener	See p. 5T for a Key to Standards.		**Explore Activity:** Infer how plants lose water, p. 127 **Before You Read,** p. 127
Section 1 Photosynthesis and Respiration ⏱ 2 sessions 📦 1 block 1. **Explain** how plants take in and give off gases. 2. **Compare and contrast** relationships between photosynthesis and respiration. 3. **Discuss** why photosynthesis and respiration are important.	National Content Standards: UCP1, A1, C1, C3		**Health Integration,** p. 129 **MiniLAB:** Inferring What Plants Need to Produce Chlorophyll, p. 131 **Science Online,** p. 132 **Activity:** Stomata in Leaves, p. 136
Section 2 Plant Responses ⏱ 3 sessions 📦 1.5 blocks 1. **Identify** the relationship between a stimulus and a tropism in plants. 2. **Compare and contrast** long-day and short-day plants. 3. **Explain** how plant hormones and responses are related.	National Content Standards: UCP1, A1, C1, C3, G1		**Physics Integration,** p. 138 **Math Skills Activity:** Calculating Averages, p. 139 **MiniLAB:** Observing Ripening, p. 140 **Visualizing Plant Hormones,** p. 141 **Science Online,** p. 142 **Activity:** Tropism in Plants, pp. 144–145 **Science and Language Arts:** Sunkissed: An Indian Legend, pp. 146–147

NATIONAL GEOGRAPHIC

Teacher's Corner

PRODUCTS AVAILABLE FROM GLENCOE
To order call 1-800-334-7344:
CD-ROM
NGS PictureShow: Plants: What It Means to Be Green
Curriculum Kit
GeoKits: Plants

Transparency Set
NGS PicturePack: Plants: What It Means to Be Green
Videodisc
STV: Plants

PRODUCTS AVAILABLE FROM NATIONAL GEOGRAPHIC SOCIETY
To order call 1-800-368-2728:
Video
Photosynthesis: Life Energy

Activity Materials	Reproducible Resources	Section Assessment	Technology
Explore Activity: self-sealing plastic bag, aluminum foil, small potted plant	**Chapter Resources Booklet** Foldable Worksheet, p. 15 Directed Reading Overview, p. 17 Note-taking Worksheets, pp. 29–31	GLENCOE'S **ASSESSMENT** ADVANTAGE	
MiniLAB: black construction paper, plant with leaves, scissors, tape **Activity:** lettuce in dish of water, coverslip, microscope, microscope slide, salt solution, forceps *Need materials?* Contact Science Kit at 1-800-828-7777 or www.sciencekit.com on the Internet.	**Chapter Resources Booklet** Transparency Activity, p. 40 MiniLAB, p. 3 Enrichment, p. 27 Reinforcement, p. 25 Directed Reading, p. 18 Activity Worksheet, pp. 5–6 Transparency Activity, pp. 43–44 Lab Activity, pp. 9–10 **Science Inquiry Labs,** p. 35 **Life Science Critical Thinking/ Problem Solving,** p. 8	**Portfolio** Science Journal, p. 131 **Performance** MiniLAB, p. 131 Skill Builder Activities, p. 135 **Content** Section Assessment, p. 135	Section Focus Transparency Interactive CD-ROM Teaching Transparency Guided Reading Audio Program
MiniLAB: 2 green bananas, paper bag **Activity:** paper towel, 30 × 30-cm sheet of aluminum foil, water, mustard seeds, marking pen, 1-L clear glass or plastic jar	**Chapter Resources Booklet** Transparency Activity, p. 41 MiniLAB, p. 4 Enrichment, p. 28 Reinforcement, p. 26 Directed Reading, pp. 19, 20 Activity Worksheet, pp. 7–8 Lab Activity, pp. 11–14 **Home and Community Involvement,** p. 45 **Lab Management and Safety,** p. 58	**Portfolio** Curriculum Connection, p. 142 Reteach, p. 143 **Performance** MiniLAB, p. 140 Skill Builder Activities, p. 143 **Content** Section Assessment, p. 143	Section Focus Transparency Interactive CD-ROM Guided Reading Audio Program

End of Chapter Assessment

GLENCOE'S **ASSESSMENT** ADVANTAGE

Blackline Masters	Technology	Professional Series
Chapter Resources Booklet Chapter Review, pp. 33–34 Chapter Tests, pp. 35–38 **Standardized Test Practice by The Princeton Review,** pp. 51–54	MindJogger Videoquiz Interactive CD-ROM Vocabulary PuzzleMakers ExamView Pro Test Bank Interactive Lesson Planner Interactive Teacher Edition	Performance Assessment in the Science Classroom (PASC)

Transparencies

Section Focus

This is a representation of key blackline masters available in the Teacher Classroom Resources. See Resource Manager boxes within the chapter for additional information.

Key to Teaching Strategies

The following designations will help you decide which activities are appropriate for your students.

L1 Level 1 activities should be appropriate for students with learning difficulties.

L2 Level 2 activities should be within the ability range of all students.

L3 Level 3 activities are designed for above-average students.

ELL ELL activities should be within the ability range of English Language Learners.

COOP LEARN Cooperative Learning activities are designed for small group work.

LS Multiple Learning Styles logos, as described on page 22T, are used throughout to indicate strategies that address different learning styles.

P These strategies represent student products that can be placed into a best-work portfolio.

Assessment

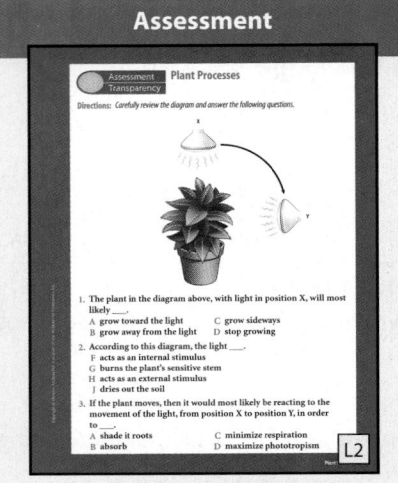

Teaching

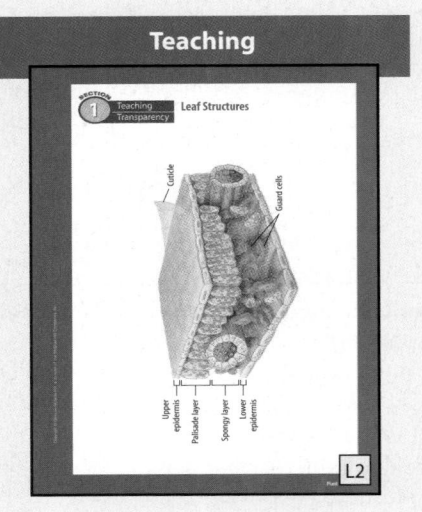

Hands-on Activities

Activity Worksheets

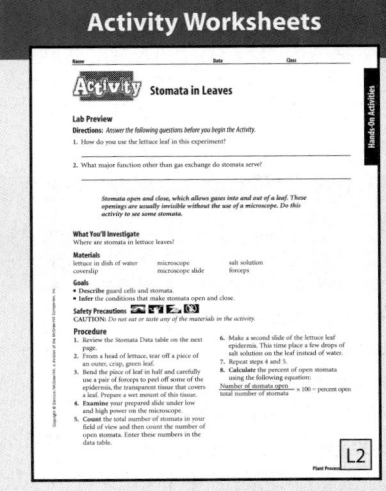

Laboratory Activities

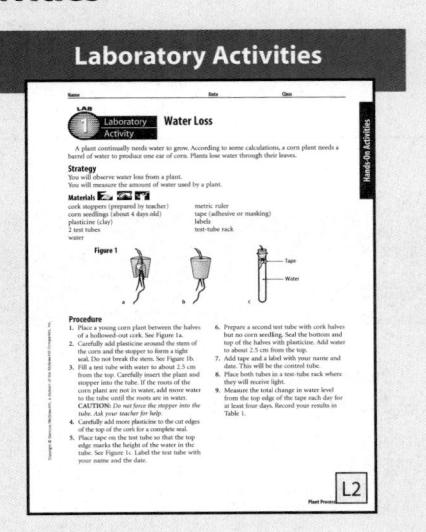

RESOURCE MANAGER

Meeting Different Ability Levels

Content Outline

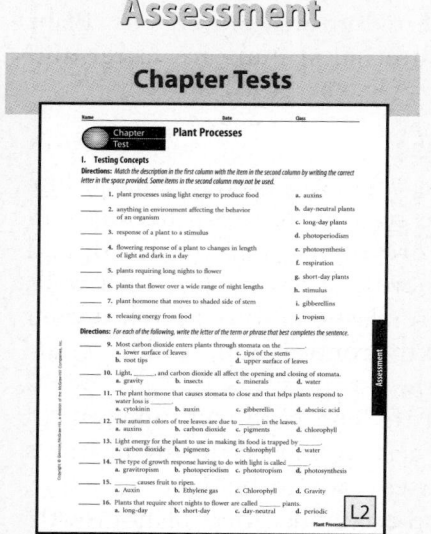

L2

Reinforcement

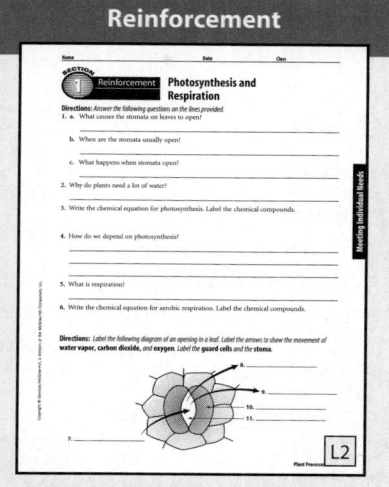

L2

Directed Reading

L1

Assessment

Chapter Tests

L2

Enrichment

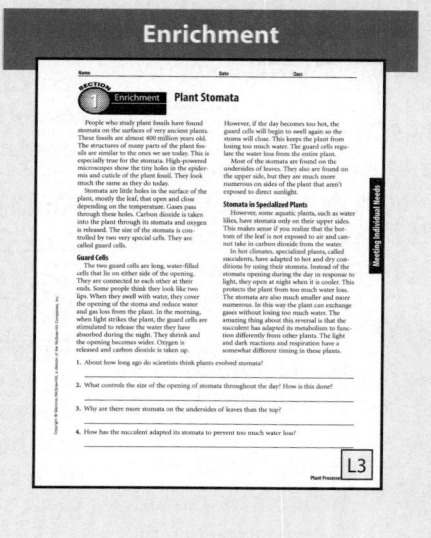

L3

Spanish Directed Reading

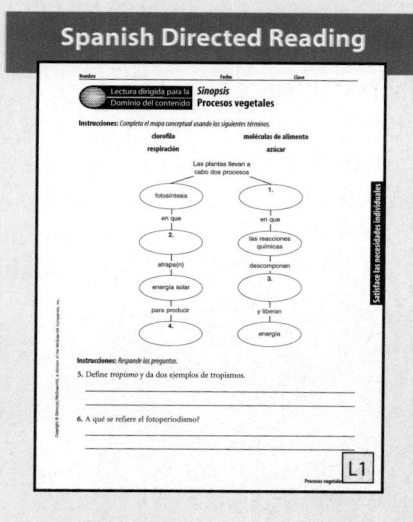

L1

Test Practice Workbook

L2

Chapter Review

L2

Science Content Background

Photosynthesis and Respiration

The Food-Making Process

During the light-dependent cycle, a chemical reaction occurs between light and chlorophyll. Electrons from this reaction combine with hydrogen ions from water and stored chemical energy called NADPH + H+. The NADPH is the source of energy for the light-independent cycle. During this cycle, most plants utilize the NADPH energy to synthesize carbohydrates, including glucose, from carbon dioxide.

Respiration, the mechanism by which energy is released from stored fuel, is always preceded by glycolysis. Glycolysis, which occurs in cell cytoplasm, breaks down one glucose molecule into two molecules of pyruvic acid, producing only a small amount of energy. If oxygen is not required or is unavailable during respiration, the process continues as anaerobic reactions, sometimes producing lactic acid. If alcohol is produced, the process is called fermentation. These two inefficient processes extract only a small amount of energy from the pyruvic acid. Aerobic respiration uses oxygen and releases all the energy in the chemical bonds of pyruvic acid. The end products of this process are carbon dioxide, water, and energy.

Jean Paul/FPG International

Student Misconception

Plants do not take in oxygen or give off carbon dioxide.

Refer to the facing page for teaching strategies to address this misconception. Refer to pages 131–133 for content related to this topic.

Plant Responses

Types of Responses

Plant responses to external stimuli, called tropisms, are slow, permanent, directed growth movements. Plant responses to internal stimuli are faster and reversible.

Plant Hormones

Plant hormones, chemicals produced in specific plant cells, are transported to other sites in the plant, where they cause physiological changes. The hormone auxin causes cell walls to become more elastic and to stretch during active cell growth, controls suppression of lateral bud growth, and prevents leaf abscission, or leaf drop. Ethylene regulates ripening of fruits. Abscisic acid, produced mainly in leaves and fruits, causes buds to become dormant. Gibberellins and cytokinins affect plant growth.

SCIENCE *Online*

For additional content background on this topic, go to the Glencoe Science Web site at science.glencoe.com.

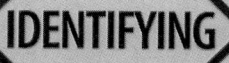

IDENTIFYING Misconceptions

Find Out What Students Think

Students may think that . . .

- **Plants do not take in oxygen or give off carbon dioxide.**

- **Photosynthesis is a plant's way of breathing.**

Textbooks and science activity books frequently include diagrams showing a cycle in which plants produce oxygen and take in carbon dioxide and animals take in oxygen while giving off carbon dioxide. From diagrams like these, students draw the conclusion that plants exist to give off oxygen for the benefit of animals. They also equate photosynthesis with breathing because it involves taking in one gas and giving off another. Students who do know that plants can give off carbon dioxide often believe it only occurs in the dark, when the plant cannot get sunlight.

Activity

Write the words *oxygen, carbon dioxide, plant, animal, glucose, light,* and *water* on the board. Ask students to copy the words and then construct concept maps showing how all these terms interrelate. Students will most likely make diagrams showing oxygen moving from plant to animal and carbon dioxide moving from animal to plant. They may not know where to place glucose and water.

Promote Understanding

Demonstrations

After students have learned that glucose is a product of photosynthesis, ask them why they think plants make glucose. A possible answer may be "Plants make glucose for animals to eat." The following demonstrations will help students understand that plants make glucose for their own use.

- Show students a soaked bean seed. Open the seed and apply iodine as a test for starch. After several minutes the starchy endosperm of the seed should turn blue-black. Use a diagram or snap-lock beads to help explain that starch molecules are chains of glucose molecules. Explain that the bean plant stored starch in the bean seed. Ask students what advantage this might have for the plant. Some students may think that the starch is food for animals, while others may understand that it is food for the embryonic plant.

- Place viable bean seeds in a flask until it is one-third full. Add enough water to completely cover the seeds. Insert a stopper with a glass tube. Attach one end of a length of rubber tubing to the glass tube. Insert the other end into a small flask of limewater. Let the apparatus sit in a warm, well-lighted place. As the seeds absorb water and begin germination, they will metabolize the stored starch in their endosperm and will give off carbon dioxide. Carbon dioxide bubbling slowly through the limewater will cause the liquid to turn cloudy.

Assess

After completing the chapter, see *Identifying Misconceptions* in the Study Guide.

Chapter Vocabulary

What do you think?

Science Journal The picture shows *Elodea* leaves giving off oxygen bubbles. Oxygen is a by-product of the process of photosynthesis, which requires light.

Plant Processes

From crabgrass to giant sequoias, many plants start as small seeds. Some trees may grow to be more than 20 m tall. One tree can be cut up to produce many pieces of lumber. Where does all that wood come from? You may have seen a plant on a windowsill with all its leaves growing toward the window. Why do they grow that way? In this chapter, find the answers to these questions. In addition, learn how plants are essential to the survival of all animals on Earth—including you!

What do you think?

Science Journal Look at the picture below with a classmate. Discuss what you think this might be or what is happening. Here's a hint: *This would never happen without light.* Write your answer or best guess in your Science Journal.

126

Theme Connection

Systems and Interactions The systems and structures involved in the processes of photosynthesis and respiration work together. Through interactions, these processes, along with the stimuli-response mechanisms discussed in the second part of the chapter, allow a plant to maintain homeostasis.

EXPLORE ACTIVITY

Plants are similar to other living things because they are made of cells, reproduce, make and use substances, and need water. If you forgot to water a houseplant, what do you think would happen? From your own experiences, you probably know that the houseplant would wilt. Do the following activity to discover one way plants lose water.

Infer how plants lose water

1. Obtain a self-sealing plastic bag, some aluminum foil, and a small potted plant from your teacher.

2. Using the foil, carefully cover the soil around the plant in the pot. Place the potted plant in the plastic bag.

3. Seal the bag and place it in a sunny window. Wash your hands.

4. Look at the plant at the same time every day for a few days.

Observe

In your Science Journal, describe what happens in the bag. If enough water is lost by a plant and not replaced, predict what will happen to the plant.

FOLDABLES
Reading & Study Skills

Before You Read

Making a Compare and Contrast Study Fold As you study plant processes, use the following Foldable to help you compare and contrast plant respiration and animal respiration.

1. Place a sheet of paper in front of you so the long side is at the top. Fold the paper in half from top to bottom.

2. Write *Respiration* across the front, as shown.

3. Unfold the paper. Draw a picture of an animal on the top half and a plant on the bottom half. Leave room to write below the drawings.

4. Before you read the chapter write what you know about animal respiration and plant respiration on the appropriate flaps.

5. As you read the chapter, add to or change your information.

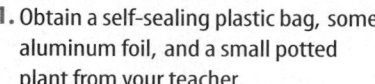

Respiration

127

EXPLORE ACTIVITY

Purpose Use the Explore Activity to introduce students to plant processes. Inform students that they will be learning more about plant processes as they read the chapter. ELL IS **Kinesthetic**

Preparation The seedlings should be large enough to transpire an observable amount of water.

Materials large self-sealing plastic bags, seedling plants in pots, aluminum foil

Teaching Strategies

• Have students record their hypotheses about what will happen after the plants are sealed in the plastic bags.

• Discuss why the soil is covered with foil. to reduce evaporation from the soil

Observe

Students should explain that most of the water that gathers in the bag came from the plant. The plant will wilt or even die if it loses too much water.

✓ **Assessment**

Process Have students diagram the pathway of water through a plant, drawing on prior knowledge to label their diagrams with terms such as *roots*, *stems*, *vascular tissue*, and *xylem*. Use **Performance Assessment in the Science Classroom**, p. 127.

FOLDABLES
Reading & Study Skills

Before You Read

Dinah Zike Study Fold

Purpose Students make and use a Foldable to collect information on plant respiration. Students use this information to compare and contrast plant and animal respiration. How are they the same? How do they differ?

📁 For additional help, see Foldables Worksheet, p. 15 in **Chapter Resources Booklet,** or go to the Glencoe Science Web site at **science.glencoe.com.** See After You Read in the Study Guide at the end of this chapter.

1 Motivate

Bellringer Transparency

Display the Section Focus
Transparency for Section 1.
Use the accompanying Transparency Activity Master. L2
ELL

Tie to Prior Knowledge

Ask if students know why
plants are green. Explain that
plants are green because they
contain chlorophyll, a pigment
that traps most of light's energy
but reflects green wavelengths
of light.

As You Read

What You'll Learn

- **Explain** how plants take in and give off gases.
- **Compare and contrast** relationships between photosynthesis and respiration.
- **Discuss** why photosynthesis and respiration are important.

Vocabulary

stomata   photosynthesis
chlorophyll   respiration

Why It's Important

Understanding photosynthesis and
respiration in plants will help you
understand how life is maintained
on Earth.

Figure 1
**Plants take in raw materials
through their roots and
leaves and get rid of wastes
through their leaves.**

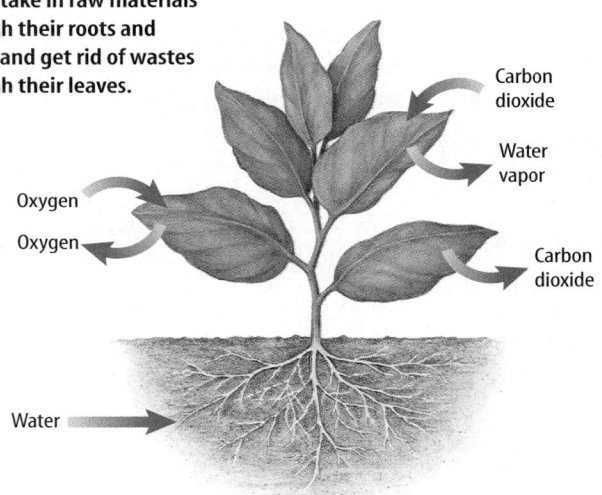

Carbon dioxide

Water vapor

Oxygen

Oxygen

Carbon dioxide

Water

Taking in Raw Materials

Sitting in the cool shade under a tree, you finish eating your
lunch. The food you eat is one of the raw materials that you
need to grow. Oxygen is another. It enters your lungs and eventually reaches every cell in your body. Your cells use oxygen to
help release the energy from the food that you eat. The process
that uses oxygen to release the energy from food produces carbon dioxide and water as wastes. These wastes move in your
blood to your lungs where they are removed as gases when you
exhale. You look up at the tree and wonder, "Does a tree need to
eat? Does it use oxygen? How does a tree get rid of wastes?

Movement of Materials in Plants No one packs a sack
lunch for the tree. Trees and other plants don't take in foods the
way you do. Plants make their own foods using the raw materials water, carbon dioxide, and inorganic chemicals in the soil.
Just like you, plants also produce waste products.

Most of the water used by plants is taken in through roots, as
shown in **Figure 1.** Water moves into root cells and then up
through the plant to where it is
used. When you pull up a plant,
some of its roots are damaged. If
you replant it, the plant will
need extra water until new roots
grow to replace those that were
damaged.

Leaves, instead of lungs, are
where most gas exchange occurs
in plants. Most of the water
taken in through the roots exits
through the leaves of a plant.
Carbon dioxide, oxygen, and
water vapor exit and enter the
plant through the leaf. The leaf's
structure helps explain how it
functions in gas exchange.

Section ✓Assessment Planner

PORTFOLIO
Science Journal, p. 131
PERFORMANCE ASSESSMENT
MiniLAB, p. 131
Skill Builder Activities, p. 135
See page 150 for more options.

CONTENT ASSESSMENT
Section, p. 135
Challenge, p. 135
Chapter, pp. 150–151

Figure 2
A leaf's structure determines its function. Food is made in the inner layers. Most stomata are found on the lower epidermis.

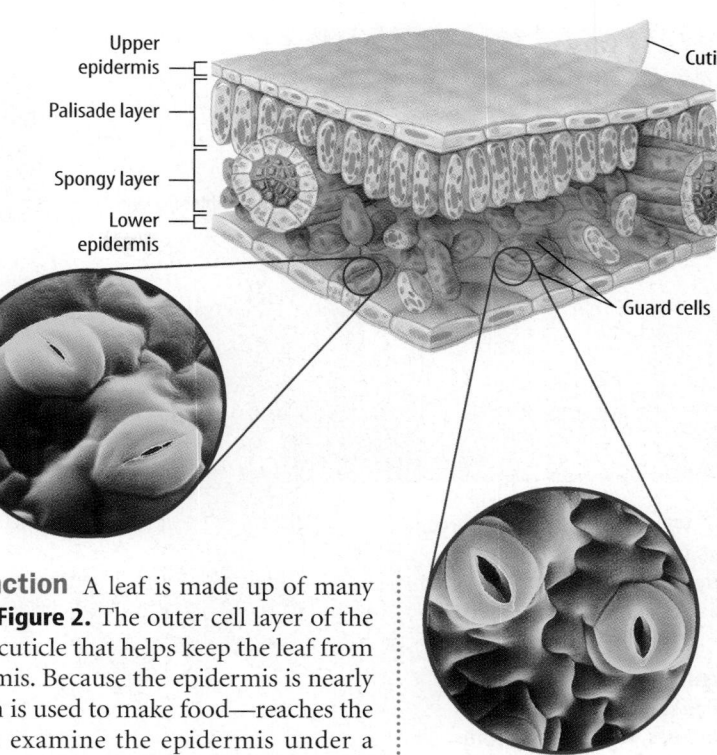

Upper epidermis
Palisade layer
Spongy layer
Lower epidermis
Cuticle
Guard cells

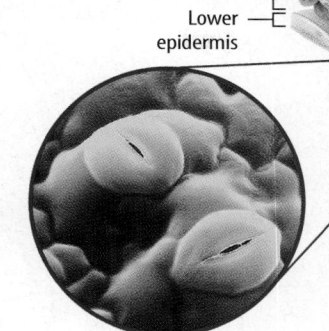

A Closed stomata

B Open stomata

Leaf Structure and Function A leaf is made up of many different layers, as shown in **Figure 2.** The outer cell layer of the leaf is the epidermis. A waxy cuticle that helps keep the leaf from drying out covers the epidermis. Because the epidermis is nearly transparent, sunlight—which is used to make food—reaches the cells inside the leaf. If you examine the epidermis under a microscope, you will see that it contains many small openings. These openings, called **stomata** (stoh MAH tuh) (singular, *stoma*), act as doorways for raw materials such as carbon dioxide, water vapor, and waste gases to enter and exit the leaf. Stomata also are found on the stems of many plants. More than 90 percent of the water plants take in through their roots is lost through the stomata. In one day, a growing tomato plant can lose up to 1 L of water.

Two cells called guard cells surround each stoma and control its size. As water moves into the guard cells, they swell and bend apart, opening a stoma. When guard cells lose water, they deflate, closing the stoma. **Figures 2A** and **2B** show closed and open stomata.

Stomata usually are open during the day when most plants need to take in raw materials to make food. They usually are closed at night when food making slows down. Stomata also close when a plant is losing too much water. This adaptation conserves water, because less water vapor escapes from the leaf.

Inside the leaf are two layers of cells, the spongy layer and the palisade layer. Carbon dioxide and water vapor, which are needed in the food-making process, fill the spaces of the spongy layer. Most of the food is made in the palisade layer.

Health
INTEGRATION

Vitamins are substances needed for good health. You get most of the vitamins you need from the plants you eat. Research to learn about four vitamins and the plant foods you would need to eat to get them. Display your results on a poster.

2 Teach

Taking in Raw Materials

Quick Demo

Demonstrate how guard cells change shape. Show students an uninflated oblong balloon along whose length you have placed a strip of cellophane tape. Blow up the balloon, and again show it to the class. Explain that when the balloon is inflated, its shape changes just like a guard cell's shape changes when it swells with water. The guard cell takes this shape because it has a thickened cell wall on the side next to the stoma.

Make a Model

Have students use two balloons like the one in the demo above to model how two guard cells bracket a stoma. Point out the tape, which represents the thickened cell wall that adjoins the stoma.

Health
INTEGRATION

Answer Answers will vary, but should include four vitamins, their sources, and their functions.

Visual Learning

Figure 2 Make sure students understand that the primary function of the stomata is to allow for the exchange of gases by the plant.

Resource Manager

Chapter Resources Booklet
Transparency Activity, p. 40
Directed Reading for Content Mastery, pp. 17, 18
Note-taking Worksheets, pp. 29–31

IDENTIFYING
Misconceptions

Many students will think that all plant cells contain chlorophyll. Explain that cells deep within the plant where light does not penetrate and cells in underground plant parts lack this pigment and are not directly involved in photosynthesis. Ask: **What parts of a tree probably do not contain chlorophyll?** Woody parts that are not green, such as the stem (trunk), roots, and branches, do not contain chlorophyll.

Extension

Some students might investigate which plant pigments cause specific plant colors. Suggest that students study trees or other plants that turn particular colors in your area of the country. Anthocyanins are red; carotenoids are yellow. Leaves change color in fall because declining temperatures and short days lead to a breakdown of chlorophyll which allows other pigments to become visible. L2

✔ Reading Check

Answer They contain a green pigment called chlorophyll.

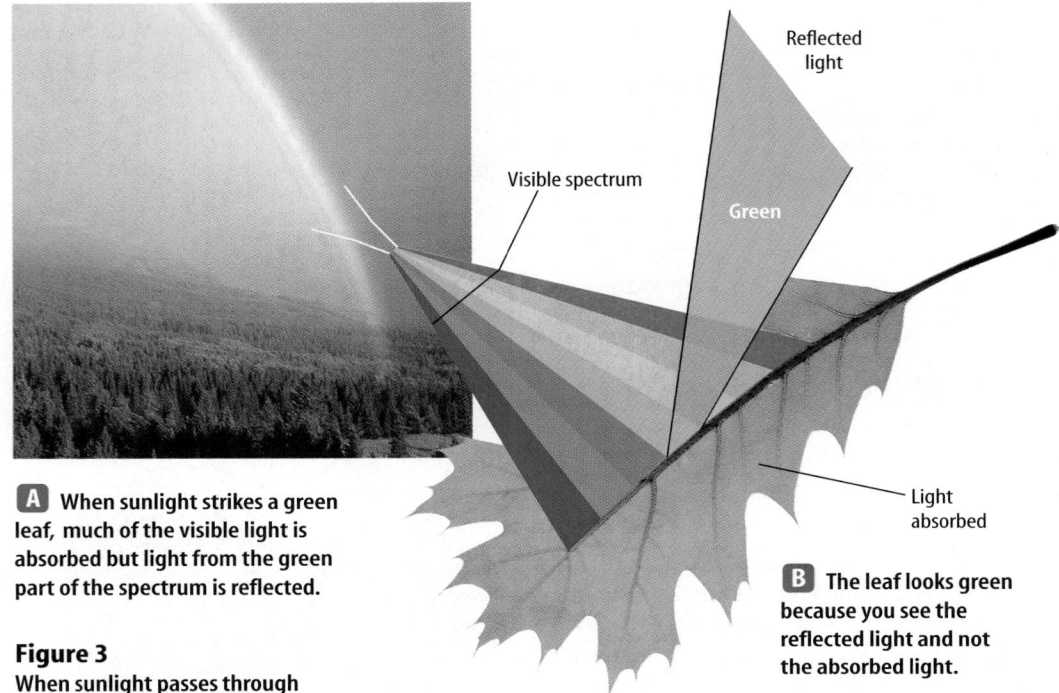

A When sunlight strikes a green leaf, much of the visible light is absorbed but light from the green part of the spectrum is reflected.

Reflected light

Visible spectrum

Green

Light absorbed

B The leaf looks green because you see the reflected light and not the absorbed light.

Figure 3
When sunlight passes through raindrops, they act like prisms. Light separates into the colors of the visible spectrum. You see a rainbow when this happens.

Chloroplasts and Plant Pigments If you look closely at the leaf in **Figure 2,** you'll see that some of the cells contain small, green structures called chloroplasts. Most leaves look green because their cells contain so many chloroplasts. Chloroplasts are green because they contain a green pigment called **chlorophyll** (KLOR uh fihl).

✔ Reading Check   *Why are chloroplasts green?*

As shown in **Figure 3,** light from the Sun contains all colors of the visible spectrum. A pigment is a substance that reflects a particular part of the visible spectrum and absorbs the rest. When you see a green leaf, you are seeing green light energy reflected from chlorophyll. Most of the other colors of the spectrum, especially red and blue, are absorbed by chlorophyll. In the spring and summer, most leaves have so much chlorophyll that it hides all other pigments. In fall, the chlorophyll in some leaves breaks down and the leaves change color as other pigments become visible. Pigments, especially chlorophyll, are important to plants because the light energy that they absorb is used to make food. For plants, this food-making process—photosynthesis—happens in the chloroplasts.

130   CHAPTER 5 Plant Processes

LAB DEMONSTRATION

Purpose to show that the colors we see are the colors objects reflect
Materials prism, light source, objects of different colors
Preparation Collect materials and have them grouped together to save time.

Procedure Place a prism in a bright light source so that the colors of white light entering the prism separate. Place objects of different colors in the paths of the separated beams.
Expected Outcome Objects will absorb all colors except the color they reflect.

✔ Assessment

What would happen if you placed a red rose with green leaves in a red beam of light in a darkened room? The rose would appear red and the leaves would appear black.

The Food-Making Process

Photosynthesis (foh toh SIHN thuh suhs) is the process during which a plant's chlorophyll traps light energy and sugars are produced. In plants, photosynthesis occurs only in cells with chloroplasts. For example, photosynthesis occurs only in a carrot plant's lacy green leaves, shown in **Figure 4.** Because a carrot's root cells lack chlorophyll and normally do not receive light, they can't perform photosynthesis. But excess sugar produced in the leaves is stored in the familiar orange root that you and many animals eat.

Besides light, plants also need the raw materials carbon dioxide and water for photosynthesis. The overall chemical equation for photosynthesis is shown below. What happens to each of the raw materials in the process?

$$6CO_2 + 6H_2O + \text{light energy} \xrightarrow{\text{chlorophyll}} C_6H_{12}O_6 + 6O_2$$

carbon dioxide   water   glucose   oxygen

Light-Dependent Reactions Some of the chemical reactions that take place during photosynthesis need light but others do not. Those that need light can be called the light-dependent reactions of photosynthesis. During light-dependent reactions, chlorophyll and other pigments trap light energy that eventually will be stored in sugar molecules. Light energy causes water molecules, which were taken up by the roots, to split into oxygen and hydrogen. The oxygen leaves the plant through the stomata. This is the oxygen that you breathe. Leftover hydrogen is used in photosynthesis reactions that occur when there is no light.

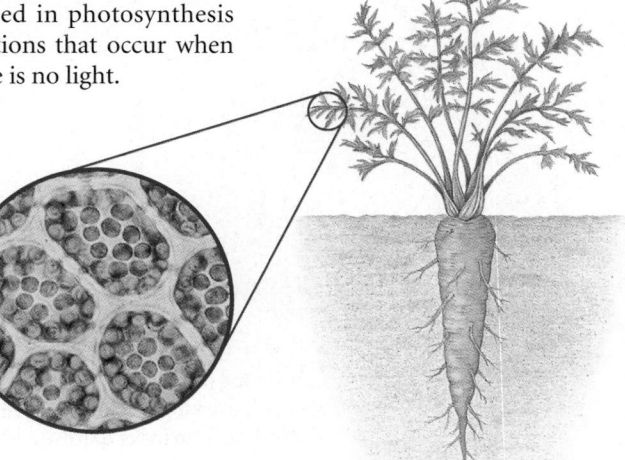

Figure 4
Because they contain chloroplasts, cells in the leaf of the carrot plant are the sites for photosynthesis.

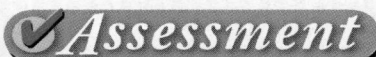

Inferring What Plants Need to Produce Chlorophyll

Procedure
1. Cut two pieces of **black construction paper** large enough so that each one completely covers one leaf on a **plant.**
2. Cut a square out of the center of each piece of paper.
3. Sandwich the leaf between the two paper pieces and **tape** the pieces together along their edges.
4. Place the plant in a sunny area. Wash your hands.
5. After seven days, carefully remove the paper and observe the leaf.

Analysis
In your **Science Journal,** describe how the color of the areas covered by paper compare to the areas not covered. Infer why this happened.

Purpose to determine if plants require light to produce and maintain chlorophyll ⬜L2

[LS] Kinesthetic

Materials black construction paper, plant, tape, scissors

Teaching Strategy Record results immediately upon removing the construction paper.

Analysis
The covered area should be less green than the uncovered area. Light is needed in the production and maintenance of chlorophyll.

✓Assessment

Process Have students suggest a way in which they could determine why they got their results. Use **PASC,** p. 99.

Science Journal

Carbon Dioxide Have students research how the buildup of carbon dioxide in the atmosphere might affect photosynthesis. Have them summarize their findings in their Science Journals. Increased carbon dioxide may correlate with increased photosynthesis in certain localities such as rain forests and marine environments with large amounts of plankton. ⬜L2 P

Resource Manager

Chapter Resources Booklet
    MiniLAB, p. 3
    Lab Activity, pp. 9–10
Science Inquiry Labs, p. 35

The Food-Making Process, continued

Quick Demo

Place a sprig of *Elodea* in a test tube with 5 mL of water and 1 mL of bromothymol blue indicator. Have students note the yellow color. Place the tube in strong light. The solution should turn blue as *Elodea* takes up carbon dioxide in light.

IDENTIFYING Misconceptions

Students may think that plants do not take in oxygen or give off carbon dioxide. Refer to page 126F for teaching strategies that address this misconception.

Fun Fact

A place where food is stored or used in a plant is called a sink. Depending on the plant, roots, stems, and leaves can be sinks.

Use Science Words

Word Meaning Have students look up the word *photosynthesis* and relate the meaning of its word parts to the process. *Photo-* means light; *synthesis* means the combining of parts to make a whole. So photosynthesis is the process that uses light to combine carbon dioxide and water into a larger sugar molecule.

Research Besides glucose, what other sugars do plants produce? Visit the Glencoe Science Web site at **science.glencoe.com** for more information about plant sugars. In your Science Journal list three sugars produced by plants.

Light-Independent Reactions Reactions that don't need light are called the light-independent reactions of photosynthesis. Carbon dioxide, the raw material from the air, is used in these reactions. The light energy trapped during the light-dependent reactions is used to combine carbon dioxide and hydrogen to make sugars. One important sugar that is made is glucose. The chemical bonds that hold glucose and other sugars together are stored energy. **Figure 5** compares what happens during each stage of photosynthesis.

What happens to the oxygen and glucose that were made during photosynthesis? Most of the oxygen from photosynthesis is a waste product and is released through stomata. Glucose is the main form of food for plant cells. A plant usually produces more glucose than it can use. Excess glucose is stored in plants as other sugars and starches. When you eat carrots, as well as beets, potatoes, or onions, you are eating the stored product of photosynthesis.

Glucose also is the basis of a plant's structure. You don't grow larger by breathing in and using carbon dioxide. However, that's exactly what plants do as they take in carbon dioxide gas and convert it into glucose. Cellulose, an important part of plant cell walls, is made from glucose. Leaves, stems, and roots are made of cellulose and other substances produced using glucose. The products of photosynthesis are used by plants to grow.

Figure 5
Photosynthesis includes two sets of reactions, the light-dependent reactions and the light-independent reactions.

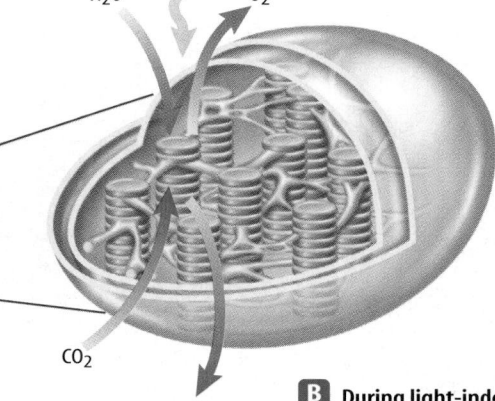

Standard plant cell

Chloroplast

Sunlight

H_2O O_2

CO_2

$C_6H_{12}O_6$

A During light-dependent reactions, light energy is trapped and water is split into hydrogen and oxygen. Oxygen leaves the plant.

B During light-independent reactions, energy is used to combine carbon dioxide and hydrogen to make glucose and other sugars.

Inclusion Strategies

Gifted Have students form an acrostic using the letters of the word *photosynthesis* to describe the process. L3

Internet Addresses _____

_____

_____

_____

Explore the Glencoe Science Web site at **science.glencoe.com** to find out more about topics in this section.

Figure 6
Tropical rain forests contain large numbers of photosynthetic plants.

Importance of Photosynthesis Why is photosynthesis important to living things? First, photosynthesis produces food. Organisms that carry on photosynthesis provide food directly or indirectly for nearly all the other organisms on Earth. Second, photosynthetic organisms, like the plants in **Figure 6,** use carbon dioxide and release oxygen. This removes carbon dioxide from the atmosphere and adds oxygen to it. Most organisms, including humans, need oxygen to stay alive. As much as 90 percent of the oxygen entering the atmosphere today is a result of photosynthesis.

The Breakdown of Food

Look at the photograph in **Figure 7.** Do the fox and the plants in the photograph have anything in common? They don't look alike, but the fox and the plants are made of cells that break down food, and release energy in a process called respiration. How does this happen?

Respiration is a series of chemical reactions that breaks down food molecules and releases energy. Respiration occurs in cells of most organisms. The breakdown of food might or might not require oxygen. Respiration that uses oxygen to break down food chemically is called aerobic respiration. In plants and many organisms that have one or more cells, a nucleus, and other organelles, aerobic respiration occurs in the mitochondria (singular, *mitochondrion*). The overall chemical equation for aerobic respiration is shown below.

$$C_6H_{12}O_6 + 6O_2 \longrightarrow 6CO_2 + 6H_2O + energy$$

glucose oxygen carbon dioxide water

Figure 7
You know that animals such as this red fox carry on respiration, but so do all the plants that surround the fox.

Discussion
Write the general equation for photosynthesis on the board. Use one color of chalk for the raw materials and another for the products. During the discussion, guide students to an understanding of what the equation means in terms of energy capture and conversion. L2
LS **Visual-Spatial and Interpersonal**

The Breakdown of Food

Quick Demo
Demonstrate respiration in yeast by adding 1 mL of bromothymol blue to a mixture of 1 mL sugar syrup (0.5 g of granulated sugar in 100 mL water), 5 mL water, and 2 mL yeast suspension. The color will change from blue to green and eventually to yellow as the yeasts respire and give off carbon dioxide.

Use an Analogy
Use these analogies to help clarify the processes of photosynthesis and respiration. A chloroplast where photosynthesis occurs is like a factory in which small parts are used to assemble a larger whole. A mitochondrion, in which respiration occurs, is like a powerhouse that uses fuel as an energy source for the production of goods.

✔ **Reading Check**

Answer all living things

Teacher FYI

Fermentation is a type of anaerobic respiration. Anaerobic means "without oxygen." It results in increased waste products that build up in cells. Also, it is a less efficient method of respiration and cannot produce as much energy as aerobic respiration. To perform the same amount of work, a cell using fermentation must consume up to 20 times more glucose per second than a cell using aerobic respiration. In the human body, if the amount of oxygen delivered to muscle cells during strenuous activity is inadequate, the cells temporarily use fermentation. The waste products that build up in the cells add to muscle fatigue.

Figure 8
Aerobic respiration takes place in the mitochondria of plant cells.

B Oxygen is used in the mitochondrion to break down these two molecules.

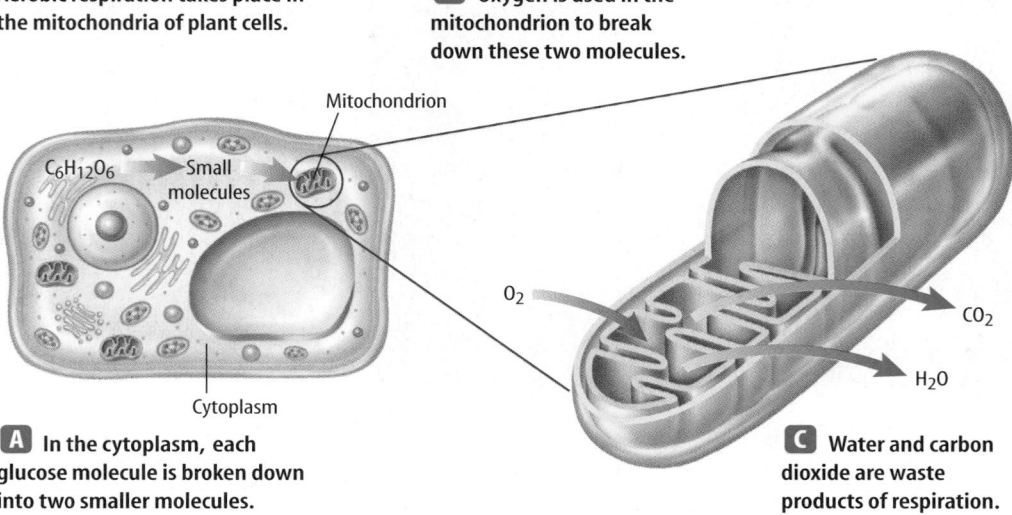

Mitochondrion

$C_6H_{12}O_6$ → Small molecules

Cytoplasm

O_2

CO_2

H_2O

A In the cytoplasm, each glucose molecule is broken down into two smaller molecules.

C Water and carbon dioxide are waste products of respiration.

Figure 9
Plants use the energy released from the respiration of food to carry out many functions.

Plant structure and function

Production of chlorophyll

Sprouting of seeds

Aerobic Respiration Before aerobic respiration begins, glucose molecules are broken down into two smaller molecules. This happens in the cytoplasm. The smaller molecules then enter a mitochondrion, where aerobic respiration takes place. Oxygen is used in the reactions that break the small molecules into the waste products water and carbon dioxide. The reactions also release energy. Every cell in the organism needs this energy. **Figure 8** shows aerobic respiration in a plant cell.

Importance of Respiration Although food contains energy, it is not in a form that can be used by cells. Respiration changes food energy into a form all cells can use. This energy drives the life processes of almost all organisms on Earth.

✔ **Reading Check** *What organisms use respiration?*

Plants use energy produced by respiration to transport sugars and open and close stomata. Some of the energy is used to produce substances needed for photosynthesis, such as chlorophyll. When seeds sprout, they use energy from the respiration of stored food in the seed. **Figure 9** shows uses of energy in plants.

The waste product carbon dioxide is also important. Aerobic respiration returns carbon dioxide to the atmosphere, where it can be used again by plants and some other organisms for photosynthesis.

134 CHAPTER 5 Plant Processes

Resource Manager

Chapter Resources Booklet
   Enrichment, p. 27
   Reinforcement, p. 25
Performance Assessment in the Science Classroom, p. 59

Visual Learning

Figure 8 Have students trace the pathways of the reactants and products of respiration in the mitochondrion. Help them understand that the arrows indicate materials moving in and out of the organelle.

Table 1 Comparing Photosynthesis and Aerobic Respiration

	Energy	Raw Materials	End Products	Where
Photosynthesis	stored	water and carbon dioxide	glucose and oxygen	cells with chlorophyll
Aerobic Respiration	released	glucose and oxygen	water and carbon dioxide	cells with mitochondria

Comparison of Photosynthesis and Respiration

Look back in the chapter to find the equations for photosynthesis and aerobic respiration. Do they resemble each other? If you look closely, you can see that overall, aerobic respiration is almost the reverse of photosynthesis. Photosynthesis combines carbon dioxide and water by using light energy. The end products are glucose (food) and oxygen. During photosynthesis, energy is stored in food. Photosynthesis occurs only in cells that contain chlorophyll, such as those in the leaves of plants. Aerobic respiration combines oxygen and food to release the energy in the chemical bonds of the food. The end products of aerobic respiration are energy, carbon dioxide, and water. Because all plant cells contain mitochondria, all plant cells and any cell with mitochondria can use the process of aerobic respiration. **Table 1** compares photosynthesis and aerobic respiration.

Section 1 Assessment

1. Explain how a leaf exchanges carbon dioxide and water vapor.
2. Why are photosynthesis and respiration important?
3. What must happen to glucose molecules before respiration begins?
4. Compare the number of organisms that respire to those that photosynthesize.
5. **Think Critically** Humidity is water vapor in the air. How do plants contribute to the amount of humidity in the air?

Skill Builder Activities

6. **Forming Hypotheses** White potatoes sometimes have green areas on their skins. Hypothesize what process can take place in the green part but not in the white part of the potato. **For more help, refer to the** Science Skill Handbook.
7. **Solving One-Step Equations** How many CO_2 molecules result from the aerobic respiration of a glucose molecule ($C_6H_{12}O_6$)? Refer to the equation in this section. **For more help, refer to the** Math Skill Handbook.

Comparison of Photosynthesis and Respiration

Activity

Have students make up songs that include the equations for photosynthesis and respiration. Then have them sing their songs to the class.

3 Assess

Reteach

Have students place one plant in the light and another in a dark area while keeping all other variables constant. Have them observe the plants once each day for a week. Then have students explain any changes that occur.

Challenge

How many atoms of oxygen are needed to produce six molecules of glucose? 6 atoms of oxygen × 6 molecules = 36 atoms

✓Assessment

Performance Using molecular model kits, have groups of students make the reactants of either photosynthesis or aerobic respiration. Exchange reactants between opposite groups and have them make the products of those reactants. Students should find that the reactants of one are the products of the other. Use **Performance Assessment in the Science Classroom,** p. 123.

Answers to Section Assessment

1. Carbon dioxide and water vapor are exchanged by diffusion through the stomata on leaf surfaces.
2. Photosynthesis provides the basic food source used by most organisms on Earth, either directly or indirectly. Respiration releases the energy stored in the product of photosynthesis (glucose) for use in cells.
3. Glucose molecules must be broken down into simpler molecules in the cytoplasm before respiration can begin.
4. Only organisms that contain chlorophyll photosynthesize, but all organisms respire.
5. Plants transpire water from their leaves, contributing water vapor to the air.
6. Photosynthesis can occur in the green areas of a potato but not in the white areas.
7. For every sugar molecule respired, six carbon dioxide molecules are produced.

Activity

BENCH TESTED

Activity

Stomata in Leaves

Purpose Students observe the activity of stomata in green plants. L2 ELL COOP LEARN

IS Visual-Spatial

Process Skills observing and inferring, recognizing cause and effect

Time Required 45 minutes

Alternate Materials Celery or onion epidermis may be substituted for lettuce.

Safety Precaution Emphasize that students should be careful when using microscopes.

Teaching Strategy Remind students that osmosis is diffusion of water through a semipermeable membrane.

Troubleshooting If an alternative tissue is used, try the activity beforehand to make sure observations will be appropriate.

Answers to Questions

1. the wet mount with plain water
2. Salt water causes water to leave the guard cells, causing them to become limp and close.
3. Stomata provide an entry and exit site in the leaf for gases such as carbon dioxide.

Assessment

Performance To further assess students' understanding of stomata, have them repeat the activity using one of the alternate materials and describe the outcome. Use **Performance Assessment in the Science Classroom,** p. 97.

Stomata open and close, which allows gases into and out of a leaf. These openings are usually invisible without the use of a microscope. Do this activity to see some stomata.

What You'll Investigate
Where are stomata in lettuce leaves?

Materials
lettuce in dish of water   microscope slide
coverslip   salt solution
microscope   forceps

Goals
- **Describe** guard cells and stomata.
- **Infer** the conditions that make stomata open and close.

Safety Precautions

WARNING: *Do not eat or taste any of the materials in the activity.*

Procedure

1. Copy the Stomata Data table into your Science Journal.
2. From a head of lettuce, tear off a piece of an outer, crisp, green leaf.
3. Bend the piece of leaf in half and carefully use a pair of forceps to peel off some of the epidermis, the transparent tissue that covers a leaf. Prepare a wet mount of this tissue.
4. **Examine** your prepared slide under low and high power on the microscope.
5. **Count** the total number of stomata in your field of view and then count the number of open stomata. Enter these numbers in the data table.

136   CHAPTER 5 Plant Processes

Stomata Data	Wet Mount	Salt-Solution Mount
Total Number of Stomata	50	60
Number of Open Stomata	40	5
Percent Open	80	8

6. Make a second slide of the lettuce leaf epidermis. This time place a few drops of salt solution on the leaf instead of water.
7. Repeat steps 4 and 5.
8. **Calculate** the percent of open stomata using the following equation:

$$\frac{\text{number of open stomata}}{\text{total number of stomata}} \times 100 = \text{percent open}$$

Conclude and Apply

1. Determine which slide preparation had a greater percentage of open stomata.
2. **Infer** why fewer stomata were open in the salt-solution mount.
3. What can you infer about the function of stomata in a leaf?

Communicating
Your Data

Collect data from other students in your class. Compare your data to the class data. Discuss any differences you find and why these differences occurred. **For more help, refer to the** Science Skill Handbook.

Communicating
Your Data

Data should be similar throughout the class. Differences might occur if students don't all use the same side of the leaf tissue. Upper and lower leaf surfaces often have different numbers of stomata.

Resource Manager

Chapter Resources Booklet
Activity Worksheet, pp. 5–6

Plant Responses

What are plant responses?

It's dark. You're alone in a room watching a horror film on television. Suddenly, the telephone near you rings. You jump, and your heart begins to beat faster. You've just responded to a stimulus. A stimulus is anything in the environment that causes a response in an organism. The response often involves movement either toward the stimulus or away from the stimulus. A stimulus may come from outside (external) or inside (internal) the organism. The ringing telephone is an example of an external stimulus. It caused you to jump, which is a response. Your beating heart is a response to an internal stimulus. Internal stimuli are usually chemicals produced by organisms. Many of these chemicals are hormones. Hormones are substances made in one part of an organism for use somewhere else in the organism.

All living organisms, including plants, respond to stimuli. Many different chemicals are known to act as hormones in plants. These internal stimuli have a variety of effects on plant growth and function. Plants respond to external stimuli such as touch, light, and gravity. Some responses, such as the response of the Venus's-flytrap plant in **Figure 10,** are rapid. Other plant responses are slower because they involve changes in growth.

As You Read

What You'll Learn
- **Identify** the relationship between a stimulus and a tropism in plants.
- **Compare and contrast** long-day and short-day plants.
- **Explain** how plant hormones and responses are related.

Vocabulary
tropism
auxin
photoperiodism
long-day plant
short-day plant
day-neutral plant

Why It's Important
You will be able to grow healthier plants if you understand how they respond to certain stimuli.

Figure 10
A Venus's-flytrap has three small trigger hairs on the surface of its toothed leaves. When two hairs are touched at the same time, the plant responds by closing its trap in less than 1 second.

SECTION 2 Plant Responses **137**

Plant Responses

Discussion

Have students brainstorm a list of possible ways to determine the cause of various plant responses. Lead them to understand the difference between external and internal stimuli. External stimuli include touch, light, and gravity. Internal stimuli include hormones.

Tropisms

Activity

Small groups of students can grow a pea plant from seed. As the plant begins to grow, they place a stick in the pot. The stem and tendrils will respond by growing around the stick. Have students identify the type of response this illustrates. thigmatropism Challenge students to record and graph the growth of the pea plant. L3

Quick Demo

Bring a Venus's-flytrap to class to demonstrate nastic movements. The trap of the Venus's-flytrap is triggered when three or more of the sensitive hairs on the upper surfaces of the hinged leaves are touched. Use the fine tip of a needle or pencil to manipulate the hairs.

Physics
INTEGRATION

Students may propose various experiments. Look for those that include a control and a method that would include a true test of the effects of gravity.

Figure 11
Tropisms are responses to external stimuli.

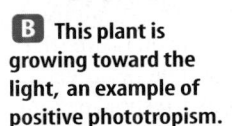

A The pea plant's tendrils respond to touch by coiling around things.

B This plant is growing toward the light, an example of positive phototropism.

C This plant was turned on its side. With the roots visible, you can see that they are showing positive gravitropism.

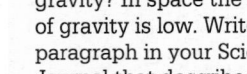
Physics
INTEGRATION

Gravity is a stimulus that affects how plants grow. Can plants grow without gravity? In space the force of gravity is low. Write a paragraph in your Science Journal that describes your idea for an experiment aboard a space shuttle to test how low gravity affects plant growth.

Tropisms

Some responses of a plant to an external stimuli are called tropisms. A **tropism** (TROH pih zum) can be seen as movement caused by a change in growth and can be positive or negative. For example, plants might grow toward a stimulus—a positive tropism—or away from a stimulus—a negative tropism.

Touch One stimulus that can result in a change in a plant's growth is touch. When the pea plant, shown in **Figure 11A,** touches a solid object, it responds by growing faster on one side of its stem than on the other side. As a result the stem bends and twists around any object it touches.

Light Did you ever see a plant leaning toward a window? Light is an important stimulus to plants. When a plant responds to light, the cells on the side of the plant opposite the light get longer than the cells facing the light. Because of this uneven growth, the plant bends toward the light. This response causes the leaves to turn in such a way that they can absorb more light. When a plant grows toward light it is called a positive response to light, as shown in **Figure 11B.**

Gravity Plants respond to gravity. The downward growth of plant roots is a positive response to gravity, as shown in **Figure 11C.** A stem growing upward is a negative response to gravity. Plants also may respond to electricity, temperature, and darkness.

138 CHAPTER 5 Plant Processes

Visual Learning

Figure 11 Use these photographs to launch a discussion on plant responses caused by various external stimuli. **Where have you seen responses such as these? How might they help a plant meet its needs?** Answers will vary. Many of these responses help a plant grow toward the light, their source of energy.

Teacher FYI

Unlike tropisms, nastic movements are independent of the direction of the stimulus. The most common are "sleep" or nyctinastic movements. These movements position leaves of some plants horizontally during the daylight and vertically at night. This response results from turgor pressure changes in cells.

Plant Hormones

Hormones control the changes in growth that result from tropisms and affect other plant growth. Plants often need only millionths of a gram of a hormone to stimulate a response.

Ethylene Many plants produce the hormone ethylene (EH thuh leen) gas and release it into the air around them. This means that ethylene produced by one plant can cause a response in a nearby plant. One plant response to ethylene causes a layer of cells to form between a leaf and the stem. That's why most leaves fall from plants.

Ethylene is produced in cells of ripening fruit, which stimulates the ripening process. Commercially, fruits such as oranges and bananas are picked when they are still green. During shipping the green fruits are exposed to ethylene and they ripen.

Math Skills Activity

Calculating Averages

Example Problem

What is the average height of control bean seedlings after 14 days?

Solution

1 *This is what you know:*
height of control seedlings after 14 days
number of control seedlings

2 *This is what you need to find:*
average height of control seedlings after14 days

3 *This is what you must do:*
total the heights of all control seedlings
$15 + 12 + 14 + 13 + 10 + 11 = 75$ cm

4 *Divide the total height by the total number of control seedlings:*
75 cm/6
average height of control seedlings = 12.5 cm

Practice Problem

Calculate the average height of seedlings treated with gibberellin.

For more help, refer to the Math Skill Handbook.

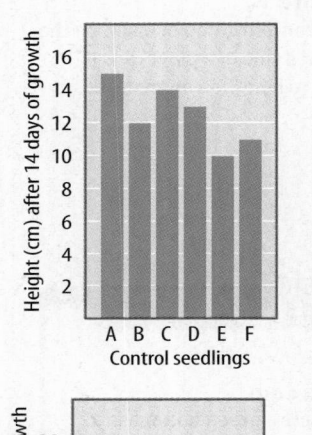

Control seedlings

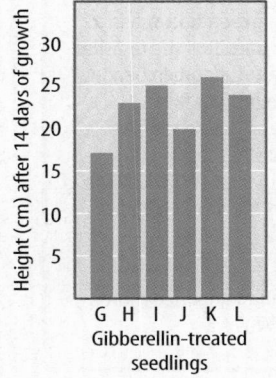

Gibberellin-treated seedlings

Resource Manager

Chapter Resources Booklet
Transparency Activity, p. 41
Directed Reading for Content Mastery, pp. 19, 20
Mathematics Skill Activities, p. 25

☑ Active Reading

Quickwrites This strategy, sometimes called freewrites, lets students use spontaneous writing to discover what they already know. Have students write a list of ideas about a topic, then share these ideas with the class. Next, have students write their ideas freely in a paragraph without worrying about punctuation, spelling, and grammar. Have students use a Quickwrite to share ideas about plant responses.

Plant Hormones

Activity

Use an activity kit for rapidly growing plants of the genus *Brassica*, available from biological supply houses, to demonstrate plant responses to hormones. These plants can grow from seed to flower in about 15 days.

Discussion

Review the names of the parts of flowering plants with students. Ask if they think every structure responds equally to every stimulus. Possible answer: different parts of a flowering plant respond to different stimuli.

Math Skills Activity

National Math Standards
Correlation to Mathematics Objectives
1, 2, 4, 6, 8, 9

Teaching Suggestion:

Students may be asked to provide the following information from the graph:
a. range of heights for control seedlings
b. range of heights for gibberellin-treated seedlings
c. percent difference in height of gibberellin-treated seedlings compared to control seedlings

It may be necessary to help students interpolate the height values on the graph.

Answer to Practice Problem

135 cm ÷ 6 = 22.5 cm

Note: Students' answers may differ slightly from the answer provided. Accept answers that are reasonably close. Variation in answers may be caused by differing interpolations of seedling heights as read from the graph.

Plant Hormones, continued

✔ Reading Check

Answer Auxin is the hormone that causes stems and leaves to exhibit positive phototropism.

Quick Demo

Obtain two coleus cuttings. Apply a rooting hormone to one cutting before planting both stems. After several days, have students observe the roots of both stems and explain the results. The cutting with the hormone should show greater root growth due to the presence of the chemical.

TRY AT HOME Mini LAB

Purpose to observe the effects of ethylene on ripening fruit

L1 | ELL | LS | **Kinesthetic**

Materials two green bananas, paper bag

Teaching Strategies
• Tell students to choose two green bananas that are at the same stage of ripeness.

Analysis
The green banana in the bag; the ethylene produced by the ripening banana was trapped in the bag, causing the fruit to ripen more quickly.

Oral Have students explain their results to the class. Use **Performance Assessment in the Science Classroom,** p. 143.

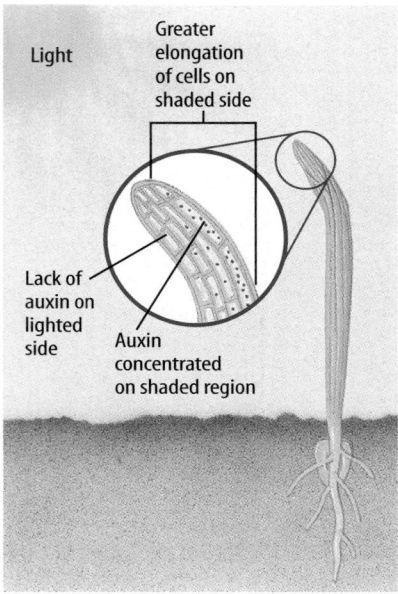

Figure 12
The concentration of auxin on the shaded side of a plant causes cells to lengthen on that side.

Light | Greater elongation of cells on shaded side

Lack of auxin on lighted side

Auxin concentrated on shaded region

TRY AT HOME Mini LAB

Observing Ripening

Procedure
1. Place a **green banana** in a **paper bag.** Roll the top shut.
2. Place another green banana on a counter or table.
3. After two days check the bananas to see how they have ripened. **WARNING:** *Do not eat the materials used in the lab.*

Analysis
Which banana ripened more quickly? Why?

Auxin Scientists identified the plant hormone, **auxin** (AWK sun) more than 100 years ago. Auxin is a type of plant hormone that causes plant stems and leaves to exhibit positive response to light. When light shines on a plant from one side, the auxin moves to the shaded side of the stem where it causes a change in growth, as shown in **Figure 12.** Auxins also control the production of other plant hormones, including ethylene.

✔ Reading Check   *How are auxins and positive response to light related?*

Development of many parts of the plant, including flowers, roots, and fruit, is stimulated by auxins. Because auxins are so important in plant development, synthetic auxins have been developed for use in agriculture. Some of these synthetic auxins are used in orchards so that all plants produce flowers and fruit at the same time. Other synthetic auxins damage plants when they are applied in high doses and are used as weed killers.

Gibberellins and Cytokinins Two other groups of plant hormones that also cause changes in plant growth are gibberellins and cytokinins. Gibberellins (jih buh REH lunz) are chemical substances that were isolated first from a fungus. The fungus caused a disease in rice plants called "foolish seedling" disease. The fungus infects the stems of plants and causes them to grow too tall. Gibberellins can be mixed with water and sprayed on plants and seeds to stimulate plant stems to grow and seeds to germinate.

Like gibberellins, cytokinins (si tuh KI nunz) also cause rapid growth. Cytokinins promote growth by causing faster cell divisions. Like ethylene, the effect of cytokinins on the plant also is controlled by auxin. Interestingly, cytokinins can be sprayed on stored vegetables to keep them fresh longer.

Abscisic Acid Because hormones that cause growth in plants were known to exist, biologists suspected that substances that have the reverse effect also must exist. Abscisic (ab SIH zihk) acid is one such substance. Many plants grow in areas that have cold winters. Normally, if seeds germinate, or buds develop on plants during the winter, they will die. Abscisic acid is the substance that keeps seeds from sprouting and buds from developing during the winter. This plant hormone also causes stomata to close and helps plants respond to water loss on hot summer days. **Figure 13** summarizes how plant hormones affect plants and how hormones are used.

Cultural **Diversity**

Ewiti Kurosawa Japanese scientist Ewiti Kurosawa discovered gibberellin while investigating the cause of "foolish seedling disease." He discovered that rice plants grew so tall that they fell over (thus, "foolish seedlings") after being infected with a fungus that secreted the substance. He named gibberellin after the genus of the fungus, *Gibberella fujikuroi.*

Figure 13

Chemical compounds called plant hormones help determine how a plant grows. There are five main types of hormones. They coordinate a plant's growth and development, as well as its responses to environmental stimuli, such as light, gravity, and changing seasons. Most changes in plant growth are a result of plant hormones working together, but exactly how hormones cause these changes is not completely understood.

◀ GIBBERELLINS The larger mustard plant in the photo at left was sprayed with gibberellins, plant hormones that stimulate stem elongation and fruit development.

▲ ETHYLENE By controlling the exposure of these tomatoes to ethylene, a hormone that stimulates fruit ripening, farmers are able to harvest unripe fruit and make it ripen just before it arrives at the supermarket.

Lateral buds

Lateral branches

◀ CYTOKININS Lateral buds do not usually develop into branches. However, if a plant's main stem is cut, as in this bean plant, naturally occurring cytokinins will stimulate the growth of lateral branches, causing the plant to grow "bushy."

▼ AUXINS Powerful growth hormones called auxins regulate responses to light and gravity, stem elongation, and root growth. The root growth on the plant cuttings, center and right, is the result of auxin treatment.

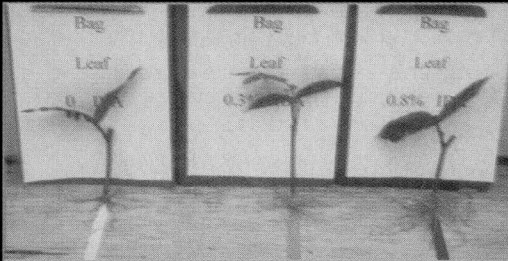

▶ ABA (ABSCISIC ACID) In plants such as the American basswood, right, abscisic acid causes buds to remain dormant for the winter. When spring arrives, ABA stops working and the buds sprout.

SECTION 2 Plant Responses **141**

Visualizing Plant Hormones

Have students examine the pictures and read the captions. Then ask the following questions.

Which of the hormones here do not stimulate plant growth? What functions do these hormones serve? ABA causes dormancy instead of growth, and ethylene stimulates fruit ripening instead of growth.

How could farmers use plant hormones to enhance their profits? By controlling plant growth, budding, dormancy periods and ripening of fruits, farmers can deliver more product to the market.

What plant hormone has most likely been studied by researchers working in space? Auxins, which control a plant's response to gravity would be of great interest to those studying a plant's response to the reduced gravity in space.

Activity

Have students work in teams to write a poem with five verses. Each verse should name a type of plant hormone, and tell the function of the hormone and the particular parts of the plant the hormone acts on.

Extension

Evidence exists that a plant hormone called florigen controls flowering in plants, but scientists haven't isolated it yet. Have students research some of the experiments scientists have done in their search for florigen. Students should report their findings to the class.

Resource Manager

Chapter Resources Booklet
MiniLAB, p. 4
Lab Activity, pp. 11–14
Home and Community Involvement, p. 45

Photoperiods

Extension

Take the class on a field trip to a commercial greenhouse. Have students interview the staff to find out how they encourage plants to flower at times other than their normal flowering seasons. Growers often plan six to twelve months ahead in order to supply plants that are blooming out of season.

✔ Reading Check

Answer A specific amount of darkness is needed, which varies depending on the species of plant.

Figure 14
When short-day plants receive less darkness than required to produce flowers, they produce larger leaves instead.

Photoperiods

Earth Science INTEGRATION

Sunflowers bloom in the summer, and cherry trees flower in the spring. Some plant species produce flowers at specific times during the year. A plant's response to the number of hours of daylight and darkness it receives daily is **photoperiodism** (foh toh PIHR ee uh dih zum).

Earth revolves around the Sun once each year. As Earth moves in its orbit, it also rotates. One rotation takes about 24 h. Because Earth is tilted about 23.5° from a line perpendicular to its orbit, the hours of daylight and darkness vary with the seasons. As you probably have noticed, the Sun sets later in summer than in winter. These changes in lengths of daylight and darkness affect plant growth.

Darkness and Flowers Many plants require a specific length of darkness to begin the flowering process. Generally, plants that require less than 10 h to 12 h of darkness to flower are called **long-day plants.** You may be familiar with some long-day plants such as spinach, lettuce, and beets. Plants that need 12 or more hours of darkness to flower are called **short-day plants.** Some short-day plants are poinsettias, strawberries, and ragweed. **Figure 14** shows what happens when a short-day plant receives less darkness than it needs to flower.

✔ Reading Check
What is needed to begin the flowering process?

Day-Neutral Plants Plants like dandelions and roses are **day-neutral plants.** They have no specific photoperiod, and the flowering process can begin within a range of hours of darkness.

In nature, photoperiodism affects where flowering plants can grow and produce flowers and fruit. Even if a particular environment has the proper temperature and other growing conditions for a plant, it will not flower and produce fruit without the correct photoperiod. **Table 2** shows how day length affects flowering in all three types of plants.

Sometimes the photoperiod of a plant has a narrow range. For example, some soybeans will flower with 9.5 h of darkness but will not flower with 10 h of darkness. Farmers must choose the variety of soybeans with a photoperiod that matches the hours of darkness in the section of the country where they plant their crop.

Curriculum Connection

Geography Have students research the place of origin for different plants and plot the locations on a world map. Challenge students to determine whether location of origin correlates with the length of darkness a plant needs to flower.

 L3 P

Table 2 Photoperiodism

	Long-Day Plants	Short-Day Plants	Day-Neutral Plants
Early Summer Noon 6 AM 6 PM Midnight			
Late Fall Noon 6 AM 6 PM Midnight			
	An iris is a long-day plant that is stimulated by short nights to flower in the early summer.	Goldenrod is a short-day plant that is stimulated by long nights to flower in the fall.	Roses are day-neutral plants and have no specific photoperiod.

Today, greenhouse growers are able to provide any length of artificial daylight or darkness. This means that you can buy short-day flowering plants during the summer and long-day flowering plants during the winter.

Section 2 Assessment

1. Give an example of an internal stimulus and an external stimulus in plants.
2. Compare and contrast photoperiodism and phototropism.
3. Some red raspberries produce fruit in late spring, then again in the fall. What term describes their photoperiod?
4. How do the effects of abscisic acid differ from those of gibberellins?
5. **Think Critically** What is the relationship between plant hormones and tropisms?

Skill Builder Activities

6. **Comparing and Contrasting** Different plant parts exhibit positive and negative tropisms. Compare and contrast the responses of roots and stems to gravity. **For more help, refer to the** Science Skill Handbook.
7. **Communicating** For three years a farmer in Costa Rica grew healthy strawberry plants. But the plants never produced fruit. In your Science Journal, explain why this happened. **For more help, refer to the** Science Skill Handbook.

Section 2 Plant Responses **143**

Answers to Section Assessment

1. Possible answers: Internal stimuli include hormones; external stimuli include environmental factors such as gravity and light.
2. Photoperiodism is plant responses to the length of the period of darkness; phototropism is any growth response to light.
3. short-day
4. Abscisic acid slows growth; gibberellins speed growth in plants.
5. Plant hormones are responsible for some tropisms.
6. Roots show positive gravitropism and grow downward. Stems show negative gravitropism and grow upward.
7. Strawberries are short-day plants. Because Costa Rica is near the equator, the days are about the same length as the nights, so there are too few hours of darkness to produce flowering in strawberries.

Activity

What You'll Investigate

Purpose

Students experiment to observe plant responses to gravity. [L2]

ELL [LS] **Logical-Mathematical**

Process Skills

observing and inferring, communicating, making and using tables, comparing and contrasting, recognizing cause and effect, separating and controlling variables, interpreting data, using numbers

Time Required

1 class period to set up; 20 minutes one day each week for up to two weeks

Materials

clear jar, marking pen, mustard seeds, aluminum foil, paper towel, water

Alternate Materials

Bean seeds can be substituted for mustard seeds.

Safety Precautions

Some kinds of seeds are poisonous. Do not allow students to put seeds in their mouths.

Activity

Tropism in Plants

Grapevines can climb on trees, fences, or other nearby structures. This growth is a response to the stimulus of touch. Tropisms are specific plant responses to stimuli outside of the plant. One part of a plant can respond positively while another part of the same plant can respond negatively to the same stimulus. Gravitropism is a response to gravity. Why might it be important for some plant parts to have a positive response to gravity while other plant parts have a negative response? You can design an experiment to test how some plant parts respond to the stimulus of gravity.

What You'll Investigate

Do stems and roots respond to gravity in the same way?

Materials

paper towel
30 cm × 30 cm sheet of aluminum foil
water
mustard seeds
marking pen
1-L clear glass or plastic jar

Goals

- **Describe** how roots and stems respond to gravity.
- **Observe** how changing the stimulus changes the growth of plants.

Safety Precautions

WARNING: *Some kinds of seeds are poisonous. Do not put any seed in your mouth. Wash your hands after handling the seeds.*

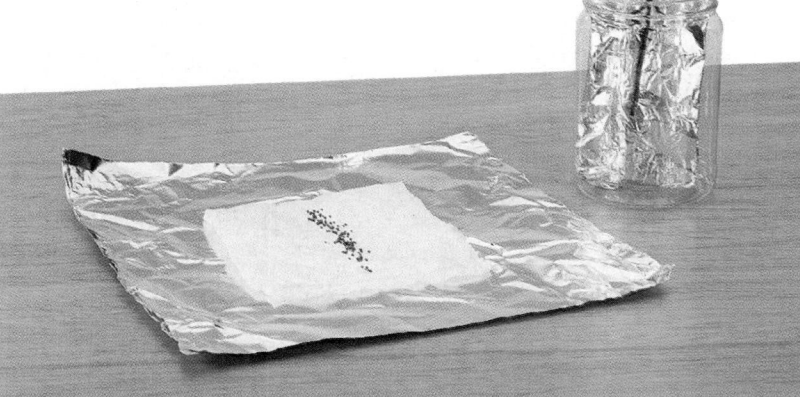

Inclusion Strategies

Learning Disabled Provide clear directions both orally and in writing. Assign a buddy to each student to help him or her assemble the seed packets.

Science Journal

Old Seeds Ask students if they think the age of the seeds used would make a difference in the results. Have them write their hypotheses and possible investigations in their Science Journals.

Procedure

1. Copy the following data table in your Science Journal.

2. Moisten the paper towel with water so that it's damp but not dripping. Fold it in half twice.

3. In the center of the foil, place the folded paper towel and sprinkle mustard seeds in a line across the center of the towel.

4. Fold the foil around the towel and seal each end by folding the foil over. Make sure the paper towel is completely covered by the foil.

5. Use a marking pen to draw an arrow on the foil, and place the foil package in the jar with the arrow pointing upward.

6. After five days carefully open the package and record your observations in the data table. (Note: *If no stems or roots are growing yet, reseal the package and place it back in the jar, making sure that the arrow points upward. Reopen the package in two days.*)

Response to Gravity		
Position of Arrow on Foil Package	Observations of Seedling Roots	Observations of Seedling Stems
Arrow Up	Growing away from arrow	Growing toward arrow
Arrow Down	Growing toward arrow	Growing away from arrow

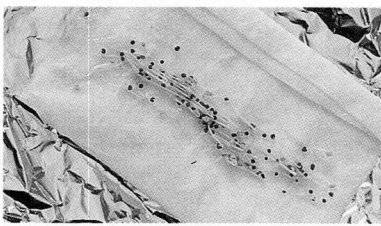

7. Reseal the foil package, being careful not to disturb the seedlings. Place it in the jar so that the arrow points downward instead of upward.

8. After five more days reopen the package and observe any new growth of the seedlings' roots and stems. Record your observations in your data table.

Conclude and Apply

1. **Classify** the responses you observed as positive or negative tropisms.

2. **Explain** why the plants' growth changed when you placed them upside down.

3. Why was it important that no light reach the seedlings during your experiment?

4. What are some other ways you could have changed the position of the foil package to test the seedlings' response?

Communicating
Your Data

Use drawings to **compare** the growth of the seedlings before and after you turned the package. **Compare** your drawing with those of other students in your class. **For more help, refer to the** Science Skill Handbook.

Resource Manager

Chapter Resources Booklet
 Activity Worksheet, pp. 7–8
Lab Management and Safety, p. 58

Communicating
Your Data

Drawings will indicate that roots grow downward and shoots grow upward, notwithstanding the orientation of the seed.

Procedure

Teaching Strategy Explain to students that there may be more than one variable at work and that stems and roots may be responding differently to these stimuli.

Troubleshooting Be sure that students always place the seeds back in the dish with the arrow pointing up.

Expected Outcome

Roots will grow downward and shoots will grow upward.

Conclude and Apply

1. Stem growth upward is negative gravitropism; root growth downward is positive gravitropism.

2. The plants' growth continued to respond to the stimulus provided by gravity, even though the direction of this stimuli had changed.

3. If light reached the seedlings, they could have responded to it (phototropism), and results due to gravitropism would be uncertain.

4. Possible answers: The packages could have been laid flat or put on a spinning turntable.

Error Analysis

Have students compare their data with that of others and explain any differences they encounter.

✓Assessment

Portfolio Have students make a labeled poster of their experimental results and share it with the class. Use **Performance Assessment in the Science Classroom**, p. 145.

Sunkissed: An Indian Legend
as told by Alberto and Patricia De La Fuente

Pre-Reading Activity

Ask students what they know about the Sun before they read the retelling of this fable by the De La Fuentes. Encourage all kinds of responses, from what the Sun looks like throughout the day, to more scientific facts about the Sun such as how it helps support life on Earth. Write down student responses on the board as they are being called out.

Respond to the Reading

Active Reading Strategies

Visualize Keep the events and setting in your mind's eye as you read. Form pictures in your mind. The fable goes to great lengths to describe the natural setting of the story. **Is the setting a fictional place?**

Review Review what you have read. By looking back over several paragraphs, you can see how the information fits together. **Why do they characterize the flower as a human, or in this case, a girl?**

Answers to Questions

1. The plants need the Sun to survive and grow.
2. The flowers need water to survive and grow.
3. Student answers will vary. Some students might suggest that it does not give enough detail about photosynthesis. Others might suggest that the visual imagery of the story is enough to convey the message.

Respond to the Reading

1. What does this passage tell you about the relationship between the Sun and plants?
2. What does this passage tell you about the relationship between water and the growth of flowers?
3. Do you think this passage is effective in making the reader understand the importance of light and darkness to a growing plant? Why or why not?

A long time ago, deep down in the very heart of the old Mexican forests, so far away from the sea that not even the largest birds ever had time to fly that far, there was a small, beautiful valley. A long chain of snow-covered mountains stood between the valley and the sea. . . . Each day the mountains were the first ones to tell everybody that Tonatiuh, the King of Light, was coming to the valley. The meadows would see the shining white tops of the mountains and spread out their flowery skirts for the Sun.

"Good morning, Tonatiuh!" cried a little meadow.

"Hurry up and bring us warmth and light!" sang all the wild roses along the river bank together as an opening line. . . .

The wild flowers always started their fresh new day with a kiss of golden sunlight from Tonatiuh, but it was necessary to first wash their sleepy baby faces with the dew that Metztli, the Moon, sprinkled for them out of her bucket onto the nearby leaves during the night. . . .

. . . All night long, then, Metztli Moon would walk her night-field making sure that by sun-up all flowers had the magic dew that made them feel beautiful all day long.

However, much as flowers love to be beautiful as long as possible, they want to be happy too. So every morning Tonatiuh himself would give each one a single golden kiss of such power that it was possible to be happy all day long after it. As you can see, then, a flower needs to feel beautiful in the first place, but if she does not feel beautiful, she will not be ready for her morning sun-kiss. If she cannot wash her little face with the magic dew, the whole day is lost.

146 CHAPTER 5 Plant Processes

Reading Further

American Indian Myths and Legends by Richard Erdoes (Editor) and Alfonso Ortiz (Editor), Pantheon Books, 1985.

Old Indian Legends by Zitkala-Sa, Sa Zitkala, and Angela Decora (Illustrator), University of Nebraska Press, 1985.

Understanding Literature

Legends and Oral Traditions A legend is a traditional story often told orally and believed to be based on actual people and events. Legends are believed to be true even if they cannot be proved. *Sunkissed: An Indian Legend* is a legend about a little flower that is changed forever by the Sun. What in this story indicates that it is a legend? This legend also is an example of an oral tradition. Oral traditions are stories or skills that are handed down by word of mouth. They can be stories about real people and events, fictional stories, recipes, or crafts.

Science Connection In this chapter, you learned about the processes of photosynthesis and respiration. The passage from *Sunkissed: An Indian Legend* does not teach us the details about photosynthesis or respiration. However, it does show how sunshine and water are important to plant life. The difference between the legend and the information contained in your textbook is this— photosynthesis and respiration can be proved scientifically, and the legend, although fun to read, cannot.

Linking Science and Writing

Creating Oral Traditions
Create an idea for a fictional story that explains why the sky becomes so colorful during a sunset. Write a few short notes about your story on a piece of paper. Then retell your story to your classmates using only your short notes and your imagination. When you retell your story, remember that good storytellers are enthusiastic and entertaining. An oral tradition is started because listeners want to pass the story along.

Career Connection

Horticulturist/Landscape Designer

Jill Nokes is a horticulturist who studies plants and how to grow them. Many horticulturists work in large nurseries as managers or plant breeders. Nokes works as a landscape designer, a person who creates gardens for homes and businesses. There are two important parts to a landscape designer's job. Designers must first create attractive landscapes for their clients. They also have to be plant experts so they can choose plants that will thrive in the local climate and with other plants in the design.

SCIENCE *Online* To learn more about careers in horticulture, visit the Glencoe Science Web site at **science.glencoe.com.**

Career Connection

While landscape designers design gardens, there is also the landscape architect. Landscape architecture is defined as "the art of arranging land and the objects upon it for human use and enjoyment." Landscape architecture includes site planning, land planning, master planning, urban design, and environmental planning.

SCIENCE Online
Internet Addresses

_____

_____

_____

Explore the Glencoe Science Web site at **science.glencoe.com** to find out more about topics in this feature.

Understanding Literature

Answer to Question

Answers will vary but should include that a legend is usually a fictional story relaying information about a specific culture, in this case Mexican.

Science Connection

The study of photosynthesis began in 1771, with observations made by the English chemist Joseph Priestley. Priestly had burned a candle in a closed container until the air within the container could no longer support combustion. He then placed a sprig of mint plant in the container and discovered that after several days the mint had produced some substance (later recognized as oxygen) that enabled the confined air to again support combustion. In 1779 the Dutch physician Jan Ingenhouz showed that the plant must be exposed to light if oxygen is to be restored.

Linking Science and Writing

Teaching Strategies

Lead students in brainstorming to come up with reasons that sunsets are colorful. Let them know that causes of pigment in the sky are not always natural. For example, some sky color can be caused by pollution. This exercise will give them a start on the writing activity.

Chapter 5 Study Guide

Reviewing Main Ideas

Preview

Students can answer the questions in their Science Journals. Discuss the answers as you go through the chapter. **Linguistic**

Review

Students can write their answers, then compare them with those of other students. **Interpersonal**

Reteach

Students can look at the illustrations and describe details that support the main ideas of the chapter. **Visual-Spatial**

Answers to Chapter Review

SECTION 1

3. They produce food for themselves and consumers.
5. Respiration provides energy the sprouting seed needs for growth and development.

SECTION 2

2. Gravity; some students may say light.
3. They do not depend on length of dark periods to trigger flowering.

Reviewing Main Ideas

Section 1 Photosynthesis and Respiration

1. Carbon dioxide and water vapor gases enter and leave a plant through openings in the epidermis called stomata. Guard cells cause a stoma to open and close.

2. Photosynthesis takes place in the chloroplasts of plant cells. Light energy is used to produce glucose and oxygen from carbon dioxide and water.

3. Photosynthesis provides the food for most organisms on Earth. *Why are plants called producers?*

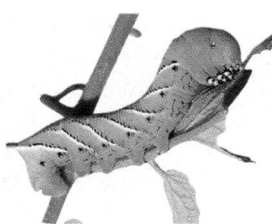

4. All organisms use respiration to release the energy stored in food molecules. Oxygen is used in the mitochondria to complete respiration in plant cells and many other types of cells. Energy, carbon dioxide, and water are produced.

5. The energy produced from respiration is needed by most living organisms including plants. *Why is respiration important to this sprouting seed?*

6. Photosynthesis and respiration are almost the reverse of each other. The end products of photosynthesis are the raw materials needed for aerobic respiration. The end products of aerobic respiration are the raw materials needed for photosynthesis.

Section 2 Plant Responses

1. Plants respond positively and negatively to stimuli. The response may be a movement, a change in growth, or the beginning of some process such as flowering.

2. A stimulus from outside the plant is called a tropism. Outside stimuli include such things as light, gravity, and touch. *What outside stimulus is affecting the growth of this plant?*

3. The length of darkness each day can affect flowering times of plants. *Why can day-neutral plants, such as this one, flower almost any time?*

4. Hormones control changes from inside plants. These chemicals affect plants in many ways. Some hormones cause plants to exhibit tropisms. Other hormones cause changes in plant growth.

FOLDABLES
Reading & Study Skills

After You Read

Use the information in your Compare and Contrast Study Fold to compare and contrast aerobic respiration that occurs in plants and animals.

FOLDABLES
Reading & Study Skills

After You Read

After students have read the chapter and completed the Foldable described in Before You Read, have them do the activity on the student page.

Dinah Zike

Visualizing Main Ideas

Complete the following cycle concept map that shows how photosynthesis and respiration are related.

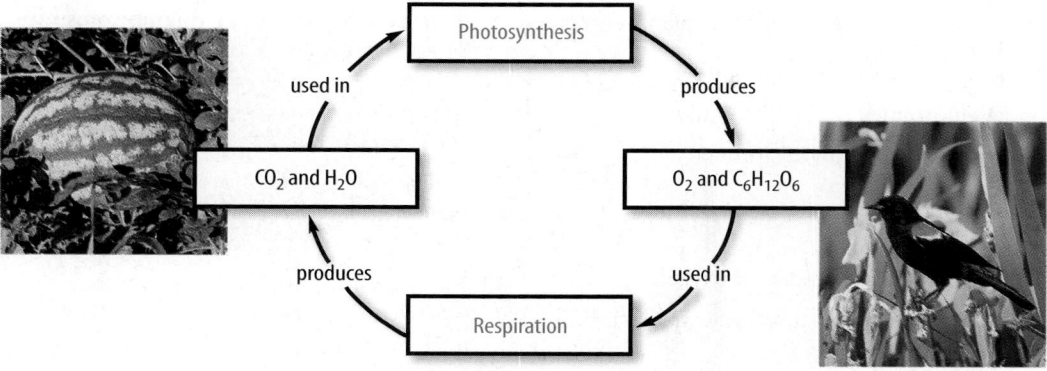

```
                Photosynthesis
        used in              produces
  CO₂ and H₂O                    O₂ and C₆H₁₂O₆
        produces              used in
                Respiration
```

Vocabulary Review

Vocabulary Words

a. auxin
b. chlorophyll
c. day-neutral plant
d. long-day plant
e. photoperiodism
f. photosynthesis
g. respiration
h. short-day plant
i. stomata
j. tropism

Using Vocabulary

Replace the underlined definition with the correct vocabulary word from the list above.

1. A plant hormone causes plant stems and leaves to exhibit positive phototropism.

Study Tip

Outline the chapters to make sure that you understand the key ideas that are presented. Writing down the main points of the chapter will help you remember important details and understand larger themes.

2. An important process of green plants is using light to make glucose and oxygen.

3. A green pigment is important in the process of photosynthesis.

4. A poinsettia, often seen flowering during December holidays, is a plant that requires long nights to flower.

5. The process of energy release from food occurs in most living things.

6. Spinach is a plant that requires only ten hours of darkness at night to flower.

7. A response of a plant to an outside stimulus can cause the plant to bend toward light.

8. Plants usually take in carbon dioxide through tiny pores in their leaves.

9. A plant's response to the number of hours of darkness it receives daily determines many plant processes.

10. Marigolds are plants that flower without regard to the length of darkness.

CHAPTER STUDY GUIDE 149

Chapter 5
Assessment

Checking Concepts

1. C
2. D
3. D
4. C
5. D
6. A
7. D
8. C
9. A
10. B

Thinking Critically

11. Put them in a brown paper bag to retain ethylene.
12. a. negative gravitropism; b. positive gravitropism; c. positive phototropism; d. positive thigmotropism
13. Oxygen is a by-product of photosynthesis. Until organisms that used carbon dioxide for photosynthesis evolved, little free oxygen was available.
14. Apple trees bloom in the spring when the days are short and nights are long. The number of dark hours in the summer is less than an apple tree's photoperiod.
15. Day-neutral plants will flower anywhere if they receive a minimum number of hours of darkness and if other environmental conditions are favorable. Long-day plants require the number of hours of darkness that occurs near the equator.

Checking Concepts

Choose the word or phrase that best answers the question.

1. What raw material needed by plants enters through open stomata?
   - A) sugar
   - B) chlorophyll
   - C) carbon dioxide
   - D) cellulose

2. What is a function of stomata?
   - A) photosynthesis
   - B) to guard the interior cells
   - C) to allow sugar to escape
   - D) to permit the release of oxygen

3. What plant process produces water, carbon dioxide, and energy?
   - A) cell division
   - B) photosynthesis
   - C) growth
   - D) respiration

4. What type of plant needs short nights in order to flower?
   - A) day-neutral
   - B) short-day
   - C) long-day
   - D) nonvascular

5. What do you call things such as light, touch, and gravity that cause plant growth responses?
   - A) tropisms
   - B) growth
   - C) responses
   - D) stimuli

6. What are the products of photosynthesis?
   - A) glucose and oxygen
   - B) carbon dioxide and water
   - C) chlorophyll and glucose
   - D) carbon dioxide and oxygen

7. What are plant substances that affect plant growth called?
   - A) tropisms
   - B) glucose
   - C) germination
   - D) hormones

8. Leaves change colors because what substance breaks down?
   - A) hormone
   - B) carotenoid
   - C) chlorophyll
   - D) cytoplasm

9. Which of these is a product of respiration?
   - A) CO_2
   - B) O_2
   - C) C_2H_4
   - D) H_2

10. What is a plant's response to gravity called?
    - A) phototropism
    - B) gravitropism
    - C) thigmotropism
    - D) hydrotropism

Thinking Critically

11. You buy pears at the store that are not completely ripe. What could you do to help them ripen more rapidly?

12. Name each tropism and state whether it is positive or negative.
    - a. Stem grows up.
    - b. Roots grow down.
    - c. Plant grows toward light.
    - d. A vine grows around a pole.

13. Scientists who study sedimentary rocks and fossils suggest that oxygen was not in Earth's atmosphere until plantlike, one-celled organisms appeared. Why?

14. Explain why apple trees bloom in the spring but not in the summer.

15. Why do day-neutral and long-day plants grow best in countries near the equator?

Developing Skills

16. **Forming Hypotheses** Make a hypothesis about when guard cells open and close in desert plants.

17. **Identifying and Manipulating Variables and Controls** Plan an experiment to test your hypothesis in question 16.

18. **Predicting** Make a prediction about how the number and location of stomata differ in land plants and water plants whose leaves float on the water's surface.

Chapter ✓Assessment Planner

Portfolio Encourage students to place in their portfolios one or two items of what they consider to be their best work. Examples include:
- Science Journal, p. 131
- Curriculum Connection, p. 140
- Reteach, p. 141

Performance Additional performance assessments, Performance Task Assessment Lists, and rubrics for evaluating these activities can be found in Glencoe's **Performance Assessment in the Science Classroom.**

19. Concept Mapping Complete the following concept map about photoperiodism using the following information: flower year-round—*corn, dandelion, tomato;* flower in the spring, fall, or winter—*chrysanthemum, rice, poinsettia;* flower in summer—*spinach, lettuce, petunia.*

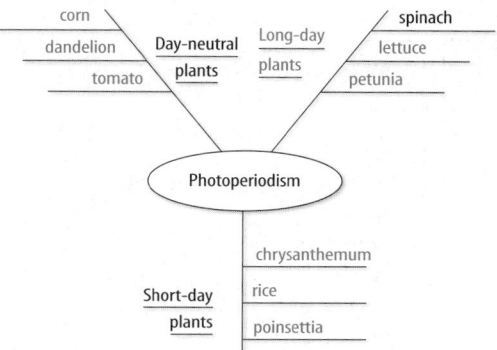

20. Comparing and Contrasting Compare and contrast the action of auxin and the action of ethylene on a plant.

Performance Assessment

21. Coloring Book Create a coloring book of day-neutral plants, long-day plants, and short-day plants. Use pictures from magazines and seed catalogs to get your ideas. Label the drawings with the plant's name and how it responds to darkness. Let a younger student color the flowers in your book.

TECHNOLOGY

Go to the Glencoe Science Web site at **science.glencoe.com** or use the **Glencoe Science CD-ROM** for additional chapter assessment.

THE PRINCETON REVIEW **Test Practice**

Eileen and Logan wanted to learn more about the materials that plants use during photosynthesis. They designed the following data table to record the results of their investigation.

Resources Used During Photosynthesis

Plant	Water Used	Carbon Dioxide Used	Light Absorbed	Oxygen Produced
Plant X				
Plant Y				
Plant Z				

Study the table and answer the following questions.

1. Using your knowledge of photosynthesis, which of the data columns would not be needed for recording results from the investigation?
A) water used
B) carbon dioxide used
C) light absorbed
D) oxygen produced

2. The most likely source of energy for the plants during this investigation is _____.
F) water
G) carbon dioxide
H) light
J) oxygen

THE PRINCETON REVIEW **Test Practice**

The Test-Taking Tip was written by The Princeton Review, the nation's leader in test preparation.
1. D
2. H

Developing Skills

16. Desert plants' stomata might open at night and close during the day in order to conserve moisture. This is opposite to most other plants.
17. Experimental designs will differ but should include a comparison of several species of plants from deserts and other environments.
18. Floating water plants have stomata on the upper leaf surfaces, whereas land plants usually have more stomata on lower leaf surfaces.
19. See student page.
20. Both are hormones. Auxin makes stems grow toward light; ethylene makes fruit ripen.

Performance Assessment

21. At a minimum each plant's drawing should include its name and photoperiod. Use **Performance Assessment in the Science Classroom,** p. 133.

✓**Assessment** **Resources**

📁 **Reproducible Masters**

Chapter Resources Booklet
Chapter Review, pp. 33–34
Chapter Tests, pp. 35–38
Assessment Transparency Activity, p. 45

Glencoe Science Web site
Interactive Tutor
Chapter Quizzes

Glencoe Technology
🖱 Assessment Transparency
💿 Interactive CD-ROM Chapter Quizzes
💿 ExamView Pro Test Bank
💿 Vocabulary PuzzleMaker Software
📼 MindJogger Videoquiz

Section/Objectives	Standards		Activities/Features
	National	**State/Local**	
Chapter Opener	See p. 5T for a Key to Standards.		**Explore Activity:** Measure breathing rate, p. 153 **Before You Read,** p. 153
Section 1 The Respiratory System 🕐 2 sessions 📦 1 block 1. **Describe** the functions of the respiratory system. 2. **Explain** how oxygen and carbon dioxide are exchanged in the lungs and in tissues. 3. **Identify** the pathway of air in and out of the lungs. 4. **Explain** the effects of smoking on the respiratory system.	National Content Standards: UCP1, A1, C1, F1		**Earth Science Integration,** p. 155 **Science Online,** p. 157 **MiniLAB:** Comparing Surface Area, p. 158 **Visualizing Abdominal Thrusts,** p. 159 **Science Online,** p. 160
Section 2 The Excretory System 🕐 3 sessions 📦 1.5 blocks 1. **Distinguish** between the excretory and urinary systems. 2. **Describe** how the kidneys work. 3. **Explain** what happens when urinary organs don't work.	National Content Standards: UCP1, A1, C1, F1, G3		**MiniLAB:** Modeling Kidney Function, p. 165 **Problem-Solving Activity:** How does your body gain and lose water?, p. 166 **Earth Science Integration,** p. 167 **Activity:** Kidney Structure, p. 169 **Activity:** Simulating the Abdominal Thrust Maneuver, pp. 170–171 **Science and History:** Overcoming the Odds, pp. 172–173

NATIONAL GEOGRAPHIC

Teacher's Corner

Activity Materials	Reproducible Resources	Section Assessment	Technology
Explore Activity: stopwatch or clock with second hand, calculator	**Chapter Resources Booklet** Foldables Worksheet, p. 15 Directed Reading Overview, p. 17 Note-taking Worksheets, pp. 29–31	GLENCOE'S ASSESSMENT ADVANTAGE	
MiniLAB: bathroom-tissue cardboard tube, bowl, marbles, calculator	**Chapter Resources Booklet** Transparency Activity, p. 40 MiniLAB, p. 3 Enrichment, p. 27 Reinforcement, p. 25 Directed Reading, p. 18 Lab Activity, pp. 9–12, 13–14 **Performance Assessment in the Science Classroom,** p. 48 **Reading and Writing Skill Activities,** p. 39 **Life Science Critical Thinking/Problem Solving,** p. 17	**Portfolio** Extension, p. 157 **Performance** MiniLAB, p. 158 Skill Builder Activities, p. 162 **Content** Section Assessment, p. 162	Section Focus Transparency Interactive CD-ROM Guided Reading Audio Program
MiniLAB: 3 cups, soil, fine gravel, water, funnel, small piece of wire screen, filter paper **Activity:** large animal kidney, scalpel, hand lens, disposable gloves **Activity:** cardboard tube, paper, clay, bicycle pump, sports bottle, scissors *Need materials?* Contact Science Kit at 1-800-828-7777 or www.sciencekit.com on the Internet.	**Chapter Resources Booklet** Transparency Activity, p. 41 MiniLAB, p. 4 Enrichment, p. 28 Reinforcement, p. 26 Directed Reading, pp. 19, 20 Activity Worksheet, pp. 5–6, 7–8 Transparency Activity, pp. 43–44 **Lab Management and Safety,** p. 77 **Mathematics Skill Activities,** p. 1 **Home and Community Involvement,** p. 40	**Portfolio** Assessment, p. 165 **Performance** MiniLAB, p. 165 Problem-Solving Activity, p. 166 Skill Builder Activities, p. 168 **Content** Section Assessment, p. 168	Section Focus Transparency Teaching Transparency Interactive CD-ROM Guided Reading Audio Program

End of Chapter Assessment

Blackline Masters	Technology	Professional Series
Chapter Resources Booklet Chapter Review, pp. 33–34 Chapter Tests, pp. 35–38 **Standardized Test Practice by The Princeton Review,** pp. 87–90	MindJogger Videoquiz Interactive CD-ROM Vocabulary PuzzleMakers ExamView Pro Test Bank Interactive Lesson Planner Interactive Teacher Edition	Performance Assessment in the Science Classroom (PASC)

Transparencies

Section Focus

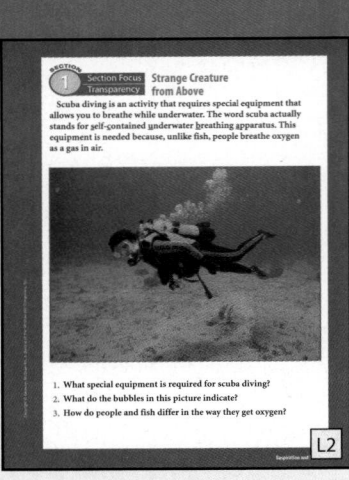

Strange Creature from Above

Scuba diving is an activity that requires special equipment that allows you to breathe while underwater. The word scuba actually stands for self-contained underwater breathing apparatus. This equipment is needed because, unlike fish, people breathe oxygen as a gas in air.

1. What special equipment is required for scuba diving?
2. What do the bubbles in this picture indicate?
3. How do people and fish differ in the way they get oxygen?

L2

Liquid Wastes

Have you ever thought of your skin as an organ that rids your body of waste? You probably perspire most heavily when you exercise. Perspiration is a liquid waste given off by the body.

1. How is perspiring helpful to the body?
2. Why is it important to drink plenty of fluids before, during, and after periods of intense physical activity?
3. What other body system is involved with the removal of liquid wastes?

L2

This is a representation of key blackline masters available in the Teacher Classroom Resources. See Resource Manager boxes within the chapter for additional information.

Key to Teaching Strategies

The following designations will help you decide which activities are appropriate for your students.

L1 Level 1 activities should be appropriate for students with learning difficulties.

L2 Level 2 activities should be within the ability range of all students.

L3 Level 3 activities are designed for above-average students.

ELL ELL activities should be within the ability range of English Language Learners.

COOP LEARN Cooperative Learning activities are designed for small group work.

LS Multiple Learning Styles logos, as described on page 22T, are used throughout to indicate strategies that address different learning styles.

P These strategies represent student products that can be placed into a best-work portfolio.

Assessment

Respiration and Excretion

Directions: Carefully review the graph and answer the following questions.

Percentage of Cigarette Smokers, Organized by Gender 1965–1990 (Selected Years)

1. Between which two years did the percentage of female smokers decrease the most?
A 1965 and 1974   C 1979 and 1983
B 1974 and 1979   D 1988 and 1990
2. A reasonable conclusion is that between the years 1965 and 1990 ___.
F a greater percentage of women quit smoking
G a greater percentage of men quit smoking
H more women smoked than men
J it is more difficult for men to quit smoking
3. From the information in the graph, which statement would best describe the number of smokers in 1991?
A More people probably smoked.
B More women than men probably smoked.
C Fewer people probably smoked.
D There were no more smokers.
4. Which year had the highest difference in percentages between men and women?
F 1965   G 1974   H 1979   J 1988

L2

Teaching

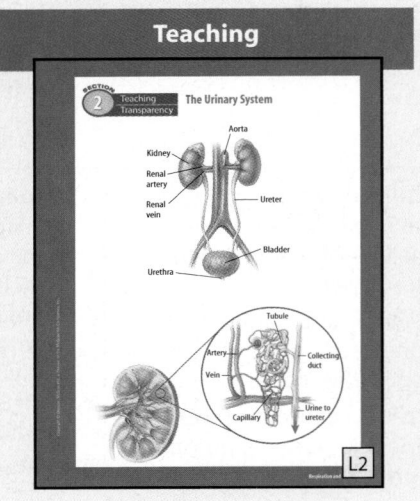

The Urinary System

L2

Hands-on Activities

Activity Worksheets

Kidney Structure

L2

Laboratory Activities

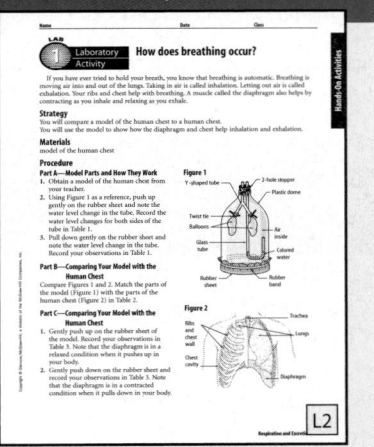

How does breathing occur?

L2

Meeting Different Ability Levels

Content Outline

Note-taking Worksheet — Respiration and Excretion

Section 1   The Respiratory System

A. Functions of the respiratory system—supply _____ to the body
  1. _____ is the movement of the chest that brings air into the lungs and removes waste gases.
  2. _____—oxygen is used by the cells to release energy from glucose
  3. The waste products of cellular respiration are _____ and water.

B. Organs of the respiratory system
  1. The _____ is a tubelike passageway used by food, liquid, and air; lower end has a tissue flap called the epiglottis, to prevent food or liquid from entering the airway.
  2. Air passes through the _____ which contains the vocal cords used to speak.
  3. _____—tube held open by rings of cartilage;
  4. At the lower end of the trachea, two short tubes called _____ branch into smaller tubes
  5. Smallest tubes are bronchioles, which end in clusters of _____
  6. The alveoli are surrounded by _____. This is where oxygen enters the blood and waste products exit the blood.

C. Why do you _____?
  1. Signals from your brain tell muscles in your chest and abdomen to _____ and relax.
    a. If carbon dioxide level in the blood increases, your _____ rate increases.
    b. If _____ levels decrease, breathing rate decreases.
  2. _____—muscle that contracts and relaxes to move gas into and out of the lungs

D. Diseases and Disorders of Respiratory System
  1. Respiratory infections—colds, the flu, _____
  2. _____—bronchial tubes become irritated and swell; too much mucus is produced; excess coughing can damage cilia, form scar tissue, and reduce respiratory system function

L2

Reinforcement

Reinforcement — The Respiratory System

Directions: Label the parts of the respiratory system shown in the diagram below.

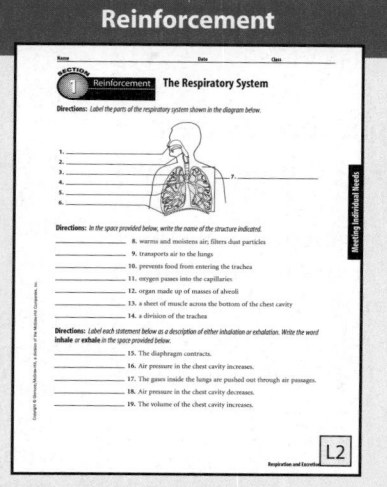

1. _____
2. _____
3. _____
4. _____
5. _____
6. _____
7. _____

Directions: In the space provided below, write the name of the structure indicated.

_____ 8. warms and moistens air; filters dust particles
_____ 9. transports air to the lungs
_____ 10. prevents food from entering the trachea
_____ 11. oxygen passes into the capillaries
_____ 12. organ made up of masses of alveoli
_____ 13. a sheet of muscle across the bottom of the chest cavity
_____ 14. a division of the trachea

Directions: Label each statement below as a description of either inhalation or exhalation. Write the word **inhale** or **exhale** in the space provided below.

_____ 15. The diaphragm contracts.
_____ 16. Air pressure in the chest cavity increases.
_____ 17. The gases inside the lungs are pushed out through air passages.
_____ 18. Air pressure in the chest cavity decreases.
_____ 19. The volume of the chest cavity increases.

L2

Directed Reading

Directed Reading for Content Mastery — *Overview* Respiration and Excretion

Directions: Use the following terms to label the diagram below.

alveoli   bronchi   diaphragm   pharynx
lungs   nasal cavity   trachea

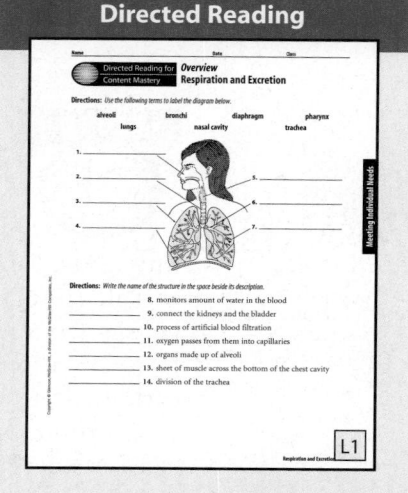

1. _____
2. _____
3. _____
4. _____
5. _____
6. _____
7. _____

Directions: Write the name of the structure in the space beside its description.

_____ 8. monitors amount of water in the blood
_____ 9. connect the kidneys and the bladder
_____ 10. process of artificial blood filtration
_____ 11. oxygen passes from them into capillaries
_____ 12. organs made up of alveoli
_____ 13. sheet of muscle across the bottom of the chest cavity
_____ 14. division of the trachea

L1

Assessment

Chapter Tests

Chapter Test — Respiration and Excretion

I. Testing Concepts

Directions: Match the description in Column I with the item in Column II by writing the correct letter in the space provided. Some items in Column II are not used.

Column I	Column II
_____ 1. structure to which vocal cords are attached	a. alveoli
_____ 2. tube with cartilage, mucous membranes, and cilia	b. asthma
_____ 3. branches of the trachea	c. bladder
_____ 4. clusters of thin-walled air sacs	d. bronchi
_____ 5. muscle beneath lungs that helps air move in and out	e. chronic bronchitis
_____ 6. disease resulting in the alveoli losing their ability to expand and contract	f. diaphragm
	g. emphysema
_____ 7. major organs of urinary system	h. kidneys
_____ 8. filtering units of the kidneys	i. larynx
_____ 9. tubes that lead from each kidney to the bladder	j. nephrons
_____ 10. organ that holds urine until it leaves the body	k. trachea
	l. ureters
	m. urethra

Directions: For each of the following, write the letter of the term or phrase that best completes each sentence.

_____ 11. When you breathe, your lungs take in oxygen and remove _____.
  a. air   b. carbon dioxide   c. nitrogen   d. nitrogen dioxide

_____ 12. Cell respiration involves supplying your body's cells with _____.
  a. oxygen   b. blood   c. bone marrow   d. enzymes

_____ 13. The _____ is a tubelike passageway for both food and air.
  a. epiglottis   b. larynx   c. pharynx   d. trachea

_____ 14. Within the lungs, the exchange of oxygen and carbon dioxide occurs between the _____ and the capillaries.
  a. trachea   b. bronchi   c. alveoli   d. diaphragm

_____ 15. The _____ prevents food or liquid from entering your trachea.
  a. alveoli   b. bronchi   c. epiglottis   d. larynx

_____ 16. People whose _____ don't work may have to undergo dialysis.
  a. alveoli   b. bladders   c. kidneys   d. lungs

L2

Enrichment

Enrichment — Exhaling

How much air do you exhale in one breath? One way to find out might be to blow up a balloon and see how big it gets. A better way to measure how much air you exhale in a single breath is to see how much water is displaced by the air you exhale. Try the following activity.

Materials
plastic milk jug (3.79 liter)
measuring cup (0.5 liter)
water
marking pen
sink with stopper
flexible plastic tubing (60 cm)

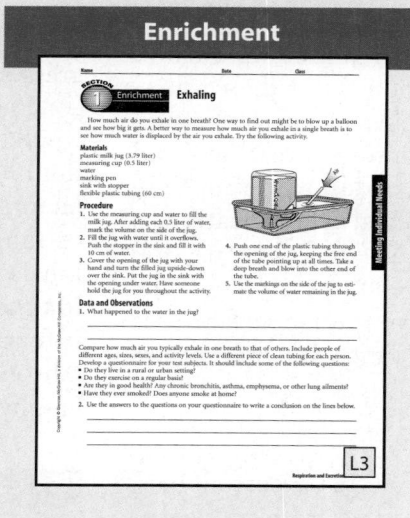

Procedure
1. Use the measuring cup and water to fill the milk jug. After adding each 0.5 liter of water, mark the volume on the side of the jug.
2. Fill the jug with water until it overflows. Push the stopper in the sink and fill it with 10 cm of water.
3. Cover the opening of the jug with your hand and turn the filled jug upside-down over the sink. Put the jug in the sink with the opening under water. Have someone hold the jug for you throughout the activity.
4. Push one end of the plastic tubing through the opening of the jug, keeping the free end of the tube pointing up at all times. Take a deep breath and blow into the other end of the tube.
5. Use the markings on the side of the jug to estimate the volume of water remaining in the jug.

Data and Observations
1. What happened to the water in the jug?
_____

Compare how much air you typically exhale in one breath to that of others. Include people of different ages, sizes, sexes, and activity levels. Use a different piece of clean tubing for each person. Develop a questionnaire for your test subjects. It should include some of the following questions:
• Do they live in a rural or urban setting?
• Do they exercise on a regular basis?
• Are they in good health? Any chronic bronchitis, asthma, emphysema, or other lung ailments?
• Have they ever smoked? Does anyone smoke at home?
2. Use the answers to the questions on your questionnaire to write a conclusion on the lines below.
_____

L3

Spanish Directed Reading

Lectura dirigida para Dominio del contenido — *Sinopsis* Respiración y excreción

Instrucciones: Rotula el diagrama con los siguientes términos.

alvéolos   bronquios   diafragma   faringe
pulmones   cavidad nasal   tráquea

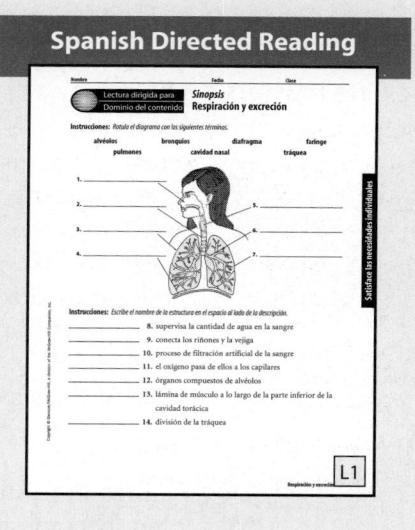

1. _____
2. _____
3. _____
4. _____
5. _____
6. _____
7. _____

Instrucciones: Escribe el nombre de la estructura en el espacio al lado de la descripción.

_____ 8. supervisa la cantidad de agua en la sangre
_____ 9. conecta los riñones y la vejiga
_____ 10. proceso de filtración artificial de la sangre
_____ 11. el oxígeno pasa de ellos a los capilares
_____ 12. órganos compuestos de alvéolos
_____ 13. lámina de músculo a lo largo de la parte inferior de la cavidad torácica
_____ 14. división de la tráquea

L1

Test Practice Workbook

Standardized Test Practice
Teacher Edition

Glencoe
Science

LEVEL GREEN

L2

Chapter Review

Chapter Review — Respiration and Excretion

Part A. Vocabulary Review
Directions: Unscramble the letters to form the correct word for each definition.

_____ 1. rnhxeye — tubelike passageway for both food and air
_____ 2. ryalxn — structure to which vocal cords are attached
_____ 3. crhicaet — tube with cartilage, mucous membranes, and cilia
_____ 4. hobirn — branches of the trachea
_____ 5. iavello — clusters of thin-walled air sacs in the lungs
_____ 6. prislamgh — muscle under lungs that helps air move in and out
_____ 7. rarxuyi uemsty — tubes that lead from each kidney to the bladder
_____ 8. enrdylk — system made up of excretory organs
_____ 9. sponrhee — major organs of urinary system
_____ 10. neiru — filtering units of the kidneys
_____ 11. dernlabl — waste fluid that is excreted from the body
_____ 12. etrours — organ that holds urine until it is excreted
_____ 13. rutruhe — tube that leads to the outside of the body

Directions: Complete the following lists.
14. List four diseases or disorders of the respiratory system.
  a. _____
  b. _____
  c. _____
  d. _____

15. List the five major excretory organs.
  a. _____
  b. _____
  c. _____
  d. _____
  e. _____

L2

Science Content Background

SECTION 1

The Respiratory System

Functions of the Respiratory System

In order to function, cells need nutrients, which must be oxidized in order to release energy. The process of obtaining energy from nutrients is called cellular respiration. In respiration the most commonly used carbohydrate is glucose. The oxidation of glucose produces water and carbon dioxide, and releases energy.

$$C_6H_{12}O_6 + 6O_2 \rightarrow 6H_2O + 6CO_2 + energy$$

Obtaining oxygen and removing carbon dioxide are the major functions of the respiratory system. These processes occur in two successive phases of functioning—breathing and transporting gases. In order to effectively exchange the gases involved in respiration, a large surface area is required. There are 300 million to 400 million alveoli in each lung. The air sacs of both lungs have a total surface area of about 93 m², nearly 50 times the total surface area of the skin.

The Lungs

Lungs are pink at birth, but as a person ages, they become gray and mottled from tiny particles breathed in with the air. Usually people who live in cities and industrial areas have darker lungs than those who live in the country.

In the adult human, the left lung is divided into two sections, or lobes—the superior and the inferior. The right lung is somewhat larger than the left lung and is divided into three lobes—the superior, middle, and inferior. The two lungs are separated by an area which contains the heart, trachea, esophagus, and blood vessels.

Fun Fact

Your lungs inhale and exhale about 500 mL of air with an average breath. This may increase to 2,000 mL of air per breath when you do strenuous physical activity.

The movement of air in and out of the lungs is possible due to three factors: the ability of the thoracic cavity to change size, the elasticity of the lung tissue, and the difference in pressure between the lungs and chest.

Diseases and Disorders of the Respiratory System

Many diseases and disorders affect the health of the human respiratory system and interfere with its effectiveness. Allergies affect so many people that pollen counts of the atmosphere are reported in the media. The worst allergens include the pollen of wind-pollinated trees, grasses, and ragweed, and air pollutants.

Pneumonia is the term used to describe any condition that results in alveoli filling up with fluid. It can be caused by a number of different factors, including chemicals, bacteria, viruses, or fungi. Blood infections, chronic alcoholism, inhalation of fluids into the lungs, or even prolonged bed rest can predispose a person to infection of the lungs by microorganisms. Chronic smoking has the potential to promote emphysema and lung cancer.

SECTION 2

The Excretory System

The Urinary System

The metabolic processes of the body produce waste products. The respiratory system rids the body of carbon dioxide and other waste gases. The digestive system eliminates solid wastes. The urinary system removes a variety of dissolved salts and nitrogenous wastes from the blood and lymph systems.

The major organs of the urinary system are a pair of bean-shaped structures called kidneys, each of which is approximately 10 cm long and 5 cm wide. They weigh about 170 g each. The functioning unit of the kidney is the nephron. All of the blood in the body flows through the kidneys about once every five minutes.

Fun Fact

Protozoans are complete organisms (most are one-celled) that ingest food, digest food, expel waste, and breathe without the benefit of separate organs such as those that humans have.

Urine

Urea and uric acid are wastes from the metabolism of proteins. The straw color of fresh urine is due to a pigment called urochrome. The average pH of urine is approximately 6.0, making it slightly acidic.

The urinary system also functions in maintaining the homeostasis of body fluids and electrolytes and keeps the levels of acids and bases in proper balance. All of this provides for the uniform composition of the blood components.

Urinary Disease and Disorders

Urinary tract infections are common, second only to respiratory infections. Normally urine is sterile. An infection occurs when microbes, usually bacteria from the digestive tract, adhere to the opening of the urethra and begin to multiply. Most urinary tract infections can be traced to one type of colon bacteria, *Escherichia coli (E. coli)*. Often the bacteria move from the urethra to the bladder causing a bladder infection. Such infections are usually treated with specific antibacterial drugs.

SCIENCE *Online*

For additional content background on this topic, go to the Glencoe Science Web site at science.glencoe.com.

Greg Vaughn/Tom Stack & Associates

Respiration and Excretion

Chapter Vocabulary

pharynx, p. 156
larynx, p. 157
trachea, p. 157
bronchi, p. 157
alveoli, p. 157
diaphragm, p. 158
emphysema, p. 161
asthma, p. 162
urinary system, p. 163
urine, p. 164
kidneys, p. 164
nephron, p. 165
ureter, p. 166
bladder, p. 166
urethra, p. 166

What do you think?

Science Journal The wormlike things are cilia, hairlike structures in the nasal cavity. They help trap foreign material that comes into the nose and move it to the back of the throat.

CHAPTER 6

Respiration and Excretion

How do you feel when you've just finished running a mile, or sliding into home base, or slamming a soccer ball into the goal past your opponent? If you're like most people, you probably breathe hard and perspire. Maybe you have even felt your lungs would burst. You need a constant supply of oxygen to keep your body cells functioning. Your body is adapted to meet that need.

What do you think?

Science Journal Look at the picture below. What do you think these wormlike things are? Here's a hint: *You are glad you have them on a dusty day.* Write your answer or best guess in your Science Journal.

152

Theme Connection

Energy Energy transformation is a central theme in this text. Human cells require oxygen in order to utilize nutrients and provide energy for cellular activities. Chemical energy is transformed into thermal and mechanical energy.

Your body can store food and water, but it cannot store much oxygen. Breathing brings oxygen into your body. In the following activity, find out about one factor that can change your breathing rate.

Measure breathing rate

1. Put your hand on the side of your rib cage. Take a deep breath. Notice how your rib cage moves out and upward when you inhale.

2. Count the number of breaths you take for 15 s. Multiply this number by four to calculate your normal breathing rate for 1 min.

3. Repeat step 2 two more times, then calculate your average breathing rate.

4. Do a physical activity described by your teacher for 1 min and repeat step 2 to determine your breathing rate now.

5. Time how long it takes for your breathing rate to return to normal.

Observe

How does breathing rate appear to be related to physical activity? Write your answer in your Science Journal.

Before You Read

Making a Know-Want-Learn Study Fold **Make the following Foldable to help identify what you already know and what you want to know about respiration.**

1. Place a sheet of paper in front of you so the long side is at the top. Fold the paper in half from top to bottom.

2. Fold in both sides to divide the paper into thirds. Unfold the paper.

3. Cut through the top thickness of paper along each of the fold lines to the top fold to form three tabs. Label each tab as shown.

4. Before you read the chapter, write *I breathe* under the left tab. Write *Why do I breathe?* under the middle tab.

5. As you read the chapter, write the answer you learn under the right tab.

Know	Want	Learn

153

Purpose Use the Explore Activity to introduce students to respiration. Students will discover how the respiratory system responds to physical activity. L2 ELL LS **Kinesthetic**

Preparation Check with the school nurse to determine whether any students should not jog or engage in activities that stress the heart and respiratory system.

Materials watch or clock with second hand, calculator

Teaching Strategies

- Any students not able to participate in the physical part of this activity can be designated as timekeepers or recorders.

- Review the reason for multiplying by four to obtain the pulse rate for one minute.

Observe

Breathing rates increase after physical activity.

Performance Have students design another activity that will result in an increase in breathing rate, do the activity, and gather the data. Use **Performance Assessment in the Science Classroom,** p. 105.

Before You Read

Dinah Zike Study Fold

Purpose Use this activity to get students thinking about respiration before they read the chapter by asking them to pose questions to guide their reading. Students record answers to their questions in a Foldable that becomes a study guide.

📁 For additional help, see Foldables Worksheet, p. 15 in **Chapter Resources Booklet,** or go to the Glencoe Science Web site at **science.glencoe.com.** See After You Read in the Study Guide at the end of this chapter.

The Respiratory System

1 Motivate

Bellringer Transparency

Display the Section Focus Transparency for Section 1. Use the accompanying Transparency Activity Master. L2

ELL

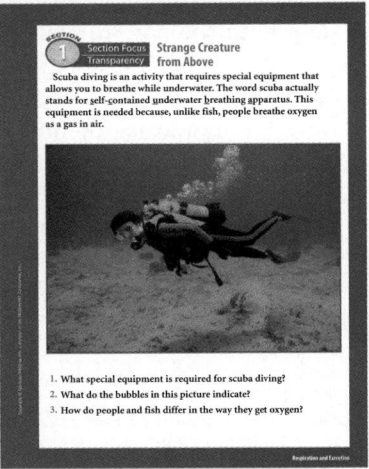

SECTION
1 Section Focus
Transparency
Strange Creature
from Above

Scuba diving is an activity that requires special equipment that allows you to breathe while underwater. The word scuba actually stands for self-contained underwater breathing apparatus. This equipment is needed because, unlike fish, people breathe oxygen as a gas in air.

1. What special equipment is required for scuba diving?
2. What do the bubbles in this picture indicate?
3. How do people and fish differ in the way they get oxygen?

Respiration and Excretion

Tie to Prior Knowledge

Students are aware that they need oxygen to live. Ask students how they get oxygen into their bodies. Most will say breathing. Point out that oxygen taken in by the respiratory system is transported to the body's cells by the circulatory system.

The Respiratory System

As You Read

What You'll Learn

- **Describe** the functions of the respiratory system.
- **Explain** how oxygen and carbon dioxide are exchanged in the lungs and in tissues.
- **Identify** the pathway of air in and out of the lungs.
- **Explain** the effects of smoking on the respiratory system.

Vocabulary

pharynx   alveoli
larynx   diaphragm
trachea   emphysema
bronchi   asthma

Why It's Important

Your body's cells depend on your respiratory system to supply oxygen and remove carbon dioxide.

Figure 1
Air, which is needed by most organisms, is only 21 percent oxygen.

Functions of the Respiratory System

Can you imagine an astronaut walking on the Moon without a space suit or a diver exploring the ocean without scuba gear? Of course not. You couldn't survive in either location under those conditions because you need to breathe air. Earth is surrounded by a layer of gases called the atmosphere (AT muh sfihr). You breathe atmospheric gases that are closest to Earth. As shown in **Figure 1,** oxygen is one of those gases.

For thousands of years people have known that air, food, and water are needed for life. However, the gas in the air that is necessary for life was not identified as oxygen until the late 1700s. At that time, a French scientist experimented and discovered that an animal breathed in oxygen and breathed out carbon dioxide. He measured the amount of oxygen that the animal used and the amount of carbon dioxide produced by its bodily processes. After his work with animals, the French scientist used this knowledge to study the way that humans use oxygen. He measured the amount of oxygen that a person uses when resting and when exercising. These measurements were compared, and he discovered that more oxygen is used by the body during exercise.

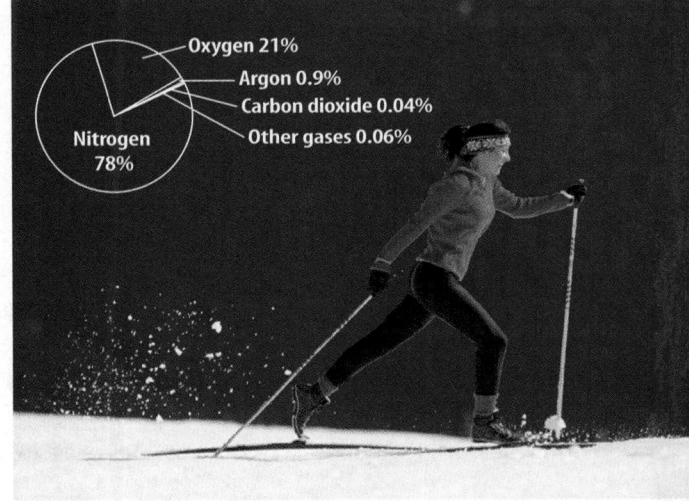

Oxygen 21%
Argon 0.9%
Carbon dioxide 0.04%
Other gases 0.06%
Nitrogen 78%

Section ✓Assessment Planner

PORTFOLIO
Extension, p. 157
PERFORMANCE ASSESSMENT
Try at Home MiniLAB, p. 158
Skill Builder Activities, p. 162
See page 176 for more options.

CONTENT ASSESSMENT
Section, p. 162
Challenge, p. 162
Chapter, pp. 176–177

Figure 2
Several processes are involved in how the
body obtains, transports, and uses oxygen.

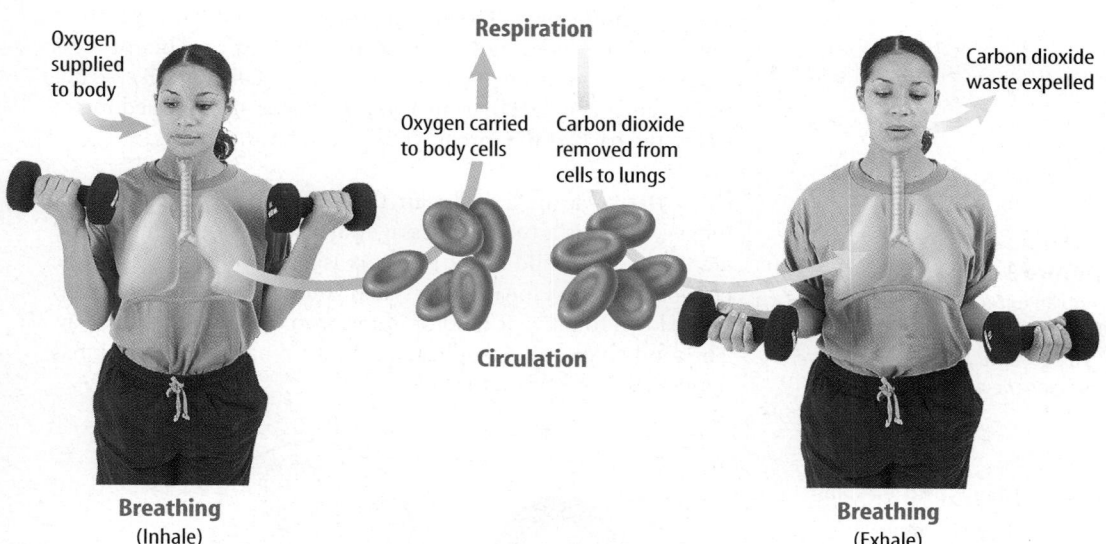

$$C_6H_{12}O_6 + 6O_2 \longrightarrow 6CO_2 + 6H_2O + Energy$$

Glucose + Oxygen ⟶ Carbon + Water + Energy
                              dioxide

Respiration

Oxygen
supplied
to body

Oxygen carried
to body cells

Carbon dioxide
removed from
cells to lungs

Carbon dioxide
waste expelled

Circulation

Breathing
(Inhale)

Breathing
(Exhale)

Breathing and Respiration People often confuse the terms
breathing and *respiration*. Breathing is the movement of the
chest that brings air into the lungs and removes waste gases. The
air entering the lungs contains oxygen. It passes from the lungs
into the circulatory system because there is less oxygen in the
blood than in cells of the lungs. Blood carries oxygen to individual cells. At the same time, the digestive system supplies glucose
from digested food to the same cells. The oxygen delivered to
the cells is used to release energy from glucose. This chemical
reaction, shown in the equation in **Figure 2,** is called cellular
respiration. Without oxygen, this reaction would not take place.
Carbon dioxide and water molecules are waste products of cellular respiration. They are carried back to the lungs in the
blood. Exhaling, or breathing out, eliminates waste carbon dioxide and some water molecules.

> **Reading Check** *What is respiration?*

Earth Science
INTEGRATION

The amount of water vapor
in the atmosphere varies
from almost none over
deserts to nearly four percent in tropical rain forest
areas. This means that
every 100 molecules that
make up air include only
four molecules of water.
In your Science Journal,
infer how breathing dry air
can stress your respiratory
system.

Functions of the Respiratory System

Earth Science
INTEGRATION

Breathing dry air can irritate
nasal and throat passages.

> **Reading Check**

Answer A cellular chemical reaction in
which glucose and oxygen combine and
produce CO_2 and H_2O with the release of
energy.

Quick Demo

If possible, obtain pig lungs
from a meat-packing house or
biological supply company for
students to examine. Students
are often surprised at the light
weight of the organs. Lead a
discussion on why lungs aren't
heavy. Lungs are composed of alveoli,
which are hollow.

Extension

A person can experience oxygen deficiency in carbon
monoxide poisoning. Have students research how carbon
monoxide impairs the delivery
of oxygen to tissues. Prepare a
chart to show how to avoid carbon monoxide poisoning in the
home. L2

Activity

Have students blow through a
straw into a test tube one-fourth
full of limewater. Note the
change from a clear liquid to a
cloudy liquid. This indicates the
presence of carbon dioxide. L1
Kinesthetic

Resource Manager

Chapter Resources Booklet
   Transparency Activity, p. 40
   Directed Reading for Content Mastery,
     pp. 17, 18

Inclusion Strategies

Gifted An opera singer's ability to be heard over
an orchestra in a large auditorium for an
extended period of time is a result of breath
control. Breath control enables singers to sustain a long musical phrase, and change volume
for dramatic effect. Invite students who have
studied voice or a wind instrument to perform
for the class and demonstrate their breathing
techniques. ELL **Auditory-Musical**

Organs of the Respiratory System

Text Question Answer
The food or drink gets into your airway.

Caption Answer
Figure 3 It can be cleaned, warmed, and moistened before moving to the pharynx.

Make a Model
Blow up a balloon and stretch the opening into a narrow slit. Explain to students that the balloon represents a lung and its neck is the trachea. Stretch the slit to make it longer and release a bit to make it shorter, noting the changes in pitch. Correlate the higher-pitched sounds and tighter stretch with the shorter vocal cords of females and the lower-pitched sounds and looser stretch with the longer vocal cords of males.

Use an Analogy
The nasal cavity traps air particles just as a dust mask traps dust and pollen from the air.

Organs of the Respiratory System

The respiratory system, shown in **Figure 3,** is made up of structures and organs that help move oxygen into the body and waste gases out of the body. Air enters your body through two openings in your nose called nostrils or through the mouth. Fine hairs inside the nostrils trap dust from the air. Air then passes through the nasal cavity, where it gets moistened and warmed by the body's heat. Glands that produce sticky mucus line the nasal cavity. The mucus traps dust, pollen, and other materials that were not trapped by nasal hairs. This process helps filter and clean the air you breathe. Tiny, hairlike structures, called cilia (SIHL ee uh), sweep mucus and trapped material to the back of the throat where it can be swallowed.

Pharynx Warmed, moist air then enters the **pharynx** (FER ingks), which is a tubelike passageway used by food, liquid, and air. At the lower end of the pharynx is a flap of tissue called the epiglottis (ep uh GLAHT us). When you swallow, your epiglottis folds down to prevent food or liquid from entering your airway. The food enters your esophagus instead. What do you think has happened if you begin to choke?

Figure 3
Air can enter the body through the nostrils and the mouth. *What is an advantage of having air enter through the nostrils?*

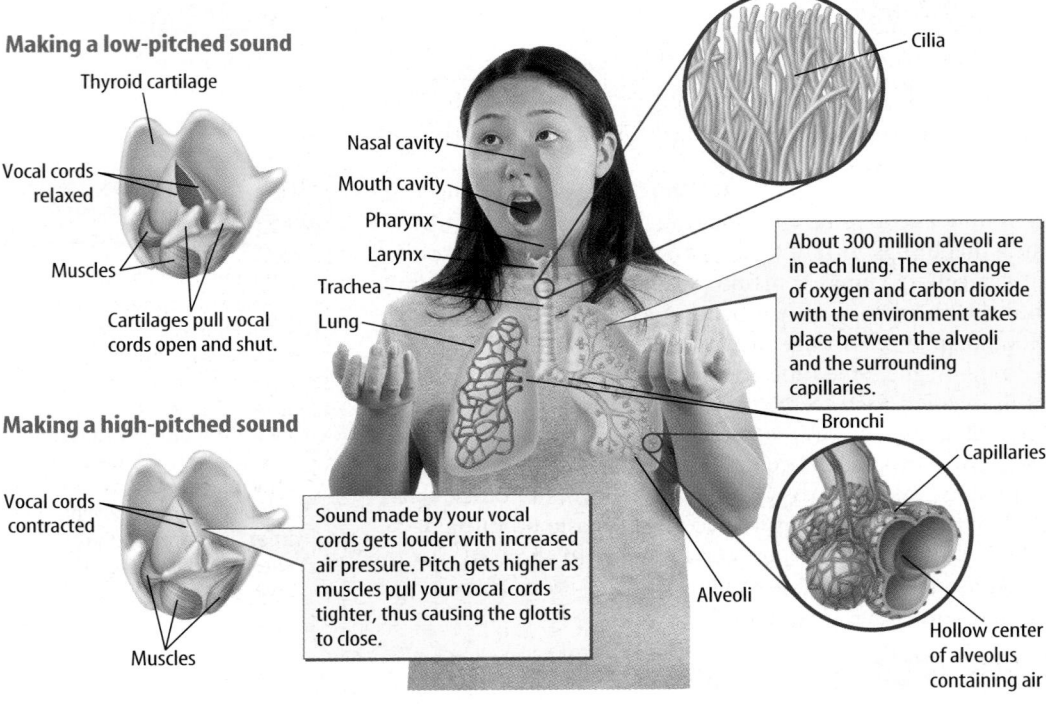

Making a low-pitched sound
Thyroid cartilage
Vocal cords relaxed
Muscles
Cartilages pull vocal cords open and shut.

Making a high-pitched sound
Vocal cords contracted
Muscles

Sound made by your vocal cords gets louder with increased air pressure. Pitch gets higher as muscles pull your vocal cords tighter, thus causing the glottis to close.

Nasal cavity
Mouth cavity
Pharynx
Larynx
Trachea
Lung

Cilia

About 300 million alveoli are in each lung. The exchange of oxygen and carbon dioxide with the environment takes place between the alveoli and the surrounding capillaries.

Bronchi
Capillaries
Alveoli
Hollow center of alveolus containing air

Curriculum Connection

Health The pharynx serves as the passageway of food into the esophagus and air into the trachea. The epiglottis is a small flap of tissue that normally closes over the tracheal opening when food is swallowed. Sometimes food or liquid gets past the epiglottis and goes into the trachea, triggering the choking reflex. Ask students to discuss ways to prevent choking. [L2]
Logical-Mathematical

Cultural Diversity

Living at High Altitudes People living at high altitudes must deal with a slightly reduced pull of gravity, gas molecules that are spread out in the air, and a reduced pressure gradient. Have students research how the bodies of people native to high altitudes have adapted to these changes. Possible answers: number of red blood cells and amount of hemoglobin increase; increase in the number of small blood vessels. [L3]

Larynx and Trachea Next, the air moves into your larynx (LER ingks). The **larynx** is the airway to which two pairs of horizontal folds of tissue, called vocal cords, are attached as shown in **Figure 3.** Forcing air between the cords causes them to vibrate and produce sounds. When you speak, muscles tighten or loosen your vocal cords, resulting in different sounds. Your brain coordinates the movement of the muscles in your throat, tongue, cheeks, and lips when you talk, sing, or just make noise. Your teeth also are involved in forming letter sounds and words.

From the larynx, air moves into the **trachea** (TRAY kee uh), which is a tube about 12 cm in length. Strong, C-shaped rings of cartilage prevent the trachea from collapsing. The trachea is lined with mucous membranes and cilia, as shown in **Figure 3,** that trap dust, bacteria, and pollen. Why must the trachea stay open all the time?

Bronchi and the Lungs Air is carried into your lungs by two short tubes called **bronchi** (BRAHN ki) (singular, *bronchus)* at the lower end of the trachea. Within the lungs, the bronchi branch into smaller and smaller tubes. The smallest tubes are called bronchioles (BRAHN kee ohlz). At the end of each bronchiole are clusters of tiny, thin-walled sacs called **alveoli** (al VEE uh li). Air passes into the bronchi, then into the bronchioles, and finally into the alveoli. As shown in **Figure 3,** lungs are masses of alveoli arranged in grapelike clusters. The capillaries surround the alveoli like a net.

The exchange of oxygen and carbon dioxide takes place between the alveoli and capillaries. This easily happens because the walls of the alveoli (singular, *alveolus)* and the walls of the capillaries are each only one cell thick, as shown in **Figure 4.** Oxygen moves through the cell membranes of the alveoli and then through the cell membranes of the capillaries into the blood. There the oxygen is picked up by hemoglobin (HEE muh gloh bun), a molecule in red blood cells, and carried to all body cells. At the same time, carbon dioxide and other cellular wastes leave the body cells. The wastes move through the cell membranes of the capillaries. Then they are carried by the blood. In the lungs, waste gases move through the cell membranes of the capillaries and through the cell membranes of the alveoli. Then waste gases leave the body during exhalation.

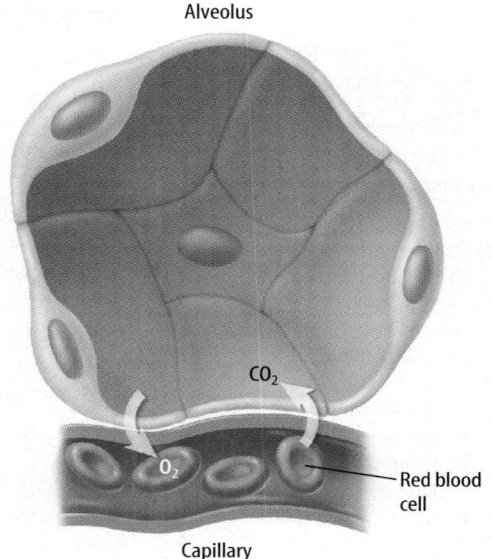

Alveolus

CO_2

O_2

Red blood cell

Capillary

Figure 4
The thin capillary walls allow gases to be exchanged easily between the alveoli and the capillaries.

Research Visit the Glencoe Science Web site at **science.glencoe.com** for more information about how speech sounds are made. Report to your class what you learn.

Internet Addresses

_____
_____
_____
_____

Explore the Glencoe Science Web site at **science.glencoe.com** to find out more about topics in this section.

Fun Fact

During one minute, while the body is at rest, approximately 12.5 mL of oxygen per kg of body weight are used by body cells; an equal amount of carbon dioxide is produced.

Resource Manager

Chapter Resources Booklet
Note-taking Worksheets, pp. 29–31
Reading and Writing Skill Activities, p. 39

TRY AT HOME Mini LAB

Purpose Students observe the increased surface area provided by alveoli. [L2] [ELL]

[IS] **Logical-Mathematical**

Materials bathroom-tissue cardboard tube, marbles, bowl, calculator

Teaching Strategy Gently shake the tube when half-full of marbles to settle them and avoid gaps.

Analysis

1. Answers will vary depending on stacking techniques, but will usually indicate a more than twofold increase in the surface area when using marbles.
2. The marbles represent the alveoli.
3. More gas can be exchanged because there is greater surface area within the same space.

✓ Assessment

Performance Have students calculate the surface area of a cube that is 10 cm x 5 cm x 2 cm and compare this with the surface area of one hundred 1 cm x 1 cm x 1 cm cubes that have the same volume as the larger cube. Use **PASC,** p. 101.

✓ Reading Check

Answer It helps move gases into and out of the body.

Visual Learning

Figure 5 The position of the diaphragm during the process of inhaling and expanding is shown. Compare this process with the squeezing of the plastic bottle discussed in the text.

TRY AT HOME Mini LAB

Comparing Surface Area

Procedure

1. Stand a **bathroom-tissue cardboard tube** in an **empty bowl.**
2. Drop **marbles** into the tube, filling it to the top.
3. Count the number of marbles used.
4. Repeat steps 2 and 3 two more times. Calculate the average number of marbles needed to fill the tube.
5. The tube's inside surface area is approximately 161.29 cm². Each marble has a surface area of approximately 8.06 cm². Calculate the surface area of the average number of marbles.

Analysis

1. Compare the inside surface area of the tube with the surface area of the average number of marbles needed to fill the tube.
2. If the tube represents a bronchus, what do the marbles represent?
3. Using this model, explain what makes gas exchange in the lungs efficient.

Figure 5
Your lungs inhale and exhale about 500 mL of air with an average breath. This increases to 2,000 mL of air per breath when you do strenuous activity.

158   CHAPTER 6 Respiration and Excretion

Why do you breathe?

Signals from your brain tell the muscles in your chest and abdomen to contract and relax. You don't have to think about breathing to breathe, just like your heart beats without you telling it to beat. Your brain can change your breathing rate depending on the amount of carbon dioxide present in your blood. If a lot of carbon dioxide is present, your breathing rate increases. It decreases if less carbon dioxide is in your blood. You do have some control over your breathing—you can hold your breath if you want to. Eventually, though, your brain will respond to the buildup of carbon dioxide in your blood. The brain's response will tell your chest and abdomen muscles to work automatically, and you will breathe whether you want to or not.

Inhaling and Exhaling Breathing is partly the result of changes in air pressure. Under normal conditions, a gas moves from an area of high pressure to an area of low pressure. When you squeeze an empty, soft-plastic bottle, air is pushed out. This happens because air pressure outside the top of the bottle is less than the pressure you create inside the bottle when you squeeze it. As you release your grip on the bottle, the air pressure inside the bottle becomes less than it is outside the bottle. Air rushes back in, and the bottle returns to its original shape.

Your lungs work in a similar way to the squeezed bottle. Your **diaphragm** (DI uh fram) is a muscle beneath your lungs that contracts and relaxes to help move gases into and out of your lungs. **Figure 5** illustrates breathing.

✓ Reading Check   *How does your diaphragm help you breathe?*

When a person is choking, a rescuer can use abdominal thrusts, as shown in **Figure 6,** to save the life of the choking victim.

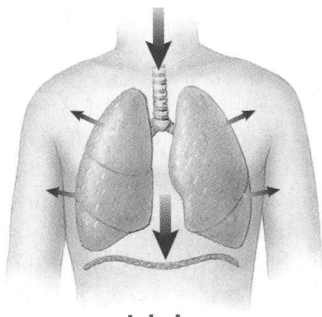

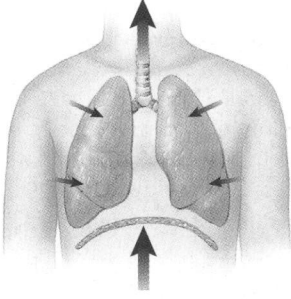

Inhale   **Exhale**

Resource Manager

Chapter Resources Booklet
 MiniLAB, p. 3
 Lab Activity, pp. 9–12

Life Science Critical Thinking/Problem Solving, p. 17

Teacher FYI

Hiccups are caused by spasmodic contractions of the diaphragm. The result is a sudden inhaling of air. Choking could result if a reflex action did not automatically cause the epiglottis to close over the trachea and prevent any food from entering.

Figure 6

When food or other objects become lodged in the trachea, airflow between the lungs and the mouth and nasal cavity is blocked. Death can occur in minutes. However, prompt action by someone can save the life of a choking victim. The rescuer uses abdominal thrusts to force the victim's diaphragm up. This decreases the volume of the chest cavity and forces air up in the trachea. The result is a rush of air that dislodges and expels the food or other object. The victim can breathe again. This technique is shown at right and should only be performed in emergency situations.

Food is lodged in the victim's trachea.

The rescuer places her fist against the victim's stomach.

The rescuer's second hand adds force to the fist.

A The rescuer stands behind the choking victim and wraps her arms around the victim's upper abdomen. She places a fist (thumb side in) against the victim's stomach. The fist should be below the ribs and above the navel.

B With a violent, sharp movement, the rescuer thrusts her fist up into the area below the ribs. This action should be repeated as many times as necessary.

An upward thrust dislodges the food from the victim's trachea.

SECTION 1 The Respiratory System **159**

Visualizing Abdominal Thrusts

Have students examine the pictures and read the captions. Then ask the following questions.

Why should abdominal thrusts only be performed in emergencies, and never performed on other people for practice or for fun? Abdominal thrusts could cause injury if performed on a person who is not choking .

Why is it important that the rescuer's fist be located below the ribs of the choking victim? The fist must be below the diaphragm in order for an upward force to be applied to the diaphragm. A fist located on the rib cage or breastbone could cause injury to the victim.

Activity

Have students work in small groups to develop a mnemonic, or memory device, that will allow them to quickly and accurately remember the steps of proper abdominal thrusts to save a choking victim.

Extension

Have students use the non-emergency number to contact the local rescue squad. Have the students obtain statistics on the number of choking incidents that occur each year in your area, and share the information with the class.

Visual Learning

Figure 6 Review the theory of how abdominal thrusts work. This maneuver is often called the Heimlich maneuver. Abdominal thrusts lift the diaphragm and force enough air from the lungs to create an artificial cough. The cough is intended to move and expel an obstructing foreign body from an airway.

Curriculum Connection

Health Arrange a visit to a Red Cross center or have a health specialist come to school and demonstrate how to use abdominal thrusts and cardiopulmonary resuscitation (CPR) to revive a person who is not breathing. Ask students to find out where CPR training is available in their area. L2

Diseases and Disorders of the Respiratory System

✔ Reading Check

Answer all parts, but usually the upper part, from the nose to the pharynx

---

Table 1 Smokers' Risk of Death from Disease	
Disease	**Smokers' Risk Compared to Nonsmokers' Risk**
Lung Cancer	23 times higher for males, 11 times higher for females
Chronic Bronchitis and Emphysema	5 times higher
Heart Disease	2 times higher

Diseases and Disorders of the Respiratory System

Environmental Science INTEGRATION

If you were asked to list some of the things that can harm your respiratory system, you probably would put smoking at the top. As you can see in **Table 1,** many serious diseases are related to smoking. The chemical substances in tobacco—nicotine and tars—are poisons and can destroy cells. The high temperatures, smoke, and carbon monoxide produced when tobacco burns also can injure a smoker's cells. Even if you are a nonsmoker, inhaling smoke from tobacco products—called secondhand smoke—is unhealthy and has the potential to harm your respiratory system. Smoking, polluted air, coal dust, and asbestos (as BES tus) have been related to respiratory problems such as bronchitis (brahn KITE us), emphysema (em fuh SEE muh), asthma (AZ muh), and cancer.

Respiratory Infections Bacteria, viruses, and other microorganisms can cause infections that affect any of the organs of the respiratory system. The common cold usually affects the upper part of the respiratory system—from the nose to the pharynx. The cold virus also can cause irritation and swelling in the larynx, trachea, and bronchi. The cilia that line the trachea and bronchi can be damaged. However, cilia usually heal rapidly. A virus that causes influenza, or flu, can affect many of the body's systems. The virus multiplies in the cells lining the alveoli and damages them. Pneumonia is an infection in the alveoli that can be caused by bacteria, viruses, or other microorganisms. Before antibiotics were available to treat these infections, many people died from pneumonia.

✔ Reading Check
What parts of the respiratory system are affected by the cold virus?

LAB DEMONSTRATION

Purpose to compare cilia functionality in the presence and absence of tar

Materials fine-tooth comb, water, black pepper, molasses, newspaper

Preparation Cover work area with newspaper. The comb teeth represent cilia, pepper represents dust, and the molasses represents tar.

Procedure Put the fine-toothed end of the comb in a cup of water. Remove and sprinkle with pepper. Run a finger over the teeth five times, making them vibrate. Wash the comb and repeat the process using molasses instead of water.

Expected Outcome Students will see how tar prevents cilia from removing dust particles.

✔*Assessment*

Why do foreign particles need to be removed from the bronchial tubes? The particles can irritate the tissues, and bacteria can cause infections. **In addition to preventing normal cilia action, why are tars dangerous?** They are poisons that can kill cells.

Chronic Bronchitis When bronchial tubes are irritated and swell and too much mucus is produced, a disease called bronchitis develops. Sometimes, bacterial infections occur in the bronchial tubes because the mucus there provides nearly ideal conditions for bacteria to grow. Antibiotics are effective treatments for this type of bronchitis.

Many cases of bronchitis clear up within a few weeks, but the disease sometimes lasts for a long time. When this happens, it is called chronic (KRAHN ihk) bronchitis. A person who has chronic bronchitis must cough often to try to clear the excess mucus from the airway. However, the more a person coughs, the more the cilia and bronchial tubes can be harmed. When cilia are damaged, they cannot move mucus, bacteria, and dirt particles out of the lungs effectively. Then harmful substances, such as sticky tar from burning tobacco, build up in the airways. Sometimes, scar tissue forms and the respiratory system cannot function properly.

Emphysema A disease in which the alveoli in the lungs enlarge is called **emphysema** (em fuh SEE muh). When cells in the alveoli are reddened and swollen, an enzyme is released that causes the walls of the alveoli to break down. As a result, alveoli can't push air out of the lungs, so less oxygen moves into the bloodstream from the alveoli. When blood becomes low in oxygen and high in carbon dioxide, shortness of breath occurs. Some people with emphysema require extra oxygen as shown in **Figure 7C.** Because the heart works harder to supply oxygen to body cells, people who have emphysema often develop heart problems, as well.

Figure 7
Lung diseases can have major effects on breathing.

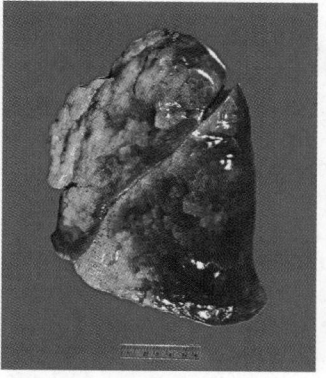
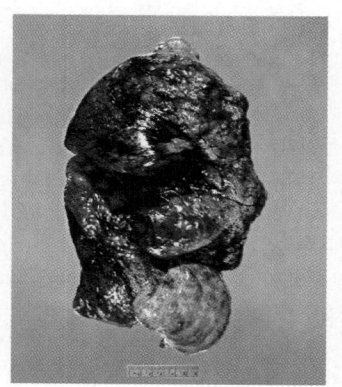

A A normal, healthy lung can exchange oxygen and carbon dioxide effectively.

B A diseased lung carries less oxygen to body cells.

C Emphysema may take 20 to 30 years to develop.

Many people believe that being exposed to cold drafts or cold rain will cause a cold. Colds are caused by viruses and not by exposure to cold and wet conditions. People already infected by cold germs who get cold and wet and then develop the full symptoms may thereby associate the two events.

Teacher FYI

Inhaling tobacco smoke or other chemical irritants stimulates an increase in goblet cells and the enlargement of mucous cells in the lining of the bronchial tubes. This is the cause of the increased mucus in the bronchi of bronchitis sufferers.

Use Science Words

Word Origin The word *emphysema* comes from two Greek words: *em-*, meaning "*in*," and *physan*, meaning "*blow*." **How does the origin of the word relate to the symptoms of the disease?** Persons with the disease have difficulty "blowing" air in and out of their lungs.

Use an Analogy

The alveoli of persons with emphysema are like balloons that have been blown up too many times and with too much air. In both cases the walls have been stretched, become thin, and can rupture.

Resource Manager

Chapter Resources Booklet
  Enrichment, p. 27
  Lab Activity, pp. 13–14

**Performance Assessment in the Science
  Classroom,** p. 48

Curriculum Connection

Health To test for healthy lungs, a doctor may thump the back or chest of the patient. If there is a hollow sound, the lungs are filled with air. If there is a dull sound, it is evidence of fluid in the lungs. Have students find out which respiratory infections can cause fluid buildup in the lungs.

3 Assess

Reteach

Use a lung demonstration apparatus to illustrate how the downward movement of the diaphragm causes reduced pressure within the chest cavity.

Challenge

Have students write a paragraph describing why air moves into the lungs when the ribs move upward and the diaphragm moves downward. This action reduces air pressure within the chest cavity, and the higher external air pressure causes air to rush into the lungs.

✔ **Assessment**

Process Have students use a chart of the respiratory system to describe the passage of air into and out of the lungs. Use **Performance Assessment in the Science Classroom**, p. 143.

Labels: Mouth, Esophagus, Larynx, Pancreas, Kidney, Bladder

Figure 8
More than 85 percent of all lung cancer is related to smoking. Smoking also can play a part in the development of cancer in other body organs indicated above.

Lung Cancer The third leading cause of death in men and women in the United States is lung cancer. Inhaling the tar in cigarette smoke is the greatest contributing factor to lung cancer. Tar and other ingredients found in smoke act as carcinogens (kar SIHN uh junz) in the body. Carcinogens are substances that can cause an uncontrolled growth of cells. In the lungs, this is called lung cancer. Lung cancer is not easy to detect in its early stages. Smoking also has been linked to the development of cancers of the mouth, esophagus, larynx, pancreas, kidney, and bladder. See **Figure 8.**

✔ **Reading Check** *What do you think will happen to the lungs of a young person who begins smoking?*

Asthma Shortness of breath, wheezing, or coughing can occur in a lung disorder called **asthma.** When a person has an asthma attack, the bronchial tubes contract quickly. Inhaling medicine that relaxes the bronchial tubes is the usual treatment for an asthma attack. Asthma is often an allergic reaction. An allergic reaction occurs when the body overreacts to a foreign substance. An asthma attack can result from breathing certain substances such as cigarette smoke or certain plant pollen, eating certain foods, or stress in a person's life.

Section ① Assessment

1. What is the main function of the respiratory system?
2. How are oxygen, carbon dioxide, and other waste gases exchanged in the lungs and body tissues?
3. What causes air to move into and out of a person's lungs?
4. How does smoking affect the respiratory and circulatory systems?
5. **Think Critically** How is the work of the digestive and circulatory systems related to the respiratory system?

Skill Builder Activities

6. **Researching Information** Nicotine in tobacco is a poison. Using library references, find out how nicotine affects the body. **For more help, refer to the** Science Skill Handbook.
7. **Communicating** Use references to find out about lung disease common among coal miners, stonecutters, and sandblasters. Find out what safety measures are required now for these trades. In your Science Journal, write a paragraph about these safety measures. **For more help, refer to the** Science Skill Handbook.

Answers to Section Assessment

1. supply oxygen and remove carbon dioxide
2. Oxygen, carbon dioxide, and waste gases are exchanged by diffusion into and out of the blood.
3. movement of the diaphragm and rib cage; differences in pressure
4. Smoking damages the lungs, making breathing labored and causing the heart to work harder.
5. digestive system—provides food for cell respiration; circulatory system—transports oxygen for food break down and carries respiration
waste products to the lungs for expulsion
6. Nicotine causes blood vessels to constrict, resulting in increased blood pressure. It also causes nausea, headaches, and gastric upset.
7. Students answers will vary.

2 The Excretory System

Functions of the Excretory System

It's your turn to take out the trash. You carry the bag outside and put it in the trash can. The next day, you bring out another bag of trash, but the trash can is full. When trash isn't collected, it piles up. Just as trash needs to be removed from your home to keep it livable, your body must eliminate wastes to remain healthy. Undigested material is eliminated by your large intestine. Waste gases are eliminated through the combined efforts of your circulatory and respiratory systems. Some salts are eliminated when you sweat. These systems function together as parts of your excretory system. If wastes aren't eliminated, toxic substances build up and damage organs. If not corrected, serious illness or death occurs.

The Urinary System

The **urinary system** rids the blood of wastes produced by the cells. **Figure 9** shows how the urinary system functions as a part of the excretory system. The urinary system also controls blood volume by removing excess water produced by body cells during respiration.

As You Read

What You'll Learn
- **Distinguish** between the excretory and urinary systems.
- **Describe** how the kidneys work.
- **Explain** what happens when urinary organs don't work.

Vocabulary
urinary system	ureter
urine	bladder
kidney	urethra
nephron	

Why It's Important
The urinary system helps clean your blood of cellular wastes.

Figure 9
The urinary system, along with the digestive and respiratory systems, and the skin make up the excretory system.

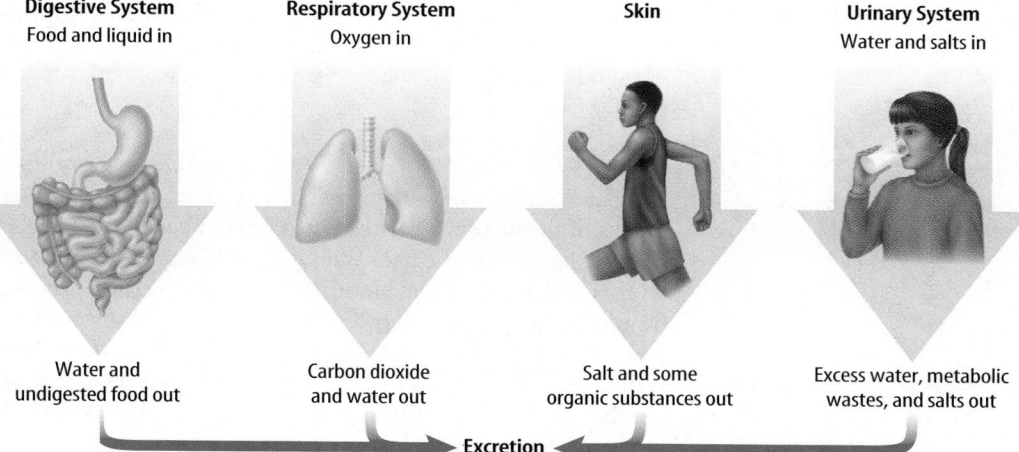

Digestive System
Food and liquid in

Water and undigested food out

Respiratory System
Oxygen in

Carbon dioxide and water out

Skin

Salt and some organic substances out

Urinary System
Water and salts in

Excess water, metabolic wastes, and salts out

Excretion ←

SECTION 2 The Excretory System **163**

SECTION

2

The Excretory System

1 Motivate

Bellringer Transparency
Display the Section Focus Transparency for Section 2. Use the accompanying Transparency Activity Master. [L2] ELL

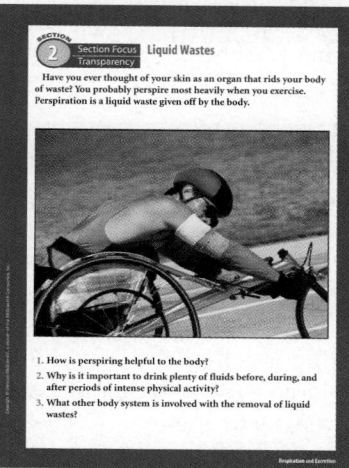

SECTION
2 Section Focus Transparency **Liquid Wastes**

Have you ever thought of your skin as an organ that rids your body of waste? You probably perspire most heavily when you exercise. Perspiration is a liquid waste given off by the body.

1. How is perspiring helpful to the body?
2. Why is it important to drink plenty of fluids before, during, and after periods of intense physical activity?
3. What other body system is involved with the removal of liquid wastes?

Tie to Prior Knowledge
Remind students of how the filter on a coffeemaker works. Only liquid is allowed to flow through. Explain that, in a similar way, the urinary system acts as a filter.

Section ✓*Assessment* Planner

PORTFOLIO
Assessment, p. 165

PERFORMANCE ASSESSMENT
MiniLAB, p. 165
Problem-Solving Activity, p. 166
Skill Builder Activities, p. 168
See page 176 for more options.

CONTENT ASSESSMENT
Section, p. 168
Challenge, p. 168
Chapter, pp. 176–177

Figure 10
The amount of urine that you eliminate each day is determined by the level of a hormone that is produced by your hypothalamus.

Hypothalamus

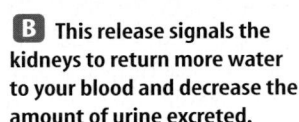

A Your brain detects too little water in your blood. Your hypothalamus then releases a larger amount of hormone.

B This release signals the kidneys to return more water to your blood and decrease the amount of urine excreted.

Regulating Fluid Levels To stay in good health, the fluid levels within the body must be balanced and normal blood pressure must be maintained. An area in the brain, the hypothalamus (hi poh THAL uh mus), constantly monitors the amount of water in the blood. When the brain detects too much water in the blood, the hypothalamus releases a lesser amount of a specific hormone. This signals the kidneys to return less water to the blood and increase the amount of wastewater, called **urine,** that is excreted. **Figure 10** shows what happens when too little water is in the blood.

✔ Reading Check
How does the urinary system control the volume of water in the blood?

A specific amount of water in the blood is also important for the movement of gases and excretion of solid wastes from the body. The urinary system also balances the amounts of certain salts and water that must be present for all cell activities to take place.

Organs of the Urinary System Excretory organs is another name for the organs of the urinary system. The main organs of the urinary system are two bean-shaped **kidneys.** Kidneys are located on the back wall of the abdomen at about waist level. The kidneys filter blood that contains wastes collected from cells. In approximately 5 min, all of the blood in your body passes through the kidneys. The red-brown color of the kidneys is due to their enormous blood supply. In **Figure 11A,** you can see that blood enters the kidneys through a large artery and leaves through a large vein.

164 CHAPTER 6 Respiration and Excretion

Filtration in the Kidney The kidney, shown in **Figure 11B,** is a two-stage filtration system. It is made up of about 1 million tiny filtering units called **nephrons** (NEF rahnz), shown in **Figure 11C.** Each nephron has a cuplike structure and a tubelike structure called a duct. Blood moves from a renal artery to capillaries in the cuplike structure. The first filtration occurs when water, sugar, salt, and wastes from the blood pass into the cuplike structure. Left behind in the blood are the red blood cells and proteins. Next, liquid in the cuplike structure is squeezed into a narrow tubule. Capillaries that surround the tubule perform the second filtration. Most of the water, sugar, and salt are reabsorbed and returned to the blood. These collection capillaries merge to form small veins, which merge to form a renal vein in each kidney. Purified blood is returned to the main circulatory system. The liquid left behind flows into collecting tubules in each kidney. This wastewater, or urine, contains excess water, salts, and other wastes that are not reabsorbed by the body. An average-sized person produces about 1 L of urine per day.

Figure 11
The urinary system removes wastes from the blood.

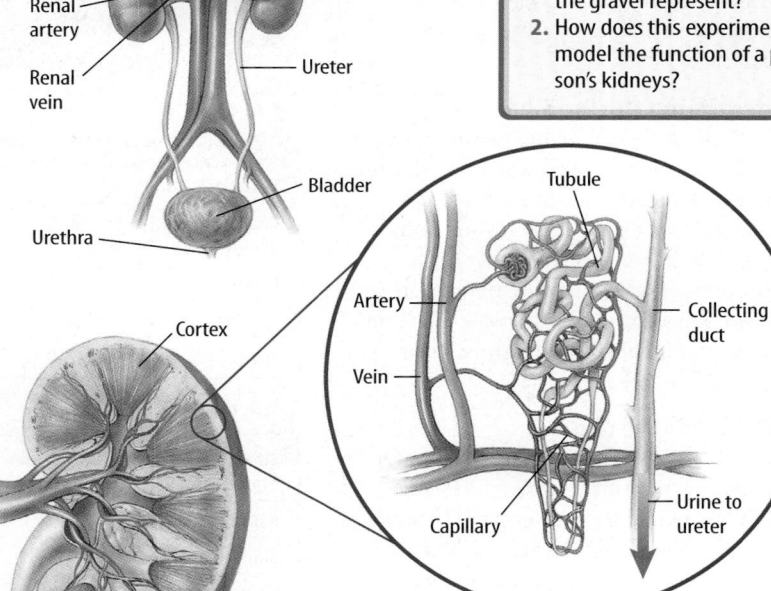

A **The urinary system includes the kidneys, the bladder, and the connecting tubes.**

B **Kidneys are made up of many nephrons.**

C A single nephron is shown in detail. *What is the main function of the nephron?*

SECTION 2 The Excretory System **165**

Caption Answer
Figure 11C to filter blood

The Urinary System, continued

Use an Analogy

In the filtering model constructed in the MiniLAB, have students infer what each part (muddy water, gravel, filter, clear water) represents within the human body. gravel—blood cells; filter—kidney; muddy water—blood containing waste; clear water—filtered blood with wastes removed

Extension

Adult kidneys weigh only about 170 g each. The kidneys of an average adult process about 1,600 L of liquid per day, most of which is recycled. Have students calculate how many liters an adult's kidneys process in a year, in a decade, and in 75 years. 584,000 L; 5,840,000 L; 43,800,000 L L2

IS **Logical-Mathematical**

Urine Collection and Release The urine in each collecting tubule drains into a funnel-shaped area of each kidney that leads to the ureter (YER ut ur). **Ureters** are tubes that lead from each kidney to the bladder. The **bladder** is an elastic, muscular organ that holds urine until it leaves the body. The elastic walls of the bladder can stretch to hold up to 0.5 L of urine. When empty, the bladder looks wrinkled and the cells lining the bladder are thick. When full, the bladder looks like an inflated balloon and the cells lining the bladder are stretched and thin. A tube called the **urethra** (yoo REE thruh) carries urine from the bladder to the outside of the body.

Problem-Solving Activity

How does your body gain and lose water?

Your body depends on water. Without water, your cells could not carry out their activities and body systems could not function. Water is so important to your body that your brain and other body systems are involved in balancing water gain and water loss.

Identifying the Problem

Table A shows the major sources by which your body gains water. Oxidation of nutrients occurs when energy is released from nutrients by your body's cells. Water is a waste product of these reactions. **Table B** lists the major sources by which your body loses water. The data show you how daily gain and loss of water are related.

Solving the Problem

1. What is the greatest source of water gained by your body?
2. How would the percentages of water gained and lost change in a person who was working in extremely warm temperatures? In this case, what organ of the body would be the greatest contributor to water loss?

Table A

Major Sources by Which Body Water Is Gained		
Source	Amount (mL)	Percent
Oxidation of Nutrients	250	10
Foods	750	30
Liquids	1,500	60
Total	2,500	100

Table B

Major Sources by Which Body Water Is Lost		
Source	Amount (mL)	Percent
Urine	1,500	60
Skin	500	20
Lungs	350	14
Feces	150	6
Total	2,500	100

166 CHAPTER 6 Respiration and Excretion

Science Journal

Making an Analogy Ask students to write an essay in which they compare a kidney to a recycling center. Have them consider substances that can and cannot be recycled. Kidney—water, salt, and sugar can be recycled, waste cannot; recycling center—paper, glass, and plastic can be recycled, some synthetic materials cannot. L2 IS **Linguistic**

Curriculum Connection

Health Small stones made up of precipitated minerals such as uric acid or calcium salts may form in the kidneys. These kidney stones may move into the ureter and can cause severe pain. Drinking large quantities of water can help prevent the formation of the stones. Ask students to investigate what foods may contribute to the formation of kidney stones. L2

Other Organs of Excretion

Large amounts of liquid wastes are lost every day by your body in other ways, as shown in **Figure 12.** The liver also filters the blood to remove wastes. Certain wastes are converted to other substances. For example, excess amino acids are changed to urea (yoo REE uh), which is a chemical that ends up in urine. Hemoglobin from broken-down red blood cells becomes part of bile, which is the digestive fluid from the liver.

Figure 12
On average, the volume of water lost daily by exhaling is a little more than the volume of a soft-drink can. The volume of water lost by your skin each day is about the volume of a 20-ounce soft-drink bottle.

Urinary Diseases and Disorders

What happens when someone's kidneys don't work properly or stop working? Waste products that are not removed build up and act as poisons in body cells. Water that normally is removed from body tissues accumulates and causes swelling of the ankles and feet. Sometimes these fluids also build up around the heart, and it has to work harder to move blood to the lungs.

Without excretion, an imbalance of salts occurs. The body responds by trying to restore this balance. If the balance isn't restored, the kidneys and other organs can be damaged. Kidney failure occurs when the kidneys don't work as they should. This is always a serious problem because the kidneys' job is so important to the rest of the body.

Infections caused by microorganisms can affect the urinary system. Usually, the infection begins in the bladder. However, it can spread and involve the kidneys. Most of the time, these infections can be cured with antibiotics.

Because the ureters and urethra are narrow tubes, they can be blocked easily in some disorders. A blockage of one of these tubes can cause serious problems because urine cannot flow out of the body properly. If the blockage is not corrected, the kidneys can be damaged.

 Reading Check *Why is a blocked ureter or urethra a serious problem?*

Detecting Urinary Diseases Urine can be tested for any signs of a urinary tract disease. A change in the urine's color can suggest kidney or liver problems. High levels of glucose can be a sign of diabetes. Increased amounts of a protein called albumin (al BYEW mun) indicate kidney disease or heart failure. When the kidneys are damaged, albumin can get into the urine, just as a leaky water pipe allows water to drip.

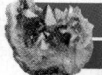 **Earth Science
INTEGRATION**

Nearly 80 percent of Earth's surface is covered by water. Ninety-seven percent of this water is salt water. Humans cannot drink salt water, so they depend on the less than one percent of freshwater that is available for use. In your Science Journal, infer how your kidneys would need to be different for you to be able to drink salt water.

Other Organs of Excretion

Discussion

What organ of the body is most likely to filter out drugs? The liver is able to filter out a number of chemicals, including drugs. **What prevents the liver from being destroyed by the chemicals it filters?** The liver can detoxify most chemicals and render them harmless.

Urinary Diseases and Disorders

 **Earth Science
INTEGRATION**

In order to be able to drink seawater, the kidneys would have to be able to filter out more salt and remove it from the body, in order to keep a balance of salt and water within the body.

Reading Check

Answer It can lead to kidney damage.

Resource Manager

Chapter Resources Booklet
Enrichment, p. 28
Transparency Activity, pp. 43–44
Mathematics Skill Activities, p. 1

Curriculum Connection

History Physician-scientists of ancient times noted that there was no blood in the arteries of dissected corpses, but that veins, which entered and left the liver, were full of blood. They concluded that it was the liver that made blood and pumped it to the body, and the heart that gave blood a "vital spirit" as it passed by. Have students write a paragraph explaining the relationship of the liver to the heart. L2 LS **Linguistic**

Figure 13
A dialysis machine can replace or help with some of the activities of the kidneys in a person with kidney failure. Like the kidney, the dialysis machine removes wastes from the blood.

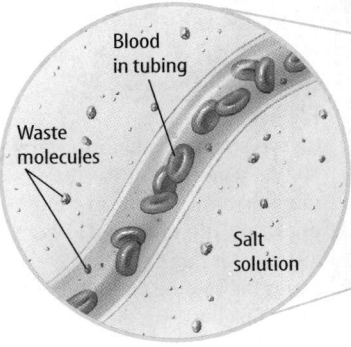

Blood in tubing

Waste molecules

Salt solution

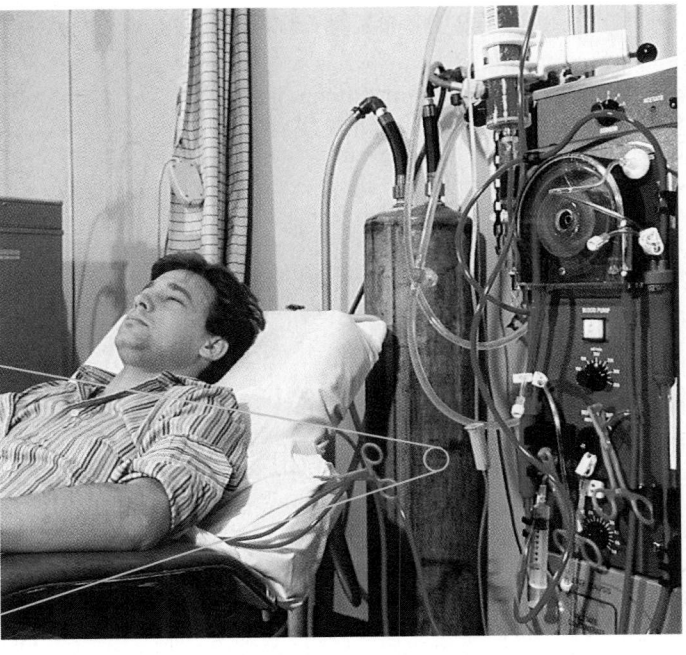

Dialysis A person who has only one kidney still can live normally. The remaining kidney increases in size and works harder to make up for the loss of the other kidney. However, if both kidneys fail, the person will need to have his or her blood filtered by an artificial kidney machine in a process called dialysis (di AL uh sus), as shown in **Figure 13.**

Section Assessment

1. Describe the functions of a person's urinary system.
2. Explain how the kidneys remove wastes and keep fluids and salts in balance.
3. Describe what happens when the urinary system does not function properly.
4. Compare the excretory system and urinary system.
5. **Think Critically** Explain why reabsorption of certain materials in the kidneys is important to your health.

Skill Builder Activities

6. **Concept Mapping** Using a network tree concept map, compare the excretory functions of the kidneys and the lungs. **For more help, refer to the** Science Skill Handbook.
7. **Solving One-Step Equations** In approximately 5 min, all 5 L of blood in the body pass through the kidneys. Calculate the average rate of flow through the kidneys in liters per minute. **For more help, refer to the** Math Skill Handbook.

168 CHAPTER 6 Respiration and Excretion

Answers to Section Assessment

1. rids the body of wastes, controls blood volume, balances salts and water
2. Kidneys filter the blood to remove wastes, sugar, water, and salt. Necessary amounts of water, sugar, and salt are returned to the blood.
3. Waste products not removed cause the destruction of cells. Fluids not removed from body tissues cause swellings in the extremities and buildup of fluids around the heart. Salts are in imbalance in body fluids, which can lead to organ damage.
4. excretory system—includes all systems that rid the body of wastes; urinary system—consists of organs that produce urine as waste
5. Many of the substances are needed by the body to maintain homeostasis.
6. Wastes in blood are carried to the lungs, which remove water and carbon dioxide, and to the kidneys, which remove water and excess salts, and other wastes.
7. 5 liters per 5 minutes = 1 liter per minute rate of flow

Activity

Kidney Structure

As your body uses nutrients, wastes are created. One role of the kidneys is to filter waste products out of the bloodstream and excrete this waste outside the body. How can these small structures filter all the blood in the body in 5 min?

What You'll Investigate
How does the structure of the kidney relate to the function of a kidney?

Materials
large animal kidney
*model of a kidney
scalpel
hand lens
disposable gloves
*Alternate material

Goal
■ **Observe** the external and internal structures of a kidney.

Safety Precautions

WARNING: *Use extreme care when using sharp instruments. Wear disposable gloves. Wash your hands with soap after completing this activity.*

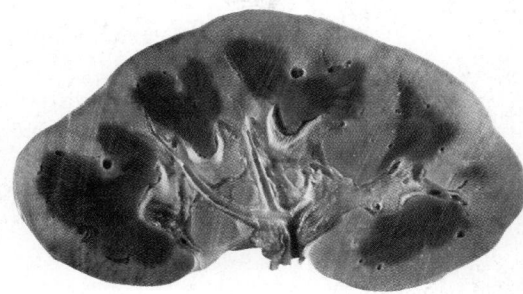

Procedure
1. **Examine** the outside of the kidney supplied by your teacher.
2. If the kidney still is encased in fat, peel off the fat carefully.
3. Using a scalpel, carefully cut the tissue in half lengthwise around the outline of the kidney. This cut should result in a section similar to the illustration on this page.

4. **Observe** the internal features of the kidney using a hand lens, or view these features in a model.
5. **Compare** the specimen or model with the kidney in the illustration.
6. **Draw** the kidney in your Science Journal and label its structures.

Conclude and Apply
1. What part makes up the cortex of the kidney? Why is this part red?
2. What is the main function of nephrons?
3. The medulla of the kidney is made up of a network of tubules that come together to form the ureter. What is the function of this network of tubules?
4. How can the kidney be compared to a portable water-purifying system?

*C*ommunicating
Your Data
Compare your conclusions with those of other students in your class. **For more help, refer to the** Science Skill Handbook.

ACTIVITY 169

Activity

Purpose Students examine the structures in a kidney and relate each structure to its function.
L2 IS **Kinesthetic**
Process Skills observing and inferring; interpreting scientific illustrations; comparing and contrasting
Time Required 50 minutes

Safety Precautions
Caution students about using sharp objects.

Teaching Strategies
• You may wish to have some kidneys remain intact.
• Other kidneys may be already sliced longitudinally.
• Kidneys can be reused.

Troubleshooting Demonstrate proper techniques for scalpel usage.

Answers to Questions
1. Nephrons; the color is caused by the blood in the nephrons.
2. to filter blood within the kidneys
3. The network of tubules moves the fluid from the kidney to the bladder so it can be excreted.
4. Both are filtering mechanisms.

Oral Have students describe the evidence that two kidneys are more than enough to take care of excretory functions. Possible answer: people who have only one kidney are still able to function normally. Use **PASC**, p. 143.

---

*C*ommunicating
Your Data
Students should discuss why their conclusions did or did not agree. They can prepare a listing of references that support their findings.

Resource Manager

Chapter Resources Booklet
   Activity Worksheet, pp. 5–6
   Reinforcement, p. 26
Home and Community Involvement, p. 40

Activity

BENCH TESTED

Recognize the Problem

Purpose
Students model a blocked trachea and demonstrate how the abdominal thrust maneuver is used to remove the blockage. L2

Kinesthetic

Process Skills
recording observations, making models, analyzing results, recognizing cause and effect, drawing conclusions

Time Required
40 minutes

Thinking Critically
Discussion Tell students that the trachea is a tube that carries air from the mouth to the lungs. This passageway is the only normal path for air to flow into the lungs. **What might happen if this passage were blocked?** The oxygen supply would be cut off, and the person would die within a few minutes. Explain that the abdominal thrust maneuver is a simple method of removing a blockage from this passageway.

Possible Materials
paper towel roll tube or other tube, paper, clay, bellows, bicycle pump, sports bottle, scissors

Safety Precautions
Caution students to use care with scissors.

Activity *Model and Invent*

Simulating the Abdominal Thrust Maneuver

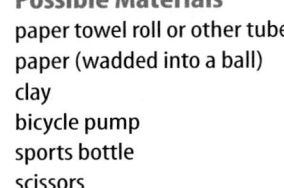

Have you ever taken a class in CPR or learned about how to help a choking victim? Using the abdominal thrust maneuver, or Heimlich maneuver, is one way to remove food or another object that is blocking someone's airway. What happens internally when the maneuver is used? How can you simulate the internal effects of the abdominal thrust maneuver?

Recognize the Problem
How can you simulate the removal of an object from the trachea when the abdominal thrust maneuver is used?

Thinking Critically
What can you use to make a model of the trachea? How can you simulate what happens during an abdominal thrust maneuver using your model?

Goals
- **Construct** a model of the trachea with a piece of food stuck in it.
- **Demonstrate** what happens when the abdominal thrust maneuver is performed on someone.
- **Predict** another way that air could get into the lungs if the food could not be dislodged with an abdominal thrust maneuver.

Possible Materials
paper towel roll or other tube
paper (wadded into a ball)
clay
bicycle pump
sports bottle
scissors

Safety Precautions

Always be careful when you use scissors.

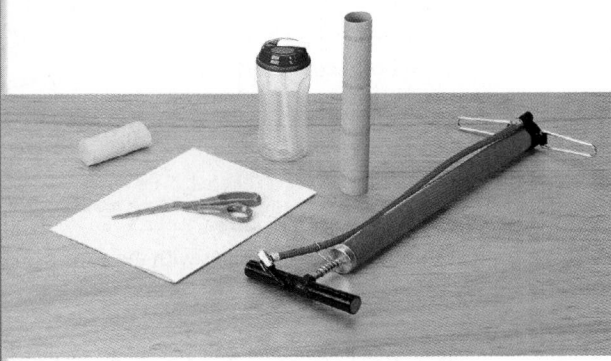

SCIENCE *Online*
Internet Addresses

Explore the Glencoe Science Web site at **science.glencoe.com** to find out more about topics in this activity.

Resource Manager

Chapter Resources Booklet
 Activity Worksheet, pp. 7–8
Lab Management and Safety, p. 77

Planning the Model

1. **List** the materials that you will need to construct your model. What will represent the trachea and a piece of food or other object blocking the airway?

2. How can you use your model to simulate the effects of an abdominal thrust maneuver?

3. Suggest a way to get air into the lungs if the food could not be dislodged. How would you simulate this method in your model?

Check the Model Plans

1. **Compare** your plans for the model and the abdominal thrust maneuver simulation with those of other students in your class. Discuss why each of you chose the plans and materials that you did.

2. Make sure your teacher approves your plan and materials for your model before you start.

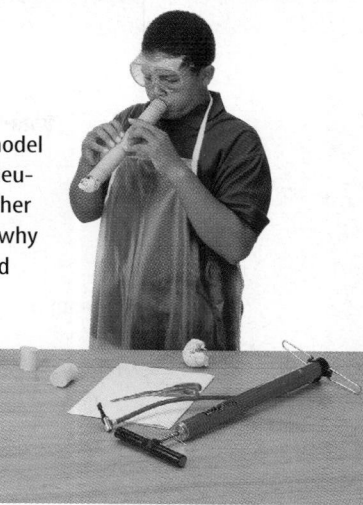

Making the Model

1. **Construct** your model of a trachea with an object stuck in it. Make sure that air cannot get through the trachea if you try blowing softly through it.

2. Simulate what happens when an abdominal thrust maneuver is used. Record your observations. Was the object dislodged? How hard was it to dislodge the object?

3. Replace the object in the trachea. Use your model to simulate how you could get air into the lungs if an abdominal thrust maneuver did not remove the object. Is it easy to blow air through your model now?

4. Model a crushed trachea. Is it easy to blow air through the trachea in this case?

Analyzing and Applying Results

1. **Describe** how easy it was to get air through the trachea in each step in the Making the Model section above. Include any other observations that you made as you worked with your model.

2. Think about what you did to get air into the trachea when the object could not be dislodged with an abdominal thrust maneuver. How could this be done to a person? Do you know what this procedure is called?

3. **Explain** why the trachea has cartilage around it to protect it. What might happen if it did not?

Explain to your family or friends what you have learned about how the abdominal thrust maneuver can help choking victims.

ACTIVITY 171

Planning the Model

Teaching Strategies

- A model or anatomy wall chart showing the mouth, trachea, and lungs will help students conceptualize the problems caused by a blocked trachea.

- Encourage students to make a checklist of items they need to include in their models.

Making the Model

Expected Outcome

Students will build a model that simulates a trachea. They will simulate food blockage and the abdominal thrust maneuver and brainstorm ways to get oxygen to the lungs if the blockage cannot be dislodged.

Analyzing and Applying Results

1. Students should find that the abdominal thrust maneuver successfully dislodges most obstructions.

2. Students will likely suggest that a small incision could be cut below the blockage to allow air into the lungs. This procedure is called tracheostomy or tracheotomy.

3. Cartilage protects the trachea from being punctured and keeps it from collapsing.

Assessment

Oral Ask students if they can think of other instances where the trachea might become blocked and a tracheostomy or tracheotomy would need to be performed. Possible answers: an accident that causes severe damage to the mouth or neck, cancerous or tumorous growths that block the trachea Use **Performance Assessment in the Science Classroom,** p. 89.

Encourage students to use drawings showing that the trachea is the only pathway to the lungs. Then they can better describe the importance of the abdominal thrust maneuver.

Content Background

It is important to know the function of the kidney and to relay this information to students. The kidney washes the blood as a filtering system, ridding it of toxins and balancing the body's water levels by producing urine to get rid of this waste. In fact, your blood goes through your kidney about 288 times a day.

Before making discoveries with regard to kidney transplants, Samuel Kountz had to overcome many odds, indeed. He was born in extreme poverty in an all-black town in Arkansas in 1930. His grandmother was born a slave. She was his encouragement and inspiration while trying to get into college. He became the first African-American to be accepted to the University of Arkansas Medical School.

While interning at Stanford, Kountz started to research the rejection process for kidney transplants. He discovered that large amounts of the steroid methylprednisolone given to the patient after the transplant operation helped to reverse the rejection of the new organ. Kountz was a man of many achievements. He received several awards during his career including an Outstanding Investigator Award from the American College of Cardiology in 1964. At the University of California in San Francisco he built one of the largest kidney transplant training and research centers in the nation.

Overcoming the Odds

Guts and determination helped one pioneering doctor to save the lives of thousands

Overcoming the odds—especially when the odds seem stacked against you—is a challenge that many people face. Dr. Samuel Lee Kountz, Jr. (photo, right) had the odds stacked against him. Thanks to his determination he beat them.

Samuel Kountz decided at age eight to become a doctor. He faced his first challenge when he failed the entrance exam to his local Arkansas college. That didn't stop him, though. He asked the college president to give him another chance, and the president did. Kountz got into school and earned As and Bs. Kountz went on to get a graduate degree in biochemistry and was admitted to the University of Arkansas's medical school. For many, these achievements would be more than enough. But for Dr. Kountz, it was just the beginning of his quest to improve medicine—and to change history.

172

Resources for Teachers and Students

"The Black Surgeon in the Twentieth Century: A Tribute to Samuel L. Kountz," by Claude Organ. *Journal of the National Medical Association,* (September 1978).

Understanding Kidney Transplantation by Edith T. Oberley and Neal R. Glass. Thomas; Springfield, Ill. 1987.

Dr. Kountz was especially interested in a process that was still brand new in the 1950s—the kidney transplant. For many patients, a kidney transplant added months or a year to one's life. But then a patient's body would reject the kidney, and the patient would die. Dr. Kountz was determined to see that kidney transplants saved lives and kept patients healthy for years.

Fixing the Problem

A donated organ is on its way to save a life.

Kountz discovered the root of the problem—why and how a patient's body rejected the transplanted kidney. He discovered that the patient's cells attacked and destroyed the small blood vessels of the transplanted kidney. So the new kidney would die from lack of blood-supplied oxygen. He and others at Stanford University developed a way for doctors to watch the flow of the kidney's blood supply following surgery. Then doctors can give patients the right kinds of drugs at the right time, so that their bodies can overcome the rejection process.

In 1959, Kountz performed the first successful kidney transplant. He went on to develop a procedure to keep body organs healthy for up to 60 hours after being taken from a donor. He also set up a system of organ donor cards through the National Kidney Foundation. And in his career, Dr. Kountz transplanted more than 1,000 kidneys himself—and paved the way for thousands more.

CONNECTIONS Research What kinds of medical breakthroughs has the last century brought? Locate an article that explains either a recent advance in medicine or the work that doctors and medical researchers are doing. Share your findings with your class.

Online

For more information, visit science.glencoe.com

CONNECTIONS First, ask students to focus on one part of medicine or one specialization in medicine that interests them. If a student is interested in the brain, suggest a search for an article about neurological advancements in medicine. Perhaps a student is interested in premature babies and advancements in obstetrics. Suggest avenues that are available for your students to successfully fulfill research in whatever interests they present for this project.

Online

Internet Addresses

_____

_____

_____

Explore the Glencoe Science Web site at **science.glencoe.com** to find out more about topics in this feature.

Discussion

What did Kountz discover was the reason kidneys were being rejected after transplant surgeries? Possible answer: The patient's cells attacked and destroyed the small blood vessels of the transplanted kidney, thus, the kidney would die from lack of blood-supplied oxygen.

Historical Significance

The significance of Kountz's work for people who suffer from kidney disease is obvious. Point out to students, that Kountz's work also had a significant impact on other transplant surgeries. Because other transplant procedures were associated with similar rejection problems, similar immunosuppressive drug treatments have been developed for heart, liver, and lung transplants.

The first successful kidney transplant without the use of immunosuppressive drugs was performed in 1954. The transplant was successful because the donor was the recipient's twin. In this case, organ rejection was lessened because the donor and recipient had identical genes. Further evidence shows that the likelihood of rejection can be lessened when the donor is a sibling or other family member.

As a prelude to the Connections Research activity, have students create a timeline of transplant history starting from the early 1900s. This should give them some historical perspective on the history of kidney transplants as well as provide other information about other medical discoveries. Have students use posterboard and ask them to include photographs and illustrations that illustrate transplant history.
L2 [LS] **Visual-Spatial**

Chapter 6 Study Guide

Reviewing Main Ideas

Preview

Students can answer the questions in their Science Journals. Discuss the answers as you go through the chapter. **Linguistic**

Review

Students can write their answers, then compare them with those of other students. **Interpersonal**

Reteach

Students can look at the illustrations and describe details that support the main ideas of the chapter. **Visual-Spatial**

Answers to Chapter Review

SECTION 1

2. The cartilage rings reinforce the structure of the trachea. If the trachea collapsed, the organism would be unable to breathe. Movement of gases in the trachea is not dependent upon muscular action. The movement of substances in the esophagus relies on peristalsis, and cartilage rings would inhibit this action.

5. the circulatory system

SECTION 2

1. The kidneys help maintain a balance of fluids in the body and filter wastes.

Reviewing Main Ideas

Section 1 The Respiratory System

1. The respiratory system brings oxygen into the body and removes carbon dioxide.

2. Inhaled air passes through the nasal cavity, pharynx, larynx, trachea, bronchi, and into the alveoli of the lungs. *Why does the trachea, shown in the illustration, have cartilage but the esophagus does not?*

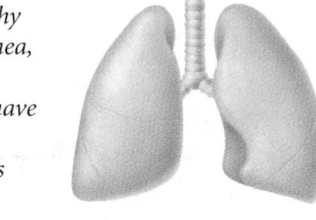

3. Breathing is the movement of the chest that brings air into the lungs and removes waste gases. The chemical reaction in the cells that needs oxygen to release energy from glucose is called cellular respiration.

4. The exchange of oxygen and carbon dioxide happens by the process of diffusion. In the lungs, oxygen diffuses into the capillaries from the alveoli. Carbon dioxide diffuses from the capillaries into the alveoli. In the body tissues, oxygen diffuses from the capillaries into the cells. Carbon dioxide diffuses from the cells into the capillaries.

5. Smoking causes many problems throughout the respiratory system, including chronic bronchitis, emphysema, and lung cancer. *What other body system is affected severely by smoking?*

SHE'S ALREADY UP TO A PACK A DAY.

Section 2 The Excretory System

1. The kidneys are the major organs of the urinary system. They filter wastes from all of the blood in the body. *How does a kidney, shown in the photo regulate fluid levels in the body?*

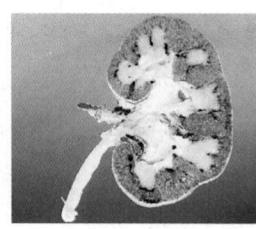

2. The kidney is a two-stage filtration system. The first filtration occurs when water, sugar, salt, and wastes from the blood pass into the cuplike part of the nephron. The capillaries surrounding the tubule part of the nephron perform the second filtration. In this filtration, most of the water, sugar, and salt are reabsorbed and returned to the blood.

3. The urinary system is part of the excretory system. The skin, lungs, liver, and large intestine are also excretory organs.

4. Urine can be tested for signs of urinary tract disease and other diseases.

5. A person who has only one kidney still can live normally. When kidneys fail to work, an artificial kidney can be used to filter the blood in a process called dialysis.

FOLDABLES
Reading & Study Skills

After You Read

Now that you've read the chapter, write the answer to the *Want* question under the *Learned* tab of your Foldable.

FOLDABLES
Reading & Study Skills

After You Read

After students have read the chapter and completed the Foldable described in Before You Read, have them do the activity on the student page.

Dinah Zike

Visualizing Main Ideas

Complete the following table on the respiratory and excretory systems.

Human Body Systems		
	Respiratory System	**Excretory System**
Major Organs	lungs	kidneys, lungs, large intestine, skin, liver
Wastes Eliminated	carbon dioxide, water vapor	water, salts, toxins
Disorders	chronic bronchitis, emphysema, lung cancer, asthma	buildup of wastes, infections

Vocabulary Review

Vocabulary Words

a. alveoli
b. asthma
c. bladder
d. bronchi
e. diaphragm
f. emphysema
g. kidney
h. larynx
i. nephron
j. pharynx
k. trachea
l. ureter
m. urethra
n. urinary system
o. urine

THE PRINCETON REVIEW

Study Tip

Listening is a learning tool, too. Try recording a reading of your notes on tape and replaying it for yourself a few times a week.

Using Vocabulary

For each set of vocabulary words below, explain the relationship that exists.

1. alveoli, bronchi
2. bladder, urine
3. larynx, pharynx
4. ureter, urethra
5. alveoli, emphysema
6. nephron, kidney
7. urethra, bladder
8. asthma, bronchi
9. kidney, urine
10. diaphragm, alveoli

CHAPTER STUDY GUIDE 175

Chapter 6 Study Guide

Visualizing Main Ideas

See student page.

Vocabulary Review

Using Vocabulary

1. Both are structures of the respiratory system.
2. Urine is stored in the bladder until it can be eliminated from the body.
3. Both are structures in the passageway leading to the esophagus.
4. The ureter carries urine to the bladder, and the urethra carries urine away from the bladder.
5. Alveoli are structures in the lungs that are damaged by the disease emphysema.
6. A nephron is the filtering unit of the kidney.
7. The urethra is a tube that carries urine away from the bladder.
8. Asthma is a disorder that causes the bronchi to contract.
9. The kidney filters blood and discharges liquid wastes, called urine.
10. Both are structures of the respiratory system.

Checking Concepts

1. B
2. C
3. A
4. A
5. B
6. D
7. B
8. A
9. C
10. C

Thinking Critically

11. Small objects can be sucked into and block their small windpipes, causing the child to choke.
12. Having many air sacs increases the surface area for gas exchange.
13. Tars coat cilia, making them less flexible and unable to move particles out of the lungs; alveoli lose elasticity, decreasing the total surface area of the lungs available for gas exchange; carcinogens cause the growth of cancerous cells in lung tissue.
14. If the kidneys stopped working, blood would accumulate waste products from the body's organs. These wastes would act as poisons, and the person would need immediate medical care.
15. Kidney stones in the ureter extend and block the tube and cause severe pain. Infections may also occur.

Chapter 6 Assessment

Checking Concepts

Choose the word or phrase that best answers the question.

1. When you inhale, which of the following contracts and moves down?
   A) bronchioles   C) nephrons
   B) diaphragm   D) kidneys

2. Air is moistened, filtered, and warmed in which of the following structures?
   A) larynx   C) nasal cavity
   B) pharynx   D) trachea

3. Exchange of gases occurs between capillaries and which of the following structures?
   A) alveoli   C) bronchioles
   B) bronchi   D) trachea

4. Which of the following is a lung disorder that can occur as an allergic reaction?
   A) asthma   C) emphysema
   B) atherosclerosis D) cancer

5. When you exhale, which way does the rib cage move?
   A) up   C) out
   B) down   D) stays the same

6. Which of the following conditions does smoking worsen?
   A) arthritis   C) excretion
   B) respiration   D) emphysema

7. Urine is held temporarily in which of the following structures?
   A) kidneys   C) ureter
   B) bladder   D) urethra

8. What are the filtering units of the kidneys?
   A) nephrons   C) neurons
   B) ureters   D) alveoli

9. Approximately 1 L of water is lost per day through which of the following?
   A) sweat   C) urine
   B) lungs   D) large intestine

10. Which of the following substances is not reabsorbed by blood after it passes through the kidneys?
    A) salt   C) wastes
    B) sugar   D) water

Thinking Critically

11. Explain why certain foods, such as peanuts, can cause choking in small children.

12. Why is it an advantage to have lungs with many smaller air sacs instead of having just two large sacs, like balloons?

13. Explain the damage to cilia, alveoli, and lungs from smoking.

14. What happens to the blood if the kidneys stop working?

15. Small, solid particles called kidney stones can form in the kidneys. Explain why it is often painful when a kidney stone passes into the ureter.

Developing Skills

16. **Interpreting Data** Study the data below. How much of each substance is reabsorbed into the blood in the kidneys? What substance is excreted completely in the urine?

Materials Filtered by the Kidneys		
Substance Filtered in Urine	Amount Moving Through Kidney	Amount Excreted
Water	125 L	1 L
Salt	350 g	10 g
Urea	1 g	1 g
Glucose	50 g	0 g

17. **Recognizing Cause and Effect** Discuss how lack of oxygen is related to lack of energy.

Chapter ✔Assessment Planner

Portfolio Encourage students to place in their portfolios one or two items of what they consider to be their best work. Examples include:
- Extension, p. 157
- Assessment, p. 165
- Science Journal, p. 166

Performance Additional performance assessments, Performance Task Assessment Lists, and rubrics for evaluating these activities can be found in Glencoe's **Performance Assessment in the Science Classroom.**

18. **Making and Using Graphs** Make a circle graph of total lung capacity using the following data:
    - volume of air in a normal inhalation or exhalation = 500 mL
    - volume of additional air that can be inhaled forcefully after a normal inhalation = 3,000 mL
    - volume of additional air that can be exhaled forcefully after a normal expiration = 1,100 mL
    - volume of air still left in the lungs after all the air that can be exhaled has been forcefully exhaled = 1,200 mL

19. **Forming Hypotheses** Make a hypothesis about the number of breaths a person might take per minute in each of these situations: asleep, exercising, and on top of Mount Everest. Give a reason for each hypothesis.

20. **Concept Mapping** Make an events chain concept map showing how urine forms in the kidneys. Begin with, "In the nephron …"

Performance Assessment

21. **Questionnaire and Interview** Prepare a questionnaire that can be used to interview a health specialist who works with lung cancer patients. Include questions on reasons for choosing the career, new methods of treatment, and the most encouraging or discouraging part of the job.

TECHNOLOGY

Go to the Glencoe Science Web site at **science.glencoe.com** or use the **Glencoe Science CD-ROM** for additional chapter assessment.

THE PRINCETON REVIEW — Test Practice

For one week, research scientists collected and accurately measured the amount of body water lost and gained per day for four different patients. They placed their results in the following table.

Person	Day 1 (L)	Day 2 (L)	Day 3 (L)	Day 4 (L)
Mr. Stoler	+ 0.05	+ 0.15	− 0.35	+ 0.12
Mr. Jemma	− 0.01	0.00	− 0.20	− 0.01
Mr. Lowe	0.00	+ 0.10	− 0.28	+ 0.01
Mr. Cheng	− 0.50	− 0.50	− 0.55	− 0.32

Body Water Gained (+) and Lost (−)

Study the table and answer the following questions.

1. According to this information, which patient may be suffering from dehydration or an excessive amount of body water loss?
   A) Mr. Stoler
   B) Ms. Jemma
   C) Mr. Lowe
   D) Mr. Cheng

2. According to the table, it was probably very hot in each patient's hospital room during _____ .
   F) day one
   G) day two
   H) day three
   J) day four

THE PRINCETON REVIEW — Test Practice

The Test-Taking Tip was written by The Princeton Review, the nation's leader in test preparation.
1. D
2. H

Developing Skills

16. Water: 124 L; salt: 340 g; glucose: 50 g; all urea is excreted.
17. Cells need oxygen to break down food and release energy.
18. Check student graphs for accuracy: 500 mL = 9% of circle (32°); 3,000 mL = 52% (187°); 1,100 mL = 19% (68°); 1,200 mL = 21% (76°).
19. Possible answers: Sleeping—breathing rate is low because less respiration is occurring; exercising—breathing rate would increase to get oxygen to the muscles; on Mount Everest—breathing rate would increase because less oxygen is present.
20. In the nephron, wastes, water, salt, and sugar are removed from blood; water, sugar, and salt are reabsorbed; urine is produced and removed from the kidneys through the ureter.

Performance Assessment

21. Students should prepare questionnaires and conduct interviews. Use **PASC**, p. 91.

✔Assessment Resources

📁 **Reproducible Masters**

Chapter Resources Booklet
Chapter Review, pp. 33–34
Chapter Tests, pp. 35–38
Assessment Transparency Activity, p. 45

Glencoe Science Web site
Interactive Tutor
Chapter Quizzes

Glencoe Technology
- 🔖 Assessment Transparency
- 💿 Interactive CD-ROM Chapter Quizzes
- 💿 ExamView Pro Test Bank
- 💿 Vocabulary PuzzleMaker Software
- 📼 MindJogger Videoquiz

Section/Objectives	Standards		Activities/Features
	National	**State/Local**	
Chapter Opener	See p. 5T for a Key to Standards.		**Explore Activity:** Observe how humans communicate without using sound, p. 179 **Before You Read,** p. 179
Section 1 Types of Behavior 🕐 2 sessions 📦 1 block 1. **Identify** the differences between innate and learned behavior. 2. **Explain** how reflexes and instincts help organisms survive. 3. **Identify** examples of imprinting and conditioning.	National Content Standards: UCP3, A1, C3, C5, G3		**Health Integration,** p. 181 **Science Online,** p. 183 **MiniLAB:** Observing Conditioning, p. 184
Section 2 Behavioral Interactions 🕐 3 sessions 📦 1.5 blocks 1. **Explain** why behavioral adaptations are important. 2. **Describe** how courtship behavior increases reproductive success. 3. **Explain** the importance of social behavior and cyclic behavior.	National Content Standards: UCP3, A1, A2, C2, C3, C5, G1		**MiniLAB:** Demonstrating Chemical Communication, p. 189 **Chemistry Integration,** p. 190 **Visualizing Bioluminescence,** p. 191 **Science Online,** p. 192 **Problem-Solving Activity:** How can you determine which animals hibernate?, p. 193 **Activity:** Observing Earthworm Behavior, p. 195 **Activity:** Animal Habitats, p. 196 **Oops! Accidents in Science:** Going to the Dogs, p. 198

NATIONAL GEOGRAPHIC

Teacher's Corner

PRODUCTS AVAILABLE FROM GLENCOE
To order call 1-800-334-7344:
CD-ROMs
Mammals: A Multimedia Encyclopedia
NGS PictureShow: Structure of Vertebrates 1

NGS PictureShow: Structure of Vertebrates 2
Transparency Sets
NGS PicturePack: Structure of Vertebrates 1
NGS PicturePack: Structure of Vertebrates 2

PRODUCTS AVAILABLE FROM NATIONAL GEOGRAPHIC SOCIETY
To order call 1-800-368-2728:
Book
National Geographic Book of Mammals

Activity Materials	Reproducible Resources	Section Assessment	Technology
Explore Activity: Science Journal	**Chapter Resources Booklet** Foldables Worksheet, p. 15 Directed Reading Overview, p. 17 Note-taking Worksheets, pp. 29–31	*GLENCOE'S* **ASSESSMENT** *ADVANTAGE*	
MiniLAB: photos of different foods and landscapes *Need materials?* Contact Science Kit at 1-800-828-7777 or www.sciencekit.com on the Internet.	**Chapter Resources Booklet** Transparency Activity, p. 40 MiniLAB, p. 3 Enrichment, p. 27 Reinforcement, p. 25 Directed Reading, p. 18 Lab Activity, pp. 9–11 Transparency Activity, pp. 43–44 **Science Inquiry Labs,** p. 11 **Home and Community Involvement,** p. 44	**Portfolio** Reteach, p. 185 **Performance** MiniLAB, p. 184 Skill Builder Activities, p. 185 **Content** Section Assessment, p. 185 Challenge, p. 185	Section Focus Transparency Teaching Transparency Interactive CD-ROM Guided Reading Audio Program
MiniLAB: sample of perfume, air freshener, or flavoring oil **Activity:** scissors, shoe box with lid, flashlight, tape, paper, moist paper towels, earthworms, timer **Activity:** poster board, markers or colored pencils, materials to make a scale model	**Chapter Resources Booklet** Transparency Activity, p. 41 MiniLAB, p. 4 Enrichment, p. 28 Reinforcement, p. 26 Directed Reading, pp. 19, 20 Activity Worksheet, pp. 5–6, 7–8 Lab Activity, pp. 13–14 **Reading and Writing Skill Activities,** p. 5 **Lab Management and Safety,** p. 43	**Portfolio** Cultural Diversity, p. 190 Curriculum Connection, p. 193 **Performance** MiniLAB, p. 189 Skill Builder Activities, p. 194 **Content** Section Assessment, p. 194 Challenge, p. 194	Section Focus Transparency Interactive CD-ROM Guided Reading Audio Program

End of Chapter Assessment

Blackline Masters	Technology	Professional Series
Chapter Resources Booklet Chapter Review, pp. 33–34 Chapter Tests, pp. 35–38 **Standardized Test Practice by The Princeton Review,** pp. 71–74	MindJogger Videoquiz Interactive CD-ROM Vocabulary PuzzleMakers ExamView Pro Test Bank Interactive Lesson Planner Interactive Teacher Edition	Performance Assessment in the Science Classroom (PASC)

Transparencies

Section Focus

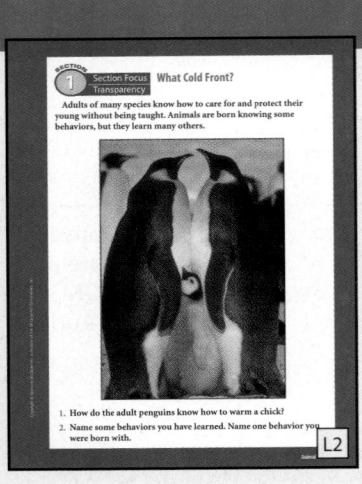

Section Focus Transparency 1 — What Cold Front?

Adults of many species know how to care for and protect their young without being taught. Animals are born knowing some behaviors, but they learn many others.

1. How do the adult penguins know how to warm a chick?
2. Name some behaviors you have learned. Name one behavior you were born with.

L2

Section Focus Transparency 2 — Jump Back!

The snow leopard, which is sometimes called an ounce, is on the endangered species list. Found mainly in the mountains of Asia, the snow leopard tends to live alone. Though snow leopards are solitary animals, they still must interact with other snow leopards as well as with other species.

1. How would you describe this animal's behavior?
2. What are some ways the snow leopard might interact with other animals?

L2

This is a representation of key blackline masters available in the Teacher Classroom Resources. See Resource Manager boxes within the chapter for additional information.

Key to Teaching Strategies

The following designations will help you decide which activities are appropriate for your students.

L1 Level 1 activities should be appropriate for students with learning difficulties.

L2 Level 2 activities should be within the ability range of all students.

L3 Level 3 activities are designed for above-average students.

ELL ELL activities should be within the ability range of English Language Learners.

COOP LEARN Cooperative Learning activities are designed for small group work.

LS Multiple Learning Styles logos, as described on page 22T, are used throughout to indicate strategies that address different learning styles.

P These strategies represent student products that can be placed into a best-work portfolio.

Assessment

Assessment Transparency — Animal Behavior

Directions: *Carefully review the table and answer the following questions.*

Fall Bird Migration–Long Island (New York)		
Bird	**Approximate arrival date**	**Approximate departure date**
Oldsquaw	November 1	April 1
Sanderling	August 1	October 1
White-winged scoter	September 1	May 1
Yellow-crowned night heron	July 1	November 1

1. Which two birds have the greatest chance of not encountering one another in the Long Island Sound area?
   A Sanderling and white-winged scoter
   B Sanderling and yellow-crowned night heron
   C Oldsquaw and white-winged scoter
   D Oldsquaw and yellow-crowned night heron
2. The bird that remains in the Long Island Sound area for the shortest period of time is the ___.
   F white-winged scoter
   G oldsquaw
   H sanderling
   J yellow-crowned night heron
3. The bird that remains in the Long Island Sound area for the longest period of time is the ___.
   A white-winged scoter   C sanderling
   B oldsquaw   D yellow-crowned night heron

L2

Teaching

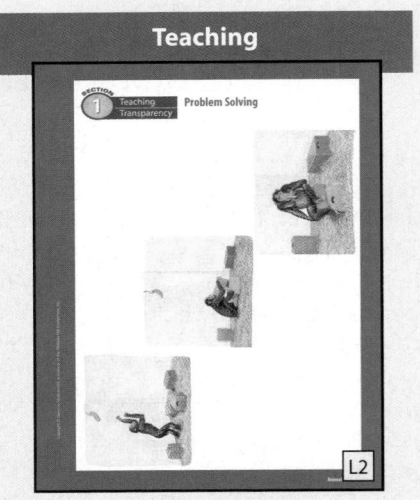

Teaching Transparency — Problem Solving

L2

Hands-on Activities

Activity Worksheets

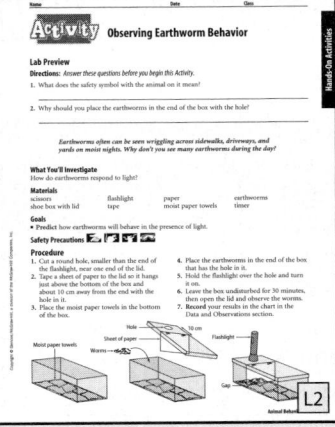

Activity — Observing Earthworm Behavior

Lab Preview
Directions: *Answer these questions before you begin this Activity.*
1. What does the safety symbol with the animal on it mean?

2. Why should you place the earthworms in the end of the box with the hole?

Earthworms often can be seen wriggling across sidewalks, driveways, and yards on moist nights. Why don't you see many earthworms during the day?

What You'll Investigate
How do earthworms respond to light?

Materials
scissors   flashlight   paper   earthworms
shoe box with lid tape   moist paper towels timer

Goals
• **Predict** how earthworms will behave in the presence of light.

Safety Precautions

Procedure
1. Cut a round hole, smaller than the end of the flashlight, near one end of the lid.
2. Tape a sheet of paper to the lid so it hangs just above the bottom of the box and about 10 cm away from the end with the hole in it.
3. Place the moist paper towels in the bottom of the box.
4. Place the earthworms in the end of the box that has the hole in it.
5. Hold the flashlight over the hole and turn it on.
6. Leave the box undisturbed for 30 minutes, then open the lid and observe the worms.
7. **Record** your results in the chart in the Data and Observations section.

L2

Laboratory Activities

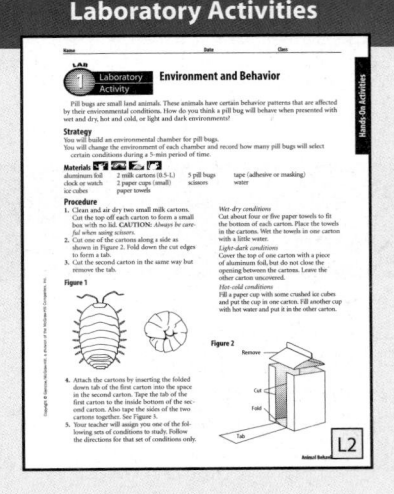

Laboratory Activity — Environment and Behavior

Pill bugs are small land animals. These animals have certain behavior patterns that are affected by their environmental conditions. How do you think a pill bug will behave when presented with wet and dry, hot and cold, or light and dark environments?

Strategy
You will build an environmental chamber for pill bugs.
You will change the environment of each chamber and record how many pill bugs will select certain conditions during a 5-min period of time.

Materials
aluminum foil   2 milk cartons (0.5-L)   5 pill bugs   tape (adhesive or masking)
clock or watch   2 paper cups (small)   scissors   water
ice cubes   paper towels

Procedure
1. Clean and air dry two small milk cartons. Cut the top off each carton to form a small box with no lid. CAUTION: *Always be careful when using scissors.*
2. Cut one of the cartons along a side as shown in Figure 2. Fold down the cut edges to form a tab.
3. Cut the second carton in the same way but remove the tab.

Wet-dry conditions
Cut about four or five paper towels to fit the bottom of each carton. Place the towels in the cartons. Wet the towels in one carton with a little water.

Light-dark conditions
Cover the top of one carton with a piece of aluminum foil, but do not close the opening between the cartons. Leave the other carton uncovered.

Hot-cold conditions
Fill a paper cup with some crushed ice cubes and put the cup in one carton. Fill another cup with hot water and put it in the other carton.

Figure 1

4. Attach the cartons by inserting the folded-down tab of the first carton into the space in the second carton. Tape the tab of the first carton to the inside bottom of the second carton. Also tape the sides of the two cartons together. See Figure 3.
5. Your teacher will assign you one of the following sets of conditions to study. Follow the directions for that set of conditions only.

Figure 2

L2

Meeting Different Ability Levels

Content Outline

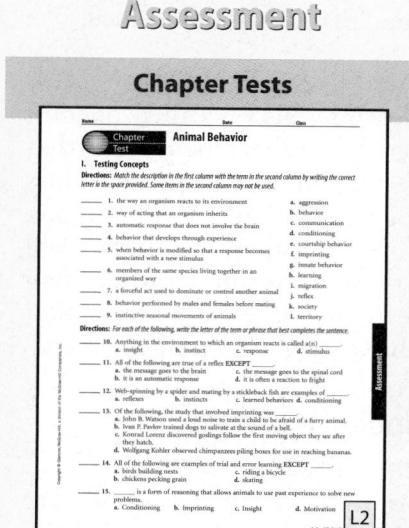

Note-taking Worksheet — **Animal Behavior** — L2

Reinforcement

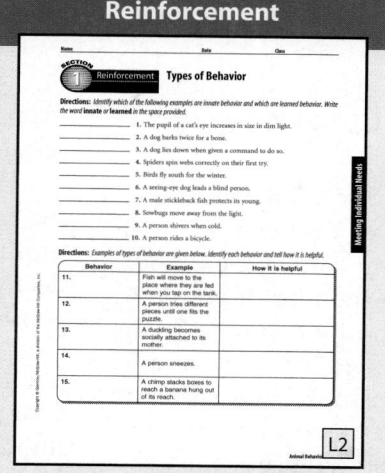

Reinforcement — **Types of Behavior** — L2

Directed Reading

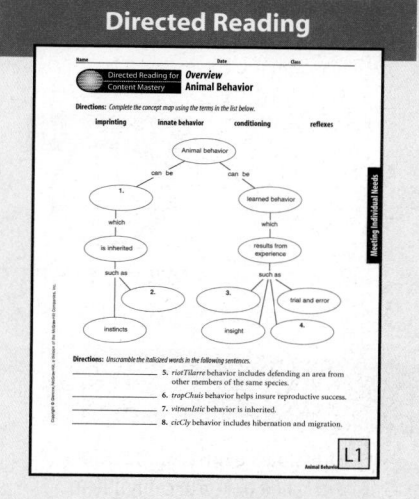

Directed Reading for Content Mastery — **Overview Animal Behavior** — L1

Assessment

Chapter Tests

Chapter Test — **Animal Behavior** — L2

Enrichment

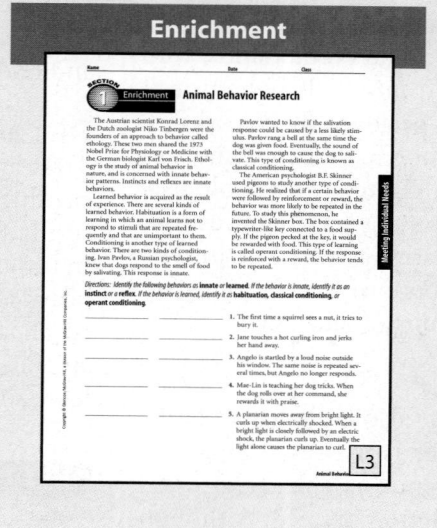

Enrichment — **Animal Behavior Research** — L3

Spanish Directed Reading

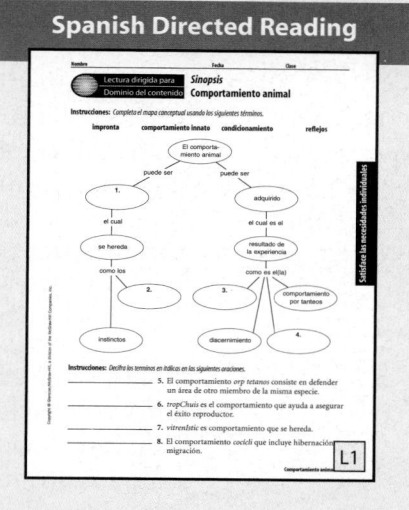

Lectura dirigida para Dominio del contenido — **Sinopsis Comportamiento animal** — L1

Test Practice Workbook

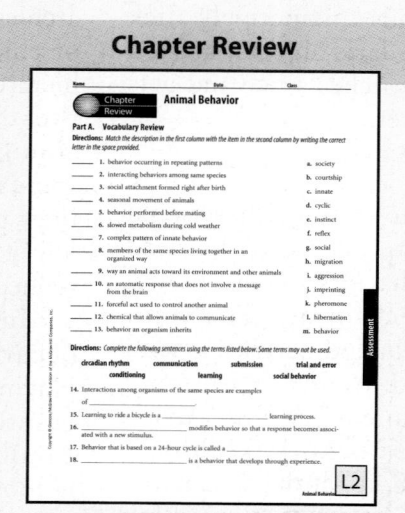

Standardized Test Practice — Teacher Edition — Glencoe Science — LEVEL GREEN — L2

Chapter Review

Chapter Review — **Animal Behavior** — L2

Science Content Background

SECTION 1

Types of Behavior

Ethology

The scientific study of animal behavior as it occurs in an organism's natural environment is called ethology. Konrad Z. Lorenz, a founder of ethology, studied the behavior of birds and developed a theory of animal behavior that stressed its inherited aspects. Lorenz and two other ethologists—Karl von Frisch of Austria, who studied bee communication, and Nikolaas Tinbergen of the Netherlands, who studied gull and fish behavior—received the 1973 Nobel prize for their work.

Early ethologists thought that most behaviors were instinctual. In contrast, psychologists thought that the environment modified instinctual behavior and that learning was more important. Today, ideas from both of these groups are combined in studies of animal behavior.

> **Fun Fact**
>
> Mice missing a gene that codes for a protein called oxytocin cannot learn to identify other mice. Oxytocin seems to regulate social memory.

Innate Behavior

Innate behavior is often also called instinctive behavior. Innate behavior is triggered by a specific environmental stimulus that triggers a behavior called a fixed action pattern. Although innate behaviors are inherited, environment plays a role in the development of the behavior. For example, young toads instinctively flick their tongues out at all dark objects, a fixed action pattern. If a toad catches a bee and gets stung it learns to avoid bees.

Learned Behavior

It is sometimes difficult to distinguish between innate behavior and learned behavior. Learned behaviors and innate behaviors involve neural and often hormonal mechanisms. The complexity of an animal's brain and nervous system is genetically determined. Animals with more complex brains receive more input from experience and exhibit learned behavior. Though learning is not instinctive, it can be automatic. For example, people learn how to use eating utensils. After a while, this action does not require conscious thought.

Habituation is learning to tune out unimportant stimuli. When animals ignore unimportant stimuli they conserve energy to deal with relevant stimuli. A person may ignore constant noises, such as traffic outside a window.

Imprinting

Goats, sheep, and the Alaskan fur seals are imprinted during the first few minutes after the birth of their offspring to recognize the offspring by their odor. The mother will accept any young that they smell during this critical period and reject any young that they did not smell.

Trial and Error

Trial and error learning also is called operant conditioning. Animals repeat behaviors that result in positive stimuli and avoid behaviors that result in negative stimuli. For example, bears soon learn by trial and error that they will catch a fish by remaining quiet rather than splashing about in the water. The toad that learned to avoid bees learned by trial and error.

SECTION 2

Social Behavior

Animal Societies

Some animal societies are organized into dominance hierarchies, such as a pecking order within a society of chickens. Animals with a high rank in the hierarchy usually have access to more food and thus have more reproductive success. The young of these dominant animals will have some of the same characteristics that helped their parents survive. If food is scarce, animals lower in the hierarchy die and the population is reduced to a number the habitat can support.

In many animal societies, reproduction occurs at the same time within the group. Having many young in a population at once ensures that some will survive to adulthood. Ethologists think that this type of behavior is more common when members of a group are related.

A group of animals is more likely to be successful in finding food than an individual alone. Some animals, like wolves and hyenas, hunt in groups so they can more easily corner prey.

Territorial Behavior

Dominant individuals are usually more successful in defending a territory. Because only individuals with territories mate, genes of the best-adapted individuals are likely to pass on to the next generation. Some territories are only large enough for mating. Other larger territories help ensure an adequate food supply for offspring.

Sound Communication

Whales "sing," and dolphins emit clicking noises that can travel more than 100 kilometers underwater. Elephants emit low-frequency sounds called infrasound. These sounds are in the same sound range as earthquakes and cannot be heard by humans. Elephants emit these sounds as warnings and female elephants "sing" at this frequency to attract mates.

Migration

Animals use a variety of navigational devices to find their way. Honeybees use polarized light. Birds use the Sun during the day or the stars at night, much as humans use a compass and map.

SCIENCE *Online*

For additional content background on this topic, go to the Glencoe Science Web site at science.glencoe.com.

Brandon D. Cole/Corbis

Animal Behavior

Chapter Vocabulary

What do you think?

Science Journal The photograph shows birds waiting to be fed. This response is triggered by the arrival of the parents at the nest.

Animal Behavior

E ye contact is made, dirt flies, and the silence is shattered. Massive horns clash as two bighorn sheep butt heads. Nearby, a spider spins a web to catch its food. Overhead, the honking of a V-shaped string of geese echoes through the valley. Do organisms learn these actions or do they occur automatically? In this chapter, you will examine the unique behaviors of animals. Also, you'll read about different types of behavior and learn about animal communication.

What do you think?

Science Journal Look at the picture below with a classmate. Discuss what you think this might be or what is happening. Here's a hint: *This instinctive reaction is triggered by their parent's arrival.* Write your answer or best guess in your Science Journal.

178

Theme Connection

Stability and Change Survival of a species is dependent upon the ability of its members to respond to changes in the environment by changing either themselves or their behaviors. Complex patterns of behavior have evolved in animals to help them successfully compete in a variety of environments.

 **EXPLORE ACTIVITY**

One way you communicate is by speaking. Other animals communicate without the use of sound. For example, a gull chick pecks at its parent's beak to get food. Try the activity below to see if you can communicate without speaking.

Observe how humans communicate without using sound

1. Form groups of students. Have one person choose an object and describe that object using gestures.
2. The other students observe and try to identify the object that is being described.
3. Each student in the group should choose an object and describe it without speaking while the others observe and identify the object.

Observe

In your Science Journal, describe how you and the other students were able to communicate without speaking to one another.

 Before You Read

FOLDABLES
Reading & Study Skills

Making a Compare and Contrast Study Fold As you study behaviors, make the following Foldable to help find the similarities and differences between the behaviors of two animals.

1. Place a sheet of paper in front of you so the short side is at the top. Fold the paper in half from the left to the right side. Fold top to bottom but do not crease. Then unfold.
2. Label *Observed Behaviors of Animal 1* and *Observed Behaviors of Animal 2* across the front of the paper, as shown.
3. Through one thickness of paper, cut along the middle fold line to form two tabs, as shown.
4. Before you read the chapter, choose two animals to compare.
5. As you read the chapter, list the behaviors you learn about Animal 1 and Animal 2 under the tabs.

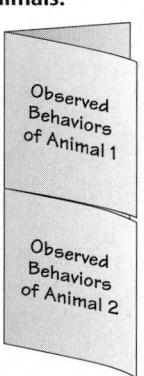

Observed Behaviors of Animal 1

Observed Behaviors of Animal 2

179

EXPLORE ACTIVITY

Purpose Use this Explore Activity to demonstrate to students that humans can communicate without using sound. L1 ELL COOP LEARN 〖K〗 **Kinesthetic**

Preparation Discuss how humans and other animals communicate.

Teaching Strategies
- Encourage students to choose objects with which their classmates are familiar.
- Discuss differences and similarities in their methods of communication.

Observe
Possible answers: use of hands, facial expressions, body movements, and other gestures

✔Assessment

Oral Ask how humans communicate with one another. Possible answers: frowning, smiling, looking perplexed or anxious, shaking hands, hugging, touching, posturing and body language in general, speaking, tone of voice. Use **Performance Assessment in the Science Classroom,** p. 89.

FOLDABLES
Reading & Study Skills

Before You Read

Dinah Zike Study Fold

Purpose Students make and use a Foldable to collect information on two observable animals and then use what they have learned to compare and contrast the behavior of these animals.

📁 For additional help, see Foldables Worksheet, p. 15 in **Chapter Resources Booklet,** or go to the Glencoe Science Web site at **science.glencoe.com.** See After You Read in the Study Guide at the end of this chapter.

Bellringer Transparency

Display the Section Focus Transparency for Section 1. Use the accompanying Transparency Activity Master. L2

ELL

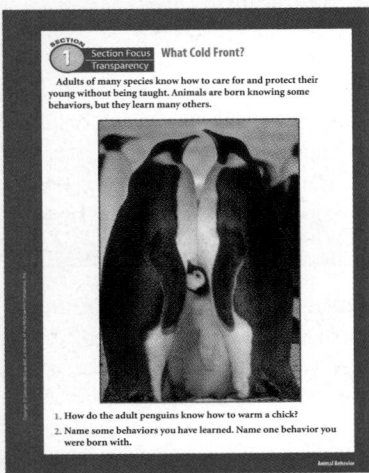

Tie to Prior Knowledge

Ask students to define *communication*. Have them explain how they communicate with their pets and other animals. Invite volunteers to describe how a pet communicates with its owner.

Types of Behavior

As You Read

What You'll Learn
- **Identify** the differences between innate and learned behavior.
- **Explain** how reflexes and instincts help organisms survive.
- **Identify** examples of imprinting and conditioning.

Vocabulary
behavior
innate behavior
reflex
instinct
imprinting
conditioning
insight

Why It's Important
Innate behavior helps you survive on your own.

Behavior

When you come home from school, does your dog run to meet you? Your dog barks and wags its tail as you scratch behind its ears. Sitting at your feet, it watches every move you make. Why do dogs do these things? In nature, dogs are pack animals that generally follow a leader. They have been living with people for about 12,000 years. Domesticated dogs treat people as part of their own pack, as shown in **Figure 1B.**

Animals are different from one another in their behavior. They are born with certain behaviors, and they learn others. **Behavior** is the way an organism interacts with other organisms and its environment. Anything in the environment that causes a reaction is called a stimulus. A stimulus can be external, such as a rival male entering another male's territory, or internal, such as hunger or thirst. You are the stimulus that causes your dog to bark and wag its tail. Your dog's reaction to you is a response.

Figure 1
Dogs are pack animals by nature. **A** This pack of wild dogs must work together to survive. **B** This domesticated dog has accepted a human as its leader.

Section ✓*Assessment* Planner

PORTFOLIO
Reteach, p. 185
PERFORMANCE ASSESSMENT
MiniLAB, p. 184
Skill Builder Activities, p. 185
See page 202 for more options.

CONTENT ASSESSMENT
Section, p. 185
Challenge, p. 185
Chapter, pp. 202–203

Innate Behavior

A behavior that an organism is born with is called an **innate behavior.** These types of behaviors are inherited. They don't have to be learned.

Innate behavior patterns occur the first time an animal responds to a particular internal or external stimulus. For birds like the swallows in **Figure 2A** and the hummingbird in **Figure 2B** building a nest is innate behavior. When it's time for the female weaverbird to lay eggs, the male weaverbird builds an elaborate nest, as shown in **Figure 2C.** Although a young male's first attempt may be messy, the nest is constructed correctly.

The behavior of animals that have short life spans is mostly innate behavior. Most insects do not learn from their parents. In many cases, the parents have died or moved on by the time the young hatch. Yet every insect reacts innately to its environment. A moth will fly toward a light, and a cockroach will run away from it. They don't learn this behavior. Innate behavior allows animals to respond instantly. This quick response often means the difference between life and death.

Reflexes The simplest innate behaviors are reflex actions. A **reflex** is an automatic response that does not involve a message from the brain. Sneezing, shivering, yawning, jerking your hand away from a hot surface, and blinking your eyes when something is thrown toward you are all reflex actions.

In humans a reflex message passes almost instantly from a sense organ along the nerve to the spinal cord and back to the muscles. The message does not go to the brain. You are aware of the reaction only after it has happened. Your body reacts on its own. A reflex is not the result of conscious thinking.

Figure 2
Bird nests come in different sizes and shapes. **A** Cliff swallows build nests out of mud. **B** Hummingbirds build delicate cup-shaped nests on branches of trees. **C** This male weaverbird is knotting the ends of leaves together to secure the nest.

Health
INTEGRATION

A tap on a tendon in your knee causes your leg to stretch. This is known as the knee-jerk reflex. Abnormalities in this reflex tell doctors of a possible problem in the central nervous system. Research other types of reflexes and write a report about them in your Science Journal.

SECTION 1 Types of Behavior **181**

Innate Behavior,
continued

Quick Demo
Reinforce students' understanding of innate behaviors by demonstrating reflex actions. The response of the pupil to light in a dark room is an automatic response.

Reading Check

Answer reflex: automatic response, does not involve the brain; instinct: complex pattern of innate behavior developed over time

Extension
Many students will find animal communication interesting. Have them research and design a project that involves tape-recording and analyzing animal sounds. L2 IS **Auditory-Musical**

Discussion
Why are reflexes important? They allow an animal to rapidly respond to sudden change.

Learned Behavior

Caption Answer
Figure 4 It protects them until they can learn to distinguish between harmful and nonthreatening organisms.

Figure 3
Spiders, like this orb weaver spider, know how to spin webs as soon as they hatch.

Figure 4
As they grow older, these quail chicks will learn which organisms to avoid. *Why is it important for young quail to react the same toward all organisms?*

Instincts An **instinct** is a complex pattern of innate behavior. Spinning a web like the one in **Figure 3** is complicated, yet spiders spin webs correctly on the first try. Unlike reflexes, instinctive behaviors can take weeks to complete. Instinctive behavior begins when the animal recognizes a stimulus and continues until all parts of the behavior have been performed.

Reading Check *What is the difference between a reflex and an instinct?*

Learned Behavior

All animals have innate and learned behaviors. Learned behavior develops during an animal's lifetime. Animals with more complex brains exhibit more behaviors that are the result of learning. However, the behavior of insects, spiders, and other arthropods is mostly instinctive behavior. Fish, reptiles, amphibians, birds, and mammals all learn. Learning is the result of experience or practice.

Learning is important for animals because it allows them to respond to changing situations. In changing environments, animals that have the ability to learn a new behavior are more likely to survive. This is especially important for animals with long life spans. The longer an animal lives, the more likely it is that the environment in which it lives will change.

Learning also can modify instincts. For example, grouse and quail chicks, shown in **Figure 4,** leave their nests the day they hatch. They can run and find food, but they can't fly. When something moves above them, they instantly crouch and keep perfectly still until the danger has passed. They will crouch without moving even if the falling object is only a leaf. Older birds have learned that leaves will not harm them, but they freeze when a hawk moves overhead.

LAB DEMONSTRATION

Purpose to observe fruit fly responses

Materials 2 vials of fruit flies, ice, black construction paper, masking tape, jars, bananas

Preparation Put 2 jars containing bananas outdoors. After fruit flies collect, wrap black paper around each jar. Invert a vial over a jar. Shine a light on the vial and insert plug after flies move into it. Do the same with the other vial and jar.

Procedure Place one vial in ice. Cover half of the second vial with black paper. Leave both undisturbed for 10–15 minutes. Have students record their observations.

Expected Outcome Fruit flies in ice become sluggish. Those in the second vial move toward the light.

Assessment

How does the behavior of fruit flies help them survive? Their body processes slow when it is cold. Since fruit flies do not internally regulate their body temperatures, their positive response to light helps them stay warm and remain active.

Imprinting Learned behavior includes imprinting, trial and error, conditioning, and insight. Have you ever seen young ducks following their mother? This is an important behavior because the adult bird has had more experience in finding food, escaping predators, and getting along in the world. **Imprinting** occurs when an animal forms a social attachment, like the condor in **Figure 5,** to another organism within a specific time period after birth or hatching.

Konrad Lorenz, an Austrian naturalist, developed the concept of imprinting. Working with geese, he discovered that a gosling follows the first moving object it sees after hatching. The moving object, whatever it is, is imprinted as its parent. This behavior works well when the first moving object a gosling sees is an adult female goose. But goslings hatched in an incubator might see a human first and imprint on him or her. Animals that become imprinted toward animals of another species have difficulty recognizing members of their own species.

Trial and Error Can you remember when you learned to ride a bicycle? You probably fell many times before you learned how to balance on the bicycle. After a while you could ride without having to think about it. You have many skills that you have learned through trial and error such as feeding yourself and tying your shoes, as shown in **Figure 6.**

Behavior that is modified by experience is called trial-and-error learning. Many animals learn by trial and error. When baby chicks first try feeding themselves, they peck at many stones before they get any food. As a result of trial and error, they learn to peck only at food particles.

Figure 6
Were you able to tie your shoes on the first attempt? *What other things do you do every day that required learning?*

Activity

Separate a large puzzle into six sections. Place the disassembled pieces for each section in a paper bag. Divide the class into six groups, each with one of the bags. Have groups work together to reassemble the sections. Then, have students combine the sections to the complete puzzle. Ask students what type of behavior they demonstrated. learned L2   ELL   COOP LEARN

Caption Answer

Figure 6 Possible answers: reading, writing, brushing teeth, using the telephone, walking

Resource Manager

Chapter Resources Booklet
   Enrichment, p. 27
   Lab Activity, pp. 9–11
   Transparency Activity, pp. 43–44

Visual Learning
Figure 5 The use of puppets of adult condors ensures that expected imprinting occurs. Predict what would likely occur if puppets of adult geese had been used to feed the condor chicks. Because of imprinting, the chicks would form a social attachment to adult geese instead of to adult condors. L2
Logical-Mathematical

Learned Behavior,
continued

Mini LAB

Purpose to observe the affects of conditioning [L1] [ELL]

IS Visual-Spatial

Materials photos of food and landscapes

Teaching Strategy Have students show their partners several different types of food.

Analysis

1. Usually, staring at pictures of food causes a person to feel hungry.
2. Generally, landscape pictures remind people of places, but they do not stimulate a response or feeling. At times, landscapes can evoke feelings of nostalgia.
3. Large pictures of appetizing foods condition consumers to feel hungry and crave the food product.

Assessment

Performance Have students design another experiment in which they test for conditioning. Use **PASC,** p. 95.

Reading Check

Answer Conditioning causes a response to one stimulus to become associated with a different stimulus.

Mini LAB

Observing Conditioning

Procedure

1. Obtain several **photos of different foods and land-scapes** from your teacher.
2. Show each picture to a classmate for 20 s.
3. Record how each photo made your partner feel.

Analysis

1. How did your partner feel after looking at the photos of food?
2. What effect did the land-scape pictures have on your partner?
3. Infer how advertising might condition consumers to buy specific food products.

Figure 7
In Pavlov's experiment, a dog was conditioned to salivate when a bell was rung. It associated the bell with food.

Conditioning Do you have an aquarium in your school or home? If you put your hand above the tank, the fish probably will swim to the top of the tank expecting to be fed. They have learned that a hand shape above them means food. What would happen if you tapped on the glass right before you fed them? After a while the fish probably will swim to the top of the tank if you just tap on the glass. Because they are used to being fed after you tap on the glass, they associate the tap with food.

Animals often learn new behaviors by conditioning. In **conditioning,** behavior is modified so that a response to one stimulus becomes associated with a different stimulus. There are two types of conditioning. One type introduces a new stimulus before the usual stimulus. Russian scientist Ivan P. Pavlov performed experiments with this type of conditioning. He knew that the sight and smell of food made hungry dogs secrete saliva. Pavlov added another stimulus. He rang a bell before he fed the dogs. The dogs began to connect the sound of the bell with food. Then Pavlov rang the bell without giving the dogs food. They salivated when the bell was rung even though he did not show them food. The dogs, like the one in **Figure 7,** were conditioned to respond to the bell.

In the second type of conditioning, the new stimulus is given after the affected behavior. Getting an allowance for doing chores is an example of this type of conditioning. You do your chores because you want to receive your allowance. You have been conditioned to perform an activity that you may not have done if you had not been offered a reward.

✓ Reading Check *How does conditioning modify behavior?*

Insight How does learned behavior help an animal deal with a new situation? Suppose you have a new math problem to solve. Do you begin by acting as though you've never seen it before, or do you use what you have learned previously in math to solve the problem? If you use what you have learned, then you have used a kind of learned behavior called insight. **Insight** is a form of reasoning that allows animals to use past experiences to solve new problems. In experiments with chimpanzees, as shown in **Figure 8,** bananas were placed out of the chimpanzees' reach. Instead of giving up, they piled up boxes found in the room, climbed them, and reached the bananas. At some time in their lives, the chimpanzees must have solved a similar problem. The chimpanzees demonstrated insight during the experiment. Much of adult human learning is based on insight. When you were a baby, you learned by trial and error. As you grow older, you will rely more on insight.

Figure 8
This illustration shows how chimpanzees may use insight to solve problems.

Section ① **Assessment**

1. How is innate behavior different from learned behavior?
2. Compare a reflex with an instinct.
3. What is the difference between an internal and external stimulus?
4. Compare imprinting and conditioning.
5. **Think Critically** Use what you know about conditioning to explain how the term *mouthwatering food* might have come about.

Skill Builder Activities

6. **Researching Information** How are dogs trained to sniff out certain substances? **For more help,** refer to the Science Skill Handbook.
7. **Using an Electronic Spreadsheet** Make a spreadsheet of the behaviors in this section. Sort the behaviors according to whether they are innate or learned behaviors. Then identify the type of innate or learned behavior. **For more help,** refer to the Technology Skill Handbook.

Teacher FYI
Much of human learning is based on insight. Babies first learn by trial and error. As they grow older, they rely on insight. Solving problems is an example of using insight.

③ Assess

Reteach
Have students make a concept map using all vocabulary terms in this section. L2 IS **Visual-Spatial** P

Challenge
How would a lack of innate behavior patterns affect animals? Many would not live long enough to reproduce, which could result in species eventually becoming extinct.

✓Assessment

Portfolio Have students write a paragraph in their Science Journals describing the type of learning that occurs when crows in a farmer's field do not react to a scarecrow that has been in place for a month. Use **Performance Assessment in the Science Classroom,** p. 99.

Answers to Section Assessment

1. innate: behavior an animal is born with; learned: develops through experience
2. reflex: automatic response, doesn't involve brain; instinct: complex pattern of innate behavior
3. An internal stimulus originates inside the body; an external stimulus comes from outside the body.
4. Imprinting occurs when an animal forms a social attachment to another organism within a specific time period after birth or hatching. Conditioning occurs when a response to one stimulus becomes associated with a different stimulus.
5. The response to the stimulus of food is the production of saliva. Upon conditioning, the sight, smell, or thought of food can cause the production of saliva.
6. Look for understanding of innate and learned behaviors in student responses.
7. innate: reflexes and instincts; learned: imprinting, trial and error, conditioning, and insight; An example should be provided for each

1 Motivate

Bellringer Transparency

Display the Section Focus Transparency for Section 2. Use the accompanying Transparency Activity Master. L2 ELL

Tie to Prior Knowledge

Students will be familiar with aggressive and territorial behaviors of pets and other animals. Discuss familiar examples of territorial displays and threatening behaviors.

✔ Reading Check

Answer It provides advantages for survival of the species.

What **You'll Learn**
- **Explain** why behavioral adaptations are important.
- **Describe** how courtship behavior increases reproductive success.
- **Explain** the importance of social behavior and cyclic behavior.

Vocabulary
social behavior
society
aggression
courtship behavior
pheromone
cyclic behavior
hibernation
migration

Why **It's Important**
Organisms must be able to communicate with each other to survive.

Figure 9
When several zebras are close together their stripes make it difficult for predators to pick out one individual.

Instinctive Behavior Patterns

Complex interactions of innate behaviors between organisms result in many types of animal behavior. For example, courtship and mating within most animal groups are instinctive ritual behaviors that help animals recognize possible mates. Animals also protect themselves and their food sources by defending their territories. Instinctive behavior, just like natural hair color, is inherited.

Social Behavior

Animals often live in groups. One reason, shown in **Figure 9,** is that large numbers provide safety. A lion is less likely to attack a herd of zebras than a lone zebra. Sometimes animals in large groups help keep each other warm. Also, migrating animal groups are less likely to get lost than animals that travel alone.

Interactions among organisms of the same species are examples of **social behavior.** Social behaviors include courtship and mating, caring for the young, claiming territories, protecting each other, and getting food. These inherited behaviors provide advantages that promote survival of the species.

 Reading Check *Why is social behavior important?*

Section ✔ *Assessment* Planner

PORTFOLIO
Cultural Diversity, p. 190
Curriculum Connection, p. 193
PERFORMANCE ASSESSMENT
Try at Home MiniLAB, p. 189
Skill Builder Activities, p. 194
See page 202 for more options.

CONTENT ASSESSMENT
Section, p. 194
Challenge, p. 194
Chapter, pp. 202–203

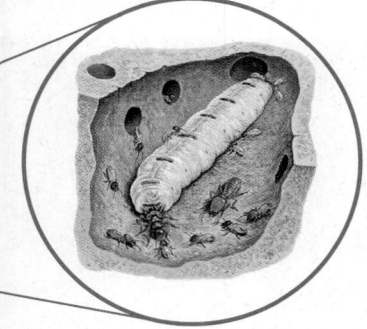

Societies Insects such as ants, bees, and the termites shown in **Figure 10,** live together in societies. A **society** is a group of animals of the same species living and working together in an organized way. Each member has a certain role. Usually a specific female lays eggs, and a male fertilizes them. Workers do all the other jobs in the society.

Some societies are organized by dominance. Wolves usually live together in packs. A wolf pack has a dominant female. The top female controls the mating of the other females. If plenty of food is available, she mates and then allows the others to do so. If food is scarce, she allows less mating. During such times, she is usually the only one to mate.

Territorial Behavior

Many animals set up territories for feeding, mating, and raising young. A territory is an area that an animal defends from other members of the same species. Ownership of a territory occurs in different ways. Songbirds sing, sea lions bellow, and squirrels chatter to claim territories. Other animals leave scent marks. Some animals, like the tiger in **Figure 11,** patrol an area and attack other animals of the same species who enter their territory. Why do animals defend their territories? Territories contain food, shelter, and potential mates. If an animal has a territory, it will be able to mate and produce offspring. Defending territories is an instinctive behavior. It improves the survival rate of an animal's offspring.

Figure 10
Termites built this large mound in Australia. The mound has a network of tunnels and chambers for the queen to deposit eggs into.

Figure 11
A tiger's territory may include several miles. It will confront any other tiger who enters it.

Social Behavior

Make a Model
Have students work in groups of three to make a model of animals with social behavior, such as honeybees, hornets, ants, beavers or wolves. Ask them to identify the members of the group modeled and explain their roles. L2

Discussion
How do fish benefit from forming schools? When swimming in a school, a fish is less vulnerable to attack by a predator.

Territorial Behavior

Use an Analogy
Discuss the meaning of the expression: *The best defense is a good offense.* Explain that some animals that travel together will mount an attack against predators as a means of protection. For example, some monkeys will throw sticks at an approaching leopard.

Discussion
Some male lions roar to compete for mates. Roaring takes a lot of strength. **How might roaring prevent a fight between two males?** The roar's intensity illustrates the strength of a male. A weaker male will likely leave the area rather than fight.

Resource Manager

Chapter Resources Booklet
    Transparency Activity, p. 41
    Directed Reading for Content Mastery, pp. 19, 20
Mathematics Skill Activities, p. 49

Visual Learning

Figure 11 What other animals defend their territories? Possible answers: songbirds, sea lions, squirrels

IDENTIFYING
Misconceptions

Students may typically describe animal behavior in human terms using such words as *pain*, *emotions*, and *desire*. There is a tendency to relate all animal behavior in terms of human reactions. Caution students not to think of animal behavior in terms of their own behavior.

Use Science Words

Word Origin The term *anthropomorphism* is derived from the Greek terms *anthropos*, meaning "man," and *morphe*, meaning "form." Have students use a dictionary to find the meaning of *anthropomorphism* and use the word in a sentence. It is the application of human characteristics to anything not human.

Communication

Quick Demo

Shake a student's hand. Ask what message was communicated by the action. Have class members identify other actions that send messages. Point out that animals have many forms of nonverbal communication.

Figure 12
Young wolves roll over and make themselves as small as possible to show their submission to adult wolves.

Figure 13
During the waggle dance, if the source is far from the hive, the dance takes the form of a figure eight. The angle of the waggle is equal to the angle from the hive between the Sun and nectar source.

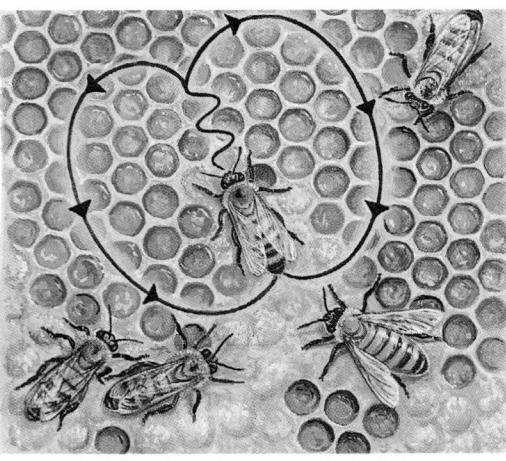

Aggression Have you ever watched as one dog approached another dog that was eating a bone? What happened to the appearance of the dog with the bone? Did its hair on its back stick up? Did it curl its lips and make growling noises? This behavior is aggression. **Aggression** is a forceful behavior used to dominate or control another animal. Fighting and threatening are aggressive behaviors animals use to defend their territories, protect their young, or to get food.

Many animals demonstrate aggression. Some birds let their wings droop below their tail feathers. It may take another bird's perch and thrust its head forward in a pecking motion as a sign of aggression. Cats lay their ears flat, arch their backs, and hiss.

Submission Animals of the same species seldom fight to the death. Teeth, beaks, claws, and horns are used for killing prey or for defending against members of a different species.

To avoid being attacked and injured by an individual of its own species, an animal shows submission. Postures that make an animal appear smaller often are used to communicate surrender. In some animal groups, one individual is usually dominant. Members of the group show submissive behavior toward the dominant individual. This stops further aggressive behavior by the dominant animal. Young animals also display submissive behaviors toward parents or dominant animals, as shown in **Figure 12.**

Communication

In all social behavior, communication is important. Communication is an action by a sender that influences the behavior of a receiver. How do you communicate with the people around you? You may talk, make noises, or gesture like you did in this chapter's Explore Activity. Honeybees perform a dance, as shown in **Figure 13,** to communicate to other bees in the hive where a food source is. Animals in a group communicate with sounds, scents, and actions. Alarm calls, chemicals, speech, courtship behavior, and aggression are forms of communication.

Inclusion Strategies

Learning Disabled Write all the letters of the alphabet in random order on a sheet of paper. Provide each student three copies of the sheet and have them mark the copies 1, 2, and 3. Give students 10 seconds to find the letters and draw a line to connect them in alphabetical order. Time the students for three trials. L1 IS **Kinesthetic**

Curriculum Connection

Health Studies show that the health of hospitalized and institutionalized people often improves when they develop a relationship with an animal. Have students research capuchin monkeys or guide dogs and write reports explaining how the interaction of animals and people is thought to promote better health.

Figure 14
This male Emperor of Germany bird of paradise attracts mates by posturing and fanning its tail.

Courtship Behavior A male bird of paradise, shown in **Figure 14,** spreads its tail feathers and struts. A male sage grouse fans its tail, fluffs its feathers, and blows up its two red air sacs. These are examples of behavior that animals perform before mating. This type of behavior is called **courtship behavior.** Courtship behaviors allow male and female members of a species to recognize each other. These behaviors also stimulate males and females so they are ready to mate at the same time. This helps ensure reproductive success.

In most species the males are more colorful and perform courtship displays to attract a mate. Some courtship behaviors allow males and females to find each other across distances.

Chemical Communication

Ants are sometimes seen moving single file toward a piece of food. Male dogs frequently urinate on objects and plants. Both behaviors are based on chemical communication. The ants have laid down chemical trails that others of their species can follow. The dog is letting other dogs know he has been there. In these behaviors, the animals are using a chemical called a pheromone to communicate. A **pheromone** (FER uh mohn) is a chemical that is produced by one animal to influence the behavior of another animal of the same species. They are powerful chemicals needed only in small amounts. They remain in the environment so that the sender and the receiver can communicate without being in the same place at the same time. They can advertise the presence of an animal to predators, as well as to the intended receiver of the message.

Males and females use pheromones to establish territories, warn of danger, and attract mates. Certain ants, mice, and snails release alarm pheromones when injured or threatened.

TRY AT HOME
Mini LAB

Demonstrating Chemical Communication

Procedure
1. Obtain a **sample of perfume or air freshener.**
2. Spray it into the air to leave a scent trail as you move around the house or apartment to a hiding place.
3. Have someone try to discover where you are by following the scent of the substance.

Analysis
1. What was the difference between the first and last room you were in?
2. Would this be an efficient way for humans to communicate? Explain.

TRY AT HOME
Mini LAB

Purpose to observe a method of chemical communication
Materials perfume, air freshener, or flavoring oil
Teaching Strategy Have students choose a strong scent with a pleasant odor.
Analysis
1. The scent would be stronger in the last room.
2. Yes; a person could be located by the scent.

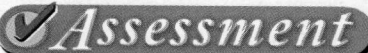

Oral How do law enforcement officers help trained dogs pick up the scent of a missing person? They have the dog smell an object that belonged to the missing person. Use **Performance Assessment in the Science Classroom,** p. 143.

SECTION 2 Behavioral Interactions **189**

Resource Manager

Chapter Resources Booklet
Enrichment, p. 28
MiniLAB, p. 4

Teacher FYI

Ants make a "pheromone trail" from their nest to food sources for other ants to follow. Some female insects give off pheromones that attract males. Scientists have developed artificial pheromones for use in pest control. Traps contain the female pheromones, which attract the males to the trap.

Figure 15
Many animals use sound to communicate.

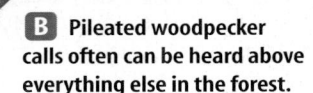

A Frogs often croak loud enough to be heard far away.

B Pileated woodpecker calls often can be heard above everything else in the forest.

C Howler monkeys got their name because of the sounds they make.

Sound Communication Male crickets rub one forewing against the other forewing. This produces chirping sounds that attract females. Each cricket species produces several calls that are different from other cricket species. These calls are used by researchers to identify different species. Male mosquitoes have hairs on their antennae that sense buzzing sounds produced by females of their same species. The tiny hairs vibrate only to the frequency emitted by a female of the same species.

Vertebrates use a number of different forms of sound communication. Rabbits thump the ground, gorillas pound their chests, beavers slap the water with their flat tails, and frogs, like the one in **Figure 15,** croak. Do you think that sound communication in noisy environments is useful? Seabirds that live where waves pound the shore rather than in some quieter place must rely on visual signals, not sound, for communication.

Chemistry INTEGRATION

The light produced by fireflies is a particle of visible light that radiates when chemicals produce a high-energy state and then return to their normal state. Hypothesize how this helps fireflies survive. Write your hypothesis in your Science Journal.

Light Communication Certain kinds of flies, marine organisms, and beetles have a special form of communication called bioluminescence. Bioluminescence, shown in **Figure 16,** is the ability of certain living things to give off light. This light is produced through a series of chemical reactions in the organism's body. Probably the most familiar bioluminescent organisms in North America are fireflies. They are not flies, but beetles. The flash of light is produced on the underside of the last abdominal segments and is used to locate a prospective mate. Each species has its own characteristic flashing. Males fly close to the ground and emit flashes of light. Females must flash an answer at exactly the correct time to attract males.

190 CHAPTER 7 Animal Behavior

Figure 16

Many marine organisms use bioluminescence as a form of communication. This visible light is produced by a chemical reaction and often confuses predators or attracts mates. Each organism on this page is shown in its normal and bioluminescent state.

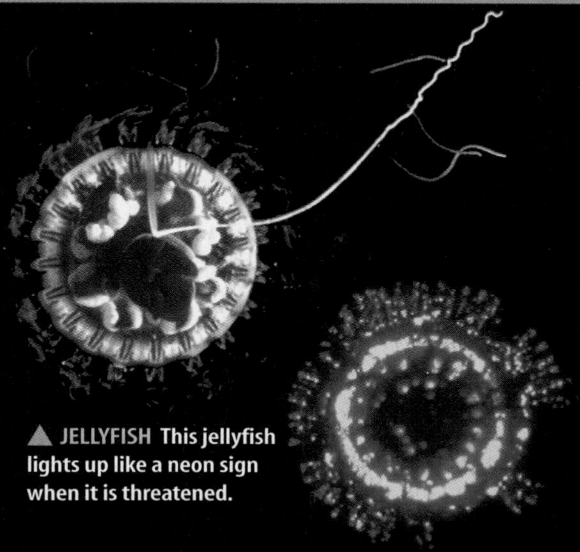

▼ **KRILL** The blue dots shown below this krill are all that are visible when krill bioluminesce. The krill may use bioluminescence to confuse predators.

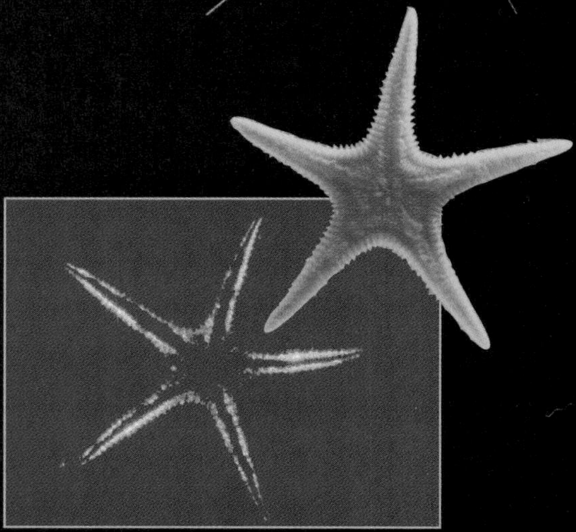

▲ **JELLYFISH** This jellyfish lights up like a neon sign when it is threatened.

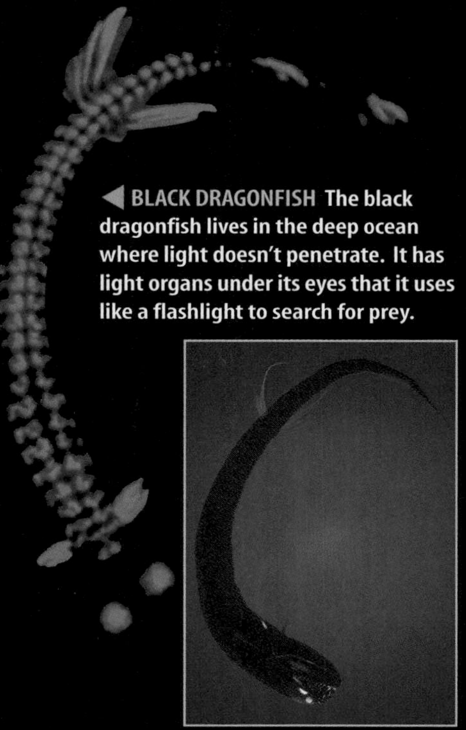

◄ **BLACK DRAGONFISH** The black dragonfish lives in the deep ocean where light doesn't penetrate. It has light organs under its eyes that it uses like a flashlight to search for prey.

▲ **DEEP-SEA SEA STAR** The sea star uses light to warn predators of its unpleasant taste.

SECTION 2 Behavioral Interactions **191**

Visualizing Bioluminescence

Have students examine the pictures and read the captions. Then ask the following questions.

During which times are organisms bioluminescent? Possible answers: Organisms that live near the surface are bioluminescent at night. Organisms that live in the deep sea, where there is no light, can use bioluminescence all the time.

Explain how bioluminescence can be used to attract prey. Possible answer: Prey organisms are attracted to the light, which is often coming from the mouthparts or a fleshy lure of the predator. As the unsuspecting prey approaches to investigate, it nears the mouth and is gobbled up.

Activity

Have students find examples of land animals that are bioluminescent and record where in the world they can be found living. Students can make a simple map of the world and draw in the representative bioluminescent animals found in different locations. Possible answers: fireflies are found east of the continental divide in the U.S., a type of beetle larvae called railroad worms is found in Central and South America, glowworms, which are fly larvae, can be found in caves in New Zealand, and land snails in Malaysia. Other bioluminescent land animals include some types of earthworms, centipedes and millipedes.

Resource Manager

Chapter Resources Booklet
   Lab Activity, pp. 13–14
Reading and Writing Skill Activities, p. 5

Extension

Have students investigate why there are almost no bioluminescent animals in found fresh water. Possible answer: Scientists hypothesize that the different chemical composition of fresh water may account for the lack of bioluminescence. Some essential chemical may be missing in the fresh water that will not allow the reaction to proceed.

Cyclic Behavior

Use Science Words

Word Origin The term *circadian* comes from the Latin word *circum*, meaning "around," and *dies*, meaning "day." Have students make a list of additional words derived from the Latin word *circum*. Possible answers: circuit, circulate, circumference, circumvent
L2 **LS Linguistic**

Extension

Have students use encyclopedias and other resources to find out what environmental factors might trigger an animal's urge to hibernate. Examples include decreasing temperature, shorter day length, and weather conditions. L2

Internet Addresses

Explore the Glencoe Science Web site at **science.glencoe.com** to find out more about topics in this section.

✔ Reading Check

Answer when an animal is active during the day

Caption Answer

Figure 17 cyclic behavior called nocturnal behavior

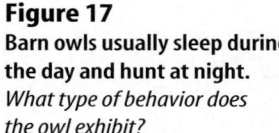

Research Visit the Glencoe Science Web site at **science.glencoe.com** for more information about owl behavior. Communicate to your class what you learn.

Figure 17
Barn owls usually sleep during the day and hunt at night.
What type of behavior does the owl exhibit?

Uses of Bioluminescence Many bioluminescent animals are found deep in oceans where sunlight does not reach. The ability to produce light may serve several functions. One species of fish dangles a special luminescent organ in front of its mouth. This lures prey close enough to be caught and eaten. Deep-sea shrimp secrete clouds of a luminescent substance when disturbed. This helps them escape their predators. Patterns of luminescence on an animal's body may serve as marks of recognition similar to the color patterns of animals that live in sunlit areas.

Cyclic Behavior

Why do most songbirds rest at night while some species of owls rest during the day? Some animals like the owl in **Figure 17** show regularly repeated behaviors such as sleeping in the day and feeding at night.

A **cyclic behavior** is innate behavior that occurs in a repeating pattern. It often is repeated in response to changes in the environment. Behavior that is based on a 24-hour cycle is called a circadian rhythm. Most animals come close to this 24-hour cycle of sleeping and wakefulness. Experiments show that even if animals can't tell whether it is night or day, they continue to behave in a 24-hour cycle.

Animals that are active during the day are diurnal (dy UR nul). Animals that are active at night are nocturnal. Owls are nocturnal. They have round heads, big eyes, and flat faces. Their flat faces reflect sound and help them navigate at night. Owls also have soft feathers that make them almost silent while flying.

✔ Reading Check *What is a diurnal behavior?*

Curriculum Connection

Health Point out that people function according to a circadian rhythm. The most familiar aspect of this is the sleep-wake cycle. Have students research what body changes occur during sleep and how people behave when they are deprived of sleep for several days. Sleep deprivation can cause fatigue, inability to concentrate, and visual or tactile illusions and hallucinations. L3 P

Science Journal

Problems in Studying Behavior Have students list some of the problems of using animals, including humans, in behavioral studies. Possible answers: Animals other than humans cannot communicate in words. Equating animal responses with those of humans may not always work.

Hibernation Some cyclic behaviors also occur over long periods of time. **Hibernation** is a cyclic response to cold temperatures and limited food supplies. During hibernation, an animal's body temperature drops to near that of its surroundings, and its breathing rate is greatly reduced. Animals in hibernation, such as the bats in **Figure 18,** survive on stored body fat. The animal remains inactive until the weather becomes warm in the spring. Some mammals and many amphibians and reptiles hibernate.

Animals that live in desertlike environments also go into a state of reduced activity. This period of inactivity is called estivation. Desert animals sometimes estivate due to extreme heat, lack of food, or periods of drought.

Figure 18
Many bats find a frost-free place like this abandoned coal mine to hibernate for the winter when food supplies are low.

Problem-Solving Activity

How can you determine which animals hibernate?

Many animals hibernate in the winter. During this period of inactivity, they survive on stored body fat. While they are hibernating, they undergo several physical changes. Heart rate slows down and body temperature decreases. The degree to which the body temperature decreases varies among animals. Scientists have disagreed about whether some animals truly hibernate or if they just reduce their activity and go into a light sleep. Usually, a true hibernator's body temperature will decrease significantly while it is hibernating.

Identifying the Problem
The table on the right shows the difference between the normal body temperature and the hibernating body temperature of several animals. What similarities do you notice?

Average Body Temperatures of Hibernating Animals		
Animal	**Normal Body Temperature (°C)**	**Hibernating Body Temperature (°C)**
Woodchuck	37	3
Squirrel	32	4
Grizzly Bear	32–37	27–32
Whippoorwill	40	18
Hoary Marmot	37	10

Solving the Problem
1. Which animals would you classify as true hibernators and which would you classify as light sleepers? Explain.
2. Some animals such as snakes and frogs also hibernate. Why would it be difficult to record their normal body temperature on this table?
3. Which animal has the least amount of change in body temperature?

SECTION 2   Behavioral Interactions   **193**

Extension

More than 100 million monarch butterflies migrate from Canada and the eastern United States to Mexico every fall. Gray whales migrate from the Bering Sea to the coastal region of California. Have students trace these routes and others on a map or globe.

L1 LS **Visual-Spatial**

③ Assess

Reteach

Label 3 x 5 cards with examples of social behavior, territorial behavior, communication, and cyclic behavior. Ask students to choose a card, classify the type of behavior, and provide reasons for their responses.

Challenge

Have students research what causes jet lag. Jet lag is the temporary disruption of the body's normal biological rhythms after high-speed air travel through several time zones. People suffering from jet lag often feel fatigued and have lowered efficiency for several days after travel. This is because the body is still functioning on its "regular" time. It takes about a day per hour of time change to reset the body's clock.

✓ Assessment

Content Have pairs of students make posters that explain social behavior, territorial behavior, communication, or cyclic behavior. Use **Performance Assessment in the Science Classroom,** p. 145.

Figure 19
Many monarch butterflies travel from the United States to Mexico for the winter.

Migration Instead of hibernating, many birds and mammals move to new locations when the seasons change. This instinctive seasonal movement of animals is called **migration.** Most animals migrate to find food or reproduce in an environment that is more favorable for the survival of its offspring. Many species of birds fly for hours or days without stopping. The blackpoll warbler flies more than 4,000 km nonstop from North America to its winter home in South America. The trip takes nearly 90 hours. Monarch butterflies, shown in **Figure 19,** can migrate as much as 2,900 km. Gray whales swim from cold arctic waters to the waters off the coast of northern Mexico. After the young are born, they make the return trip.

Section ② Assessment

1. What are some examples of courtship behavior? How does this behavior help organisms survive?
2. How are cyclic behaviors, such as hibernation, a response to stimuli in the environment?
3. Give two reasons why animals migrate.
4. What is the difference between hibernation and migration?
5. **Think Critically** Suppose a species of frog lives close to a loud waterfall. It often waves a bright blue foot in the air. What might the frog be doing?

Skill Builder Activities

6. **Testing a Hypothesis** Design an experiment that tests the hypothesis that ants leave chemical trails to show other ants where food can be found. **For more help, refer to the** Science Skill Handbook.
7. **Solving One-Step Equations** Some cicadas emerge from the ground every 17 years. The population of one type of caterpillar peaks every five years. If the peak cycle of the caterpillars and the emergence of cicadas coincided in 1990, in what year will they coincide again? **For more help, refer to the** Math Skill Handbook.

194 CHAPTER 7 Animal Behavior

Answers to Section Assessment

1. Answers will vary. These behaviors help ensure reproductive success.
2. They are responses to changes in the environment, such as decrease in the number of daylight hours or temperature changes.
3. to find food and to reproduce in a favorable environment for offspring
4. An animal that hibernates stays in the same place and becomes inactive until environmental conditions become favorable. An animal that migrates moves to a location with favorable conditions.
5. Possible answer: signalling other frogs, either to attract a mate or to defend its territory
6. Students should identify a variable, a constant, and a control.
7. Since 17 and 5 are prime numbers, the cycles will again coincide in 17×5, or 85 years from 1990; $1990 + 85 = 2075$.

Activity

Observing Earthworm Behavior

Earthworms often can be seen wriggling across sidewalks, driveways, and yards on moist nights. Why don't you see many earthworms during the day?

What You'll Investigate
How do earthworms respond to light?

Materials
scissors	paper
shoe box with lid	moist paper towels
flashlight	earthworms
tape	timer

Goals
- **Predict** how earthworms will behave in the presence of light.

Safety Precautions 🔲 🔲 🔲 🔲

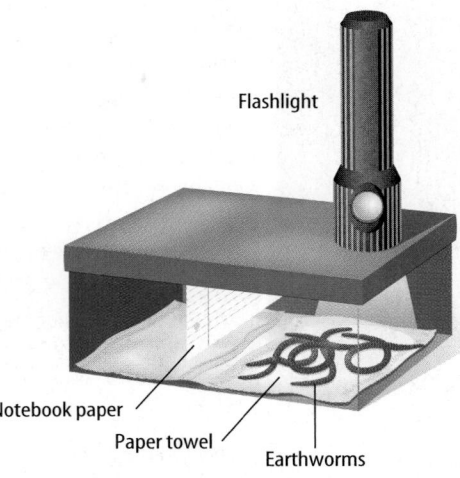

Flashlight

Notebook paper

Paper towel

Earthworms

Procedure

1. Cut a round hole, smaller than the end of the flashlight, near one end of the lid.

2. Tape a sheet of paper to the lid so it hangs just above the bottom of the box and about 10 cm away from the end with the hole in it.

3. Place the moist paper towels in the bottom of the box.

4. Place the earthworms in the end of the box that has the hole in it.

5. Hold the flashlight over the hole and turn it on.

6. Leave the box undisturbed for 30 minutes, then open the lid and observe the worms.

7. **Record** the results of your experiment in your Science Journal.

Conclude and Apply

1. Which direction did the earthworms move when the light was turned on?

2. Based on your observations, what can you infer about earthworms?

3. What type of behavior did the earthworms exhibit? Explain.

4. **Predict** where you would need to go to find earthworms during the day.

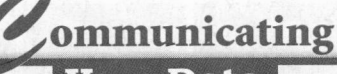

Communicating Your Data

Write a story that describes a day in the life of an earthworm. List activities, dangers, and problems an earthworm can face. Include a description of its habitat. **For more help, refer to the** Science Skill Handbook.

ACTIVITY 195

Activity

BENCH TESTED

Purpose Students observe earthworm responses to light. [L2]
[IS] **Kinesthetic**

Process Skills observing and inferring, recognizing cause and effect

Time Required 45 minutes

Safety Precautions Caution students to wash their hands after handling earthworms.

Teaching Strategy Have students keep their hands moist while handling earthworms. Remind them to handle worms gently.

Answers to Questions

1. away from the light
2. Earthworms prefer darkness to light.
3. Innate behavior; the earthworms instinctively move away from the light and toward the darkened area.
4. in the soil

Assessment

Process Have students use their observations to list what they think an earthworm needs to survive. soil, darkness, moisture Use **Performance Assessment in the Science Classroom,** p. 89.

Inclusion Strategies

Visually Impaired Have visually impaired students dampen their hands and gently run their fingers over the body of an earthworm. Encourage them to describe both the worm's segments and its setae—bristle-like structures found on each segment that anchor the worm to the ground as it contracts its muscles for movement. [L1] [IS] **Kinesthetic**

Communicating Your Data

Students should base their story on their knowledge of earthworms and their habitat.

Resource Manager

Chapter Resources Booklet
Activity Worksheet, pp. 5–6
Reinforcement, p. 26

ACTIVITY 195

Activity

Recognize the Problem

Purpose

Students research information about animals in their natural habitats, and then design and build a model of a habitat that supports the survival of that animal. L2

IS Logical-Mathematical

Process Skills

making models, researching information, predicting, collecting data, measuring in SI, recognizing cause and effect, interpreting data, communicating, using proportions

Time Required

one to two weeks

Thinking Critically

Discussion Direct students to think about the types of animals with which they are familiar. **What types of food do they eat? What kind of environment do they need to survive?** Have students discuss and research other types of animals that could live in the same environments. Provide reference materials or allow students to use library resources and the Internet.

Possible Materials

Provide basic materials for making models such as modeling clay, scrap paper, scissors, and glue. Encourage reusing and recycling by having students bring in scrap materials from home.

Activity Model and Invent

Animal Habitats

Zoos, animal parks, and aquariums are safe places for wild animals. Years ago, captive animals were kept in small cages or behind glass windows. Almost no attempt was made to provide natural habitats for the animals. People who came to see the animals could not observe the animal's normal behavior. Now, most captive animals are kept in exhibit areas that closely resemble their natural habitats. These areas provide suitable environments for the animals so that they can interact with members of their same species and have healthier, longer lives.

Recognize the Problem

What types of environments are best suited for raising animals in captivity?

Thinking Critically

How can the habitats provided at an animal park affect the behavior of animals?

Goals

- **Research** the natural habitat and basic needs of one animal.
- **Design** and model an appropriate zoo, animal park, or aquarium environment for this animal. Working cooperatively with your classmates, design an entire zoo or animal park.

Possible Materials

poster board
markers or colored pencils
materials that can be used to make a scale model

Data Source

SCIENCE_Online_ Go to the Glencoe Science Web site at **science.glencoe.com** for more information about existing zoos, animal parks, and aquariums.

Resource Manager

Chapter Resources Booklet
  Activity Worksheet, pp. 7–8
Lab Management and Safety, p. 43

SCIENCE _Online_
Internet Addresses
_____
_____
_____
_____

Explore the Glencoe Science Web site at **science.glencoe.com** to find out more about topics in this activity.

Planning the Model

1. Choose an animal to research. Find out where this animal is found in nature. What does it eat? What are its natural predators? Does it exhibit unique territorial, courtship, or other types of behavior? How is this animal adapted to its natural environment?

2. **Design** a model of a proposed habitat in which this animal can live successfully. Don't forget to include all of the things, such as shelter, food, and water, that your animal will need to survive. Will there be any other organisms in the habitat?

Check the Model Plans

1. **Research** how zoos, animal parks, or aquariums provide habitats for animals. Information may be obtained by viewing the Glencoe Science Web site and contacting scientists who work at zoos, animal parks, and aquariums.

2. **Present** your design to your class in the form of a poster, slide show, or video. Compare your proposed habitat with that of the animal's natural environment. Make sure you include a picture of your animal in its natural environment.

Making the Model

1. Using all of the information you have gathered, create a model exhibit area for your animal.

2. Indicate what other plants and animals may be present in the exhibit area.

Analyzing and Applying Results

1. **Decide** whether all of the animals studied in this activity can coexist in the same zoo or wildlife preserve.

2. **Predict** which animals could be grouped together in exhibit areas.

3. **Determine** how large your zoo or wildlife preserve needs to be. Which animals require a large habitat?

4. Using the information provided by the rest of your classmates, design an entire zoo or aquarium that could include the majority of animals studied.

5. **Analyze** problems that might exist in your design. Suggest some ways you might want to improve your design.

Communicating Your Data

Give an oral presentation to another class on the importance of providing natural habitats for captive animals. **For more help, refer to the** Science Skill Handbook.

ACTIVITY 197

Planning the Model

Teaching Strategies

- Distribute lists of zoo web sites.
- Encourage students to make a checklist of items they need to include in their models.

Making the Model

Expected Outcome

Students should build a model that is appropriate for their chosen animal. Area of concern might include sufficient land and water area and climate control.

Analyzing and Applying Results

Direct students to record and then discuss the answers to these questions in small groups. Decisions to combine different animals in one habitat should be based on environmental concerns such as land and water requirements and climate considerations, including temperature and amount of precipitation. In the event of unfavorable conditions, adequate shelter must be available. Animals that have predator-prey relationships must also be separated geographically.

Safety Precautions

Discuss the dangers of any materials being used, such as sharp scissors or glue with strong fumes.

✓ *Assessment*

Performance Have students make pamphlets encouraging the public to visit the model animal habitats they have devised. Use **Performance Assessment in the Science Classroom,** p. 129.

Communicating Your Data

Show students how to outline their presentations as a way of organizing their ideas. Suggest that they practice several times before giving the presentation.

Content Background

Dogs can be trained to help people in many capacities. Many police departments have special K-9 units. The dogs in these units are specially trained to help the officer in a variety of ways, including searching for people or finding drugs. Dogs are often used in search and rescue after disasters such as earthquakes or avalanches. Dogs can also be used to help the hearing impaired, as well as acting as companion animals to people who are physically challenged. Guide dogs for the visually impaired learn that things like curbs and moving cars are dangerous and that they must stop for these in order to warn their master. The dogs are also trained to be aware of and lead their masters around things like trees and low-hanging obstructions such as signs and awnings. Even though the dog can walk underneath such obstacles, a person could be injured if they had no warning. Other dogs work as sled dogs, sheep or cattle herders, or even to help carry newspapers on a delivery route.

Discussion

Arrange for a patrol dog and its handler to come to the classroom. Before the guests arrive, have students make a list of questions for the officer. Questions can be about the acquisition of the dogs, information on the training procedures, at home handling, or retiring a patrol dog.

Oops!

Oops! Accidents in SCIENCE

SOMETIMES GREAT DISCOVERIES HAPPEN BY ACCIDENT!

Going to the Dogs

A simple and surprising stroll showed that dogs really are humans' best friends

German shepherds make excellent guide dogs.

198

You've probably seen visually impaired people walking with their trusted and gentle four-legged guides—or "seeing-eye" dogs. The specially trained dogs serve as eyes for people who can't see, making it possible for them to lead independent lives. But what you probably didn't know is that about 80 years ago, a doctor and his patient discovered this canine ability entirely by accident!

Many people were killed or injured during World War I. Near the end of that war, Dr. Gerhard Stalling and his dog strolled with a patient—a German soldier who had been blinded—around hospital grounds in Germany.

Resources for Teachers and Students

Dogs With Jobs, by Merrily Weisbord and Kim Kachanoff, Pocket Books, 2000.

Working Dogs: Tales from Animal Planet's K-9 to 5 World, by Colleen Needles and Kit Carlson, Discovery Books, 2000.

A Dog's Gotta Do What A Dog's Gotta Do: Dogs at Work, by Marilyn Singer, Henry Holt and Company, Inc., 2000.

A dog safely guides its owner across a street.

While they were walking, the doctor was briefly called away. The dog and the soldier stayed outside. A few moments later, when the doctor returned, the dog and the soldier were gone! Searching the paths frantically, Dr. Stalling made an astonishing discovery. His pet had led the soldier safely around the hospital grounds. And together the two strolled peacefully back toward the doctor.

School for Dogs

Inspired by what his dog could do, Dr. Stalling set up the first school in the world dedicated to training dogs as guides. Dorothy Eustis, an American woman working as a dog trainer for the International Red Cross in Switzerland, traveled to Stalling's school about ten years later. A report of her visit and study of the way Stalling trained dogs appeared in a New York City newspaper in 1927.

Hearing the story, Morris Frank, a visually impaired American, became determined to get himself a guide dog. He wrote to Dorothy Eustis and asked that she train a dog for him. She accepted his request on one condition.

She wanted Frank to join her in Switzerland for the training process. Frank and his guide dog Buddy returned to New Jersey in 1928. Within a year, Frank set up a training facility in New Jersey, "The Seeing Eye, Inc."

German shepherds, golden retrievers, and Labrador retrievers seem to make the best guide dogs. They learn hand gestures and simple commands to lead visually impaired people across streets and safely around obstacles. This is what scientists call "learned behavior." Animals gain learned behavior through experience. Learning happens gradually and in steps. In fact, scientists say that learning is a somewhat permanent change in behavior due to experience. But, a guide dog not only learns to respond to special commands, it must also know when *not* to obey. If its human owner urges the dog to cross the street and the dog sees that a car is approaching and refuses, the dog has learned to disobey the command. This trait, called "intelligent disobedience," ensures the safety of the owner and the dog—a sure sign that dogs are still humans' best friends.

This girl gets to help train a future guide dog for The Seeing Eye, Inc.

CONNECTIONS Write Lead a blindfolded partner around the classroom. Help your partner avoid obstacles. Then trade places. Write in your Science Journal about your experience leading and being led.

SCIENCE *Online*
For more information, visit
science.glencoe.com

Activity

Have students investigate other capacities in which dogs can help people. Students can also research any other animals that help or have helped people in the past, such as carrier pigeons or capuchin monkeys. Students should make a poster showing their results. They could act out a story as a skit. Encourage students to share with the class any heartwarming or amazing stories that they come across in their research.

Analyze the Event

Have students discuss what elements may be involved in the training of guide dogs. **What traits should a guide dog have? How should the training progress? What should the dogs learn first? How are the dogs taught to respond to dangers such as curbs and cars?** Possible answers: The breeds of dogs usually used as guides are all described as being smart, even-tempered, and friendly animals. They are also strong and make good partners for work. During training, dogs are rewarded with praise and pats on the head when they do something correctly. When the dog needs to be corrected, the instructor says "no" loudly and may pull on the leash. The dogs are never hit or yelled at. This training is repeated many times until the dog achieves the desired goal. Simpler commands, such as "come" and "sit," are taught first. More difficult tasks such as stopping for curbs or cars are learned later.

Chapter 7 Study Guide

Preview

Students can answer the questions in their Science Journals. Discuss the answers as you go through the chapter. **IS** **Linguistic**

Review

Students can write their answers, then compare them with those of other students. **IS** **Interpersonal**

Reteach

Students can look at the illustrations and describe details that support the main ideas of the chapter. **IS** **Visual-Spatial**

Answers to Chapter Review

SECTION 1
1. learned behavior

SECTION 2
3. courtship behavior
4. The ant has left a chemical trail that other ants can follow.

Reviewing Main Ideas

Section 1 Types of Behavior

1. Behavior that an animal has when it's born is innate behavior. Other animal behaviors are learned through experience. *In the figure below, what type of behavior is the dog exhibiting?*

2. Reflexes are simple innate behaviors. An instinct is a complex pattern of innate behavior.

3. Learned behavior includes imprinting, in which an animal forms a social attachment immediately after birth.

4. Behavior modified by experience is learning by trial and error.

5. Conditioning occurs when the response to one stimulus becomes associated with another. Insight uses past experiences to solve new problems.

Section 2 Behavioral Interactions

1. Behavioral adaptations such as defense of territory, courtship behavior, and social behavior help species of animals survive and reproduce.

2. Courtship behaviors allow males and females to recognize each other and prepare to mate.

3. Interactions among members of the same species are social behaviors. *What type of social behavior is this male peacock displaying?*

4. Communication among organisms occurs in several ways including chemical, sound, and light. *How will other ants, like the one shown, be able to locate food that is far from their nest?*

5. Cyclic behaviors are behaviors that occur in repeating patterns. Animals that are active during the day are diurnal. Animals that are active at night are nocturnal.

FOLDABLES
Reading & Study Skills

After You Read

Compare and contrast the behaviors of Animal 1 and Animal 2 listed in your foldable. How many of the behaviors you listed were innate? Learned?

FOLDABLES
Reading & Study Skills

After You Read

After students have read the chapter and completed the Foldable described in Before You Read, have them do the activity on the student page.

Dinah Zike

Visualizing Main Ideas

Complete the following concept map on types of behavior.

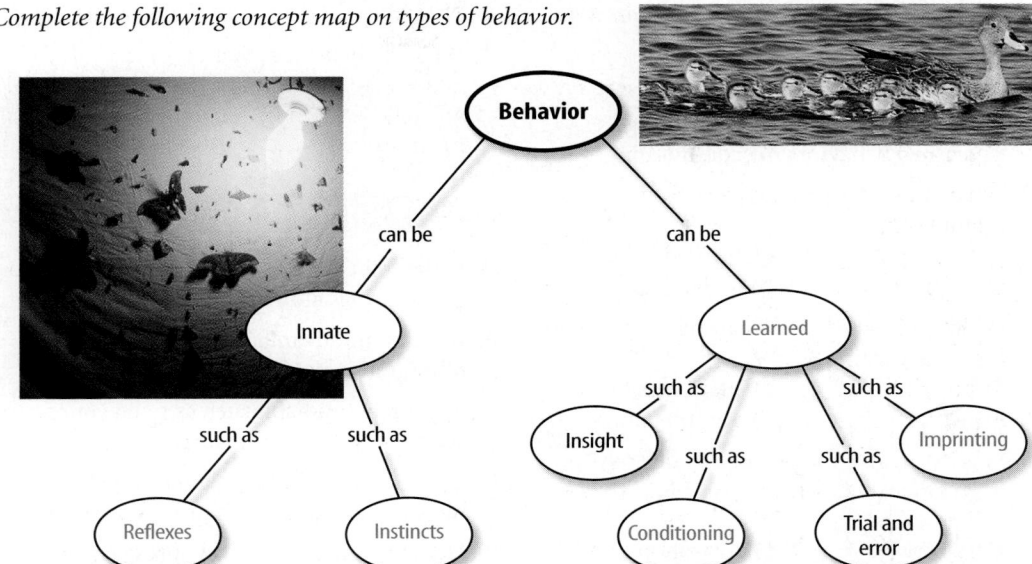

Vocabulary Review

Vocabulary Words

a. aggression
b. behavior
c. conditioning
d. courtship behavior
e. cyclic behavior
f. hibernation
g. imprinting
h. innate behavior

i. insight
j. instinct
k. migration
l. pheromone
m. reflex
n. social behavior
o. society

Using Vocabulary

Explain the differences between the vocabulary words given below. Then explain how the words are related.

1. conditioning, imprinting
2. innate behavior, social behavior
3. insight, instinct
4. social behavior, society
5. instinct, reflex
6. hibernation, migration
7. courtship behavior, pheromone
8. cyclic behavior, migration
9. aggression, social behavior
10. behavior, reflex

CHAPTER STUDY GUIDE 201

Visualizing Main Ideas

See student page.

Vocabulary Review

Using Vocabulary

1. Conditioning is modification of established behaviors. Imprinting is the formation of a new behavior. Both are learned behaviors.
2. Not all innate behaviors are social behaviors, but all social behaviors are innate behaviors.
3. Instinct is an innate behavior, and insight is a learned behavior. Both can be complex patterns of behavior.
4. Social behavior is an innate behavior. The social behaviors within an animal population form a society.
5. Instinct: complex pattern of innate behavior; reflex: simple innate behavior.
6. Hibernation is a period of inactive behavior, and migration is the seasonal movement of an animal or animal populations. Both are cyclic behaviors.
7. Courtship behavior is a social behavior between males and females of a species. Chemicals called pheromones usually stimulate courtship behavior.
8. All migrations are cyclic behaviors, but not all cyclic behaviors are migrations.
9. Aggression is just one of the many types of social behaviors.
10. Behavior is the interaction of one organism with another organism. Some behaviors are learned and others are instinctive. Reflex is the simplest innate behavior.

Checking Concepts

1. A
2. D
3. C
4. B
5. C
6. B
7. C
8. A
9. C
10. A

Thinking Critically

11. Leaving the room when the bell rings is a conditioned learned response.
12. Migration allows organisms to survive changes in weather. Some organisms may not survive the long, stressful journey.
13. A habit is a learned behavior that has become automatic. A reflex is an innate behavior.
14. Behaviors that help obtain food, are protective, or are defensive help organisms survive.
15. A farmer can artificially lengthen the amount of "daylight" hens are exposed to by using lights, which stimulate the hens to lay more eggs.

Checking Concepts

Choose the word or phrase that best answers the question.

1. What is an instinct an example of?
   A) innate behavior   C) imprinting
   B) learned behavior   D) conditioning

2. What is a spider spinning a web an example of?
   A) conditioning   C) learned behavior
   B) imprinting   D) an instinct

3. Which animals depend least on instinct and most on learning?
   A) birds   C) mammals
   B) fish   D) amphibians

4. What is an area that an animal defends from other members of the same species called?
   A) society   C) migration
   B) territory   D) aggression

5. What is a forceful act used to dominate or control?
   A) courtship   C) aggression
   B) reflex   D) hibernation

6. Which of the following is NOT an example of courtship behavior?
   A) fluffing feathers
   B) taking over a perch
   C) singing songs
   D) releasing pheromones

7. What is an organized group of animals doing specific jobs called?
   A) community   C) society
   B) territory   D) circadian rhythm

8. What is the response of inactivity and slowed metabolism that occurs during cold conditions?
   A) hibernation   C) migration
   B) imprinting   D) circadian rhythm

9. Which of the following is a reflex?
   A) writing   C) sneezing
   B) talking   D) riding a bicycle

10. What are behaviors that occur in repeated patterns called?
    A) cyclic   C) reflex
    B) imprinting   D) society

Thinking Critically

11. Explain the type of behavior involved when the bell rings at the end of class.

12. Discuss the advantages and disadvantages of migration as a means of survival.

13. Explain how a habit such as tying your shoes, is different from a reflex.

14. Use one example to explain how behavior increases an animal's chance for survival.

15. Hens lay more eggs in the spring when the number of daylight hours increases. How can farmers use this knowledge of behavior to their advantage?

Developing Skills

16. **Testing a Hypothesis** Design an experiment to test a hypothesis about a specific response to a stimulus from an animal.

17. **Recording Observations** Make observations of a dog, cat, or bird for a week. Record what you see. How did the animal communicate with other animals and with you?

Chapter ✓Assessment Planner

Portfolio Encourage students to place in their portfolios one or two items of what they consider to be their best work. Examples include:
- Reteach, p. 185
- Cultural Diversity, p. 190
- Curriculum Connection, p. 193

Performance Additional performance assessments, Performance Task Assessment Lists, and rubrics for evaluating these activities can be found in Glencoe's **Performance Assessment in the Science Classroom.**

18. Forming a Hypothesis Make a hypothesis about how frogs communicate with each other. How could you test your hypothesis?

19. Classifying Make a list of 25 things that you do regularly. Classify each as an innate or learned behavior. Which behaviors do you have more of?

20. Concept Mapping Complete the following concept map about communication. Use these words: *light, sound, chirping, biolumi-nescence,* and *buzzing.*

Communication
- can be → Light
  - such as → Bioluminescence
- can be → Sound
  - such as → Chirping
  - such as → Buzzing

Performance Assessment

21. Poster Draw a map showing the migration route of monarch butterflies, gray whales, or blackpoll warblers.

TECHNOLOGY

Go to the Glencoe Science Web site at **science.glencoe.com** or use the **Glencoe Science CD-ROM** for additional chapter assessment.

THE PRINCETON REVIEW **Test Practice**

A biologist is given illustrations of different behaviors. The different types of behaviors are listed below.

Types of Behavior	
Behavior	Example
1	
2	
3	
4	

Study the table and answer the following questions.

1. A reflex is an automatic response to a stimulus. Which one of the behaviors in the table is an example of a reflex?

A) one   C) three
B) two   D) four

2. Trial and error is a type of learned behavior that is modified by experience. Which of the behaviors in the table is an example of a trial-and-error behavior?

F) one   H) three
G) two   J) four

THE PRINCETON REVIEW **Test Practice**

The Test-Taking Tip was written by The Princeton Review, the nation's leader in test preparation.

1. A
2. H

Developing Skills

16. Answers should follow the basic plan Pavlov followed.
17. Answers will be determined by the animal the student observes.
18. Students will likely hypothesize that frogs communicate by using vocal-izations. Accept all logical ways to test this hypothesis.
19. Possible answers may include: innate—sneezing, yawning, hic-cups, jerking your hand away from something hot; learned—tying shoes, reading, writing, solving problems, riding a bike. Learned behaviors are probably more numerous.
20. See student page.

Performance Assessment

21. Maps should indicate both spring and fall migration routes. Use **Performance Assessment in the Science Classroom,** p. 145.

✓Assessment Resources

📁 **Reproducible Masters**
Chapter Resources Booklet
Chapter Review, pp. 33–34
Chapter Tests, pp. 35–38
Assessment Transparency Activity, p. 45
Glencoe Science Web site
Interactive Tutor
Chapter Quizzes

Glencoe Technology
🖋 Assessment Transparency
💿 Interactive CD-ROM Chapter Quizzes
💿 ExamView Pro Test Bank
💿 Vocabulary PuzzleMaker Software
📼 MindJogger Videoquiz

Reading Comprehension

Question 1: C

Students must use information from the passage to identify the best-supported conclusion.

- **Choice A** No; this is not supported by the passage.
- **Choice B** No; this is not supported by the passage.
- **Choice C** Yes; this is supported by the passage.
- **Choice D** No; this is not supported by the passage.

Question 2: H

Students must use information from the passage to identify the correct cause. Students should use the clue *important to human health*.

- **Choice F** No; this is not supported by the passage.
- **Choice G** No; although this is a detail from the passage, it is not the reason enzymes are important to human health.
- **Choice H** Yes; this is the reason enzymes are important to human health.
- **Choice J** No; although this is a detail from the passage, it is not the reason enzymes are important to human health.

Reading Comprehension

Read the passage. Then read each question that follows the passage. Decide which is the best answer to each question.

Enzymes in Humans

A catalyst is a substance that makes a chemical reaction happen faster than it would happen by itself. Interestingly, it affects the rate of the reaction without permanently entering into the reaction. More than 2,000 catalysts are necessary for the human body to function well. These catalysts are called enzymes.

Enzymes are a kind of protein. How an enzyme works depends on what shape it has. A special place on an enzyme attaches to chemicals. This site is called the active site. Enzyme activity can be compared to a lock and a key. Only the correct chemicals, or keys, will fit into the enzyme, or lock. The enzyme brings chemicals together so they can react. This is how enzymes speed up reactions—by making the reactants come together in a more direct way than if they were left to just bump into each other <u>randomly</u>. One enzyme can be used over and over to activate the same reaction. Some enzymes can help reactions go in either direction. In order for an enzyme to work properly, the temperature and pH must be within a certain range. Enough energy and enough reactants also must be present.

Two main types of enzymes are metabolic and digestive. Metabolic enzymes catalyze the reactions within cells. They help phosphorus turn into bone, iron attach to red blood cells, and wounds to heal. Digestive enzymes help with the breakdown of foods, allowing nutrients to be absorbed into the bloodstream and used by the body.

Enzymes are essential for many reactions within the human body. Amylase is an enzyme found in saliva. It starts digesting your food before you even swallow!

An enzyme called carbonic anhydrase helps remove carbon dioxide from your cells. You breathe the carbon dioxide out and replace it with oxygen. Carbonic anhydrase enzyme makes the reaction 107 times faster than if it had to happen on its own! You can see how people depend on enzyme catalysts to maintain health.

Enzymes can be found in all living things. Enzymes also have been used in industry for nearly 100 years. Some of the products that depend on the action of enzymes are leather, alcohol, medications, baking products, detergents, and even fruit juice!

Test-Taking Tip Make sure that you understand what you are reading as you read a passage. If you are confused by something, stop and read the information again.

1. Based on the information in the passage, it can be concluded that _____.
   - A) enzymes are found only in humans
   - B) amylase is an enzyme that removes oxygen
   - C) humans have more than 2,000 enzymes
   - D) another word for the locks found in doors is enzyme

2. Enzymes are important to human health because they _____.
   - F) are used to help open locks
   - G) are used to make leather and fruit juice
   - H) control the reactions in human bodies
   - J) are found in all living things

Reasoning and Skills

Read each question and select the best answer.

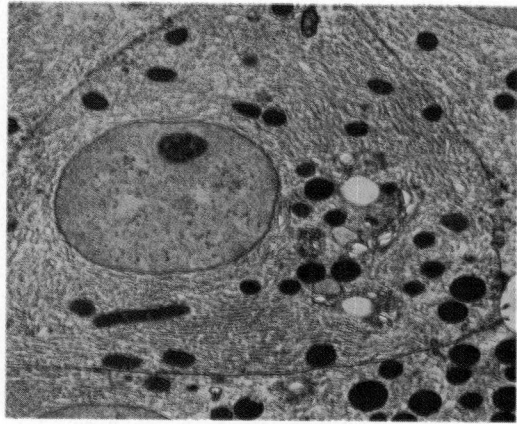

1. The object shown here is a(n) _____ because it contains structures surrounded by membranes.
  A) prokaryotic cell
  B) mitochondrion
  C) Golgi body
  D) eukaryotic cell

Test-Taking Tip Think about the way cells are classified into groups.

2. Which of the following chemical compounds does not influence the growth of plants?
  F) cytokinins
  G) gibberellins
  H) auxins
  J) pheromones

Test-Taking Tip Think about the roles of hormones in plants and animals.

3. Campers dig a hole to bury their food scraps. Before they leave, they refill the hole with soil and place several large rocks on top. Later, a pair of raccoons explores the campground area, sniffing the ground. Eventually, the animals dig around and under the rocks to get to the food scraps. This is an example of how animals _____.
  A) can be affected by pheromones.
  B) use insight.
  C) show cyclic behavior.
  D) prepare for hibernation.

Test-Taking Tip Think about the definition of each type of animal behavior listed.

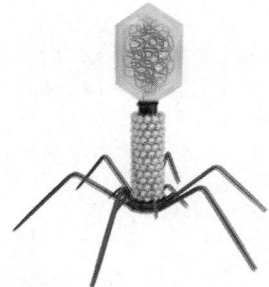

Consider this question carefully before writing your answer on a separate sheet of paper.

4. The virus particle pictured above is not inside a host cell. Give at least one good reason why it could be considered a living organism and one good reason why it could not.

Test-Taking Tip Compare the characteristics of a virus with the characteristics of living organisms.

Reasoning and Skills

QUESTION 1: D

Students must understand that the structures in a *eukaryotic cell* are surrounded by membranes.

QUESTION 2: J

Students must understand that choices F, G, and H are different kinds of plant hormones that affect growth.

QUESTION 3: A

Students must understand how animals pick up the scent of humans.

- **Choice A** Yes; this is how animals pick up the scent.
- **Choice B** No; raccoons are not capable of such abstract reasoning.
- **Choice C** No; there is nothing cyclical about this behavior.
- **Choice D** No; raccoons sleep in their dens, but they do not hibernate.

QUESTION 4: Answers will vary.

Students should mention that viruses have genetic material (DNA or RNA) and are capable of multiplying inside a host cell.

Teaching Tip

Suggest students make an outline of their essays before they begin writing.

UNIT 3

Unit Contents

Pre-Reading Activity

Have students look for pictures of cells and identify differences among them.

SCIENCE Online

Internet Addresses

Explore the Glencoe Science Web site at **science.glencoe.com** to find out more about topics in this unit.

UNIT 3 Reproduction and Heredity

How Are Cargo Ships & Cancer Cells Connected?

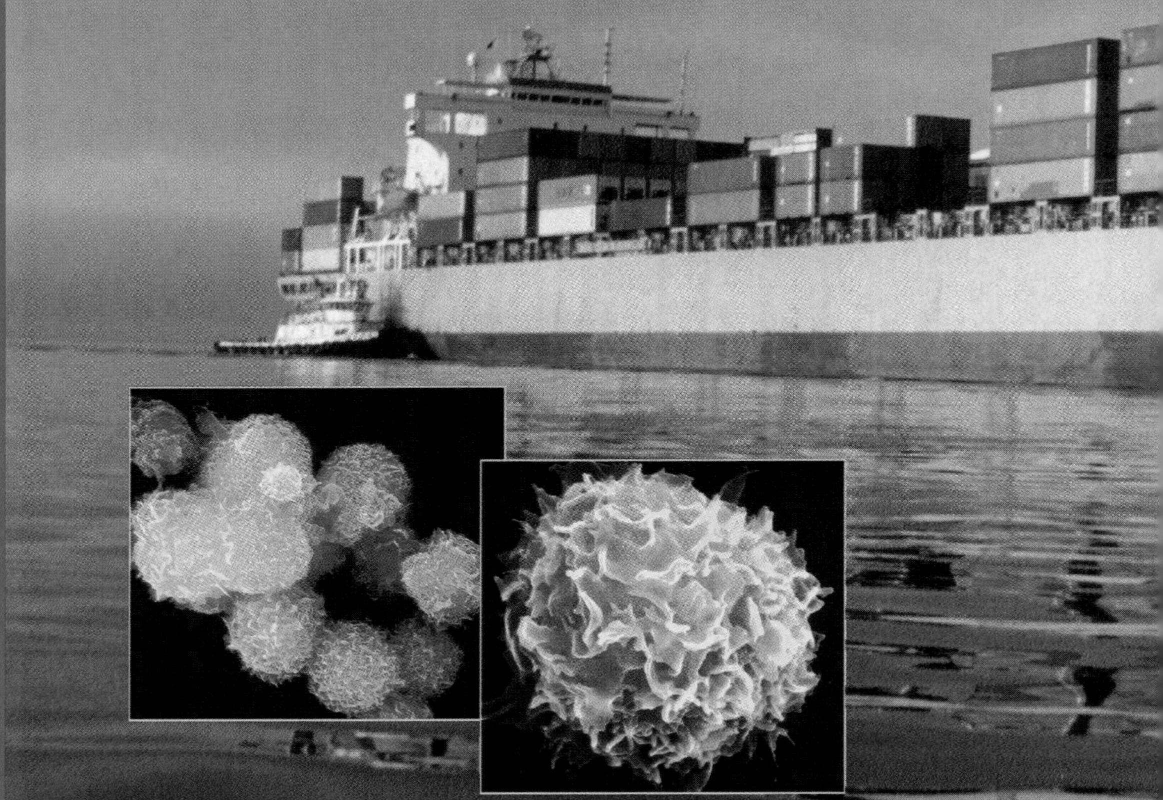

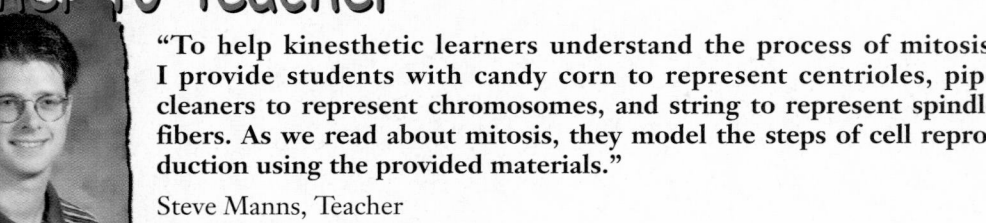

Teacher to Teacher

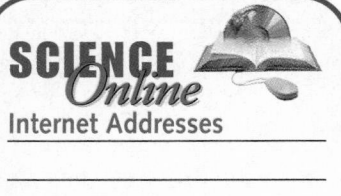

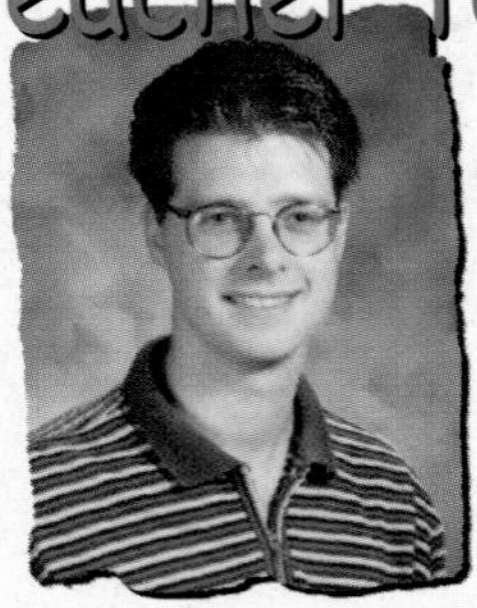

"To help kinesthetic learners understand the process of mitosis, I provide students with candy corn to represent centrioles, pipe cleaners to represent chromosomes, and string to represent spindle fibers. As we read about mitosis, they model the steps of cell reproduction using the provided materials."

Steve Manns, Teacher
Derry Area Middle School
Derry, PA

Below, a present-day cargo ship glides through a harbor in New Jersey. In 1943, during World War II, another cargo ship floated in an Italian harbor. The ship carried a certain type of chemical. When a bomb struck the ship, the chemical accidentally was released. Later, when doctors examined the sailors who were exposed to the chemical, they noticed that the sailors had low numbers of white blood cells. The chemical had interfered with the genetic material in certain cells, preventing the cells from reproducing. Since cancer cells (such as the ones at lower left) are cells that reproduce without control, scientists wondered whether this chemical could be used to fight cancer. A compound related to the chemical became the first drug developed to fight cancer. Since then, many other cancer-fighting drugs have been developed.

SCIENCE CONNECTION

CANCER AND CELL REPRODUCTION Cancer is characterized by the uncontrolled reproduction of cells. Scientists have learned that normal cells can become cancer cells when the genes that control cell reproduction are changed by chemicals, radiation, or viruses. Find out which types of cancer are most common in the United States, and investigate what steps people can take to help reduce the chances of getting cancer. Create a brochure that presents your findings.

Introducing the Unit

How Are Cargo Ships & Cancer Cells Connected?

Mitosis is the process by which a nucleus divides. It is normally followed by the entire cell dividing. Each division of each cell requires that the DNA be completely and accurately copied. Specific segments of DNA, or genes, are the genetic "blueprints" that direct the synthesis of 100,000 or more different proteins, each of which will direct a cellular activity. Certain enzyme proteins control DNA replication itself. The rate and frequency of cell division is also under the control of various proteins. A mutation is simply a change in the sequence of bases in DNA. If a mutation occurs in a gene for a protein regulating cell division, cells can begin to divide uncontrollably. This can result in the formation of a cancerous tumor. Cancer-fighting drugs target the DNA of rapidly dividing cells, stopping or slowing the uncontrolled cell division.

SCIENCE CONNECTION
Activity

The cells that are most likely to develop cancers are those that undergo mitosis most frequently. The more cells divide, the greater the chance for a mutation in DNA. Some of the cell types that are most susceptible are those that line the digestive tract and lungs, the cells in the bone marrow, which continually replace red and white blood cells, and cells in the skin. Increased rates of cancers in these tissues are clearly associated with dietary factors (too much saturated fat, low fiber), and behaviors (smoking, chewing tobacco, exposure to UV radiation). The risk of developing some cancers can be reduced significantly by altering these habits. Have students research a particular type of cancer and write a report on preventative measures that can reduce an individual's chances of getting that type of cancer.

Section/Objectives	Standards		Activities/Features
	National	State/Local	
Chapter Opener	See p. 5T for a Key to Standards.		**Explore Activity:** Infer about seed growth, p. 209 **Before You Read,** p. 209
Section 1 Cell Division and Mitosis 🕐 2 sessions 📦 1 block 1. **Explain** why mitosis is important. 2. **Examine** the steps of mitosis. 3. **Compare** mitosis in plant and animal cells. 4. **List** two examples of asexual reproduction.	National Content Standards: UCP3, A1, C1		**Health Integration,** p. 211 **Science Online,** p. 211 **MiniLAB:** Modeling Mitosis, p. 215 **Activity:** Mitosis in Plant Cells, p. 217
Section 2 Sexual Reproduction and Meiosis 🕐 2 sessions 📦 1 block 1. **Describe** the stages of meiosis and how sex cells are produced. 2. **Explain** why meiosis is needed for sexual reproduction. 3. **Name** the cells that are involved in fertilization. 4. **Explain** how fertilization occurs in sexual reproduction.	National Content Standards: UCP3, UCP4, C2		**Chemistry Integration,** p. 219 **Problem-Solving Activity:** How can chromosome numbers be predicted? p. 221 **Visualizing Polyploidy in Plants,** p. 221
Section 3 DNA 🕐 3 sessions 📦 1.5 blocks 1. **Identify** the parts of a DNA molecule and its structure. 2. **Explain** how DNA copies itself. 3. **Describe** the structure and function of each kind of RNA.	National Content Standards: UCP3, UCP4, A1, C1, C2, E2, F5, G1		**MiniLAB:** Modeling DNA Replication, p. 224 **Science Online,** p. 226 **Science Online,** p. 228 **Activity:** Mutations, p. 229 **Oops! Accidents in Science:** A Tangled Tale, p. 231

NATIONAL GEOGRAPHIC

Teacher's Corner

PRODUCTS AVAILABLE FROM GLENCOE
To order call 1-800-334-7344:
CD-ROM
NGS PictureShow: The Cell
NGS PictureShow: Plants: What It Means to Be Green
Curriculum Kit
GeoKit: Cells and Microorganisms

Transparency Sets
NGS PicturePack: The Cell
NGS PicturePack: What It Means to Be Green

PRODUCTS AVAILABLE FROM NATIONAL GEOGRAPHIC SOCIETY
To order call 1-800-368-2728:

Video
DNA: Laboratory of Life

INDEX TO NATIONAL GEOGRAPHIC SOCIETY
The following articles may be used for research relating to this chapter:
"The Rise of Life on Earth," by Richard Monastersky, March 1998.

Activity Materials	Reproducible Resources	Section Assessment	Technology
Explore Activity: soaked bean seeds, water, paper towels, self-sealing plastic bags, hand lens	**Chapter Resources Booklet** Foldables Worksheet, p. 15 Directed Reading Overview, p. 17 Note-taking Worksheets, pp. 31–33	GLENCOE'S ASSESSMENT ADVANTAGE	
MiniLAB: colored paper, poster board, markers, toothpicks, yarn, thread, glue, scissors **Activity:** prepared slide of onion root tip, microscope	**Chapter Resources Booklet** Transparency Activity, p. 42 MiniLAB, p. 3 Enrichment, p. 28 Reinforcement, p. 25 Transparency Activity, pp. 45–46 Activity Worksheet, pp. 5–6 Directed Reading, p. 18 Lab Activity, pp. 9–10	**Portfolio** Visual Learning, p. 211 **Performance** MiniLAB, p. 215 Skill Builder Activities, p. 216 **Content** Section Assessment, p. 216 Challenge, p. 216	Section Focus Transparency Teaching Transparency Interactive CD-ROM Guided Reading Audio Program
Need materials? Contact Science Kit at 1-800-828-7777 or www.sciencekit.com on the Internet.	**Chapter Resources Booklet** Transparency Activity, p. 43 Enrichment, p. 29 Reinforcement, p. 26 Directed Reading, p. 18 **Life Science Critical Thinking/ Problem Solving,** p. 19 **Mathematics Skill Activities,** p. 3 **Performance Assessment in the Science Classroom,** p. 57	**Portfolio** Make a Model, p. 221 **Performance** Skill Builder Activities, p. 223 **Content** Section Assessment, p. 223 Challenge, p. 223	Section Focus Transparency Interactive CD-ROM Guided Reading Audio Program
MiniLAB: pencil, paper **Activity:** Web sites and other resources on mutations	**Chapter Resources Booklet** Transparency Activity, p. 44 MiniLAB, p. 4 Enrichment, p. 30 Reinforcement, p. 27 Directed Reading, pp. 19, 20 Activity Worksheet, pp. 7–8 Lab Activity, pp. 11–13 **Home and Community Involvement,** p. 36 **Lab Management and Safety,** p. 58	**Portfolio** Extension, p. 227 **Performance** MiniLAB, p. 225 Skill Builder Activities, p. 229 **Content** Section Assessment, p. 229 Challenge, p. 229	Section Focus Transparency Interactive CD-ROM Guided Reading Audio Program

End of Chapter Assessment

GLENCOE'S ASSESSMENT ADVANTAGE

Blackline Masters	Technology	Professional Series
Chapter Resources Booklet Chapter Review, pp. 35–36 Chapter Tests, pp. 37–40 **Standardized Test Practice by The Princeton Review,** pp. 23–26	MindJogger Videoquiz Interactive CD-ROM Vocabulary PuzzleMakers ExamView Pro Test Bank Interactive Lesson Planner Interactive Teacher Edition	Performance Assessment in the Science Classroom (PASC)

Transparencies

Section Focus

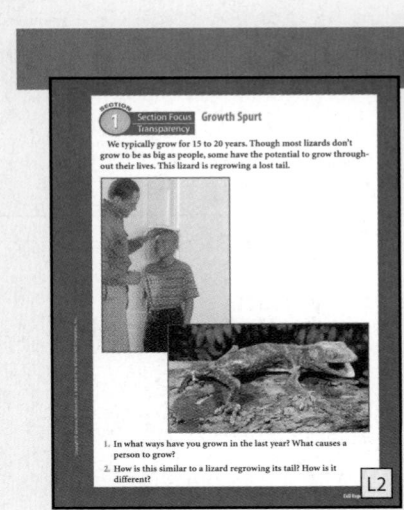

Section Focus Transparency 1 — Growth Spurt

We typically grow for 15 to 20 years. Though most lizards don't grow to be as big as people, some have the potential to grow throughout their lives. This lizard is regrowing a lost tail.

1. In what ways have you grown in the last year? What causes a person to grow?
2. How is this similar to a lizard regrowing its tail? How is it different?

L2

Section Focus Transparency 2 — I Think He Has Your Eyes

The Santa Gertrudis bull flourishes in the arid plains of Texas. The King Ranch developed the Santa Gertrudis by cross-breeding Brahman cattle with Shorthorns. As you can see, the Santa Gertrudis inherited characteristics from both of its parents.

1. Why might ranchers have wanted to cross-breed Brahmans and Shorthorns?
2. Which of the Santa Gertrudis' traits can you identify in the Brahman and the Shorthorn?

L2

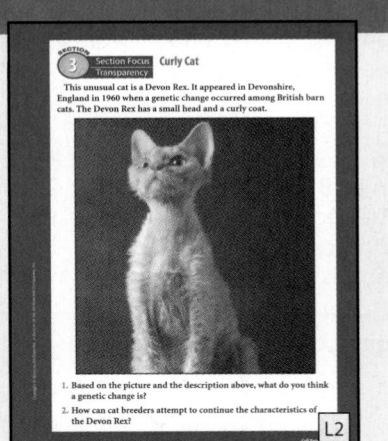

Section Focus Transparency 3 — Curly Cat

This unusual cat is a Devon Rex. It appeared in Devonshire, England in 1960 when a genetic change occurred among British barn cats. The Devon Rex has a small head and a curly coat.

1. Based on the picture and the description above, what do you think a genetic change is?
2. How can cat breeders attempt to continue the characteristics of the Devon Rex?

L2

This is a representation of key blackline masters available in the Teacher Classroom Resources. See Resource Manager boxes within the chapter for additional information.

Key to Teaching Strategies

The following designations will help you decide which activities are appropriate for your students.

L1 Level 1 activities should be appropriate for students with learning difficulties.

L2 Level 2 activities should be within the ability range of all students.

L3 Level 3 activities are designed for above-average students.

ELL ELL activities should be within the ability range of English Language Learners.

COOP LEARN Cooperative Learning activities are designed for small group work.

LS Multiple Learning Styles logos, as described on page 22T, are used throughout to indicate strategies that address different learning styles.

P These strategies represent student products that can be placed into a best-work portfolio.

Assessment

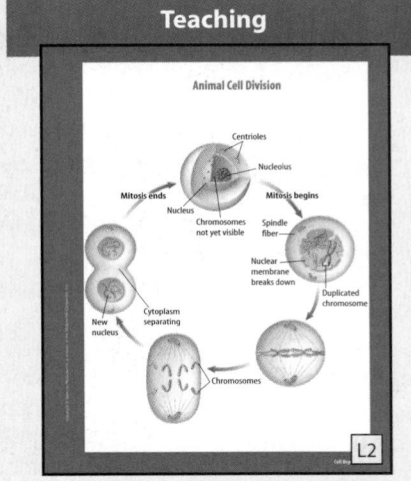

Assessment Transparency — Cell Reproduction

Directions: *Carefully review the diagram and answer the following questions.*

1. A cell produced by the fruit fly cell pictured above will most likely be ___.
   A identical to the fruit fly cell
   B a combination of its two parent fruit fly cells.
   C unable to reproduce
   D a genetic mutation
2. In which part of the cell are the chromosomes located?
   F Cell membrane
   G Cytoplasm
   H Nucleus
   J Mitochondrion
3. The fruit fly cell above contains eight chromosomes. How many chromosomes will cells produced by the above cell probably have?
   A sixteen   B eight   C four   D sixty-four

L2

Teaching

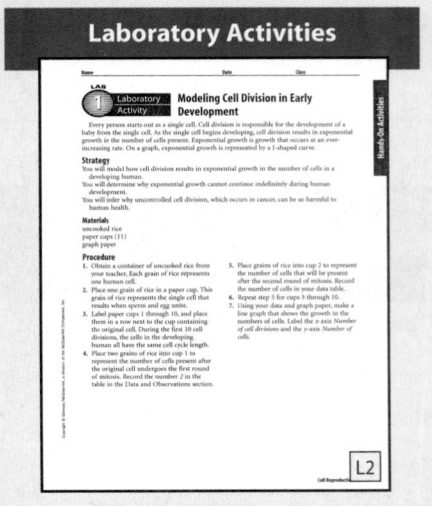

Teaching Transparency — Animal Cell Division

L2

Hands-on Activities

Activity Worksheets

Activity — Mitosis in Plant Cells

L2

Laboratory Activities

Laboratory Activity 1 — Modeling Cell Division in Early Development

L2

RESOURCE MANAGER

Meeting Different Ability Levels

Content Outline

Reinforcement

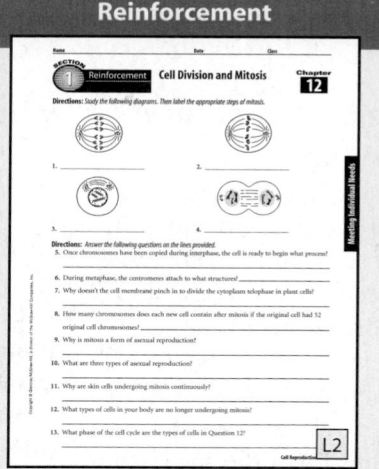

Directed Reading

Assessment

Chapter Tests

Enrichment

Spanish Directed Reading

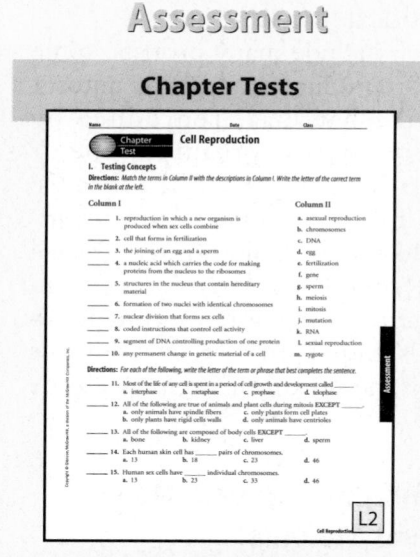

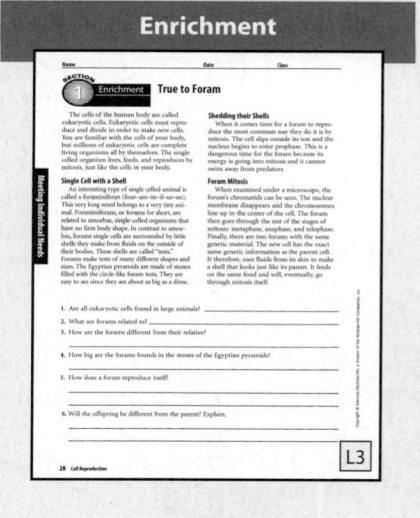

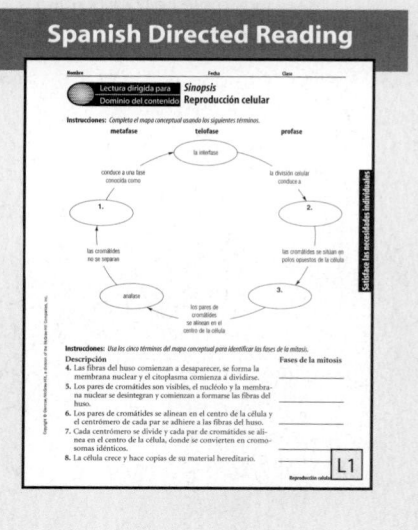

Test Practice Workbook

Chapter Review

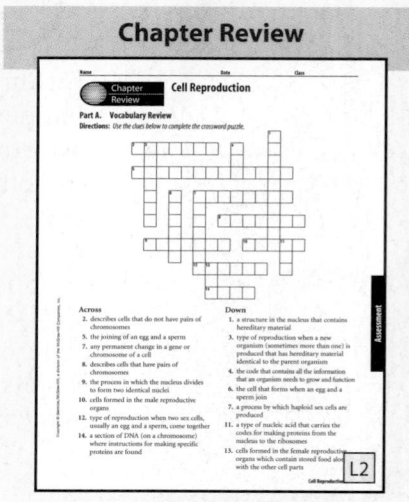

Science Content Background

SECTION 1

Cell Division and Mitosis

Results of Mitosis

Every species has a characteristic number of chromosomes in each cell. A cat has 38 chromosomes, whereas a potato and a chimpanzee each have 48 chromosomes. In all sexually reproducing organisms, chromosomes occur in homologous pairs. Except for some sex chromosomes, homologous chromosomes are of equal length and have the same genes at the same relative

> **Fun Fact**
>
> The first pigs were cloned in 2000. Scientists think that organs from pigs could be transplanted into humans.

locations. The alleles may or may not be identical. For example, the gene for hair color would be at the same location on homologous chromosomes but may code for brunette on one chromosome and blonde on the other.

Animals and some plants have one pair of sex chromosomes. In most animals, including humans, the sex chromosomes of the female are truly homologous, whereas the male sex chromosomes are of unequal lengths and have many different genes. This is reversed in birds and butterflies, with males having the truly homologous sex chromosomes.

Asexual Reproduction

Eukaryotes, which include many protists, some fungi, and plants, reproduce asexually by mitosis. Prokaryotes, like bacteria, reproduce by fission. Depending on the organism, one or several new organisms can be created that are genetically identical to, or clones of, the original organism. Most animals do not use asexual reproduction. Recently scientists have been able to stimulate cells from adult animals to divide by mitosis and reproduce new animals that are clones of the organism from which the cells were taken.

SECTION 2

Sexual Reproduction and Meiosis

Sexual Reproduction

Sex cells, or gametes, are the result of meiosis. Because of a process that happens at metaphase I called independent assortment, the possible combination of chromosomes for each sex cell varies every time sex cells form. When duplicated homologous chromosomes line up at a cell's center during metaphase I, there are no rules about how a particular pair is aligned relative to any other pair. The only requirement is that the alignment results in one half of each duplicated chromosome moving in one direction and the other half

Reuters New Media, Inc./Corbis

moving in the opposite direction during anaphase I. The offspring formed by fertilization has its own unique combination of genetic material. This produces variation between parents and offspring and may give offspring a better chance of surviving in a changing environment.

Meiosis and Sex Cells

This process is often called reduction division since the number of chromosomes in the cells produced is half that of the original cell. Meiosis provides for great diversity within a species because of the many ways the chromosomes can align during metaphase I. There are more than 8 million possible gametes that can be produced from the 23 pairs of human chromosomes.

In animals, meiosis results in haploid egg and sperm cells. In plants, meiosis results in haploid spores that later produce egg and sperm cells.

SECTION 3

DNA

What is DNA?

The information in DNA that determines what an organism will be is contained in a code dictated by the order of subunits called nucleotides. A nucleotide consists of the sugar deoxyribose, a phosphate molecule, and one of the four possible nitrogen bases. A DNA molecule is two chains of nucleotides. These two chains are antiparallel and run in opposite directions. One chain ends with a phosphate, and the other chain ends with

SCIENCE Online

For additional content background on this topic, go to the Glencoe Science Web site at science.glencoe.com.

deoxyribose. Just as the order of letters on this page determines what words you are reading, the order of nucleotides determines the message on the DNA. Because DNA is copied from one generation to the next, any change, or mutation, in a gene is also preserved. If the change occurs in cells that become gametes, it is passed on to future generations in a process called heredity.

A DNA Model

The process of DNA replication is directed by the enzyme called DNA polymerase. It moves along the separated DNA molecule and inserts the correct, complementary nucleotides onto the exposed nitrogen bases. This happens at many locations along the length of the DNA molecule simultaneously. Otherwise the time it would take to match up the millions of nitrogen bases would be astronomical.

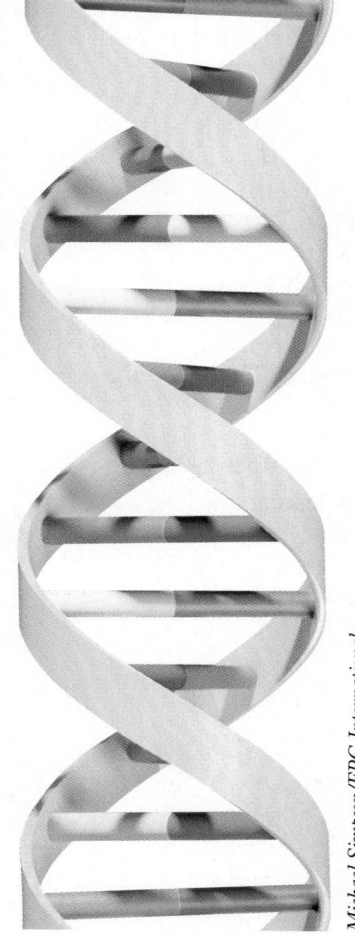

Michael Simpson/FPG International

Mutations

A change in a cell's genetic message is called a mutation. Some mutations affect the message itself, altering the sequence of DNA nucleotides. Other classes of mutations involve sequences of DNA that can move from place to place and are often called jumping genes. When a particular gene is mutated, its function is often destroyed.

Fun Fact

Barbara McClintock first published a paper on jumping genes in the 1940s. In 1983 she received the Nobel Prize for her work.

Chapter Vocabulary

What do you think?

Science Journal The structures in the picture are duplicated chromosomes, which contain genetic information for the organism they belong to.

How does a cut on your skin heal? Why doesn't a baby chicken grow up to look like a duck? Why do turtles, like the one in the photo to the right, and most other animals need to have two parents, when a sweet potato plant can be grown from just one potato? In this chapter, you will find answers to these questions as you learn about cell reproduction. You also will learn what genetic material is and how it functions.

What do you think?

Science Journal Look at the picture below with a classmate. Discuss what you think this might be. Here is a hint: *These structures contain important information for cells.* Write your answer or best guess in your Science Journal.

Theme Connection

Stability and Change DNA controls all cell activities by directing the production of proteins in living organisms. Changes in DNA can result in evolutionary changes that are inherited.

Most flower and vegetable seeds sprout and grow into entire plants in just a few weeks. Although all of the cells in a seed have information and instructions to produce a new plant, only some of the cells in the seed use the information. Where are these cells in seeds? Do the following activity to find out.

Infer about seed growth

1. Carefully split open two bean seeds that have soaked in water overnight.
2. Observe both halves and record your observations.
3. Wrap all four halves in a moist paper towel. Then put them into a self-sealing, plastic bag and seal the bag. Wash your hands.
4. Make observations for a few days.

Observe

In your Science Journal, describe what you observe. Hypothesize about which cells in seeds use information about how plants grow.

Purpose Use the Explore Activity to introduce students to growth; as they read the chapter, they will understand that growth is the result of mitosis. L2

KS Kinesthetic

Preparation Soak pinto beans or other large seeds for 24 hours.

Materials 2 soaked seeds, paper towels, self-sealing plastic bag, hand lens

Teaching Strategy After soaking, the seeds should split easily. If students have difficulty, forceps can be used to separate the seeds.

Observe

Students should observe and record the growth of a new plant from one half of each seed. They should predict that the cells of the seed embryo are able to use the information needed to grow into a plant.

✔**Assessment**

Performance Have students repeat the experiment using corn seeds and observe the new plant that grows from each seed. Use **Performance Assessment in the Science Classroom,** p. 89.

Before You Read

FOLDABLES
Reading & Study
Skills

Making an Organizational Study Fold When information is grouped into clear categories, it is easier to make sense of what you are learning. Make the following Foldable to help you organize information about cell reproduction.

1. Place a sheet of paper in front of you so the long side is at the top. Fold the paper in half from the left side to the right side and then unfold.
2. Fold in each side to the center line to divide the paper into fourths.
3. Use a pencil to draw a cell on the front of your Foldable as shown.
4. As you read the chapter, use a pen to illustrate how the cell divides into two cells. Under the flaps, list how cells divide. In the middle section, list why cells divide.

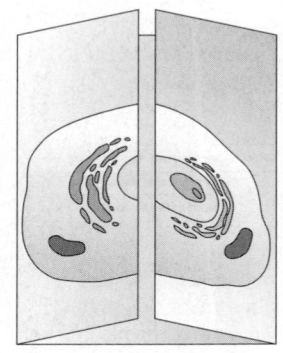

209

Before You Read

FOLDABLES
Reading & Study
Skills

Dinah Zike Study Fold

Purpose Students should use this Foldable to diagram cells and organize information on cells and cell division as they read.

📁 For additional help, see Foldables Worksheet p. 15 in **Chapter Resources Booklet,** or go to the Glencoe Science Web site at **science.glencoe.com.** See After You Read in the Study Guide at the end of this chapter.

Cell Division and Mitosis

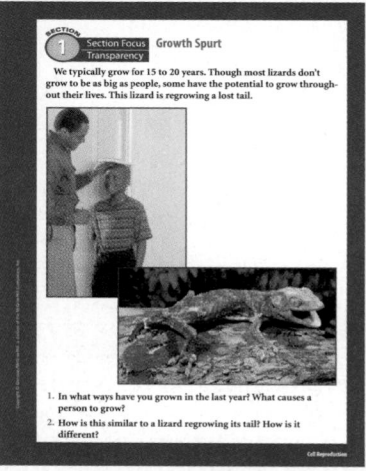
As You Read

What You'll Learn

- **Explain** why mitosis is important.
- **Examine** the steps of mitosis.
- **Compare** mitosis in plant and animal cells.
- **List** two examples of asexual reproduction.

Vocabulary

mitosis
chromosome
asexual reproduction

Why It's Important

Your growth, like that of many organisms, depends on cell division.

Figure 1
All organisms use cell division.

A Many-celled organisms, such as this octopus, grow by increasing the numbers of their cells.

Why is cell division important?

What do you, an octopus, and an oak tree have in common? You share many characteristics, but an important one is that you are all made of cells—trillions of cells. Where did all of those cells come from? As amazing as it might seem, many organisms start as just one cell. That cell divides and becomes two, two become four, four become eight, and so on. Many-celled organisms, including you, grow because cell division increases the total number of cells in an organism. Even after growth stops, cell division is still important. Every day, billions of red blood cells in your body wear out and are replaced. During the few seconds it takes you to read this sentence, your bone marrow produced about six million red blood cells. Cell division is important to one-celled organisms, too—it's how they reproduce themselves, as shown in **Figure 1B.** Cell division isn't as simple as just cutting the cell in half, so how do cells divide?

The Cell Cycle

A living organism has a life cycle. A life cycle begins with the organism's formation, is followed by growth and development, and finally ends in death. Right now, you are in a stage of your life cycle called adolescence, which is a period of active growth and development. Individual cells also have life cycles.

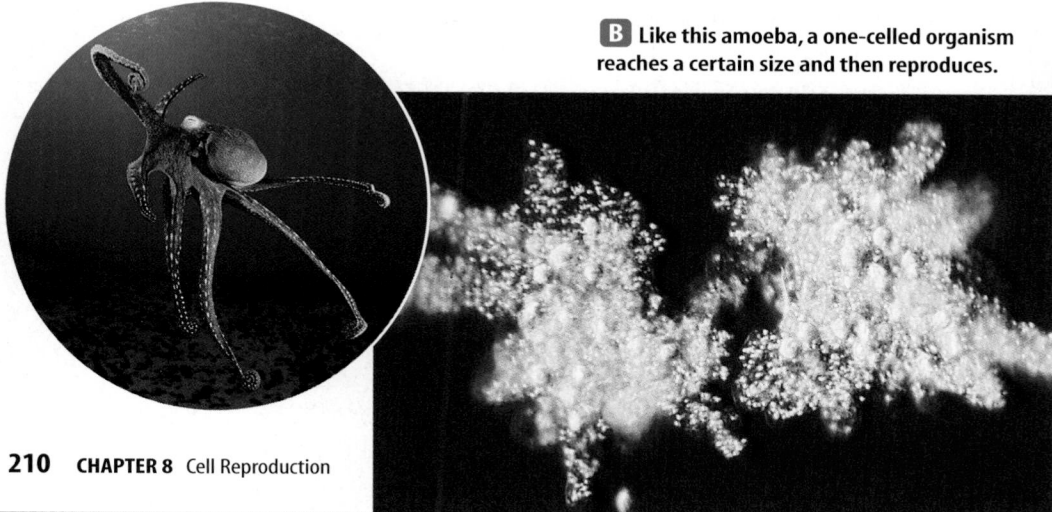

B Like this amoeba, a one-celled organism reaches a certain size and then reproduces.

210 CHAPTER 8 Cell Reproduction

Section ✓ Assessment Planner

PORTFOLIO
Visual Learning, p. 211
PERFORMANCE ASSESSMENT
MiniLAB, p. 215
Skill Builder Activities, p. 216
See page 236 for more options.

CONTENT ASSESSMENT
Section, p. 216
Challenge, p. 216
Chapter, pp. 236–237

Figure 2
Interphase is the longest part of the cell cycle. *When do chromosomes duplicate?*

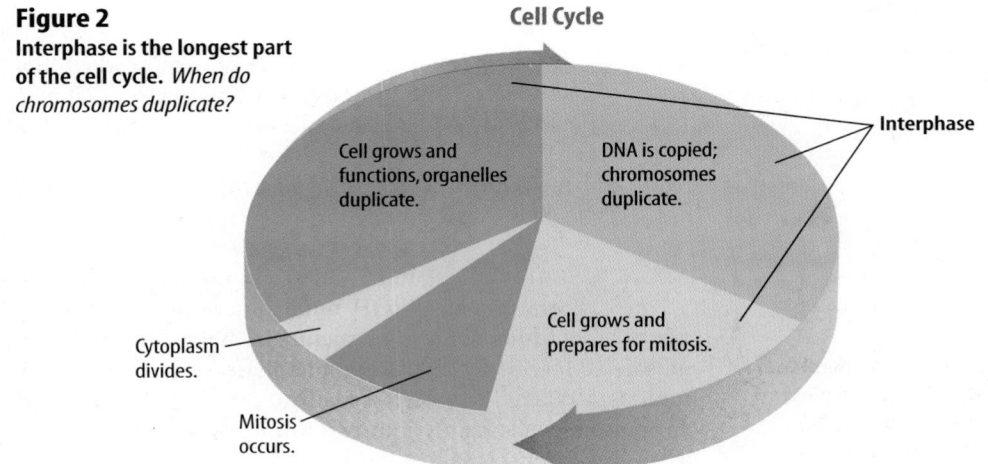

Cell Cycle

- Cell grows and functions, organelles duplicate.
- DNA is copied; chromosomes duplicate.
- Interphase
- Cell grows and prepares for mitosis.
- Mitosis occurs.
- Cytoplasm divides.

Length of Cycle The cell cycle, as shown in **Figure 2,** is a series of events that takes place from one cell division to the next. The time it takes to complete a cell cycle is not the same in all cells. For example, the cycle for cells in some bean plants takes about 19 h to complete. Cells in animal embryos divide rapidly and can complete their cycles is less than 20 min. In some human cells, the cell cycle takes about 16 h. Cells in humans that are needed for repair, growth, or replacement, like skin and bone cells, constantly repeat the cycle.

Interphase Most of the life of any eukaryotic cell—a cell with a nucleus—is spent in a period of growth and development called interphase. Cells in your body that no longer divide, such as nerve and muscle cells, are always in interphase. An actively dividing cell, such as a skin cell, copies its hereditary material and prepares for cell division during interphase.

Why is it important for a cell to copy its hereditary information before dividing? Imagine that you have a part in a play and the director has one complete copy of the script. If the director gave only one page to each person in the play, no one would have the entire script. Instead the director makes a complete, separate copy of the script for each member of the cast so that each one can learn his or her part. Before a cell divides, a copy of the hereditary material must be made so that each of the two new cells will get a complete copy. Just as the actors in the play need the entire script, each cell needs a complete set of hereditary material to carry out life functions.

After interphase, cell division begins. The nucleus divides, and then the cytoplasm separates to form two new cells.

Health
INTEGRATION

In most cells, the cell cycle is well controlled. However, cancerous cells have uncontrolled cell division. Some cancerous cells form a mass of cells called a tumor. Find out why some tumors are harmful to an organism. Write what you find out in your Science Journal.

SCIENCE *Online*

Research Nerve cells in adults usually do not undergo mitosis. Visit the Glencoe Science Web site at **science.glencoe.com** for more information about nerve cell regeneration. Communicate to your class what you learn.

The Cell Cycle

Caption Answer
Figure 2 during interphase

Visual Learning

Figure 2 Have students make an events chain concept map that outlines the steps of the cell cycle as illustrated in **Figure 2.**
L2 | LS | **Visual-Spatial** | P

Health
INTEGRATION

Cancerous tumors grow rapidly and sometimes invade healthy tissue.

SCIENCE *Online*
Internet Addresses
_____
_____
_____

Explore the Glencoe Science Web site at **science.glencoe.com** to find out more about topics in this section.

Resource Manager

Chapter Resources Booklet
Transparency Activity, p. 42
Directed Reading for Content Mastery, pp. 17, 18

Science **Journal**

Life of a Cell Have students write creative stories about the life cycle of a cell from its beginning to its end. Have them use section vocabulary as they describe what happens in the cell. L2 | LS | **Linguistic**

Mitosis

Use an Analogy

Compare chromosome thickening to a coiled telephone cord. When stretched out, the cord is long and thin, like chromosomes during interphase. When the cord returns to its usual position, it shortens and thickens, like chromosomes preparing to divide. L1

LS Visual-Spatial

✔ Reading Check

Answer A duplicated chromosome is made up of two chromatids.

Fun Fact

Most cells are not actively engaged in mitosis. Skin cells spend 15–20 days in interphase. After infancy, nerve cells stay in interphase.

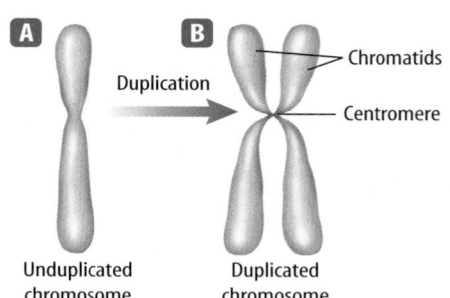

Duplication

Chromatids

Centromere

Unduplicated chromosome

Duplicated chromosome

Figure 3
DNA is copied during interphase.
A An unduplicated chromosome has one strand of DNA. **B** A duplicated chromosome has two identical DNA strands, called chromatids, that are held together at a region called the centromere.

Figure 4
The cell plate shown in this plant cell appears when the cytoplasm is being divided.

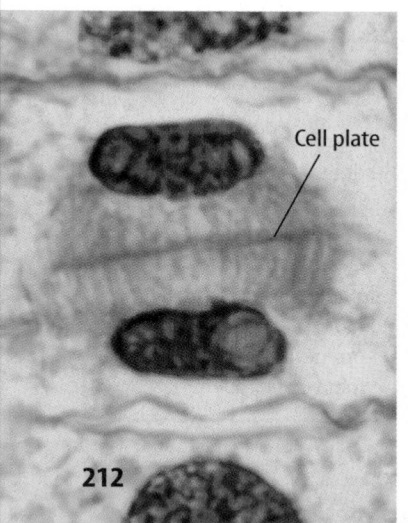

Cell plate

212

Mitosis

Mitosis (mi TOH sus) is the process in which the nucleus divides to form two identical nuclei. Each new nucleus also is identical to the original nucleus. Mitosis is described as a series of phases, or steps. The steps of mitosis in order are named prophase, metaphase, anaphase, and telophase.

Steps of Mitosis When any nucleus divides, the chromosomes (KROH muh sohmz) play the important part. A **chromosome** is a structure in the nucleus that contains hereditary material. During interphase, each chromosome duplicates. When the nucleus is ready to divide, each duplicated chromosome coils tightly into two thickened, identical strands called chromatids, as shown in **Figure 3.**

✔ Reading Check *How are chromosomes and chromatids related?*

During prophase, the pairs of chromatids are fully visible when viewed under a microscope. The nucleolus and the nuclear membrane disintegrate. Two small structures called centrioles (SEN tree olz) move to opposite ends of the cell. Between the centrioles, threadlike spindle fibers begin to stretch across the cell. Plant cells also form spindle fibers during mitosis but do not have centrioles.

In metaphase, the pairs of chromatids line up across the center of the cell. The centromere of each pair usually becomes attached to two spindle fibers—one from each side of the cell.

In anaphase, each centromere divides and the spindle fibers shorten. Each pair of chromatids separates, and chromatids begin to move to opposite ends of the cell. The separated chromatids are now called chromosomes. In the final step, telophase, spindle fibers start to disappear, the chromosomes start to uncoil, and a new nucleus forms.

Division of the Cytoplasm For most cells, after the nucleus has divided, the cytoplasm separates and two new cells are formed. In animal cells, the cell membrane pinches in the middle, like a balloon with a string tightened around it, and the cytoplasm divides. In plant cells, the appearance of a cell plate, as shown in **Figure 4,** tells you that the cytoplasm is being divided. New cell walls form along the cell plate, and new cell membranes develop inside the cell walls. Following division of the cytoplasm, most new cells begin the period of growth, or interphase, again. Review cell division for an animal cell using the illustrations in **Figure 5.**

Figure 5

Cell division for an animal cell is shown here. Each micrograph shown in this figure is magnified 600 times.

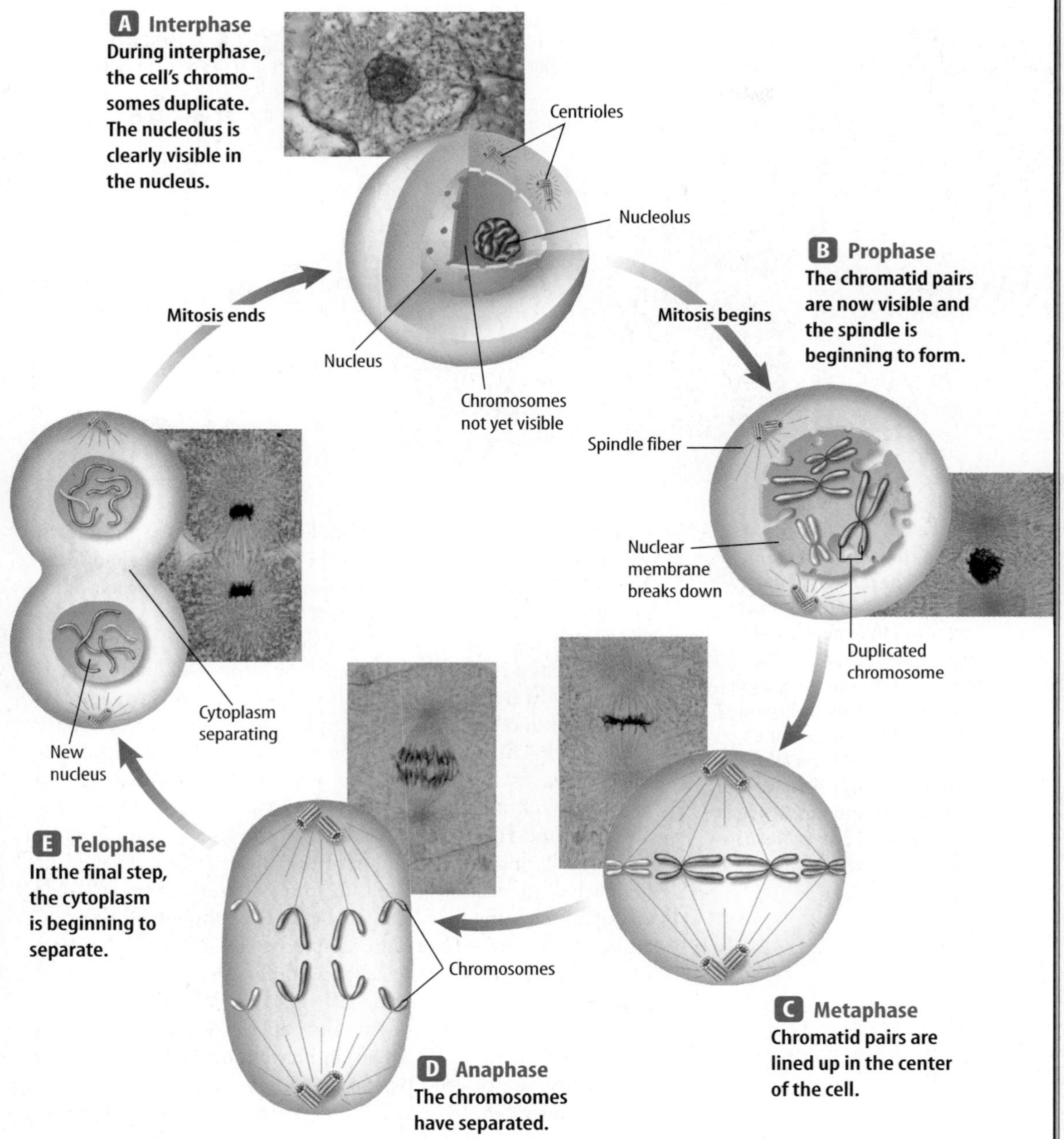

A Interphase
During interphase, the cell's chromosomes duplicate. The nucleolus is clearly visible in the nucleus.

Centrioles

Nucleolus

Mitosis ends

Nucleus

Chromosomes not yet visible

Mitosis begins

B Prophase
The chromatid pairs are now visible and the spindle is beginning to form.

Spindle fiber

Nuclear membrane breaks down

Duplicated chromosome

New nucleus

Cytoplasm separating

E Telophase
In the final step, the cytoplasm is beginning to separate.

Chromosomes

D Anaphase
The chromosomes have separated.

C Metaphase
Chromatid pairs are lined up in the center of the cell.

SECTION 1 Cell Division and Mitosis **213**

Mitosis, continued

Discussion

Have students use their knowledge of the cell cycle to infer why even slight injuries to the brain and spinal cord can be serious and permanent. Because nerve cells do not undergo mitosis, damaged cells are not replaced, although some repair does occur.

Discussion

Many nonliving things such as icicles, stalagmites, crystals, and sand dunes appear to grow. Ask students to give examples of other nonliving things that appear to grow. Possible answers: highway systems, buildings, developments, shopping malls Have students distinguish between the processes involved in the growth of living things and the growth of nonliving things. In nonliving things, growth is caused by the surrounding environment. In living things, growth is caused by processes within the organism.

Caption Answer

Figure 6 the sex of the organism

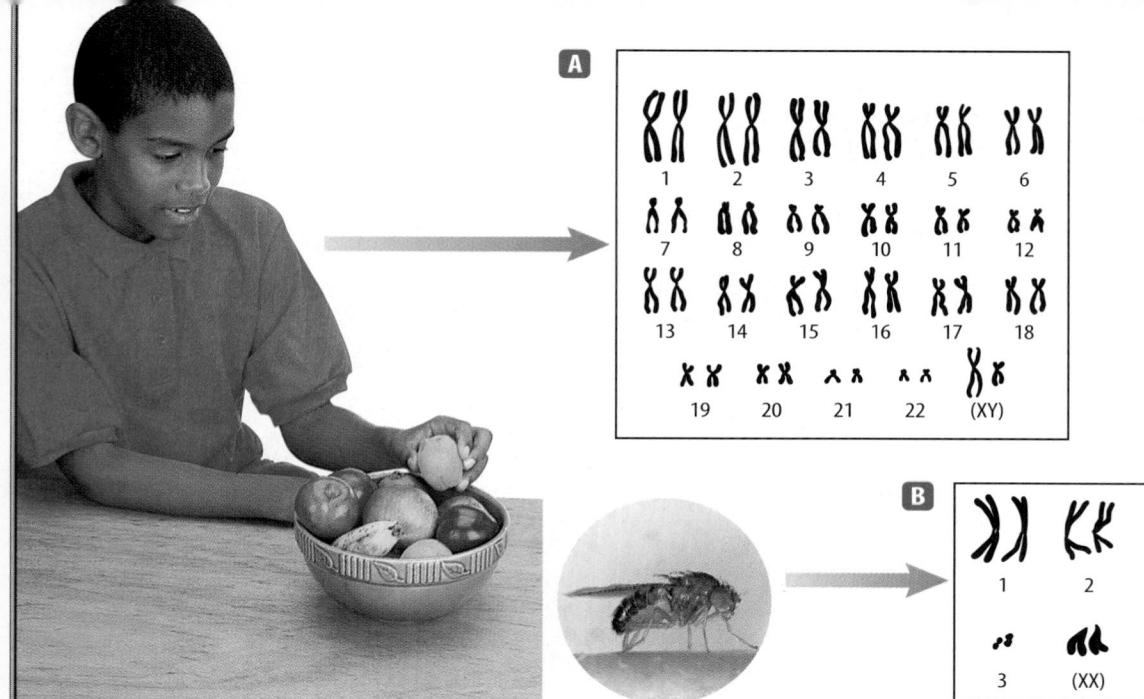

Figure 6
Pairs of chromosomes are found in the nucleus of most cells. All chromosomes shown here are in their duplicated form. **A** Most human cells have 23 pairs of chromosomes including one pair of chromosomes that help determine sex such as the XY pair above. **B** Most fruit fly cells have four pairs of chromosomes. *What do you think the XX pair in fruit flies helps determine?*

Results of Mitosis You should remember two important things about mitosis. First, it is the division of a nucleus. Second, it produces two new nuclei that are identical to each other and the original nucleus. Each new nucleus has the same number and type of chromosomes. Every cell in your body, except sex cells, has a nucleus with 46 chromosomes—23 pairs. This is because you began as one cell with 46 chromosomes in its nucleus. Skin cells, produced to replace or repair your skin, have the same 46 chromosomes as the original single cell you developed from. Each cell in a fruit fly has eight chromosomes, so each new cell produced by mitosis has a copy of those eight chromosomes. **Figure 6** shows the chromosomes found in most human cells and those found in most fruit fly cells.

Each of the trillions of cells in your body, except sex cells, has a copy of the same hereditary material. Even though all actors in a play have copies of the same script, they do not learn the same lines. Likewise, all of your cells use different parts of the same hereditary material to become different types of cells.

Cell division allows growth and replaces worn out or damaged cells. You are much larger and have more cells than a baby mainly because of cell division. If you cut yourself, the wound heals because cell division replaces damaged cells. Another way some organisms use cell division is to produce new organisms.

LAB DEMONSTRATION

Purpose to observe asexual reproduction in a sweet potato

Materials sweet potato with leaf buds, water, widemouthed glass jar, 4 toothpicks

Preparation Obtain a sweet potato that has purple leaf buds growing at its scarred end.

Procedure Fill a jar almost full of water, and place sweet potato with buds or scarred end up so at least half of the potato is in water. Toothpicks can hold the potato in place. Keep water level constant and observe for three weeks.

Expected Outcome Students should observe the formation of roots and leaf growth.

✔Assessment

What part of the sweet potato produced leaves and roots? Leaves developed from the buds; roots grew from the bottom half of the sweet potato. **Is this an example of sexual or asexual reproduction? Explain.** Asexual; a new organism is produced from one parent.

Asexual Reproduction

Reproduction is the process by which an organism produces others of its same kind. Among living organisms, there are two types of reproduction—sexual and asexual. Sexual reproduction usually requires two organisms. In **asexual reproduction,** a new organism (sometimes more than one) is produced from one organism. The new organism will have hereditary material identical to the hereditary material of the parent organism.

✔ Reading Check *How many organisms are needed for asexual reproduction?*

Cellular Asexual Reproduction Organisms with eukaryotic cells asexually reproduce by cell division. A sweet potato growing in a jar of water is an example of asexual reproduction. All the stems, leaves, and roots that grow from the sweet potato have been produced by cell division and have the same hereditary material. New strawberry plants can be reproduced asexually from horizontal stems called runners. **Figure 7** shows asexual reproduction in a potato and a strawberry plant.

Recall that mitosis is the division of a nucleus. However, bacteria do not have a nucleus so they can't use mitosis. Instead, bacteria reproduce asexually by fission. During fission, an organism whose cells do not contain a nucleus copies its genetic material and then divides into two identical organisms.

Figure 7
Many plants can reproduce asexually.

A A new potato plant can grow from each sprout on this potato.

B *How does the genetic material in the small strawberry plant compare to the genetic material in the large strawberry plant?*

Modeling Mitosis
Procedure
1. Make models of cell division using **materials supplied by your teacher.**
2. Use four chromosomes in your model.
3. When finished, arrange the models in the order in which mitosis occurs.

Analysis
1. In which steps is the nucleus visible?
2. How many cells does a dividing cell form?

Asexual Reproduction

✔ Reading Check

Answer one

Purpose to construct a model of mitosis L2 ELL
Kinesthetic and Visual-Spatial
Materials colored paper, poster board, markers, toothpicks, yarn, thread, glue, scissors
Teaching Strategy Student models should resemble mitosis as shown in **Figure 4.**
Analysis
1. prophase and telophase
2. two new cells

Assessment

Performance Assess students' understanding of mitosis by making flash cards of the stages and having students arrange them in the proper order. Use **PASC**, p. 163.

Caption Answer
Figure 7 They are identical.

Resource Manager

Chapter Resources Booklet
MiniLAB, p. 3
Transparency Activity, pp. 45–46
Lab Activity, pp. 9–10

Science Journal

Cloning Have students use science reference books, newspapers, and the Internet to research cloning, a process that artificially reproduces an exact duplicate of a single parent. Have students write reports in their Science Journals on the medical uses as well as the negative ethical implications of cloning technology. L2 **Linguistic**

Asexual Reproduction, continued

Activity

Add one package of yeast and one teaspoon of sugar to a .5 L container of warm water. Let the container stand in a warm place for a few hours. Allow students to examine microscope slides of the mixture to observe budding in yeast cells. L2
ℕ Visual-Spatial

Text Question Answers

Sea star numbers would increase because of regeneration.

③ Assess

Reteach

Have students draw the nucleus or chromosomes on cell cycle outlines and describe what is occurring at each stage. L1
ELL ℕ Visual-Spatial

Challenge

At one time, interphase was called the resting stage. Why is this not a good description of interphase? A cell in interphase is carrying out all of the life processes.

✔Assessment

Oral How is mitosis different from cell division? Mitosis is the division of the nucleus. Cell division includes mitosis and the division of the cytoplasm and its contents. Use **Performance Assessment in the Science Classroom**, p. 89.

Figure 8
Some organisms use cell division for budding and regeneration.

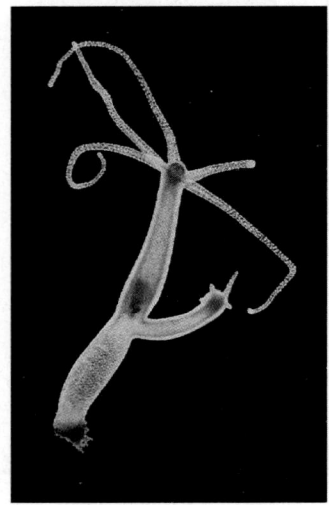

A Hydra, a freshwater animal, can reproduce asexually by budding. The bud is a small exact copy of the adult.

B Some sea stars reproduce asexually by shedding arms. Each arm can grow into a new sea star.

Budding and Regeneration Look at **Figure 8A.** A new organism is growing from the body of the parent organism. This organism, called a hydra, is reproducing by budding. Budding is a type of asexual reproduction made possible because of cell division. When the bud on the adult becomes large enough, it breaks away to live on its own.

Could you grow a new finger? Some organisms can regrow damaged or lost body parts, as shown in **Figure 8B.** Regeneration is the process that uses cell division to regrow body parts. Sponges, planaria, sea stars, and some other organisms can use regeneration for asexual reproduction. If these organisms break into pieces, a whole new organism will grow from each piece. Because sea stars eat oysters, oyster farmers dislike them. What would happen if an oyster farmer collected sea stars, cut them into pieces, and threw them back into the ocean?

Section ① Assessment

1. What is mitosis and how does it differ in plants and animals?

2. Give two examples of asexual reproduction in many-celled organisms.

3. What happens to chromosomes before mitosis begins?

4. After a cell undergoes mitosis, how are the two new cells alike?

5. **Think Critically** Why is it important for the nuclear membrane to disintegrate during mitosis?

Skill Builder Activities

6. **Testing a Hypothesis** A piece of leaf, stem, or root can grow into a new plant. Hypothesize how you would use one of these plant parts to grow a new plant. Test your idea. **For more help, refer to the** Science Skill Handbook.

7. **Solving One-Step Equations** If a cell undergoes cell division every 5 min, how many cells will there be after 1 h? Calculate and record the answer in your Science Journal. **For more help, refer to the** Math Skill Handbook.

Answers to Section Assessment

1. A process in which a cell nucleus divides into two nuclei, each of which has the same genetic information; in animal cells, the cytoplasm divides as the cell membrane pinches in the middle of the cell. In plant cells, the appearance of the cell plate indicates that the cytoplasm is being divided.

2. Possible answers: budding and regeneration

3. The chromosomes duplicate.

4. They both have the same genetic information.

5. Otherwise, the chromosomes would not be able to move to opposite ends of the cell.

6. Hypotheses will vary. Students may separate plant parts and place them in water or soil.

7. 60 minutes divided by 5 minutes = 12 cell divisions; $2^{12} = 4{,}096$ cells

Activity

Mitosis in Plant Cells

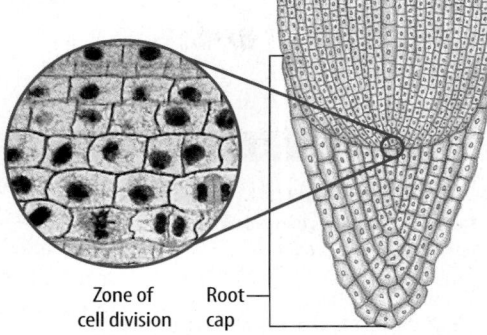

Zone of cell division   Root cap

Reproduction of most cells in plants and animals uses mitosis and cell division. In this activity, you will study mitosis in plant cells by examining prepared slides of onion root-tip cells.

What You'll Investigate
How can plant cells in different stages of mitosis be distinguished from each other?

Materials
prepared slide of an onion root tip
microscope

Goals
- **Compare** cells in different stages of mitosis and observe the location of their chromosomes.
- **Observe** what stage of mitosis is most common in onion root tips.

Safety Precautions

Procedure

1. Copy the data table in your Science Journal.
2. **Obtain** a prepared slide of cells from an onion root tip.
3. Set your microscope on low power and examine the onion root tip. Move the slide until you can see the tip of the root. You will see several large, round cells. These cells are called the root cap. Move your slide until you see the cells in the area just behind the root cap. Turn the nosepiece to high power.
4. Find one area of cells where you can see the most stages of mitosis. Count how many cells you see in each stage and record your data in the table.
5. Turn the microscope back to low power. Remove the onion root-tip slide.

Conclude and Apply

1. **Compare** the cells in the region behind the root cap to those in the root cap.
2. **Calculate** the percent of cells found in each stage of mitosis. Infer which stage of mitosis takes the longest period of time.

Number of Root-Tip Cells Observed

Stage of Mitosis	Number of Cells Observed	Percent of Cells Observed
Prophase	78	65
Metaphase	23	19
Anaphase	12	10
Telophase	7	6
Total	120	100

*C*ommunicating Your Data

Write a story as if you were a cell in an onion root tip. Describe what changes occur as you go through mitosis. Use some of your drawings to illustrate the story. Share your story with your class. **For more help, refer to the Science Skill Handbook.**

Purpose Students observe the stages of mitosis. L2 ELL
LS Visual-Spatial

Process Skills observing, inferring, comparing and contrasting

Time Required 40 minutes

Teaching Strategy Review the stages of mitosis before beginning the activity.

Troubleshooting Students may have difficulty locating all the phases. You may want to place an onion root tip slide on the microprojector and point out the phases.

Answers to Questions

1. The cells behind the root cap are smaller than those in the root cap. Mitosis occurs at a faster rate in cells behind the root cap.
2. See student page; prophase takes the longest.

Assessment

Performance To further assess students' understanding of mitosis, give each one a sheet of paper listing a stage and have them describe what comes before and after that stage. Use **Performance Assessment in the Science Classroom,** p. 163.

Resource Manager

Chapter Resources Booklet
Reinforcement, p. 25
Activity Worksheet, pp. 5–6

*C*ommunicating Your Data

The story and drawings should include the stages in mitosis.

Bellringer Transparency

Display the Section Focus Transparency for Section 2. Use the accompanying Transparency Activity Master. L2

ELL

Tie to Prior Knowledge

As a review, ask students to describe the stages in mitosis. Then tell the students that for certain cells, the nucleus divides twice. They will learn why in this section.

Sexual Reproduction and Meiosis

As You Read

What **You'll Learn**

- **Describe** the stages of meiosis and how sex cells are produced.
- **Explain** why meiosis is needed for sexual reproduction.
- **Name** the cells that are involved in fertilization.
- **Explain** how fertilization occurs in sexual reproduction.

Vocabulary

sexual reproduction	zygote
sperm	diploid
egg	haploid
fertilization	meiosis

Why **It's Important**

Because of meiosis and sexual reproduction, no one is exactly like you.

Figure 9
A human sperm or egg contains 23 chromosomes. The chromosomes are shown in their duplicated form.

Human egg and many sperm   Magnification: 790×

Sexual Reproduction

Sexual reproduction is another way that a new organism can be produced. During **sexual reproduction,** two sex cells, sometimes called an egg and a sperm, come together. Sex cells, like those in **Figure 9,** are formed from cells in reproductive organs. **Sperm** are formed in the male reproductive organs. **Eggs** are formed in the female reproductive organs. The joining of an egg and a sperm is called **fertilization,** and the cell that forms is called a **zygote** (ZI goht). Generally, the egg and the sperm come from two different organisms of the same species. Following fertilization, cell division begins. A new organism with a unique identity develops.

Diploid Cells Your body forms two types of cells—body cells and sex cells. Body cells far outnumber sex cells. Your brain, skin, bones, and other tissues and organs are formed from body cells. A typical human body cell has 46 chromosomes. Each chromosome has a mate that is similar to it in size and shape and has similar DNA. Human body cells have 23 pairs of chromosomes. When cells have pairs of similar chromosomes, they are said to be **diploid** (DIH ployd).

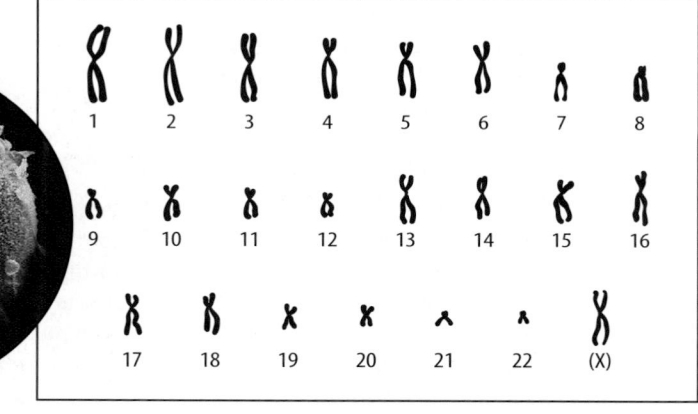

Section ✓ *Assessment* Planner

PORTFOLIO
Make a Model, p. 221
PERFORMANCE ASSESSMENT
Skill Builder Activities, p. 223
See page 236 for more options.

CONTENT ASSESSMENT
Section, p. 223
Challenge, p. 223
Chapter, pp. 236–237

Haploid Cells

Because sex cells do not have pairs of chromosomes, they are said to be **haploid** (HA ployd). They have only half the number of chromosomes as body cells. *Haploid* means "single form." Human sex cells have only 23 chromosomes—one from each of the 23 pairs of similar chromosomes. Compare the chromosomes found in a sex cell, as shown in **Figure 9,** to the full set of human chromosomes seen in **Figure 6A.**

 **Reading Check** *How many chromosomes are usually in each human sperm?*

Meiosis and Sex Cells

A process called **meiosis** (mi OH sus) produces haploid sex cells. What would happen in sexual reproduction if two diploid cells combined? The offspring would have twice as many chromosomes as its parent. Although plants with twice the number of chromosomes as the parent plants are often produced, most animals do not survive with a double number of chromosomes. Meiosis ensures that the offspring will have the same diploid number as its parent, as shown in **Figure 10.** After two haploid sex cells combine, a diploid zygote is produced that develops into a new diploid organism.

During meiosis, two divisions of the nucleus occur. These divisions are called meiosis I and meiosis II. The steps of each division have names like those in mitosis and are numbered for the division in which they occur.

Chemistry
INTEGRATION

The human egg releases a chemical into the surrounding fluid that attracts sperm. Usually, only one sperm fertilizes the egg. After the sperm nucleus enters the egg, the cell membrane of the egg changes in a way that prevents other sperm from entering. What adaptation in this process guarantees that the zygote will be diploid? Write a paragraph describing your ideas in your Science Journal.

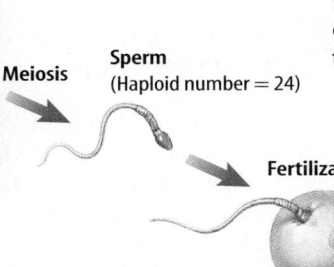

Figure 10
When sex cells join, a zygote forms. The zygote divides by cell division and develops into a new organism. Compare the number of chromosomes present in the different cells.

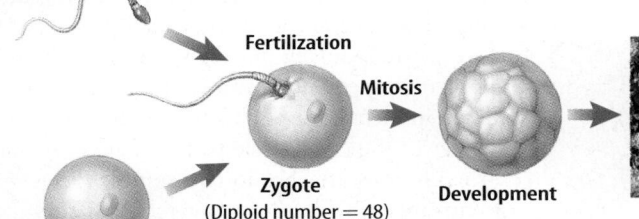

Meiosis
Sperm
(Haploid number = 24)

Fertilization

Mitosis

Meiosis
Egg
(Haploid number = 24)

Zygote
(Diploid number = 48)

Development

SECTION 2 Sexual Reproduction and Meiosis **219**

Teacher FYI

In vitro fertilization is a procedure that joins sperm and eggs outside the body. Fertilized eggs (actually two-day-old embryos) are then implanted into the female.

Extension

Have students research and report on the contribution of African American cell biologist Everett Anderson to the modern understanding of meiosis. Anderson is one of the leading researchers in developing electron microscopic techniques to study meiosis. L2
IS Linguistic

✓ Reading Check

Answer The duplicated chromosomes of each similar pair are pulled to opposite ends of the cell.

Use Science Words

Word Meaning Have students use a dictionary to find out what *triploid* and *tetraploid* mean. Have them write an explanation of how this condition occurs. *Triploid*—each cell in the organism contains three sets of chromosomes; plant endosperm is triploid and normal. *Tetraploid* organisms have four sets of chromosomes in each cell; these conditions arise from total nondisjunction during mitosis or meiosis. L2 **IS Linguistic**

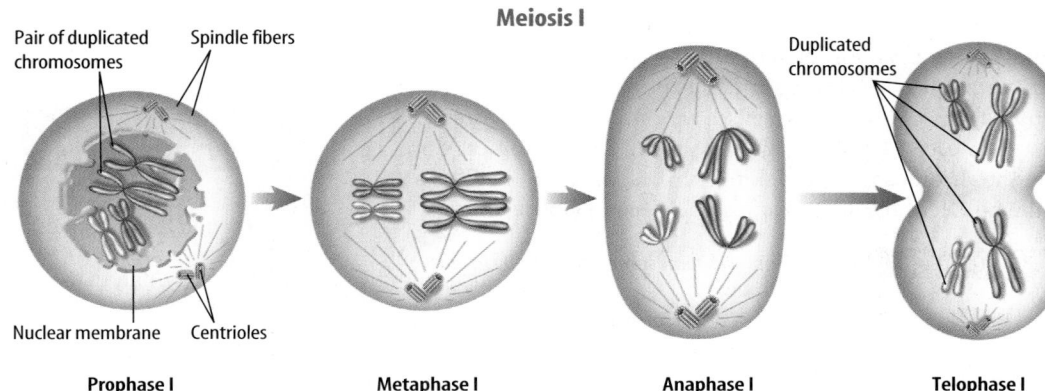

Meiosis I

Prophase I   Metaphase I   Anaphase I   Telophase I

Figure 11
Meiosis has two divisions of the nucleus—meiosis I and meiosis II. *How many sex cells are finally formed after both divisions are completed?*

Meiosis I Before meiosis begins, each chromosome is duplicated, just as in mitosis. When the cell is ready for meiosis, each duplicated chromosome is visible under the microscope as two chromatids. As shown in **Figure 11,** the events of prophase I are similar to those of prophase in mitosis. In meiosis, each duplicated chromosome comes near its similar duplicated mate. In mitosis they do not come near each other.

In metaphase I, the pairs of duplicated chromosomes line up in the center of the cell. The centromere of each chromatid pair becomes attached to one spindle fiber so, the chromatids do not separate in anaphase I. The two pairs of chromatids of each similar pair move away from each other to opposite ends of the cell. Each duplicated chromosome still has two chromatids. Then, in telophase I, the cytoplasm divides, and two new cells form. Each new cell has one duplicated chromosome from each similar pair.

✓ Reading Check   *What happens to duplicated chromosomes during anaphase I?*

Meiosis II The two cells formed during meiosis I now begin meiosis II. The chromatids of each duplicated chromosome will be separated during this division. In prophase II, the duplicated chromosomes and spindle fibers reappear in each new cell. Then in metaphase II, the duplicated chromosomes move to the center of the cell. Unlike what occurs in metaphase I, each centromere now attaches to two spindle fibers instead of one. The centromere divides during anaphase II, and the chromatids separate and move to opposite ends of the cell. Each chromatid now is an individual chromosome. As telophase II begins, the spindle fibers disappear, and a nuclear membrane forms around the chromosomes at each end of the cell. When meiosis II is finished, the cytoplasm divides.

Resource Manager

Chapter Resources Booklet
Enrichment, p. 29
Mathematics Skill Activities, p. 3

Inclusion Strategies

Learning Disabled Students who are dyslexic may have trouble distinguishing between the first and second parts of meiosis. Instead of Roman numbers, as in prophase I and prophase II, use Arabic numbers for easier identification (prophase 1 and prophase 2).

Meiosis II

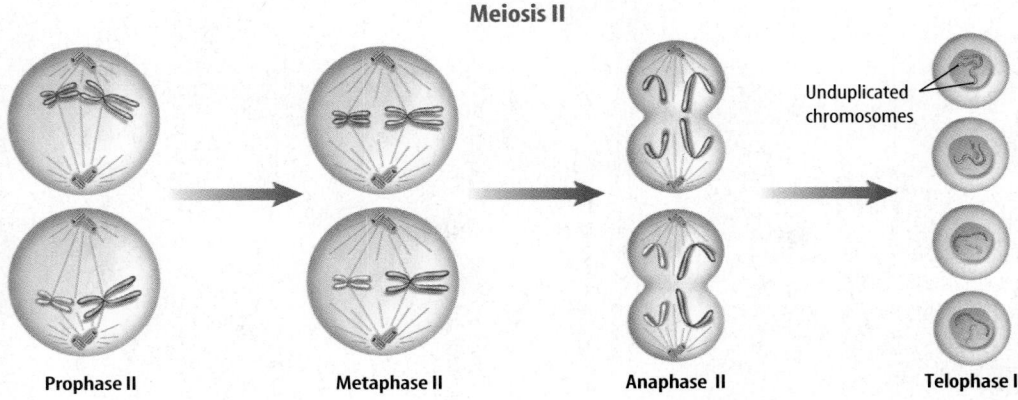

Prophase II   Metaphase II   Anaphase II   Telophase II

Unduplicated chromosomes

Summary of Meiosis Two cells form during meiosis I. In meiosis II, both of these cells form two cells. The two divisions of the nucleus result in four sex cells. Each has one-half the number of chromosomes in its nucleus that was in the original nucleus. From a human cell with 46 paired chromosomes, meiosis produces four sex cells each with 23 unpaired chromosomes.

Problem-Solving Activity

How can chromosome numbers be predicted?

Offspring get half of their chromosomes from one parent and half from the other. What happens if each parent has a different diploid number of chromosomes?

Identifying the Problem

A zebra and a donkey can mate to produce a zonkey. Zebras have a diploid number of 46. Donkeys have a diploid number of 62.

Solving the Problem

1. How many chromosomes would the zonkey receive from each parent?
2. What is the chromosome number of the zonkey?
3. What would happen when meiosis occurs in the zonkey's reproductive organs?
4. Predict why zonkeys are usually sterile.

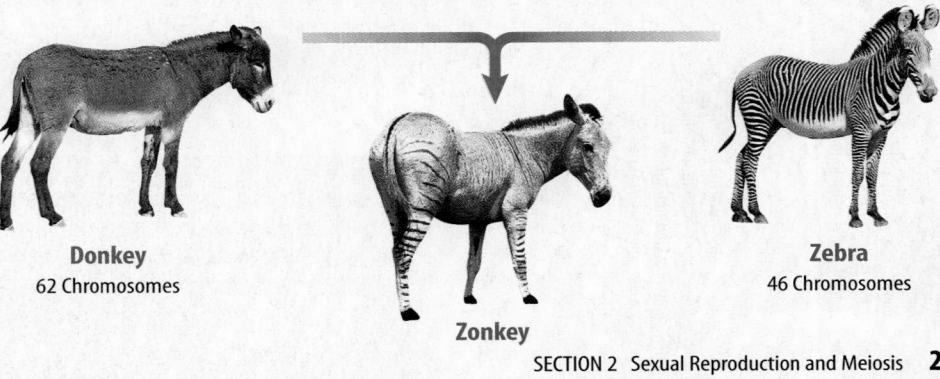

Donkey
62 Chromosomes

Zonkey

Zebra
46 Chromosomes

SECTION 2 Sexual Reproduction and Meiosis **221**

☑ Active Reading

Flow Chart A flow chart helps students logically sequence events. Students will write major stages of the sequence in large ovals and write substages in smaller ovals under the larger ovals. Have students design a flow chart for a concept in this section. Sample flow chart:

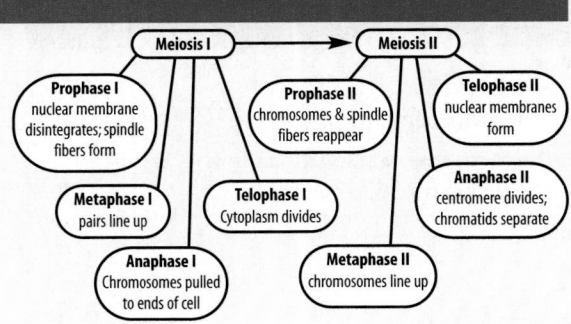

Meiosis I → Meiosis II

Prophase I nuclear membrane disintegrates; spindle fibers form

Metaphase I pairs line up

Anaphase I Chromosomes pulled to ends of cell

Telophase I Cytoplasm divides

Prophase II chromosomes & spindle fibers reappear

Metaphase II chromosomes line up

Anaphase II centromere divides; chromatids separate

Telophase II nuclear membranes form

NATIONAL GEOGRAPHIC

Visualizing Polyploidy in Plants

Have students examine the pictures and read the captions. Then ask the following questions.

What kinds of mistakes in meiosis or mitosis could result in a polyploid plant? A mistake that caused chromosome sets not to separate, allowing more than one full set to be present in a cell after division to form sex cells.

What is the main advantage of bananas being triploid? Triploid plants have very small seeds, so people can eat bananas without removing seeds.

Why wouldn't you find triploid peanuts in the grocery store? The part of a peanut plant you eat is a seed, but triploid plants have little or no seeds.

Activity

Have students use pipe cleaners to model the chromosomes of one of the plants featured here. For example, a banana with 3 sets of 11 chromosomes, a strawberry with 8 sets of 7 chromosomes or a peanut with 4 sets of 10 chromosomes.

Extension

Have students research the meaning of the terms *allopolyploidy* and *autopolyploidy*. Have the students find and list some examples of plants that each term applies to.

NATIONAL GEOGRAPHIC **VISUALIZING POLYPLOIDY IN PLANTS**

Figure 12

You received a haploid (n) set of chromosomes from each of your parents, making you a diploid (2n) organism. In nature, however, many plants are polyploid—they have three (3n), four (4n), or more sets of chromosomes. We depend on some of these plants for food.

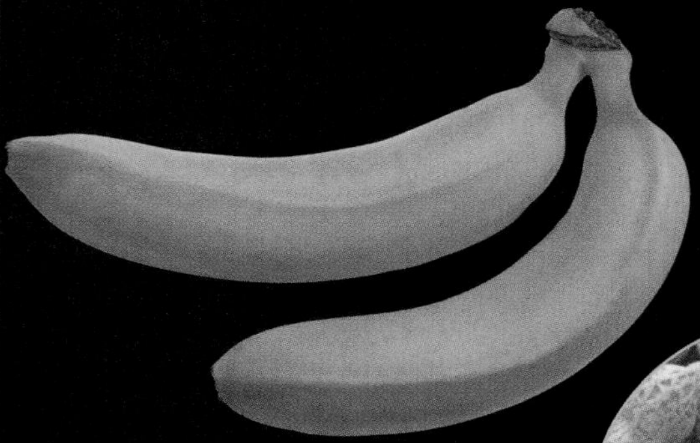

▲ TRIPLOID Bright yellow bananas typically come from triploid (3n) banana plants. Plants with an odd number of chromosome sets usually cannot reproduce sexually and have very small seeds or none at all.

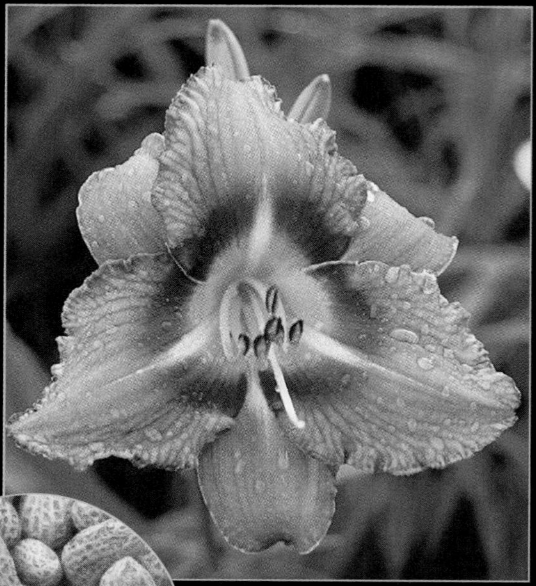

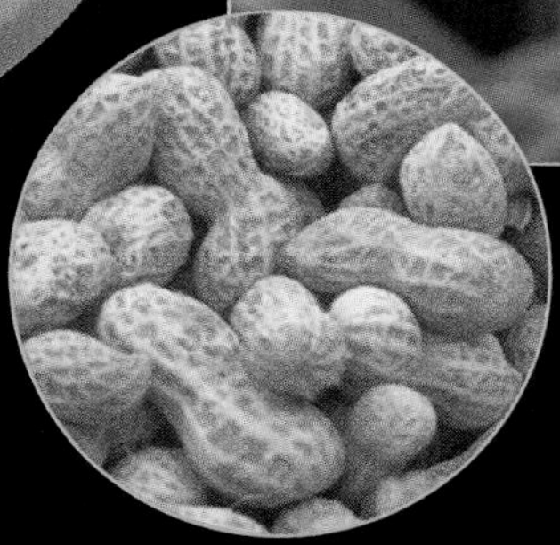

▲ TETRAPLOID Polyploidy occurs naturally in many plants—including peanuts and daylilies—due to mistakes in mitosis or meiosis.

▼ HEXAPLOID Modern cultivated strains of oats have six sets of chromosomes, making them hexaploid (6n) plants.

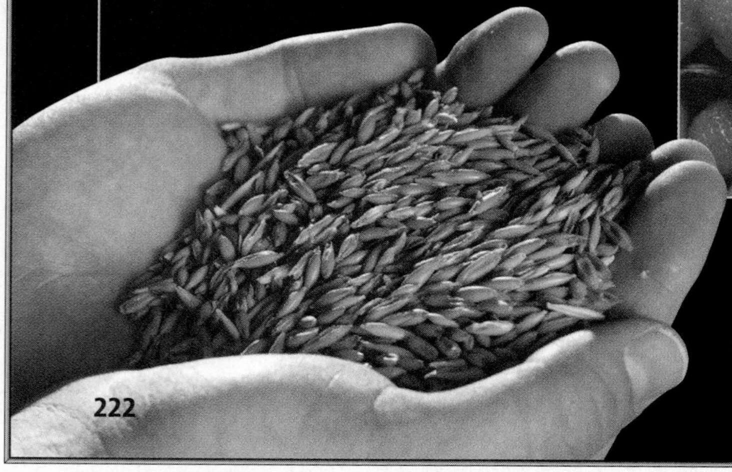

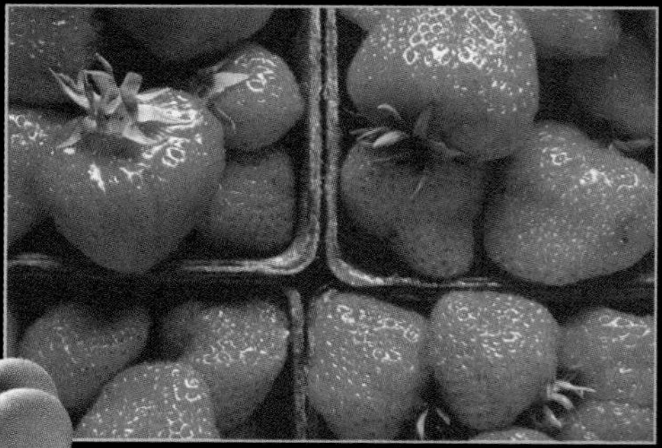

▲ OCTAPLOID Polyploid plants often are bigger than nonpolyploid plants and may have especially large leaves, flowers, or fruits. Strawberries are an example of octaploid (8n) plants.

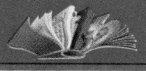

Resource Manager

Chapter Resources Booklet
Reinforcement, p. 26

Performance Assessment in the Science Classroom, p. 57

Visual Learning

Figure 13 Have students follow the unseparated chromosome pair through each stage of meiosis. **How did this error affect the sex cells?** Some had too many chromosomes; others not enough.

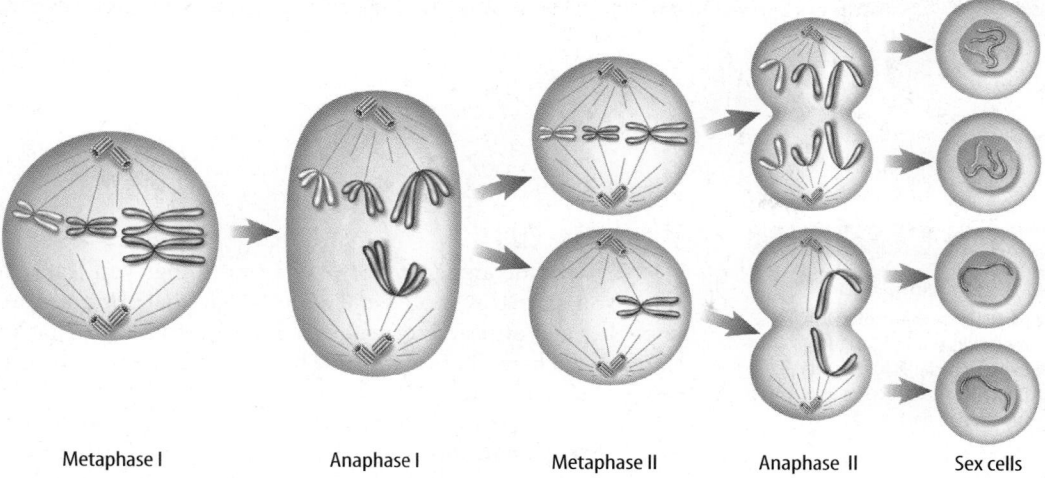

Metaphase I   Anaphase I   Metaphase II   Anaphase II   Sex cells

Mistakes in Meiosis Meiosis occurs many times in reproductive organs. Although mistakes in plants, as shown in **Figure 12,** are common, mistakes are less common in animals. These mistakes can produce sex cells with too many or too few chromosomes, as shown in **Figure 13.** Sometimes, zygotes produced from these sex cells die. If the zygote lives, every cell in the organism that grows from that zygote usually will have the wrong number of chromosomes. Organisms with the wrong number of chromosomes may not grow normally.

Figure 13
This diploid cell has four chromosomes. During anaphase I, one pair of duplicated chromosomes did not separate. *How many chromosomes does each sex cell usually have?*

Meiosis and Sex Cells, continued

Activity
Show students pictures of karyotypes with abnormal numbers of chromosomes and have them find the abnormalities. L2
ELL LS **Visual-Spatial**

Caption Answer
Figure 13 two

3 Assess

Reteach
Show the phases of meiosis out of sequence. Have students identify each phase and place the phases in order. L2 ELL
LS **Visual-Spatial**

Challenge
How are the cells at the end of meiosis different from those at the beginning? The original cell is diploid, and each of the new cells is haploid.

✓ Assessment

Content Write these chromosome numbers on the board: horse—66; pig—40; cat—38; potato—48; dog—78; corn—20. **How many chromosomes would be in a cell of each organism produced by mitosis and meiosis?** horse—66, 33; pig—40, 20; cat—38, 19; potato—48, 24; dog—78, 39; corn—20, 10 Use **PASC,** p. 101.

Section ② Assessment

1. Compare and contrast sexual and asexual reproduction.

2. What is a zygote, and how is it formed?

3. Give two examples of sex cells. Where are sex cells formed?

4. Compare what happens to chromosomes during anaphase I and anaphase II.

5. **Think Critically** Plants grown from runners and leaf cuttings have the same traits as the parent plant. Plants grown from seeds can vary from the parent plants in many ways. Suggest an explanation for why this can happen.

Skill Builder Activities

6. **Making and Using Tables** Make a table to compare mitosis and meiosis in humans. Vertical headings should include: *What Type of Cell (Body or Sex), Beginning Cell (Haploid or Diploid), Number of Cells Produced, End-Product Cell (Haploid or Diploid),* and *Number of Chromosomes in Cells Produced.* **For more help, refer to the** Science Skill Handbook.

7. **Communicating** Write a poem, song, or another memory device to help you remember the steps and outcome of meiosis. **For more help, refer to the** Science Skill Handbook.

SECTION 2 Sexual Reproduction and Meiosis **223**

Answers to Section Assessment

1. Sexual reproduction: offspring is produced when sex cells combine; asexual reproduction: genetically identical offspring produced from one parent.

2. A zygote is the cell that forms when sperm fertilizes an egg.

3. sperm cells—form in male reproductive organs; egg cells— form in female reproductive organs

4. Anaphase I—duplicated chromosome pairs separate and move to opposite ends of the cell; anaphase II—chromatids separate and move to opposite ends of the cell.

5. Plants produced by asexual reproduction are the result of mitosis, which duplicates the genetic material of the parent. Plants grown from seeds have a combination of traits from their parents, because seeds are produced by sexual reproduction.

6. See table.

7. Allow students to share their memory devices with the class.

Feature	Mitosis	Meiosis
Type of cell	Body cell	Sex cell
Beginning cell	Diploid	Diploid
Number of cells produced	Two	Four
End-product	Diploid	Haploid
Number of chromosomes	Same as original cell	Half the original cell

SECTION

3

DNA

1 Motivate

Bellringer Transparency

Display the Section Focus Transparency for Section 3. Use the accompanying Transparency Activity Master. **L2**

ELL

Tie to Prior Knowledge

Students should be familiar with template systems, such as keys and locks and peg-and-hole games. Ask for other examples. Use this knowledge to explain that DNA in the nucleus serves as a template for RNA.

As You Read

What You'll Learn

- **Identify** the parts of a DNA molecule and its structure.
- **Explain** how DNA copies itself.
- **Describe** the structure and function of each kind of RNA.

Vocabulary

DNA   RNA
gene   mutation

Why It's Important

DNA helps determine nearly everything your body is and does.

Figure 14
DNA is part of the chromosomes found in a cell's nucleus.

What is DNA?

Why was the alphabet one of the first things you learned when you started school? Letters are a code that you need to know before you learn to read. A cell also uses a code that is stored in its hereditary material. The code is a chemical called deoxyribonucleic (dee AHK sih ri boh noo klay ihk) acid, or **DNA.** It contains information for an organism's growth and function. **Figure 14** shows how DNA is stored in cells that have a nucleus. When a cell divides, the DNA code is copied and passed to the new cells. In this way, new cells receive the same coded information that was in the original cell. Every cell that has ever been formed in your body or in any other organism contains DNA.

Chemistry INTEGRATION

Discovering DNA Since the mid-1800s, scientists have known that the nuclei of cells contain large molecules called nucleic acids. By 1950, chemists had learned what the nucleic acid DNA was made of, but they didn't understand how the parts of DNA were arranged.

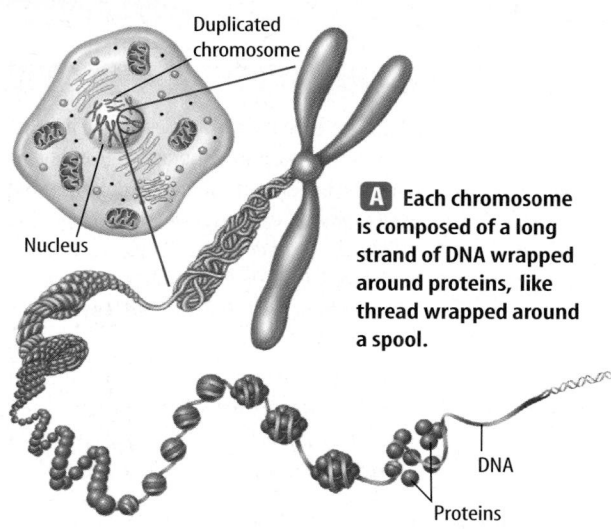

Duplicated chromosome

Nucleus

A Each chromosome is composed of a long strand of DNA wrapped around proteins, like thread wrapped around a spool.

B The large DNA molecule, called a double helix, looks like a twisted ladder. The sides of the ladder are made of smaller sugar-phosphate molecules.

DNA

Proteins

224 CHAPTER 8 Cell Reproduction

Section ✓ Assessment Planner

PORTFOLIO
Extension, p. 227
PERFORMANCE ASSESSMENT
Try at Home MiniLAB, p. 225
Skill Builder Activities, p. 229
See page 236 for more options.

CONTENT ASSESSMENT
Section, p. 229
Challenge, p. 229
Chapter, pp. 236–237

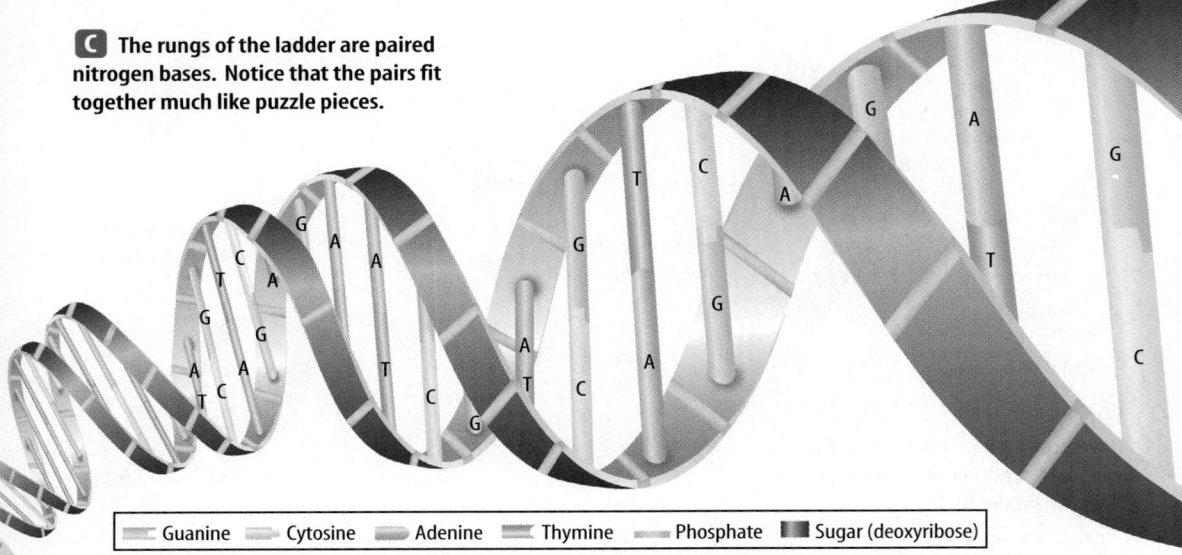

C The rungs of the ladder are paired nitrogen bases. Notice that the pairs fit together much like puzzle pieces.

Guanine — Cytosine — Adenine — Thymine — Phosphate ■ Sugar (deoxyribose)

DNA's Structure In 1952, scientist Rosalind Franklin discovered that DNA is two chains of molecules in a spiral form. By using an X-ray technique, Dr. Franklin showed that the large spiral was probably made up of two spirals. As it turned out, the structure of DNA is similar to a twisted ladder. In 1953, using the work of Franklin and others, scientists James Watson and Francis Crick made a model of a DNA molecule.

A DNA Model What does DNA look like? According to the Watson and Crick DNA model, each side of the ladder is made up of sugar-phosphate molecules. Each molecule consists of the sugar called deoxyribose (dee AHK sih ri bohs) and a phosphate group. The rungs of the ladder are made up of other molecules called nitrogen bases. Four kinds of nitrogen bases are found in DNA—adenine (AD un een), guanine (GWAHN een), cytosine (SITE uh seen), and thymine (THI meen). The bases are represented by the letters A, G, C, and T. The amount of cytosine in cells always equals the amount of guanine, and the amount of adenine always equals the amount of thymine. This led to the hypothesis that these bases occur as pairs in DNA. **Figure 14** shows that adenine always pairs with thymine, and guanine always pairs with cytosine. Like interlocking pieces of a puzzle, each base bonds only with its correct partner.

✔ **Reading Check** *What are the nitrogen base pairs in a DNA molecule?*

TRY AT HOME
Mini LAB

Modeling DNA Replication

Procedure
1. Suppose you have a segment of DNA that is six nitrogen base pairs in length. On **paper,** using the letters A, T, C, and G, write a combination of six pairs remembering that A and T are always a pair and C and G are always a pair.
2. Duplicate your segment of DNA. On paper, diagram how this happens and show the new DNA segments.

Analysis
Compare the order of bases of the original DNA to the new DNA molecules.

SECTION 3 DNA **225**

Use an Analogy

Students are probably familiar with Morse code. Morse code uses only two symbols—the dot and the dash—in combinations to represent numbers and letters of the alphabet. DNA has four symbols. The order of nitrogen bases, rather than the sequence of dots and dashes, expresses the information needed for life processes.

Discussion

How can you predict the base sequence of a second strand of DNA? by knowing the base pairing rules and the sequence of the original DNA strand

Genes

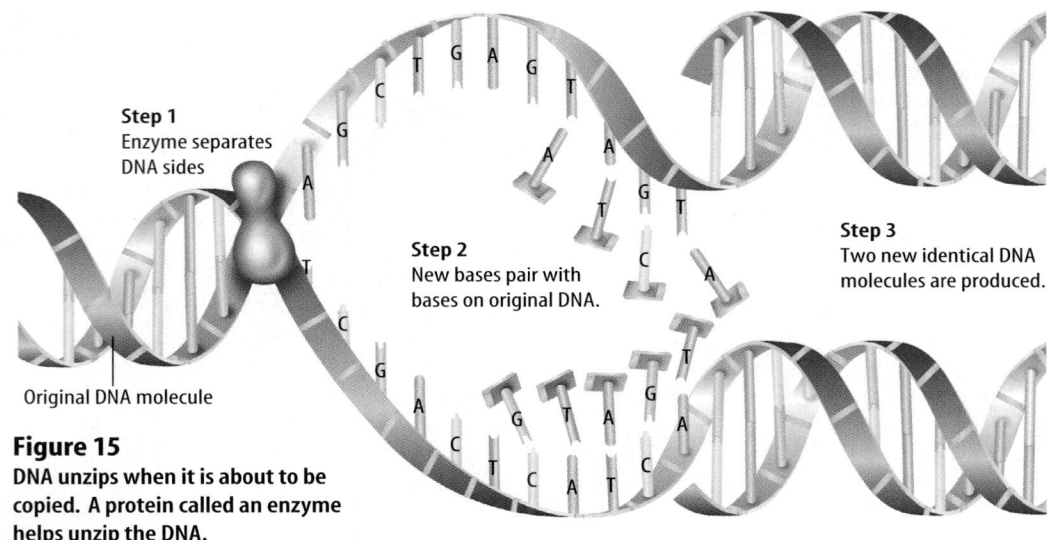

Figure 15
DNA unzips when it is about to be copied. A protein called an enzyme helps unzip the DNA.

Step 1
Enzyme separates DNA sides

Step 2
New bases pair with bases on original DNA.

Step 3
Two new identical DNA molecules are produced.

Original DNA molecule

Figure 16
This diagram shows just a few of the genes that have been identified on human chromosome 7. The bold print is the name that has been given to each gene.

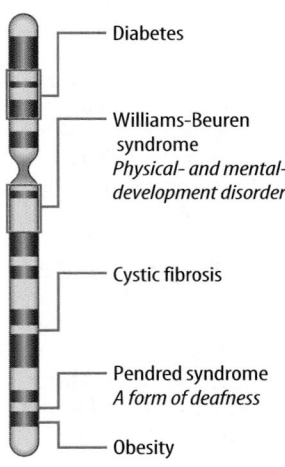

Chromosome 7

- Diabetes
- Williams-Beuren syndrome
  Physical- and mental-development disorder
- Cystic fibrosis
- Pendred syndrome
  A form of deafness
- Obesity

Copying DNA When chromosomes are duplicated before mitosis or meiosis, the amount of DNA in the nucleus is doubled. The Watson and Crick model shows how this takes place. The two sides of DNA unwind and separate. Each side then becomes a pattern on which a new side forms, as shown in **Figure 15.** The new DNA has bases that are identical to those of the original DNA and are in the same order.

Genes

Most of your characteristics, such as the color of your hair, your height, and even how things taste to you, depend on the kinds of proteins your cells make. DNA in your cells stores the instructions for making these proteins.

Proteins build cells and tissues or work as enzymes. The instructions for making a specific protein are found in a **gene** which is a section of DNA on a chromosome. As shown in **Figure 16,** each chromosome contains hundreds of genes. Proteins are made of chains of hundreds or thousands of amino acids. The gene determines the order of amino acids in a protein. Changing the order of the amino acids makes a different protein. What might occur if an important protein couldn't be made or if the wrong protein was made in your cells?

Making Proteins Genes are found in the nucleus, but proteins are made on ribosomes in cytoplasm. The codes for making proteins are carried from the nucleus to the ribosomes by another type of nucleic acid called ribonucleic acid, or **RNA.**

Text Question Answer

It could cause serious health problems.

Science Journal

DNA as Evidence Have students research the use of DNA technology in law enforcement and write a report in their Science Journals. Have them use the Internet, news magazines, reference books, and interview forensic scientists. L2 LS **Linguistic**

Curriculum Connection

Math The DNA code is written in four "letters" and the cell "reads" the code in groups of three. Have students determine how many different ways the four "letters" (A, T, G, and C) can be arranged in groups of three. There are 64 possible combinations. L2 LS **Logical-Mathematical**

Ribonucleic Acid RNA is made in the nucleus on a DNA pattern. However, RNA is different from DNA. If DNA is like a ladder, RNA is like a ladder that has all its rungs sawed in half. Compare the DNA molecule in **Figure 14** to the RNA molecule in **Figure 17**. RNA has the bases A, G, and C like DNA but has the base uracil (U) instead of thymine (T). The sugar-phosphate molecules in RNA contain the sugar ribose, not deoxyribose.

The three main kinds of RNA made from DNA in a cell's nucleus are messenger RNA (mRNA), ribosomal RNA (rRNA), and transfer RNA (tRNA). Protein production begins when mRNA moves into the cytoplasm. There, ribosomes attach to it. Ribosomes are made of rRNA. Transfer RNA molecules in the cytoplasm bring amino acids to these ribosomes. Inside the ribosomes, three nitrogen bases on the mRNA temporarily match with three nitrogen bases on the tRNA. The same thing happens for the mRNA and another tRNA molecule, as shown in **Figure 17**. The amino acids that are attached to the two tRNA molecules bond. This is the beginning of a protein. The code carried on the mRNA directs the order in which the amino acids bond. After a tRNA molecule has lost its amino acid, it can move about the cytoplasm and pick up another amino acid just like the first one. The ribosome moves along the mRNA. New tRNA molecules with amino acids match up and add amino acids to the protein molecule.

SCIENCE Online

Data Update The Human Genome Project was begun in 1990. One of its goals is to identify all of the genes on human chromosomes. To find out how the project is progressing, visit the Glencoe Science Web site at **science.glencoe.com.** Communicate to your class what you learn.

SCIENCE Online

Internet Addresses

_____

_____

_____

Explore the Glencoe Science Web site at **science.glencoe.com** to find out more about topics in this section.

Make a Model

Have students draw a cell on poster board and make a model demonstrating protein synthesis using materials such as craft sticks, beads, yarn, and so on. L2 IS **Visual-Spatial**

Activity

On the board or an overhead transparency, write the sequence for one strand of DNA. Have students copy the sequence and write the corresponding sequence for mRNA and tRNA. L2 IS **Visual-Spatial**

Extension

Have students choose one of the following DNA pioneers for a written report: Francis Crick, James Watson, Barbara McClintock, Maurice Wilkins, Martha Chase, A.D. Hershey, Rosalind Franklin. L2 IS **Linguistic** P

Visual Learning

Figure 17 Have students make an events chain concept map to outline the stages of protein synthesis. L2 IS **Visual-Spatial**

Figure 17
Cells need DNA, RNA, and amino acids to make proteins.

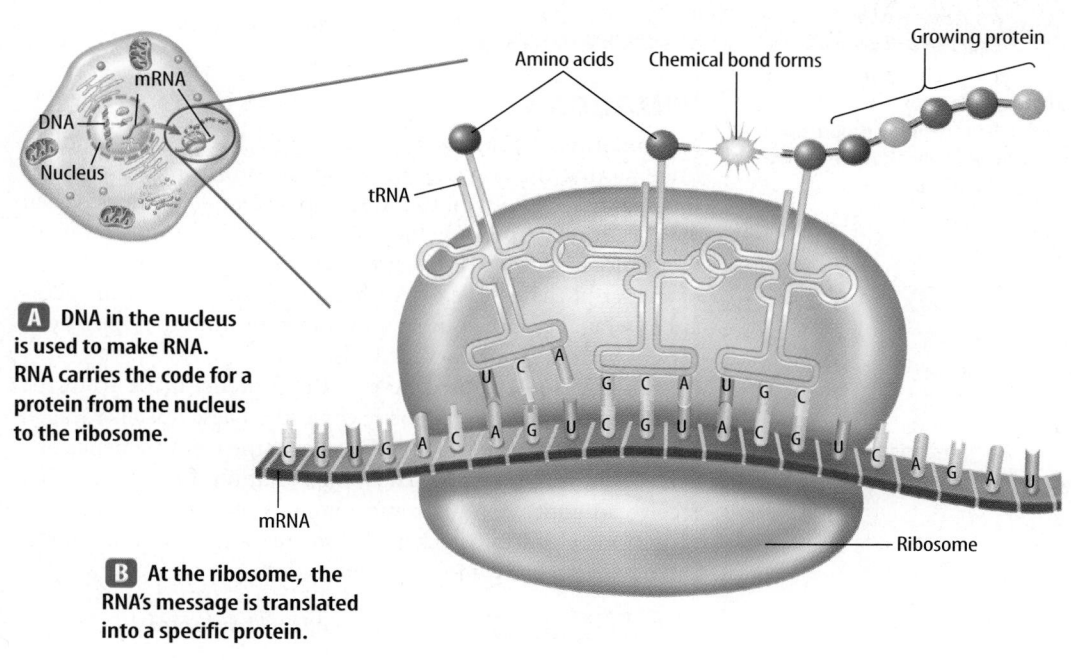

A DNA in the nucleus is used to make RNA. RNA carries the code for a protein from the nucleus to the ribosome.

B At the ribosome, the RNA's message is translated into a specific protein.

SECTION 3 DNA **227**

Resource Manager

Chapter Resources Booklet
   Enrichment, p. 30
   Directed Reading for Content Mastery,
      pp. 19, 20
Cultural Diversity, p. 19

Curriculum Connection

History Have students study the history of DNA research. Then using poster board, students should draw and label a timeline showing the events of DNA research since DNA was first removed from a cell nucleus in 1869. L2 IS **Visual-Spatial and Kinesthetic**

Mutations

Cells in the iris of the eye produce proteins needed for eye color.

Muscle cells produce proteins that help make muscles move.

Cells in the stomach produce proteins necessary to digest food.

Figure 18
Each cell in the body produces only the proteins that are necessary to do its job.

Controlling Genes You might think that because most cells in an organism have exactly the same chromosomes and the same genes, they would make the same proteins, but they don't. In many-celled organisms like you, each cell uses only some of the thousands of genes that it has to make proteins. Just as each actor uses only the lines from the script for his or her role, each cell uses only the genes that direct the making of proteins that it needs. For example, muscle proteins are made in muscle cells, as represented in **Figure 18,** but not in nerve cells.

Cells must be able to control genes by turning some genes off and turning other genes on. They do this in many different ways. Sometimes the DNA is twisted so tightly that no RNA can be made. Other times, chemicals bind to the DNA so that it cannot be used. If the incorrect proteins are produced, the organism cannot function properly.

Mutations

Sometimes mistakes happen when DNA is being copied. Imagine that the copy of the script the director gave you was missing three pages. You use your copy to learn your lines. When you begin rehearsing for the play, everyone is ready for one of the scenes except for you. What happened? You check your copy of the script against the original and find that three of the pages are missing. Because your script is different from the others, you cannot perform your part correctly.

If DNA is not copied exactly, the proteins made from the instructions might not be made correctly. These mistakes, called **mutations,** are any permanent change in the DNA sequence of a gene or chromosome of a cell. Some mutations include cells that receive an entire extra chromosome or are missing a chromosome. Outside factors such as X rays, sunlight, and some chemicals have been known to cause mutations.

✔ **Reading Check** *When are mutations likely to occur?*

Figure 19
Because of a defect on chromosome 2, the mutant fruit fly has short wings and cannot fly. *Could this defect be transferred to the mutant's offspring? Explain.*

Results of a Mutation Genes control the traits you inherit. Without correctly coded proteins, an organism can't grow, repair, or maintain itself. A change in a gene or chromosome can change the traits of an organism, as illustrated in **Figure 19.**

If the mutation occurs in a body cell, it might or might not be life threatening to the organism. However, if a mutation occurs in a sex cell, then all the cells that are formed from that sex cell will have that mutation. Mutations add variety to a species when the organism reproduces. Many mutations are harmful to organisms, often causing their death. Some mutations do not appear to have any effect on the organism, and some can even be beneficial. For example, a mutation to a plant might cause it to produce a chemical that certain insects avoid. If these insects normally eat the plant, the mutation will help the plant survive.

SCIENCE *Online*

Research Visit the Glencoe Science Web site at **science.glencoe.com** for more information about what genes are present on the chromosomes of a fruit fly. Make a poster that shows one of the chromosomes and some of the genes found on that chromosome.

Section 3 Assessment

1. How does DNA make a copy of itself?
2. How are the codes for proteins carried from the nucleus to the ribosomes?
3. A single strand of DNA has the bases AGTAAC. Using letters, show a matching DNA strand from this pattern.
4. How is tRNA used when cells build proteins?
5. **Think Critically** You begin as one cell. Compare the DNA in one of your brain cells to the DNA in one of your heart cells.

Skill Builder Activities

6. **Concept Mapping** Using a network tree concept map, show how DNA and RNA are alike and how they are different. **For more help, refer to the** Science Skill Handbook.
7. **Using a Word Processor** Use a word processor to make an outline of the events that led up to the discovery of DNA. Use library resources to find this information. **For more help, refer to the** Technology Skill Handbook.

Answers to Section Assessment

1. The two sides unwind and separate; a complementary strand is formed for each, and the resulting double-stranded DNA has one original strand and one new strand.
2. The codes are carried by mRNA from the nucleus to the ribosome.
3. TCATTG

4. The tRNA in the cytoplasm brings amino acids to the ribosomes. There, three nitrogen bases on the mRNA template match with three bases on the tRNA. The amino acids bond, and protein synthesis begins.
5. The DNA is identical.

6. Answers should be similar to the table for question 16 in the Chapter Assessment.
7. Students should be sure to include the contributions of Miescher, Griffith, Avery, Hershey, Chase, Chargraff, Wilkins, Franklin, Crick, and Watson.

Caption Answer
Figure 19 yes, if it affects reproductive cells

SCIENCE *Online*
Internet Addresses

_____
_____
_____
_____

Explore the Glencoe Science Web site at **science.glencoe.com** to find out more about topics in this section.

3 Assess

Reteach
Have students make a drawing of DNA replication and protein synthesis. L2 IS **Visual-Spatial**

Challenge
Why does the mutation of a sperm or egg cell have a potential for different results from that of a body cell? A mutation in a reproductive cell will affect offspring. A mutation in a body cell will affect only the individual.

✓ Assessment

Oral What are the three kinds of RNA and their functions? Messenger RNA, transfer RNA, and ribosomal RNA; mRNA is copied from DNA and moves from the nucleus to a ribosome; tRNA carries amino acids to ribosomes; rRNA makes up ribosomes. Use **Performance Assessment in the Science Classroom,** p. 89.

Activity

Recognize the Problem

Internet Students will use Internet sites that can be accessed through the Glencoe Science Web site. They will observe genetic traits and mutations in animals.

Non-Internet Sources Collect books describing animals and their genetic traits.

Time Required

about three days

Preparation

Internet Access the Glencoe Science Web site to run through the steps that students will follow.

Non-Internet Have students use books to select an animal and one of its traits to investigate.

Form a Hypothesis

Possible Hypotheses

Most students will select a phenotype to hypothesize about. For example, a tiger's white fur is a mutation that can become a common trait.

Activity *Use the Internet*

Mutations

Fantail Pigeon

Mutations can result in dominant or recessive genes. A recessive characteristic can appear only if an organism has two recessive genes for that characteristic. However, a dominant characteristic can appear if an organism has one or two dominant genes for that characteristic. Why do some mutations result in more common traits while others do not?

Recognize the Problem

How can a mutation become a common trait?

Form a Hypothesis

Form a hypothesis about how a mutation can become a common trait.

Goals
- ■ **Observe** traits of various animals.
- ■ **Research** how mutations become traits.
- ■ Gather data about mutations.
- ■ Make a frequency table of your findings and communicate them to other students.

Data Source

SCIENCE*Online* Go to the Glencoe Science Web site at **science.glencoe. com** for more information on common genetic traits in different animals, recessive and dominant genes, and data from other students.

White tiger

Resource Manager

Chapter Resources Booklet
  Activity Worksheet, pp. 7–8
Lab Management and Safety, p. 58

SCIENCE *Online*
Internet Addresses

_____

_____

_____

Explore the Glencoe Science Web site at **science.glencoe.com** to find out more about topics in this activity.

Test Your Hypothesis

Plan

1. **Observe** common traits in various animals, such as household pets or animals you might see in a zoo.
2. **Learn** what genes carry these traits in each animal.
3. **Research** the traits to discover which ones are results of mutations. Are all mutations dominant? Are any of these mutations beneficial?

Do

1. Make sure your teacher approves your plan before you start.
2. Visit the Glencoe Science Web site for links to different sites about mutations and genetics.
3. **Decide** if a mutation is beneficial, harmful, or neither. Record your data in your Science Journal.

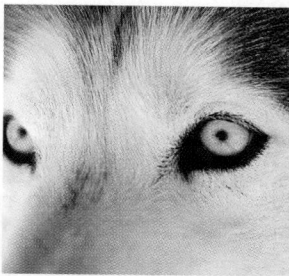

Siberian Husky's eyes

Analyze Your Data

1. **Record** in your Science Journal a list of traits that are results of mutations.
2. **Describe** an animal, such as a pet or an animal you've seen in the zoo. Point out which traits are known to be the result of a mutation.
3. Make a chart that compares recessive mutations to dominant mutations. Which are more common?
4. Share your data with other students by posting it on the Glencoe Science Web site.

Draw Conclusions

1. **Compare** your findings to those of your classmates and other data on the Glencoe Science Web site. What were some of the traits your classmates found that you did not? Which were the most common?
2. Look at your chart of mutations. Are all mutations beneficial? When might a mutation be harmful to an organism?
3. How would your data be affected if you had performed this activity when one of these common mutations first appeared? Do you think you would see more or less animals with this trait?
4. Mutations occur every day but we only see a few of them. Infer how many mutations over millions of years can lead to a new species.

Communicating Your Data

SCIENCE Online Find this *Use the Internet* activity on the Glencoe Science Web site at **science.glencoe.com**. **Post** your data in the table provided. Combine your data with that of other students and make a chart that shows all of the data.

ACTIVITY 231

Assessment

Oral Students describe mutations they researched and discuss how helpful they are to animals. Show pictures of animals with the mutation. Use **Performance Assessment in the Science Classroom**, p. 143.

Test Your Hypothesis

Teaching Strategy

Have students use animal population data to see how often that mutation is found.

Analyze Your Data

1. Answers will vary. Color can result from a mutation.
2. Answers will depend upon animals chosen.
3. Answers will vary, but dominant genes are not necessarily more common.
4. Students may need help posting data.

Draw Conclusions

1. Answers will vary. Remind students that the most common traits may be the result of mutations.
2. Answers will vary. Have students think about the mutation they are investigating and how helpful or harmful it is to the animal.
3. If you had investigated the mutation when it first appeared, you may have seen fewer animals with the trait. With the passage of time, you can determine if the mutation is beneficial.
4. Organisms with mutations may be better suited to a particular environment. These traits would be passed on to their offspring. Many mutations may lead to a new species.

Content Background

Cytogenetics is the branch of science that studies heredity both through genetics and studies of the cell. In 1956, modern human cytogenetics began, thanks to the discovery of the number of human chromosomes present in each cell of the body. As early as 1905, scientists had determined that chromosomes are found in pairs, and in 1915, Thomas Hunt Morgan discovered that genes were found on chromosomes. It was not until 1952 that Dr. Hsu's work occurred, and 1953 when Watson and Crick used Rosalind Franklin's work to determine the structure of DNA. Studies of human chromosomes and genes have progressed at an astounding rate since that time. Scientists have determined the particular chromosome that carries the gene for many human diseases and other traits.

Discussion

Explain what type of mistake the lab technician in Dr. Hsu's lab might have made while mixing the solution that caused mysterious behavior of the chromosomes. Possible answer: The technician either added too little of the solute to a set amount of water, or too much water to a set amount of solute, causing the solution to have a higher water content than the cells.

A Tangled

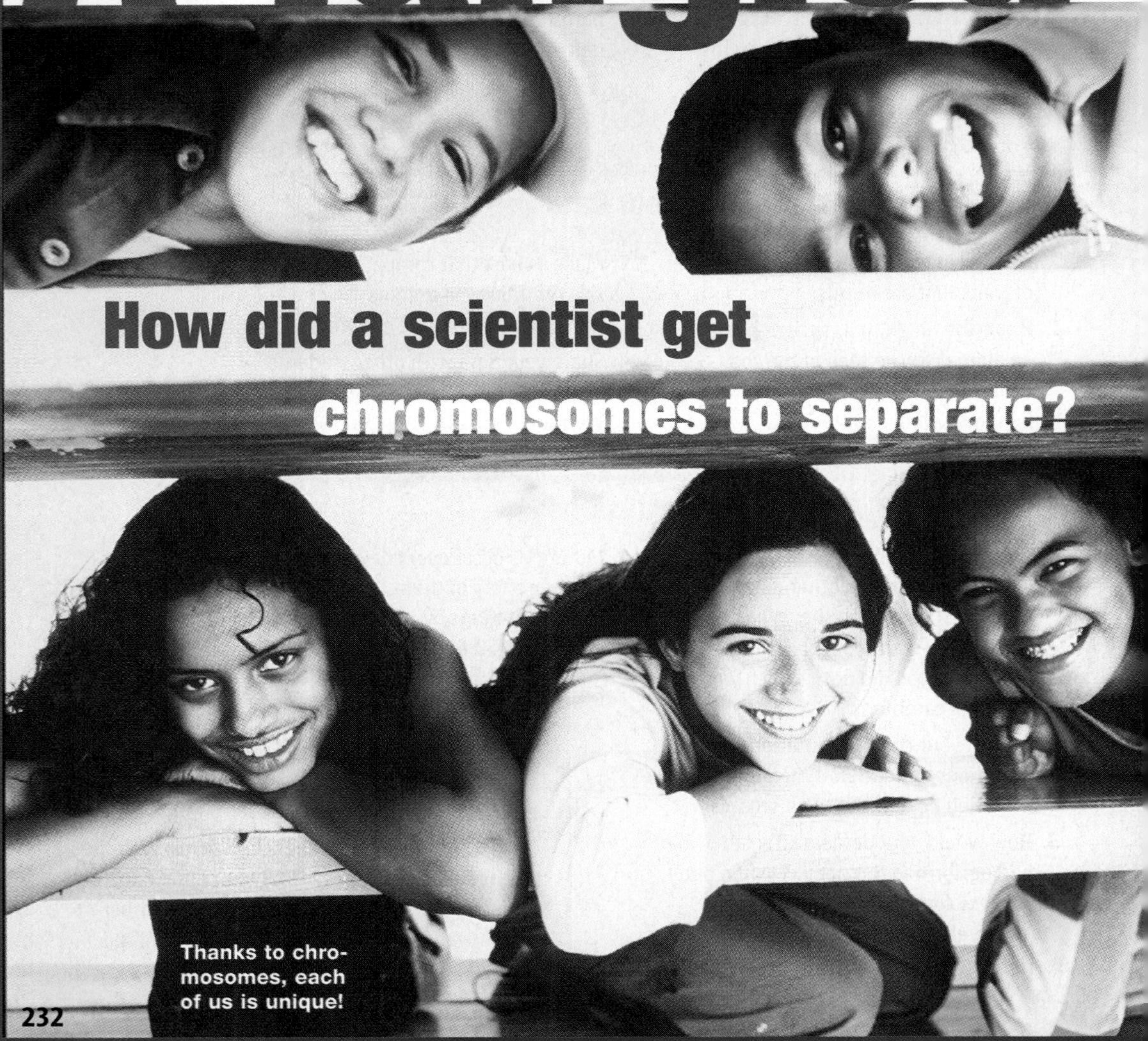

How did a scientist get chromosomes to separate?

Thanks to chromosomes, each of us is unique!

232

Resources for Teachers and Students

"Genetics and Genetic Engineering," by Lisa Yount, Facts on File, Inc., 1997.

The Big Idea, by Paul Strathern. New York: Doubleday, 1999.

The History of Genetics, by Robert Snedden. New York: Raintree Steck-Vaughn Publishers, 1995.

Viewed under a microscope, chromosomes in cells sometimes look a lot like tangled spaghetti. That's why during the early 1900s, scientists had such a hard time figuring out how many chromosomes are in each human cell.

Tale

Imagine then, how Dr. Tao-Chiuh Hsu (dow shew•SEW) must have felt when he looked into a microscope and saw "beautifully scattered chromosomes." The problem was, Hsu didn't know what he had done to separate the chromosomes into countable strands.

"I tried to study those slides and set up some more cultures to repeat the miracle," Hsu explained. "But nothing happened."

For three months, Hsu toiled in the lab, changing every variable he could think of to make the chromosomes separate again.

In April 1952, he reduced the amount of salt and increased the amount of water in the solution used to prepare the cells for study, and his efforts were finally rewarded. Hsu quickly realized that the chromosomes separated because of osmosis.

Osmosis is the movement of water molecules through cell membranes. This movement occurs in predictable ways. The water molecules move from areas with higher concentrations of water to areas with lower concentrations of water. In Hsu's case, the solution had a higher concentration of water than the cell did. So water moved from the solution into the cell and the cell swelled until it finally exploded. The chromosomes suddenly were visible as separate strands.

What made the cells swell the first time? Apparently, a lab technician had mixed the solution incorrectly. "Since nearly four months had elapsed, there was no way to trace who actually had prepared that particular [solution]," Hsu noted. "Therefore, this heroine must remain anonymous."

The Real Count

Although Hsu's view of the chromosomes was fairly clear, he mistakenly estimated the number of chromosomes in a human cell. He put the count at 48, which was the number that most scientists of the day accepted. By 1956, however, other scientists improved upon Hsu's techniques and concluded that there are 46 chromosomes in a human cell. Because chromosomes contain the genes that determine each person's characteristics, this discovery helped scientists better understand genetic diseases and disorders. Scientists also have a better idea of why every person, including you, is unique.

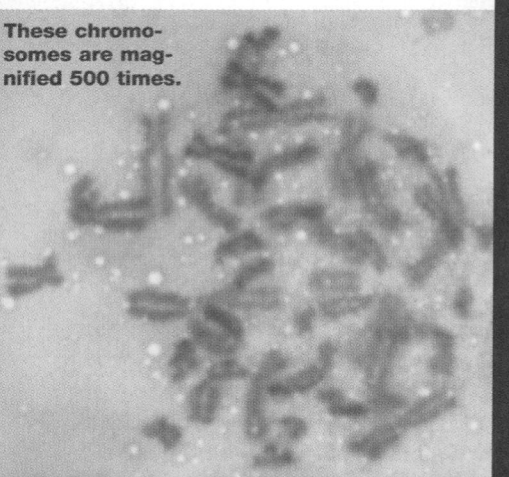

These chromosomes are magnified 500 times.

CONNECTIONS
Research Until the 1950s, scientists believed that there were 48 chromosomes in a human cell. Research the developments that led scientists to the conclusion that the human cell has 46 chromosomes. Use the Glencoe Science Web site to get started.

SCIENCE *Online*
For more information, visit science.glencoe.com

Activity
Have students work in teams to research the major discoveries in the field of genetics. Have each team display their results on a timeline made on a long piece of paper. Students should be encouraged to include discoveries from early research until present times, and to include the names of the scientists who made the discoveries.

Analyze the Event
Ask the students to brainstorm what other positive or negative effects a mistake in making a lab solution could have. Possible answers: In some cases a mistake could result in better than expected results or a discovery that would not have otherwise been made. Negative results could include work that can't be repeated, the need to re-do the entire experiment, skewed results, or potential fire or poisoning hazards. Point out to students that because Dr. Hsu's results were due to a mistake it took him months to find the cause of the good results. In general, mistakes of this type in the lab bring only negative outcomes.

CONNECTIONS
As students research the history of research on human chromosomes, have them consider the rate at which discoveries occurred then and now. Point out that the Human Genome Project has increased the knowledge of genetics at an amazing rate.

SCIENCE *Online*
Internet Addresses

_____

_____

_____

Explore the Glencoe Science Web site at **science.glencoe.com** to find out more about topics in this feature.

Reviewing Main Ideas

Preview

Students can answer the questions in their Science Journals. Discuss the answers as you go through the chapter. **LS Linguistic**

Review

Students can write their answers, then compare them with those of other students. **LS Interpersonal**

Reteach

Students can look at the illustrations and describe details that support the main ideas of the chapter. **LS Visual-Spatial**

Answers to Chapter Review

SECTION 1

4. Cell division produces new bone cells to replace damaged ones.

SECTION 2

4. 26

SECTION 3

4. It has a mutation that affects its number of wings.

Reviewing Main Ideas

Section 1 Cell Division and Mitosis

1. The life cycle of a cell has two parts—growth and development and cell division. Cell division includes mitosis and the division of the cytoplasm.

2. In mitosis, the nucleus divides to form two identical nuclei. Mitosis occurs in four continuous steps, or phases—prophase, metaphase, anaphase, and telophase.

3. Cell division in animal cells and plant cells is similar, but plant cells do not have centrioles and animal cells do not form cell walls.

4. Organisms use cell division to grow, to replace cells, and for asexual reproduction. Asexual reproduction produces organisms with DNA identical to the parent's DNA. Fission, budding, and regeneration can be used for asexual reproduction. *How would cell division help heal this broken bone?*

Section 2 Sexual Reproduction and Meiosis

1. Sexual reproduction results when a male sex cell enters the female sex cell. This event is called fertilization, and the cell that forms is called the zygote.

2. Before fertilization, meiosis occurs in the reproductive organs, producing four haploid sex cells from one diploid cell.

3. During meiosis, two divisions of the nucleus occur.

4. Meiosis ensures that offspring produced by fertilization have the same number of chromosomes as their parents. *If the diploid number of a frog is 26, how many chromosomes does this tadpole have?*

Section 3 DNA

1. DNA—the genetic material of all organisms—is a large molecule made up of two twisted strands of sugar-phosphate molecules and nitrogen bases.

2. All cells contain DNA. The section of DNA on a chromosome that directs the making of a specific protein is a gene.

3. DNA can copy itself and is the pattern from which RNA is made. Messenger RNA, ribosomal RNA, and transfer RNA are used to make proteins.

4. Sometimes changes in DNA occur. Permanent changes in DNA are called mutations. *Why does this fruit fly have four wings instead of the normal two?*

FOLDABLES Reading & Study Skills

After You Read

To help you review cell reproduction, use the Organizational Study Fold about the cell you made at the beginning of the chapter.

FOLDABLES Reading & Study Skills

After You Read

After students have read the chapter and completed the Foldable described in Before You Read, have them do the activity on the student page.

Dinah Zike

Visualizing Main Ideas

Think of four ways that organisms can use mitosis and fill out the spider diagram below.

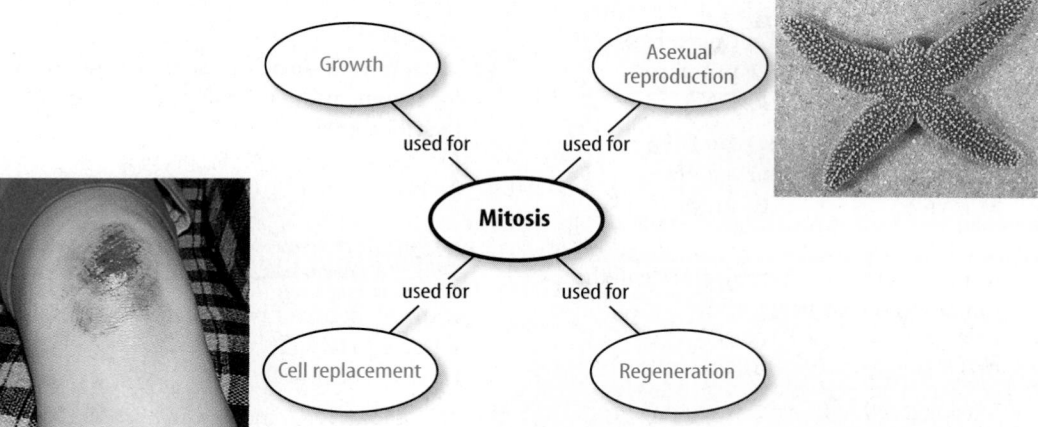

Vocabulary Review

Vocabulary Words

a. asexual reproduction
b. chromosome
c. diploid
d. DNA
e. egg
f. fertilization
g. gene
h. haploid
i. meiosis
j. mitosis
k. mutation
l. RNA
m. sexual reproduction
n. sperm
o. zygote

Study Tip

Be a teacher—organize a group of friends and instruct each person to review a section of the chapter for the group. Teaching helps you remember and understand information thoroughly.

Using Vocabulary

Replace each underlined word in the following statements with the correct vocabulary word.

1. <u>Muscle</u> and <u>skin</u> cells are sex cells.

2. <u>Digestion</u> produces two identical cells.

3. An example of a nucleic acid is <u>sugar</u>.

4. A <u>cell</u> is the code for a protein.

5. A <u>diploid</u> sperm is formed during meiosis.

6. Budding is a type of <u>meiosis</u>.

7. A <u>ribosome</u> is a structure in the nucleus that contains hereditary material.

8. <u>Respiration</u> produces four sex cells.

9. As a result of <u>fission</u>, a new organism develops that has its own unique identity.

10. An error made during the copying of DNA is called a <u>protein</u>.

CHAPTER STUDY GUIDE   235

Visualizing Main Ideas

See student page.

Vocabulary Review

Using Vocabulary

1. Egg, sperm
2. Mitosis
3. DNA or RNA
4. gene
5. haploid
6. asexual reproduction
7. chromosome
8. Meiosis
9. Fertilization, meiosis, or sexual reproduction
10. mutation

Chapter 8 Assessment

Checking Concepts

1. D
2. D
3. B
4. C
5. A
6. A
7. D
8. D
9. C
10. B

Thinking Critically

11. TAGGCAG
12. UAGGCAG
13. No; in order for a mutation to be passed to offspring, the mutation must take place in a sex cell.
14. the copying of chromosomes in interphase; the separation of the copies at anaphase; the separation of two new cells at telophase
15. This could happen if nondisjunction (failure of like chromosomes or chromatids to separate) occurs during anaphase I or II.

Checking Concepts

Choose the word or phrase that best answers the question.

1. Which of the following is a double spiral molecule with pairs of nitrogen bases?
   A) RNA
   B) amino acid
   C) protein
   D) DNA

2. What is in RNA but NOT in DNA?
   A) thymine
   B) thyroid
   C) adenine
   D) uracil

3. If a diploid tomato cell has 24 chromosomes, how many chromosomes will the tomato's sex cells have?
   A) 6
   B) 12
   C) 24
   D) 48

4. During a cell's life cycle, when do chromosomes duplicate?
   A) anaphase
   B) metaphase
   C) interphase
   D) telophase

5. When do chromatids separate during mitosis?
   A) anaphase
   B) prophase
   C) metaphase
   D) telophase

6. How many chromosomes are in the original cell compared to those in the new cells formed by cell division?
   A) the same amount
   B) half as many
   C) twice as many
   D) four times as many

7. What can budding, fission, and regeneration be used for?
   A) mutations
   B) sexual reproduction
   C) cell cycles
   D) asexual reproduction

8. What is any permanent change in a gene or a chromosome called?
   A) fission
   B) reproduction
   C) replication
   D) mutation

9. What does meiosis produce?
   A) cells with the diploid chromosome number
   B) cells with identical chromosomes
   C) sex cells
   D) a zygote

10. What type of nucleic acid carries the codes for making proteins from the nucleus to the ribosome?
   A) DNA
   B) RNA
   C) protein
   D) genes

Thinking Critically

11. If the sequence of bases on one side of DNA is ATCCGTC, what is the sequence on its other side?

12. A strand of RNA made using the DNA pattern ATCCGTC would have what base sequence? Look at **Figure 14** for a hint.

13. Will a mutation in a human skin cell be passed on to the person's offspring? Explain.

14. What occurs in mitosis that gives the new cells identical DNA?

15. How could a zygote end up with an extra chromosome?

Developing Skills

16. **Classifying** Copy and complete this table about DNA and RNA.

DNA and RNA		
	DNA	**RNA**
Number of Strands	2	1
Type of Sugar	deoxyribose	ribose
Letter Names of Bases	G, A, C, T	G, A, C, U
Where Found	nucleus	nucleus & cytoplasm

Chapter ✓Assessment Planner

Portfolio Encourage students to place in their portfolios one or two items of what they consider to be their best work. Examples include:
- Visual Learning, p. 211
- Make a Model, p. 221
- Extension, p. 227

Performance Additional performance assessments, Performance Task Assessment Lists, and rubrics for evaluating these activities can be found in Glencoe's **Performance Assessment in the Science Classroom.**

17. Concept Mapping Complete the events chain concept map of DNA synthesis.

DNA unwinds.

↓

Each side becomes a pattern.

↓

Two new molecules of DNA form.

18. Comparing and Contrasting Meiosis is two divisions of a reproductive cell's nucleus. It occurs in a continuous series of steps. Compare and contrast the steps of meiosis I to the steps of meiosis II.

19. Forming Hypotheses Make a hypothesis about the effect of an incorrect mitotic division on the new cells produced.

20. Concept Mapping Make an events chain concept map of what occurs from interphase in the parent cell to the formation of the zygote. Tell whether the chromosome's number at each stage is haploid or diploid.

Performance Assessment

21. Flash Cards Make a set of 11 flash cards with drawings of a cell that show the different stages of meiosis. Shuffle your cards and then put them in the correct order. Give them to another student in the class to try.

TECHNOLOGY

Go to the Glencoe Science Web site at **science.glencoe.com** or use the **Glencoe Science CD-ROM** for additional chapter assessment.

 **Test Practice**

A scientist studied the reproduction of human skin cells. The scientist examined several skin cells using a microscope. The table below summarizes what she learned.

Skin Cells		
Cell	**Phase of Division**	**Characteristic**
1	Anaphase	Chromosome separation
2	Telophase	Cytoplasm division
3	Prophase	Visible chromosomes
4	Metaphase	Chromosomes line up

Use the information in the table to answer the following questions.

1. What process is taking place in all of the cells?
A) cell division
B) fertilization
C) cytoplasm division
D) chromosome separation

2. Which is the correct order of the stages, from first to last, in the cell division of a skin cell?
F) 3, 4, 1, 2   **H)** 1, 2, 4, 3
G) 1, 3, 2, 4   **J)** 2, 1, 3, 4

3. Since the process described in the table produces two new identical cells, before it begins the chromosomes in the cell must _____ .
A) divide in half   **C)** duplicate
B) find a mate   **D)** disintegrate

 **Test Practice**

The Test-Taking Tip was written by The Princeton Review, the nation's leader in test preparation.
1. A
2. F
3. C

Developing Skills

16. See student page.
17. See student page.
18. Student answers should reflect the information in Section 2 and **Figure 11.**
19. Incorrect division can result in an incorrect number of chromosomes, often leading to abnormal offspring.
20. The order of events given for meiosis should reflect **Figure 11** and formation of the zygote, **Figure 10.** The cell at the beginning of meiosis is diploid. The four cells at the end of meiosis are all haploid.

Performance Assessment

21. Cards should be sequenced as shown in **Figure 11.** If interphase is included, it should come before prophase I. Use **Performance Assessment in the Science Classroom**, p. 163.

 ✓**Assessment** **Resources**

📁 **Reproducible Masters**

Chapter Resources Booklet
Chapter Review, pp. 35–36
Chapter Tests, pp. 37–40
Assessment Transparency Activity, p. 47

Glencoe Science Web site
Interactive Tutor
Chapter Quizzes

Glencoe Technology
🖱 Assessment Transparency
💿 Interactive CD-ROM Chapter Quizzes
💿 ExamView Pro Test Bank
💿 Vocabulary PuzzleMaker Software
📼 MindJogger Videoquiz

Section/Objectives	Standards		Activities/Features
	National	State/Local	
Chapter Opener	See p. 5T for a Key to Standards.		**Explore Activity:** Predict where seeds are found, p. 239 **Before You Read,** p. 239
Section 1 Introduction to Plant Reproduction 🕐 2 sessions 📦 1 block 1. **Distinguish** between the two types of plant reproduction. 2. **Describe** the two stages in a plant's life cycle.	National Content Standards: UCP3, A1, C1, C2		**MiniLAB:** Observing Asexual Reproduction, p. 241 **Science Online,** p. 242
Section 2 Seedless Reproduction 🕐 2 sessions 📦 1 block 1. **Examine** the life cycles of a moss and a fern. 2. **Explain** why spores are important to seedless plants. 3. **Identify** some special structures used by ferns for reproduction.	National Content Standards: UCP5, A1, C1, C2, C5		**Physics Integration,** p. 246 **Activity:** Comparing Seedless Plants, p. 248
Section 3 Seed Reproduction 🕐 3 sessions 📦 1.5 blocks 1. **Examine** the life cycles of typical gymnosperms and angiosperms. 2. **Describe** the structure and function of the flower. 3. **Discuss** methods of seed dispersal in seed plants.	National Content Standards: UCP5, A1, C1, C2, C5, E2, F5		**Science Online,** p. 250 **Environmental Science Integration,** p. 252 **MiniLAB:** Modeling Seed Dispersal, p. 256 **Visualizing Seed Dispersal,** p. 257 **Math Skills Activity:** Calculating the Number of Seeds That Will Germinate, p. 258 **Activity:** Germination Rate of Seeds, pp. 260–261 **Science and Society:** Genetic Engineering, pp. 262–263

NATIONAL GEOGRAPHIC

Teacher's Corner

PRODUCTS AVAILABLE FROM GLENCOE
To order call 1-800-334-7344:
CD-ROM: NGS PictureShow: *Plants: What It Means to Be Green*
Transparency Set
NGS PicturePack: *Plants: What It Means to Be Green*

PRODUCTS AVAILABLE FROM NATIONAL GEOGRAPHIC SOCIETY
To order call 1-800-368-2728:
Video: *Pollination*

INDEX TO NATIONAL GEOGRAPHIC SOCIETY
The following articles may be used for research relating to this chapter:

"Bats—The Cactus Connection," by Merlin D. Tuttle, June 1991; "Hummingbirds: The Nectar Connection," by Paul W. Ewald, Feb. 1982; "The Exquisite Orchids," by Luis Marden, April 1971; "The Wasp That Plays Cupid to a Fig," by Robert F. Sisson, Nov. 1970; "Crossroads of the Insect World," by J.W. MacSwain, Dec. 1966.

Activity Materials	Reproducible Resources	Section Assessment	Technology
Explore Activity: 2 different types of grapes, plastic knife, paper towels	**Chapter Resources Booklet** Foldables Worksheet, p. 15 Directed Reading Overview, p. 17 Note-taking Worksheets, pp. 31–33	GLENCOE'S ASSESSMENT ADVANTAGE	
MiniLAB: scissors, coleus or other houseplant, cup, water, small container of soil	**Chapter Resources Booklet** Transparency Activity, p. 42 MiniLAB, p. 3 Enrichment, p. 28 Reinforcement, p. 25 Directed Reading, p. 18 **Cultural Diversity,** p. 19	**Portfolio** Assessment, p. 243 **Performance** MiniLAB, p. 241 Skill Builder Activities, p. 243 **Content** Section Assessment, p. 243	Section Focus Transparency Interactive CD-ROM Guided Reading Audio Program
Activity: live mosses, liverworts, and ferns with gametophytes and sporophytes; hand lens; forceps; dropper; microscope slide and coverslip (2); microscope; dissecting needle; pencil with eraser	**Chapter Resources Booklet** Transparency Activity, p. 43 Enrichment, p. 29 Reinforcement, p. 26 Directed Reading, p. 18 Transparency Activity, pp. 45–46 Activity Worksheet, pp. 5–6	**Portfolio** Make a Model, p. 246 **Performance** Skill Builder Activities, p. 247 **Content** Section Assessment, p. 247	Section Focus Transparency Teaching Transparency Interactive CD-ROM Guided Reading Audio Program
MiniLAB: buttons, glue, paper, string, other common materials **Activity:** seeds, water, salt, potting soil, plant trays or plastic cups, thermometer, graduated cylinder, beakers	**Chapter Resources Booklet** Transparency Activity, p. 44 MiniLAB, p. 4 Enrichment, p. 30 Reinforcement, p. 27 Directed Reading, pp. 19, 20 Lab Activity, pp. 9–12, 13–14 Activity Worksheet, pp. 7–8 **Lab Management and Safety,** p. 38	**Portfolio** Activity, p. 251 **Performance** MiniLAB, p. 256 Math Skills Activity, p. 258 Skill Builder Activities, p. 259 **Content** Section Assessment, p. 259	Section Focus Transparency Interactive CD-ROM Guided Reading Audio Program

Need materials? Contact Science Kit at 1-800-828-7777 or www.sciencekit.com on the Internet.

End of Chapter Assessment

GLENCOE'S ASSESSMENT ADVANTAGE

Blackline Masters	Technology	Professional Series
Chapter Resources Booklet Chapter Review, pp. 35–36 Chapter Tests, pp. 37–40 **Standardized Test Practice by The Princeton Review,** pp. 47–50	MindJogger Videoquiz Interactive CD-ROM Vocabulary PuzzleMakers ExamView Pro Test Bank Interactive Lesson Planner Interactive Teacher Edition	Performance Assessment in the Science Classroom (PASC)

Transparencies

Section Focus

Section Focus Transparency 1 — It's a Jungle Out There

If you traveled from Alaska to Key West, Florida, you would expect to see many different plants. There's one place, however, where you could see more plants per square kilometer than any place else on Earth—a tropical rain forest.

1. What factors make the rainforest a good environment for plant growth and reproduction?
2. Why are the upper layers of a rainforest so dense, while the lowest levels may be almost bare?
3. Why is the destruction of rainforests an important concern?

L2

Section Focus Transparency 2 — It's Raining, It's Sporing

While flowering plants uses seeds to reproduce, mosses use a different strategy. As seen below, one part of moss reproduction involves releasing spores into the environment. Each spore is capable of growing into a new plant.

1. Judging from the picture, how are moss spores dispersed?
2. Why does the moss produce so many spores?

L2

Section Focus Transparency 3 — A Bee's-Eye View

A beautiful bright yellow flower you might notice in a field looks different to a bee. Bees can see ultraviolet light. To them the flower includes markings not visible to the human eye.

1. How do the ultraviolet markings help the bee?
2. How do the bee's actions benefit the flower?

L2

This is a representation of key blackline masters available in the Teacher Classroom Resources. See Resource Manager boxes within the chapter for additional information.

Key to Teaching Strategies

The following designations will help you decide which activities are appropriate for your students.

L1 Level 1 activities should be appropriate for students with learning difficulties.

L2 Level 2 activities should be within the ability range of all students.

L3 Level 3 activities are designed for above-average students.

ELL ELL activities should be within the ability range of English Language Learners.

COOP LEARN Cooperative Learning activities are designed for small group work.

LS Multiple Learning Styles logos, as described on page 22T, are used throughout to indicate strategies that address different learning styles.

P These strategies represent student products that can be placed into a best-work portfolio.

Assessment

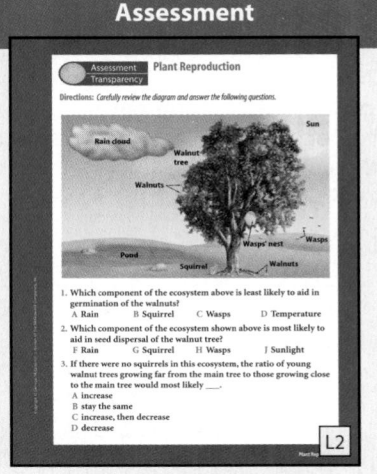

Assessment Transparency — Plant Reproduction

Directions: Carefully review the diagram and answer the following questions.

1. Which component of the ecosystem above is least likely to aid in germination of the walnuts?
   A Rain   B Squirrel   C Wasps   D Temperature
2. Which component of the ecosystem shown above is most likely to aid in seed dispersal of the walnut tree?
   F Rain   G Squirrel   H Wasps   J Sunlight
3. If there were no squirrels in this ecosystem, the ratio of young walnut trees growing far from the main tree to those growing close to the main tree would most likely ___.
   A increase
   B stay the same
   C increase, then decrease
   D decrease

L2

Teaching

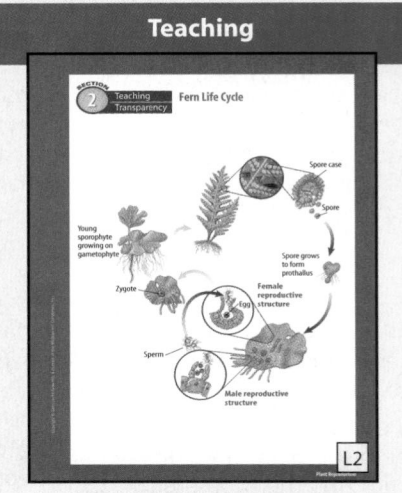

Teaching Transparency 2 — Fern Life Cycle

L2

Hands-on Activities

Activity Worksheets

Laboratory Activities

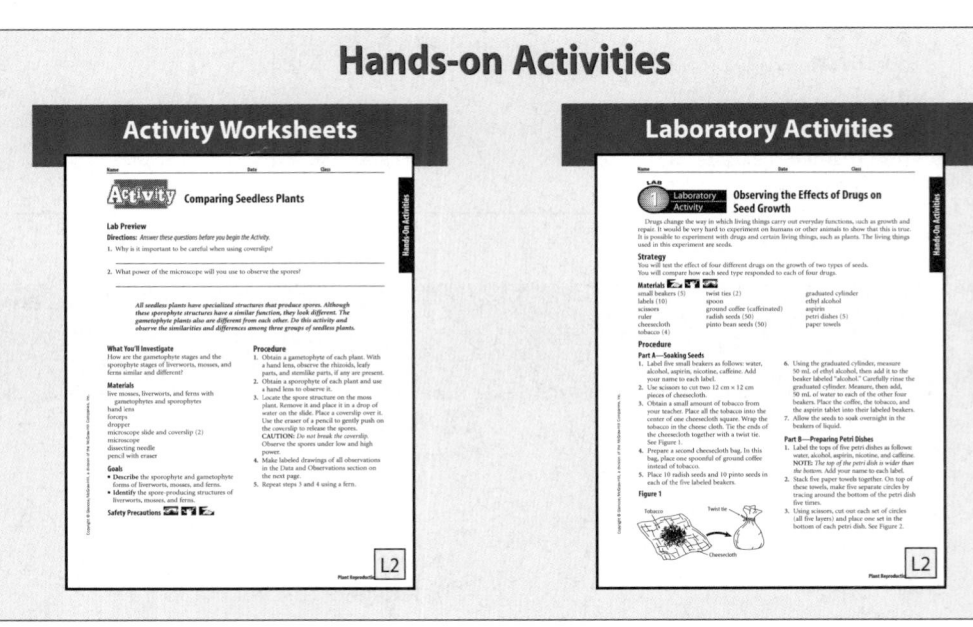

Activity — Comparing Seedless Plants

L2

Laboratory Activity 1 — Observing the Effects of Drugs on Seed Growth

L2

Meeting Different Ability Levels

Content Outline

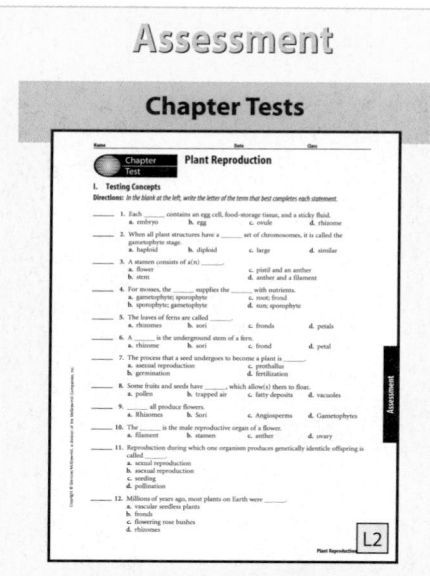

L2

Reinforcement

L2

Directed Reading

L1

Assessment

Chapter Tests

L2

Enrichment

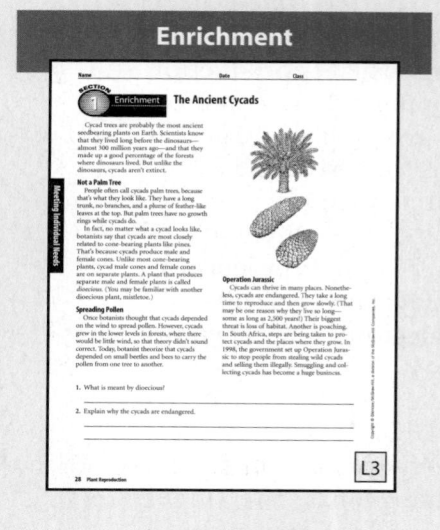

L3

Spanish Directed Reading

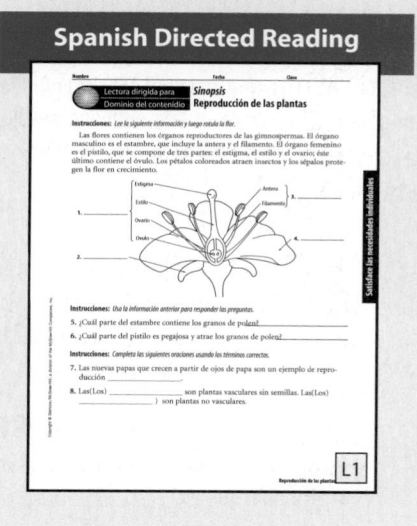

L1

Test Practice Workbook

Standardized Test Practice
Teacher Edition

Glencoe
Science

LEVEL GREEN

L2

Chapter Review

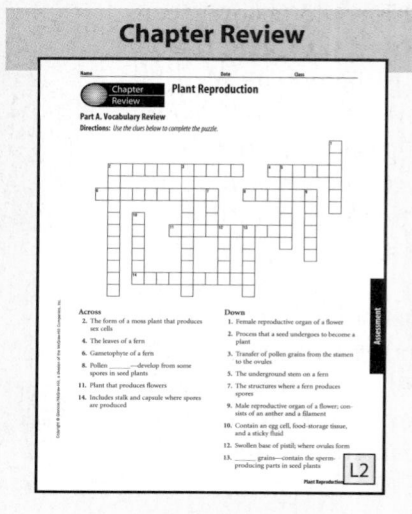

L2

Science Content Background

SECTION 1

Introduction to Plant Reproduction

Types of Reproduction

Asexual reproduction is a common method of reproduction in plants. Asexual reproduction works best in appropriate environments that change little over long periods of time. The advantage of asexual reproduction is the ability to produce large numbers of offspring that have the same genetic makeup as the parent plant. Such asexual reproduction is cloning. Many commercially grown plants, such as orchids and African violets, are routinely cloned.

The genetic diversity of plants is increased through sexual reproduction. Sexual reproduction allows plants to evolve and invade new habitats or adapt when the environment changes.

> ### Fun Fact
>
> Of the approximate 230,000 known species of flowering plants, the *Wolffia augusta* is one of the tiniest. One will easily fit through the eye of an ordinary sewing needle. Five thousand will easily fit in a sewing thimble.

Haploid and Diploid Stages

In all plant life cycles, there are haploid and diploid stages. In some plants, the stages are separate and unique and referred to as an alternation of generations. Alternation of generations evolved with the ancestors of the plant kingdom, the ancient Chlorophyta, or green algae. A diploid sporophyte ($2n$) generation alternates with a haploid gametophyte generation (n). *Sporophyte* means "spore-producing" and *gametophyte* means "gamete-producing." These terms indicate the reproductive function of the plant. In some plants these are distinct organisms, but in others they are part of the larger organism.

Meiosis occurs in specialized cells of the sporophyte, the spore mother cells, and results in the production of spores. Spores produce the gametophyte by mitosis. In time, gametophytes produce haploid gametes. A male and a female gamete unite to form a diploid zygote, the first cell in the multicellular sporophyte.

SECTION 2

Seedless Reproduction

Seedless Plants

In mosses, liverworts, and hornworts, the gametophyte is the familiar plant that makes its own food by photosynthesis. The sporophyte generation in mosses is found at the tip of the gametophyte and consists of a stalk with a capsule in which spores are produced by meiosis.

Fern spores germinate into a filamentous

D. Cavagnaro/DRK Photo

plant that eventually grows into an inconspicuous heart-shaped gametophyte called a prothallus. The gameto-phyte is independent and carries on photosynthesis. Fern sporophytes have leaves called fronds. Fronds produce spores in specialized packets called sori (singular, *sorus*) that are often misidentified as a plant disease.

SECTION 3

Seed Reproduction

Gymnosperm Reproduction

Gymnosperms are unique among seed plants because the ovules of their seeds are not completely enclosed by tissue produced by the sporophyte.

D. Cavagnaro/DRK Photo

The sporophytes, or $2n$ generations of gymnosperms, are familiar trees and shrubs like pines, junipers, and spruces. Ovulate cones and pollen-bearing cones are produced on separate stems. The female cones of gymnosperms vary from the familiar woody cones to fleshy, berry-like cones. Berrylike cones are often colorful, such as the red ones on yews and the bluish ones on junipers. Many gymnosperm cones complete their life cycle in one year, but some take two or three years for maturation.

All but about 35,000 of the 235,000 species of plants today are characterized by their production of seeds.

Germination

Seeds are efficient units of dispersal for plants, and many have elaborate adaptations for moving away from the parent plant. Germination, the growth of a plant from a seed, is affected by many factors, such as temperature, amount of light, presence of moisture and presence of oxygen. Some seeds lay dormant, waiting for the appropriate set of conditions for germination.

Fun Fact

The number of seeds per fruit ranges from one—in fruits such as peaches and plums—to several hundred in pumpkins and other squashes. It has been reported that a tropical plant, *Rafflesia keithii*, produced a fruit with 273,000 seeds.

SCIENCE Online

For additional content background on this topic, go to the Glencoe Science Web site at science.glencoe.com.

Plant Reproduction

Chapter Vocabulary

spore, p. 243
gametophyte stage, p. 243
sporophyte stage, p. 243
frond, p. 246
rhizome, p. 246
sori, p. 246
prothallus, p. 246
pollen grain, p. 249
pollination, p. 249
ovule, p. 250
stamen, p. 252
pistil, p. 252
ovary, p. 252
germination, p. 258

What do you think?

Science Journal The photo shows a flower of grass. This is not the typical showy flower most students are familiar with, but many plants have flowers of this type.

Plant Reproduction

Saplings and other plants grow among the remains of trees that were destroyed by fire. Where did these new plants come from? Did they grow from seeds that survived the fire? Perhaps they grew from plant roots and stems that survived underground. In either case, these plants are the result of plant reproduction. In this chapter, you will learn how different groups of plants reproduce and how plants can be dispersed from place to place.

What do you think?

Science Journal Look at the picture below with a classmate. Discuss what this might be. Here's a hint: *In many plants these are colorful and have pleasant aromas.* Write your answer or best guess in your Science Journal.

238

Theme Connection

Systems and Interactions This chapter emphasizes the mechanisms and systems of reproduction in plants.

You might know that most plants grow from seeds. Seeds are usually found in the fruits of plants. When you eat watermelon, it can contain many small seeds. Do all fruits contain seeds? Do this activity to find out.

Predict where seeds are found

1. Obtain two grapes from your teacher. Each grape should be from a different plant.
2. Split each grape in half and examine the insides of each grape. **WARNING:** *Do not eat the grapes.*

Observe

Were seeds found in both grapes? Hypothesize how new grape plants could be grown if no seeds are produced. In your Science Journal list three other fruits you know of that do not contain seeds.

Before You Read

Making a Venn Diagram Study Fold Make the following Foldable to compare and contrast sexual and asexual characteristics of a plant.

1. Place a sheet of paper in the front of you so the long side is at the top. Fold the paper in half from top to bottom.

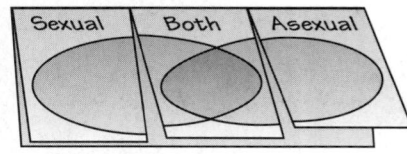

2. Fold both sides in. Unfold the paper so three sections show.
3. Through the top thickness of the paper, cut along each of the fold lines to the top fold, forming three tabs. Label each tab *Sexual, Both,* and *Asexual* as shown.
4. Before you read the chapter, draw circles across the front of the page, as shown.
5. As you read the chapter write information about sexual and asexual reproduction under the left and right tabs.

239

SECTION

Introduction to Plant Reproduction

1 Motivate

Bellringer Transparency

Display the Section Focus Transparency for Section 1. Use the accompanying Transparency Activity Master. L2 ELL

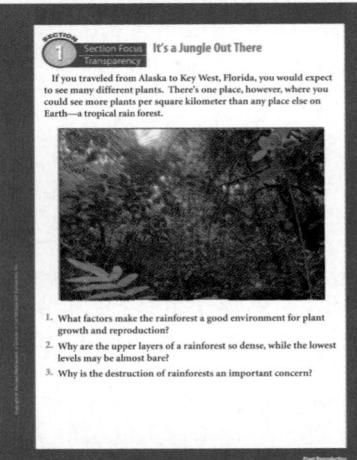

Tie to Prior Knowledge

Ask students if they have ever seen a plant being rooted from a leaf cutting. Students may have seen an African violet or similar plant being propagated in this way. Explain that what they have observed is a form of asexual reproduction and that this is one way some plants reproduce.

Introduction to Plant Reproduction

As You Read

What You'll Learn
- **Distinguish** between the two types of plant reproduction.
- **Describe** the two stages in a plant's life cycle.

Vocabulary
spore
gametophyte stage
sporophyte stage

Why It's Important
You can grow new plants without using seeds.

Types of Reproduction

Do people and plants have anything in common? You don't have leaves or roots, and a plant doesn't have a heart or a brain. Despite these differences, you are alike in many ways—you need water, oxygen, energy, and food to grow. Like humans, plants also can reproduce and make similar copies of themselves. Although humans have only one type of reproduction, most plants can reproduce in two different ways, as shown in **Figure 1.**

Sexual reproduction in plants and animals requires the production of sex cells—usually called sperm and eggs—in reproductive organs. The offspring produced by sexual reproduction are genetically different from either parent organism.

A second type of reproduction is called asexual reproduction. This type of reproduction does not require the production of sex cells. During asexual reproduction, one organism produces offspring that are genetically identical to it. Most plants have this type of reproduction, but humans and most other animals don't.

Figure 1
Many plants reproduce sexually with flowers that contain male and female parts.

A In crocus flowers, bees and other insects help get the sperm to the egg.

B Other plants can reproduce asexually. A cutting from this impatiens plant can be placed in water and will grow new roots. This new plant can then be planted in soil.

240 CHAPTER 9 Plant Reproduction

Section ✓*Assessment* Planner

PORTFOLIO
Assessment, p. 243
PERFORMANCE ASSESSMENT
Try at Home MiniLAB, p. 241
Skill Builder Activities, p. 243
See page 266 for more options.

CONTENT ASSESSMENT
Section, p. 243
Challenge, p. 243
Chapter, pp. 266–267

Figure 2
Asexual reproduction in plants takes many forms.

A The eyes on these potatoes have begun to sprout. If a potato is cut into pieces, each piece that contains an eye can be planted and will grow into a new potato plant.

B The grass plants spread by reproducing asexually.

Asexual Plant Reproduction Do you like to eat oranges and grapes that have seeds, or do you like seedless fruit? If these plants do not produce seeds, how do growers get new plants? Growers can produce new plants by asexual reproduction because many plant cells have the ability to grow into a variety of cell types. New plants can be grown from just a few cells in the laboratory. Under the right conditions, an entire plant can grow from one leaf or just a portion of the stem or root. When growers use these methods to start new plants, they must make sure that the leaf, stem, or root cuttings have plenty of water and anything else that they need to survive.

Asexual reproduction has been used to produce plants for centuries. The white potatoes shown in **Figure 2A** were probably produced asexually. Many plants, such as lawn grasses shown in **Figure 2B**, can spread and cover wide areas because their stems grow underground and produce new grass plants asexually along the length of the stem.

Sexual Plant Reproduction Although plants and animals have sexual reproduction, there are differences in the way that it occurs. An important event in sexual reproduction is fertilization. Fertilization occurs when a sperm and egg combine to produce the first cell of the new organism, the zygote. How do the sperm and egg get together in plants? In some plants, water or wind help bring the sperm to the egg. For other plants, animals such as insects help bring the egg and sperm together.

 **Reading Check** *How does fertilization occur in plants?*

Mini LAB

Observing Asexual Reproduction

Procedure
1. Using a pair of **scissors**, cut a stem with at least two pairs of leaves from a **coleus or another houseplant.**
2. Carefully remove the bottom pair of leaves.
3. Place the cut end of the stem into a **cup that is half-filled with water** for two weeks. Wash your hands.
4. Remove the new plant from the water and plant it in a small **container** of **soil.**

Analysis
1. Draw and label your results in your **Science Journal.**
2. Predict how the new plant and the plant from which it was taken are genetically related.

SECTION 1 Introduction to Plant Reproduction **241**

Teacher FYI

Tissue culture allows many plants to be grown quickly from one plant with a desirable trait. This method also produces disease-free plants. Plants routinely cloned using tissue culture include orchids, tobacco, chrysanthemums, potatoes, strawberries, asparagus, and gladioli.

---

2 Teach

Types of Reproduction

Mini LAB

Purpose Students will observe the asexual reproduction of a houseplant. L2 ELL
IS Kinesthetic
Materials coleus plant, glass of water, scissors, container of soil
Teaching Strategy Tell students to choose a young stem rather than a tougher, older one.
Analysis
1. Drawings should show the growth of a new plant in the soil. Plants should have roots, stems, and leaves.
2. The plants are genetically identical.

✓ Assessment

Performance Have students repeat the activity with a different plant that can be propagated from a leaf or a root. Use **PASC**, p. 97.

Quick Demo

Show students a strawberry plant with runners. Explain that runners are one means of reproducing asexually.

Extension

If there is a university nearby, arrange a field trip to see a tissue culture laboratory, or have individual students arrange such a visit and report their observations to the class.

✓ Reading Check

Answer Wind, water, or animals may carry the sperm to the egg in plants.

Types of Reproduction, continued

Extension

Have students research cloning as it relates to asexual reproduction of plants and write about how cloning is an important activity in tree farming.

SCIENCE *Online*
Internet Addresses

_____

_____

_____

_____

Explore the Glencoe Science Web site at **science.glencoe.com** to find out more about topics in this section.

Plant Life Cycles

Use Science Words

Word Meaning Have students research the meanings of the prefixes and suffixes that make up the words *sporophyte* and *gametophyte*. *Spor-* is derived from a Greek word meaning "seed;" *-phyte* from a Greek word meaning "plant;" *gamet-* from a Greek word meaning "to marry." Thus the gametophytes produce sex cells that will "marry" to form the sporophyte, or seed-producing stage in a plant's life cycle. L2 IN **Linguistic**

Figure 3
Some plants can fertilize themselves. Others require two different plants before fertilization can occur.

A Flowers of pea plants contain male and female structures, and each flower can fertilize itself.

B These holly flowers contain only male reproductive structures, so they can't fertilize themselves.

C Compare the flowers of this female holly plant to those of the male plant.

SCIENCE *Online*

Research Visit the Glencoe Science Web site at **science.glencoe.com** to find out more about male and female plants. In your Science Journal, list four plants that have male and female reproductive structures on separate plants.

Reproductive Organs A plant's female reproductive organs produce eggs and male reproductive organs produce sperm. Depending on the species, these reproductive organs can be on the same plant or on separate plants, as shown in **Figure 3.** If a plant has both organs, it usually can reproduce by itself. However, some plants that have both sex organs still must exchange sex cells with other plants of the same type to reproduce.

In some plant species, the male and female reproductive organs are on separate plants. For example, holly plants are either female or male. For fertilization to occur, holly plants with flowers that have different sex organs must be near each other. In that case, after the eggs in female holly flowers are fertilized, berries can form.

Another difference between you and a plant is how and when plants produce sperm and eggs. You will begin to understand this difference as you examine the life cycle of a plant.

Plant Life Cycles

All organisms have life cycles. Your life cycle started when a sperm and an egg came together to produce the zygote that would grow and develop into the person you are today. A plant also has a life cycle. It can start when an egg and a sperm come together, eventually producing a mature plant.

Resource Manager

Chapter Resources Booklet
  Note-taking Worksheets, pp. 31–33
  Enrichment, p. 28
  Reinforcement, p. 25
Cultural Diversity, p. 19

Visual Learning

Figure 4 Plant life cycles can be very confusing. Help students break down the words *haploid* and *diploid* and relate them to the numbers of chromosomes contained in the cells of each plant stage. haploid—half the number of chromosomes; diploid—full number of chromosomes

Two Stages During your life cycle, all structures in your body are formed by cell division and made up of diploid cells—cells with a full set of chromosomes. However, sex cells form by meiosis and are haploid—they have half a set of chromosomes.

Plants have a two-stage life cycle, as shown in **Figure 4.** The two stages are the gametophyte (guh MEE tuh fite) stage and the sporophyte (SPOHR uh fite) stage.

Gametophyte Stage When cells in reproductive organs undergo meiosis and produce haploid cells called **spores,** the **gametophyte stage** begins. Some plants release spores into their surroundings. Spores divide by cell division to form plant structures or an entire new plant. The cells in these structures or plants are haploid. Some of these cells undergo cell division and form sex cells.

Sporophyte Stage Fertilization—the joining of haploid sex cells—begins the **sporophyte stage.** Cells formed in this stage have the diploid number of chromosomes. Meiosis occurs in some of these plant structures to form spores, and the cycle begins again.

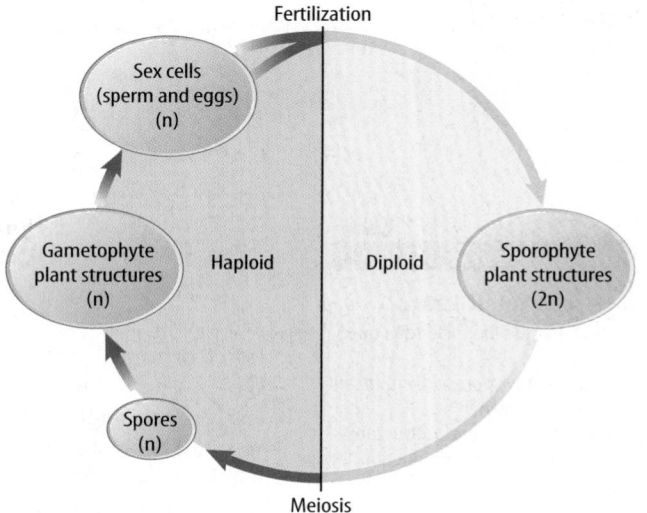

Figure 4
Plants produce diploid and haploid plant structures.

Section 1 Assessment

1. Name two types of plant reproduction.
2. Compare and contrast the gametophyte stage and the sporophyte stage.
3. Describe how plants can be grown using asexual reproduction.
4. Explain how sexual reproduction is different in plants and animals.
5. **Think Critically** You see a plant that you like and want to grow an identical one. What type of plant reproduction would you use? Why?

Skill Builder Activities

6. **Drawing Conclusions** You use a microscope to observe the nuclei of several cells from a plant. Each one has only half the number of chromosomes you would expect. What do you conclude about this stage of its life cycle? **For more help, refer to the** Science Skill Handbook.
7. **Communicating** In your Science Journal write your own analogy about the diploid and haploid stages of a plant life cycle. **For more help, refer to the** Science Skill Handbook.

3 Assess

Reteach
Have students work in small groups to prepare three multiple-choice questions about the general types of plant reproduction. Have groups take turns asking and answering each other's questions. COOP LEARN

Challenge
Work with students to make a list of the advantages and disadvantages of asexual reproduction. When the list has been compiled, have students debate this statement: Asexual reproduction has no advantages over sexual reproduction. Advantages—asexual reproduction is usually faster than sexual reproduction; it takes only one plant, so there is no need to find a "mate"; and in a stable environment, lack of genetic variation may be advantageous. Disadvantages—asexual reproduction does not provide genetic diversity because there is no genetic recombination.

✓ Assessment

Portfolio Have students write a poem that includes information about sexual and asexual reproduction. Use **Performance Assessment in the Science Classroom,** p. 151. P

Answers to Section Assessment

1. asexual and sexual
2. The gametophyte stage is haploid. The sporophyte stage is diploid.
3. Some plants grow asexually from leaves, stems, roots, runners, or other plant parts.
4. In animals, only sex cells are haploid. In plants, all the cells in the gametophyte stage of the life cycle are haploid.
5. A type of asexual reproduction (stem, leaf, or tip cutting); plants produced through these methods are identical to the parent plant.
6. Based on the number of chromosomes, students should conclude that it is in the haploid stage.
7. Answers will vary. Analogies should have alternating parts such as up and down, or in and out, for example.

SECTION

2

Seedless Reproduction

Bellringer Transparency

 Display the Section Focus Transparency for Section 2. Use the accompanying Transparency Activity Master. L2 ELL

Tie to Prior Knowledge

Ask students to tell where they have seen mosses growing in nature. Most will indicate that they have seen these plants growing in damp places in wooded areas. Tell students that in this section, they will learn why these plants need to be in damp areas.

As You Read

What You'll Learn
- **Examine** the life cycles of a moss and a fern.
- **Explain** why spores are important to seedless plants.
- **Identify** some special structures used by ferns for reproduction.

Vocabulary
frond   sori
rhizome   prothallus

Why It's Important
Seedless plants have adaptations for reproduction on land.

Figure 5
Spores come in a variety of shapes. All spores are small and have a waterproof coating. Some, like the horsetail spores, have winglike structures that uncoil and allow them to be blown easily by the wind.

The Importance of Spores

If you want to grow plants like ferns and moss plants, you can't go to a garden store and buy a package of seeds—they don't produce seeds. You could, however, grow them from spores. These plants produce haploid spores at the end of their sporophyte stage in structures called spore cases. When the spore case breaks open, the spores are released and spread by wind or water. The spores, shown in **Figure 5,** can grow into plants that will produce sex cells.

Seedless plants include all nonvascular plants and some vascular plants. Nonvascular plants do not have structures that transport water and substances throughout the plant. Instead, water and substances simply move from cell to cell. Vascular plants have tubelike cells that transport water and substances throughout the plant.

Nonvascular Seedless Plants

If you walked in a damp, shaded forest, you probably would see mosses covering the ground or growing on a log. Mosses, liverworts, and hornworts are all nonvascular plants.

The sporophyte stage of most nonvascular plants is so small that it can be easily overlooked. Moss plants have a life cycle that is typical of how sexual reproduction occurs in this plant group.

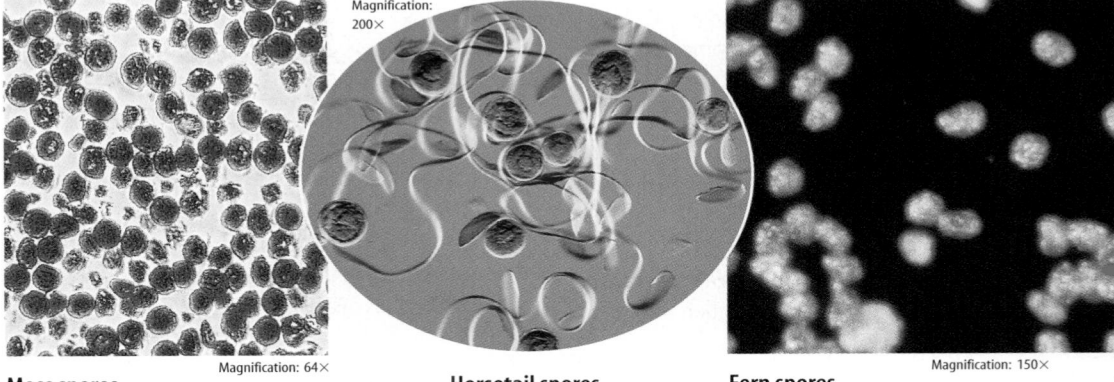

Magnification: 200×

Moss spores
Magnification: 64×

Horsetail spores

Fern spores
Magnification: 150×

244   CHAPTER 9 Plant Reproduction

Section ✓*Assessment* Planner

PORTFOLIO
Make a Model, p. 246
PERFORMANCE ASSESSMENT
Skill Builder Activities, p. 247
See page 266 for more options.

CONTENT ASSESSMENT
Section, p. 247
Challenge, p. 247
Chapter, pp. 266–267

The Moss Life Cycle You recognize mosses as green, low-growing masses of plants. This is the gametophyte stage, which produces the sex cells. But the next time you see some moss growing, get down and look at it closely. If you see any brownish stalks growing up from the tip of the gametophyte plants, you are looking at the sporophyte stage. The sporophyte stage does not carry on photosynthesis. It depends on the gametophyte for nutrients and water. On the tip of the stalk is a tiny capsule. Inside the capsule millions of spores have been produced. When environmental conditions are just right, the capsule opens and the spores either fall to the ground or are blown away by the wind. New moss gametophytes can grow from each spore and the cycle begins again, as shown in **Figure 6.**

Figure 6
The life cycle of a moss alternates between gametophyte and sporophyte stages. *What is produced by the gametophyte stage?*

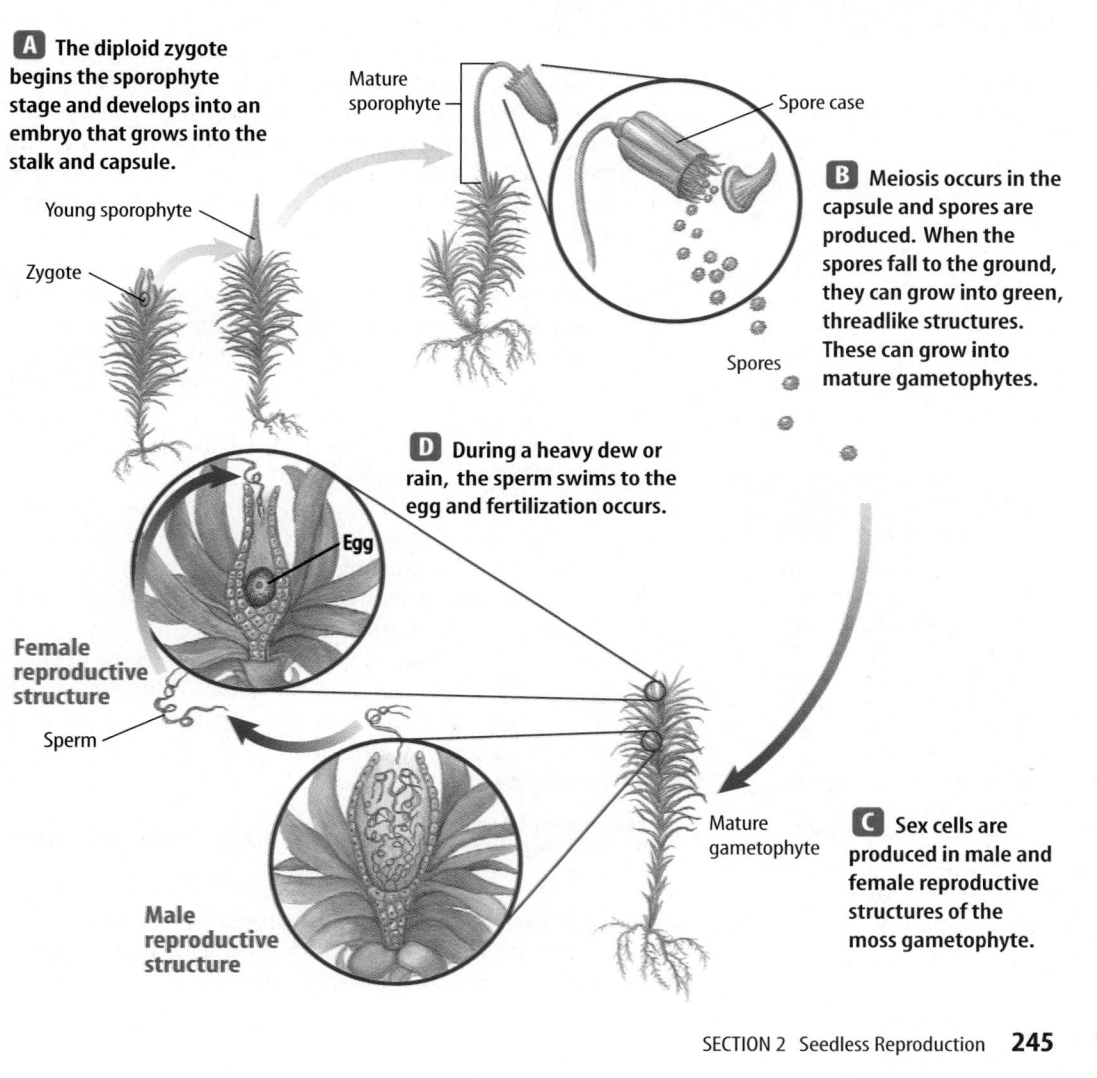

A The diploid zygote begins the sporophyte stage and develops into an embryo that grows into the stalk and capsule.

Mature sporophyte

Spore case

Young sporophyte

Zygote

B Meiosis occurs in the capsule and spores are produced. When the spores fall to the ground, they can grow into green, threadlike structures. These can grow into mature gametophytes.

Spores

D During a heavy dew or rain, the sperm swims to the egg and fertilization occurs.

Egg

Female reproductive structure

Sperm

Male reproductive structure

Mature gametophyte

C Sex cells are produced in male and female reproductive structures of the moss gametophyte.

SECTION 2 Seedless Reproduction **245**

Curriculum Connection

History Have students find out how humans have used moss gametophytes historically. Have students make posters to present their findings. Mosses were once used as bandages during wars because of their absorbency and antiseptic properties.

Resource Manager

Chapter Resources Booklet
Transparency Activity, p. 43
Directed Reading for Content Mastery, p. 18
Enrichment, p. 29

2 Teach

Nonvascular Seedless Plants

Discussion

Explain that a single moss capsule may release 50 million spores. Ask students what advantages the production of so many spores provides to moss plants. It increases the likelihood that some spores will find a suitable environment and develop into new moss plants, thus aiding in the survival of the species.

Caption Answer

Figure 6 sex cells (eggs and sperm)

Activity

Have the class make a terrarium that includes mosses. Have students observe these plants as they grow, mature, and produce spores from their capsules.

Visual Learning

Figure 6 Have students trace the different stages in the diagram, following the arrows. Again emphasize that the gametophyte produces sex cells (egg and sperm) that unite to form the sporophyte, which produces spores. Review with students the number of chromosomes contained by cells at each stage. Then give student pairs drawings of the stages of moss life cycle on 3 × 5 cards. Have students sequence and label the drawings.

Teacher FYI

Some mosses possess strands of vascular tissue. This tissue is not arranged or differentiated to the extent found in other vascular plants.

Nonvascular Seedless Plants, continued

Visual Learning

Figure 7 Ask students to explain why the balls of cells that grow in the cups shown in the picture are a form of asexual reproduction. These balls of cells do not need to be fertilized in order to grow into a new plant. Thus, they are a form of asexual reproduction.

Make a Model

Have students make drawings, flowcharts, or other models to show the stages of a moss's or fern's life cycle. Their models should include both gametophyte and sporophyte generations. P

Vascular Seedless Plants

Discussion

Ask students to hypothesize how much time a plant spends in each phase of its life cycle. Allow them to explain their answers. Nonvascular plants spend most of their life cycle in the gametophyte phase. Most vascular plants spend most of their life cycle in the sporophyte stage.

Physics
INTEGRATION

Possible answers: machines that toss tennis balls and skeet throwers

Reading Check

Answer prothallus

Figure 7
Small balls of cells grow in cup-like structures on the surface of the liverwort.

Physics
INTEGRATION

Catapults have been used by humans for thousands of years to launch objects. The spore cases of ferns act like tiny catapults as they eject their spores. In your Science Journal list tools, toys, and other objects that use catapult technology to work.

Nonvascular Plants and Asexual Reproduction Nonvascular plants also can reproduce asexually. For example, if a piece of a moss gametophyte plant breaks off, it can grow into a new plant. Liverworts can form small balls of cells on the surface of the gametophyte plant, as shown in **Figure 7.** These are carried away by water and grow into new gametophyte plants if they settle in a damp environment.

Vascular Seedless Plants

Millions of years ago most plants on Earth were vascular seedless plants. Today they are not as widespread.

Most vascular seedless plants are ferns. Other plants in this group include horsetails and club mosses. All of these plants have vascular tissue to transport water from their roots to the rest of the plant. Unlike the nonvascular plants, the gametophyte of vascular seedless plants is the part that is small and often overlooked.

The Fern Life Cycle The fern plants that you see in nature or as houseplants are fern sporophyte plants. Fern leaves are called **fronds.** They grow from an underground stem called a **rhizome.** Roots that anchor the plant and absorb water and nutrients also grow from the rhizome. Fern sporophytes make their own food by photosynthesis. Fern spores are produced in structures called **sori** (singular, *sorus*), usually located on the underside of the fronds. Sori can look like crusty rust-, brown-, or dark-colored bumps. Sometimes they are mistaken for a disease or for something growing on the fronds.

If a fern spore lands on damp soil or rocks, it can grow into a small, green, heart-shaped gametophyte plant called a **prothallus** (proh THA lus). A prothallus is hard to see because most of them are only about 5 mm to 6 mm in diameter. The prothallus contains chlorophyll and can make its own food. It absorbs water and nutrients from the soil. The life cycle of a fern is shown in **Figure 8.**

Reading Check *What is the gametophyte plant of a fern called?*

Ferns may reproduce asexually, also. Fern rhizomes grow and form branches. New fronds and roots develop from each branch. The new rhizome branch can be separated from the main plant. It can grow on its own and form more fern plants.

Resource Manager

Chapter Resources Booklet
  Reinforcement, p. 26
  Transparency Activity, pp. 45–46
  Activity Worksheet, pp. 5–6

Using Definitions *Frond* is the name given to leaves of ferns and palms. Have students look in a dictionary to find the derivation and meaning of the word *frond* and then write a paragraph in their journals to suggest why the word is used for these leaves. *Frond* comes from the Latin word for *leaf.*

Figure 8
A fern's life cycle and a moss's are similar. However, the fern sporophyte and gametophyte are photosynthetic and can grow on their own.

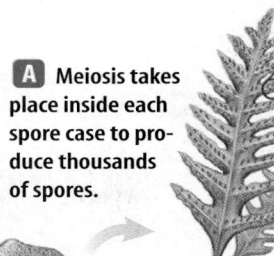
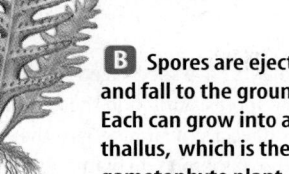

A Meiosis takes place inside each spore case to produce thousands of spores.

Spore case

Spore

B Spores are ejected and fall to the ground. Each can grow into a prothallus, which is the gametophyte plant.

Spore grows to form prothallus

Young sporophyte growing on gametophyte

Zygote

Female reproductive structure

Egg

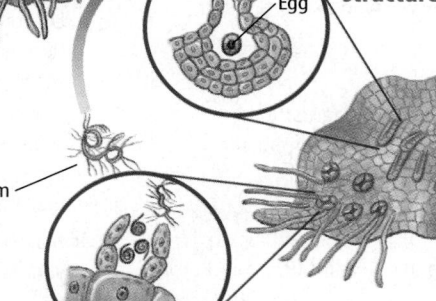

E The zygote is the beginning of the sporophyte stage and grows into the familiar fern plant.

Sperm

D Water is needed for the sperm to swim to the egg. Fertilization occurs and a zygote is produced.

Male reproductive structure

C The prothallus contains the male and female reproductive structures where sex cells form.

Section 2 Assessment

1. Describe the life cycle of mosses.
2. Explain the stages in the life cycle of a fern.
3. Compare and contrast the gametophyte plant of the moss with the gametophyte plant of the fern.
4. List several ways that seedless plants reproduce asexually.
5. **Think Critically** Why might some seedless plants reproduce only asexually during dry times of the year?

Skill Builder Activities

6. **Concept Mapping** Use an events-chain concept map to show the events in the life cycle of either a moss or fern. **For more help, refer to the** Science Skill Handbook.
7. **Solving One-Step Equations** Moss spores are usually no more than 0.1 mm in diameter. About how many spores would it take to equal the diameter of a penny? **For more help, refer to the** Math Skill Handbook.

SECTION 2 Seedless Reproduction **247**

Visual Learning

Figure 8 Again, have students trace with their fingers the sequence of events in a fern's life cycle. This time, have students explain the difference between the sporophyte and the gametophyte generations.

3 Assess

Reteach
Provide students with a list of the terms used in this section. Have students identify each term as being part of the moss life cycle, fern life cycle, or both. L2 ELL COOP LEARN **LS** Interpersonal

Challenge
Have students write essays that describe, compare, and contrast the life cycles of mosses and ferns. **LS** Linguistic

Assessment

Performance Give each student a 3 × 5 card on which is written a description of a fern or moss structure. Have each student identify his or her structure. Then divide the class into groups (two for each plant)—one for students whose structure is part of the sporophyte stage, and one for students whose structure is part of the gametophyte stage of their plant's life cycle. Have students work together to arrange themselves into a physical model of their plant's life cycle. Use **PASC**, p. 123.

Section 2 Seedless Reproduction **247**

Activity

Purpose Students will observe the stages in the life cycles of liverworts, mosses, and ferns. [L2]

ELL COOP LEARN [LS] **Visual-Spatial**

Process Skills observing, classifying, comparing and contrasting

Time Required 50 minutes

Safety Precautions Remind students not to eat any plant parts and to be careful when using microscopes.

Teaching Strategy Be sure students have properly focused their microscopes.

Troubleshooting If moss spores are not liberated using water, add an equal amount of glycerin to the water. This mixture allows the spores to come out of the capsule more easily.

Answers to Questions

1. Moss gametophyte: green, low-growing structure with leaves in a whorl around a stalk; liverwort gametophyte: green, flat, leaflike form. Sporophytes of mosses are a non-green stalk with a spore-containing capsule at the top. Liverwort sporophytes form on the gametophytes as green umbrella-like structures with spores in cases underneath. Fern gametophytes: green, heart-shaped structures; their sporophytes are familiar green plants.

2. gametophyte, sporophyte, rhizoid, spores, leaflike structures

3. Many spores do not land where conditions are right for growth. The greater the number of spores produced, the greater the chances that some will grow.

Activity

Comparing Seedless Plants

All seedless plants have specialized structures that produce spores. Although these sporophyte structures have a similar function, they look different. The gametophyte plants also are different from each other. Do this activity and observe the similarities and differences among three groups of seedless plants.

What You'll Investigate
How are the gametophyte stages and the sporophyte stages of liverworts, mosses, and ferns similar and different?

Materials
live mosses, liverworts, and ferns
    with gametophytes and sporophytes
hand lens
forceps
dropper
microscope slides and coverslips (2)
microscope
dissecting needle
pencil with eraser

Goals
■ **Describe** the sporophyte and gametophyte forms of liverworts, mosses, and ferns.
■ **Identify** the spore-producing structures of liverworts, mosses, and ferns.

Safety Precautions

Procedure

1. Obtain a gametophyte of each plant. With a hand lens, observe the rhizoids, leafy parts, and stemlike parts, if any are present.

2. Obtain a sporophyte of each plant and use a hand lens to observe it.

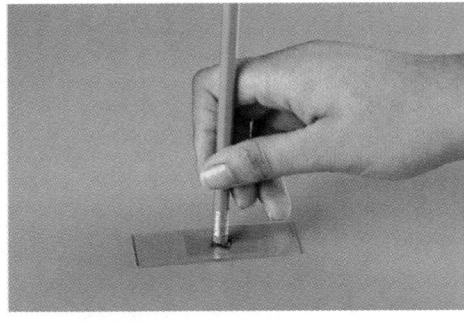

3. Locate the spore structure on the moss plant. Remove it and place it in a drop of water on the slide. Place a coverslip over it. Use the eraser of a pencil to gently push on the coverslip to release the spores. **WARNING:** *Do not break the coverslip.* Observe the spores under low and high power.

4. Make labeled drawings of all observations in your Science Journal.

5. Repeat steps 3 and 4 using a fern.

Conclude and Apply

1. For each plant, compare the gametophyte's appearance to the sporophyte's appearance.

2. **List** structure(s) common to all three plants.

3. **Hypothesize** about why each plant produces a large number of spores.

*C*ommunicating
Your Data

Prepare a bulletin board that shows differences between the sporophyte and gametophyte stages of liverworts, mosses, and ferns. **For more help, refer to the** Science Skill Handbook.

---

*C*ommunicating
Your Data

The bulletin board should illustrate differences between the life cycle stages of the plants examined. Encourage students to use Internet sources to research photographs and information for the bulletin board.

✔*Assessment*

Performance Assess students' understanding of the parts of mosses, liverworts, and ferns by having them identify parts of living specimens and by describing the functions of each. Use **Performance Assessment in the Science Classroom,** p. 89.

Seed Reproduction

The Importance of Pollen and Seeds

All the plants described so far have been seedless plants. However, the fruits and vegetables that you eat come from seed plants. Oak, maple, and other shade trees are also seed plants. All flowers are produced by seed plants. In fact, most of the plants on Earth are seed plants. How do you think they became such a successful group? Reproduction that involves pollen and seeds is part of the answer.

Pollen In seed plants, some spores develop into small structures called pollen grains. A **pollen grain,** as shown in **Figure 9,** has a water-resistant covering and contains gametophyte parts that can produce the sperm. The sperm of seed plants do not need to swim to the female part of the plant. Instead, they are carried as part of the pollen grain by gravity, wind, water currents, or animals. The transfer of pollen grains to the female part of the plant is called **pollination.**

After the pollen grain reaches the female part of a plant, sperm and a pollen tube are produced. The sperm moves through the pollen tube, then fertilization can occur.

SECTION

Seed Reproduction

As You Read

What You'll Learn
- **Examine** the life cycles of typical gymnosperms and angiosperms.
- **Describe** the structure and function of the flower.
- **Discuss** methods of seed dispersal in seed plants.

Vocabulary
pollen grain   pistil
pollination   ovary
ovule   germination
stamen

Why It's Important
Seeds from cones and flowers produce most plants on Earth.

1 Motivate

Bellringer Transparency
Display the Section Focus Transparency for Section 3. Use the accompanying Transparency Activity Master. L2 ELL

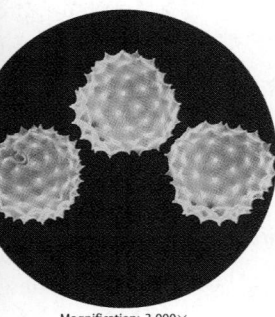

Magnification: 3,000×

Figure 9
The waterproof covering of a pollen grain is unique and can be used to identify the plant that it came from. This pollen from a ragweed plant is a common cause of hay fever.

SECTION 3 Seed Reproduction **249**

Tie to Prior Knowledge
Ask students to recall a time when they dispersed seeds. One answer may be when they were eating fruit such as watermelon. Others may have actually planted seeds in a garden. Still others may have walked through a field and found seeds stuck to their clothing.

Section ✔Assessment Planner

PORTFOLIO
Activity, p. 251
PERFORMANCE ASSESSMENT
Try at Home MiniLAB, p. 256
Skill Builder Activities, p. 259
See page 266 for more options.

CONTENT ASSESSMENT
Section, p. 259
Challenge, p. 259
Chapter, pp. 266–267

Resource Manager

Chapter Resources Booklet
Transparency Activity p. 44
Directed Reading for Content Mastery, pp. 19, 20

Section 3 Seed Reproduction **249**

The Importance of Pollen and Seeds

IDENTIFYING Misconceptions

Many students assume that plants fertilize themselves. Point out that many plants must be cross-pollinated in order to reproduce.

Caption Answer

Figure 10 Wings allow seeds to catch the wind and be dispersed farther from the parent plant.

✔ Reading Check

Answer seed coat, stored food, embryo

SCIENCE Online
Internet Addresses
_____
_____
_____
_____

Explore the Glencoe Science Web site at **science.glencoe.com** to find out more about topics in this section.

Figure 10
Seeds have three main parts—a seed coat, stored food, and an embryo. This pine seed also has a wing. *What is the function of the wing?*

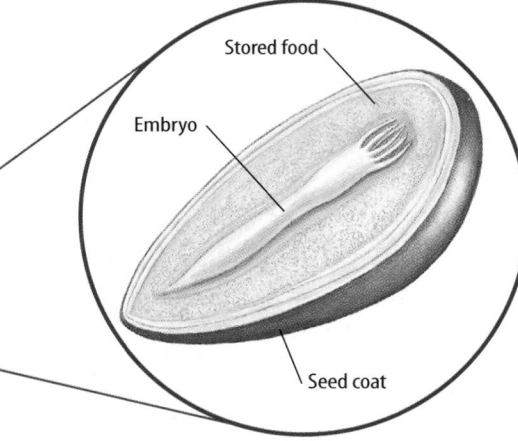

Stored food
Embryo
Seed coat

SCIENCE Online

Research Seed banks conserve seeds of many useful and endangered plants. Visit the Glencoe Science Web site at **science.glencoe.com** to find out more about seed banks. In your Science Journal list three organizations that manage seed banks.

Field GUIDE

Do all gymnosperm plants produce the same type of cones? To find out more about cones, see the **Cones Field Guide** at the back of this book.

Seeds Following fertilization, the female part can develop into a seed. A seed consists of an embryo, stored food, and a protective seed coat, as shown in **Figure 10.** The embryo has structures that eventually will produce the plant's stem, leaves, and roots. In the seed, the embryo grows to a certain stage and then stops until the seed is planted. The stored food provides energy that is needed when the plant embryo begins to grow into a plant. Because the seed contains an embryo and stored food, a new plant can develop more rapidly from a seed than from a spore.

✔ Reading Check   *What are the three parts of a seed?*

Gymnosperms (JIHM nuh spurmz) and angiosperms are seed plants. One difference between the two groups is the way seeds develop. In gymnosperms, seeds usually develop in cones—in angiosperms, seeds develop in flowers.

Gymnosperm Reproduction

If you have collected pine cones or used them in a craft project, you probably noticed that many shapes and sizes of cones exist. You probably also noticed that some cones contain seeds. Cones are the reproductive structures of gymnosperms. Each gymnosperm species has a different cone.

Gymnosperm plants include pines, firs, cedars, cycads, and ginkgoes. The pine is a familiar gymnosperm. Production of seeds in pines is typical of most gymnosperms.

Cones A pine tree or shrub is a sporophyte plant that produces male cones and female cones as shown in **Figure 11.** Male and female gametophyte structures are produced in the cones but you'd need a magnifying glass to see these structures clearly.

Curriculum Connection

Geography Gymnosperms are the dominant plant of the taiga biome. In North America, most of this area is located between 45° and 60° north latitude. Have students locate on a world map countries where taiga is the primary biome. Then have students list the climactic conditions of these areas. Canada, Norway, Sweden, and Russia are examples. These countries experience harsh winters and short summers. L2

Resource Manager

Reading and Writing Skill Activities, p. 1

Life Science Critical Thinking/Problem Solving, p. 8

A mature female cone consists of a spiral of woody scales on a short stem. At the base of each scale are two ovules. The egg is produced in the **ovule.** Pollen grains are produced in the smaller male cones. In the spring, clouds of pollen are released from the male cones. Anything near pine trees might be covered with the yellow, dustlike pollen.

Figure 11
Seed formation in pines, as in most gymnosperms, involves male and female cones.

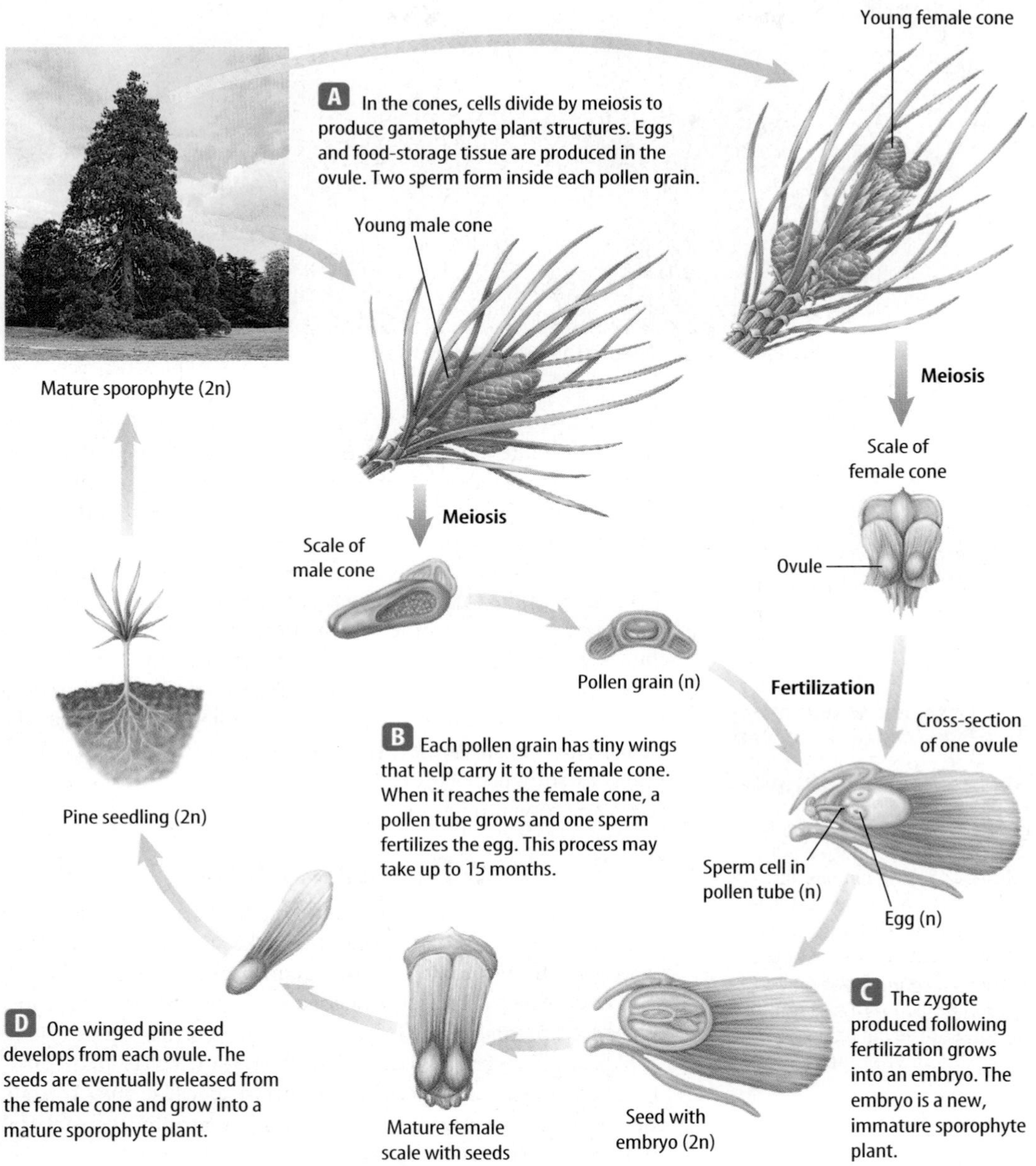

Mature sporophyte (2n)

Young female cone

A In the cones, cells divide by meiosis to produce gametophyte plant structures. Eggs and food-storage tissue are produced in the ovule. Two sperm form inside each pollen grain.

Young male cone

Meiosis

Scale of female cone

Meiosis

Scale of male cone

Ovule

Pollen grain (n)

Pine seedling (2n)

Fertilization

Cross-section of one ovule

B Each pollen grain has tiny wings that help carry it to the female cone. When it reaches the female cone, a pollen tube grows and one sperm fertilizes the egg. This process may take up to 15 months.

Sperm cell in pollen tube (n)

Egg (n)

D One winged pine seed develops from each ovule. The seeds are eventually released from the female cone and grow into a mature sporophyte plant.

Mature female scale with seeds

Seed with embryo (2n)

C The zygote produced following fertilization grows into an embryo. The embryo is a new, immature sporophyte plant.

SECTION 3 Seed Reproduction **251**

Gymnosperm Reproduction

Visual Learning

Figure 11 Have students discuss the primary differences in the life cycles of nonseed plants and gymnosperms. In gymnosperms and other seed plants, the gametophyte stage is usually microscopic. In nonseed plants, this stage can be larger than the sporophyte.

Activity

Have students write a description of a cone for someone who is visually impaired. After reviewing all the descriptions, share the best two or three with the class. **LS** **Linguistic** P

Extension

Have students visit a botanical garden to identify plants from your area and around the world. Ask students to make drawings of the plants they observe and to note any unique features of the plants. Students can present their drawings and a summary of their observations in an oral presentation.

Active Reading

Double-Bubble Map This strategy utilizes two bubble maps to compare concepts. Each cluster has ideas that are unique to that idea. In the middle are connecting ideas shared by both clusters. Have students design a Double-Bubble Map summarizing gymnosperm and angiosperm reproduction. A sample is shown.

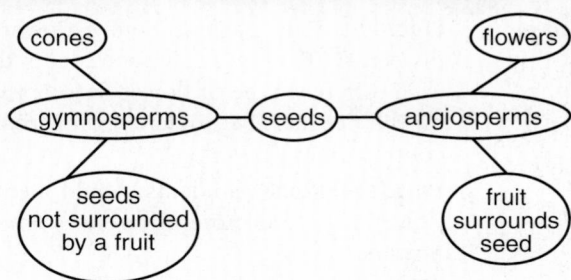

cones — gymnosperms — seeds — angiosperms — flowers

seeds not surrounded by a fruit

fruit surrounds seed

Section 3 Seed Reproduction **251**

Gymnosperm Reproduction,
continued

Angiosperm Reproduction

Figure 12
Seed development can take more than one year in pines. The female cone looks different at various stages of the seed-production process.

Cone at pollination | Cone at the end of the first year | Mature, second-year cone

Gymnosperm Seeds Wind usually carries the pollen from male cones to female cones. However, most of the pollen falls on other plants, the ground, and bodies of water. To be useful, the pollen has to be blown between the scales of a female cone. There it can be trapped in the sticky fluid secreted by the ovule. If the pollen grain and the female cone are the same species, fertilization and the formation of a seed can take place.

If you are near a pine tree when the female cones release their seeds, you might hear a crackling noise as the cones' scales open. It can take a long time for seeds to be released from a female pine cone. From the moment a pollen grain falls on the female cone until the seeds are released, can take two or three years, as shown in **Figure 12.** In the right environment, each seed can grow into a new pine sporophyte.

Angiosperm Reproduction

You might not know it, but you are already familiar with angiosperms. If you had cereal for breakfast or bread in a sandwich for lunch, you ate parts of angiosperms. Flowers that you send or receive for special occasions are from angiosperms. Most of the seed plants on Earth today are angiosperms.

All angiosperms have flowers. The sporophyte plant produces the flowers. Flowers are important because they contain the reproductive organs that contain gametophyte structures that produce sperm or eggs for sexual reproduction.

252 CHAPTER 9 Plant Reproduction

LAB DEMONSTRATION

Purpose to identify the parts of a flower

Materials a variety of monocot and dicot flowers, plastic knives, tape, paper

Preparation Collect or purchase enough flowers so that each student can have one flower.

Safety Caution students to be careful with the knives.

Procedure Give each student a flower to dissect. As they work, have students tape each different type of flower part in a line on the paper. Have students compare and contrast their dissections.

Expected Outcome Students should identify flower parts and note differences among flowers.

☑ Assessment

Have students describe any differences they have observed. The numbers of flower parts vary from plant to plant. Dicot flower parts occur in fours and fives; monocot flower parts occur in threes.

The Flower When you think of a flower, you probably imagine something with a pleasant aroma and colorful petals. Although many such flowers do exist, some flowers are drab and have no aroma, like the flowers of the maple tree shown in **Figure 13.** Why do you think such variety among flowers exists?

Most flowers have four main parts—petals, sepals, stamen, and pistil—as shown in **Figure 14.** Generally, the colorful parts of a flower are the petals. Outside the petals are usually leaflike parts called sepals. Sepals form the outside of the flower bud. Sometimes petals and sepals are the same color.

Inside the flower are the reproductive organs of the plant. The **stamen** is the male reproductive organ. Pollen is produced in the stamen. The **pistil** is the female reproductive organ. The **ovary** is the swollen base of the pistil where ovules are found. Not all flowers have every one of the four parts. Remember the holly plants you learned about at the beginning of the chapter? What flower part would be missing on a flower from a male holly plant?

✔ **Reading Check** *Where are ovules found in the flower?*

Figure 13
Maple trees produce clusters of flowers early in the spring. *How are these flowers different from those of the crocus seen earlier?*

Figure 14
The color of a flower's petals can attract insect pollinators. *What are the male and female parts of this flower?*

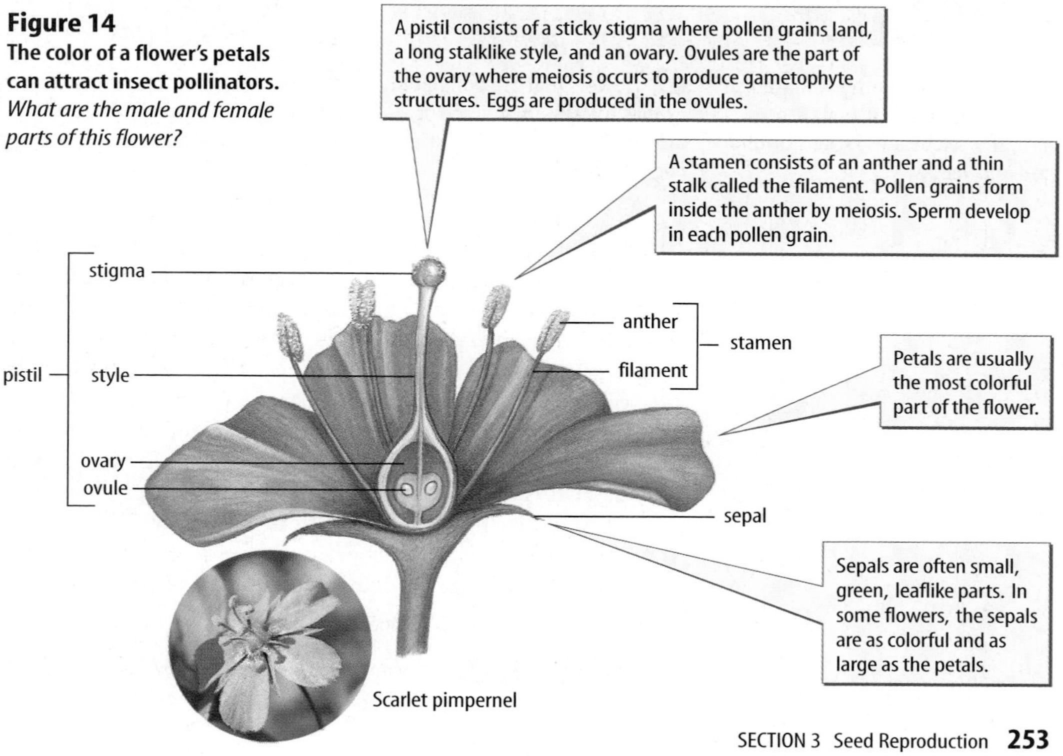

A pistil consists of a sticky stigma where pollen grains land, a long stalklike style, and an ovary. Ovules are the part of the ovary where meiosis occurs to produce gametophyte structures. Eggs are produced in the ovules.

A stamen consists of an anther and a thin stalk called the filament. Pollen grains form inside the anther by meiosis. Sperm develop in each pollen grain.

stigma

pistil — style

ovary
ovule

anther
filament
} stamen

Petals are usually the most colorful part of the flower.

sepal

Sepals are often small, green, leaflike parts. In some flowers, the sepals are as colorful and as large as the petals.

Scarlet pimpernel

SECTION 3   Seed Reproduction   **253**

Figure 15 After students have studied the pollination mechanisms shown, have them work in teams to write a short story about a particular kind of flower and its pollination mechanism. The story should include a day in the life of a flower. L2
COOP LEARN LS Linguistic

Fun Fact

It would take more than ten million orchid seeds to equal the mass of a single coconut.

✔ Reading Check

Answer An animal may pick up pollen as it eats the flower, its nectar, or its pollen. The pollen is then spread to other flowers that the animal visits.

Figure 15
Looking at flowers will give you a clue about how each one is pollinated.

A Honeybees are important pollinators. They are attracted to brightly colored flowers, especially blue and yellow flowers.

B Flowers that are pollinated at night, like this cactus flower being pollinated by a bat, are usually white.

C Flowers that are pollinated by hummingbirds usually are brightly colored, especially bright red and yellow.

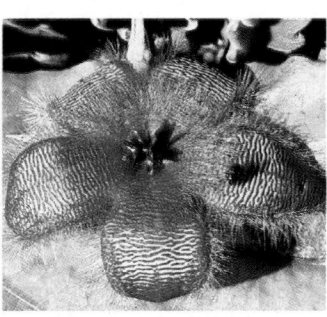

D Flowers that are pollinated by flies usually are dull red or brown. They often have a strong odor like rotten meat.

E The flower of this wheat plant does not have a strong odor and is not brightly colored. Wind, not an animal, is the pollinator of wheat and most other grasses.

Importance of Flowers The appearance of a plant's flowers can tell you something about the life of the plant. Large flowers with brightly colored petals often attract insects and other animals, as shown in **Figure 15.** These animals might eat the flower, its nectar, or pollen. As they move about the flower, the animals get pollen on their wings, legs, or other body parts. Later, these animals spread the flower's pollen to other plants that they visit. Other flowers depend on wind, rain, or gravity to spread their pollen. Their petals can be small or absent. Flowers that open only at night, such as the cactus flower in **Figure 15B,** usually are white or yellow and have strong scents to attract animal pollinators. Following pollination and fertilization, the ovules of flowers can develop into seeds.

✔ Reading Check *How do animals spread pollen?*

Resource Manager

Chapter Resources Booklet
   Enrichment, p. 30
Home and Community Involvement, p. 41

Inclusion Strategies

Learning Disabled Play "plant bingo." Have students make a game board by writing all the bold-faced terms from this section in squares on a sheet of paper. Then read a definition of a plant term. Students who can correctly identify the term can cover that term on their board. The first student to have all terms covered wins.

Angiosperm Seeds The development of angiosperm seeds is shown in **Figure 16.** Pollen grains reach the stigma in a variety of ways. Pollen is carried by wind, rain, or animals such as insects, birds, and mammals. A flower is pollinated when pollen grains land on the sticky stigma. A pollen tube grows from the pollen grain down through the style. The pollen tube enters the ovary and reaches an ovule. The sperm then travels down the pollen tube and fertilizes the egg in the ovule. A zygote forms and grows into the plant embryo.

Visual Learning

Figure 16 After students have read and discussed the information, have them make an events chain concept map to summarize seed formation in angiosperms.
L2 [JS] **Visual-Spatial**

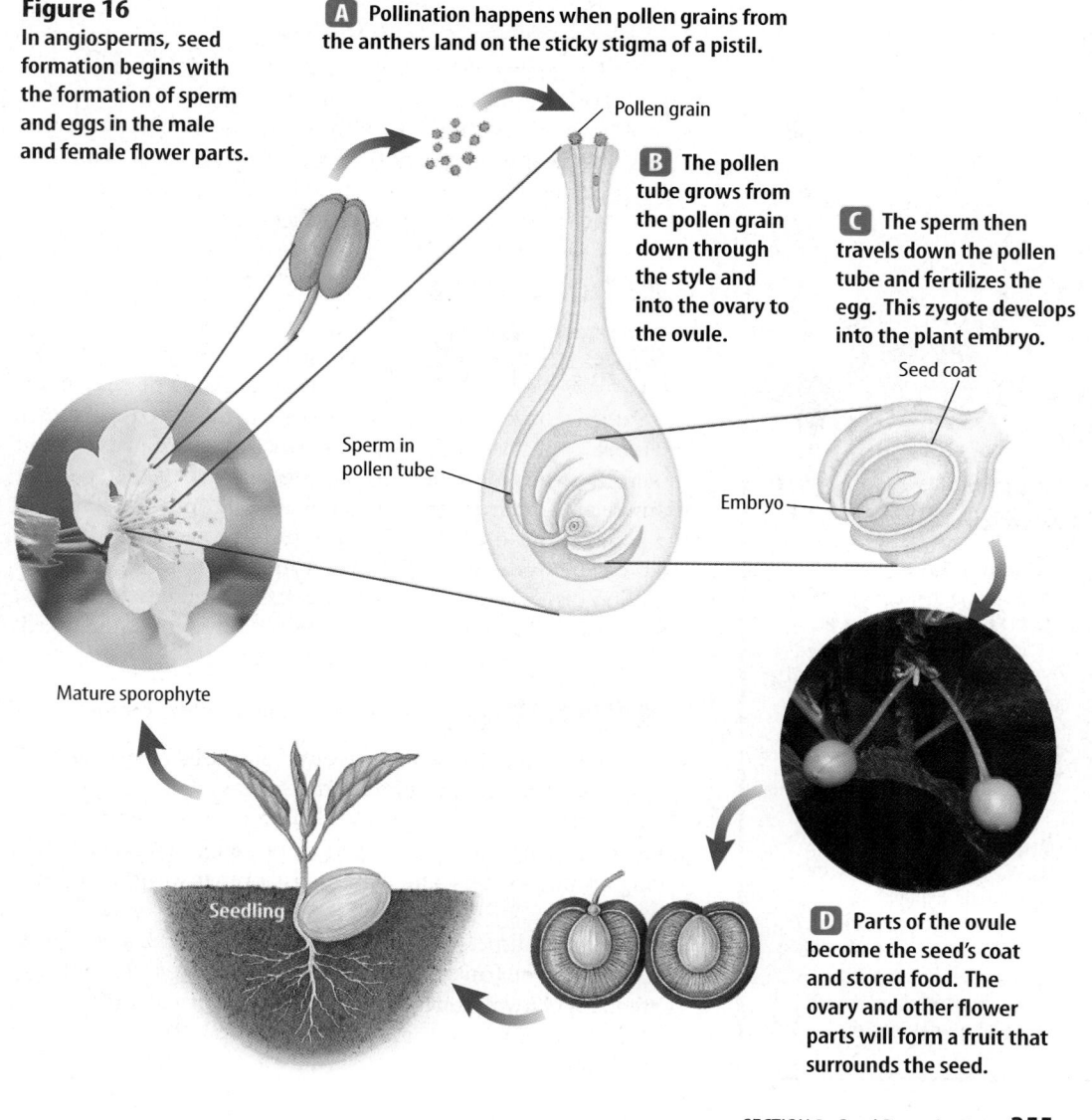

Figure 16
In angiosperms, seed formation begins with the formation of sperm and eggs in the male and female flower parts.

A Pollination happens when pollen grains from the anthers land on the sticky stigma of a pistil.

Pollen grain

B The pollen tube grows from the pollen grain down through the style and into the ovary to the ovule.

C The sperm then travels down the pollen tube and fertilizes the egg. This zygote develops into the plant embryo.

Seed coat

Sperm in pollen tube

Embryo

Mature sporophyte

Seedling

D Parts of the ovule become the seed's coat and stored food. The ovary and other flower parts will form a fruit that surrounds the seed.

SECTION 3 Seed Reproduction **255**

Teacher FYI

Bees and flowers have a symbiotic, or mutually beneficial, relationship. More flowers are pollinated by bees than any other kind of insect. Many flowers also have a highly complicated structure that discourages self-pollination and encourages cross-pollination of plants with single flowers. This means that while a bee is getting nectar from the flower, it is able to touch the pistil, but not the stamen. As the bee is leaving, however, it is able to touch the stamen, but not the pistil. This way, the bee leaves pollen from another flower rather than the pollen from the flower from which the bee is taking nectar.

Cultural Diversity

Drip Irrigation Crop production on a Navajo reservation in Arizona was once limited because of the scarcity of water. In 1984, David Mazigh, manager of an experimental farm in Israel, was invited to visit the reservation. Mazigh shared his knowledge of drip irrigation with the Navajos. Some Israeli farmers use drip irrigation to get water to plants in their desert lands. Water is pumped from a well and mixed with fertilizer. The fertilizer solution travels in thick pipes to thin drip lines that lie beside rows of planted seeds in the fields. Small nozzles allow the solution to drip out, providing plants with a slow and constant supply of water and fertilizer. Encourage students to visit a garden store and examine the drip irrigation systems available for home use.

Seed Dispersal

Use an Analogy

The way many seeds attach themselves to passing animals is like the way that two pieces of hook and loop tape stick together. In fact, hook and loop tape was inspired by the mechanism cockleburs use to stick to fur and clothing.

✔ Reading Check

Answer Small seeds may become airborne when the plant releases them. Some seeds have structures that allow them to move with air currents.

Figure 17
Seeds of land plants are capable of surviving unfavorable environmental conditions.
1. Immature plant
2. Cotyledon(s)
3. Seed coat
4. Endosperm

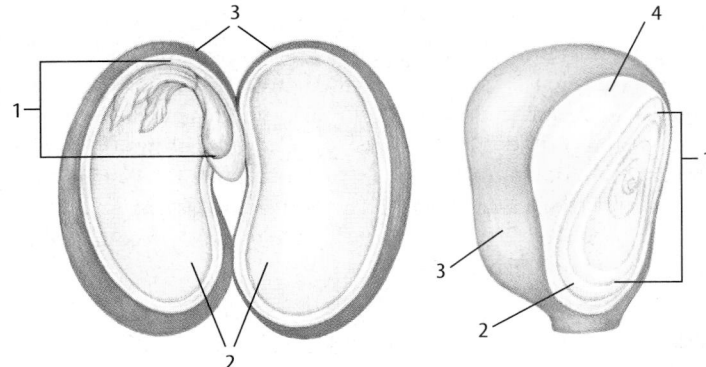

Seed Development Parts of the ovule develop into the stored food and the seed coat that surround the embryo, and a seed is formed, as shown in **Figure 17.** In the seeds of some plants, like beans and peanuts, the food is stored in structures called cotyledons. The seeds of other plants, like corn and wheat, have food stored in a tissue called endosperm.

Seed Dispersal

Earth Science INTEGRATION Sometimes, plants just seem to appear. They probably grew from a seed, but where did the seed come from? Plants have many ways of dispersing their seeds, as shown in **Figure 18.** Most seeds grow only when they are placed on or in soil. Do you know how seeds naturally get to the soil? For many seeds, gravity is the answer. They fall onto the soil from the parent plant on which they grew. However, in nature some seeds can be spread great distances from the parent plant.

Wind dispersal usually occurs because a seed has an attached structure that moves it with air currents. Sometimes, small seeds become airborne when released by the plant.

✔ Reading Check   *How can wind be used to disperse seeds?*

Animals can disperse many seeds. Some seeds are eaten with fruits, pass through an animal's digestive system, and are dispersed as the animal moves from place to place. Seeds can be carried great distances and stored or buried by animals. Hitchhiking on fur, feathers, and clothing is another way that animals disperse seeds.

Water also disperses seeds. Raindrops can knock seeds out of a dry fruit. Some fruits and seeds float on flowing water or ocean currents. When you touch the seedpod of an impatiens flower, it explodes. The tiny seeds are ejected and spread some distance from the plant.

Figure 18

Plants have many adaptations for dispersing seeds, often enlisting the aid of wind, water, or animals.

▲ Equipped with tiny hooks, burrs cling tightly to fur and feathers.

▼ Dandelion seeds are easily dislodged and sail away on a puff of wind.

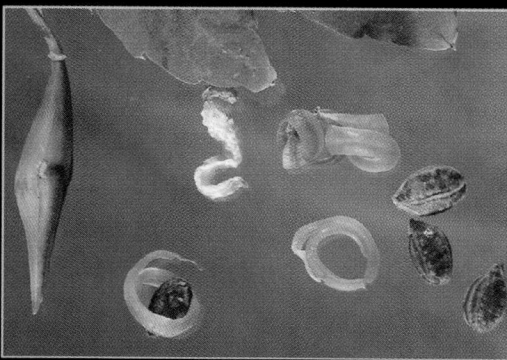

▲ Pressure builds within the seed-pods of this jewelweed plant until the pod bursts, flinging seeds far and wide.

▼ Some seeds buried by animals, such as this squirrel, go uneaten and sprout the next spring.

▲ Encased in a thick, buoyant husk, a coconut may be carried hundreds of kilometers by ocean currents.

▶ Blackberry seeds eaten by this white-footed mouse will pass through its digestive tract and be deposited in a new location.

SECTION 3   Seed Reproduction   **257**

Visualizing Seed Dispersal

Have students examine the pictures and read the captions. Then ask the following question.

What advantage does wide dispersal of seeds give a plant species? Possible answers: less competition for resources between parent plant and offspring, better chance of finding a suitable environment for growth

Activity

Have students complete a chart of the different methods of seed dispersal illustrated and give more examples for each method. Sample chart:

Dispersal Method	Examples
In Fur of Animals	burdock, burr clover, foxtails, sticktights
Buried by Animals	oak
Excreted by Animals	raspberries, strawberries, tomatoes
Floating	red mangroves, sedge
Shotgun Dispersal	mistletoe, "touch-me-not" (impatiens), "squirting cucumbers" (ecballium), sandbox tree
Wind Dispersal	maple, orchids, milkweed, tumbleweeds

Extension

Have students research the importance of bats and their role in pollination and seed dispersal in rain forests around the world. Have them make posters showing their results. Possible research findings: Bats are important in seed dispersal as they excrete seeds from the fruits they consume. Bats also are important in pollination of plants in tropical areas. Plants that rely on bats for pollination only bloom at night, when bats are active.

 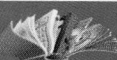
Teacher FYI

Force may be defined as a push or a pull. Some dry fruits open with such great force when ripe, that their seeds are dispersed some distance from the plants. Witch hazel seeds may be propelled more than 12 m by the force of its splitting ripe fruit.

Seed Dispersal, continued

Discussion

Why might some gardeners soak their bean seeds before planting? Soaking softens the seed coat and speeds germination.

Activity

Have students collect as many different kinds of seeds as possible. Once collected, students can germinate the seeds and draw pictures of differences they note among the germinating seeds. They also can record and graph the various rates of germination. L2 ELL LS **Kinesthetic and Visual-Spatial**

Math Skills Activity

National Math Standards

Correlation to Mathematics Objectives

1, 2, 6, 8, 9

Answer to Practice Problem

$$\frac{98}{100} = \frac{x}{50}$$

$$x = \frac{98 \times 50}{100}$$

$$x = \frac{4,900}{100}$$

$$x = 49$$

Resource Manager

Chapter Resources Booklet
Reinforcement, p. 27
Activity Worksheet, pp. 7–8
Lab Management and Safety, p. 38

Germination A series of events that results in the growth of a plant from a seed is called **germination.** When dispersed from the plant, some seeds germinate in just a few days and other seeds take weeks or months to grow. Some seeds can stay in a resting stage for hundreds of years. In 1982, seeds of the East Indian lotus sprouted after 466 years.

Seeds will not germinate until environmental conditions are right. Temperature, the presence or absence of light, availability of water, and amount of oxygen present can affect germination. Sometimes the seed must pass through an animal's digestive system before it will germinate. Germination begins when seed tissues absorb water. This causes the seed to swell and the seed coat to break open.

Math Skills Activity

Calculating the Number of Seeds That Will Germinate

Example Problem

The label on a packet of carrot seeds says that it contains about 200 seeds. It also claims that 95 percent of the seeds will germinate. How many seeds should germinate if the packet is correct?

1 *This is what you know:*
  quantity = 200
  percentage = 95

2 *This is what you need to find:*
  95 percent of 200

3 *This is the equation you need to use:*
$$\frac{95}{100} = \frac{x}{200}$$

4 *Solve the equation for* x:
$$x = \frac{95 \times 200}{100}$$

Check your answer by dividing by 200 then multiplying by 100. Do you get the original percentage of 95?

Practice Problem

The label on a packet of 50 corn kernels claims that 98 percent will germinate. How many kernels will germinate if the packet is correct?

For more help, refer to the Math Skill Handbook.

Inclusion Strategies

Learning Disabled To reinforce the conditions needed for germination, have students carry out this activity. Place a sponge in a shallow dish with enough water to soak the sponge. Be sure the sponge rises above the water level. Sprinkle a small amount of birdseed on the sponge. Pat the seeds into the sponge. Place the sponge in a bright but not sunny location. Add water to keep the sponge moist. Have students use hand lenses to examine the sponge each day. Have them record their observations as drawings with explanatory labels. Be sure they note when they see cracking in the seeds and the sprouting of the embryo. In five to seven days, the seedlings can be scraped off the sponge and into a container of potting soil. Continue to have students monitor growth of the young plants. L1 ELL LS **Kinesthetic**

Figure 19
Although germination in all seeds is similar, some differences exist.

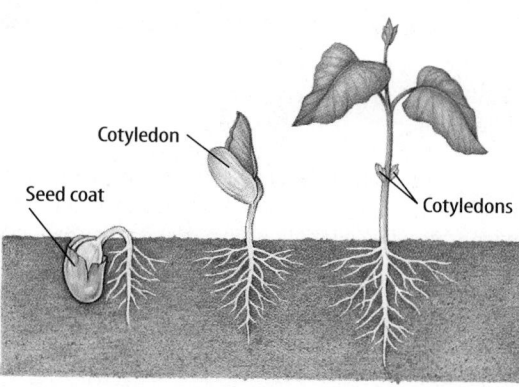

Cotyledon

Seed coat

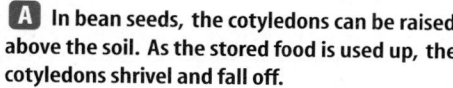

Cotyledons

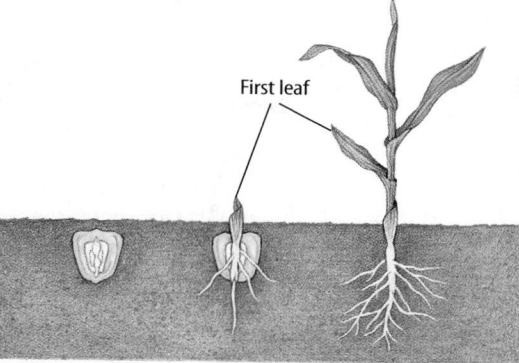

First leaf

A In bean seeds, the cotyledons can be raised above the soil. As the stored food is used up, the cotyledons shrivel and fall off.

B In corn, the stored food in the endosperm remains in the soil and is gradually used up as the young plant grows.

Next, a series of chemical reactions occurs that releases energy from the stored food in the cotyledons or endosperm for growth. Eventually, a root grows from the seed, followed by a stem and leaves as shown in **Figure 19.** After the plant emerges from the soil, photosynthesis can begin. Photosynthesis provides food as the plant continues to grow.

Section Assessment

1. Compare and contrast life cycles of angiosperms and gymnosperms.
2. Diagram a flower that has all four parts and label them.
3. List three methods of seed dispersal in plants.
4. Describe the three parts of a seed and give the function of each.
5. **Think Critically** Some conifers have female cones on the top half of the tree and male cones on the bottom half. Why would this arrangement of cones on a tree be important?

Skill Builder Activities

6. **Researching Information** Find out what conditions are needed for seed germination of three different garden plants, such as corn, peas, and beans. How long does each type of seed take to germinate? **For more help, refer to the** Science Skill Handbook.
7. **Communicating** Observe live specimens of several different types of flowers. In your Science Journal, describe their structures. Include numbers of petals, sepals, stamens, and pistil. **For more help, refer to the** Science Skill Handbook.

SECTION 3 Seed Reproduction **259**

Activity

Recognize the Problem

Purpose

Students design and carry out an experiment to explore how germination rate varies with an environmental factor. L2 COOP LEARN

IS Logical-Mathematical

Process Skills

designing an experiment; collecting, interpreting and analyzing data; drawing conclusions; communicating; making and using tables and graphs; comparing and contrasting; recognizing cause and effect; forming a hypothesis; separating and controlling variables; measuring in SI

Time Required

one class period, plus 10 minutes per day for two weeks

Alternate Materials

Use any fast-germinating seeds. Epsom salts may be substituted for table salt. Seedling warming cables provide another variable to test.

Safety Precautions

Have students review safety symbols and precautions on the student page.

Form a Hypothesis

Possible Hypotheses

Students may predict that seeds will germinate at a higher rate with water than with salt solutions. They may predict that warmer soil will increase the rate of germination. The presence and absence of light and planting depth are other variables that may be tested.

Activity — *Design Your Own Experiment*

Germination Rate of Seeds

Many environmental factors affect the germination rate of seeds. Among these are soil temperature, air temperature, moisture content of soil, and salt content of soil. What happens to the germination rate when one of these variables is changed? Can you determine a way to predict the best conditions for seed germination?

Recognize the Problem

How do environmental factors affect seed germination?

Form a Hypothesis

Based on your knowledge of seed germination, state a hypothesis about how environmental factors affect germination rates.

Possible Materials

seeds
water
salt
potting soil
plant trays or plastic cups
*seedling warming cables
thermometer
graduated cylinder
beakers
*Alternate materials

Goals

■ **Design** an experiment to test the effect of an environmental factor on seed germination rate.

■ **Compare** germination rates under different conditions.

Safety Precautions

Some kinds of seeds are poisonous. Do not place any seeds in your mouth. Be careful when using any electrical equipment to avoid shock hazards.

260

Test Your Hypothesis

Possible Procedures

Students will plant seeds in shallow trays or plastic cups. They may test one variable in their procedure. Students using salt solutions should be encouraged to use at least two solution strengths with distilled water as the control. If students use the warming cables as a variable, then seeds without added heat will be the control. If planting depth is the variable, the control is the recommended depth.

Test Your Hypothesis

Plan

1. As a group, agree upon and write your hypothesis and decide how you will test it. Identify which results will confirm the hypothesis.

2. **List** the steps you need to take to test your hypothesis. Be specific, and describe exactly what you will do at each step. List your materials.

3. **Prepare** a data table in your Science Journal to record your observations.

4. Reread your entire experiment to make sure that all of the steps are in a logical order.

5. **Identify** all constants, variables, and controls of the experiment.

Do

1. Make sure your teacher approves your plan and your data table before you proceed.

2. Use the same type and amount of soil in each tray.

3. While the experiment is going on, record your observations accurately and complete the data table in your Science Journal.

Analyze Your Data

1. **Compare** the germination rate in the two groups of seeds.

2. **Compare** your results with those of other groups.

3. Did changing the variable affect germination rates? Explain.

4. Make a bar graph of your experimental results.

Draw Conclusions

1. **Interpret** your graph to estimate the conditions that give the best germination rate.

2. What things affect the germination rate?

Communicating
Your Data

Write a short article for a local newspaper telling about this experiment. Give some ideas about when and how to plant seeds in the garden and the conditions needed for germination.

SECTION 3   Seed Reproduction   **261**

Teaching Strategy

Have students examine seed packets to gain additional information about normal germination rates.

Troubleshooting Students may confuse rate of germination (how quickly seeds germinate) with germination rate (the percent of seeds that actually germinate).

Expected Outcome

Some environmental conditions enhance seed germination; others do not.

Analyze Your Data

1. One group should have had a higher germination rate than the other.

2. Groups testing the same variable should have similar results.

3. Rates of germination and germination rates vary with environmental conditions for each variable, depending on species of plant tested.

4. Graphs should accurately reflect experimental data.

Error Analysis

Have students try to explain differences in their results from others who tested the same variable.

Draw Conclusions

1. Graphs will vary, but each should indicate a range for best germination of the variable tested.

2. Answers may include water quality, amount of water, planting depth, and other similar variables.

✓Assessment

Performance Have students test other temperatures, chemicals, or light conditions and compare their results to those obtained in this activity. Use **Performance Assessment in the Science Classroom,** p. 97.

Communicating
Your Data

Have students include graphs in their articles.

TIME

SCIENCE AND
Society

TIME

SCIENCE AND
Society

SCIENCE
ISSUES
THAT AFFECT
YOU!

Content Background

Genetic engineering is possible because all living organisms, from viruses and single-celled bacteria to humans, use the same genetic code. This allows the possibility of combining DNA from various organisms. The resulting product is called *recombinant DNA*. Organisms that contain DNA from different species are called *transgenic*.

Bacteria contain circular chromosomes called *plasmids*. Favorable genes can be spliced into these plasmids and replicated in great numbers as the bacteria undergo cell division. When the plasmids are introduced to other species, the new gene is transferred to the recipient's DNA, making it possible for the organism to produce a new protein with a certain desired effect. This technique is often used in transferring genes to plant species.

Viruses are little more than molecules of DNA surrounded by a protein coat. Many viruses are specialized and target specific tissues in plants and animals. Viruses work by injecting their DNA into a cell. The viral DNA then is spliced into the recipient's DNA and can be replicated in the host's body. The part of the viral DNA that causes disease can be disabled, making it non-infectious. Favorable genes are spliced into this DNA and then injected into a host. The virus will then target a specific cell type and deliver its modified DNA, allowing the cell to produce an otherwise missing protein. This technique is being developed as a potential means for curing a number of genetic disorders. Favorable results have been seen in this kind of treatment of muscular dystrophy, diabetes, and cystic fibrosis.

What would happen if you crossed a cactus with a rose? Well, you'd either get an extra spiky flower, or a bush that didn't need to be watered very often. Until recently, this sort of mix was the stuff science fiction was made of. But now, with the help of genetic engineering, it may be possible.

Genetic engineering is a way of taking genes from one species and giving them to another. One purpose of genetic engineering is to transfer an organism's traits. For example, scientists have changed grass by adding to it the gene from another grass species. This gene makes the grass grow so slowly, it doesn't have to be mowed very often.

How is this done? It all starts with genes—sections of DNA found in the cells of all living things. Genes produce certain characteristics, or traits, in an organism, like the color of a flower or whether a person has blond hair or black hair. Scientists have found a way to exchange genes and their traits among bacteria, viruses, plants, animals, and even humans. In 1983, the first plant was genetically modified, or changed. Since then, many crops in the U.S. have been modified in this way, including soybeans, potatoes, and tomatoes.

One common genetically engineered crop is corn. To modify it, scientists took a gene from a particular bacterium.

The gene "instructed" the bacterium to produce a natural toxin that killed certain insects. This gene was placed into another bacterium, which was placed into a corn plant. This bacterial "taxi" carried the gene into the plant's DNA, giving it the new trait. The seeds from the genetically modified corn produced crops that resisted harmful insects.

Genetic

Resources for Teachers and Students

The Food Safety Educator, Available from: USDA/FSIS/Food Safety Education, Room 2944-South Building, 1400 Independence Ave., SW, Washington, DC 20250-3700

Genetic Engineering: Fast Forwarding to Future Foods, by John Henkel, April 1995, *FDA Consumer Magazine*.

"Are Bioengineered Foods Safe?," by Larry Thompson, January-February 2000, *FDA Consumer Magazine*.

"Methods For Genetically Engineering a Plant," January-February 2000, *FDA Consumer Magazine*.

Clifton Poodry: Biologist

Clifton Poodry was born in Buffalo, New York, on the Tonawanda Seneca Indian reservation. On the reservation, Native Americans took a great deal of pride in free thinking. "This way of thinking helps if you want to do scientific research," said Poodry. "As a scientist, one thing you get to do is pursue a question that is of interest to you, even if it is not of interest to someone else."

In graduate school, Poodry studied how cells were organized and how they develop structures in the human body.

He was especially interested in learning how an organism develops from one cell to an organism with many different cells. He based his work on the fruit fly.

But equally exciting to Poodry was the fact that in college he shared the labs with men and women from many different ethnic backgrounds—all of whom were interested in research and science. That excitement, and the idea of many people coming together to share knowledge, led him to become a university professor. Today, he works to increase the number of minority students who go into scientific research. He heads the Division of Minority Opportunities in Research, a part of the National Institutes of Health.

Engineering

In addition to making plants resist insects, genetic engineering can make plants grow bigger and faster. Genetic engineering also has produced herbicide-resistant plants. This allows farmers to produce more crops with less chemicals. Scientists predict that genetic engineering will soon produce crops that are more nutritious and that can resist cold, heat, or even drought. This will help farmers increase their harvests and make more food available.

However, not everyone thinks genetic engineering is so great. Since it is a relatively new process, some people are worried about the long-term risks. One concern is that people might be allergic to modified foods and not realize it until it's too late. Other people say that genetic engineering is unnatural. Also, farmers must purchase the patented genetically modified seeds each growing season from the companies that make them, rather than saving and replanting the seeds from their current crops.

Genetically modified "super" tomatoes and "super" corn can resist heat, cold, drought, and insects.

People in favor of genetic engineering reply that there are always risks with new technology, but proper precautions are being taken. Each new plant is tested and then approved by U.S. governmental agencies. And they say that most "natural" crops aren't really natural. They are really hybrid plants bred by agriculturists, and they couldn't survive on their own.

As genetic engineering continues, so does the debate.

CONNECTIONS Debate Research the pros and cons of genetic engineering on the Glencoe Science Web site and in your school's media center. Decide whether you are for or against genetic engineering. Debate your conclusions with your classmates.

SCIENCE Online

For more information, visit science.glencoe.com

SCIENCE Online

Internet Addresses

_____

_____

_____

Explore the Glencoe Science Web site at **science.glencoe.com** to find out more about topics in this feature.

Discussion

What other methods could be used to transfer genes from one species to another without using viruses? Possible answer: A so-called gene gun can be used to "shoot" microscopic metallic pellets coated with plasmids into a cell.

What are some of the fears associated with the technology of genetic engineering? Possible answers: Bacteria and viruses that have been disabled may regain their ability to cause disease after they are injected; some viruses that are used cause very serious diseases prior to being disabled for such a use.

Extension

Have students research which human conditions may be beneficially treated with gene therapy. Suggest students make a collage of pictures and descriptions of these disorders that demonstrates the potential benefits of genetic medicine in the future. **IS Visual-Spatial**

Investigate the Issue

Many of the fears regarding genetic engineering involve the use of this technology in altering many food items. Have students research and identify the foods that have already been subjected to this engineering. **What are the goals of this work?** Many possible answers: tomatoes with longer shelf life; corn and wheat with resistance to insects, etc. Some fears are that modified foods will produce new allergies, cause diseases, result in crop pests that are resistant to insecticides.

Reviewing Main Ideas

Preview

Students can answer the questions in their Science Journals. Discuss the answers as you go through the chapter. **LS** **Linguistic**

Review

Students can write their answers, then compare them with those of other students. **LS** **Interpersonal**

Reteach

Students can look at the illustrations and describe details that support the main ideas of the chapter. **LS** **Visual-Spatial**

Answers to Chapter Review

SECTION 1

2. They are identical.

SECTION 2

3. The production of many spores increases the chances that some will encounter an environment suitable for germination and growth.

SECTION 3

3. Orchid flowers are usually pollinated by insects.

Reviewing Main Ideas

Section 1 Introduction to Plant Reproduction

1. Plants reproduce sexually and asexually. Sexual reproduction involves the formation of sex cells and fertilization.

2. Asexual reproduction does not involve sex cells and produces plants genetically identical to the parent plant. *How do fern plants produced from the same rhizome compare genetically?*

3. Plant life cycles include a gametophyte and a sporophyte stage. The gametophyte stage begins with meiosis. The sporophyte stage begins when the egg is fertilized by a sperm.

4. In some plant life cycles, the sporophyte and gametophyte stages are separate and not dependent on each other. In other plant life cycles, they are part of the same organism.

Section 2 Seedless Reproduction

1. For liverworts and mosses, the gametophyte stage is the familiar plant form. The sporophyte stage produces spores.

2. In ferns, the sporophyte stage, not the gametophyte stage, is the familiar plant form.

3. Seedless plants, like mosses and ferns, use sexual reproduction to produce spores. *Why do seedless plants such as these produce so many small spores?*

Section 3 Seed Reproduction

1. In seed plants the male reproductive organs produce pollen grains that eventually contain sperm. Eggs are produced in the ovules of the female reproductive organs.

2. The male and female reproductive organs of gymnosperms are called cones. Wind usually moves pollen from the male cone to the female cone for pollination.

3. The reproductive organs of angiosperms are in a flower. The male reproductive organ is the stamen, and the female reproductive organ is the pistil. Gravity, wind, rain, and animals can pollinate a flower. *How would these flowers become pollinated?*

4. Seeds of gymnosperms and angiosperms are dispersed in many ways. Wind, water, and animals spread seeds. Some plants can eject their seeds.

5. Germination is a series of events that results in the growth of a plant from a seed.

FOLDABLES
Reading & Study Skills

After You Read

On the front of your Venn Diagram Study Fold where the circles overlap, write common characteristics of sexual and asexual reproduction.

FOLDABLES
Reading & Study Skills

After You Read

After students have read the chapter and completed the Foldable described in Before You Read, have them do the activity on the student page.

Dinah Zike

Chapter 9 Study Guide

Visualizing Main Ideas

Complete the following table that compares reproduction in different plant groups.

Plant Reproduction

Plant Group	Seeds?	Pollen?	Cones?	Flowers?
Mosses	No	No	No	No
Ferns	No	No	No	No
Gymnosperms	Yes	Yes	Yes	No
Angiosperms	Yes	Yes	No	Yes

Vocabulary Review

Vocabulary Words

a. frond
b. gametophyte stage
c. germination
d. ovary
e. ovule
f. pistil
g. pollen grain

h. pollination
i. prothallus
j. rhizome
k. sori
l. spore
m. sporophyte stage
n. stamen

THE PRINCETON REVIEW

Study Tip

Read the chapter before you go over it in class. Being familiar with the material before your teacher explains it gives you better understanding and an opportunity to ask questions.

Using Vocabulary

Replace the underlined word or phrase with the correct vocabulary word(s).

1. A <u>sori</u> is the leaf of a fern.

2. In seed plants, the <u>anther</u> contains the egg.

3. The plant structures in the <u>sporophyte stage</u> are made up of haploid cells.

4. The green, leafy moss plant is part of the <u>prothallus</u> in the moss life cycle.

5. Two parts of a sporophyte fern are <u>stamen</u> and <u>pistil</u>.

6. The female reproductive organ of the flower is the <u>rhizome</u>.

7. The <u>ovule</u> is the swollen base of the pistil.

CHAPTER STUDY GUIDE   265

Chapter 9 Study Guide

Visualizing Main Ideas

See student page.

Vocabulary Review

Using Vocabulary

1. frond
2. ovule
3. gametophyte stage
4. gametophyte stage
5. frond; rhizome; sori (any two)
6. pistil
7. ovary

Chapter 9 Assessment

Checking Concepts

1. A
2. A
3. A
4. A
5. A
6. C
7. C
8. D
9. D
10. D

Thinking Critically

11. Large numbers of pollen grains increase the chances that any one pollen grain will be blown to a female cone and fertilize an ovule.
12. No; the embryo is the young plant; without it, no plant can grow.
13. Nonvascular plants and ferns require water to transport the sperm to egg cells.
14. The sporophyte is not photosynthetic, so it depends on the photosynthetic gametophyte for nutrition.
15. Brightly colored structures, scents, and flower form help to ensure pollination by specialized pollinators.

Checking Concepts

Choose the word or phrase that best answers the question.

1. How are colorful flowers usually pollinated?
   A) insects   C) clothing
   B) wind   D) gravity

2. What type of reproduction produces plants that are genetically identical?
   A) asexual   C) spore
   B) sexual   D) flower

3. Which of the following terms describes the cells in the gametophyte stage?
   A) haploid   C) diploid
   B) prokaryote   D) missing a nucleus

4. What structures do ferns form when they reproduce sexually?
   A) spores   C) seeds
   B) anthers   D) flowers

5. What contains food for the plant embryo?
   A) endosperm   C) stigma
   B) pollen grain D) root

6. What disperses most dandelion seeds?
   A) rain   C) wind
   B) animals   D) insects

7. What is the series of events that results in a plant growing from a seed?
   A) pollination C) germination
   B) prothallus   D) fertilization

8. In plants, meiosis is used to produce what before fertilization?
   A) prothallus   C) flowers
   B) seeds   D) spores

9. Ovules and pollen grains take part in what process?
   A) germination
   B) asexual reproduction
   C) seed dispersal
   D) sexual reproduction

10. What part of the flower receives the pollen grain from the anther?
    A) sepal   C) stamen
    B) petal   D) stigma

Thinking Critically

11. Explain why male cones produce so many pollen grains.

12. Could a seed without an embryo germinate? Explain your answer.

13. Discuss the importance of water in the sexual reproduction of nonvascular plants and ferns.

14. In mosses, why is the sporophyte stage dependent on the gametophyte stage?

15. What features of flowers ensure pollination?

Developing Skills

16. **Making and Using Graphs** Make a bar graph for the following data table about onion seeds. Put days on the horizontal axis and temperature on the vertical axis.

Onion Seed Data						
Temperature (°C)	10	15	20	25	30	35
Days to Germinate	13	7	5	4	4	13

17. **Comparing and Contrasting** Describe the differences and similarities between the fern sporophyte and gametophyte stages.

Chapter ✓Assessment Planner

Portfolio Encourage students to place in their portfolios one or two items of what they consider to be their best work. Examples include:
- Assessment, p. 243
- Make a Model, p. 246
- Activity, p. 251

Performance Additional performance assessments, Performance Task Assessment Lists, and rubrics for evaluating these activities can be found in Glencoe's **Performance Assessment in the Science Classroom.**

18. **Predicting** Observe pictures of flowers or actual flowers and predict how they are pollinated. Explain your prediction.

19. **Interpreting Scientific Illustrations** Using **Figure 16,** sequence these events.
    pollen is trapped on the stigma
    pollen tube reaches the ovule
    fertilization
    pollen released from the anther
    pollen tube forms through the style
    a seed forms

20. **Concept Mapping** Complete this concept map of a typical plant life cycle.

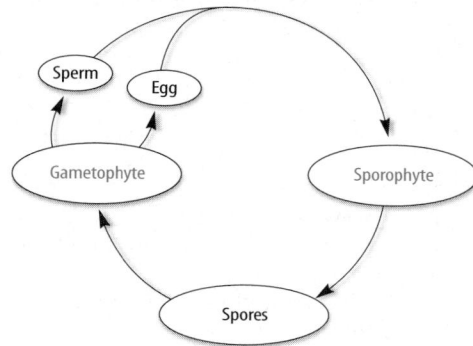

Performance Assessment

21. **Seed Mosaic** Collect several different types of seeds and use them to make a mosaic picture of a flower.

22. **Newspaper Story** Write a newspaper story to tell people about the importance of gravity, water, wind, insects, and other animals in plant life cycles.

TECHNOLOGY

 Go to the Glencoe Science Web site at **science.glencoe.com** or use the **Glencoe Science CD-ROM** for additional chapter assessment.

 **THE PRINCETON REVIEW** **Test Practice**

Four groups containing 15 plants each were set up to determine how many flowers were pollinated in a 24-h period. Each plant had five flowers. A botanist recorded the data in the following table.

Pollination Data			
Plant Group (15 plants per group)	Number of Bees	Number of Birds	Number of Flowers Pollinated after 24 hrs.
1	5	1	16
2	10	1	35
3	15	1	49
4	20	1	73

Study the table and answer the following questions.

1. Which hypothesis probably is being tested in this experiment?
   A) A greater number of bees increases the rate of pollination.
   B) Birds increase the chance of pollination.
   C) A combination of birds and bees gives the best chance of successful pollination.
   D) Increasing the number of plants in a group results in increased pollination.

2. The pollination that is taking place in this experiment is part of which process?
   F) asexual reproduction
   G) sexual reproduction
   H) seed dispersal
   J) germination

Chapter ⑨ Assessment

 **THE PRINCETON REVIEW** **Test Practice**

The Test-Taking Tip was written by The Princeton Review, the nation's leader in test preparation.
1. A
2. G

Developing Skills

16. Onion Seed Germination

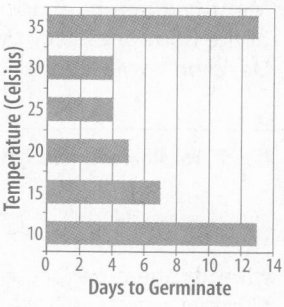

Onion Seed Data

17. Haploid gametophyte stage—small and inconspicuous; diploid sporophyte stage—large and conspicuous; both stages are independent and photosynthetic.

18. Answers will vary depending on flowers observed.

19. 1—pollen is released from the anther; 2—pollen is trapped on the stigma; 3—pollen tube forms through style; 4—pollen tube reaches the ovule; 5—fertilization; 6—a seed forms

20. See student page.

Performance Assessment

21. Seed mosaics will vary depending on seed selection and flower chosen. Look for all parts of a flower in the mosaics. Use **PASC**, p. 135.

22. Stories should include information about plant life cycles and the importance of mechanisms of pollination. Use **PASC**, p. 141.

✓Assessment Resources

📁 **Reproducible Masters**

Chapter Resources Booklet
  Chapter Review, pp. 35–36
  Chapter Tests, pp. 37–40
  Assessment Transparency Activity, p. 47

Glencoe Science Web site
  Interactive Tutor
  Chapter Quizzes

Glencoe Technology
  🔖 Assessment Transparency
  💿 Interactive CD-ROM Chapter Quizzes
  💿 ExamView Pro Test Bank
  💿 Vocabulary PuzzleMaker Software
  📼 MindJogger Videoquiz

Section/Objectives	Standards		Activities/Features
Chapter Opener	National	State/Local	**Explore Activity:** Model a chemical message, p. 269 **Before You Read,** p. 269
	See p. 5T for a Key to Standards.		
Section 1 The Endocrine System ⏱ 2 sessions 📦 1 block 1. **Define** how hormones function. 2. **Identify** different endocrine glands and the effects of the hormones they produce. 3. **Describe** how a feedback system works in your body.	National Content Standards: UCP1, UCP5, C1, C3		**Earth Science Integration,** p. 271 **Math Skills Activity:** Calculating Blood Sugar Percentage, p. 271 **Visualizing the Endocrine System,** p. 272–273
Section 2 The Reproductive System ⏱ 2 sessions 📦 1 block 1. **Identify** the function of the reproductive system. 2. **Compare and contrast** the major structures of the male and female reproductive systems. 3. **Sequence** the stages of the menstrual cycle.	National Content Standards: UCP1, UCP3, A1, C1, C2, C3, F1		**Science Online,** p. 277 **MiniLAB:** Graphing Hormone Levels, p. 278 **Activity:** Interpreting Diagrams, p. 280
Section 3 Human Life Stages ⏱ 3 sessions 📦 1.5 blocks 1. **Describe** the fertilization of a human egg. 2. **List** the major events in the development of an embryo and fetus. 3. **Describe** the developmental stages of infancy, childhood, adolescence, and adulthood.	National Content Standards: UCP5, A1, C1, C2, C3, F1		**MiniLAB:** Interpreting Fetal Development, p. 284 **Science Online,** p. 285 **Physics Integration,** p. 288 **Activity:** Changing Body Proportions, p. 290–291 **Science Stats:** Facts About Infants, p. 292–293

◻ NATIONAL GEOGRAPHIC

Teacher's Corner

PRODUCTS AVAILABLE FROM GLENCOE
To order call 1-800-334-7344:
CD-ROM
NGS PictureShow: Human Body 3
Curriculum Kit
GeoKit: Human Body 2

Transparency Set
NGS PicturePack: Human Body 3
Videodisk
STV: Human Body
PRODUCTS AVAILABLE FROM NATIONAL GEOGRAPHIC SOCIETY
To order call 1-800-368-2728:

Videos
Reproductive System (The Human Body Series)
Incredible Human Machine

Activity Materials	Reproducible Resources	Section Assessment	Technology
Explore Activity: filter paper; metric ruler; plastic, ceramic, or glass plate; baking soda; salt; dropper; vinegar	**Chapter Resources Booklet** Foldables Worksheet, p. 15 Directed Reading Overview, p. 17 Note-taking Worksheets, pp. 31–33	GLENCOE'S ASSESSMENT ADVANTAGE	
Need materials? Contact Science Kit at 1-800-828-7777 or www.sciencekit.com on the Internet.	**Chapter Resources Booklet** Transparency Activity, p. 42 Enrichment, p. 28 Reinforcement, p. 25 Directed Reading, p. 18 Lab Activity, pp. 9–11 Transparency Activity, pp. 45–46	Portfolio Visual Learning, p. 273 Performance Math Skills Activity, p. 271 Skill Builder Activities, p. 274 Content Section Assessment, p. 274	♪ Section Focus Transparency ♪ Teaching Transparency ⊙ Interactive CD-ROM ⌒ Guided Reading Audio Program
MiniLAB: graph paper **Activity:** paper, pencil	**Chapter Resources Booklet** Transparency Activity, p. 43 MiniLAB, p. 3 Enrichment, p. 29 Reinforcement, p. 26 Directed Reading, p. 18 Activity Worksheet, pp. 5–6	Portfolio Science Journal, p. 277 Performance MiniLAB, p. 278 Skill Builder Activities, p. 279 Content Section Assessment, p. 279	♪ Section Focus Transparency ⊙ Interactive CD-ROM ⌒ Guided Reading Audio Program
MiniLAB: graph paper **Activity:** tape measure, erasable pencil, graph paper	**Chapter Resources Booklet** Transparency Activity, p. 44 MiniLAB, p. 4 Enrichment, p. 30 Reinforcement, p. 27 Directed Reading, pp. 19, 20 Activity Worksheet, pp. 7–8 Lab Activity, pp. 13–14 **Lab Management and Safety,** p. 70 **Home and Community Involvement,** p. 43 **Reading and Writing Skill Activities,** p. 39 **Life Science Critical Thinking/ Problem Solving,** p. 19	Portfolio Make a Model, p. 282 Performance MiniLAB, p. 284 Skill Builder Activities, p. 289 Content Section Assessment, p. 289	♪ Section Focus Transparency ⊙ Interactive CD-ROM ⌒ Guided Reading Audio Program

End of Chapter Assessment

GLENCOE'S ASSESSMENT ADVANTAGE

Blackline Masters	Technology	Professional Series
Chapter Resources Booklet Chapter Review, pp. 35–36 Chapter Tests, pp. 37–40 **Standardized Test Practice by The Princeton Review,** pp. 95–98	▭ MindJogger Videoquiz ⊙ Interactive CD-ROM ⊙ Vocabulary PuzzleMakers ⊙ ExamView Pro Test Bank ⊙ Interactive Lesson Planner ⊙ Interactive Teacher Edition	Performance Assessment in the Science Classroom (PASC)

Transparencies

Section Focus

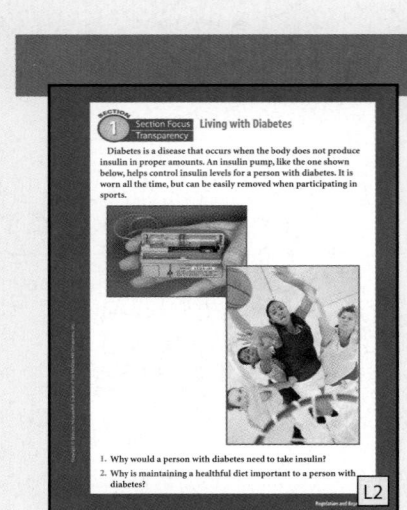

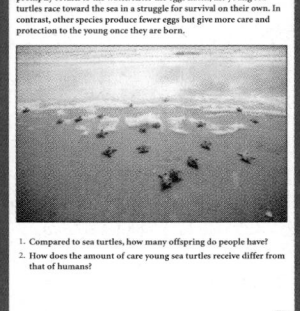

This is a representation of key blackline masters available in the Teacher Classroom Resources. See Resource Manager boxes within the chapter for additional information.

Assessment

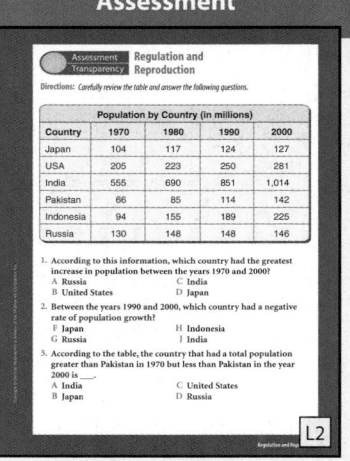

Teaching

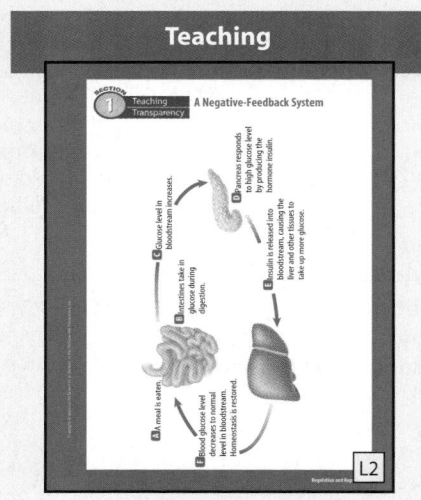

Key to Teaching Strategies

The following designations will help you decide which activities are appropriate for your students.

L1 Level 1 activities should be appropriate for students with learning difficulties.

L2 Level 2 activities should be within the ability range of all students.

L3 Level 3 activities are designed for above-average students.

ELL ELL activities should be within the ability range of English Language Learners.

COOP LEARN Cooperative Learning activities are designed for small group work.

LS Multiple Learning Styles logos, as described on page 22T, are used throughout to indicate strategies that address different learning styles.

P These strategies represent student products that can be placed into a best-work portfolio.

Hands-on Activities

Activity Worksheets

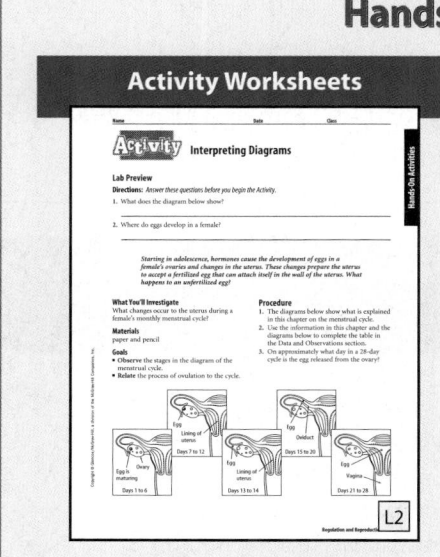

Laboratory Activities

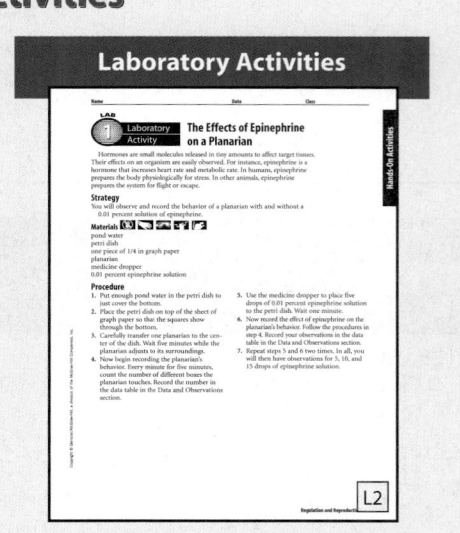

Meeting Different Ability Levels

Content Outline

Note-taking Worksheet — Regulation and Reproduction

Section 1   The Endocrine System

A. _____ of the endocrine system—help regulate and coordinate body systems
   1. _____—chemical messengers manufactured in glands throughout the body
   2. Endocrine glands release hormones directly into the blood because they are _____
B. Negative-feedback system—endocrine system gives _____ messages to control the production and release of hormones.

Section 2   The Reproductive System

A. Endocrine system hormones are key factors in the _____ of human reproduction systems.
B. Male reproductive system—has both internal and external organs
   1. _____—organs that produce male hormone testosterone and reproductive cells called **sperm**
   2. Internal organs combine sperm with a fluid energy source producing _____.
C. Female reproductive system—internal organs called _____ produce egg cells.
   1. Once a month the _____ process releases an egg.
   2. A hollow, pear-shaped, muscular organ in which fertilized eggs develop is called the _____.
   3. The _____, or birth canal, is a muscular tube that opens to the outside of the body.
D. Menstrual cycle—monthly cycle of _____ in the female reproductive system
   1. Endocrine _____ including estrogen and progesterone control the menstrual cycle.
   2. _____, which is the release of blood and uterine lining tissue, occurs in _____ phases.
      a. Phase 1 begins when _____ starts and usually lasts about 4 to 6 days.
      b. Phase 2 involves thickening of the uterus lining and _____, or egg release.
      c. Phase 3 continues with uterine preparation and ends with _____ hormone levels and uterine lining breakdown if no fertilized egg occurs.
   3. _____—the gradual shutdown of the ovaries which ends ovulation and menstrual periods

L2

Reinforcement

Reinforcement 1 — The Endocrine System

Directions: *Listed below are some of the endocrine glands. Describe the function of each gland and label the figure below.*
1. pituitary gland

2. thyroid gland

3. parathyroid glands

4. adrenal glands

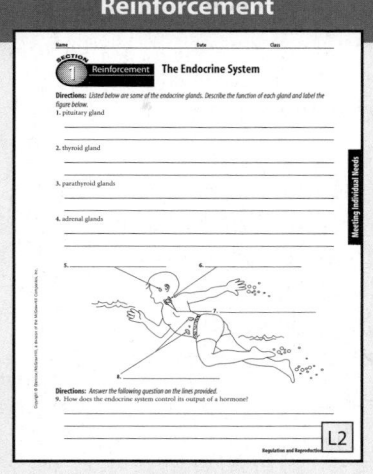

Directions: *Answer the following question on the lines provided.*
9. How does the endocrine system control its output of a hormone?

L2

Directed Reading

Directed Reading for Content Mastery — *Overview* Regulation and Reproduction

Directions: *Complete the sentences using the terms listed below.*

| hormones | endocrine | umbilical cord |
| adulthood | childhood | negative feedback |

1. _____ secreted by glands in the _____ system are necessary for sexual development.
2. The endocrine system controls the level of hormones in the body by a _____ system.
3. At birth the baby is still attached to the _____.
4. The stages of life are infancy, _____, adolescence, and _____.

Directions: *Use the following terms to complete the concept map below.*

| egg | oviduct | sperm |
| semen | fertilized egg | urethra |

An ovary → produces a(n) ___ that travels through the ___ and is penetrated by the male's sperm to become a(n) ___

Testes → produce ___ that combine with semen and travel through the ___ to penetrate the female's egg to create a(n) ___

L1

Assessment

Chapter Tests

Chapter Test — Regulation and Reproduction

I. Testing Concepts

Directions: *Match the terms in Column I with the definitions in Column I. Write the letter of the correct term in the blank at the left. Some items in the second column may not be used.*

Column I
___ 1. passageway leading from the uterus to outside the female's body
___ 2. process of releasing eggs on a monthly basis
___ 3. monthly discharge of the lining of the uterus
___ 4. control body activities deposited directly into the bloodstream
___ 5. the period in human growth that begins around age 12 to 14 and lasts until age 20
___ 6. fertilized egg during first two months of pregnancy
___ 7. mixture of sperm and a fluid that nourishes the sperm and helps them to move
___ 8. a developing baby after the first two months of pregnancy
___ 9. age one to age 12
___ 10. period between fertilization and birth

Column II
a. adolescence
b. amniotic sac
c. childhood
d. embryo
e. fetus
f. hormones
g. menstruation
h. ovaries
i. ovulation
j. pregnancy
k. semen
l. uterus
m. vagina

Directions: *For each of the following, write the letter of the term or phrase that best completes the sentence.*

___ 11. Egg cells are produced in the ___.
   a. ovaries   b. oviduct   c. uterus   d. vagina
___ 12. An egg is usually fertilized in the a(n) ___.
   a. oviduct   b. uterus   c. vagina   d. womb
___ 13. The womb, or ___, is a muscular organ in which a fertilized egg can develop into a baby.
   a. amnion   b. oviduct   c. uterus   d. vagina
___ 14. Hormones from the ___ gland control the menstrual cycle.
   a. hypothalamus   b. pituitary   c. prostate   d. thyroid
___ 15. Nearly ___ sperm are deposited in the female during fertilization.
   a. 2000 to 3000   c. 200 thousand to 300 thousand
   b. 28,000 to 30,000   d. 200 million to 300 million

L2

Enrichment

Enrichment 1 — Transplantation

Each year, millions of Americans develop Type I or insulin-dependent diabetes mellitus. People with Type I diabetes don't produce enough insulin because the disease destroys the cells in the pancreas that make insulin. Although diabetes is often managed with insulin injections, it is a serious—sometimes deadly—disease. It can cause heart disease, high blood pressure, blindness, and more. In fact, diabetes is the leading cause of kidney failure, affecting almost 30 percent of people with Type I diabetes.

A New Kidney
That's why diabetic patients with kidney failure often undergo surgery to get a new kidney. This surgery, called kidney transplantation, has a better success rate than another kind of treatment called dialysis. Dialysis acts as an artificial kidney that removes a patient's blood, purifies it, and returns it to the bloodstream. Unfortunately, Type I diabetic patients treated with dialysis for a long time are more likely to die at a young age.
Doctors trying to save lives have, in a single operation, transplanted both kidneys and pancreases into diabetic patients. The simultaneous transplantation of a pancreas and kidney, called SPK transplantation. With SPK transplantation, patients can live longer, healthier lives.

Ten years after SPK transplantation, between 70 and 80 percent of patients are still alive. With ten years on dialysis, less than 20 percent of patients survive. But SPK transplantation isn't perfect. There are risks involved, such as infection and organ rejection. Plus, patients must stay in the hospital for several days after surgery and recover at home for another four to six weeks.

Another Type of Transplant
Diabetics can also consider islet cell transplantation. With this procedure, islets or nests of hormone-producing cells are freed from nearby pancreatic tissue. The tissue is processed to purify the cells, then injected into a vein that leads directly to the liver. If the operation is successful, the islet cells survive and produce insulin.
Islet cell transplantation has none of the side effects of SPK transplantation. Even though it's been around as long as SPK transplantation, islet cell transplantation is still considered experimental. That's because its success rate is much lower than SPK transplantation. Only five to ten percent of islet cell transplantation patients are able to go off insulin after one year, compared with more than 80 percent of pancreatic transplant patients. But both methods provide hope to diabetic patients.

1. Explain the difference between SPK transplantation and islet cell transplantation.

2. What are the biggest advantages of either kind of transplantation surgery?

3. Do you think it's accurate to call SPK transplantation a "life-saving operation"? Why or why not?

4. Besides having a lower success rate than SPK transplantation, why else might islet cell transplantation be considered experimental?

28   Regulation and Reproduction

L3

Spanish Directed Reading

Lectura dirigida para Dominio del contenido — *Sinopsis* Regulación y reproducción

Instrucciones: *Completa las oraciones usando los siguientes términos.*

| hormonas | endocrine | cordón umbilical |
| edad adulta | childhood | retroalimentación negativa |

1. Las glándulas en el sistema _____ secretan _____ que son necesarias para el desarrollo sexual.
2. El sistema endocrino controla los niveles de hormonas en el cuerpo mediante un sistema de _____.
3. Al nacer, el bebé aún está adherido al(a la) _____.
4. Las etapas de la vida son lactancia, _____, adolescencia y _____.

Instrucciones: *Usa los siguientes términos para completar el mapa conceptual.*

| óvulo | oviducto | espermatozoides |
| semen | óvulo fecundado | uretra |

Los ovarios → producen un ___ que viaja por el(la) ___ que es penetrado(a) por los espermatozoides y se convierte en un(a) ___

Los testículos → producen ___ que se combinan con el semen y viajan a través de(l) ___ hasta penetrar el óvulo femenino para crear un(a) ___

L1

Test Practice Workbook

Standardized Test Practice
Teacher Edition

Glencoe Science

- Correlated to the National Science Standards
- Prepares students for ITBS, SAT-9, and Terra Nova
- Four pages of questions for each chapter
- Written by The Princeton Review

LEVEL GREEN

L2

Chapter Review

Chapter Review — Regulation and Reproduction

Part A. Vocabulary Review

Directions: *Select the term from the following list that matches each description.*

amniotic sac	embryo	fetus	hormones
menopause	menstrual cycle	menstruation	ovaries
ovulation	pregnancy	sperm
target tissues	testes	uterus	vagina

___ 1. tissues affected by hormones
___ 2. male reproductive cells
___ 3. produce eggs in the female
___ 4. muscular organ in which a fertilized egg develops into a baby
___ 5. birth canal
___ 6. process of releasing eggs on a monthly basis
___ 7. monthly discharge of the lining of the uterus
___ 8. menstrual cycle becomes irregular, then stops
___ 9. fertilized egg during first two months of pregnancy
___ 10. mixture of sperm and fluid
___ 11. monthly cycle of changes in the female reproductive system
___ 12. cushions the developing baby
___ 13. developing baby after two months of pregnancy
___ 14. period of fetal development lasting nine months
___ 15. endocrine secretions
___ 16. produce male reproductive cells

Directions: *State the function of the following glands.*

17. Pituitary gland: _____

18. Thyroid gland: _____

L2

Science Content Background

The Endocrine System

Regulation

The endocrine system backs up the regulatory functions of the nervous system. The endocrine system uses hormones to control body functions such as defense, hunger, growth and reproduction. All organs of the endocrine system are glands that produce and empty hormones into the circulatory system.

The anterior lobe of the pituitary gland produces hormones that cause the stimulation of growth, the production of milk, the regulation of thyroid gland secretions, the regulation of adrenal cortex secretions, the stimulation of egg and sperm production, and egg release.

The posterior lobe of the pituitary gland aids in the regulation of water secretion by the kidneys, muscle contractions during labor, and the contraction of milk-producing glands.

The pituitary's intermediate lobe controls melanin production, which determines skin color.

Student Misconception

Fertilization and embryonic development are mysterious processes that are not understandable.

Refer to the facing page for teaching strategies to address this misconception. Refer to pages 281–284 for content related to this topic.

The Reproductive System

Hormones

Hormones produced by the endocrine system control sexual development, maturation, and functioning of the reproductive system. Hormones stimulate the production and release of sperm and semen in the male reproductive system. In the female reproductive system, hormones stimulate the production and release of ova, or eggs. A mature ovum is about 0.10 mm in diameter. Hormones also play a role during labor and birth. In later years, menopause is brought on when the body stops producing certain hormones.

Human Life Stages

Embryonic Development

Fertilization is the union of a sperm cell from a male with an egg from a female. Fertilization results in two events: (1) fusion of the sperm and egg cells, including fusion of the two nuclei, to form a cell called a zygote, and (2) activation of the new cell to begin division and growth.

Once a sperm fertilizes an egg, the egg produces an outer protective layer. Next, the zygote divides into thousands of smaller cells that cling together like a ball of soap bubbles. After several days and until about two weeks later, the ball of cells begins to differentiate into three parts: an outer layer of cells that attaches to the uterus of the mother, an inner mass of cells that develops into the embryo, and a fluid-filled sac that surrounds the embryo.

The next phase, which occurs between two and eight weeks after fertilization, involves specialization of cells into primary organ systems. This set of events marks the end of the embryo stage and the beginning of the fetal stage.

SCIENCE Online

For additional content background on this topic, go to the Glencoe Science Web site at science.glencoe.com.

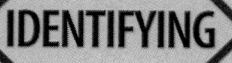

IDENTIFYING ▷ Misconceptions

Students may think that . . .

- **Fertilization and embryonic development are mysterious processes that are not understandable.**

Many students may find the concepts of fertilization and embryonic development very abstract. Using concrete demonstrations and activities will help these students understand the processes and sequences of events that occur.

Demonstration

- Using two different colors of clay, form a large ball from one color, representing an egg cell, and many smaller balls from the second color, representing sperm cells. Fertilization can be modeled by molding the "egg" and "sperm" into one ball. Explain that this fertilized cell is called a zygote. No other sperm cells can fuse with the egg cell at this point because the zygote produces a protective barrier blocking other sperm cells. Emphasize that the molding together of the sperm and egg cells is a simulation of the combining of genetic material from both.

- Next, model the phase of rapid cell division by dividing the ball into many smaller, connected balls. Explain that these cells cling together like a ball of soap bubbles. Continue by drawing the "soap bubble" stage on the board and labeling it as time from fertilization to a few days.

- Next, draw the three-part stage and the specialization. Label these drawings as "a few days to 2 weeks" and "2 weeks to 8 weeks," respectively.

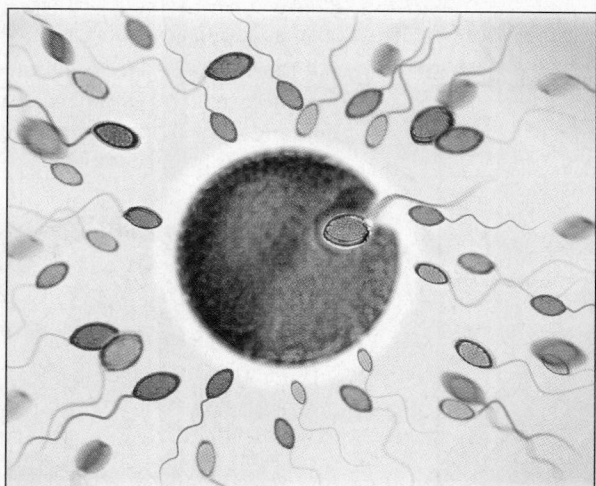

VCG/FPG International

Activity

After discussion, have students draw diagrams of the events that occur from fertilization through the stages of early development to the early fetal stage. Have students work in small groups to explain to one another their diagrams and the events that take place during each stage.

After completing the chapter, see *Identifying Misconceptions* in the Study Guide.

Regulation and Reproduction

Regulation and Reproduction

Chapter Vocabulary

What do you think?

Science Journal This bumpy-looking cluster of cells is the morula stage of human development. A morula is a ball of cells that forms by cell division following fertilization. The name morula comes from the Latin word for mulberry.

The control room blinks with monitors and panels of dials and buttons. Not much is going to get past this complex monitoring system. Your body also is designed with a system that monitors and controls the actions of many of your body's functions. In this chapter, you'll learn about this system—the endocrine system. You'll also study the human reproductive system and the stages of growth.

What do you think?

Science Journal Look at the picture below with a classmate. Discuss what this might be. Here's a hint: *This object could be considered a small beginning.* Write your answer or best guess in your Science Journal.

268

Theme Connection

Stability and Change and **Energy** The endocrine system maintains stable body functions and responds to changes. The unique functioning of the reproductive system is dependent on energy for cell division and differentiation of cells.

Your body has systems that work together to control your body's activities. One of these systems sends chemical messages through your blood to certain tissues, which, in turn, respond. You may feel the results of this system's action, but you cannot see them. Do the activity below to see how a chemical signal can be sent.

Model a chemical message

1. Cut a 10-cm-tall Y shape from filter paper and place it on a plastic, ceramic, or glass plate.

2. Sprinkle baking soda on one arm of the Y and salt on the other arm.

3. Using a dropper, place five or six drops of vinegar halfway up the leg of the Y.

Observe

Describe in your Science Journal how the chemical moves along the paper and the reaction(s) it causes.

Before You Read

Making a Sequence Study Fold
Make the following Foldable to help you predict what might occur next in the sequence of life.

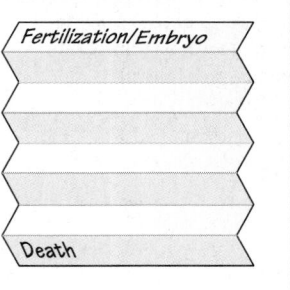
Fertilization/Embryo

Death

1. Place a sheet of paper in front of you so the short side is at the top. Fold the paper in half from top to bottom. Then fold it in half again top to bottom two more times. Unfold all the folds.

2. Using the fold lines as a guide, refold the paper into a fan. Unfold all the folds again.

3. Before you read the chapter list as many stages of life as you can on your foldable, beginning with *Fertilization/Embryo* and ending with *Death*. As you read the chapter add to your list.

269

1 Motivate

Bellringer Transparency

Display the Section Focus
Transparency for Section 1.
Use the accompanying Trans-
parency Activity Master. [L2]
[ELL]

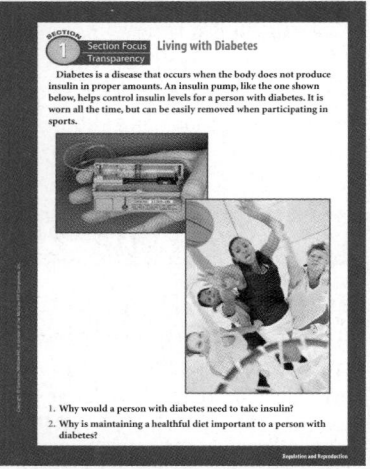

Living with Diabetes

Diabetes is a disease that occurs when the body does not produce
insulin in proper amounts. An insulin pump, like the one shown
below, helps control insulin levels for a person with diabetes. It is
worn all the time, but can be easily removed when participating in
sports.

1. Why would a person with diabetes need to take insulin?
2. Why is maintaining a healthful diet important to a person with
diabetes?

Tie to Prior Knowledge

Have students recall how their
bodies react to stimuli such as the
touching of a hot object or how
they respond to a loud noise.

The Endocrine System

As You Read

What You'll Learn

- **Define** how hormones function.
- **Identify** different endocrine glands
  and the effects of the hormones
  they produce.
- **Describe** how a feedback system
  works in your body.

Vocabulary
hormone

Why It's Important
The endocrine system uses chemicals
to control many systems in your
body.

Functions of the Endocrine System

You go through the dark hallways of a haunted house. You
can't see a thing. Your heart is pounding. Suddenly, a monster
steps out in front of you. You scream and jump backwards. Your
body is prepared to defend itself or get away. Preparing the body
for fight or flight in times of emergency, as shown in **Figure 1,** is
one of the functions of the body's control systems.

Chemical Messengers Your body is made up of systems
that are controlled, or regulated, to work together. The nervous
system and the endocrine (EN duh krun) system are the control
systems of your body. The nervous system sends messages to
and from the brain throughout the body. The endocrine system
uses **hormones** (HOR mohnz)—chemicals that are made in tissues called glands found throughout your body. Hormones
from endocrine glands are released directly into your bloodstream. They affect specific tissues called target tissues, usually
located in the body far from the hormone-producing gland.
The body doesn't react as quickly to messages from the
endocrine system as it does to those of the nervous system.

Figure 1
Your endocrine system enables
many parts of your body to
respond with an immediate
reaction to a fearful
situation.

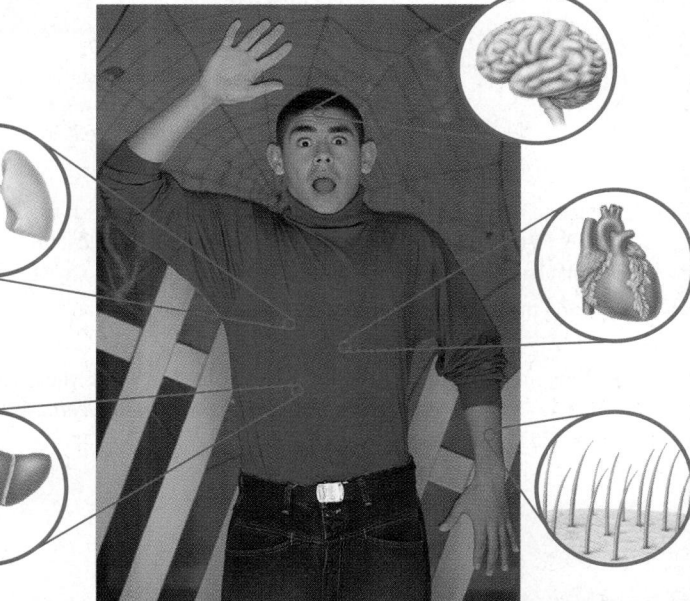

270

Section ✓ *Assessment* Planner

PORTFOLIO
Visual Learning, p. 273
PERFORMANCE ASSESSMENT
Math Skills Activity, p. 271
Skill Builder Activities, p. 274
See page 296 for more options.

CONTENT ASSESSMENT
Section, p. 274
Challenge, p. 274
Chapter, pp. 296–297

Endocrine Glands

Unlike some glands, such as your mouth's saliva glands, that release their products through small tubes called ducts, endocrine glands are ductless. Hormones from endocrine glands pour directly into the blood to reach target tissues. Hormones regulate certain cellular activities. **Figure 2** on the next page describes some of your major endocrine glands and how they function to regulate your body.

 **Reading Check** *What is the function of hormones?*

 **Earth Science**
INTEGRATION

Without the element iodine, the thyroid gland cannot function properly. Iodine is found in seawater, soil, and rocks. How does your body take in iodine? Write your answer in your Science Journal.

Math Skills Activity

Calculating Blood Sugar Percentage

Example Problem

Calculate how much higher the blood sugar (glucose) level of a diabetic is before breakfast when compared to a nondiabetic before breakfast. Express this number as a percentage of the nondiabetic sugar level before breakfast.

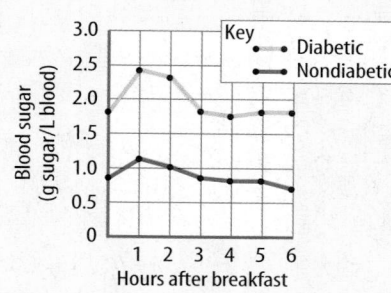

Solution

1 *This is what you know:*
blood sugar of a nondiabetic person at 0 h = 0.85 g sugar/L blood
blood sugar of a diabetic person at 0 h = 1.8 g sugar/L blood

2 *This is what you must do first:*
Find the difference between the two values. 1.8 g/L − 0.85 g/L = 0.95 g/L

3 *This is the equation you need to use:*

$$\frac{\text{difference between values}}{\text{nondiabetic value}} \times 100\% = \text{percent difference}$$

4 *Substitute in the known values:*

$$\frac{0.95}{0.85} \times 100\% = 111\%$$

At 0 h before breakfast, a diabetic's blood sugar is 111 percent higher than that of a nondiabetic.

Practice Problem

Express as a percentage how much higher the blood sugar value is for a diabetic person compared to a nondiabetic person 1 h, 3 h, and 6 h after breakfast.

For more help, refer to the Math Skill Handbook.

Teacher FYI

In addition to hormones produced by endocrine glands, other organs also produce hormones. Endocrine cells in the stomach produce a hormone that regulates the release of its digestive enzymes. The kidneys release a hormone that controls the rate of production of red blood cells. The heart makes a hormone that regulates blood pressure and volume.

Resource Manager

Chapter Resources Booklet
Transparency Activity, p. 42
Directed Reading for Content Mastery, pp. 17, 18
Note-taking Worksheets, pp. 31–33

---

2 Teach

Functions of the Endocrine System

Extension

Have students research the function of the chemical messengers called prostaglandins. Though not true hormones, they act like hormones. In reality, they are fatty-acid derivatives. L2

Endocrine Glands

 **Earth Science**
INTEGRATION

The human body absorbs iodine from food.

✔ **Reading Check**

Answer to speed up and slow down certain cellular activities

Math Skills Activity

National Math Standards

Correlation to Mathematics Objectives
1, 2, 4, 5, 6, 8, 9

Answer to Practice Problem

Hour one = 130 / 110 × 100 = 118 %
Hour three = 95 / 85 × 100 = 111 %
Hour six = 110 / 70 × 100 = 157 %

Note: student answers may vary slightly due to the values read from the graph. Accept answers that are reasonably close.

Visualizing the Endocrine System

Have students examine the pictures and read the captions. Then ask the following questions.

How do hormones from the thyroid gland and the parathyroid gland work together? Possible answers: Both glands release hormones that work together to regulate the levels of calcium in the blood.

What could be the result if a person's thymus gland was not functioning properly? Possible answer: The thymus gland produces hormones that stimulate the production of cells involved in immune reactions. Without these cells the body has difficulty fighting infection.

Activity

Have students write and act out a skit that demonstrates the negative feedback cycle of hormone regulation. Students can break into groups of 6 or 7 and produce the skits. The instructor would need to provide a different sequence of events for each student group. Each student can play the role of the brain, a hormone or an endocrine gland, and one student can be the messenger between the body and the brain.

Extension

Have students research disorders of the endocrine system such as Graves' disease, Cushing's Syndrome, Addison's disease, diabetes, gigantism and acromegaly.

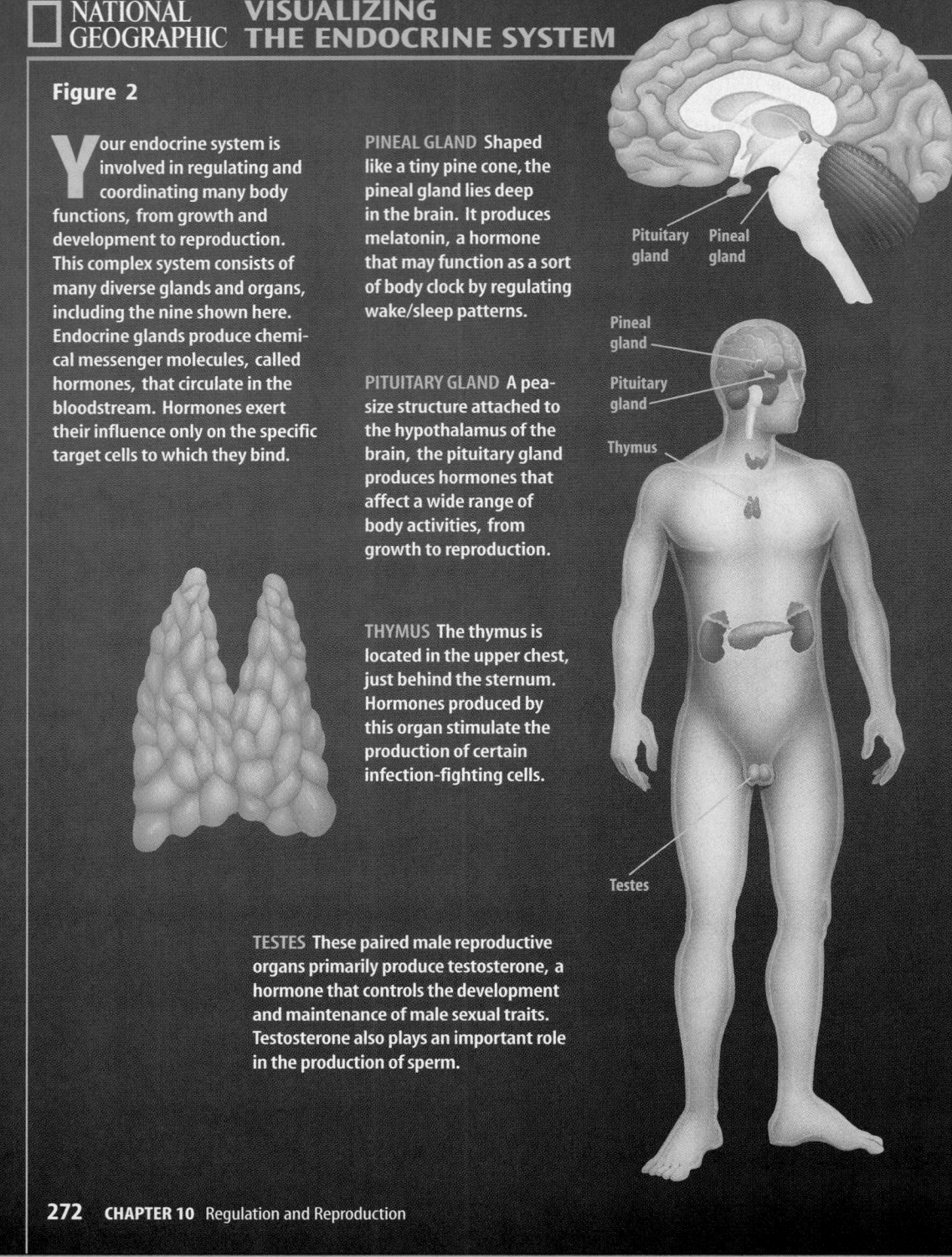

NATIONAL GEOGRAPHIC

VISUALIZING THE ENDOCRINE SYSTEM

Figure 2

Your endocrine system is involved in regulating and coordinating many body functions, from growth and development to reproduction. This complex system consists of many diverse glands and organs, including the nine shown here. Endocrine glands produce chemical messenger molecules, called hormones, that circulate in the bloodstream. Hormones exert their influence only on the specific target cells to which they bind.

PINEAL GLAND Shaped like a tiny pine cone, the pineal gland lies deep in the brain. It produces melatonin, a hormone that may function as a sort of body clock by regulating wake/sleep patterns.

PITUITARY GLAND A pea-size structure attached to the hypothalamus of the brain, the pituitary gland produces hormones that affect a wide range of body activities, from growth to reproduction.

THYMUS The thymus is located in the upper chest, just behind the sternum. Hormones produced by this organ stimulate the production of certain infection-fighting cells.

TESTES These paired male reproductive organs primarily produce testosterone, a hormone that controls the development and maintenance of male sexual traits. Testosterone also plays an important role in the production of sperm.

Pituitary gland   Pineal gland

Pineal gland

Pituitary gland

Thymus

Testes

272   CHAPTER 10 Regulation and Reproduction

Curriculum Connection

Language Arts The word *adrenal* is derived from two Latin words: *ad-* meaning "to," and *renalis*, meaning "kidneys." **How is this word related to the location of the adrenal glands?** The adrenal glands are located on top of the kidneys.

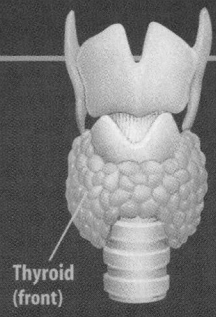

THYROID GLAND Located below the larynx, the bi-lobed thyroid gland is richly supplied with blood vessels. It produces hormones that regulate metabolic rate, control the uptake of calcium by bones, and promote normal nervous system development.

Thyroid (front)

PARATHYROID GLANDS Attached to the back surface of the thyroid are tiny para-thyroids, which help regulate calcium levels in the body. Calcium is important for bone growth and maintenance, as well as for muscle contraction and nerve impulse transmission.

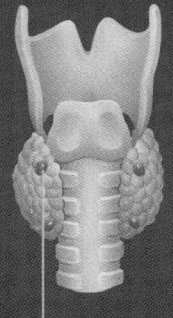

Parathyroid (back)

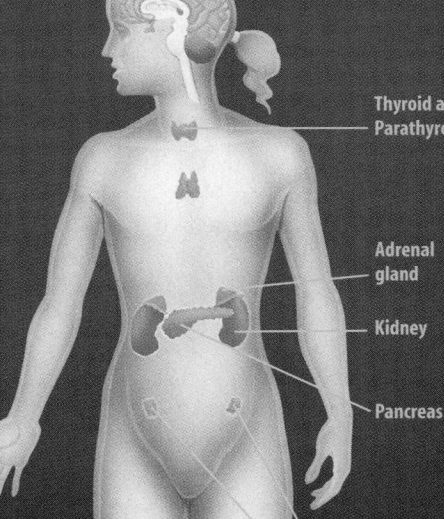

Thyroid and Parathyroid

Adrenal gland

Kidney

Pancreas

Ovaries

ADRENAL GLANDS On top of each of your kidneys is an adrenal gland. This complex endocrine gland produces a variety of hormones. Some play a critical role in helping your body adapt to physical and emotional stress. Others help stabilize blood sugar levels.

PANCREAS Scattered throughout the pancreas are millions of tiny clusters of endocrine tissue called the islets of Langerhans. Cells that make up the islets produce hormones that help control sugar levels in the bloodstream.

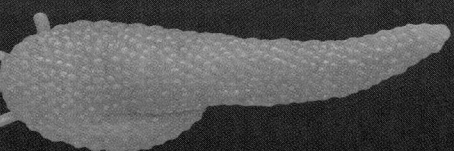

OVARIES Found deep in the pelvic cavity, ovaries produce female sex hormones known as estrogen and progesterone. These hormones regulate the female reproductive cycle and are responsible for producing and maintaining female sex characteristics.

SECTION 1 The Endocrine System **273**

NATIONAL GEOGRAPHIC

Visualizing the Endocrine System

<u>Visual</u> Learning ———o

Figure 2 Have students make a network tree concept map depicting the major endocrine glands in the human body and the function of each. [L2]
LS Visual-Spatial P

Teacher FYI

An overproduction of mela-tonin by the pineal gland is hypothesized by scientists to be one cause of Seasonal Affective Disorder (SAD). SAD is a type of depression that some people suffer when there are fewer hours of daylight during winter months. The treatment of SAD includes exposing sufferers to artificial bright light for several hours at a time.

Science Words

Word Meanings Have students research the meaning of the roots of the word *endocrine*. Students should record their findings in their Science Journal. The prefix *endo-* means "within." The Greek root word *krinein* means "to separate." The substance is separated from the gland when it moves into the blood.

Resource Manager

Chapter Resources Booklet
Enrichment, p. 28
Lab Activity, pp. 9–11
Transparency Activity, pp. 45–46
Reinforcement, p. 25

A Negative-Feedback System

Discussion

Infer the probable results of too much growth hormone in the blood of a young person. The person would grow at an accelerated rate and become abnormally tall. **What if there were too little of the hormone produced?** Shortness might result.

3 Assess

Reteach

Using a chart of the circulatory system, have students trace the pathway of a hormone to its target tissue. L2 LS **Kinesthetic**

Challenge

Why do you think the pituitary is often referred to as the "master gland?" The hormones from the pituitary control a number of body activities such as blood pressure, metabolism, growth, secretion of sex hormones, and the growth and development of the sex cells.

✓Assessment

Content Make a table describing the characteristics and components of the endocrine system. Use **Performance Assessment in the Science Classroom,** p. 109.

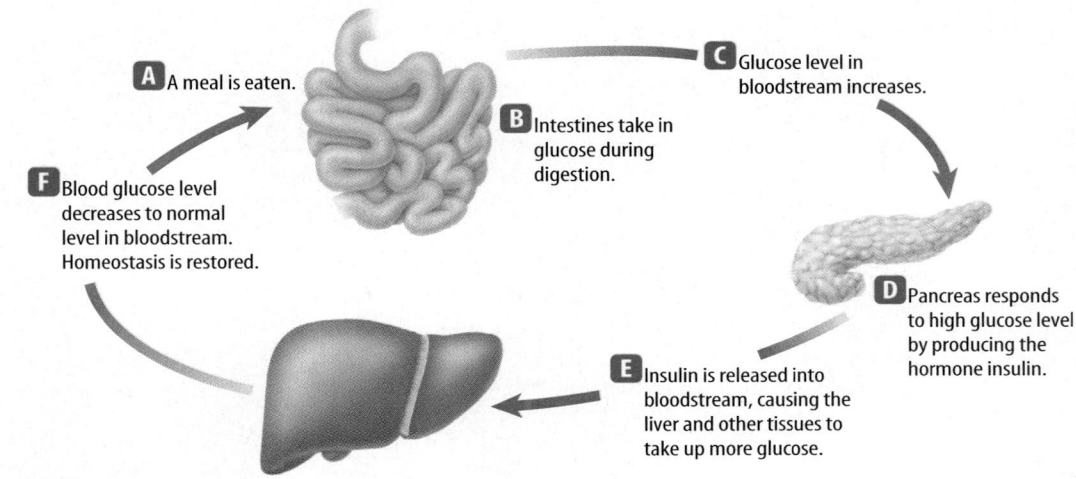

A A meal is eaten.

B Intestines take in glucose during digestion.

C Glucose level in bloodstream increases.

D Pancreas responds to high glucose level by producing the hormone insulin.

E Insulin is released into bloodstream, causing the liver and other tissues to take up more glucose.

F Blood glucose level decreases to normal level in bloodstream. Homeostasis is restored.

Figure 3
Many internal body conditions, such as hormone level, blood sugar level, and body temperature, are controlled by negative-feedback systems. Using a negative-feedback system, the pancreas controls the level of glucose in your bloodstream.

A Negative-Feedback System

To control the amount of hormones that are in your body, the endocrine system sends chemical messages back and forth within itself. This is called a negative-feedback system. It works much the way a thermostat works. When the temperature in a room drops below a set level, the thermostat signals the furnace to turn on. Once the furnace has raised the temperature in the room to the set level, the thermostat signals the furnace to shut off. It will continue to stay off until the thermostat signals that the temperature has dropped again. **Figure 3** shows how a negative-feedback system controls the level of glucose in your bloodstream.

Section ① Assessment

1. Compare and contrast the human body's two control systems.

2. What is the function of hormones?

3. Choose one endocrine gland and explain how it works.

4. What is a negative-feedback system?

5. **Think Critically** Glucose is required for cellular respiration, the process that releases energy within cells. How would lack of insulin affect this process?

Skill Builder Activities

6. **Predicting** Predict why the circulatory system is a good mechanism for delivering hormones throughout the body. **For more help, refer to the** Science Skill Handbook.

7. **Researching Information** Research recent treatments for growth disorders involving the pituitary gland. Write a brief paragraph of your results in your Science Journal. **For more help, refer to the** Science Skill Handbook.

274 CHAPTER 10 Regulation and Reproduction

Answers to Section Assessment

1. The nervous system sends messages to and from the brain throughout the body. The endocrine system uses hormones to affect specific tissues in the body.

2. Hormones regulate certain cellular activities.

3. Pancreas—secretes insulin to regulate glucose levels; refer to **Figure 2** for other possible answers.

4. a system that uses blood hormone levels to signal when a gland should and should not secrete the hormone

5. Insulin causes tissues to take up more glucose, without which cells

can't carry on respiration.

6. The circulatory system reaches every cell of the body.

7. Answers will vary. Possible topic: the use of hormone therapy to stimulate growth in young children.

2 The Reproductive System

Reproduction and the Endocrine System

Reproduction is the process that continues life on Earth. Most human body systems, such as the digestive system and the nervous system, are the same in males and females, but this is not true for the reproductive system. Males and females each have structures specialized for their roles in reproduction. Although structurally different, both the male and female reproductive systems are adapted to allow for a series of events that can lead to the birth of a baby.

Hormones are the key to how the human reproductive system functions, as shown in **Figure 4.** Sex hormones are necessary for the development of sexual characteristics, such as breast development in females and facial hair growth in males. Hormones from the pituitary gland also begin the production of eggs in females and sperm in males. Eggs and sperm transfer hereditary information from one generation to the next.

As You Read

What You'll Learn
- **Identify** the function of the reproductive system.
- **Compare and contrast** the major structures of the male and female reproductive systems.
- **Sequence** the stages of the menstrual cycle.

Vocabulary

testes	uterus
sperm	vagina
semen	menstrual cycle
ovary	menstruation
ovulation	

Why It's Important
The reproductive system helps ensure that life continues on Earth.

Figure 4
The pituitary gland produces hormones that control the male and female reproductive systems.

Brain
Pituitary gland

Produces female sex hormones

Produces male sex hormones

Stimulates egg production in ovaries

Stimulates sperm production in testes

SECTION 2 The Reproductive System **275**

SECTION

2 The Reproductive System

1 Motivate

Bellringer Transparency

Display the Section Focus Transparency for Section 2. Use the accompanying Transparency Activity Master. L2
ELL

Tie to Prior Knowledge

Ask students to think of common animals that begin life by the union of an egg and sperm. Examples may include humans, cats, dogs, horses, toads, and so on.

Section ✓Assessment Planner

PORTFOLIO
Science Journal, p. 277
PERFORMANCE ASSESSMENT
MiniLAB, p. 278
Skill Builder Activities, p. 279
See page 296 for more options.

CONTENT ASSESSMENT
Section, p. 279
Challenge, p. 279
Chapter, pp. 296–297

Resource Manager

Chapter Resources Booklet
Transparency Activity, p. 43
Directed Reading for Content Mastery, p. 18

The Male Reproductive System

Discussion

Infer why sperm have a streamlined head and an active tail. The streamlined head of a sperm reduces friction as it moves through liquids. The active tail propels the sperm in a direction that can be against gravity.

Use an Analogy

The movement of sperm is not unlike the movement of flagellate protozoans. Wavelike movements of the tail propel the organism forward. [IS] **Visual-Spatial**

Discussion

What other functions does semen have in addition to carrying the sperm? Chemical substances in semen provide energy for sperm movement. Explain that because semen is slightly alkaline, it protects sperm from acidic conditions, such as those found in the female reproductive system.

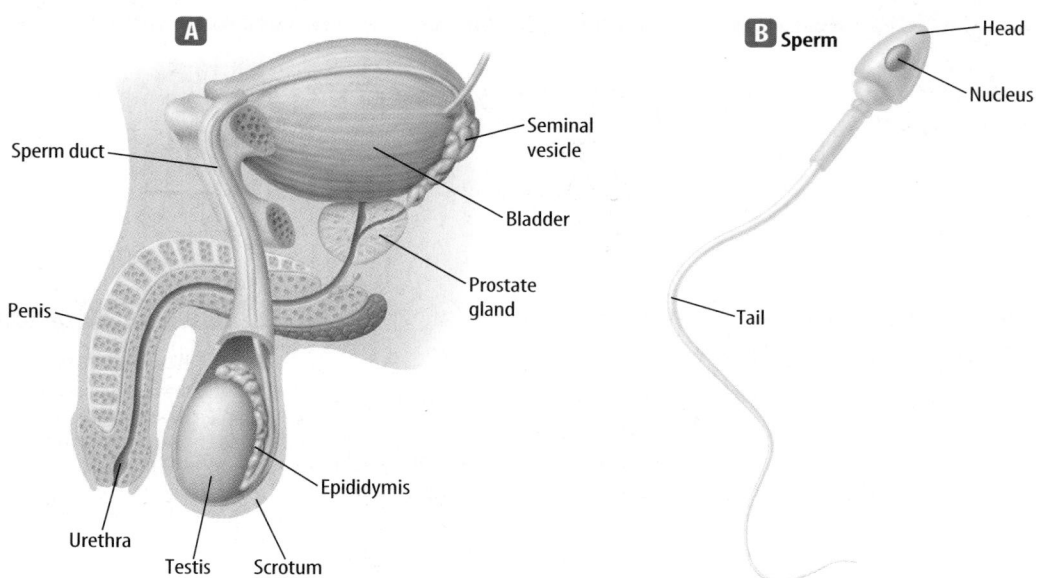

Figure 5
The structures of **A** the male reproductive system are shown with **B** a close-up of the sperm, which is produced in the testis. Sperm are produced throughout the life of a male.

The Male Reproductive System

The male reproductive system is made up of external and internal organs. The external organs of the male reproductive system are the penis and scrotum, shown in **Figure 5.** The scrotum contains two organs called testes (TES teez). As males mature sexually, the **testes** begin to produce testosterone, the male hormone, and **sperm,** which are male reproductive cells.

Sperm Each sperm cell has a head and tail. The head contains hereditary information, and the tail moves the sperm. Because the scrotum is located outside the body cavity, the testes, where sperm are produced, are kept at a lower temperature than the rest of the body. Sperm are produced in greater numbers at lower temperatures.

Many organs help in the production, transportation, and storage of sperm. After sperm are produced, they travel from the testes through sperm ducts that circle the bladder. Behind the bladder, a gland called the seminal vesicle provides sperm with a fluid. This fluid supplies the sperm with an energy source and helps them move. This mixture of sperm and fluid is called **semen** (SEE mun). Semen leaves the body through the urethra, which is the same tube that carries urine from the body. However, semen and urine never mix. A muscle at the back of the bladder contracts to prevent urine from entering the urethra as sperm leave the body.

276 CHAPTER 10 Regulation and Reproduction

Curriculum Connection

Language Arts Have students look up the words *sperm* and *ovary* and find out why the Latin roots are appropriate to their meanings. The Late Latin term *sperma* means seed; the Latin term *ovum* means egg. [L1] [IS] **Linguistic**

The Female Reproductive System

Unlike male reproductive organs, most of the reproductive organs of the female are inside the body. The **ovaries**—the female sex organs—are located in the lower part of the body cavity. Each of the two ovaries is about the size and shape of an almond. **Figure 6** shows the different organs of the female reproductive system.

The Egg When a female is born, she already has all of the cells in her ovaries that eventually will develop into eggs—the female reproductive cells. At puberty, eggs start to develop in her ovaries because of specific sex hormones.

About once a month, an egg is released from an ovary in a hormone-controlled process called **ovulation** (ahv yuh LAY shun). The two ovaries release eggs on alternating months. One month, an egg is released from an ovary. The next month, the other ovary releases an egg and so on. After the egg is released, it enters the oviduct. Sometimes a sperm fertilizes the egg. If fertilization takes place, it usually happens in an oviduct. Short, hairlike structures called cilia help sweep the egg through the oviduct toward the uterus (YEWT uh rus).

✔ Reading Check *When are eggs released by the ovaries?*

The **uterus** is a hollow, pear-shaped, muscular organ with thick walls in which a fertilized egg develops. The lower end of the uterus, the cervix, narrows and is connected to the outside of the body by a muscular tube called the **vagina** (vuh JI nuh). The vagina also is called the birth canal because during birth, a baby travels through this tube from the uterus to the outside of the mother's body.

SCIENCE *Online*

Research Visit the Glencoe Science Web site at **science. glencoe. com** for information about ovarian cysts. Make a small pamphlet explaining what cysts are and how they can be treated.

Figure 6
The structures of the female reproductive system are shown from the A side of the body and from the B front. *Where in the female reproductive system do the eggs develop?*

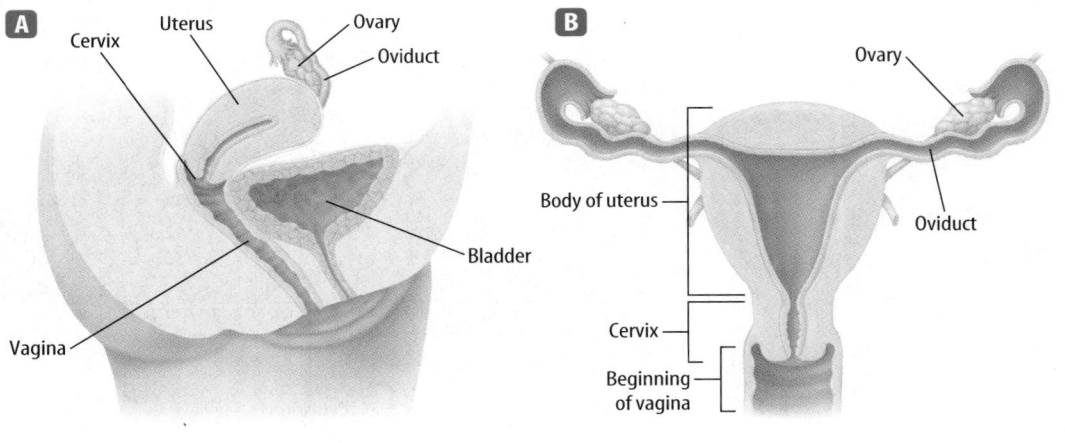

A Cervix · Uterus · Ovary · Oviduct · Bladder · Vagina

B Body of uterus · Ovary · Oviduct · Cervix · Beginning of vagina

SECTION 2 The Reproductive System **277**

The Menstrual Cycle

Use Science Words

Word Origin The Greek word for egg is *oion*. It is the root for many words related to eggs or the shape of an egg. Have students look up words with this root and explain their meanings. Possible answers: oocyte—an egg before maturation, oology—the study of bird eggs, oogenesis—the formation and maturation of an egg  **Linguistic**

✔ **Reading Check**

Answer the monthly cycle of changes in the female reproductive system

Purpose Students observe and interpret data illustrating changes in hormone levels during the menstrual cycle. L2 IS **Logical-Mathematical**

Materials graph paper

Teaching Strategy Have students note the range of the data figures before constructing their graphs.

Analysis
1. day 13
2. ovulation

✔ Assessment

Process Have students correlate the data in the MiniLAB chart with the events shown in **Figure 7**. Use **Performance Assessment in the Science Classroom**, p. 99.

Graphing Hormone Levels

Procedure
Make a line graph of this table.

Hormone Changes	
Day	**Level of Hormone**
1	12
5	14
9	15
13	70
17	13
21	12
25	8

Analysis
1. On what day is the highest level of hormone present?
2. What event takes place around the time of the highest hormone level?

The Menstrual Cycle

How is the female body prepared for having a baby? The **menstrual cycle** is the monthly cycle of changes in the female reproductive system. Before and after an egg is released from an ovary, the uterus undergoes changes. The menstrual cycle of a human female averages 28 days. However, the cycle can vary in some individuals from 20 to 40 days. Changes include the maturing of an egg, the production of female sex hormones, and the preparation of the uterus to receive a fertilized egg.

✔ **Reading Check** *What is the menstrual cycle?*

Endocrine Control Hormones control the entire menstrual cycle. The pituitary gland responds to chemical messages from the hypothalamus by releasing several hormones. These hormones start the development of eggs in the ovary. They also start the production of other hormones in the ovary, including estrogen (ES truh jun) and progesterone (proh JES tuh rohn). The interaction of all these hormones results in the physical processes of the menstrual cycle.

Phase One As shown in **Figure 7,** the first day of phase 1 starts when menstrual flow begins. Menstrual flow consists of blood and tissue cells released from the thickened lining of the uterus. This flow usually continues for four to six days and is called **menstruation** (men STRAY shun).

Figure 7
The three phases of the menstrual cycle make up the monthly changes in the female reproductive system.

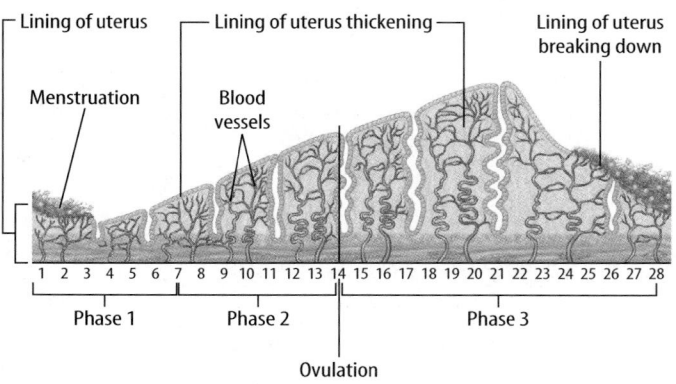

Resource Manager

Chapter Resources Booklet
Reinforcement, p. 26
MiniLAB, p. 3

Teacher FYI

The length of the menstrual period can vary. During the week before menstruation, a woman may experience premenstrual syndrome (PMS). Symptoms include depression, fatigue, headache, irritability, nervousness, and lack of concentration. Diet, exercise, aspirin, or other medicines are used to lessen the discomfort.

Phase Two Hormones cause the lining of the uterus to thicken in phase 2. Hormones also control the development of an egg in the ovary. Ovulation occurs about 14 days before menstruation begins. Once the egg is released, it must be fertilized within 24 h or it usually begins to break down. Because sperm can survive in a female's body for up to three days, fertilization can occur soon after ovulation.

Phase Three Hormones produced by the ovaries continue to cause an increase in the thickness of the uterine lining during phase 3. If a fertilized egg does arrive, the uterus is ready to support and nourish the developing embryo. If the egg is not fertilized, the lining of the uterus breaks down as the hormone levels decrease. Menstruation begins and the cycle repeats itself.

Menopause For most females the first menstrual period happens between ages nine years and 13 years and continues until 45 years of age to 60 years of age. Then, a gradual reduction of menstruation takes place as hormone production by the ovaries begins to shut down. Menopause occurs when both ovulation and menstrual periods end. It can take several years for the completion of menopause. As **Figure 8** indicates, menopause does not inhibit a woman's ability to enjoy an active life.

Figure 8
This older woman enjoys exercising with her granddaughter.

Quick Demo

With a sharp-tipped pencil, make a tiny dot on a piece of paper. This dot is about 0.5 mm in diameter. The human egg is about 5 times smaller in size. After demonstrating this, have students do it so they can get an idea of the size of a human egg.

3 Assess

Reteach

Have students diagram the pathway an egg follows as it moves from the ovary to the uterus. L1 IS **Visual-Spatial**

Challenge

Why might women going through menopause experience some of the same symptoms as women beginning their menstrual cycles? Both are experiencing changing levels of hormones.

✓ Assessment

Performance Further assess students' abilities by having them sequence the thickness of the uterus during the menstrual cycle using **Figure 7**. Use **Performance Assessment in the Science Classroom**, p. 163.

Section 2 Assessment

1. What is the major function of male and female reproductive systems in humans?

2. Explain the movement of sperm through the male reproductive system.

3. Compare and contrast the major organs and structures of the male and female reproductive systems.

4. Using diagrams and captions, sequence the stages of the menstrual cycle in a human female.

5. **Think Critically** Adolescent females often require additional amounts of iron in their diet. Explain.

Skill Builder Activities

6. **Concept Mapping** Make an events chain concept map to sequence the movement of an egg through the female reproductive system. **For more help, refer to the** Science Skill Handbook.

7. **Solving One-Step Equations** Usually, one egg is released each month during a female's reproductive years. If menstruation begins at 12 years of age and ends at 50 years of age, calculate the possible number of eggs her body can release during her reproductive years. **For more help, refer to the** Math Skill Handbook.

Answers to Section Assessment

1. to allow for a series of events that can lead to the birth of a baby
2. testes→tubes that encircle the bladder→seminal vesical→urethra
3. Sex cell production: female—ovaries within the body; male—testes in scrotum outside of body; movement of sex cells: female—eggs released

from ovary and swept into oviduct and uterus; male—sperm swim from testes through sperm duct and into the urethra.

4. Phase one: menstrual flow begins; phase two: wall of uterus thickens, ovulation occurs; phase three: wall of uterus continues to thicken; if a fertilized egg arrives, it burrows into the

wall; if a fertilized egg does not arrive, the lining deteriorates.

5. The body may have a temporary iron deficiency resulting from loss of blood.

6. ovary→oviduct→uterus→vagina.

7. 50 years − 12 years = 38 years; 38 years × 1 egg/month × 12 month/year = 456 eggs released

Activity

Purpose Students examine and interpret diagrams of the menstrual cycle. L2 LS **Visual-Spatial**

Process Skills observing, interpreting data

Time Required 40 minutes

Teaching Strategy Stress to students the importance of examining labels and captions when interpreting diagrams.

Answers to Questions

1. 28 days
2. days 7 to 28
3. If fertilization does not occur, menstruation takes place, another egg is released, and the process is repeated.
4. about 14

✓Assessment

Content Have students use the diagrams to write a summary of the process of menstruation. The lining of the uterus is shed and then builds up. The egg matures, is released, and travels to the uterus. If it is fertilized, pregnancy results. If it is not, the cycle repeats. Use **Performance Assessment in the Science Classroom,** p. 159.

Activity

Interpreting Diagrams

Starting in adolescence, hormones cause the development of eggs in the ovary and changes in the uterus. These changes prepare the uterus to accept a fertilized egg that can attach itself in the wall of the uterus. What happens to an unfertilized egg?

What You'll Investigate
What changes occur to the uterus during a female's monthly menstrual cycle?

Materials
paper and pencil

Goals
■ **Observe** the stages of the menstrual cycle in the diagram.
■ **Relate** the process of ovulation to the cycle.

Menstruation Cycle		
Days	**Condition of Uterus**	**What Happens**
1–6	breakdown of lining	menstruation
7–12	lining begins to thicken	egg matures in ovary
13–14	lining is thicker	ovulation
15–18	lining thickens	egg moves to uterus

Procedure
1. The diagrams below show what is explained in this chapter on the menstrual cycle.
2. Use the information in this chapter and the diagrams below to complete a data table.
3. On approximately what day in a 28-day cycle is the egg released from the ovary?

Conclude and Apply
1. How many days does the average menstrual cycle last?
2. On what days does the lining of the uterus build up?
3. **Infer** why this process is called a cycle.
4. **Calculate** how many days before menstruation ovulation usually occurs.

Communicating Your Data
Compare your data table with those of other students in your class. **For more help, refer to the** Science Skill Handbook.

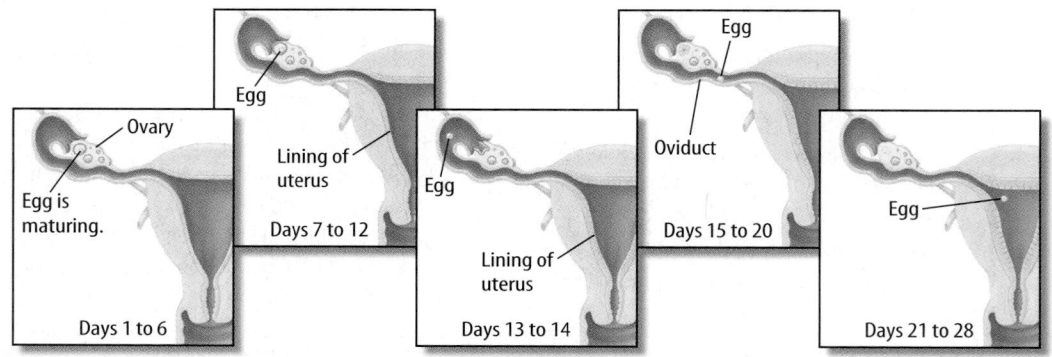

Days 1 to 6 — Egg is maturing. Ovary
Days 7 to 12 — Egg, Lining of uterus
Days 13 to 14 — Egg, Lining of uterus
Days 15 to 20 — Egg, Oviduct
Days 21 to 28 — Egg

Communicating Your Data
Students should discuss why their interpretations of the diagram did or did not agree. They can cite references to support their arguments.

Resource Manager

Chapter Resources Booklet
Activity Worksheet, pp. 5–6

SECTION

3 Human Life Stages

The Function of the Reproductive System

Before the invention of powerful microscopes, some people imagined an egg or a sperm to be a tiny person that grew inside a female. In the latter part of the 1700s, experiments using amphibians showed that contact between an egg and sperm is necessary for the development of life. With the development of the cell theory in the 1800s, scientists recognized that a human develops from an egg that has been fertilized by a sperm. The uniting of a sperm and an egg is known as fertilization. Fertilization, as shown in **Figure 9,** usually takes place in the oviduct.

Fertilization

Chemistry INTEGRATION

Although 200 millon to 300 million sperm can be deposited in the vagina, only several thousand reach an egg in the oviduct. As they enter the female, the sperm come into contact with chemical secretions in the vagina. It appears that this contact causes a change in the membrane of the sperm. The sperm then become capable of fertilizing the egg. The one sperm that makes successful contact with the egg releases an enzyme from the saclike structure on its head. Enzymes help speed up chemical reactions that have a direct effect on the protective membranes on the egg's surface. The structure of the egg's membrane is disrupted, and the sperm head can enter the egg.

Zygote Formation Once a sperm has entered the egg, changes in the electric charge of the egg's membrane prevent other sperm from entering the egg. At this point, the nucleus of the successful sperm joins with the nucleus of the egg. This joining of nuclei creates a fertilized cell called the zygote. It begins to undergo many cell divisions.

As You Read

What You'll Learn
- **Describe** the fertilization of a human egg.
- **List** the major events in the development of an embryo and fetus.
- **Describe** the developmental stages of infancy, childhood, adolescence, and adulthood.

Vocabulary
pregnancy   fetus
embryo   fetal stress
amniotic sac

Why It's Important
Fertilization begins the entire process of human growth and development.

Figure 9
After the sperm releases enzymes that disrupt the egg's membrane, it penetrates the egg.

Magnification: 425×

SECTION 3 Human Life Stages **281**

SECTION

3

Human Life Stages

1 Motivate

Bellringer Transparency
Display the Section Focus Transparency for Section 3. Use the accompanying Transparency Activity Master. L2
ELL

Tie to Prior Knowledge
Display photographs of people in different life stages, e.g., an infant, a small child, an adolescent, a young adult, and an older adult. Explain that these represent life stages and ask how many students can identify. Ask what stage they are in.

Section ✓*Assessment* Planner

PORTFOLIO
Make a Model, p. 282
PERFORMANCE ASSESSMENT
Try at Home MiniLAB, p. 284
Skill Builder Activities, p. 289
See page 296 for more options.

CONTENT ASSESSMENT
Section, p. 289
Challenge, p. 289
Chapter, pp. 296–297

Fertilization

Use Science Words

Word Usage Have students compare the biological use of the word *fertilization* to the agronomic use of the word. Biologists use fertilization to refer to the process by which two sex cells join to produce offspring. Agronomists use fertilization to refer to the application of manure or chemicals to make soil more fertile. L2
LS **Linguistic**

Multiple Births

Visual Learning

Figure 10 **What are the differences between the development of fraternal and identical twins?** Fraternal twins develop from two separate eggs that have been fertilized by two different sperm. Identical twins result when one egg is fertilized by one sperm and the resulting zygote splits.

Development Before Birth

Extension

Have students research the unusual breeding processes of such animals as the sea horse and midwife toad. In both, the fertilized eggs are carried by the male until the young are ready to be born. L2

Make a Model

Have students use polystyrene foam balls to construct four- and eight-cell models to illustrate the earliest stages of zygote growth. L2 **LS** **Kinesthetic** P

Figure 10
The development of fraternal and identical twins is different.

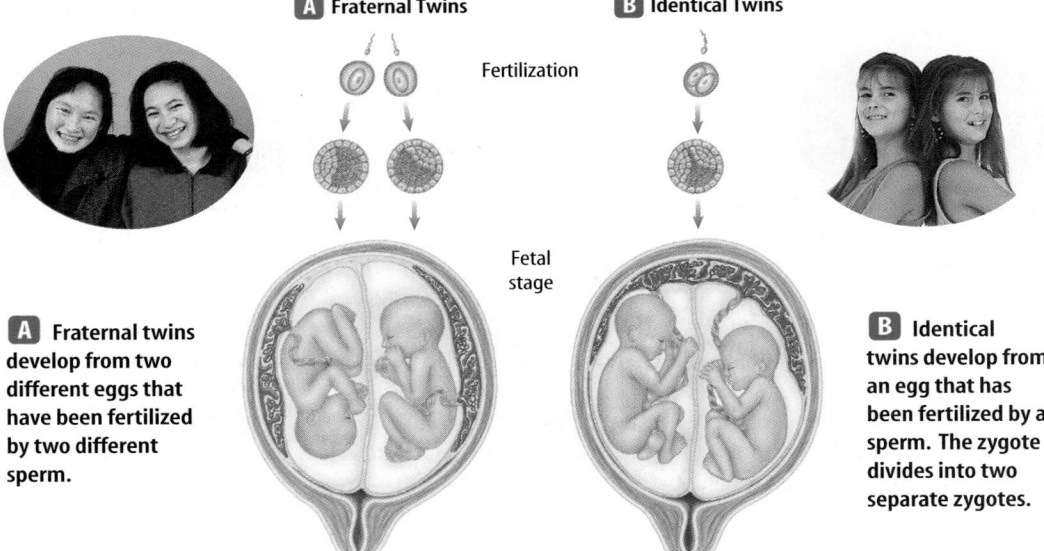

A Fraternal Twins
B Identical Twins
Fertilization
Fetal stage

A Fraternal twins develop from two different eggs that have been fertilized by two different sperm.

B Identical twins develop from an egg that has been fertilized by a sperm. The zygote divides into two separate zygotes.

Multiple Births

Sometimes two eggs leave the ovary at the same time. If both eggs are fertilized and both develop, fraternal twins are born. Fraternal twins, as shown in **Figure 10A,** can be two girls, two boys, or a boy and a girl. Because fraternal twins come from two eggs, they only resemble each other.

Because identical twin zygotes develop from the same egg and sperm, as explained in **Figure 10B,** they have the same hereditary information. These identical zygotes develop into identical twins, which are either two girls or two boys. Multiple births also can occur when three or more eggs are produced at one time or when the zygote separates into three or more parts.

Development Before Birth

After fertilization, the zygote moves along the oviduct to the uterus. During this time, the zygote is dividing and forming into a ball of cells. After about seven days, the zygote attaches to the wall of the uterus, which has been thickening in preparation to receive a zygote, as shown in **Figure 11.** If attached to the wall of the uterus, the zygote will develop into a baby in about nine months. This period of development from fertilized egg to birth is known as **pregnancy.**

282 **CHAPTER 10** Regulation and Reproduction

Curriculum Connection

Health Have students research ectopic pregnancies. **How frequently do they occur?** 1 in every 250–300 pregnancies **How does the female know there is a problem?** She experiences pain and bleeding. **What is the treatment?** Ectopic pregnancies often end in a miscarriage; if not miscarried, surgical removal of the fetus is sometimes necessary; abdominal pregnancies can be carried to term and the baby delivered by C-section. L2

✓ Active Reading

Speculation About Effects/Prediction Journal This strategy allows students to examine events and speculate about their possible long-term effects. Have students divide their papers in half. On the left side record "What happened." On the right side, write "What might/should happen as a result of this." Have students write a Speculation About Effects/Prediction Journal about an aspect of human life stages.

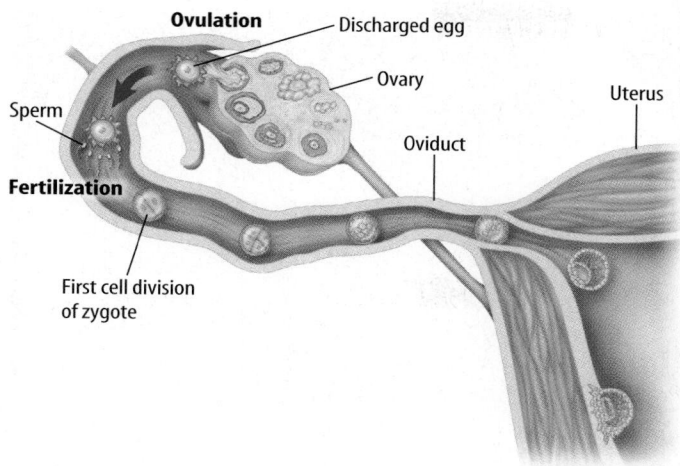

Ovulation — Discharged egg

Sperm

Fertilization

First cell division of zygote

Ovary

Oviduct

Uterus

Implantation

Figure 11
After a few days of rapid cell division, the zygote, now a ball of cells, reaches the lining of the uterus, where it attaches itself to the lining for development.

The Embryo After the zygote attaches to the wall of the uterus, it is known as an **embryo**, illustrated in **Figure 12.** It receives nutrients from fluids in the uterus until the placenta (pluh SENT uh) develops from tissues of the uterus and the embryo. An umbilical cord develops that connects the embryo to the placenta. In the placenta, materials diffuse between the mother's blood and the embryo's blood, but their bloods do not mix. Blood vessels in the umbilical cord carry nutrients and oxygen from the mother's blood through the placenta to the embryo. Other substances in the mother's blood can move into the embryo, including drugs, toxins, and disease organisms. Wastes from the embryo are carried in other blood vessels in the umbilical cord through the placenta to the mother's blood.

☑ **Reading Check** *Why must a pregnant woman avoid alcohol, tobacco, and harmful drugs?*

Pregnancy in humans lasts about 38 to 39 weeks. During the third week, a thin membrane called the **amniotic** (am nee AH tihk) **sac** begins to form around the embryo. The amniotic sac is filled with a clear liquid called amniotic fluid, which acts as a cushion for the embryo and stores nutrients and wastes.

During the first two months of development, the embryo's major organs form and the heart structure begins to beat. At five weeks, the embryo has a head with eyes, nose, and mouth features. During the sixth and seventh weeks, fingers and toes develop.

Figure 12
By two months, the developing embryo is about 2.5 cm long and is beginning to develop recognizable features.

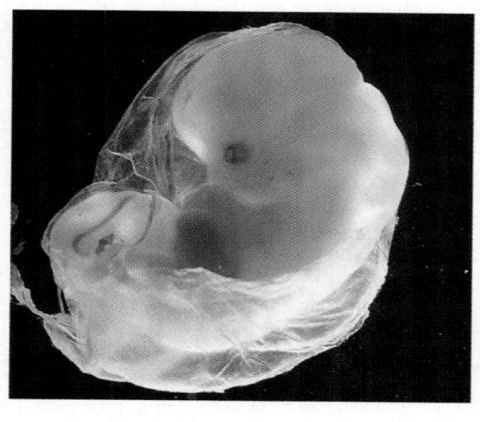

☑ **Reading Check**

Answer Any substances taken in by the mother and carried in her blood can pass to the embryo through the umbilical cord and cause the embryo damage.

Teacher FYI

In the interior of the blastocyst, a specialized mass of cells differentiates and forms the embryo. The outer layer of cells attach to the uterus and form the placenta.

IDENTIFYING Misconceptions

Students may think that fertilization and embryonic development are mysterious processes that are not understandable. Refer to page 626F for teaching strategies that address this misconception.

Development Before Birth, continued

TRY AT HOME
Mini LAB

Purpose Students observe data on the growth rate of a fetus.

L2 LS **Logical-Mathematical**

Materials graph paper

Teaching Strategy Have students note the range of the data before constructing their graphs.

Analysis
1. during the ninth month
2. about 5.7 cm per month

Performance To further assess students' understanding of fetus size, have them find and measure common household items that correspond to the various fetus sizes. Set up a display of these items. Use **PASC,** p. 97.

Activity

Have students prepare a series of actual-size cutouts of the fetus from three months to birth to have a visual demonstration of its size while developing. L2

ELL LS **Visual-Spatial**

Figure 13
A fetus at about 16 weeks is approximately 15 cm long and weighs 140 g.

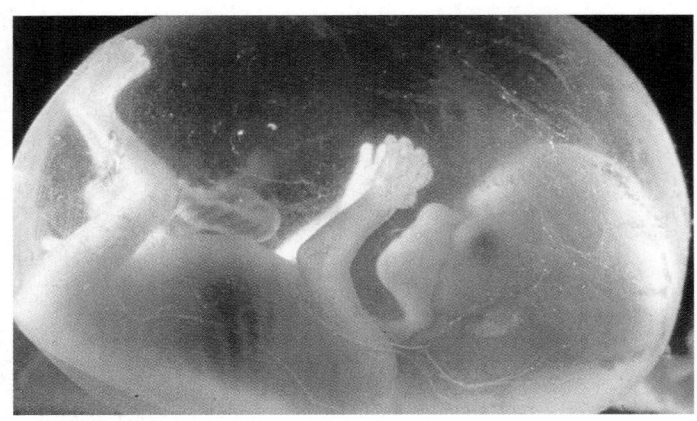

TRY AT HOME
Mini LAB

Interpreting Fetal Development

Procedure
Make a bar graph of the following data.

Fetal Development	
End of Month	**Length (cm)**
3	8
4	15
5	25
6	30
7	35
8	40
9	51

Analysis
1. During which month does the greatest increase in length occur?
2. On average, how many centimeters does the baby grow per month?

The Fetus After the first two months of pregnancy, the developing embryo is called a **fetus,** shown in **Figure 13.** At this time, body organs are present. Around the third month, the fetus is 8 cm to 9 cm long. The mother may feel the fetus move. The fetus can even suck its thumb. By the fourth month, an ultrasound test can determine the sex of the fetus. The fetus is 30 cm to 38 cm in length by the end of the seventh month of pregnancy. Fatty tissue builds up under the skin, and the fetus looks less wrinkled. By the ninth month, the fetus usually has shifted to a head-down position within the uterus, a position beneficial for delivery. The head usually is in contact with the opening of the uterus to the vagina. The fetus is about 50 cm in length and weighs from 2.5 kg to 3.5 kg.

The Birthing Process

The process of childbirth, as shown in **Figure 14,** begins with labor, the muscular contractions of the uterus. As the contractions increase in strength and number, the amniotic sac usually breaks and releases its fluid. Over a period of hours, the contractions cause the opening of the uterus to widen. More powerful and more frequent contractions push the baby out through the vagina into its new environment.

Delivery Often a mother is given assistance by a doctor during the delivery of the baby. As the baby emerges from the birth canal, a check is made to determine if the umbilical cord is wrapped around the baby's neck or any body part. When the head is free, any fluid in the baby's nose and mouth is removed by suction. After the head and shoulders appear, contractions force the baby out completely. Up to an hour after delivery, contractions occur that push the placenta out of the mother's body.

LAB DEMONSTRATION

Purpose to observe the proportions of girls and boys born in the population

Materials pennies

Preparation Collect small foam trays to deaden the sound and catch the tossed pennies.

Procedure Have students toss a penny one hundred times and record the order and number of times it lands on heads or tails.

Expected Outcome About a 50:50 ratio; there may be sequences of one side landing faceup repeatedly. Relate this to families of several boys or several girls.

Infer the chances of a family with five girls or a family with five boys having a girl if there were a sixth child born. The chance of a girl being born into either family as the next child is 50:50.

Cesarean Section Sometimes a baby must be delivered before labor begins or before it is completed. At other times, a baby cannot be delivered through the birth canal because the mother's pelvis might be too small or the baby might be in the wrong birthing position. In cases like these, surgery called a cesarean (suh SEER ee uhn) section is performed. An incision is made through the mother's abdominal wall, then through the wall of the uterus. The baby is delivered through this opening.

✔ **Reading Check** *What is a cesarean section?*

After Birth When the baby is born, it is attached to the umbilical cord. The person assisting with the birth clamps the cord in two places and cuts it between the clamps. The baby does not feel any pain from this procedure. The baby might cry, which is the result of air being forced into its lungs. The scar that forms where the cord was attached is called the navel.

SCIENCE Online

Research Visit the Glencoe Science Web site at **science.glencoe.com** for more information about cesarean section delivery. Communicate what you learn to your class.

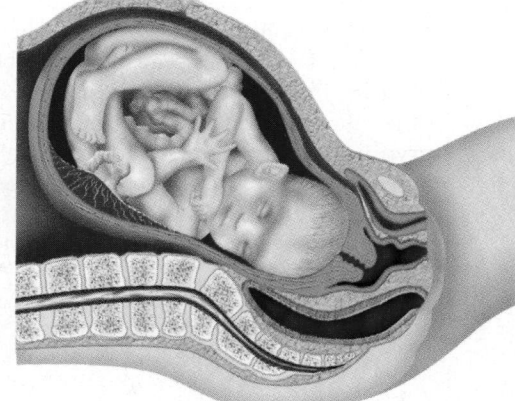

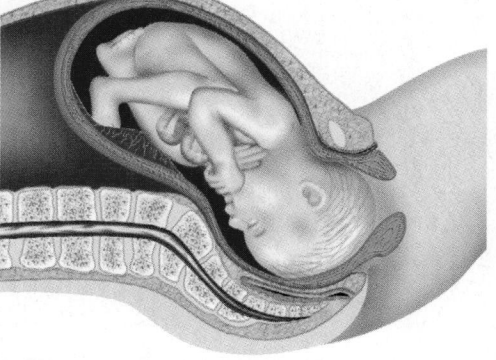

A The fetus moves into the opening of the birth canal, and the uterus begins to widen.

Figure 14
Childbirth begins with labor. The opening to the uterus widens, and the baby passes through.

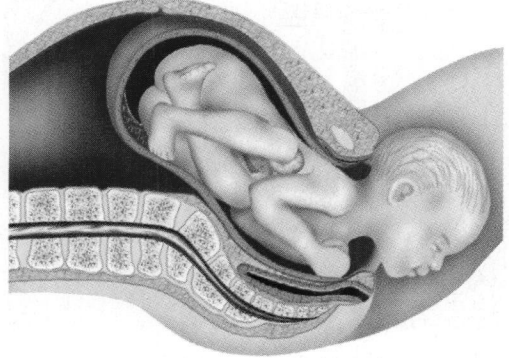

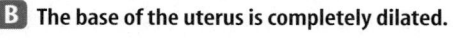

B The base of the uterus is completely dilated.

C The fetus is pushed out through the birth canal.

SECTION 3 Human Life Stages **285**

The Birthing Process

SCIENCE Online

Internet Addresses

_____
_____
_____
_____

Explore the Glencoe Science Web site at **science.glencoe.com** to find out more about topics in this section.

✔ **Reading Check**

Answer a surgical procedure in which an incision in the mother's abdomen and uterus is made and the baby removed

Use Science Words

Word Meaning Have students find out why the surgical removal of a baby from the mother is called a "cesarean section." It was named after Julius Caesar, who was supposedly delivered in this manner. L2 LS **Linguistic**

Visual Learning

Figure 14 Have students list the stages involved in childbirth. Fetus moves to opening of birth canal, base of uterus dilates, muscle contractions push fetus through the birth canal. L2 LS **Visual-Spatial**

Resource Manager

Chapter Resources Booklet
  MiniLAB, p. 4
Home and Community Involvement, p. 43
Life Science Critical Thinking/Problem Solving, p. 19

Curriculum Connection

Health Arrange a visit to an X-ray lab to view X rays of bones of infants or young children and compare them with X rays of adults to show the differences in cartilage and bone. If a visit is impractical, arrange to view X-ray photos in class. L2 LS **Visual-Spatial**

Stages After Birth

Use Science Words

Neonatal means "newborn," and refers to a child younger than one month. *Neo-* is from the Greek and means "new" or "recent." Ask students to find words with this root and explain their meanings. Neophyte is a beginner, neolithic is the new stone age, neogenic refers to newly formed rocks and minerals. L2 **Linguistic**

Discussion

How might a newborn react to loud sounds or bright lights? Possible answer: he or she might be startled by loud sounds and bright lights.

Teacher FYI

Certain animals are ready to care for themselves immediately after birth. Precocial birds such as ducks are able to immediately move around and take care of themselves. Other self-sufficient animals are deer, hares, bison, and many types of insects, fish, amphibians, and reptiles. However, many of these animals, though mobile, still depend upon their mothers for milk.

Fun Fact

The major constituents of human milk are water, proteins, fats, and lactose, a carbohydrate. In addition, there are small amounts of vitamins and electrolytes.

Stages After Birth

Defined stages of development occur after birth, based on the major developments that take place during those specific years. Infancy lasts from birth to around 18 months of age. Childhood extends from the end of infancy to sexual maturity, or puberty. The years of adolescence vary, but they usually are considered to be the teen years. Adulthood covers the years of age from the early 20s until life ends, with older adulthood considered to be over 60. The age spans of these different stages are not set, and scientists differ in their opinions regarding them.

Infancy What type of environment must the infant adjust to after birth? The experiences the fetus goes through during birth cause **fetal stress.** The fetus has emerged from an environment that was dark, watery, a constant temperature, and nearly soundless. In addition, the fetus might have been forced through the constricted birth canal. However, in a short period of time, the infant's body becomes adapted to its new world.

The first four weeks after birth are known as the neonatal(nee oh NAY tul) period. The term *neonatal* means "newborn." During this time, the baby's body begins to function normally. Unlike the newborn of some other animals, human babies, shown in **Figure 15A,** depend on other humans for their survival. In contrast, many other animals, such as horses like those shown in **Figure 15B,** begin walking a few hours after they are born.

Figure 15
Human babies are more dependent upon their caregivers than many other mammals are.

A Infants and toddlers are completely dependent upon caregivers for all their needs.

B Other young mammals are more self-sufficient. This colt is able to stand within an hour after birth.

286   CHAPTER 10   Regulation and Reproduction

Inclusion Strategies

Behaviorally Disordered Have students bring photos of themselves at various stages and describe favorite activities they remember from these stages. L1

Science Journal

Immunizations Babies and young children need certain vaccines to prevent disease. Have students find out what vaccinations are recommended between birth and age 6. Between birth and 6 yrs. old, the following vaccines are recommended: Polio; Hepatitis B; Diphtheria, Tetanus, Pertussis; Varicella or Chicken Pox; Haemophilus Influenza B; Measles, Mumps, Rubella.

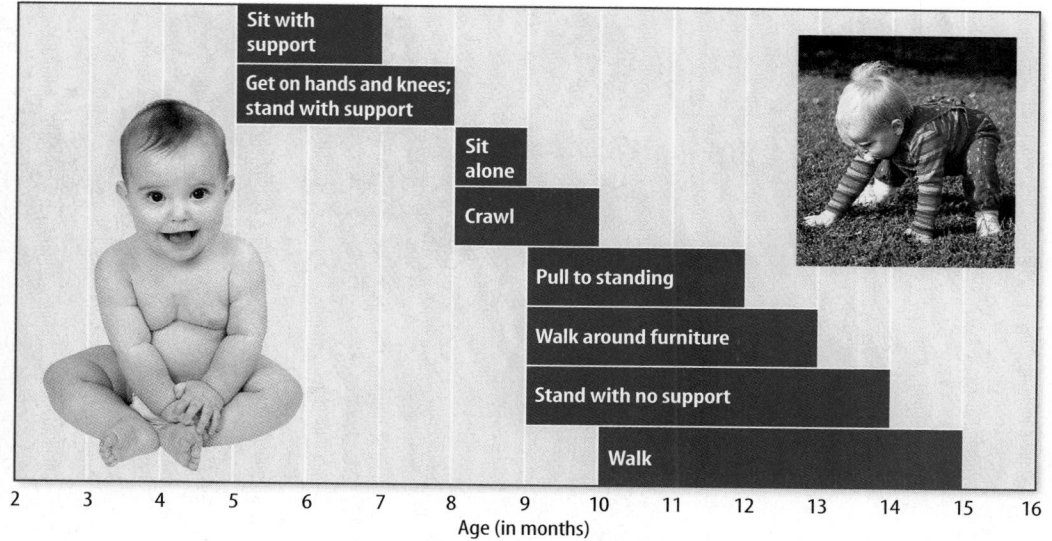

Sit with support

Get on hands and knees; stand with support

Sit alone

Crawl

Pull to standing

Walk around furniture

Stand with no support

Walk

| 2 | 3 | 4 | 5 | 6 | 7 | 8 | 9 | 10 | 11 | 12 | 13 | 14 | 15 | 16 |

Age (in months)

During these first 18 months, infants show increased physical coordination, mental development, and rapid growth. Many infants will triple their weight in the first year. **Figure 16** shows the extremely rapid development of the nervous and muscular systems during this stage, which enables infants to start interacting with the world around them.

Figure 16
Infants show rapid development in their nervous and muscular systems through 18 months of age.

Childhood   After infancy is childhood, which lasts until about puberty, or sexual maturity. Sexual maturity occurs around 12 years of age. Overall, growth during early childhood is rather rapid, although the physical growth rate for height and weight is not as rapid as it is in infancy. Between two and three years of age, the child learns to control his or her bladder and bowels. At age two to three, most children can speak in simple sentences. Around age four, the child is able to get dressed and undressed with some help. By age five, many children can read a limited number of words. By age six, children usually have lost their chubby baby appearance, as seen in **Figure 17.** However, muscular coordination and mental abilities continue to develop. Throughout this stage, children develop their abilities to speak, read, write, and reason. These ages of development are only guidelines because each child develops at a different rate.

Figure 17
Children grow and develop at different rates, like these kindergartners.

Resource Manager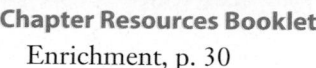

Chapter Resources Booklet
   Enrichment, p. 30
Reading and Writing Skill Activities, p. 39

Activity

Have students conduct a survey of parents with young children. Have them ask questions such as: What changes did you notice at different ages? What stage seemed to have the most changes? L2 **LS** **Interpersonal**

Make a Model

Have students make a time-line of the stages from infancy to adulthood using long pieces of paper. Identify various milestones such as the start of walking, puberty, and menopause. L2 **LS** **Kinesthetic**

Discussion

Have students think about how they learned to talk. **How might hearing problems in young children cause speech problems?** Children learn speech by listening to others. If they have a hearing problem, they cannot properly hear the sounds of speech. They are unable to reproduce sounds that other people can understand.

Inclusion Strategies

Gifted Have students observe a lower elementary or preschool classroom. What adaptations would they have to make to teach this chapter to the class they observed? Have them make a sample presentation to your class, pretending they are preschoolers. Have a class discussion on how they modified the chapter and why. L3

Caption Answer

Figure 18 A baby's head is almost one-fourth its total body length. This reduces as the child grows into an adult. In adulthood, the head is approximately one-eighth of the body's length.

Teacher FYI

The onset of puberty varies greatly in the growth patterns of adolescents. The variations are caused by a number of factors. Heredity is a key factor in determining the development of the body. Other factors are diet and illnesses. Poor diet and sickness can delay the onset of puberty. Often adolescents are disturbed that they are developing earlier or later than their peers. By age 17–18, the differences have usually disappeared.

Physics INTEGRATION

Since the body may be off balance, it is difficult to be coordinated and to do some of the maneuvers required in sports activities.

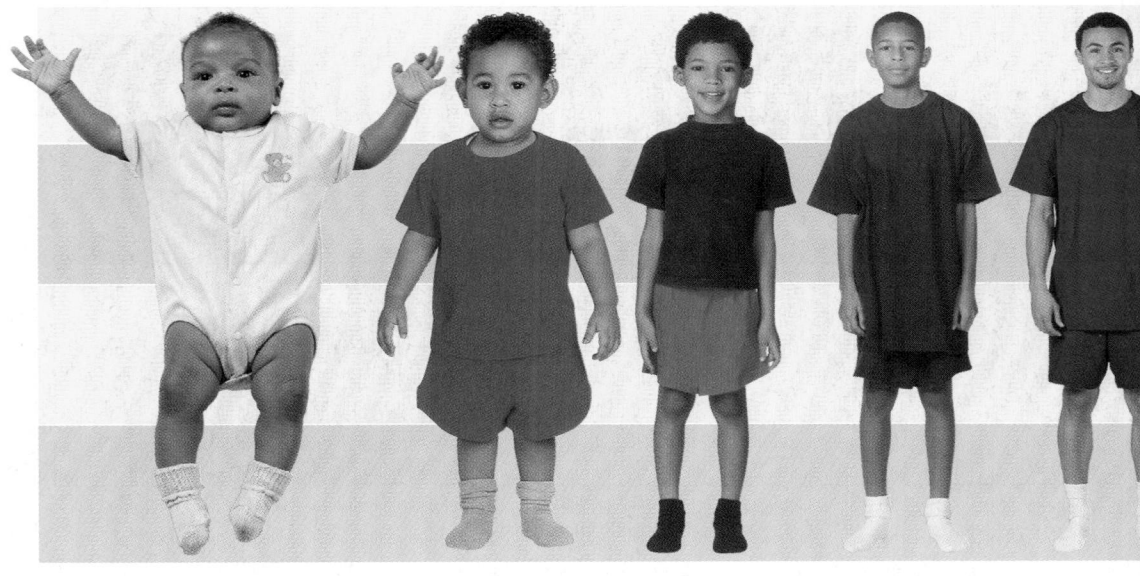

Figure 18
The proportions of body parts change over time as the body develops. *Describe how the head changes proportion.*

Physics INTEGRATION

During adolescence, the body parts do not all grow at the same rate. The legs grow longer before the upper body lengthens. This changes the body's center of gravity, the point at which the body maintains its balance. This is one cause of teenager clumsiness. In your Science Journal, write a paragraph about how this might affect playing sports.

Adolescence Adolescence usually begins around age 12 or 13. A part of adolescence is puberty—the time of development when a person becomes physically able to reproduce. For girls, puberty occurs between ages nine and 13. For boys, puberty occurs between ages 13 and 16. During puberty, hormones produced by the pituitary gland cause changes in the body. These hormones produce reproductive cells and sex hormones. Secondary sex characteristics also develop. In females, the breasts develop, pubic and underarm hair appears, and fatty tissue is added to the buttocks and thighs. In males, the hormones cause a deepened voice, an increase in muscle size, and the growth of facial, pubic, and underarm hair.

Adolescence usually is when the final growth spurt occurs. Because the time when hormones begin working varies among individuals and between males and females, growth rates differ. Girls often begin their final growth phase at about age 11 and end around age 16. Boys usually start their growth spurt at age 13 and end around 18 years of age.

Adulthood The final stage of development, adulthood, begins with the end of adolescence and continues through old age. This is when the growth of the muscular and skeletal system stops. **Figure 18** shows how body proportions change as you age.

People from age 45 to age 60 are sometimes considered middle-aged adults. During these years, physical strength begins to decline. Blood circulation and respiration become less efficient. Bones become more brittle, and the skin becomes wrinkled.

288 CHAPTER 10 Regulation and Reproduction

Cultural Diversity

Rites of Passage Have students research and write a report on ceremonies in other societies, past or present, that mark the transition of young people to adults. These ceremonies are often referred to as "rites of passage." L2
IS Linguistic

Resource Manager

Chapter Resources Booklet
Reinforcement, p. 27
Lab Activity, pp. 13–14

Older Adulthood People over the age of 60 may experience an overall decline in their physical body systems. The cells that make up these systems no longer function as well as they did at a younger age. Connective tissues lose their elasticity, causing muscles and joints to be less flexible. Bones become thinner and more brittle. Hearing and vision are less sensitive. The lungs and heart work less efficiently. However, exercise and eating well over a lifetime can help extend the health of one's body systems. Many healthy older adults enjoy full lives and embrace challenges, as shown in **Figure 19.**

Figure 19
Astronaut and Senator John Glenn traveled into space twice. In 1962, at age 40, he was the first U.S. citizen to orbit Earth. He was part of the space shuttle crew in 1998 at age 77. Senator Glenn has helped change people's views of what many older adults are capable of doing.

 **Reading Check** *What physical changes occur during late adulthood?*

Human Life Spans Seventy-five years is the average life span—from birth to death—of humans, although an increasing number of people live much longer. However, body systems break down with age, resulting in eventual death. Death can occur earlier than old age for many reasons, including diseases, accidents, and bad health choices.

Section 3 Assessment

1. What happens when an egg is fertilized in a female?
2. What happens to an embryo during the first two months of pregnancy?
3. Describe the major events that occur during childbirth.
4. What stage of development are you in? What physical changes have occurred or will occur during this stage of human development?
5. **Think Critically** Why is it hard to compare the growth and development of different adolescents?

Skill Builder Activities

6. **Making Models** Use references to construct a time line that highlights the major events in the various stages of development from the embryo to adulthood. **For more help, refer to the** Science Skill Handbook.
7. **Using an Electronic Spreadsheet** Using your text and other resources, make a spreadsheet for the stages of human development from a zygote to a fetus. Title one column *Zygote,* another *Embryo,* and a third *Fetus.* Complete the spreadsheet. **For more help, refer to the** Technology Skill Handbook.

 Reading Check

Answer Connective tissue loses elasticity, bones become brittle, hearing and vision are less sensitive, and the lungs and heart work less efficiently.

3 Assess

Reteach

Divide the class into groups and have each group write descriptions of a particular life stage—one per index card. Mix up the cards, divide the class into teams, and read the descriptions. Students take turns stating the life stage. The team with the greatest number of correct answers wins. L2 ELL **LS** Visual-Spatial

Challenge

What features of a pregnant woman protect the developing child? The woman's body has a thickened uterine wall; the placenta develops to transport food and wastes through the umbilical cord; amniotic fluid cushions the embryo.

Assessment

Performance To further assess students' understanding of neonatal development, have them construct a time line to correspond with the stages of neonatal development. Use **Performance Assessment in the Science Classroom,** p. 163.

Activity

What You'll Investigate

Purpose

Students measure the body proportions of adolescents and infer how body proportions differ between males and females. L2

LS Logical-Mathematical

Process Skills

calculating, comparing, graphing, inferring

Time Required

40 minutes

Materials

Students may use metersticks instead of a tape measure. Masking tape can be used to mark heights on the wall instead of pencil marks.

Procedure

Teaching Strategy

- Encourage students to measure each dimension twice to improve accuracy.

Activity

Changing Body Proportions

The ancient Greeks believed the perfect body was completely balanced. Arms and legs should not be too long or short. A person's head should not be too large or small. The extra large muscles of a body builder would have been ugly to the Greeks. How do you think they viewed the bodies of infants and children? Infants and young children have much different body proportions than adults, and teenagers often go through growth spurts that quickly change their body proportions. How do body proportions differ among people?

What You'll Investigate

How do the body proportions differ between adolescent males and females?

Materials

tape measure
erasable pencil
graph paper

Goals

- **Measure** specific body proportions of adolescents.
- **Infer** how body proportions differ between adolescent males and females.

290

Resource Manager

Chapter Resources Booklet
  Activity Worksheet, pp. 7–8

Lab Management and Safety, p. 70

Procedure

1. Copy the data table in your Science Journal and record the gender of each person that you measure.

2. Measure each person's head circumference by starting in the middle of the forehead and wrapping the tape measure around the head. Record these measurements.

3. Measure each person's arm length from the top of the shoulder to the tip of the middle finger while the arm is held straight out to the side of the body. Record these measurements.

4. Ask each person to remove his or her shoes and stand next to a wall. Mark their height with an erasable pencil and measure their height from the floor to the mark. Record these measurements in the data table.

5. **Combine** your data with that of your classmates. Find the averages of head circumference, arm length, and height. Then, find these averages for males and females.

6. Make a bar graph of your calculations in step 5. Plot the measurements on the *y*-axis and plot all of the averages along the *x*-axis.

7. **Calculate** the proportion of average head circumference to average height for everyone in your class by dividing the average head circumference by the average height. Repeat this calculation for males and females.

8. **Calculate** the proportion of average arm length to average height for everyone in your class by dividing the average arm length by the average height. Repeat this calculation for males and females.

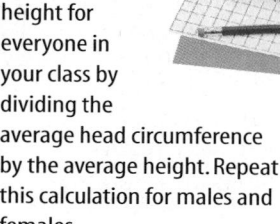

Age and Body Measurements

Gender of Person	Head Circumference (cm)	Arm Length (cm)	Height (cm)
	Answers will vary.		

Conclude and Apply

1. Do adolescent males or females have larger head circumferences or longer arms? Which group has the larger proportion of head circumference or arm length to height?

2. Does this activity support the information in this chapter about the differences between growth rates of adolescent males and females? Explain.

Communicating Your Data

On poster board, **construct** data tables showing your results and those of your classmates. Discuss with your classmates why these results might be different.

ACTIVITY   291

Expected Outcome

Because adolescent girls generally undergo growth sooner than adolescent males, their body parts will be in different proportions than those of adolescent males.

Conclude and Apply

1. Answers will vary depending on students' measurements.

2. Answers will vary but data should support chapter information about differences in growth rates between adolescent males and females.

Error Analysis

Form students into groups of four or five and have each student compare his or her data with that of other group members. If data disagree, have each group list reasons for discrepancies.

Assessment

Portfolio Ask students to draw what they envision as the Greek ideal of a perfectly proportioned body. Use **Performance Assessment in the Science Classroom,** p. 127.

Communicating Your Data

Encourage students to use a spreadsheet program to construct their data tables.

Content Background

Mammals can be divided into three groups based on their development. Humans are placentals; a mammal whose young develop in the female parent's uterus. The offspring of placental mammals are usually comparatively well developed. Marsupials, like the kangaroo shown in this feature, give birth to less-developed young, which usually develop in a pouch, or attached to the mother's body. Throughout the world, there are more than 250 species of marsupials. Monotremes are mammals that lay eggs. All montremes are found in Australia, New Guinea and Tasmania. All female mammals produce milk to feed their infants. Female marsupials and placentals have mammary glands with nipples for infants to suck on, but montreme mammary glands simply release milk through pores in the mother's skin.

Discussion

Why might a baby kangaroo need to spend such a long period of time in its mother's pouch after it is born? Possible answer: Kangaroo babies are not developed enough to survive outside of the pouch when they are born, they need a period of protected growth and development.

Activity

Assign small groups of students an animal to research. Have the students find the age at which the young become independent from their parents. Have the students compare their findings on a bar graph.

Science Stats

Facts About Infants

Did you know...

...Humans and chimpanzees share about 99 percent of their genes. Although humans look different than chimps, reproduction is similar and gestation is the same— about nine months. Youngsters of both species lose their baby teeth at about six years of age.

Female kangaroo and joey

...Unlike humans and most other mammals, the newborn kangaroo develops in its mother's pouch longer than in her uterus. About one month after fertilization, the kangaroo is born and moves from its mother's uterus into her pouch. It spends seven to ten months in the pouch, drinking milk and growing.

...The blue whale calf is the biggest newborn in the world. At birth, it measures about 7 m and weighs about 2,700 kg. The average human newborn measures about 50 cm and weighs about 3.3 kg. In its first year of life, a blue whale calf gains about 90 kg every day. Compare that to an average human baby who gains about 10 kg during his or her entire first year.

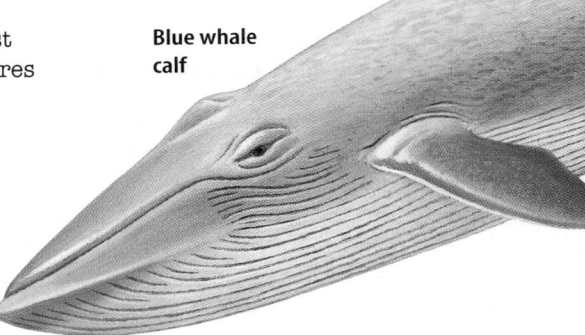

Blue whale calf

292 CHAPTER 10 Regulation and Reproduction

SCIENCE *Online*
Internet Addresses

_____

_____

_____

Explore the Glencoe Science Web site at **science.glencoe.com** to find out more about topics in this feature.

Mammal Facts

Mammal	Average Gestation	Average Birth Weight	Average Adult Weight	Average Life Span (years)
African Elephant	22 months	136 kg	4,989.5 kg	35
Blue Whale	12 months	1,800 kg	135,000 kg	60
Human	**9 months**	**3.3 kg**	**59–76 kg**	**76***
Brown Bear	7 months	0.23–0.5 kg	350 kg	22.5
Cat	2 months	99 g	2.7–7 kg	13.5
Kangaroo	1 month	0.75–1.0 g	45 kg	5
Golden Hamster	2.5 weeks	0.3 g	112 g	2

* In the United States

1-day-old to 7-day-old mice

...Of about 4,000 species of mammals, only three lay eggs. These species are the platypus, the short-beaked echidna (ih KIHD nuh), and the long-beaked echidna. No other mammals lay eggs.

Echidna

... House mice can have up to ten litters per year, each one containing up to seven mice. Mice have this many offspring because so few of them survive.

Do the Math

1. Look at the data table above. Make a generalization about a mammal's birth weight and the length of its gestation period.
2. Make a bar graph that compares the length of the human gestation period to that of two other mammals.
3. Assume that a female of each mammal listed in the table above is pregnant once during her life. Which mammal is pregnant for the greatest proportion of her life?

Go Further

Do research to find out which species of vertebrate animals has the longest life span and which has the shortest. Present your findings in a table that also shows the life span of humans.

Do the Math

Teaching Strategies

- Remind the students that they need to convert all of the numbers to the same units before they can be compared.
- Discuss the appropriate labels for both axis of the bar graph, and remind students that the graph needs a descriptive title.
- Review proportions, and remind students that the numbers being compared in a proportion must have the same units. In this case the gestation period must be converted to years, or the life span to months or weeks.

Answers

1. The larger the mammal is at birth, the longer its gestation period is—the smaller the mammal is, the shorter its gestation period is.
2. Check student's graphs.
3. elephant, about 5%

Go Further

Students can use reference material to explore the life spans of different animals. Explain that the life span of humans varies greatly between countries, so the statistic that different students use for this number may vary.

Visual Learning

Mammal Facts Ask students to compare the birth weights of humans and whales as a percent of adult weight. They will find that whales are born at about 1.5% of the weight they will be as adults, while humans are born at 4.5% to 5.5% of their adult weight. Proportionately, newborn humans are larger than newborn whales. Have students determine which animals listed in the chart are born at the smallest (brown bear) and the largest (human) proportion of their adult weight.

Chapter 10 Study Guide

Reviewing Main Ideas

Preview

Students can answer the questions in their Science Journals. Discuss the answers as you go through the chapter. IS **Linguistic**

Review

Students can write their answers, then compare them with those of other students. IS **Interpersonal**

Reteach

Students can look at the illustrations and describe details that support the main ideas of the chapter. IS **Visual-Spatial**

Answers to Chapter Review

SECTION 1

2. The gland releases a hormone into the bloodstream, which carries it to its target tissue.

SECTION 2

3. The sphere-shaped egg allows for a large volume-to-surface-area ratio. Sperm have heads that contain hereditary information and tails that enable them to swim.

SECTION 3

2. Labor is physical or mental exertion and corresponds to the activities of childbirth.

Reviewing Main Ideas

Section 1 The Endocrine System

1. Endocrine glands secrete hormones directly into the bloodstream.

2. Hormones affect specific tissues throughout the body. *How can a gland near your head control chemical activities in other parts of your body?*

3. A change in the body causes an endocrine gland to function. When homeostasis is reached, the endocrine gland receives a signal to slow or stop its production.

Section 2 The Reproductive System

1. The reproductive system allows new organisms to be formed.

2. The testes produce sperm that leave the male through the penis.

3. The female ovary produces an egg. If fertilized, it becomes a zygote and later develops into a fetus within the uterus. *How are the structures of the egg and sperm suited for their functions?*

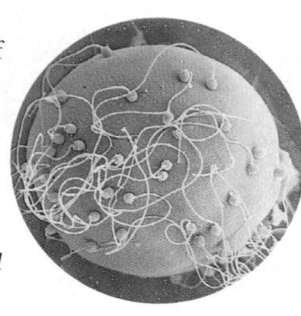

4. When an egg is not fertilized, the built-up lining of the uterus is shed in a process called menstruation. This process begins 14 days after ovulation.

Section 3 Human Life Stages

1. After fertilization, the zygote undergoes developmental changes to become an embryo, then a fetus. Twins occur when two eggs are fertilized or when a zygote divides after fertilization.

2. Birth begins with labor—muscular contractions of the uterus. The amniotic sac breaks. Then, usually after several hours, the contractions force the baby out of the mother's body. *Why is the first stage in the birthing process called labor?*

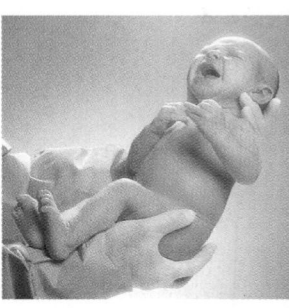

3. Infancy is the stage of development from birth to 18 months of age. It is a period of rapid growth of mental and physical skills. Childhood, which lasts until age 12, is marked by development of muscular coordination and mental abilities.

4. Adolescence is the stage of development when a person becomes physically able to reproduce. The final stage of development is adulthood. Physical development is complete and body systems become less efficient. Death occurs at the end of life.

FOLDABLES
Reading & Study Skills

After You Read

Using the information on your Foldable as an outline, explain each stage of human life.

FOLDABLES
Reading & Study Skills

After You Read

After students have read the chapter and completed the Foldable described in Before You Read, have them do the activity on the student page.

Dinah Zike

Visualizing Main Ideas

Complete the following table on life stages.

Human Development		
Stages of Life	**Age Range**	**Physical Development**
Infant	birth—18 months	sits, stands, words spoken
Childhood	18 months—12 years	walks, speaks, writes, reads
Adolescent	12—18 years	physically able to reproduce, sexual characteristics develop, final growth spurt
Adulthood	18 years—death	end of muscular and skeletal growth

Visualizing Main Ideas

See student page.

Vocabulary Review

Using Vocabulary

1. Semen
2. pregnancy
3. an embryo
4. uterus
5. amniotic sac
6. fetus
7. ovary

Vocabulary Review

Vocabulary Words

a. amniotic sac
b. embryo
c. fetal stress
d. fetus
e. hormone
f. menstrual cycle
g. menstruation
h. ovary
i. ovulation
j. pregnancy
k. semen
l. sperm
m. testes
n. uterus
o. vagina

THE PRINCETON REVIEW
Study Tip

Use lists to help you memorize facts. For example, when trying to memorize the stages of human development, write them down several times on a piece of paper until you know them.

Using Vocabulary

Replace the underlined words with the correct vocabulary word(s).

1. <u>Testes</u> is a mixture of sperm and fluid.

2. The time of the development until the birth of a baby is known as <u>menstruation</u>.

3. During the first two months of pregnancy, the unborn child is known as <u>fetal stress</u>.

4. The <u>vagina</u> is a hollow, pear-shaped muscular organ.

5. The <u>ovary</u> is the membrane that protects the unborn child.

6. After two months of pregnancy, the unborn child is known as a(n) <u>embryo</u>.

7. The <u>testes</u> is the organ that produces eggs.

IDENTIFYING ▷ Misconceptions

Assess

Use the assessment as follow-up to page 268F after students have completed the chapter.

Activity Ask students to describe the events that take place during fertilization and what the new fused cell is called. Give students a handout or write on the board the stages of development (0 to a few days, a few days to 2 weeks, and 2 weeks to 8 weeks). Have students fill in the stages with diagrams and/or verbal descriptions of the stages of development.

Expected Outcome Students should know that during fertilization the sperm and egg cells fuse, their nuclei fuse, and the fused cell is called a zygote. No other sperm can fuse with the newly formed zygote. They should draw or describe the "soap bubble" stage, the three-part state, and the differentiation stage.

Checking Concepts

1. C
2. D
3. C
4. B
5. A
6. A
7. C
8. B
9. B
10. B

Thinking Critically

11. Adrenal hormones cause your heart to beat faster, increasing blood flow to major organs and giving a sense of increased strength.

12. Both are paired organs that produce sex cells.

13. ovulation—ovary; fertilization—oviduct; implantation—uterus

14. According to the level of hormone in the blood, the target tissue sends a chemical message back to the gland to stop or start hormone secretion. Likewise, the thermostat in a house signals the heating or air conditioning unit to start or stop according to the temperature in the house. Both are negative-feedback systems.

15. Either; zygote splits into four parts—identical quadruplets; four eggs fertilized by four different sperm—fraternal quadruplets.

Chapter 10 Assessment

Checking Concepts

Choose the word or phrase that best answers the question.

1. What are the chemicals produced by the endocrine system?
   A) enzymes
   B) target tissues
   C) hormones
   D) saliva

2. Which gland produces melatonin?
   A) adrenal
   B) thyroid
   C) pancreas
   D) pineal

3. Where does the embryo develop?
   A) oviduct
   B) ovary
   C) uterus
   D) vagina

4. What is the monthly process that releases an egg called?
   A) fertilization
   B) ovulation
   C) menstruation
   D) puberty

5. What is the union of an egg and a sperm?
   A) fertilization
   B) ovulation
   C) menstruation
   D) puberty

6. Where is the egg usually fertilized?
   A) oviduct
   B) uterus
   C) vagina
   D) ovary

7. When does puberty occur?
   A) childhood
   B) adulthood
   C) adolescence
   D) infancy

8. Which sex characteristics are common to males and females?
   A) breasts
   B) pubic hair
   C) increased fat
   D) increased muscles

9. During which period does growth stop?
   A) childhood
   B) adulthood
   C) adolescence
   D) infancy

10. During what stage of development does the amniotic sac form?
    A) zygote
    B) embryo
    C) fetus
    D) newborn

Thinking Critically

11. List the effects that adrenal gland hormones can have on your body as you prepare to run a race.

12. Explain the similar functions of the ovaries and testes.

13. Identify the structure in the following diagram in which each process occurs: ovulation, fertilization, and implantation.

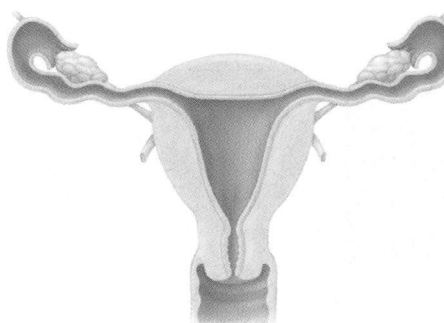

14. How is your endocrine system like the thermostat in your house?

15. Are quadruplets always identical or always fraternal, or can they be either? Explain.

Developing Skills

16. **Predicting** During the ninth month of pregnancy, the fetus develops a white, greasy coating. Predict what the function of this coating might be.

17. **Forming Hypotheses** Make a hypothesis about the effect of raising identical twins apart from each other.

18. **Classifying** Classify each of the following structures as female or male and internal or external: ovary, penis, scrotum, testes, uterus, and vagina.

Chapter ✓Assessment Planner

Portfolio Encourage students to place in their portfolios one or two items of what they consider to be their best work. Examples include:
- Visual Learning, p. 273
- Science Journal, p. 277
- Make a Model, p. 282

Performance Additional performance assessments, Performance Task Assessment Lists, and rubrics for evaluating these activities can be found in Glencoe's **Performance Assessment in the Science Classroom.**

19. Concept Mapping Complete the following concept map of egg release and implantation using the appropriate scientific words.

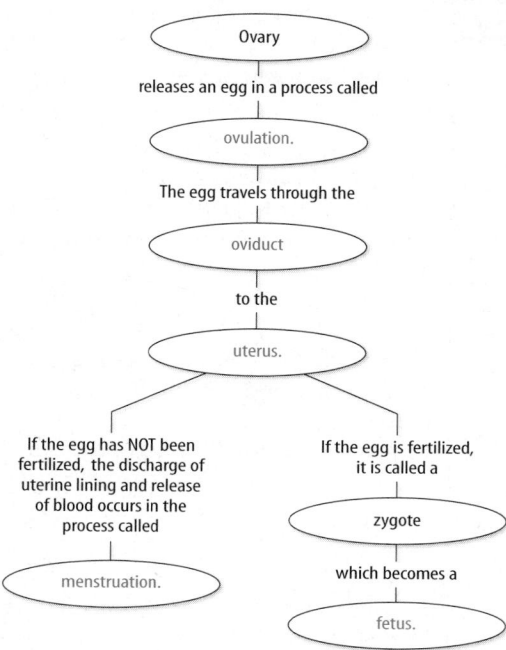

```
              Ovary
     releases an egg in a process called
            ovulation.
    The egg travels through the
            oviduct
              to the
             uterus.
        /              \
If the egg has NOT been    If the egg is fertilized,
fertilized, the discharge of    it is called a
uterine lining and release
of blood occurs in the         zygote
process called
                          which becomes a
         menstruation.
                              fetus.
```

Performance Assessment

20. Letter Find newspaper or magazine articles on the effects of smoking on the health of the developing embryo and newborn. Write a letter to the editor about why a mother's smoking is damaging her unborn baby's health.

TECHNOLOGY

Go to the Glencoe Science Web site at **science.glencoe.com** or use the **Glencoe Science CD-ROM** for additional chapter assessment.

Test Practice

In health class, Angela decided to do a report about the cases of syphilis in the United States. She brought the following graph to accompany her report, which shows syphilis rates by year between 1970 and 1997.

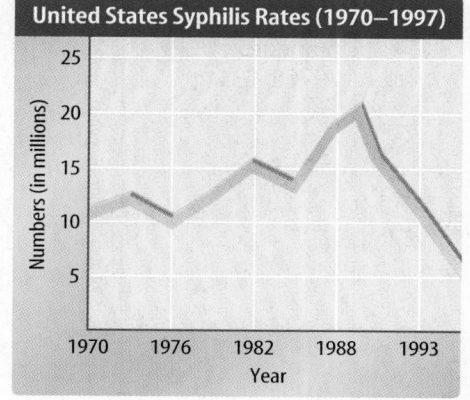

United States Syphilis Rates (1970–1997)

Study the graph and answer the following questions.

1. According to the information in the graph, when did an epidemic of syphilis occur in the United States?
A) 1970–1972
B) 1982–1984
C) 1988–1990
D) 1992–1994

2. A reasonable hypothesis for the information in the graph is that the number of people infected with syphilis _____.
F) is increasing
G) is decreasing
H) has remained the same
J) is related to gender

Test Practice

The Test-Taking Tip was written by The Princeton Review, the nation's leader in test preparation.
1. C
2. G

Developing Skills

16. This coating aids in the movement of the baby through the birth canal.
17. Students might hypothesize that they will be the same because of their genes or that the environment will have an effect, making them different.
18. female internal: ovary, uterus, vagina; male external: penis, scrotum, testes
19. See student page.

Performance Assessment

20. Information in the letter might include how smoking reduces the oxygen supply to the fetus, increases the heart rate and blood pressure, and interferes with body chemistry. Use **PASC**, p. 139.

Assessment Resources

 Reproducible Masters

Chapter Resources Booklet
Chapter Review, pp. 35–36
Chapter Tests, pp. 37–40
Assessment Transparency Activity, p. 47

Glencoe Science Web site
Interactive Tutor
Chapter Quizzes

Glencoe Technology
🖋 Assessment Transparency
💿 Interactive CD-ROM Chapter Quizzes
💿 ExamView Pro Test Bank
💿 Vocabulary PuzzleMaker Software
📼 MindJogger Videoquiz

Section/Objectives	Standards		Activities/Features
Chapter Opener	**National**	**State/Local**	**Explore Activity:** Observe dimples on faces, p. 299 **Before You Read,** p. 299
	See p. 5T for a Key to Standards.		
Section 1 Genetics 2 sessions 1 block 1. **Explain** how traits are inherited. 2. **Identify** Mendel's role in the history of genetics. 3. **Use** a Punnett square to predict the results of crosses. 4. **Compare and contrast** the difference between an individual's genotype and phenotype.	National Content Standards: UCP2, A1, C2, G3		**Science Online,** p. 301 **MiniLAB:** Comparing Common Traits, p. 302 **Visualizing Mendel's Experiments,** p. 303 **Math Skills Activity:** Calculating Probability Using a Punnett Square, p. 305 **Activity:** Predicting Results, p. 307
Section 2 Genetics Since Mendel 2 sessions 1 block 1. **Explain** how traits are inherited by incomplete dominance. 2. **Compare** multiple alleles and polygenic inheritance, and give examples of each. 3. **Describe** two human genetic disorders and how they are inherited. 4. **Explain** how sex-linked traits are passed to offspring.	National Content Standards: UCP2, A1, C2, F1		**Science Online,** p. 309 **MiniLAB:** Interpreting Polygenic Inheritance, p. 310 **Chemistry Integration,** p. 312
Section 3 Advances in Genetics 3 sessions 1.5 blocks 1. **Evaluate** the importance of advances in genetics. 2. **Sequence** the steps in making genetically engineered organisms.	National Content Standards: UCP2, A1, C2, E1, E2, F5, G1		**Environmental Science Integration,** p. 316 **Activity:** Tests for Color Blindness, p. 318 **Science Stats:** The Human Genome, p. 320

Activity Materials	Reproducible Resources	Section Assessment	Technology
Explore Activity: Science Journal	**Chapter Resources Booklet** Foldables Worksheets, p. 13 Directed Reading Overview, p. 15 Note-taking Worksheets, pp. 29–31	GLENCOE'S ASSESSMENT ADVANTAGE	
MiniLAB: paper and pencil **Activity:** 2 paper bags, 100 red beans, 100 white beans	**Chapter Resources Booklet** Transparency Activity, p. 40 MiniLAB, p. 3 Directed Reading, p. 16 Enrichment, p. 26 Reinforcement, p. 23 Activity Worksheet, pp. 5–6 Lab Activity, pp. 9–10, 11–12 **Mathematics Skill Activities,** p. 23 **Home and Community Involvement,** p. 36 **Performance Assessment in the Science Classroom,** p. 57	**Portfolio** Extension, p. 304 **Performance** MiniLAB, p. 302 Math Skills Activity, p. 305 Skill Builder Activities, p. 306 **Content** Section Assessment, p. 306	🖑 Section Focus Transparency 💿 Interactive CD-ROM 🎧 Guided Reading Audio Program
MiniLAB: paper, pencil, ruler *Need materials?* Contact Science Kit at 1-800-828-7777 or www.sciencekit.com on the Internet.	**Chapter Resources Booklet** Transparency Activity, p. 41 MiniLAB, p. 4 Enrichment, p. 27 Reinforcement, p. 24 Directed Reading, p. 16 Transparency Activity, pp. 43–44 **Life Science Critical Thinking/ Problem Solving,** p. 19	**Portfolio** Science Journal, p. 309 **Performance** MiniLAB, p. 310 Skill Builder Activities, p. 314 **Content** Section Assessment, p. 314	🖑 Section Focus Transparency 🖑 Teaching Transparency 💿 Interactive CD-ROM 🎧 Guided Reading Audio Program
Activity: white paper or poster board, colored markers	**Chapter Resources Booklet** Transparency Activity, p. 42 Enrichment, p. 28 Reinforcement, p. 25 Directed Reading, pp. 17, 18 Activity Worksheet, pp. 7–8 **Lab Management and Safety,** p. 74	**Portfolio** Assessment, p. 317 **Performance** Skill Builder Activities, p. 317 **Content** Section Assessment, p. 317	🖑 Section Focus Transparency 💿 Interactive CD-ROM 🎧 Guided Reading Audio Program

GLENCOE'S ASSESSMENT ADVANTAGE	End of Chapter Assessment		
	Blackline Masters	**Technology**	**Professional Series**
	Chapter Resources Booklet Chapter Review, pp. 33–34 Chapter Tests, pp. 35–38 **Standardized Test Practice by The Princeton Review,** pp. 27–30	📼 MindJogger Videoquiz 💿 Interactive CD-ROM 💿 Vocabulary PuzzleMakers 💿 ExamView Pro Test Bank 💿 Interactive Lesson Planner 💿 Interactive Teacher Edition	Performance Assessment in the Science Classroom (PASC)

Transparencies

Section Focus

1 Section Focus Transparency — Pass It On

You may have noticed that tall parents often have tall children and dark-haired parents often have dark-haired children. Even though offspring are similar to their parents, they do not look exactly alike.

1. Do children ever look exactly the same? When?
2. How are the members of this family different? How are they the same?
3. Why can looking at a set of parents help you predict what their children might look like?

L2

2 Section Focus Transparency — Dog Days

Humans have kept dogs for 12,000 to 14,000 years. At first, all dogs had jobs, such as herding or guarding. Today, some dogs have jobs, but many others are kept as pets.

1. What determines how big a dog can get?
2. Can a gray puppy and a brown puppy be littermates? How?
3. What environmental conditions could make one dog look different than its identical twin?

L2

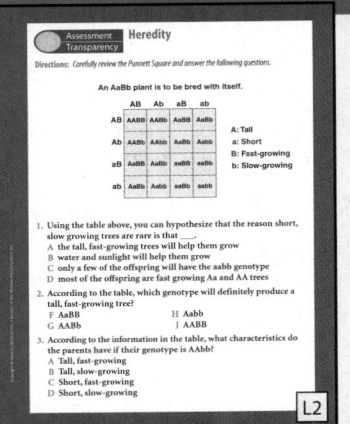

3 Section Focus Transparency — Two Quarts of Oil and a Side Salad, Please

For many years, scientists have looked for ways to raise plants and animals with traits that people want most. At the same time they try to take away unwanted traits. But how can they make a better bacteria? Recently, scientists learned how to put new parts of DNA directly into cells. By doing this, they gave certain bacteria an appetite for oil!

1. What other advantages might there be to changing an organism in this way?
2. Are there any dangers in making these sorts of changes?

L2

This is a representation of key blackline masters available in the Teacher Classroom Resources. See Resource Manager boxes within the chapter for additional information.

Key to Teaching Strategies

The following designations will help you decide which activities are appropriate for your students.

L1 Level 1 activities should be appropriate for students with learning difficulties.

L2 Level 2 activities should be within the ability range of all students.

L3 Level 3 activities are designed for above-average students.

ELL ELL activities should be within the ability range of English Language Learners.

COOP LEARN Cooperative Learning activities are designed for small group work.

LS Multiple Learning Styles logos, as described on page 22T, are used throughout to indicate strategies that address different learning styles.

P These strategies represent student products that can be placed into a best-work portfolio.

Assessment

Assessment Transparency — Heredity

Directions: Carefully review the Punnett Square and answer the following questions.

An AaBb plant is to be bred with itself.

	AB	Ab	aB	ab
AB	AABB	AABb	AaBB	AaBb
Ab	AABb	AAbb	AaBb	Aabb
aB	AaBB	AaBb	aaBB	aaBb
ab	AaBb	Aabb	aaBb	aabb

A: Tall
a: Short
B: Fast-growing
b: Slow-growing

1. Using the table above, you can hypothesize that the reason short, slow growing trees are rare is that ___.
   A the tall, fast-growing trees will help them grow
   B water and sunlight will help them grow
   C only a few of the offspring will have the aabb genotype
   D most of the offspring are fast growing Aa and AA trees
2. According to the table, which genotype will definitely produce a tall, fast-growing tree?
   F AaBB   H Aabb
   G AABb   J AABB
3. According to the information in the table, what characteristics do the parents have if their genotype is AAbb?
   A Tall, fast-growing
   B Tall, slow-growing
   C Short, fast-growing
   D Short, slow-growing

L2

Teaching

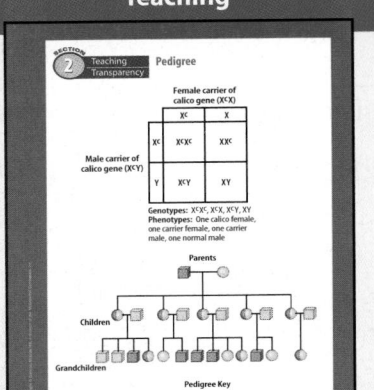

2 Teaching Transparency — Pedigree

L2

Hands-on Activities

Activity Worksheets

Activity Predicting Results

L2

Laboratory Activities

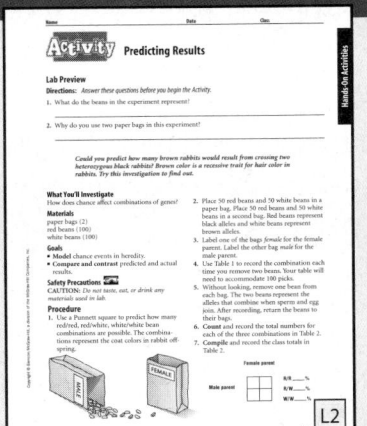

1 Laboratory Activity — Genetic Traits

L2

Meeting Different Ability Levels

Content Outline

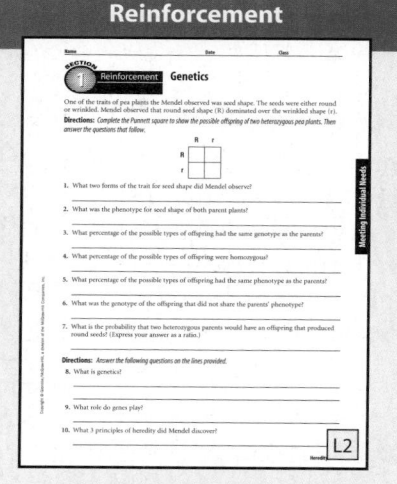

L2

Reinforcement

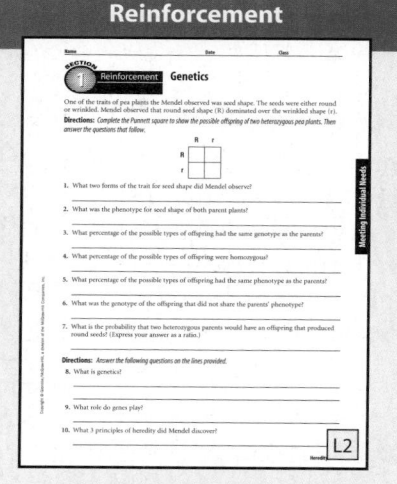

L2

Directed Reading

L1

Assessment

Chapter Tests

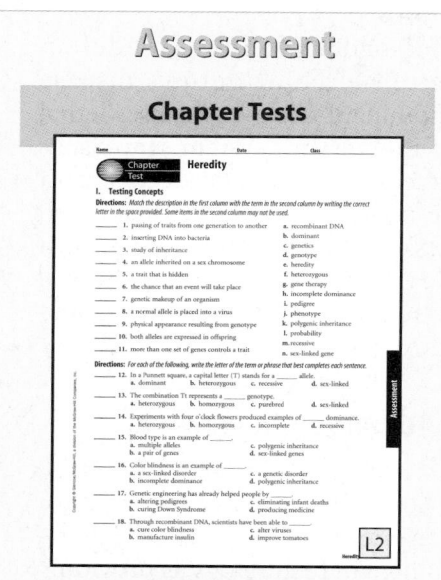

L2

Enrichment

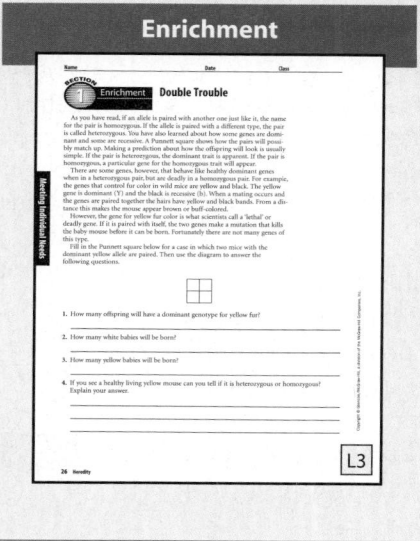

L3

Spanish Directed Reading

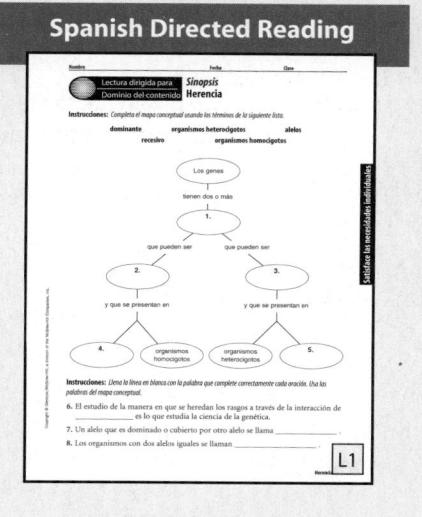

L1

Test Practice Workbook

L2

Chapter Review

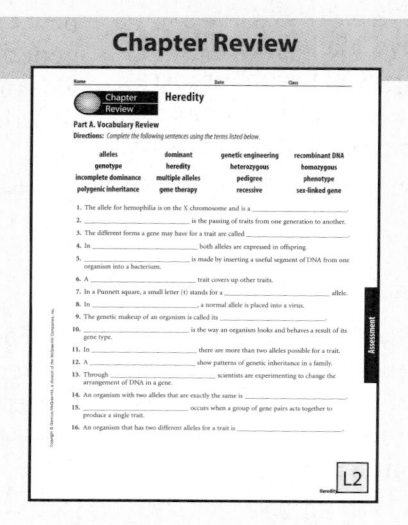

L2

Science Content Background

SECTION 1 — The Father of Genetics

Mendelian Inheritance

Gregor Mendel, an Austrian monk, was the first scientist to bring an experimental and quantitative approach to genetics, the study of heredity. Mendelian inheritance reflects the mathematical rules of probability.

Student Misconception

Dominant traits are those that occur most frequently, or those that will "take over" in a population.

Refer to the facing page for teaching strategies to address this misconception. Refer to pages 302–304 for content related to this topic.

Dominant and Recessive Factors

In Mendel's experiments, the inheritance patterns of traits each possessed two alleles. The law of dominance explains that one trait, the dominant trait, is expressed in homozygous and heterozygous conditions. The recessive trait is expressed only in the homozygous condition.

Using a Punnett Square

Mendel developed the law of segregation, which shows that recessive alleles are not lost during meiosis. In Mendel's experiments with pea hybridization, the recessive trait reappeared in approximately one-fourth of the offspring produced by crossing two heterozygous pea plants.

SECTION 2 — Genetics Since Mendel

Other Modes of Inheritance

In incomplete dominance, the heterozygous condition results in an intermediate phenotype that appears to be a blend of the dominant and recessive traits. However, when heterozygous offspring are crossed, the next generation expresses the dominant, recessive and intermediate phenotypes. In codominance, the heterozygous condition results in a phenotype that is a mixture of both dominant alleles. Sometimes there are multiple alleles for a trait, though each individual only carries two. Polygenic inheritance occurs when a trait is produced as a result of a group of genes. Mutations and chromosome disorders are caused by changes in genes such as an error made during DNA replication.

Genetic Disorders

Many human disorders follow Mendelian inheritance patterns. Huntington's disease is carried on a dominant allele and causes lethal degeneration of the nervous system. Tay-Sachs is caused by a recessive allele and occurs most often in people of Jewish descent. Sickle-cell anemia is a recessive disorder that occurs most often in people of African descent. The red blood cells are malformed and cannot effectively transport oxygen.

SECTION 3 — Advances in Genetics

Benefits of Genetic Research

Advances made in the search for the molecular basis of inheritance are phenomenal. Technology is providing new tools to aid in research, genetic testing and genetic counseling. Genetic engineering provides improved plants and efficient production of artificial chemicals such as insulin.

SCIENCE Online

For additional content background on this topic, go to the Glencoe Science Web site at science.glencoe.com.

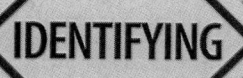

IDENTIFYING Misconceptions

Find Out What Students Think

Students may think that . . .

- **Dominant traits are the strongest, most superior, or most common traits in a population.**

Genes coding for eye color in humans comes in two alleles. The dominant allele causes brown pigment to be produced in the iris, and the recessive allele does not produce a functional protein or pigment. Each person receives two alleles of each gene, one from each parent. If a person inherits at least one "brown" allele, the person's eyes will produce pigment. If a person has only recessive alleles, no pigment is made and the eyes appear blue. Human eye color is actually somewhat more complex than this, as it is controlled by several genes (not a single pair) as opposed to simple Mendelian inheritance. The greater the number of dominant alleles a person has, the darker the eyes appear.

Discussion

Ask the class, "If brown eyes are dominant over blue eyes, does this mean that someday all people will be brown-eyed?" Let students form small discussion groups. After a set time limit, let students present their answers and supporting evidence. Their answers will reveal their preconceived notions and their reasoning.

Promote Understanding

Activity

Group students in pairs, and give each pair an envelope containing five brown and five blue squares.

- Have each student draw one brown and one blue square. These squares represent the eye color alleles of an imaginary person. Ask what color of eyes the person has (brown).

- Tell students that their two imaginary people will have a child, so each must contribute one allele. Students should randomly draw a square from the envelope. Have students lay their contributed squares side by side and determine the eye color of the child.

- Count the number of blue-eyed and brown-eyed offspring produced in the class. Ask students why some of the brown-eyed parents had a child with blue eyes.

- Poll the class to see how many students have a widow's peak hairline (dominant) versus a straight hairline (recessive), and how many have a dimple in the chin (dominant) versus no dimple in the chin (recessive). These two traits have dominant forms that are usually infrequent in a population.

Assess

After completing the chapter, see *Identifying Misconceptions* in the Study Guide.

Heredity

Chapter Vocabulary

heredity, p. 300
alleles, p. 300
genetics, p. 300
hybrid, p. 302
dominant, p. 302
recessive, p. 302
Punnett square, p. 304
genotype, p. 304
phenotype, p. 304
homozygous, p. 304
heterozygous, p. 304
incomplete dominance, p. 308
polygenic inheritance, p. 310
sex-linked gene, p. 313
genetic engineering, p. 315

What do you think?

Science Journal The cells in the picture are a human sperm and egg at the time of fertilization. The union of these cells determines a child's genetic make-up.

CHAPTER
11

Heredity

Wherever you go, look around you. You don't have the same skin color, the same kind of hair, or the same height as everyone else. Why do you resemble some people but do not look like others at all? In this chapter, you'll find out how differences are determined, and you will learn how to predict when certain traits might appear. You also will learn what causes some hereditary disorders.

What do you think?

Science Journal Look at the picture below with a classmate. Discuss what you think this might be or what is happening. Here's a hint: *The secret to why you look the way you do is found in this picture.* Write your answer or best guess in your Science Journal.

298

Theme Connection

Stability and Change Genes control stability through homeostasis at the organism level. Genetics provides background for understanding the changes involved in evolution.

EXPLORE ACTIVITY

You and your best friend enjoy the same sports, like the same food, and even have similar haircuts. But, there are noticeable differences between your appearances. Most of these differences are controlled by the genes you inherited from your parents. In the following activity, you will observe one of these differences.

Observe dimples on faces

1. Notice the two students in the photographs. One student has dimples when she smiles, and the other student doesn't have dimples.

2. Ask your classmates to smile naturally. In your Science Journal, record the name of each classmate and whether each one has dimples.

Observe

In your Science Journal, calculate the percentage of students who have dimples. Are facial dimples a common feature among your classmates?

Before You Read

FOLDABLES
Reading & Study Skills

Making a Classify Study Fold As you read this chapter about heredity, you can use the following Foldable to help you classify characteristics. When you classify, you organize objects or events into groups based on their common features.

1. Place a sheet of paper in front of you so the short side is at the top. Fold both sides in to divide the paper into thirds. Unfold the paper so three columns show.

2. Fold the paper in half from top to bottom. Then fold it in half again two more times. Unfold all the folds.

3. Trace over all the fold lines and label the columns you created as shown: *Personal Characteristics*, *Inherited*, and *Not Inherited*. List personal characteristics down the left-hand column, as shown.

4. Before you read the chapter, predict which characteristics are inherited or not inherited. As you read the chapter, check and change the table.

Personal Characteristics	Inherited	Not Inherited
eyes		
hair		
dimples		

299

Before You Read

FOLDABLES
Reading & Study Skills

Dinah Zike Study Fold

Purpose Students will define genetics by using a Foldable classification chart to record inherited and non-inherited characteristics, or traits.

📁 For additional help, see Foldables Worksheet, p. 13 in **Chapter Resources Booklet,** or go to the Glencoe Science Web site at **science.glencoe.com.** See After You Read in the Study Guide at the end of this chapter.

EXPLORE ACTIVITY

Purpose Use the Explore Activity to introduce students to inheritance. Inform students that they will be learning about inheritance and genetics as they read the chapter. L2 ELL COOP LEARN **LS** Logical-Mathematical

Preparation Discuss the photograph as a class to ensure that students recognize what dimples are.

Teaching Strategy Record data for each class and have students compare their results with those of other classes.

Observe

Percentages will vary depending upon how many students in the class have and do not have dimples. Generally, the percentage of students having dimples falls between 10 and 40 percent.

✓ Assessment

Oral Have students suggest other features that are inherited. Possible answers: hair color and texture, skin and eye color, height, shape of facial features. Use **Performance Assessment in the Science Classroom,** p. 89.

1 Motivate

Bellringer Transparency

Display the Section Focus Transparency for Section 1. Use the accompanying Transparency Activity Master. L2 ELL

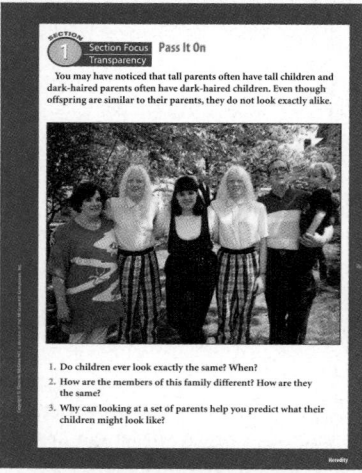

As You Read

What You'll Learn

- **Explain** how traits are inherited.
- **Identify** Mendel's role in the history of genetics.
- **Use** a Punnett square to predict the results of crosses.
- **Compare and contrast** the difference between an individual's genotype and phenotype.

Vocabulary

heredity	Punnett square
allele	genotype
genetics	phenotype
hybrid	homozygous
dominant	heterozygous
recessive	

Why It's Important

Heredity and genetics help explain why people are different.

Tie to Prior Knowledge

Show a picture of a mother dog and her puppies (or a cat and her kittens). Have students list characteristics of the offspring they think are inherited from the parents. Lead students to understand that all of the general physical traits, such as number of legs, length and shape of ears, eye color and shape, and so on, are inherited.

Inheriting Traits

Do you look more like one parent or grandparent? Do you have your father's eyes? What about Aunt Isabella's cheekbones? Eye color, nose shape, and many other physical features are some of the traits that are inherited from parents, as **Figure 1** shows. An organism is a collection of traits, all inherited from its parents. **Heredity** (huh REH duh tee) is the passing of traits from parent to offspring. What controls these traits?

What is genetics? Generally, genes on chromosomes control an organism's form and function. The different forms of a trait that a gene may have are called **alleles** (uh LEELZ). When a pair of chromosomes separates during meiosis (mi OH sus), alleles for each trait also separate into different sex cells. As a result, every sex cell has one allele for each trait, as shown in **Figure 2.** The allele in one sex cell may control one form of the trait, such as having facial dimples. The allele in the other sex cell may control a different form of the trait—not having dimples. The study of how traits are inherited through the interactions of alleles is the science of **genetics** (juh NET ihks).

Figure 1
Note the strong family resemblance among these four generations.

Section ✓ *Assessment* Planner

PORTFOLIO	CONTENT ASSESSMENT
Extension, p. 304	Section, p. 306
PERFORMANCE ASSESSMENT	Challenge, p. 306
Try at Home MiniLab, p. 302	Chapter, pp. 324–325
Math Skills Activity, p. 305	
Skill Builder Activities, p. 306	
See page 324 for more options.	

Figure 2
An allele is one form of a gene. Alleles separate into separate sex cells during meiosis. In this example, the alleles that control the trait for dimples include *D*, the presence of dimples, and *d*, the absence of dimples.

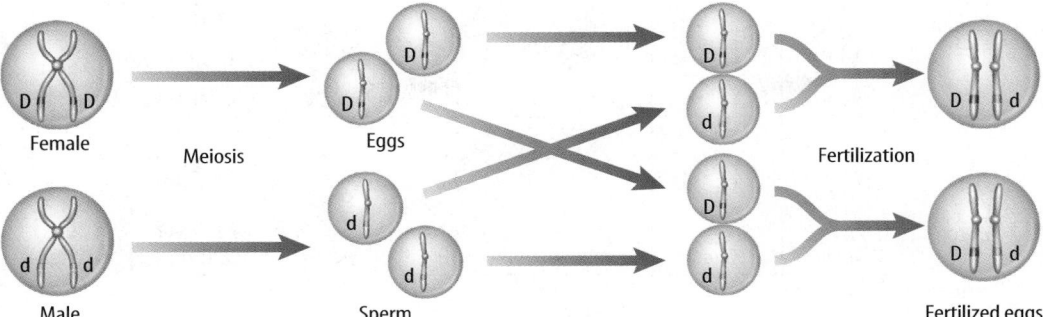

Female

Meiosis

Eggs

Fertilization

Male

Sperm

Fertilized eggs

A The alleles that control a trait are located on each duplicated chromosome.

B During meiosis, duplicated chromosomes separate.

C During fertilization, each parent donates one chromosome. This results in two alleles for the trait of dimples in the new individual formed.

Mendel—The Father of Genetics

Did you know that an experiment with pea plants helped scientists understand why your eyes are the color that they are? Gregor Mendel was an Austrian monk who studied mathematics and science but became a gardener in a monastery. His interest in plants began as a boy in his father's orchard where he could predict the possible types of flowers and fruits that would result from crossbreeding two plants. Curiosity about the connection between the color of a pea flower and the type of seed that same plant produced inspired him to begin experimenting with garden peas in 1856. Mendel made careful use of scientific methods, which resulted in the first recorded study of how traits pass from one generation to the next. After eight years, Mendel presented his results with pea plants to scientists.

Before Mendel, scientists mostly relied on observation and description, and often studied many traits at one time. Mendel was the first to trace one trait through several generations. He was also the first to use the mathematics of probability to explain heredity. The use of math in plant science was a new concept and not widely accepted then. Mendel's work was forgotten for a long time. In 1900, three plant scientists, working separately, reached the same conclusions as Mendel. Each plant scientist had discovered Mendel's writings while doing his own research. Since then, Mendel has been known as the father of genetics.

SCIENCE *Online*

Research Visit the Glencoe Science Web site at **science.glencoe.com** for more information about early genetics experiments. Write a paragraph in your Science Journal about a scientist, other than Gregor Mendel, who studied genetics.

2 Teach

Mendel—The Father of Genetics

Teacher FYI

Mendel's experiments illustrate the scientific method. Mendel worked with a single trait at a time, conducted carefully controlled experiments, collected and analyzed data, recorded his experiments so they could be repeated, worked with large samples, and shared results with his contemporaries.

SCIENCE *Online*
Internet Addresses

_____

_____

_____

Explore the Glencoe Science Web site at **science.glencoe.com** to find out more about topics in this section.

Resource Manager

Chapter Resources Booklet
Transparency Activity, p. 40
Directed Reading for Content Mastery, pp. 15, 16
Note-taking Worksheets, pp. 29–31

Purpose to observe and calculate the occurrence of various traits in dogs [L2] [ELL]

[IS] **Logical-Mathematical**

Teaching Strategies Make sure students understand that variations make each dog unique.

Safety Precautions Caution students not to touch or approach dogs they do not know.

Analysis

1. Answers will vary depending on dogs observed.
2. There are many variations. Each dog looks different.

✓ Assessment

Performance To further assess students' understanding of inherited traits, have volunteers observe and tabulate several traits among children, parents, and grandparents. Use **PASC**, p. 109.

✓ Reading Check

Answer They can be relied upon to produce the same traits generation after generation.

Some students think that dominant traits are those that will "take over" in a population. Refer to page 298F for teaching strategies that address this misconception.

Table 1 Traits Compared by Mendel							
Traits	Shape of Seeds	Color of Seeds	Color of Pods	Shape of Pods	Plant Height	Position of Flowers	Flower Color
Dominant Trait	Round	Yellow	Green	Full	Tall	At leaf junctions	Purple
Recessive Trait	Wrinkled	Green	Yellow	Flat, constricted	Short	At tips of branches	White

Genetics in a Garden

Each time Mendel studied a trait, he crossed two plants with different expressions of the trait and found that the new plants all looked like one of the two parents. He called these new plants **hybrids** (HI brudz) because they received different genetic information, or different alleles, for a trait from each parent. The results of these studies made Mendel even more curious about how traits are inherited.

Garden peas are easy to breed for pure traits. An organism that always produces the same traits generation after generation is called a purebred. For example, tall plants that always produce seeds that produce tall plants are purebred for the trait of tall height. **Table 1** shows other pea plant traits that Mendel studied.

✓ Reading Check *Why might farmers plant purebred crop seeds?*

Dominant and Recessive Factors In nature, insects randomly pollinate plants as they move from flower to flower. In his experiments, Mendel used pollen from the flowers of purebred tall plants to pollinate by hand the flowers of purebred short plants. This process is called cross-pollination. He found that tall plants crossed with short plants produced seeds that produced all tall plants. Whatever caused the plants to be short had disappeared. Mendel called the tall form the **dominant** (DAHM uh nunt) factor because it dominated, or covered up, the short form. He called the form that seemed to disappear the **recessive** (rih SES ihv) factor. Today, these are called dominant alleles and recessive alleles. What happened to the recessive form? **Figure 3** answers this question.

Comparing Common Traits

Procedure

1. Safely survey as many **dogs** in your neighborhood as you can for the presence of a solid color or spotted coat, short or long hair, and floppy ears or ears that stand up straight.
2. Make a data table that lists each of the traits. Record your data in the data table.

Analysis

1. Compare the number of dogs that have one form of a trait with those that have the other form. How do those two groups compare?
2. What can you conclude about the variations you noticed in the dogs?

NATIONAL GEOGRAPHIC VISUALIZING MENDEL'S EXPERIMENTS

Figure 3

Gregor Mendel discovered that the experiments he carried out on garden plants provided an understanding of heredity. For eight years he crossed plants that had different characteristics and recorded how those characteristics were passed from generation to generation. One such characteristic, or trait, was the color of pea pods. The results of Mendel's experiment on pea pod color are shown below.

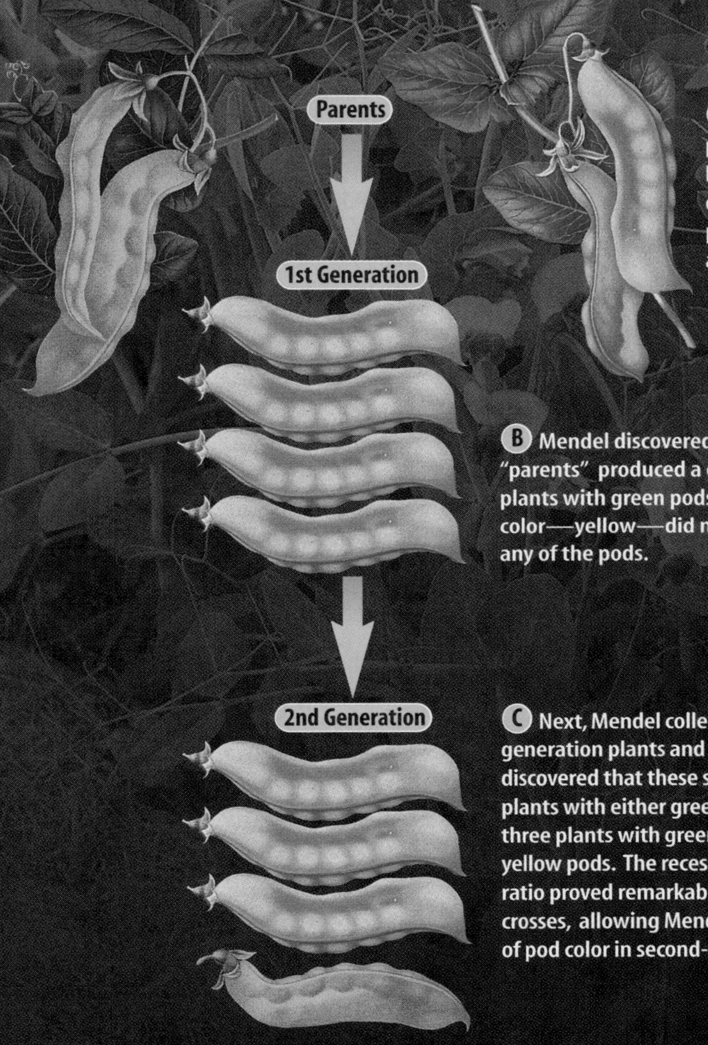

Parents

1st Generation

2nd Generation

A One of the so-called "parent plants" in Mendel's experiment had pods that were green, a dominant trait. The other parent plant had pods that were yellow, a recessive trait.

B Mendel discovered that the two "parents" produced a generation of plants with green pods. The recessive color—yellow—did not appear in any of the pods.

C Next, Mendel collected seeds from the first-generation plants and raised a second generation. He discovered that these second-generation plants produced plants with either green or yellow pods in a ratio of about three plants with green pods for every one plant with yellow pods. The recessive trait had reappeared. This 3:1 ratio proved remarkably consistent in hundreds of similar crosses, allowing Mendel to accurately predict the ratio of pod color in second-generation plants.

303

Visualizing Mendel's Experiments

Have students examine the pictures and read the captions. Then ask the following questions:

Why is it important that Mendel based his conclusions on the results of hundreds of pea plant crosses? It's important to have as much data as possible before drawing conclusions about any experiment, and in general, the larger your sample size, the more accurate your results will be.

Would the allele for the recessive trait of yellow pea pod color be present in the first generation of pea plants? Yes, the allele would be present, but it would not be expressed because none of the plants is homozygous recessive.

Activity

Have students work in small groups. Using the example shown in the Visualizing, have the students use Mendel's ratios to determine the number of yellow pea plants in the second generation if the second generation of plants contained the following: 100 total plants (25) 300 total plants (75).

Extension

Have students learn about one of the researchers who, in 1900, rediscovered Mendel's work while analyzing their own experiments, and report their findings to the class.

Genetics in a Garden, continued

Use an Analogy

The probability of genetic events is analogous to rolling a die and other games of chance.

Make a Model

Provide students with blocks of two different colors. Have them use the blocks to model the cross involving pea plant flowers described in the text. Help them use these tools to distinguish between genotype and phenotype, and homozygous and heterozygous.

Extension

Challenge students to form Punnett squares that show the results of first- and second-generation crosses between organisms pure bred for two traits. If purebred organisms are crossed, the first generation will result in all heterozygous organisms. When these are crossed, students should obtain a 9:3:3:1 ratio, as shown below. L3 ELL COOP LEARN P

Caption Answer

Figure 4 No; if red is recessive, then the genotype is homozygous recessive (rr), but if red is dominant, then the flower could be either homozygous (RR) or heterozygous (Rr).

☑ Reading Check

Answer Homozygous organisms carry the same two alleles for a trait. Heterozygous organisms carry two different alleles for a trait.

Figure 4
This snapdragon's phenotype is red. *Can you tell what the flower's genotype for color is? Explain your answer.*

Using Probability to Make Predictions If you and your sister can't agree on what movie to see, you could solve the problem by tossing a coin. When you toss a coin, you're dealing with probabilities. Probability is a branch of mathematics that helps you predict the chance that something will happen. If your sister chooses tails while the coin is in the air, what is the probability that the coin will land tail-side up? Because a coin has two sides, there are two possible outcomes, heads or tails. One outcome is tails. Therefore, the probability of one side of a coin showing is one out of two, or 50 percent.

Mendel also dealt with probabilities. One of the things that made his predictions accurate was that he worked with large numbers of plants. He studied almost 30,000 pea plants over a period of eight years. By doing so, Mendel increased his chances of seeing a repeatable pattern. Valid scientific conclusions need to be based on results that can be duplicated.

Punnett Squares Suppose you wanted to know what colors of pea plant flowers you would get if you pollinated white flowers on one pea plant with pollen from purple flowers on a different plant. How could you predict what the offspring would look like without making the cross? A handy tool used to predict results in Mendelian genetics is the **Punnett** (PUN ut) **square.** In a Punnett square, letters represent dominant and recessive alleles. An uppercase letter stands for a dominant allele. A lowercase letter stands for a recessive allele. The letters are a form of code. They show the **genotype** (JEE nuh tipe), or genetic makeup, of an organism. Once you understand what the letters mean, you can tell a lot about the inheritance of a trait in an organism.

The way an organism looks and behaves as a result of its genotype is its **phenotype** (FEE nuh tipe), as shown in **Figure 4.** If you have brown hair, then the phenotype for your hair color is brown.

Alleles Determine Traits Most cells in your body have two alleles for every trait. These alleles are located on chromosomes within the nucleus of cells. An organism with two alleles that are the same is called **homozygous** (hoh muh ZI gus). For Mendel's peas, this would be written as *TT* (homozygous for the tall-dominant trait) or *tt* (homozygous for the short-recessive trait). An organism that has two different alleles for a trait is called **heterozygous** (het uh roh ZI gus). The hybrid plants Mendel produced were all heterozygous for height, *Tt*.

☑ Reading Check
What is the difference between homozygous and heterozygous organisms?

Sample Punnett Square for Extension:

Parent 2 (RrYy)	Parent 1 (RrYy)			
		RY	Ry	rY	ry
RY	RRYY	RRYy	RrYY	RrYy
Ry	RRYy	RRyy	RrYy	Rryy
rY	RrYY	RrYy	rrYY	rrYy
ry	RrYy	Rryy	rrYy	rryy

Making a Punnett Square In a Punnett square for predicting one trait, the letters representing the two alleles from one parent are written along the top of the grid, one letter per section. Those of the second parent are placed down the side of the grid, one letter per section. Each square of the grid is filled in with one allele donated by each parent. The letters that you use to fill in each of the squares represent the genotypes of possible offspring that the parents could produce.

Math Skills Activity

Calculating Probability Using a Punnett Square

You can determine the probability of certain traits by using a Punnett square. Letters are used to represent the two alleles from each parent and are combined to determine the possible genotypes of the offspring.

Example Problem

One dog carries heterozygous, black-fur traits (Bb), and its mate carries homogeneous, blond-fur traits (bb). Calculate the probability of the puppy having black fur.

Solution

1 *This is what you know:*
dominant allele is represented by *B*
recessive allele is represented by *b*

2 *This is what you need to find:*
the probability of a puppy's fur color being black using a Punnett square

3 *This is the diagram you need to use:*

Black dog

	B	b
b		
b		

Blond dog

4 *Complete the Punnett square by taking each letter in each column and combining it with each letter from each row in the corresponding square.*

Black dog

	B	b
b	Bb	bb
b	Bb	bb

Blond dog

Genotypes of offspring:
2Bb, 2bb
Phenotypes of offspring:
2 black, 2 blond

5 *Find the needed probability. There are two Bb genotypes and four possible outcomes.*

$$P(black\ fur) = \frac{number\ of\ ways\ to\ get\ black\ fur}{number\ of\ possible\ outcomes}$$

$$= \frac{2}{4} = \frac{1}{2} = 50\%$$

Practice Problem

Use a Punnett square to determine the probability of each of the offspring's genotype and phenotype when two heterozygous, tall-dominant traits (Tt) are crossed with each other.

For more help, refer to the Math Skill Handbook.

Inclusion Strategies

Learning Disabled Have students choose one or two inherited traits (eye color, left- or right-handedness, and so on) and survey classmates to see how many of them display the characteristics. Results can be graphed. Other classrooms can be surveyed. Students can determine whether larger populations have the same ratio of the traits as subgroups. L1 COOP LEARN
 IS **Interpersonal**

Quick Demo

Use two long strings of the large plastic beads used as a toddler's toy to demonstrate alleles along a chromosome. Explain that each different shape and color of bead represents a different trait. When the two strands are brought together, you can demonstrate homozygous and heterozygous conditions.

Math Skills Activity

National Math Standards
Correlation to Mathematics Objectives
1, 2, 4, 5, 6, 8, 9, 10

Answer to Practice Problem

Genotype: p(TT) = 25%;
p(Tt) = 50%; p(tt) = 25%;
Phenotype: 75% tall, 25% short

	T	t
T	TT	Tt
t	Tt	tt

Genetics in a Garden, continued

Visual Learning

Table 2 Have students relate the principles of heredity to genetic examples they have studied in this section.

③ Assess

Reteach

Have students role play the alleles in a cross. Take the class to a paved portion of the school yard. Use masking tape to mark out a large Punnett square on the pavement. Assign students to be certain alleles and allow them to arrange themselves and announce the phenotypes and genotypes produced. L2 ELL  **Visual-Spatial**

Challenge

Have students determine the number of combinations possible in a trihybrid cross. There are 64 possibilities. L3 **Logical-Mathematical**

✓ Assessment

Performance Have students use a Punnett square to demonstrate their answer to Question 6. Use **PASC,** p. 97.

Principles of Heredity Even though Gregor Mendel didn't know anything about DNA, genes, or chromosomes, he succeeded in beginning to describe and mathematically represent how inherited traits are passed from parents to offspring. He realized that some factor in the pea plant produced certain traits. Mendel also concluded that these factors separated when the pea plant reproduced. Mendel arrived at his conclusions after years of detailed observation, careful analysis, and repeated experimentation. **Table 2** summarizes Mendel's principles of heredity.

Table 2 Principles of Heredity	
1	Traits are controlled by alleles on chromosomes.
2	An allele's effect is dominant or recessive.
3	When a pair of chromosomes separates during meiosis, the different alleles for a trait move into separate sex cells.

Section ① Assessment

1. Alleles are described as being dominant or recessive. What is the difference between a dominant and a recessive allele?

2. How are dominant and recessive alleles represented in a Punnett square?

3. Explain the difference between genotype and phenotype. Give examples.

4. Gregor Mendel, an Austrian monk who lived in the 1800s, is known as the father of genetics. Explain why Mendel has been given this title.

5. **Think Critically** If an organism expresses a recessive phenotype, can you tell the genotype? Explain your answer by giving an example.

Skill Builder Activities

6. **Predicting** Hairline shape is an inherited trait in humans. The widow's peak allele is dominant, and the straight hairline allele is recessive. Predict how both parents with widow's peaks could have a child without a widow's peak hairline. **For more help, refer to the** Science Skill Handbook.

7. **Using Percentages** One fruit fly is heterozygous for long wings, and another fruit fly is homozygous for short wings. Long wings are dominant to short wings. Using a Punnett square, find out what percent of the offspring are expected to have short wings. **For more help, refer to the** Math Skill Handbook.

Answers to Section Assessment

1. A dominant allele is expressed if an allele pair is homozygous dominant or heterozygous. A recessive allele is expressed only when an allele pair is homozygous recessive.

2. Dominant alleles are represented with an uppercase letter, recessive alleles with a lowercase letter.

3. Genotype is the combination of alleles an organism contains; phenotype is the expression of the alleles in an organism. For example, a genotype might be Tt (heterozygous dominant), and the phenotype might be tall.

4. He was the first person to explain the mechanisms of heredity.

5. Yes, because two copies of the recessive allele must be present for the recessive phenotype to show up.

6. Both parents would have to be heterozygous to produce children without the widow's peak trait.

7. 50%

Activity

Predicting Results

Could you predict how many brown rabbits would result from crossing two heterozygous black rabbits? Try this investigation to find out. Brown color is a recessive trait for hair color in rabbits.

What You'll Investigate
How does chance affect combinations of genes?

Materials
paper bags (2)   white beans (100)
red beans (100)

Goals
■ **Model** chance events in heredity.
■ **Compare and contrast** predicted and actual results.

Safety Precautions
WARNING: *Do not taste, eat, or drink any materials used in the lab.*

Procedure
1. Use a Punnett square to predict how many red/red, red/white, and white/white bean combinations are possible. The combinations represent the coat colors in rabbit offspring.
2. Place 50 red beans and 50 white beans in a paper bag. Place 50 red beans and 50 white beans in a second bag. Red beans represent black alleles and white beans represent brown alleles.
3. Label one of the bags *female* for the female parent. Label the other bag *male* for the male parent.
4. Use a data table to record the combination each time you remove two beans. Your table will need to accommodate 100 picks.

5. Without looking, remove one bean from each bag. The two beans represent the alleles that combine when sperm and egg join. After recording, return the beans to their bags.
6. **Count** and record the total numbers for each of the three combinations in your data table.
7. **Compile** and record the class totals.

Conclude and Apply
1. Which combination occurred most often?
2. **Calculate** the ratio of red/red to red/white to white/white. What hair color in rabbits do these combinations represent?
3. **Compare** your predicted (expected) results with your observed (actual) results.
4. **Hypothesize** how you could get predicted results to be closer to actual results.

Sample data

Gene Combinations			
Rabbits	**Red/Red**	**Red/White**	**White/White**
Your Total	18	52	30
Class Total	376	751	373

Communicating Your Data

Write a paragraph that clearly describes your results. Have another student read your paragraph. Ask if he or she could understand what happened. If not, rewrite your paragraph and have the other student read it again. **For more help, refer to the** Science Skill Handbook.

Communicating Your Data

Students' paragraphs should indicate methods and results, as well as how the model relates to actual heredity principles.

Activity

BENCH TESTED

Purpose Students use a model to investigate how the principles of heredity are related to chance.
L2 ELL LS **Logical-Mathematical**
Process Skills predicting, observing, recording data, interpreting data, using numbers, making and using tables

Time Required one class period

Safety Precautions Remind students not to eat or throw the beans.

Teaching Strategies
• All the beans should be approximately the same size.
• Emphasize the importance of completing all 100 trials.
• **Troubleshooting** Explain to students that beans must be returned to the bag after each draw so that the probability of choosing the different color combinations remains the same throughout the activity.

Answers to Questions
1. red/white
2. Results should be close to 1:2:1; red/red represents a black rabbit, red/white represents a black rabbit, and white/white represents a brown rabbit.
3. Answers will vary, but should follow expected results closely.
4. A larger sample could be used or more trials done.

✓*Assessment*

Performance To further assess students' knowledge of probability, have them repeat the activity using three different kinds of beans. Use the **PASC,** p. 97.

SECTION

2 Genetics Since Mendel

Bellringer Transparency

Display the Section Focus Transparency for Section 2. Use the accompanying Transparency Activity Master. L2
ELL

Tie to Prior Knowledge

Ask students if any of them have eye color different from either parent. Explain that some inherited traits involve more complex patterns of inheritance, and students will learn about them in this section.

Caption Answer

Figure 5 The palomino's coat color is intermediate between its parents' coat colors.

As You Read

What **You'll Learn**

- **Explain** how traits are inherited by incomplete dominance.
- **Compare** multiple alleles and polygenic inheritance, and give examples of each.
- **Describe** two human genetic disorders and how they are inherited.
- **Explain** how sex-linked traits are passed to offspring.

Vocabulary
incomplete dominance
polygenic inheritance
sex-linked gene

Why **It's Important**
Most of your inherited traits involve more complex patterns of inheritance than Mendel discovered.

Figure 5
When a chestnut horse is bred with **B** a cremello horse, all offspring will be **C** palomino. The Punnett square shown in **D** can be used to predict this result. *How does the color of the palomino horse in **C** show that the coat color of horses may be inherited by incomplete dominance?*

Incomplete Dominance

Not even in science do things remain the same. After Mendel's work was rediscovered in 1900, scientists repeated his experiments. For some plants, such as peas, Mendel's results proved true. However, when different plants were crossed, the results were sometimes different. One scientist crossed purebred red four-o'clock plants with purebred white four-o'clock plants. He expected to get all red flowers, but they were pink. Neither allele for flower color seemed dominant. Had the colors become blended like paint colors? He crossed the pink-flowered plants with each other, and red, pink, and white flowers were produced. The red and white alleles had not become blended. Instead, when the allele for white flowers and the allele for red flowers combined, the result was an intermediate phenotype—a pink flower. When the offspring of two homozygous parents show an intermediate phenotype, this inheritance is called **incomplete dominance.** Other examples of incomplete dominance include the feather color of some chicken breeds and the coat color of some horse breeds, as shown in **Figure 5.**

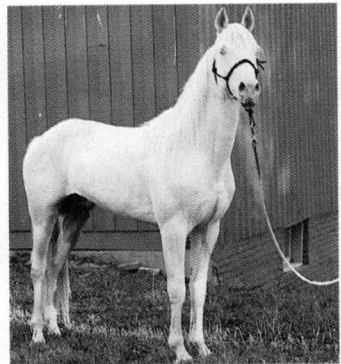

Section ✔ *Assessment* Planner

PORTFOLIO
Science Journal, p. 309
PERFORMANCE ASSESSMENT
MiniLAB, p. 310
Skill Builder Activities, p. 314
See page 324 for more options.

CONTENT ASSESSMENT
Section, p. 314
Challenge, p. 314
Chapter, pp. 324–325

Multiple Alleles Mendel studied traits in peas that were controlled by just two alleles. However, many traits are controlled by more than two alleles. A trait that is controlled by more than two alleles is said to be controlled by multiple alleles. Traits controlled by multiple alleles produce more than three phenotypes of that trait.

Imagine that only three types of coins are made—nickels, dimes, and quarters. If every person can have only two coins, six different combinations are possible. In this problem, the coins represent alleles of a trait. The sum of each two-coin combination represents the phenotype. Can you name the six different phenotypes possible with two coins?

Blood type in humans is an example of multiple alleles that produce only four phenotypes. The alleles for blood types are called A, B, and O. The O allele is recessive to both the A and B alleles. When a person inherits one A allele and one B allele for blood type, both are expressed—phenotype AB. A person with phenotype A blood has the genetic makeup, or genotype—AA or AO. Someone with phenotype B blood has the genotype BB or BO. Finally, a person with phenotype O blood has the genotype OO.

SCIENCE Online

Research Visit the Glencoe Science Web site at **science.glencoe.com** for information on the importance of blood types in blood transfusions. In your Science Journal, draw a chart showing which blood types can be used safely during transfusions.

☑ **Reading Check** *What are the six different blood type genotypes?*

C

D

Chestnut horse (CC)

	C	C
C'	CC'	CC'
C'	CC'	CC'

Cremello horse (C'C')

Genotypes: All CC'
Phenotypes: All palomino horses

---

2 Teach

Incomplete Dominance

Discussion

Discuss why traits governed by incomplete dominance or multiple alleles might be more difficult to study. Help students see that these patterns do not conform to Mendel's prediction of a simple 3:1 ratio.

Text Question Answer

Possible combinations: nickel, dime; nickel, quarter; dime, quarter; nickel, nickel; dime, dime; quarter, quarter

Fun Fact

Blood types are important to the health profession. Matching blood types—both AB, A, B, or O and Rh—is important in transfusions. The recessive blood type, O, occurs in more than 30 percent of Americans.

☑ **Reading Check**

Answer AA, AO, AB, BB, BO, OO

Science Journal

Genetics of Flower Color Explain that in hibiscus flowers, red is dominant to white. Have students explain why they can tell the genotype of a red four-o'clock, but not of a red hibiscus. Four-o'clocks inherit color by incomplete dominance. A red four-o'clock must be homozygous. If it were heterozygous, it would be pink. A red hibiscus might be heterozygous or homozygous. L2 P

Resource Manager

Chapter Resources Booklet

Transparency Activity, p. 41
Directed Reading for Content Mastery, p. 16

SCIENCE Online
Internet Addresses

_____

_____

_____

Explore the Glencoe Science Web site at **science.glencoe.com** to find out more about topics in this section.

Polygenic Inheritance

Use Science Words

Word Origin Polygenic inheritance involves many genes. The prefix *poly-* means "many." Have students use a dictionary to find other words with this prefix and explain their meanings. Possible answers: polygon—many sided figure; polychromatic—made of many colors

Purpose to determine the inheritance pattern that controls hand span [L2] [ELL]

[LS] **Logical-Mathematical**

Materials paper, pencil, ruler

Teaching Strategy It may be easier for students to have each subject place his or her hand on a piece of paper and mark the width of the hand span before measuring it.

Analysis

1. Answers will vary. Spans may range from 12.5 cm to 24 cm or more.
2. Hand spans are determined by polygenic inheritance, not by a simple Mendelian pattern.

Oral Ask students to determine if identical twins have identical hand spans. The spans are usually very close, but not identical because of environmental factors that affect growth. Use **Performance Assessment in the Science Classroom,** p. 89.

Mini LAB

Interpreting Polygenic Inheritance

Procedure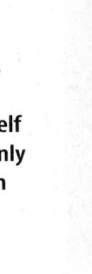

1. Measure the hand spans of your classmates.
2. Using a **ruler,** measure from the tip of the thumb to the tip of the little finger when the hand is stretched out. Read the measurement to the nearest centimeter.
3. Record the name and hand-span measurement of each person in a data table.

Analysis

1. What range of hand spans did you find?
2. Are hand spans inherited as a simple Mendelian pattern or as a polygenic or incomplete dominance pattern? Explain.

Figure 6
Himalayan rabbits have alleles for dark-colored fur. However, this allele is able to express itself only at lower temperatures. Only the areas located farthest from the rabbit's main body heat (ears, nose, feet, tail) have dark-colored fur.

310 CHAPTER 11 Heredity

Polygenic Inheritance

Eye color is an example of a trait that is produced by a combination of many genes. **Polygenic** (pahl ih JEHN ihk) **inheritance** occurs when a group of gene pairs acts together to produce a trait. The effects of many alleles produces a wide variety of phenotypes. For this reason, it may be hard to classify all the different shades of eye color.

Your height and the color of your eyes and skin are just some of the many human traits controlled by polygenic inheritance. It is estimated that three to six gene pairs control your skin color. Even more gene pairs might control the color of your hair and eyes. The environment also plays an important role in the expression of traits controlled by polygenic inheritance. Polygenic inheritance is common and includes such traits as grain color in wheat and milk production in cows. Egg production in chickens is also a polygenic trait.

Impact of the Environment Your environment plays a role in how some of your genes are expressed or whether they are expressed at all, as shown in **Figure 6.** Environmental influences can be internal or external. For example, most male birds are more brightly colored than females. Chemicals in their bodies determine whether the gene for brightly colored feathers is expressed.

Although genes determine many of your traits, you might be able to influence their expression by the decisions you make. Some people have genes that make them at risk for developing certain cancers. Whether they get cancer might depend on external environmental factors. For instance, if some people at risk for skin cancer limit their exposure to the Sun and take care of their skin, they might never develop cancer.

 **Reading Check** *What environmental factors might affect the size of leaves on a tree?*

Active Reading

Reflective Journal In this strategy, students identify activities and what they learned and record responses to the activities. Have students divide pieces of paper into several columns. Have them record their thoughts under headings such as "What I did," "What I learned," "What questions do I have," "What surprises did I experience," and "Overall response." Have students write a Reflective Journal entry for the MiniLAB.

Human Genes and Mutations

Sometimes a gene undergoes a change that results in a trait that is expressed differently. Occasionally errors occur in the DNA when it is copied inside of a cell. Such changes and errors are called mutations. Not all mutations are harmful. They might be helpful or have no effect on an organism.

Certain chemicals are known to produce mutations in plants or animals, including humans. X rays and radioactive substances are other causes of some mutations. Mutations are changes in genes.

Chromosome Disorders In addition to individual mutations, problems can occur if the incorrect number of chromosomes is inherited. Every organism has a specific number of chromosomes. However, mistakes in the process of meiosis can result in a new organism with more or fewer chromosomes than normal. A change in the total number of human chromosomes is usually fatal to the unborn embryo or fetus, or the baby may die soon after birth.

Look at the human chromosomes in **Figure 7**. If three copies of chromosome 21 are produced in the fertilized human egg, Down's syndrome results. Individuals with Down's syndrome can be short, exhibit learning disabilities, and have heart problems. Such individuals can lead normal lives if they have no severe health complications.

Figure 7
Humans usually have 23 pairs of chromosomes. Notice that three copies of chromosome 21 are present in this photo, rather than the usual two chromosomes. This change in chromosome number results in Down's syndrome. Chris Burke, a well-known actor, has this syndrome.

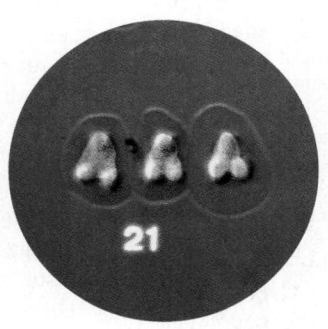

21

SECTION 2 Genetics Since Mendel **311**

Human Genes and Mutations

LAB DEMONSTRATION

Purpose to show how mutations are passed to daughter cells
Materials blue and red overhead acetate, yarn, scissors, overhead projector
Preparation Cut out several 2-, 4-, and 6-cm long pairs of blue chromosomes. Cut one 4-cm long red chromosome.
Procedure Make a circle of yarn on the projector to represent a cell. Place the blue chromosome pairs in the cell. "Mutate" one chromosome from blue to red. Divide the chromosomes to make two new cells surrounded by yarn as if the cell had undergone mitosis.
Expected Outcome One daughter cell carries a mutation.

✔ *Assessment*

What will happen when the cell carrying the mutation reproduces? The mutation will be reproduced. **How might this explain how a person could have a white stripe in his hair, while the rest of his hair remains black?** The mutation is in the hair cells. It is passed along when the hair cells undergo mitosis.

Recessive Genetic Disorders

Discussion

Point out that about 600 simple recessive human disorders are presently known. Genetic disorders caused by dominant alleles are more common. An example is Huntington's disease, which usually does not express itself until the person is an adult. **Why are fewer human genetic disorders recessive?** Humans with recessive genetic disorders rarely live to a reproductive age.

Reading Check

Answer Cystic fibrosis is a recessive disorder.

Caption Answer

Figure 8 The X chromosome is larger than the Y, and looks like an X. The Y chromosome looks like the V part of a Y.

Chemistry INTEGRATION

If both parents are heterozygous for the trait, they have a 25 percent chance of producing an offspring with PKU with each pregnancy.

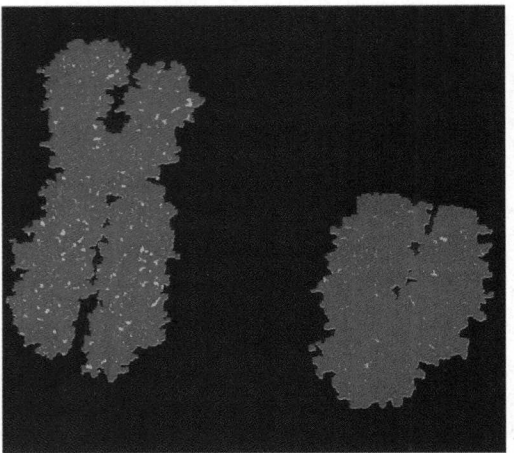
Magnification: 10,000×

Figure 8
Sex in many organisms is determined by X and Y chromosomes. *How do the X (left) and Y (right) chromosomes differ from one another in shape and size?*

Chemistry INTEGRATION

People with PKU, a recessive disorder, cannot produce the enzyme needed for the breakdown of a substance found in some artificially sweetened drinks. Soft-drink cans must be labeled to ensure that individuals with this disorder do not unknowingly consume the substance. Explain in your Science Journal how a person can be born with PKU if neither parent has this recessive disorder.

Recessive Genetic Disorders

Many human genetic disorders, such as cystic fibrosis, are caused by recessive genes. Some recessive genes are the result of a mutation within the gene. Many of these alleles are rare. Such genetic disorders occur when both parents have a recessive allele responsible for this disorder. Because the parents are heterozygous, they don't show any symptoms. However, if each parent passes the recessive allele to the child, the child inherits both recessive alleles and will have a recessive genetic disorder.

Reading Check

How is cystic fibrosis inherited?

Cystic fibrosis is a homozygous recessive disorder. It is the most common genetic disorder that can lead to death among Caucasian Americans. In most people, a thin fluid is produced that lubricates the lungs and intestinal tract. People with cystic fibrosis produce thick mucus instead of this thin fluid. The thick mucus builds up in the lungs and makes it hard to breathe. This buildup often results in repeated bacterial respiratory infections. The thick mucus also reduces or prevents the flow of substances necessary for digesting food. Physical therapy, special diets, and new drug therapies have increased the life spans of patients with cystic fibrosis.

Sex Determination

What determines the sex of an individual? Much information on sex inheritance came from studies of fruit flies. Fruit flies have only four pairs of chromosomes. Because the chromosomes are large and few in number, they are easy to study. Scientists identified one pair that contains genes that determine the sex of the organism. They labeled the pair XX in females and XY in males. Geneticists use these labels when studying organisms, including humans. You can see human X and Y chromosomes in **Figure 8.**

Each egg produced by a female normally contains one X chromosome. Males produce sperm that normally have either an X or a Y chromosome. When a sperm with an X chromosome fertilizes an egg, the offspring is a female, XX. A male offspring, XY, is the result of a Y-containing sperm fertilizing an egg. What pair of sex chromosomes is in each of your cells? Sometimes chromosomes do not separate during meiosis. When this occurs, an individual can inherit an abnormal number of sex chromosomes.

312 CHAPTER 11 Heredity

Inclusion Strategies

Learning Disabled Some students may appreciate seeing photos or videos that depict much of the information presented here. The March of Dimes and other foundations supply free or low-cost classroom materials that summarize many of these concepts. L1 LS **Visual-Spatial**

Teacher FYI

Most students will be aware of someone with a genetic disorder. Be sensitive to the possibility that students may have someone in their own family with a disorder.

Sex-Linked Disorders

Some inherited conditions are linked with the X and Y chromosomes. An allele inherited on a sex chromosome is called a **sex-linked gene.** Color blindness is a sex-linked disorder in which people cannot distinguish between certain colors, particularly red and green. This trait is a recessive allele on the X chromosome. Because males have only one X chromosome, a male with this allele on his X chromosome is color-blind. However, a color-blind female occurs only when both of her X chromosomes have the allele for this trait.

The allele for the distinct patches of three different colors found in calico cats is recessive and carried on the X chromosome. As shown in **Figure 9,** calico cats have inherited two X chromosomes with this recessive allele—one from both parents.

Pedigrees Trace Traits

How can you trace a trait through a family? A pedigree is a visual tool for following a trait through generations of a family. Males are represented by squares and females by circles. A completely filled circle or square shows that the trait is seen in that person. Half-colored circles or squares indicate carriers. A carrier is heterozygous for the trait and it is not seen. People represented by empty circles or squares do not have the trait and are not carriers. The pedigree in **Figure 10** shows how the trait for color blindness is carried through a family.

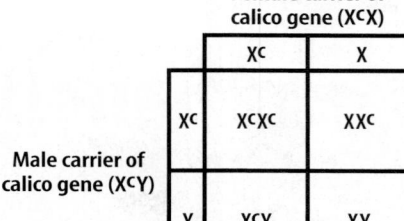

Female carrier of calico gene (XᶜX)

Genotypes: XᶜXᶜ, XᶜX, XᶜY, XY
Phenotypes: One calico female, one carrier female, one carrier male, one normal male

Figure 9
Calico cat fur is a homozygous recessive sex-linked trait. Female cats that are heterozygous are not calico but are only carriers. Two recessive alleles must be present for this allele to be expressed. *Why aren't all the females calico?*

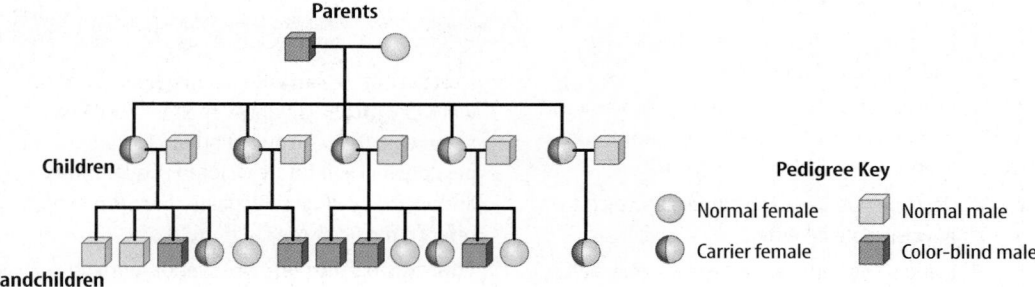

Parents

Children

Grandchildren

Pedigree Key

 Normal female

Carrier female

Normal male

Color-blind male

Figure 10
The symbols in this pedigree's key mean the same thing on all pedigree charts. The grandfather in this family was color-blind and married to a woman who was not a carrier of the color-blind allele. *Why are no women in this family color-blind?*

SECTION 2   Genetics Since Mendel   **313**

Sex-Linked Disorders

Quick Demo
Use Punnett squares to demonstrate inheritance patterns discussed in this section, such as the combination of X and Y chromosomes that determines the sex of an individual.

Make a Model
Have students use a set of cutouts of X and Y chromosomes to model how a sex-linked disorder can be inherited.

Caption Answer
Figure 9 All the females aren't calico because some are heterozygous.

Pedigrees Trace Traits

Visual Learning
Figure 10 Have students use this figure to answer the following questions. **How many children are carriers for color blindness?** 5 **How many grandchildren?** 3 **What percent is this of each generation?** 100% of children, 23% of grandchildren are carriers.

Extension
Have students find out the pros and cons of purebred breeding. For example, some purebred dog breeds have fragile bone structure or poor kidney functioning. Breeding with other breeds might lessen these weaknesses. L2

Caption Answer
Figure 10 Because color-blind women must inherit the allele from both mother and father, more women are carriers of color blindness than have the disorder.

③ Assess

Reteach

Have students compare the three inheritance patterns in this section by making a chart. L1
LS Visual-Spatial

Challenge

Which would be more difficult to predict, the results of incomplete dominance, multiple alleles, or polygenic inheritance? The number of variations is usually much greater with polygenic inheritance than with the other two patterns.

✔ Assessment

Process Have students prepare a table that lists types of inheritance, their descriptions, and examples of each. Use **PASC,** p. 109.

Resource Manager

Chapter Resources Booklet
Reinforcement, p. 24

Figure 11
A variety of traits are considered when breeding dogs. **A** Black Labrador retrievers often are bred to be sporting dogs.
B Shih tzus are usually companion or show dogs.

Using Pedigrees A pedigree is a useful tool for a geneticist. Sometimes a geneticist needs to understand who has had a trait in a family over several generations to determine its pattern of inheritance. A geneticist determines if a trait is recessive, dominant, sex-linked, or has some other pattern of inheritance. When geneticists understand how a trait is inherited, they can predict the probability that a baby will be born with a specific trait.

✔ **Reading Check** *Why is a pedigree a useful tool for a geneticist?*

Pedigrees also are important in breeding animals or plants. Because livestock and plant crops are used as sources of food, these organisms are bred to increase their yield and nutritional content. Breeders of pets and show animals, like the dogs pictured in **Figure 11,** also examine pedigrees carefully for possible desirable physical and ability traits. Issues concerning health also are considered when researching pedigrees.

Section ② Assessment

1. Compare inheritance by multiple alleles and polygenic inheritance.

2. Explain why a trait inherited by incomplete dominance, such as the color of Appaloosa horses, is not a blend of two alleles.

3. Describe two genetic disorders and discuss how they are inherited.

4. Using a Punnett square, explain why males are affected more often than females by sex-linked genetic disorders.

5. **Think Critically** Calico male cats are rare. Explain how such a cat can exist.

Skill Builder Activities

6. **Predicting** A man with blood type B marries a woman with blood type A. Their first child has blood type O. Predict what other blood types are possible for their future children. Explain your answer using a Punnett square. **For more help, refer to the** Science Skill Handbook.

7. **Communicating** In your Science Journal, write an essay that explains why the offspring of two parents may or may not show much resemblance to either parent. **For more help, refer to the** Science Skill Handbook.

Answers to Section Assessment

1. Multiple alleles involve a single pair of genes that have more than two alleles; polygenic inheritance involves multiple pairs of genes, each with two or more alleles, all affecting the same trait.

2. The two alleles are present in the offspring, and are available to be passed on. But when combined, they produce a phenotype that is intermediate between those shown by homozygous individuals.

3. Answers will vary. Sample response: cystic fibrosis, a disease affecting the lungs and other organs, is inherited as a simple recessive trait.

4. Males only need to inherit one gene encoding for the disorder to be affected. Females must inherit two genes for the disorder to appear.

5. Possible answer: A mutation may allow a male cat to inherit an extra X chromosome in addition to a Y chromosome. Both X chromosomes may carry the recessive calico trait.

6. Children may have blood types A, B, O, or AB. The Punnett square should show heterozygous parents with the alleles AO and BO.

7. There are many genes and combinations, so an individual may look very different from either parent.

Advances in Genetics

Why is genetics important?

If Mendel were to pick up a daily newspaper in any country today, he'd probably be surprised. News articles about developments in genetic research appear almost daily. The term *gene* has become a common word. The principles of heredity are being used to change the world.

Genetic Engineering

You may know that chromosomes are made of DNA and are in the nucleus of a cell. Sections of DNA in chromosomes that direct cell activities are called genes. Through **genetic engineering,** scientists are experimenting with biological and chemical methods to change the arrangement of DNA that makes up a gene. Genetic engineering already is used to help produce large volumes of medicine. Genes also can be inserted into cells to change how those cells perform their normal functions, as shown in **Figure 12.** Other research is being done to find new ways to improve crop production and quality, including the development of plants that are resistant to disease.

As You Read

***What* You'll Learn**
- **Evaluate** the importance of advances in genetics.
- **Sequence** the steps in making genetically engineered organisms.

Vocabulary
genetic engineering

***Why* It's Important**
Advances in genetics can affect your health, the foods that you eat, and your environment.

Figure 12
DNA from one organism is placed into another species. This method is used to produce human insulin, human growth hormone, and other chemicals by bacteria.

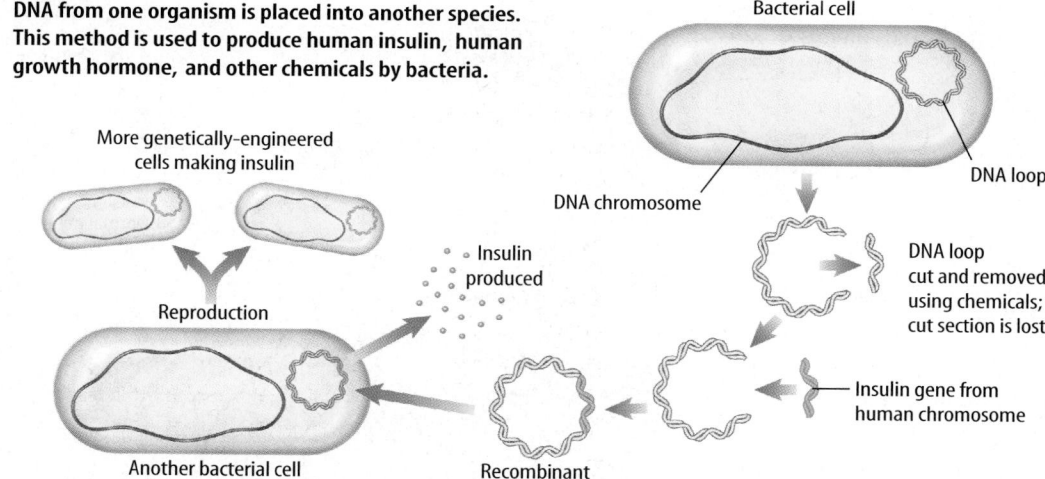

SECTION 3 Advances in Genetics **315**

Section ✓*Assessment* Planner

PORTFOLIO
Assessment, p. 317

PERFORMANCE ASSESSMENT
Skill Builder Activities, p. 317
See page 324 for more options.

CONTENT ASSESSMENT
Section, p. 317
Challenge, p. 317
Chapter, pp. 324–325

Advances in Genetics

1 Motivate

Bellringer Transparency
Display the Section Focus Transparency for Section 3. Use the accompanying Transparency Activity Master. L2
ELL

Tie to Prior Knowledge

Explain that in selective breeding, specific crosses are made to accentuate a desired trait in offspring. Discuss with students how this might be advantageous to a plant breeder trying to produce a corn plant that has higher yields. Then explain that scientists are trying to find new ways to change traits without the time involved in selective breeding. They will learn about these techniques in this section.

Genetic Engineering

Environmental Science INTEGRATION

Possible answers: The crops may begin to grow in areas where they are not wanted; weeds might inadvertently become pesticide resistant; the plants may pollinate other fields of the same crop unintentionally.

Visual Learning

Figure 13 Explain that gene therapy is still in its infancy. As more is learned, the applications are likely to extend to many more genetic disorders. Remind students of the demonstration of a mutation in a cell being propagated by mitosis. **How is gene therapy similar to the way a mutation is propagated through body cells?** The mechanisms are similar, but in gene therapy, a mutation is corrected by the propagation, instead of spread.

Teacher FYI

Transgenesis is a genetic engineering process that involves transferring a gene from one organism into another. Using transgenesis, scientists have developed tomato plants that have increased resistance to disease and spoilage. Potato, cotton, and corn plants that have a natural resistance to insects, such as moth larvae and beetles, also have been developed.

Environmental Science INTEGRATION

Crop plants are now being genetically engineered to produce chemicals that kill specific pests that feed on them. Some of the pollen from pesticide-resistant canola crops is capable of spreading up to 8 km from the plant, while corn and potato pollen can spread up to 1 km. What might be the effects of pollen landing on other plants?

Figure 13
Gene therapy involves placing a normal allele in a cell that has a mutation. When the normal allele begins to function, a genetic disorder such as cystic fibrosis (CF) may be corrected.

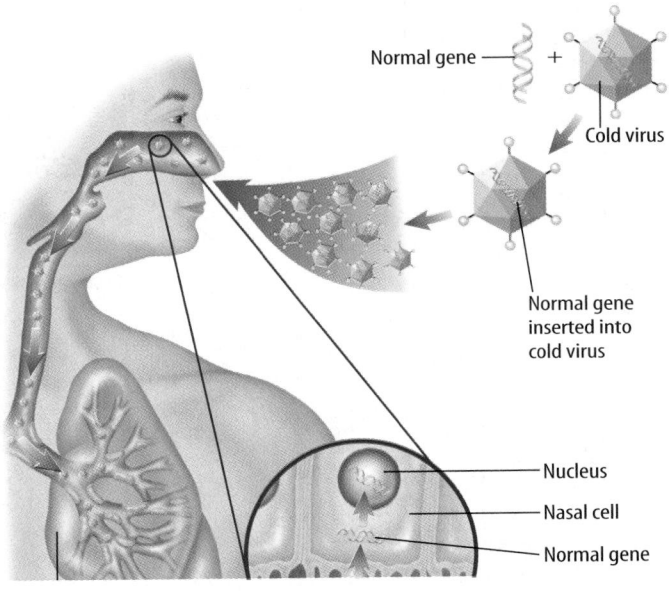

Normal gene + Cold virus
Normal gene inserted into cold virus
Nucleus
Nasal cell
Normal gene

Recombinant DNA Making recombinant DNA is one method of genetic engineering. Recombinant DNA is made by inserting a useful segment of DNA from one organism into a bacterium, as illustrated in **Figure 12.** Large quantities of human insulin are made by some genetically-engineered organisms. People with Type 1 diabetes need this insulin because their pancreases produce too little or no insulin. Other uses include the production of growth hormone to treat dwarfism and chemicals to treat cancer.

Gene Therapy Gene therapy is a kind of genetic engineering. In gene therapy, a normal allele is placed in a virus, as shown in **Figure 13.** The virus then delivers the normal allele when it infects its target cell. The normal allele replaces the defective one. Scientists are conducting experiments that use this method to test ways of controlling cystic fibrosis and some kinds of cancer. More than 2,000 people already have taken part in gene therapy experiments. Gene therapy might be a method of curing several other genetic disorders in the future.

Cultural Diversity

Genetic Engineering Research into genetic engineering, especially of crops, is taking place in many countries. Genetically engineered crops have already been planted in Europe, Canada, and the United States, though several countries in Europe have now banned the use of genetically engineered crops. Have students research to find out what countries could most benefit from agricultural advances involving genetic engineering. Have them research the staples of diets in those countries, and what, if any, research is being done on engineering those crops. Possible answer: Researchers at the International Rice Institute in the Philippines are working to produce new strains of rice.

Genetically Engineered Plants For thousands of years people have improved the plants they use for food and clothing even without the knowledge of genotypes. Until recently, these improvements were the results of selecting plants with the most desired traits to breed for the next generation. This process is called selective breeding. Recent advances in genetics have not replaced selective breeding. Although a plant can be bred for a particular phenotype, the genotype and pedigree of the plants also are considered.

Genetic engineering can produce improvements in crop plants, such as corn, wheat, and rice. One type of genetic engineering involves finding the genes that produce desired traits in one plant and then inserting those genes into a different plant. Scientists recently have made genetically engineered tomatoes with a gene that allows tomatoes to be picked green and transported great distances before they ripen completely. Ripe, firm tomatoes are then available in the local market. In the future, additional food crops may be genetically engineered so that they are not desirable food for insects.

Figure 14
Genetically engineered produce is sometimes labeled. This allows consumers to make informed choices about their foods.

 **Reading Check** *What other types of traits would be considered desirable in plants?*

Because some people might prefer foods that are not changed genetically, some stores label such produce, as shown in **Figure 14.** The long-term effects of consuming genetically engineered plants are unknown.

Section 3 Assessment

1. Give examples of areas in which advances in genetics are important.
2. Compare and contrast the technologies of using recombinant DNA and gene therapy.
3. What are some benefits of genetically engineered crops?
4. How does selective breeding differ from genetic engineering?
5. **Think Critically** Why might some people be opposed to genetically engineered plants?

Skill Builder Activities

6. **Concept Mapping** Make an events chain concept map of the steps used in making recombinant DNA. **For more help, refer to the** Science Skill Handbook.
7. **Using a Word Processor** Use a computer word processing program to write predictions about how advances in genetics might affect your life in the next ten years. **For more help, refer to the** Technology Skill Handbook.

SECTION 3 Advances in Genetics   **317**

③ Assess

Reteach
Have students make flash cards that illustrate steps in the process of genetic engineering. Have students practice identifying and ordering the steps using these cards.

Challenge
Should gene therapy be made available for all genetic disorders, or only those that are most harmful? Support your answer. Individual responses will vary. Accept all responses for which students provide support.

✓ Assessment

Performance Have students make a model that demonstrates the process of genetic engineering. Use **Performance Assessment in the Science Classroom,** p. 123. P

Resource Manager

Chapter Resources Booklet
Transparency Activity, p. 42
Reinforcement, p. 25
Directed Reading for Content Mastery, pp. 17, 18

Answers to Section Assessment

1. Answers may include agriculture, health, and medicine.
2. Recombinant DNA inserts a segment of DNA from an organism into a bacterium to produce needed substances. Gene therapy places a normal allele into a virus, which delivers the allele to its target cell. There, it replaces the defective allele.
3. They may lead to increased crop production or be pest-resistant.
4. Selective breeding relies on natural, reproductive processes. Genetic engineering may take traits from one organism and place them into another.
5. Some people are concerned about pesticide resistance in weeds or other unforeseen consequences.
6. Answers should reflect steps shown in **Figure 12.**
7. Answers may include increased food production, curing genetic disorders, or providing new medicines.

Activity

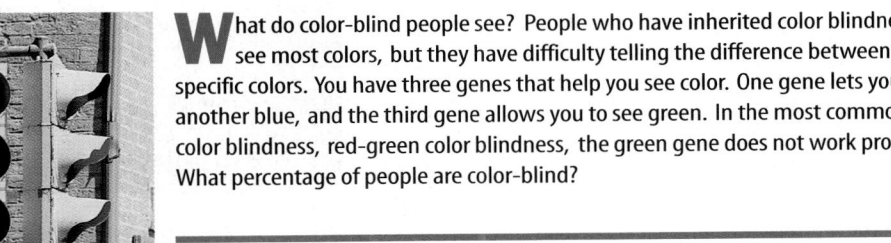

BENCH TESTED

Recognize the Problem

Purpose
Students will devise a method to test for color blindness, and administer the test to determine the percentage of affected individuals.

Process Skills
interpreting data, designing an experiment, forming a hypothesis, communicating, using numbers

Time Required
one class period

Materials
colored markers, blank white paper

Form a Hypothesis

Possible Hypothesis
Students may hypothesize that color blindness will affect more males than females.

Test Your Hypothesis

Possible Procedures
Students may choose to create a picture or number out of green circles. They can then use circles of red, orange, or yellow to surround the picture or number. Using this test, students would determine whether individuals could see the "hidden" picture or number.

Activity Design Your Own Experiment

Tests for Color Blindness

What do color-blind people see? People who have inherited color blindness can see most colors, but they have difficulty telling the difference between two specific colors. You have three genes that help you see color. One gene lets you see red, another blue, and the third gene allows you to see green. In the most common type of color blindness, red-green color blindness, the green gene does not work properly. What percentage of people are color-blind?

Recognize the Problem

What percentages of males and females in your school are color-blind?

Form a Hypothesis

Based on your reading and your own experiences, form a hypothesis about how common color blindness is among males and females.

Goals
- **Design** an experiment that tests for a specific type of color blindness in males and females.
- **Calculate** the percentage of males and females with the disorder.

Possible Materials
white paper or poster board
colored markers: red, orange, yellow, bright green, dark green, blue
*computer and color printer
*Alternate materials

To a person with red-green color blindness, bright green appears tan in color, and dark green looks like brown. The color red also looks brown, making it difficult to tell the difference between green and red. A person without red-green color blindness will see a "6" in this test, while a red-green color-blind person will not see this number.

Resource Manager

Chapter Resources Booklet
   Activity Worksheet, pp. 7–8
   Enrichment, p. 28
Lab Management and Safety, p. 74

Test Your Hypothesis

Plan

1. **Decide** what type of color blindness you will test for—the common green-red color blindness or the more rare green-blue color blindness.

2. **List** the materials you will need and describe how you will create test pictures. Tests for color blindness use many circles of red, orange, and yellow as a background, with circles of dark and light green to make a picture or number. List the steps you will take to test your hypothesis.

3. **Prepare** a data table in your Science Journal to record your test results.

4. **Examine** your experiment to make sure all steps are in logical order.

5. **Identify** which pictures you will use as a control and which pictures you will use as variables.

Do

1. Make sure your teacher approves your plan before you start.

2. **Draw** the pictures that you will use to test for color blindness.

3. Carry out your experiment as planned and record your results in your data table.

Analyze Your Data

1. **Calculate** the percentage of males and females that tested positive for color blindness.

2. **Compare** the frequency of color blindness in males with the frequency of color blindness in females.

Draw Conclusions

1. Did the results support your hypothesis? Explain.

2. Use your results to explain why color blindness is called a sex-linked disorder.

3. **Infer** how common the color-blind disorder is in the general population.

4. **Predict** your results if you were to test a larger number of people.

*C*ommunicating Your Data

Using a word processor, **write** a short article for the advice column of a fashion magazine about how a color-blind person can avoid wearing outfits with clashing colors. **For more help, refer to the** Technology Skill Handbook.

ACTIVITY 319

Teaching Strategy

Allow students to test individuals outside of class. Encourage them to test family, friends, and other teachers. Have them turn in their results after one week.

Expected Outcome

More males than females will test positive for color blindness.

Analyze Your Data

1. More males should test positive than females.

2. Males are much more likely to be color blind than females.

Error Analysis

Have students compare results to identify errors in data collection. Some possible sources of error are colors on the test pictures not being right or students overhearing the results of others so as not to give a true result.

Draw Conclusions

1. Answers will vary.

2. The allele for this trait is only located on the X chromosome. Because males only have one X chromosome, males with this allele will be color blind. A female will be color blind only when both of her X chromosomes have the color blind allele.

3. Color blindness afflicts 8 percent of males and 0.04 percent of females.

4. A larger sample will give more accurate results.

✓*Assessment*

Process Have students create a similar test for another type of color blindness. After getting results, have students make a bar graph showing the percentages of individuals affected with each type of color blindness. Use **Performance Assessment in the Science Classroom,** p. 107.

*C*ommunicating Your Data

Students might suggest that matching colors be grouped in different areas of the closet, or that a tagging system be developed so that one group of matching clothing is labeled *A*, a second group is labeled *B*, and so on.

Content Background

The human genome project, an international, cooperative effort to sequence the human genome, is making continual contributions to our knowledge of human genetics. Scientists involved in the project are quick to point out the many things they don't know, even though the genome is complete. For example, the exact mechanism that turns genes on and off as needed, the exact function of many genes, and how some genes work together to cause disease are unknown. Students may be curious to know whose genome is being sequenced. The government and private companies working on genomes are using several anonymous donors of various racial and ethnic backgrounds.

Discussion

Mice and humans have many similar genes. What is one characteristic or function shared by mice and humans that might be coded for by similar genes? Possible answer: Both mice and humans have digestive enzymes that could be coded for by similar genes.

Activity

Have students write a story from the point of view of a human gene. Students should include details such as which chromosome the gene is located on, the function of the gene, and whether the gene functions all the time or is switched on and off. Students can either use an imaginary gene, or an actual human gene. **IS Linguistic**

Science Stats

The Human Genome

Did you know...

... The human genome is not very different from the genome of mice. As shown to the right, many of the genes that are found on mouse chromosome 17 are similar to genes on human chromosomes. Humans may be more closely related to other organisms than previously thought.

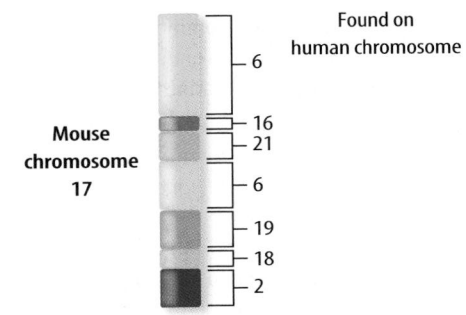

... The strands of DNA in the human genome, if unwound and connected end to end, would be more than 1.5 m long—but only about 130 trillionths of a centimeter wide. Even an average human hair is as much as 200,000 times wider than that.

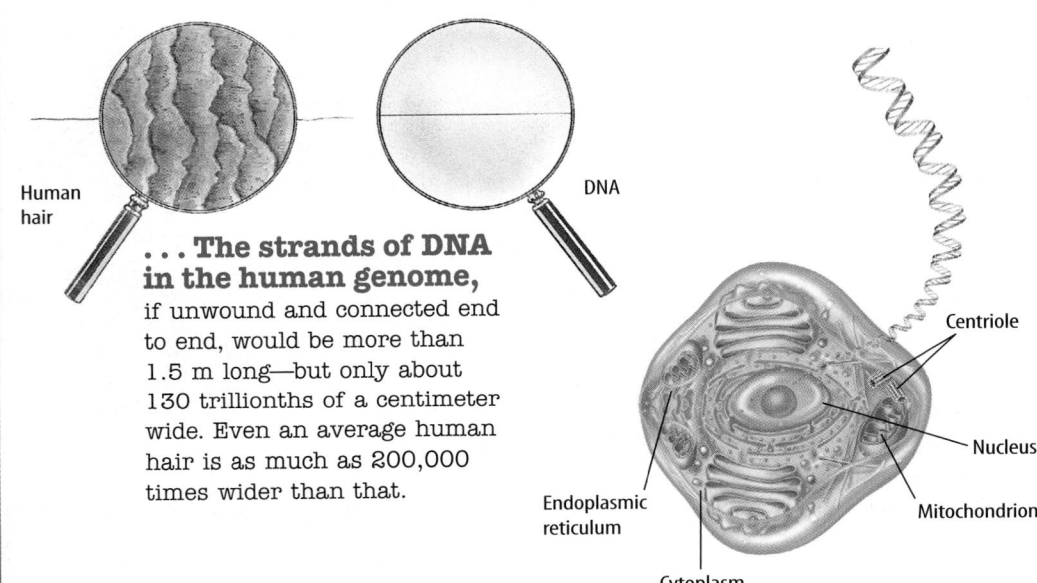

... The biggest advance in genetics in years took place in February 2001. Scientists successfully mapped the human genome. There are 30,000 to 40,000 genes in the human genome. Genes are in the nucleus of each of the several trillion cells in your body.

320 **CHAPTER 11** Heredity

SCIENCE *Online*
Internet Addresses

Explore the Glencoe Science Web site at **science.glencoe.com** to find out more about topics in this feature.

... It would take about nine and one-half years to read aloud without stopping the 3 billion bits of instructions (called base pairs) in your genome.

Teaching Strategies

- Review place value for millions and billions to help students convert units in the first problem.
- Discuss what units are used to label the Y axis of the graph for the second problem.
- Remind students of the meaning of the metric prefix *milli-* (1/1000) to help them convert units for the third problem.

Genome Sizes of Various Organisms

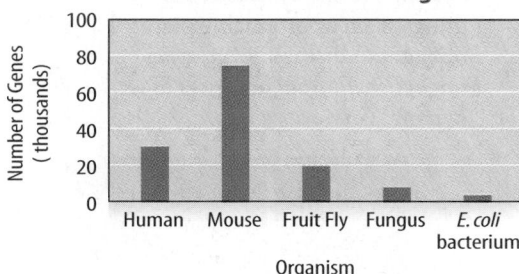

... Not all the DNA in your genes contains useful information. About 90 percent of it is "junk" DNA—meaningless sequences located in and between genes.

Answers

1. 3 gigabytes (1 million base pairs = 1 megabyte; 3 billion base pairs = 3,000 megabytes or 3 gigabytes)
2. about 10,000 genes
3. 20 m

Go Further

Have students prepare a poster with information about the genetic disease they have chosen to investigate. Children's hospitals are often an excellent source of information about genetic disorders.
LS Visual-Spatial

Do the Math

1. If one million base pairs of DNA take up 1 megabyte of storage space on a computer, how many gigabytes (1,024 megabytes) would the whole genome fill?
2. Consult the above graph. How many more genes are in the human genome than the genome of the fruit fly?
3. If you wrote the genetic information for each gene in the human genome on a separate sheet of 0.2-mm-thick paper and stacked the sheets, how tall would the stack be?

Go Further

By decoding the human genome scientists hope to identify the location of disease-causing genes. Research a genetic disease and share your results with your class.

Visual Learning

Genome Sizes of Various Organisms Have students examine the information in the graph and propose reasons for the large number of genes in the human genome as compared to the number of genes in the *E. coli* genome. As students discuss their ideas, point out the different levels of complexity in a human body and an *E. coli* bacterium.

Reviewing Main Ideas

Preview

Students can answer the questions in their Science Journals. Discuss the answers as you go through the chapter. **IS** **Linguistic**

Review

Students can write their answers, then compare them with those of other students. **IS** **Interpersonal**

Reteach

Students can look at the illustrations and describe details that support the main ideas of the chapter. **IS** **Visual-Spatial**

Answers to Chapter Review

SECTION 1

4. Punnett squares can help to predict the variations and ratios of offspring.

SECTION 3

4. Accept all reasonable answers. Common examples may include corn, wheat, rice, and various produce.

Reviewing Main Ideas

Section 1 Genetics

1. Genetics is the study of how traits are inherited. Gregor Mendel determined the basic laws of genetics.

2. Traits are controlled by alleles on chromosomes in the nuclei of cells.

3. Some alleles can be dominant and others can be recessive in action.

4. When a pair of chromosomes separates during meiosis, the different alleles for a trait move into separate sex cells. Mendel found that traits followed the laws of probability and that he could predict the outcome of genetic crosses. *How can a Punnett square help predict inheritance of traits?*

	F	f
F	FF	Ff
F	FF	Ff

Section 2 Genetics Since Mendel

1. Inheritance patterns studied since Mendel include incomplete dominance, multiple alleles, and polygenic inheritance.

2. These inheritance patterns allow a greater variety of phenotypes to be produced than would result from Mendelian inheritance.

3. Some disorders are the results of inheritance and can be harmful, even deadly, to those affected.

4. Pedigree charts help reveal patterns of the inheritance of a trait in a family. Pedigrees show that sex-linked traits are expressed more often in males than in females.

Section 3 Advances in Genetics

1. Genetic engineering uses biological and chemical methods to add or remove genes in an organism's DNA.

2. Recombinant DNA is one way genetic engineering can be performed using bacteria to make useful chemicals, including hormones.

3. Gene therapy shows promise for correcting many human genetic disorders by inserting normal alleles into cells.

4. Breakthroughs in the field of genetic engineering are allowing scientists to do many things, such as producing plants that are resistant to disease. *What types of crops might benefit from advances in genetic engineering? Give examples.*

FOLDABLES
Reading & Study Skills

After You Read

How many characteristics listed in your Classify Study Fold are inherited from your parents? How many are not inherited? Why are some not inherited?

FOLDABLES
Reading & Study Skills

After You Read

After students have read the chapter and completed the Foldable described in Before You Read, have them do the activity on the student page.

Dinah Zike

Visualizing Main Ideas

Examine the following pedigree for diabetes and explain the inheritance pattern.

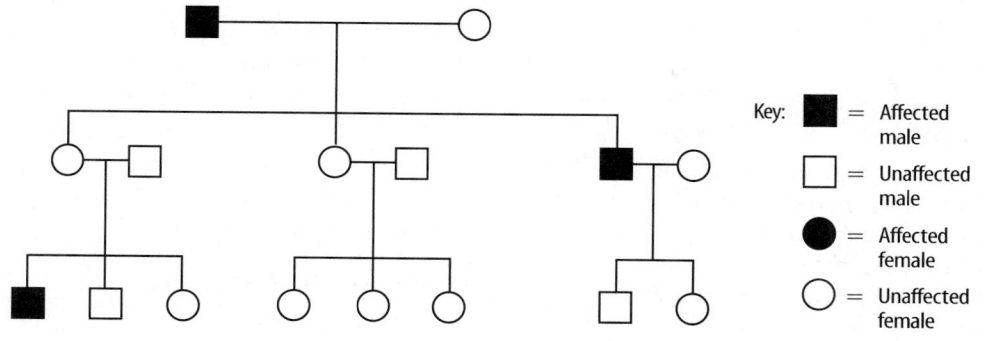

Key:
- ■ = Affected male
- □ = Unaffected male
- ● = Affected female
- ○ = Unaffected female

Vocabulary Review

Vocabulary Words

a. allele
b. dominant
c. genetic engineering
d. genetics
e. genotype
f. heredity
g. heterozygous
h. homozygous
i. hybrid
j. incomplete dominance
k. phenotype
l. polygenic inheritance
m. Punnett square
n. recessive
o. sex-linked gene

Using Vocabulary

Make the sentences to the right true by replacing the underlined word with the correct vocabulary word.

THE PRINCETON REVIEW **Study Tip**

When you encounter new vocabulary, write it down in a sentence. This will help you understand, remember, and use new vocabulary words.

1. Alternate forms of a gene are called <u>genetics</u>.
2. The outward appearance of a trait is a <u>genotype</u>.
3. Human height, eye color, and skin color are all traits controlled by <u>sex-linked genes</u>.
4. An allele that produces a trait in the heterozygous condition is <u>recessive</u>.
5. <u>Polygenic inheritance</u> is the branch of biology that deals with the study of heredity.
6. The actual combination of alleles of an organism is its <u>phenotype</u>.
7. <u>Hybrid</u> is moving fragments of DNA from one organism and inserting them into another organism.
8. A <u>phenotype</u> is a helpful device for predicting the proportions of possible genotypes.
9. <u>Genetics</u> is the passing of traits from parents to offspring.
10. Red-green color blindness and hemophilia are two human genetic disorders that are caused by a <u>genotype</u>.

CHAPTER STUDY GUIDE 323

Chapter **11** Study Guide

Visualizing Main Ideas

The trait is X-linked.

Vocabulary Review

Using Vocabulary

1. alleles
2. phenotype
3. polygenic inheritance
4. dominant
5. Genetics
6. genotype
7. Genetic engineering
8. Punnett square
9. Heredity
10. sex-linked gene

IDENTIFYING Misconceptions

Assess

Use the assessment as follow-up to page 298F after students have completed the chapter.

Procedure Repeat the question: If brown eyes are dominant over blue eyes, does this mean that someday all people will be brown eyed? Have students write and diagram their answer.

Expected Outcome Students should show that brown-eyed parents can have blue-eyed children if both parents have one blue-eyed allele. Students should show that the allele is passed directly from parent to child. It does not disappear in the parent, then reappear in the child, nor does it disappear from the population. Students should show that they understand that a dominant allele is not stronger or more frequently expressed than a recessive allele.

Checking Concepts

1. A
2. C
3. A
4. C
5. C
6. B
7. D
8. A
9. A
10. B

Thinking Critically

11. DNA is a chemical; a gene contains DNA; an allele is a form of a gene specific for a trait; genes are located on chromosomes.

12. The phenotype will show the dominant trait, whether the genotype is homozygous or heterozygous, because the recessive gene does not show up in the phenotype.

13. The coat colors of some rabbits are affected by temperature differences in the environment.

14. The normal allele is usually inserted only into the cells that cause the disorder. For this reason, the reproductive cells would not be changed by gene therapy.

Chapter 11 Assessment

Checking Concepts

Choose the word or phrase that best answers the question.

1. Which of the following are located in the nuclei on chromosomes?
   A) genes
   C) carbohydrates
   B) pedigrees
   D) zygotes

2. Which of the following describes the allele that causes color blindness?
   A) dominant
   B) carried on the Y chromosome
   C) carried on the X chromosome
   D) present only in males

3. What is it called when the presence of two different alleles results in an intermediate phenotype?
   A) incomplete dominance
   B) polygenic inheritance
   C) multiple alleles
   D) sex-linked genes

4. What separates during meiosis?
   A) proteins
   C) alleles
   B) phenotypes
   D) pedigrees

5. What controls traits in organisms?
   A) cell membrane
   C) genes
   B) cell wall
   D) Punnett squares

6. Which of the following is a use for a Punnett square?
   A) to dominate the outcome of a cross
   B) to predict the outcome of a cross
   C) to assure the outcome of a cross
   D) to number the outcome of a cross

7. What term describes the inheritance of cystic fibrosis?
   A) polygenic inheritance
   B) multiple alleles
   C) incomplete dominance
   D) recessive genes

8. What type of inheritance is eye color?
   A) polygenic inheritance
   B) multiple alleles
   C) incomplete dominance
   D) recessive genes

9. What chromosome(s) did the father contribute if a normal female is produced?
   A) X
   C) Y
   B) XX
   D) XY

10. What type of inheritance is blood type?
    A) polygenic inheritance
    B) multiple alleles
    C) incomplete dominance
    D) recessive genes

Thinking Critically

11. Explain the relationship among DNA, genes, alleles, and chromosomes.

12. Explain how the parents and offspring represented in this Punnett square have the same phenotype.

	F	f
F	FF	Ff
F	FF	Ff

13. Explain why two rabbits with the same genes might not be colored the same if one is raised in Maine and one is raised in Texas.

14. Why would a person who receives genetic therapy for a disorder still be able to pass the disorder to his or her children?

Developing Skills

15. **Predicting** Two organisms were found to have different genotypes but the same phenotype. Predict what these phenotypes might be. Explain.

Chapter ✓Assessment Planner

Portfolio Encourage students to place in their portfolios one or two items of what they consider to be their best work. Examples include:
- Extension, p. 304
- Science Journal, p. 309
- Assessment, p. 317

Performance Additional performance assessments, Performance Task Assessment Lists, and rubrics for evaluating these activities can be found in Glencoe's **Performance Assessment in the Science Classroom.**

16. Classifying Classify the inheritance pattern for each of the following:
  a. many different phenotypes produced by one pair of alleles;
  b. many phenotypes produced by more than one pair of alleles; two phenotypes from two alleles; three phenotypes from two alleles.

17. Comparing and Contrasting Compare and contrast Mendelian inheritance with incomplete dominance.

18. Interpreting Scientific Illustrations What were the genotypes of the parents that produced the following Punnett square?

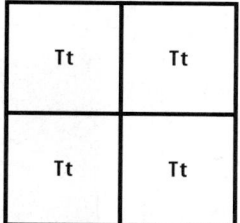

Tt	Tt
Tt	Tt

Performance Assessment

19. Newspaper Article Write a newspaper article to announce a new, genetically engineered plant. Include the method of developing the plant, the characteristic changed, and the terms that you would expect to see. Read your article to the class.

TECHNOLOGY

Go to the Glencoe Science Web site at **science.glencoe.com** or use the **Glencoe Science CD-ROM** for additional chapter assessment.

THE PRINCETON REVIEW   Test Practice

A scientist is studying pea plants. The scientist made this Punnett square to predict the color traits of the offspring of two parent pea plants.

Parent (Yy)

	Y	y
Y	YY	Yy
y	Yy	??

Parent (Yy) (left side)

Study the Punnett square and answer the following questions.

1. Which of these genotypes will complete this Punnett square?
   A) YY
   B) Yy
   C) yy
   D) Yx

2. In peas, the color yellow (Y) is dominant to the color green (y). According to this Punnett square, most of the offspring of the two yellow pea plants probably will be _____.
   F) orange
   G) green
   H) yellow
   J) red

THE PRINCETON REVIEW   Test Practice

The Test-Taking Tip was written by The Princeton Review, the nation's leader in test preparation.
1. C
2. H

Developing Skills

15. The phenotypes would be the expression of a dominant trait.
16. (a) multiple allele inheritance
    (b) polygenic inheritance
17. Mendelian inheritance has two forms of an allele that produce only two phenotypes. Incomplete dominance also has two forms of an allele, but produces three phenotypes.
18. TT and tt; both were purebred, one dominant, one recessive

Performance Assessment

19. Answers will vary, but should explain genetic engineering methods and how the methods can change the traits of organisms. Use **Performance Assessment in the Science Classroom**, p.141.

✓ *Assessment* Resources

 Reproducible Masters

Chapter Resources Booklet
  Chapter Review, pp. 33–34
  Chapter Tests, pp. 35–38
  Assessment Transparency Activity, p. 45

Glencoe Science Web site
  Interactive Tutor
  Chapter Quizzes

Glencoe Technology
  🖌 Assessment Transparency
  💿 Interactive CD-ROM Chapter Quizzes
  💿 ExamView Pro Test Bank
  💿 Vocabulary PuzzleMaker Software
  📼 MindJogger Videoquiz

Reading Comprehension

Read the passage. Then read each question that follows the passage. Decide which is the best answer to each question.

Genetic Engineering and Your Food

In recent years, scientists have made tremendous advances in the study of DNA. DNA is the material found in each cell that determines a cell's type, activities, and development. The DNA of a cell contains all the instructions that a cell inherits, including traits that help that organism survive. Scientists now can change an organism's DNA. This is called genetic engineering.

In the past, people were able to affect the DNA of organisms through breeding. The miniature poodle is a great example of this. People wanted smaller poodles, so they selected small poodles from the poodle population and bred them to produce small offspring. Eventually, a new variety of poodle, called the miniature poodle, developed. It has slightly different DNA than larger poodles.

Today, however, scientists can take small pieces of DNA from one organism and add them to another organism's DNA. Scientists have done this a lot with plants such as corn. They wanted corn to have two different traits— resistance to a weed-killing chemical often used by farmers and the ability to make a bug-killing substance called Cry1A(b). To develop a variety of corn with both of those traits, scientists took DNA from bacteria that display these traits and added it to the DNA of corn. The result was a new variety of corn that is not harmed by the weed-killing chemicals and that naturally produces Cry1A(b).

Because scientists have identified and learned about different DNA over the last few decades, they now know which traits result from different DNA. As a result, scientists are able to genetically engineer such things as new varieties of corn. Scientists also are exploring many other ideas for using genetic engineering to develop new crop varieties. Soon, these new varieties of crops will be able to be used all over the world to help feed millions of people.

Test-Taking Tip   Consider how the actions of scientists have changed over the years from breeding to genetic engineering.

1. Scientists were able to create new varieties of corn by _____.
   A) using less Cry1A(b)
   B) successfully breeding dogs
   C) asking farmers what they needed
   D) using DNA from bacteria

2. According to the passage, which of the following must have happened first?
   F) the breeding of miniature poodles
   G) the transfer of small sections of DNA from bacteria to other organisms
   H) the discovery that DNA determines a cell's traits
   J) the development of a genetically engineered variety of corn

This genetically engineered corn contains DNA from bacteria.

Standardized Test Practice

Read each question and choose the best answer.

1. The genetic makeup of an organism is called its genotype. Two plants are bred and all of their offspring have a Tt genotype. The genotype of one parent is TT. Which of the following is the most likely explanation for the Tt genotype of the offspring?
- **A)** The other parent plant's genotype is tt.
- **B)** The offspring's phenotype is controlled by the T allele.
- **C)** The offspring are called heterozygotes.
- **D)** The T and t are two alleles of the same gene.

Test-Taking Tip If a question contains a lot of information about genotypes, draw a Punnett square to keep the information organized.

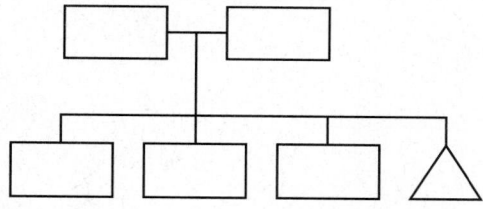

2. When an organism has a dominant and a recessive allele of a gene, only the dominant allele controls the organism's phenotype. Phenotypes can be represented by using shapes. According to the diagram above, the rectangle results from what kind of allele?
- **F)** recessive
- **G)** mutant
- **H)** dominant
- **J)** incomplete dominant

Test-Taking Tip As you read the question, remember the difference between dominant and recessive alleles.

3. Some alleles have incomplete dominance, which means they make phenotypes that are intermediate between the two alleles. The drawing above shows a cross between a shaded plant and a white plant that carry alleles with incomplete dominance for flower color. Which of the following depicts what the offsprings' flowers might look like?

A)
B)
C)
D)

Test-Taking Tip Cover up the answer choices, reread the question, and imagine what the correct answer should be. Then, read each answer choice.

Consider this question carefully before writing your answer on a separate sheet of paper.

4. The U.S. Department of Health funds many genetics research projects. How could this research help medical doctors?

Test-Taking Tip Use scratch paper to list as many different ways that genetics relates to disease and medicine as you can think of. Then, write about one or two of these.

QUESTION 1: A

Students must infer that the other parent is homozygous recessive. Encourage students to translate the question into a Punnett square or some other familiar sketch.

QUESTION 2: H

Students must understand how phenotypes and genotypes are displayed in family trees to identify the graphic depiction of genetic dominance.

QUESTION 3: B

Students must recognize which answer choice offers an *intermediate* between unshaded and shaded.

- **Choice A** No; the shaded parent flower has only incomplete dominance and was mated with a recessive plant. Therefore, none of its offspring could be completely black in color.
- **Choice B** Yes; the offspring displaying different shades would result from having a parent with incomplete dominance.
- **Choice C** No; these offspring display entirely recessive qualities, which is not possible because one of their parents had incomplete dominance.
- **Choice D** No; the shaded parent flower has only incomplete dominance and was mated with a recessive plant. Therefore, none of its offspring could be completely black.

QUESTION 4: Answers will vary.

Students should write a thorough response based upon information from the unit.

Teaching Tip

Make sure that students are familiar with the depiction of different phenotypes in family trees.

UNIT 4

Unit Contents

Pre-Reading Activity

Have students look through the unit for photographs and illustrations that show relationships between humans and the environment.

UNIT 4 Ecology

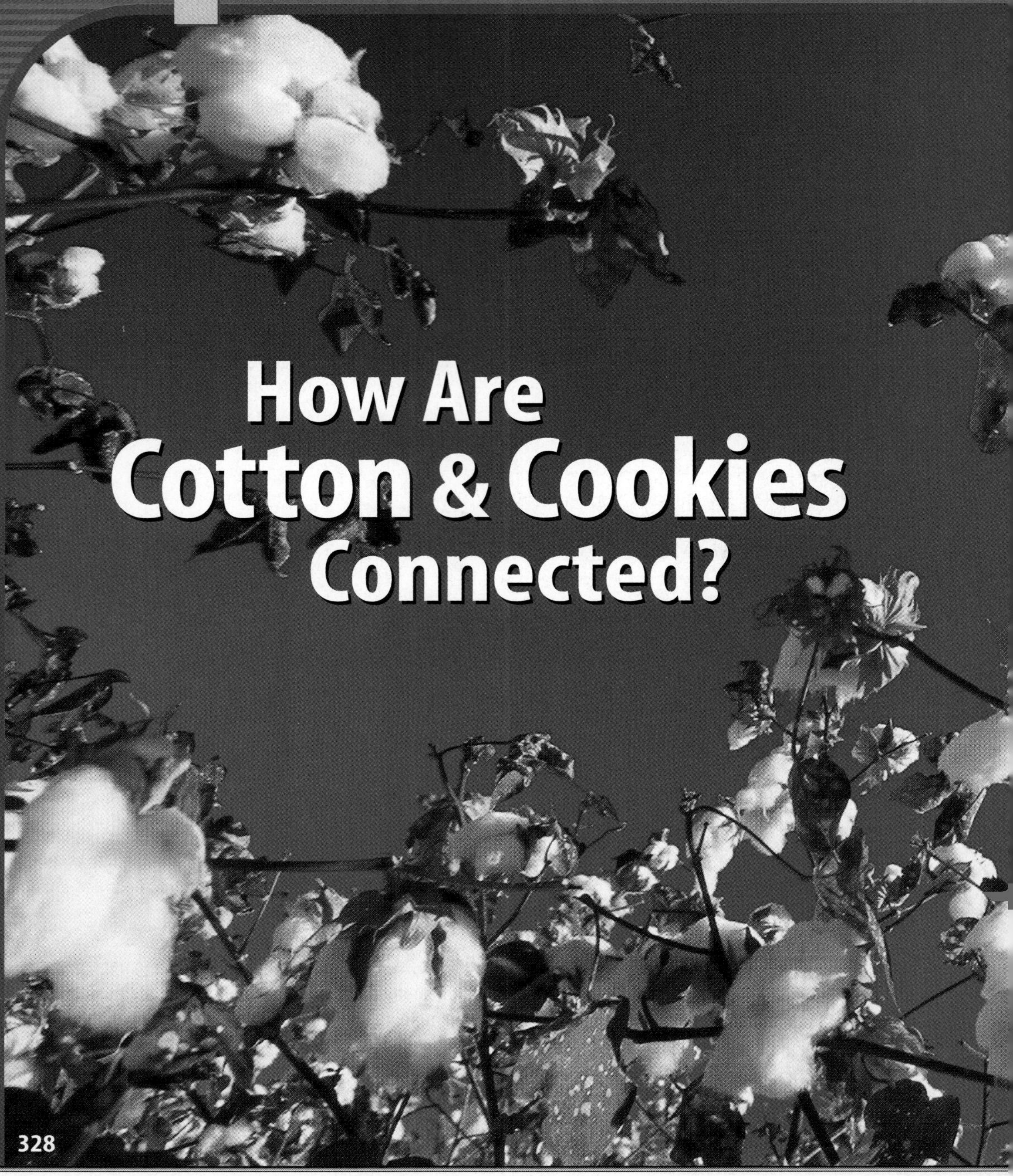

How Are Cotton & Cookies Connected?

328

Teacher to Teacher

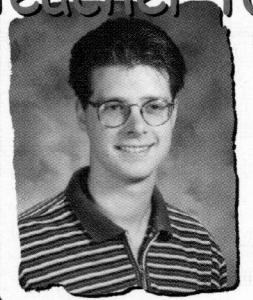

"To evaluate student understanding of abiotic and biotic factors of the environment, I take them outside and have them make two lists of the factors and how they are interrelated to one another. I also have the students make food chains from their observations."

Steve Manns, Teacher
Derry Area Middle School
Derry, PA

In the 1800s, the economy of the South depended heavily on cotton and tobacco—two crops that rob the soil of nutrients, especially nitrogen. By the late 1800s, the soil was in poor shape. A scientist named George Washington Carver set out to change that. He promoted the technique of crop rotation—alternating soil-depleting crops such as cotton with soil-enriching crops such as peanuts. Many farmers listened to Carver and began planting peanuts. However, there was little market for the crop. So Carver poured his energy into developing uses for peanuts. Ultimately, he came up with more than 300 products made from peanuts—everything from soap to axle grease. He also created the first recipe for peanut butter cookies, which have become an American favorite.

Introducing the Unit

How Are Cotton & Cookies Connected?

The human body requires water, air, and energy derived from food in order to function properly. Air quality, water, and appropriate land have an impact on the health of human populations.

George Washington Carver recognized the impact of human activity on soil quality when he observed the nitrogen depleting effects of cotton plants on soil. To remedy this situation he suggested planting peanuts, which could use nitrogen directly from the air. By rotating crops, soil could be productive again.

It is important to recognize the impact of human activities on the environment. Creative solutions, such as Carver's 300 uses for peanuts, are necessary for clean water, air, and land to sustain an ever-increasing human population.

SCIENCE CONNECTION

NITROGEN FIXATION Plants need nitrogen to grow well. Peanuts are legumes, plants that—with the help of certain bacteria—take nitrogen from the air and convert it into a form that plants can use. Conduct research to identify some other legumes and to discover how they "fix" nitrogen. In a one-page report, describe nitrogen fixation. If you were a farmer, what crops would you choose and how would you plant them to make your farm more productive?

SCIENCE CONNECTION

Activity

Borrow books from the school library on plants and nitrogen fixation and place in a classroom reference center. Give students a list of legumes. Have students develop a flow chart about nitrogen fixation.

SCIENCE Online

Internet Addresses

_____

_____

_____

Explore the Glencoe Science Web site at **science.glencoe.com** to find out more about topics in this unit.

CHAPTER 12 INTERACTIONS OF LIFE

Section/Objectives	Standards		Activities/Features
	National	State/Local	
Chapter Opener	See p. 5T for a Key to Standards.		**Explore Activity:** Examine sod from a lawn, p. 331 **Before You Read,** p. 331
Section 1 Living Earth ⏱ 2 sessions 📦 1 block 1. **Identify** places where life is found on Earth. 2. **Define** ecology. 3. **Observe** how the environment influences life.	National Content Standards: UCP1, A1, C1, C4		**Science Online,** p. 334
Section 2 Populations ⏱ 2 sessions 📦 1 block 1. **Identify** methods for estimating population sizes. 2. **Explain** how competition limits population growth. 3. **List** factors that influence changes in population size.	National Content Standards: UCP1, A1, C1, C4		**MiniLAB:** Observing Seedling Competition, p. 337 **Problem Solving Activity:** Do you have too many crickets?, p. 339 **Science Online,** p. 340 **MiniLAB:** Comparing Biotic Potential, p. 341 **Visualizing Population Growth,** p. 342
Section 3 Interactions Within Communities ⏱ 3 sessions 📦 1.5 blocks 1. **Describe** how organisms obtain energy for life. 2. **Explain** how organisms interact. 3. **Recognize** that every organism occupies a niche.	National Content Standards: UCP1, A1, C1, C4, F5, G1, G3		**Chemistry Integration,** p. 345 **Health Integration,** p. 347 **Activity:** Feeding Habits of Planaria, p. 349 **Activity:** Population Growth in Fruit Flies, pp. 350–351 **Science and History:** You Can Count On It, pp. 352–353

NATIONAL GEOGRAPHIC

Teacher's Corner

PRODUCTS AVAILABLE FROM GLENCOE
To order call 1-800-334-7344:
CD-ROMs
NGS Picture Show: Looking at Ecosystems
NGS Picture Show: Looking at Living Things

Videodisc
STV: Habitats
STV: Water

PRODUCTS AVAILABLE FROM NATIONAL GEOGRAPHIC SOCIETY
To order call 1-800-368-2728:

Videos
Ecosystem: A Struggle For Survival
Pond-Life: Food Web
Web of Life

330A **CHAPTER 12** Interactions of Life

Activity Materials	Reproducible Resources	Section Assessment	Technology
Explore Activity: a section of sod, hand lens	**Chapter Resources Booklet** Foldables Worksheet, p. 17 Directed Reading Overview, p. 19 Note-taking Worksheets, pp. 33–35	GLENCOE'S ASSESSMENT ADVANTAGE	
Need materials? Contact Science Kit at 1-800-828-7777 or www.sciencekit.com on the Internet.	**Chapter Resources Booklet** Transparency Activity, p. 44 Enrichment, p. 30 Reinforcement, p. 27 Directed Reading, p. 20 **Science Inquiry Labs,** p. 7	**Portfolio** Activity, p. 334 **Performance** Skill Builder Activities, p. 335 **Content** Section Assessment, p. 335 Challenge, p. 335	Section Focus Transparency Interactive CD-ROM Guided Reading Audio Program
MiniLAB: 2 pots of plants, moist potting soil, radish seeds, watering can, basin, metric ruler **MiniLAB:** whole fruit, plastic knife, paper towels	**Chapter Resources Booklet** Transparency Activity, p. 45 MiniLAB, pp. 3, 4 Enrichment, p. 31 Reinforcement, p. 28 Directed Reading, p. 20 Transparency Activity, pp. 47–48 **Mathematics Skill Activities,** p. 5	**Portfolio** Curriculum Connection, p. 339 **Performance** MiniLAB, p. 337 MiniLAB, p. 341 Skill Builder Activities, p. 343 **Content** Section Assessment, p. 343 Challenge, p. 343	Section Focus Transparency Teaching Transparency Interactive CD-ROM Guided Reading Audio Program
Activity: small bowl, several planarians, lettuce leaf, raw liver or meat, several guppies, pond or stream water, hand lens **Activity:** fruit flies; fruit fly culture kit; food items (banana, orange peel, or other fruit); water; culture containers; cloth, plastic, or other tops for containers; hand lens; heating or cooling source	**Chapter Resources Booklet** Transparency Activity, p. 46 Activity Worksheets, pp. 5–6, 7–8 Enrichment, p. 32 Reinforcement, p. 29 Directed Reading, pp. 21, 22 Lab Activities, pp. 9–11, 13–16 **Home and Community Involvement,** p. 47 **Lab Management and Safety,** p. 71	**Portfolio** Science Journal, p. 347 **Performance** Skill Builder Activities, p. 348 **Content** Section Assessment, p. 348 Challenge, p. 348	Section Focus Transparency Interactive CD-ROM Guided Reading Audio Program

End of Chapter Assessment

GLENCOE'S ASSESSMENT ADVANTAGE

Blackline Masters	Technology	Professional Series
Chapter Resources Booklet Chapter Review, pp. 37–38 Chapter Tests, pp. 39–42 **Standardized Test Practice by The Princeton Review,** pp. 103–106	MindJogger Videoquiz Interactive CD-ROM Vocabulary PuzzleMakers ExamView Pro Test Bank Interactive Lesson Planner Interactive Teacher Edition	Performance Assessment in the Science Classroom (PASC)

Transparencies

Section Focus

Section Focus Transparency 1 — Hot Enough for Ya?

At one time it was thought that no organisms could survive below the soil layer. Over the last twenty years, however, scientists have discovered microorganisms that like hot, high-pressure, and even radioactive conditions! These scientists are working deep in an abandoned gold mine. They are investigating bacteria that thrive in similar harsh conditions.

1. What do you find most surprising about microorganisms living in extreme conditions?
2. Name some other places where living things thrive, but humans cannot.

L2

Section Focus Transparency 2 — That's a Lot of Penguins

Every living thing on Earth has a particular environment that it calls home. These penguins like cold, icy Antarctica. This environment provides the penguins with all of the things they need for survival.

1. Name some factors that might affect penguin population.
2. How might you estimate the number of penguins in this picture?

L2

Section Focus Transparency 3 — Frolics with Sharks

Remoras are several different species of related fishes that attach themselves to sharks and other ocean organisms. Both the shark and the remora benefit from this relationship.

1. Why doesn't the shark eat the remora?
2. How do the shark and remora help each other?

L2

Assessment

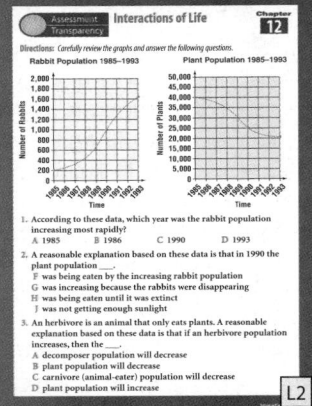

Assessment Transparency — Interactions of Life — Chapter 12

Directions: Carefully review the graphs and answer the following questions.

Rabbit Population 1985–1993   Plant Population 1985–1993

1. According to these data, which year was the rabbit population increasing most rapidly?
   A 1985   B 1986   C 1990   D 1993
2. A reasonable explanation based on these data is that in 1990 the plant population ___.
   F was being eaten by the increasing rabbit population
   G was increasing because the rabbits were disappearing
   H was being eaten until it was extinct
   J was not getting enough sunlight
3. An herbivore is an animal that only eats plants. A reasonable explanation based on these data is that if an herbivore population increases, then the ___.
   A decomposer population will decrease
   B plant population will decrease
   C carnivore (animal-eater) population will decrease
   D plant population will increase

L2

Teaching

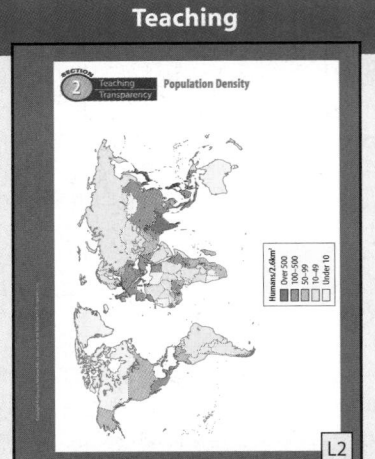

Teaching Transparency 2 — Population Density

L2

This is a representation of key blackline masters available in the Teacher Classroom Resources. See Resource Manager boxes within the chapter for additional information.

Key to Teaching Strategies

The following designations will help you decide which activities are appropriate for your students.

L1 — Level 1 activities should be appropriate for students with learning difficulties.

L2 — Level 2 activities should be within the ability range of all students.

L3 — Level 3 activities are designed for above-average students.

ELL — ELL activities should be within the ability range of English Language Learners.

COOP LEARN — Cooperative Learning activities are designed for small group work.

LS — Multiple Learning Styles logos, as described on page 22T, are used throughout to indicate strategies that address different learning styles.

P — These strategies represent student products that can be placed into a best-work portfolio.

Hands-on Activities

Activity Worksheets

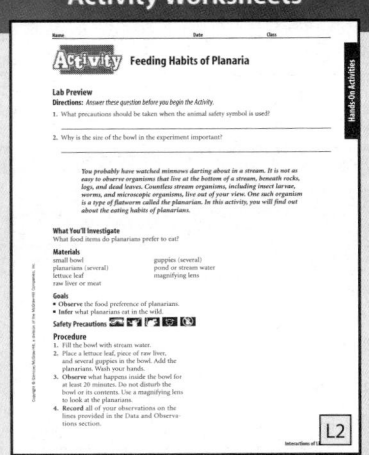

Activity — Feeding Habits of Planaria

Lab Preview
Directions: Answer these question before you begin the Activity.
1. What precautions should be taken when the animal safety symbol is used?

2. Why is the size of the bowl in the experiment important?

You probably have watched minnows darting about in a stream. It is not as easy to observe organisms that live at the bottom of a stream, beneath rocks, logs, and dead leaves. Countless stream organisms, including insect larvae, worms, and microscopic organisms, live out of your view. One such organism is a type of flatworm called the planarian. In this activity, you will find out about the eating habits of planarians.

What You'll Investigate
What food items do planarians prefer to eat?

Materials
small bowl   guppies (several)
planarians (several) pond or stream water
lettuce leaf   magnifying lens
raw liver or meat

Goals
• Observe the food preference of planarians.
• Infer what planarians eat in the wild.

Safety Precautions

Procedure
1. Fill the bowl with stream water.
2. Place a lettuce leaf, piece of raw liver, and several guppies in the bowl. Add the planarians. Wash your hands.
3. Observe what happens inside the bowl for at least 20 minutes. Do not disturb the bowl or its contents. Use a magnifying lens to look at the planarians.
4. Record all of your observations on the lines provided in the Data and Observations section.

L2

Laboratory Activities

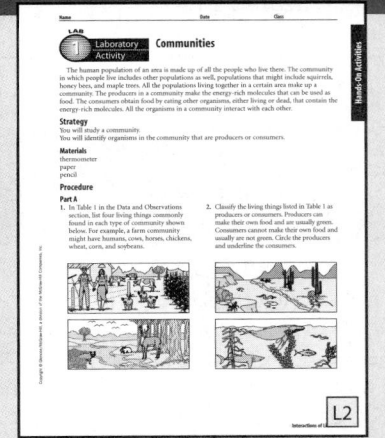

Laboratory Activities 1 — Communities

The human population of an area is made up of all the people who live there. The community in which people live includes other populations as well, populations that might include squirrels, honey bees, and maple trees. All the populations living together in a certain area make up a community. The producers in a community make the energy-rich molecules that can be used as food. The consumers obtain food by eating other organisms, either living or dead, that contain the energy-rich molecules. All the organisms in a community interact with each other.

Strategy
You will study a community.
You will identify organisms in the community that are producers or consumers.

Materials
thermometer
paper
pencil

Procedure
Part A
1. In Table 1 in the Data and Observations section, list four living things commonly found in each type of community shown below. For example, a farm community might have humans, cows, horses, chickens, wheat, corn, and soybeans.

2. Classify the living things in Table 1 as producers or consumers. Producers can make their own food and are usually green. Consumers cannot make their own food and usually are not green. Circle the producers and underline the consumers.

L2

Meeting Different Ability Levels

Content Outline

Note-taking Worksheet — Interactions of Life

Meeting Individual Needs

L2

Reinforcement

Reinforcement — Living Earth

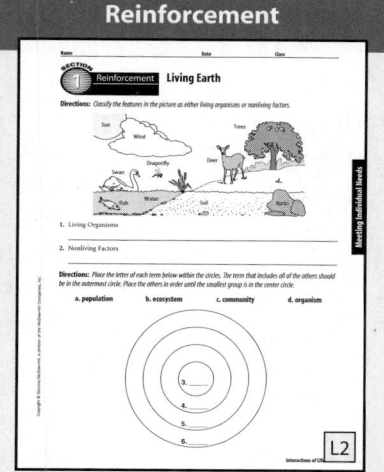

Meeting Individual Needs

L2

Directed Reading

Directed Reading for Content Mastery — Overview: Interactions of Life

Meeting Individual Needs

L1

Assessment

Chapter Tests

Chapter Test — Interactions of Life

Assessment

L2

Enrichment

Enrichment — Tropical Rain Forests

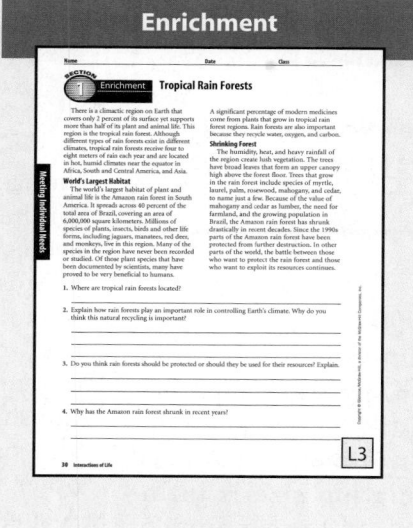

Meeting Individual Needs

L3

Spanish Directed Reading

Lectura dirigida para Dominio del contenido — Sinopsis: Interacciones de la vida

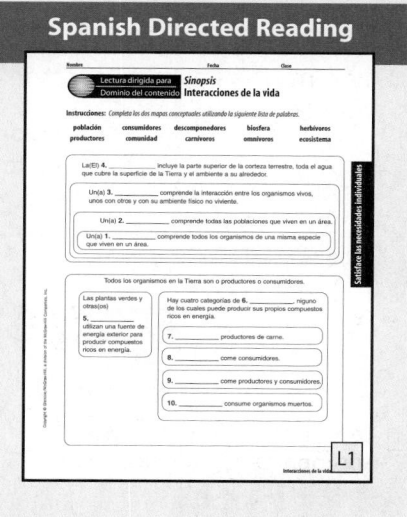

Satisface las necesidades individuales

L1

Test Practice Workbook

Standardized Test Practice
Teacher Edition

Glencoe
Science

LEVEL GREEN

L2

Chapter Review

Chapter Review — Interactions of Life

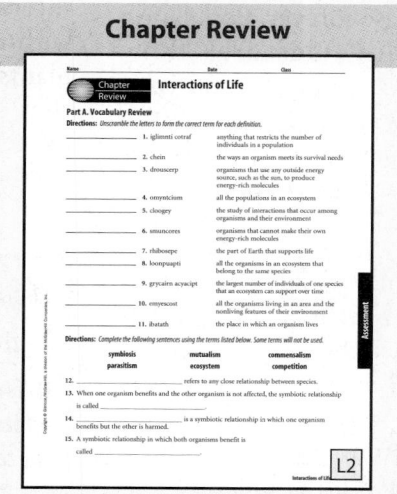

Assessment

L2

Science Content Background

Living Earth
Understanding Ecosystems

The biosphere is the total part of Earth where life can exist and includes a great variety of conditions. An ecosystem is a smaller area consisting of the organisms and nonliving features that interact in the system. Sir Arthur George Tansley, a British plant ecologist, coined the word *ecosystem* in 1935.

SCIENCE Online

For additional content background on this topic, go to the Glencoe Science Web site at science.glencoe.com.

Populations
Population Size

Population size is an important characteristic, but it can be difficult to measure. Animal population size is influenced by the amount of food and space available. Natural populations cannot increase forever. Population density measures how crowded a population is. It is always expressed as the number of individuals per unit area or volume.

Carrying Capacity

When a population's size is no longer increasing, it has reached the carrying capacity of its ecosystem. The carrying capacity is the greatest number of individuals in a certain population that

a given environment is capable of supporting under a given set of conditions. If a population is at carrying capacity, the number of organisms born in a given period of time is balanced by the number of organisms that die during that same time. Carrying capacity can vary with changing seasonal conditions. For example, cold winter weather may cause a reduction in the food supply and a resulting decrease in carrying capacity. In summer, when temperatures are favorable and food supplies increase, carrying capacity also increases.

Interactions Within Communities
Types of Interactions

Organisms within a community interact in many ways. Plants and other photosynthetic organisms produce sugars that they use as food. Animals, fungi, and other non-photosynthetic organisms must consume other organisms for food. In addition to predator/prey or producer/consumer relationships, organisms may participate in symbiotic relationships, such as mutualism, commensalism, and parasitism, or they may compete with other species with similar needs for resources. A single species interacts directly or indirectly with nearly all the other species in its community. For example, a squirrel in a forest interacts not only with the plants it eats or with the predators that eat it but also with the plants it uses for cover or shelter, with insects that share its nest, with other animals that use its abandoned nest for shelter, with the bacteria that live on its skin, and so on.

Student Misconception

Plants do not depend on other organisms.

Refer to the facing page for teaching strategies to address this misconception. Refer to pages 344–345 for content related to this topic.

Manoj Shah/DRK Photo

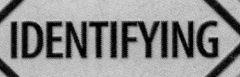

IDENTIFYING > Misconceptions

Students may think that . . .

- **Plants do not depend on other organisms.**
- **Organisms do not depend on one another.**
- **Interdependence is primarily predator/prey relationships.**

While most students can draw a picture of a natural community that includes producers, herbivores, and predators, few can explain their selections in terms of ecological relationships. Many students understand that the organisms they have depicted belong in the environment, but they don't understand how the organisms interact with one another and with the nonliving environment. While students may be able to identify predator/prey relationships, or plant/herbivore relationships, they seldom understand other types of relationships, nor do they see how interconnected one organism may be with many other organisms in its environment.

Activity
Have students draw a terrestrial community, using the local environment as a model. Their drawings should include several different types of organisms. Ask students to indicate as many interactions between organisms as they can. Then have them describe, aloud or in essay form, how each organism in the picture interacts with other organisms. Note the types and complexity of interactions that students describe.

Promote Understanding

Activity
After students read Section 3, organize the class into teams of three or four students. Assign each team a color. Have each team make ten or so flags from paper corresponding to their team's color and toothpicks.

- Take the class outside to a grassy or weedy area of the school grounds.

- Have teams hunt for examples of organisms interacting in various ways, including consumption, competition, and symbiosis, and mark each area where an interaction is occurring with a flag. On each flag, team members should identify the type of interaction and write a short description in their Science Journals of what they found. Encourage students to include drawings along with their verbal descriptions.

- After the allotted time, give students time to examine the findings of other teams before gathering up the flags and returning to the classroom.

- Give each team time to summarize their findings. Then have representatives from each team report their findings to the class. Encourage teams to include their drawings of the interactions they observed.

When all teams have reported, discuss the relationships discovered by the class. Focus the discussion on a few organisms identified by most teams. Challenge students to brainstorm a list of ways in which those organisms interact with other organisms.

Assess
After completing the chapter, see *Identifying Misconceptions* in the Study Guide.

Chapter Vocabulary

What do you think?

Science Journal These are the little mud tunnels that termites build across a non-wood surface to provide protection as they travel back and forth between their nest and their food source.

Why would a powerful rhinoceros allow birds to perch on its back? Why aren't these birds safely perched in a tree? How do they find food? You don't have to go to Africa to see birds on the back of a rhino. You can see these animals at zoos or wildlife parks. In this chapter, you will learn how living organisms interact with each other and their surroundings. You also will learn about the roles each organism plays in the flow of energy through the environment.

What do you think?

Science Journal Look at the picture below with a classmate. Discuss what you think this might be or what is happening. Here's a hint: *It's a city within a city.* Write your answer or best guess in your Science Journal.

330

Theme Connection

Systems and Interactions A discussion of ecosystems, habitats, and communities shows how organisms interact. These interactions within the system affect population sizes and organisms' abilities to survive in their environments.

EXPLORE ACTIVITY

In your lifetime, you probably have taken thousands of footsteps on grassy lawns or playing fields. If you take a close look at the grass, you'll see that each blade is attached to roots in the soil. How do the grass plants obtain everything they need to live and grow? What other kinds of organisms live in the grass? The following activity will give you a chance to take a closer look at the life in a lawn.

Examine sod from a lawn

1. Examine a section of sod from a lawn.
2. How do the roots of the grass plants hold the soil?
3. Do you see signs of other living things besides grass?

Observe

In your Science Journal, answer the above questions and describe any organisms that are present in your section of sod. Explain how these organisms might affect the growth of grass plants. Draw a picture of your section of sod.

Before You Read

FOLDABLES
Reading & Study Skills

Making a Concept Map Study Fold The following Foldable will help you organize information by diagramming ideas about your favorite wild animal.

1. Place a sheet of paper in front of you with the short side at the top. Fold the paper in half from the left side to the right side.
2. Fold from top to bottom to divide the paper into thirds, then open up the three folds.
3. Through the top thickness of paper, cut along each of the fold lines to the side fold, forming three tabs.
4. Label *Organism, Population,* and *Community* across the front of the paper, as shown. Write the name of your favorite wild animal under the *Organism* tab.
5. Before you read the chapter, write what you know about your favorite animal under the top tab. As you read the chapter, write how this animal is part of a population and a community under the middle and bottom tabs.

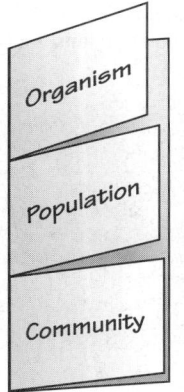

331

EXPLORE ACTIVITY

Purpose Use the Explore Activity to introduce students to characteristics of ecosystems and communities. Explain that they will be learning about interactions among organisms of the same or different species. L1
ELL LS **Kinesthetic**

Preparation Purchase sod from a garden center, or dig up a square of sod, including the soil that surrounds the roots. Temporarily fill the area with soil so you don't leave a divot. Replace the sod when you are finished. Keep the sod in a cool, moist area so that it stays fresh and retains small animal life.

Materials small piece of sod for each group, hand lens (optional)

Teaching Strategy After a few minutes of examination, instruct students to tear the sod in half. This may reveal animals that have moved to the interior of the sod.

Observe

Organisms may include one or more grasses, clover, ants, grasshopper nymphs, earthworms, fungi, or bacteria. The effects of the organisms will vary. A grasshopper might slow the growth of grass, but an earthworm might accelerate it.

✔ Assessment

Process Have students show each other an organism that they observed. Then have them infer the effect of the organism on the grass. Use **Performance Assessment in the Science Classroom,** p. 89.

Before You Read

FOLDABLES
Reading & Study Skills

Dinah Zike Study Fold

Purpose Students develop and use a Foldable concept map to describe a specific animal as part of a population and a community.

📁 For additional help, see Foldables Worksheet, p. 17 in **Chapter Resources Booklet,** or go to the Glencoe Science Web site at **science.glencoe.com.** See After You Read in the Study Guide at the end of this chapter.

SECTION

1

Living Earth

1 Motivate

Bellringer Transparency

Display the Section Focus Transparency for Section 1. Use the accompanying Transparency Activity Master. L2

ELL

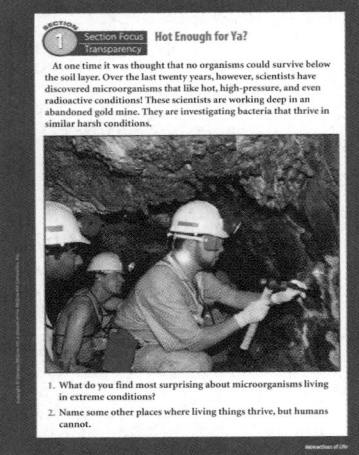

Tie to Prior Knowledge

Ask students to identify several habitats—the places where plants and animals live. Have them describe living and nonliving things in those habitats.

SECTION

1 Living Earth

As You Read

What You'll Learn

- **Identify** places where life is found on Earth.
- **Define** ecology.
- **Observe** how the environment influences life.

Vocabulary

biosphere   population
ecosystem   community
ecology   habitat

Why It's Important

All living things on Earth depend on each other for survival.

The Biosphere

What makes Earth different from other planets in the solar system? One difference is Earth's abundance of living organisms. The part of Earth that supports life is the **biosphere** (BI uh sfihr). The biosphere includes the top portion of Earth's crust, all the waters that cover Earth's surface, and the atmosphere that surrounds Earth.

✓ **Reading Check** *What three things make up the biosphere?*

As **Figure 1** shows, the biosphere is made up of different environments that are home to different kinds of organisms. For example, desert environments receive little rain. Cactus plants, coyotes, and lizards are included in the life of the desert. Tropical rain forest environments receive plenty of rain and warm weather. Parrots, monkeys, and tens of thousands of other organisms live in the rain forest. Coral reefs form in warm, shallow ocean waters. Arctic regions near the north pole are covered with ice and snow. Polar bears, seals, and walruses live in the arctic.

Figure 1
Earth's biosphere consists of many environments, including ocean waters, polar regions, and deserts.

Desert

Arctic

Coral reef

Section ✓ *Assessment* Planner

PORTFOLIO
Activity, p. 334
PERFORMANCE ASSESSMENT
Skill Builder Activities, p. 335
See page 356 for more options.

CONTENT ASSESSMENT
Section, p. 335
Challenge, p. 335
Chapter, pp. 356–357

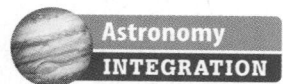

Astronomy
INTEGRATION

Life on Earth In our solar system, Earth is the third planet from the Sun. The amount of energy that reaches Earth from the Sun helps make the temperature just right for life. Mercury, the planet closest to the Sun, is too hot during the day and too cold at night to make life possible there. Venus, the second planet from the Sun, has a thick, carbon dioxide atmosphere and high temperatures. It is unlikely that life could survive there. Mars, the fourth planet, is much colder than Earth because it is farther from the Sun and has a thinner atmosphere. It might support microscopic life, but none has been found. The planets beyond Mars probably do not receive enough heat and light from the Sun to have the right conditions for life.

Ecosystems

On a visit to Yellowstone National Park in Wyoming, you might see a prairie scene like the one shown in **Figure 2.** Bison graze on prairie grass. Cowbirds follow the bison, catching grasshoppers that jump away from the bisons' hooves. This scene is part of an ecosystem. An **ecosystem** consists of all the organisms living in an area and the nonliving features of their environment. Bison, grass, birds, and insects are living organisms of this prairie ecosystem. Water, temperature, sunlight, soil, and air are nonliving features of this prairie ecosystem. **Ecology** is the study of interactions that occur among organisms and their environment. Ecologists are scientists who study these interactions.

✔ **Reading Check** *What is an ecosystem?*

Figure 2
Ecosystems are made up of living organisms and the nonliving features of their environment. In this prairie ecosystem, cowbirds eat insects and bison graze on grass. *What other kinds of organisms might live in this ecosystem?*

Populations

SCIENCE *Online*

Research Visit the Glencoe Science Web site at **science.glencoe.com** and find out the estimated human population size for the world today. In your Science Journal, create a graph that shows the population change between the year 2000 and this year.

IDENTIFYING
Misconceptions

Uses of the term *population* may lead to confusion. When discussing human population size it is common to simply say population. For example, "What is the population of San Diego?" In ecology, a population refers to all the organisms of a species in an area. A population has many characteristics, only one of which is size.

Activity

Have students observe a natural setting and draw or photograph a habitat that contains visible plant and animal life. Ask students to place their drawings or photographs, along with a list of the populations observed, in their Science Journals. ⟦L2⟧ ⟦ELL⟧

⟦IS⟧ **Naturalist** ⟦P⟧

Populations

Suppose you meet an ecologist who studies how a herd of bison moves from place to place and how the female bison in the herd care for their young. This ecologist is studying the members of a population. A **population** is made up of all the organisms in an ecosystem that belong to the same species. For example, all the bison in a prairie ecosystem are one population. All the cowbirds in this ecosystem make up a different population. The grasshoppers make up yet another population.

Ecologists often study how populations interact. For example, an ecologist might try to answer questions about several prairie species. How does grazing by bison affect the growth of prairie grass? How does grazing influence the insects that live in the grass and the birds that eat those insects? This ecologist is studying a community. A **community** refers to all the populations in an ecosystem. The prairie community is made of populations of bison, grasshoppers, cowbirds, and all other species in the prairie ecosystem. An arctic community might include populations of fish, seals that eat fish, and polar bears that hunt and eat seals. **Figure 3** shows how organisms, populations, communities, and ecosystems are related.

Figure 3
The living world is arranged in several levels of organization.

Community

Organism

Population

Ecosystem

Inclusion Strategies

Learning Disabled Give student pairs a one-inch column of newspaper text. Ask them to find, circle, and count different populations. For example, have them find the population of the letter *P* by circling each *P* and counting to determine population size. Explain that one letter is an organism, each type of letter is a population, and all the types of letters are a community. ⟦L1⟧

Resource Manager

Chapter Resources Booklet
Reinforcement, p. 27
Enrichment, p. 30
Science Inquiry Labs, p. 7

Figure 4
The trees of the forest provide a habitat for woodpeckers and other birds. This salamander's habitat is the moist forest floor.

Habitats

Each organism in an ecosystem needs a place to live. The place in which an organism lives is called its **habitat.** The animals shown in **Figure 4** live in a forest ecosystem. Trees are the woodpecker's habitat. These birds use their strong beaks to pry insects from tree bark or break open acorns and nuts. Woodpeckers usually nest in holes in dead trees. The salamander's habitat is the forest floor, beneath fallen leaves and twigs. Salamanders avoid sunlight and seek damp, dark places. This animal eats small worms, insects, and slugs. An organism's habitat provides the kinds of food and shelter, the temperature, and the amount of moisture the organism needs to survive.

Section 1 Assessment

1. What is the biosphere?
2. What is ecology?
3. How are the terms *habitat* and *biosphere* related to each other?
4. What is the major difference between a community and a population? Give one example of each.
5. **Think Critically** Does the amount of rain that falls in an area determine which kinds of organisms can live there? Why or why not?

Skill Builder Activities

6. **Forming Hypotheses** Make a hypothesis about how one nonliving feature of an ecosystem would affect the growth of dandelions in that ecosystem. **For more help, refer to the** Science Skill Handbook.
7. **Communicating** Pretend you are a non-human organism in the wild. Describe what you are and list living and nonliving features of the environment that affect you. **For more help, refer to the** Science Skill Handbook.

Habitats

Discussion

Point out that a habitat may describe a very small location, such as a nest in a tree, or a much larger area, such as a freshwater lake. **What is your habitat?** house or apartment **What is the habitat of a humpback whale?** the ocean

3 Assess

Reteach

Have students write a paragraph in their Science Journals explaining the relationships among a population, a community, and an ecosystem. They should include that populations interact to form a community and that communities and nonliving things together make up the ecosystem. L2 LS **Linguistic**

Challenge

Have students research the natural habitat of an organism and then tell the class five interesting things about this habitat. L3 LS **Naturalist**

Assessment

Content Provide students with photographs from discarded magazines. Have them identify living and nonliving things in each photograph and explain how the nonliving things might affect living things. Use **Performance Assessment in the Science Classroom,** p. 89.

Answers to Section Assessment

1. the part of Earth that supports life
2. the study of the interactions between organisms and between organisms and their environment
3. Habitat—place where organisms live; the biosphere includes all Earth's habitats.
4. A population is a single species living in an area. Example: all the maple trees of the Catskill Mountains. A community is all the populations that live in an area. Example: all the species of the Catskill Mountains.
5. Yes; organisms that need a lot of water cannot exist in areas with little rainfall.
6. Hypotheses should indicate that a nonliving factor, such as light, moisture, chemical fertilizers, or pH can have a positive or negative affect on the growth of dandelions.
7. Answers will vary but should include interactions with both the living and nonliving components of the environment.

Populations

1 Motivate

Bellringer Transparency

Display the Section Focus Transparency for Section 2. Use the accompanying Transparency Activity Master. L2

ELL

Tie to Prior Knowledge

Have students recall the needs of living things. Knowing what living things need to grow and reproduce will be helpful in understanding limiting factors.

Populations

As You Read

What You'll Learn
- **Identify** methods for estimating population sizes.
- **Explain** how competition limits population growth.
- **List** factors that influence changes in population size.

Vocabulary
limiting factor
carrying capacity

Why It's Important
Competition caused by population growth affects many organisms, including humans.

Figure 5
Gila woodpeckers make nesting holes in the saguaro cactus. Many animals compete for the shelter these holes provide.

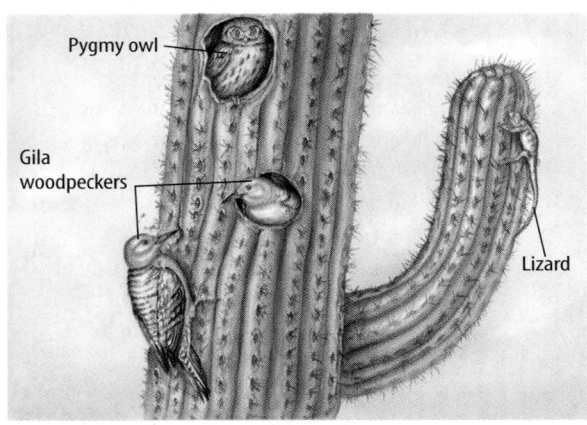

Competition

Some pet shops sell lizards, snakes, and other reptiles. Crickets are raised as a food supply for pet reptiles. In the wild, crickets come out at night and feed on plant material. During the day, they hide in dark areas, beneath leaves or under buildings. Pet shop workers who raise crickets make sure that the insects have plenty of food, water, and hiding places. As the cricket population grows, the workers increase the crickets' food supply and the number of hiding places. To avoid crowding, some of the crickets could be moved into larger containers.

Food and Space Organisms living in the wild do not always have enough food or living space. The Gila woodpecker, shown in **Figure 5,** lives in the Sonoran Desert of Arizona and Mexico. This bird makes its nest in a hole that it drills in a saguaro (suh GWAR oh) cactus. If an area has too many Gila woodpeckers or too few saguaros, the woodpeckers must compete with each other for nesting spots. Competition occurs when two or more organisms seek the same resource at the same time.

Growth Limits Competition limits population size. If the amount of available nesting space is limited, some woodpeckers will not be able to raise young. Gila woodpeckers eat cactus fruit, berries, and insects. If food becomes scarce, some woodpeckers might not survive to reproduce. Competition for food, living space, or other resources can prevent population growth.

In nature, the most intense competition is usually among individuals of the same species, because they need the same kinds of food and shelter. Competition also takes place among individuals of different species. For example, after a Gila woodpecker has abandoned its nesting hole, owls, flycatchers, snakes, and lizards compete for the shelter of the empty hole.

336 CHAPTER 12 Interactions of Life

Section ✓*Assessment* Planner

PORTFOLIO
Curriculum Connection, p. 339
PERFORMANCE ASSESSMENT
Try at Home MiniLAB, p. 337
MiniLAB, p. 341
Skill Builder Activities, p. 343
See page 356 for more options.

CONTENT ASSESSMENT
Section, p. 343
Challenge, p. 343
Chapter, pp. 356–357

Population Size

Ecologists often need to measure the size of a population. This information can indicate whether or not a population is healthy and growing. Population counts can help identify populations that could be in danger of disappearing.

Some populations are easy to measure. If you were raising crickets, you could measure the size of your cricket population simply by counting all the crickets in the container. What if you wanted to compare the cricket populations in two different containers? You would calculate the number of crickets per square meter (m^2) of your container. The size of a population that occupies a specific area is called population density. **Figure 6** shows human population density in different places in the world.

✔ Reading Check *What is population density?*

Measuring Populations Counting crickets can be tricky. They look alike, move a lot, and hide. The same cricket could be counted more than once, and others could be completely missed. Ecologists have similar problems when measuring wildlife populations. One of the methods they use is called trap-mark-release. Suppose you want to count wild rabbits. Rabbits live underground and come out at dawn and dusk to eat. Ecologists set traps that capture rabbits without injuring them. Each captured rabbit is marked and released. Later, another sample of rabbits is captured. Some of these rabbits will have marks, but many will not. By comparing the number of marked and unmarked rabbits in the second sample, ecologists can estimate the population size.

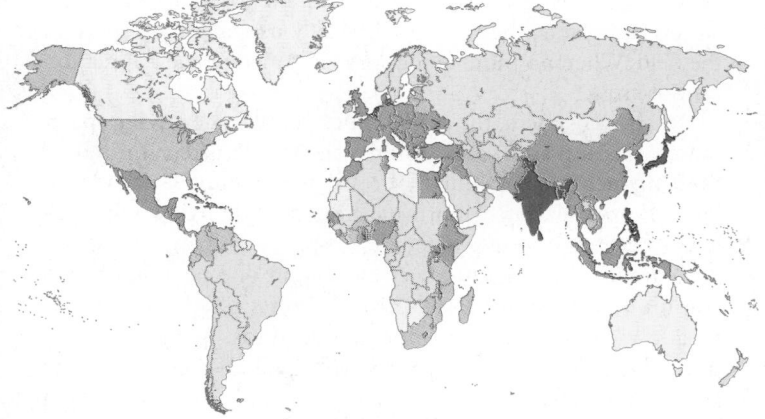

Humans/2.6 km²	
	Over 500
	100–500
	50–99
	10–49
	Under 10

Figure 6
This map shows human population density. *Which countries have the highest population density?*

SECTION 2 Populations **337**

TRY AT HOME
Mini LAB

Observing Seedling Competition

Procedure
1. Fill **two plant pots** with **moist potting soil.**
2. Plant **radish seeds** in one pot, following the spacing instructions on the seed packet. Label this pot "Recommended Spacing."
3. Plant radish seeds in the second pot, spaced half the recommended distance apart. Label this pot "Densely Populated." Wash your hands.
4. Keep the soil moist. When the seeds sprout, move them to a well-lit area.
5. Measure the height of the seedlings every two days for two weeks. Record the data in your **Science Journal.**

Analysis
1. Which plants grew faster?
2. Which plants looked healthiest after two weeks?
3. How did competition influence the plants?

---

② Teach

Population Size

TRY AT HOME
Mini LAB

Purpose Students determine if population density affects the growth of certain plants. [L2]

🅰 Logical-Mathematical

Materials 2 plant pots, potting soil, radish seeds, watering can, large basin, metric ruler

Teaching Strategies
- Avoid putting plants in hot areas.
- Have students premeasure water before adding.

Troubleshooting Follow seed packets instructions as to the number of seeds to plant per hole. Thin plants so that the density of seedlings in one pot is twice the density in the other pot.

Analysis
1. In many cases the densely planted seedlings grew faster.
2. The plants with more space will usually look healthier. They may not be as tall, but they look greener, fuller, and more robust.
3. Competition probably caused the less densely planted seedlings to grow better because they were able to get more light.

✔ Reading Check

Answer the size of a population that occupies a specific area

Caption Answer
Figure 6 India, Japan, the Philippines, and South Korea

Resource Manager 📖

Chapter Resources Booklet
Transparency Activity, p. 45
MiniLAB, p. 3
Reading and Writing Skill Activities, p. 1

✓ Assessment

Oral Have students explain why the more densely planted seedlings might have grown faster. Have them predict which plants would be healthier if the experiment was continued for another four weeks. Use **Performance Assessment in the Science Classroom,** p. 99.

Population Size,
continued

Discussion

Why would people want to know the population size of organisms such as deer? Ecologists may want the data for research. Game and Fish Departments may want the information to decide how many hunting permits to issue.

Caption Answer

Figure 7 Answers will vary. Students may suggest that they can count the number of wildebeests in the enlarged square, and then multiply by 25, the number of squares in the entire photograph.

Extension

Crabgrass is an annual plant. Assume one crabgrass plant produces 100 seeds every season, and each of those sprouts into a plant next season that will also produce 100 seeds. **If you start with one grass plant, how many will you have after three years?**
year 1-1 plant
year 2-100 plants
year 3-10,000 plants

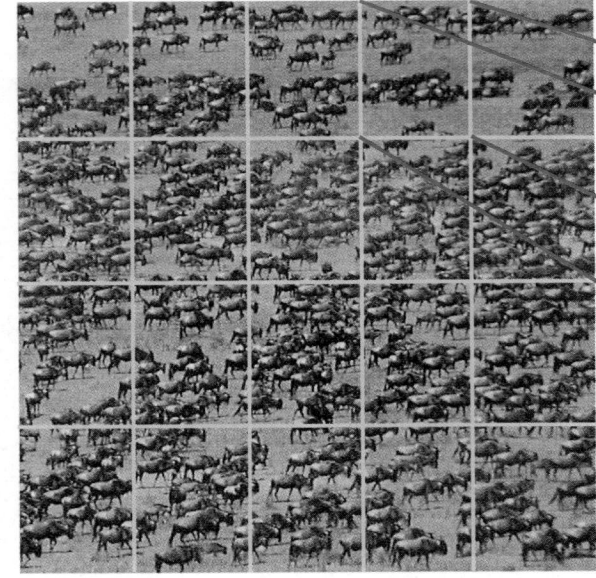
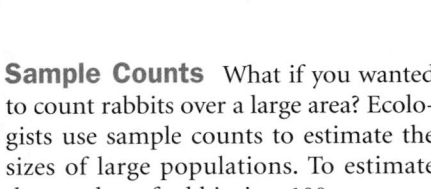

Figure 7
Ecologists can estimate population size by making a sample count. Wildebeests graze on the grassy plains of Africa. *How could you use the enlarged square to estimate the number of wildebeests in the entire photograph?*

Sample Counts What if you wanted to count rabbits over a large area? Ecologists use sample counts to estimate the sizes of large populations. To estimate the number of rabbits in a 100-acre area, for example, you could count the rabbits in one acre and multiply by 100 to estimate the population size. **Figure 7** shows another approach to sample counting.

Limiting Factors One grass plant can produce hundreds of seeds. Imagine those seeds drifting onto a vacant field. Many of the seeds sprout and grow into grass plants that produce hundreds more seeds. Soon the field is covered with grass. Can this grass population keep growing forever? Suppose the seeds of wildflowers or trees drift onto the field. If those seeds sprout, trees and flowers would compete with grasses for sunlight, soil, and water. Even if the grasses did not have to compete with other plants, they might eventually use up all the space in the field. When no more living space is available, the population cannot grow.

In any ecosystem, the availability of food, water, living space, mates, nesting sites, and other resources is often limited. A **limiting factor** is anything that restricts the number of individuals in a population. Limiting factors include living and nonliving features of the ecosystem.

A limiting factor can affect more than one population in a community. Suppose a lack of rain limits plant growth in a meadow. Fewer plants produce fewer seeds. For seed-eating mice, this reduction in the food supply could become a limiting factor. A smaller mouse population could, in turn, become a limiting factor for the hawks and owls that feed on mice.

338 CHAPTER 12 Interactions of Life

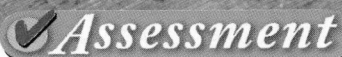

LAB DEMONSTRATION

Assessment

Purpose to estimate population size
Materials overhead projector (OHP), 4 sheets of paper, transparency, marker, ruler, cardboard to screen the OHP surface, hole punch
Preparation Punch 100 discs. Draw a grid on the transparency consisting of 25 1.25″ x 1.25″ squares.

Procedure Display the grid. Erect the screen. Evenly sprinkle 25 discs. Position papers to reveal one square. Turn on the OHP; count the discs. Repeat twice. Estimate and then count population size. Repeat for 50 and 100 discs.

Expected Outcome Estimates will approximate actual population size.

How could a better estimate be made? Collect data from a greater number of cells. **When would an ecologist use this technique?** when it is difficult or expensive to count all the organisms in an area

Carrying Capacity A population of robins lives in a grove of trees in a park. Over several years, the number of robins increases and nesting space becomes scarce. Nesting space is a limiting factor that prevents the robin population from getting any larger. This ecosystem has reached its carrying capacity for robins. **Carrying capacity** is the largest number of individuals of one species that an ecosystem can support over time. If a population begins to exceed the environment's carrying capacity, some individuals will not have enough resources. They could die or be forced to move elsewhere, like the deer shown in **Figure 8.**

Figure 8
These deer might have moved into a residential area because a nearby forest's carrying capacity for deer has been reached.

 **Reading Check** *How are limiting factors related to carrying capacity?*

Problem-Solving Activity

Do you have too many crickets?

Y ou've decided to raise crickets to sell to pet stores. A friend says you should not allow the cricket population density to go over 210 crickets/m². Use what you've learned in this section to measure the population density in your cricket tanks.

Identifying the Problem
The table on the right lists the areas and populations of your three cricket tanks. How can you determine if too many crickets are in one tank? If a tank contains too many crickets, what could you do? Explain why too many crickets in a tank might be a problem.

Cricket Population

Tank	Area (m²)	Number of Crickets
1	0.80	200
2	0.80	150
3	1.5	315

Solving the Problem
1. Do any of the tanks contain too many crickets? Could you make the population density of the three tanks equal by moving crickets from one tank to another? If so, which tank would you move crickets into?

2. The population density of wild crickets living in a field is 2.4 crickets/m². If the field has an area of 250 m², what is the approximate size of the cricket population? Why would the population density of crickets in a field be lower than the population density of crickets in a tank?

SECTION 2 Populations **339**

Curriculum Connection

Art Have students research populations that live in areas in which limiting factors severely restrict the kinds of organisms that can live there. Have them make a collage that shows several different populations and environments, such as penguins in Antarctica and cacti in a hot, dry desert.

Biotic Potential What would happen if no limiting factors restricted the growth of a population? Think about a population that has an unlimited supply of food, water, and living space. The climate is favorable. Population growth is not limited by diseases, predators, or competition with other species. Under ideal conditions like these, the population would continue to grow.

The highest rate of reproduction under ideal conditions is a population's biotic potential. The larger the number of offspring that are produced by parent organisms, the higher the biotic potential of the species will be. Compare an avocado tree to a tangerine tree. Assume that each tree produces the same number of fruits. Each avocado fruit contains one large seed. Each tangerine fruit contains a dozen seeds or more. Because the tangerine tree produces more seeds per fruit, it has a higher biotic potential than the avocado tree.

Changes in Populations

Birthrates and death rates also influence the size of a population and its rate of growth. A population gets larger when the number of individuals born is greater than the number of individuals that die. When the number of deaths is greater than the number of births, populations get smaller. Take the squirrels living in New York City's Central Park as an example. In one year, if 900 squirrels are born and 800 die, the population increases by 100. If 400 squirrels are born and 500 die, the population decreases by 100.

The same is true for human populations. **Table 1** shows birthrates, death rates, and population changes for several countries around the world. In countries with faster population growth, birthrates are much higher than death rates. In countries with slower population growth, birthrates are only slightly higher than death rates. In Germany, where the population is getting smaller, the birthrate is lower than the death rate.

Table 1 Population Growth			
	Birthrate*	**Death Rate***	**Population Increase** (percent)
Rapid-Growth Countries			
Jordan	38.8	5.5	3.3
Uganda	50.8	21.8	2.9
Zimbabwe	34.3	9.4	5.2
Slow-Growth Countries			
Germany	9.4	10.8	−1.5
Sweden	10.8	10.6	0.1
United States	14.8	8.8	0.6

*Number per 1,000 people

Figure 9
The mangrove seeds sprout while they are still attached to the parent tree. Some sprouted seeds drop into the mud below the parent tree and continue to grow. Others drop into the water and can be carried away by tides and ocean currents. When they wash ashore, they might start a new population of mangroves or add to an existing mangrove population.

Moving Around Most animals can move easily from place to place, and these movements can affect population size. For example, a male mountain sheep might wander many miles in search of a mate. After he finds a mate, their offspring might establish a completely new population of mountain sheep far from the male's original population.

Many bird species move from one place to another during their annual migrations. During the summer, populations of Baltimore orioles are found throughout eastern North America. During the winter, these populations disappear because the birds migrate to Central America. They spend the winter there, where the climate is mild and food supplies are plentiful. When summer approaches, the orioles migrate back to North America.

Even plants and microscopic organisms can move from place to place, carried by wind, water, or animals. The tiny spores of mushrooms, mosses, and ferns float through the air. The seeds of dandelions, maple trees, and other plants have feathery or winglike growths that allow them to be carried by wind. Spine-covered seeds hitch rides by clinging to animal fur or people's clothing. Many kinds of seeds can be transported by river and ocean currents. Mangrove trees growing along Florida's Gulf Coast, shown in **Figure 9,** provide an example of how water moves seeds.

Mini LAB

Comparing Biotic Potential

Procedure
1. Remove all the seeds from a **whole fruit.** Do not put fruit or seeds in your mouth.
2. Count the total number of seeds in the fruit. Wash your hands, then record these data in your Science Journal.
3. Compare your seed totals with those of classmates who examined other types of fruit.

Analysis
1. Which type of fruit had the most seeds? Which had the fewest seeds?
2. What is an advantage of producing many seeds? Can you think of a possible disadvantage?
3. To estimate the total number of seeds produced by a tomato plant, what would you need to know?

Mini LAB

Purpose Students observe and compare the number of seeds in different types of fruit. [L2]

ELL **IS** **Logical-Mathematical**

Materials plastic knives, paper towels, assorted fruits

Teaching Strategies
- Arrange for students to bring in fruits from home.
- Explain that many of our vegetables are actually fruits, including tomatoes, eggplants, and squashes.

Safety Precautions Instruct students on the proper way to handle and use the plastic knives.

Analysis
1. Tomatoes and strawberries have many seeds; avocados and peaches have one seed.
2. Advantage: There is a greater chance that a seed will find an optimal place to grow. Disadvantage: The seeds are small and carry few nutrients.
3. How many tomatoes the plant produces and about how many seeds are produced by each tomato

✓ Assessment

Oral Based on the number of seeds contained in each fruit, which has a greater biotic potential—a nectarine or a watermelon? Explain. A watermelon—it contains many seeds, while a nectarine contains only one. Use **PASC,** p. 89.

✓ Active Reading

Four-Corner Discussion This strategy encourages the class to debate a complex issue. Make four signs: Strongly Agree, Agree, Disagree, Strongly Disagree. Place one sign in each corner of the room. Write on the chalkboard a statement that will elicit reactions from students. Have students respond on paper to the statement. After several minutes, direct them to move to the corner with the sign that most closely reflects their opinions. In the corners, students share responses. Each group then selects a spokesperson to report the opinions of the group. After all groups have reported, open the floor for debate. Allow students who have changed their opinions to change corners. Have students conduct a Four-Corner Discussion about the causes of changes in populations.

Visualizing Population Growth

Have students examine the pictures and read the captions. Then ask the following question.

What happens when a population exceeds carrying capacity? Possible answer: There may not be enough resources to support all members of the population. It is likely that members will begin to die from lack of resources such as food and water.

Extension

Have students graph the following data on predator-prey cycles between lynx and snowshoe hares.

Years	# of lynx	# of hares
1845	30,000	18,000
1850	10,000	40,000
1855	30,000	78,000
1860	8,000	21,000
1865	67,000	71,000
1870	7,000	12,000
1875	40,000	99,000
1880	12,000	9,000

What is the pattern between the population numbers of the lynx and the hares? As the number of hares increases, the number of lynx increases. As the larger lynx population feeds on hares, the number of hares decreases, followed by a decrease in the number of lynx.

Figure 10

When a species enters an ecosystem that has abundant food, water, and other resources, its population can flourish. Beginning with a few organisms, the population increases until the number of organisms and available resources are in balance. At that point, population growth slows or stops. A graph of these changes over time produces an S-curve, as shown here for coyotes.

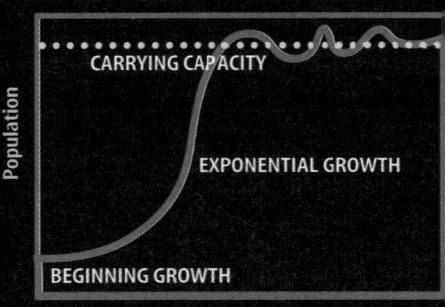

BEGINNING GROWTH During the first few years, population growth is slow, because there are few adults to produce young. As the population grows, so does the number of breeding adults.

EXPONENTIAL GROWTH As the number of adults in the population grows, so does the number of births. The coyote population undergoes exponential growth, quickly increasing in size.

CARRYING CAPACITY As resources become less plentiful, the birthrate declines and the death rate may rise. Population growth slows. The coyote population has reached the environmental carrying capacity—the maximum number of coyotes that the environment can sustain.

342

Resource Manager

Chapter Resources Booklet
Transparency Activity, pp. 47–48
Reinforcement, p. 28

Life Science Critical Thinking/Problem Solving, p. 13

Curriculum Connection

Math The bacterium *E. coli* can double in population size every twenty minutes under suitable conditions. Starting with a single bacterium, have students calculate the length of time it would take for the population to reach 1 million. The population would reach 1 million in only 6 hours and 40 minutes. L2 LS **Logical-Mathematical**

Exponential Growth

Imagine what might happen if a pair of coyotes moves into a valley where no other coyotes live. Food and water are abundant, and there are plenty of areas where female coyotes can build dens for their young. This population grows quickly in a pattern called exponential growth. Exponential growth means that the larger a population becomes, the faster it grows.

After several years, the population becomes so large that the coyotes begin to compete for food and den sites. Population growth slows, and the number of coyotes remains fairly constant and reaches equilibrium. This ecosystem has reached its carrying capacity for coyotes. A graph that describes each stage in this pattern of population growth is shown in **Figure 10.** As you can see in **Figure 11,** Earth's human population shows exponential growth. In the year 2000, Earth's human population exceeded 6 billion. By the year 2050, it is estimated that Earth's human population could reach 10 billion.

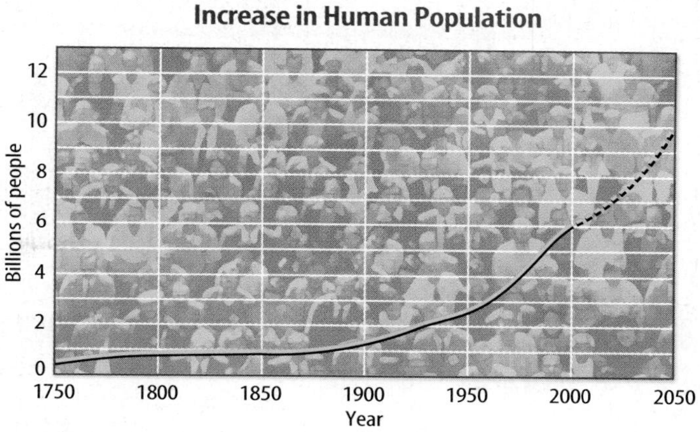

Increase in Human Population

Figure 11
The size of the human population is increasing by about 1.6 percent per year. *What factors affect human population growth?*

Section ② Assessment

1. How can an ecologist predict the size of a population without counting every organism in the population?

2. Why does competition between individuals of the same species tend to be greater than competition between individuals of different species?

3. How do birthrates and death rates influence the size of a population?

4. How does carrying capacity influence the number of organisms in an ecosystem?

5. **Think Critically** Why does the supply of food and water in an ecosystem usually affect population size more than other limiting factors?

Skill Builder Activities

6. **Making and Using Tables** Construct a table using the following data on changes in the size of a deer population in Arizona. In 1910 there were 6 deer; in 1915, 36 deer; in 1920, 143 deer; in 1925, 86 deer; and in 1935, 26 deer. Propose a hypothesis to explain what might have caused these changes. **For more help, refer to the** Science Skill Handbook.

7. **Solving One-Step Equations** A vacant lot that measures 12 m × 12 m contains 46 dandelion plants, 212 grass plants, and 14 bindweed plants. What is the population density, per square meter, of each species? **For more help, refer to the** Math Skill Handbook.

---

③ Assess

Reteach

Ask students to work in groups to (a) guess the size of your school's seventh-grade population, (b) devise a way to more accurately estimate that population size, and (c) give reasons for seventh-grade immigration and emigration. L1 COOP LEARN

Challenge

The number of a certain bacteria doubles every hour. If you start at time zero with one bacterium, how many bacteria will you have after 10 hours? Make a graph showing the number you have every hour. Graphs should show the following data:

Time (hours)	Number of Bacteria	Time (hours)	Number of Bacteria
0	1	6	64
1	2	7	128
2	4	8	256
3	8	9	512
4	16	10	1024
5	32		

✓ Assessment

Performance Have students research the population trends of an endangered species. Ask students to graph the data, showing numbers of individuals on the vertical axis and year on the horizontal axis. Have students describe the growth curve. Use **PASC**, p. 111.

Answers to Section Assessment

1. Count the organisms in a portion of an area, and then multiply that number by the number of portions needed to make a whole.

2. Organisms of the same species have similar needs.

3. If birthrate exceeds death rate, population size increases. If death rate exceeds birthrate, population size decreases. If they are equal, population size is maintained.

4. The number of organisms cannot permanently exceed the carrying capacity of the environment.

5. Food and water are critical for survival. Things such as oxygen also are critical, but they usually are not in short supply.

6. Possible answer: The population grew when predators were eliminated. When the deer exceeded the carrying capacity of their environment, their numbers were again reduced.

7. dandelion: 46/144 = 0.3; grass: 212/144 = 1.5; bindweed: 14/144 = 0.1

Interactions Within Communities

Interactions Within Communities

1 Motivate

Bellringer Transparency

Display the Section Focus Transparency for Section 3. Use the accompanying Transparency Activity Master. L2

ELL

SECTION 3 Section Focus Transparency — Frolics with Sharks

Remoras are several different species of related fishes that attach themselves to sharks and other ocean organisms. Both the shark and the remora benefit from this relationship.

1. Why doesn't the shark eat the remora?
2. How do the shark and remora help each other?

Interactions of Life

Tie to Prior Knowledge

Have students consider a familiar ecosystem. Ask them to name organisms that make up the community and describe interactions among these organisms.

As You Read

What You'll Learn

- **Describe** how organisms obtain energy for life.
- **Explain** how organisms interact.
- **Recognize** that every organism occupies a niche.

Vocabulary

producer	commensalism
consumer	parasitism
symbiosis	niche
mutualism	

Why It's Important

How organisms obtain food and meet other needs is critical for their survival.

Figure 12
Green plants, including the grasses that surround this pond, are producers. The pond also contains many other producers, including microscopic organisms like **A** *Euglena* and **B** simple plantlike organisms called algae.

Obtaining Energy

Just as a car engine needs a constant supply of gasoline, living organisms need a constant supply of energy. The energy that fuels most life on Earth comes from the Sun. Some organisms use the Sun's energy to create energy-rich molecules through the process of photosynthesis. The energy-rich molecules, usually sugars, serve as food. They are made up of different combinations of carbon, hydrogen, and oxygen atoms. Energy is stored in the chemical bonds that hold the atoms of these molecules together. When the molecules break apart—for example, during digestion—the energy in the chemical bonds is released to fuel life processes.

Producers Organisms that use an outside energy source like the Sun to make energy-rich molecules are called **producers.** Most producers contain chlorophyll (KLOR uh fihl), a chemical that is required for photosynthesis. As shown in **Figure 12,** green plants are producers. Some producers do not contain chlorophyll and do not use energy from the Sun. Instead, they make energy-rich molecules through a process called chemosynthesis (kee moh SIHN thuh sus). These organisms can be found near volcanic vents on the ocean floor. Inorganic molecules in the water provide the energy source for chemosynthesis.

A Magnification: 125×   **B** Magnification: 225×

Section *Assessment* Planner

PORTFOLIO
Science Journal, p. 347
PERFORMANCE ASSESSMENT
Skill Builder Activities, p. 348
See page 356 for more options.

CONTENT ASSESSMENT
Section, p. 348
Challenge, p. 348
Chapter, pp. 356–357

Consumers

Herbivores

Carnivores

Omnivores

Decomposers

Figure 13
Four categories of consumers are shown. *What kind of consumer is a cactus wren? A mushroom?*

Consumers Organisms that cannot make their own energy-rich molecules are called **consumers.** Consumers obtain energy by eating other organisms. **Figure 13** shows the four general categories of consumers. Herbivores are the vegetarians of the world. They include rabbits, deer, and other plant eaters. Carnivores are animals that eat other animals. Frogs and spiders are carnivores that eat insects. Omnivores, including pigs and humans, eat mostly plants and animals. Decomposers, including fungi, bacteria, and earthworms, consume wastes and dead organisms. Decomposers help recycle once-living matter by breaking it down into simple, energy-rich substances. These substances might serve as food for decomposers, be absorbed by plant roots, or be consumed by other organisms.

Chemistry
INTEGRATION

Glucose is a nutrient molecule produced during photosynthesis. Look up the chemical structure of glucose and draw it in your Science Journal.

✔ **Reading Check** *How are producers different from consumers?*

Food Chains Ecology includes the study of how organisms depend on each other for food. A food chain is a simple model of the feeding relationships in an ecosystem. For example, shrubs are food for deer, and deer are food for mountain lions, as illustrated in **Figure 14.** What food chain would include you?

Figure 14
Food chains illustrate how consumers obtain energy from other organisms in an ecosystem.

SECTION 3 Interactions Within Communities **345**

Text Question Answer
  Accept any answer that shows a human eating food derived from a plant or animal. For example, in Figure 14, humans might replace the mountain lion, because humans eat venison.

Caption Answer
Figure 13 A cactus wren is an omnivore; a mushroom is a decomposer.

2 Teach

Obtaining Energy

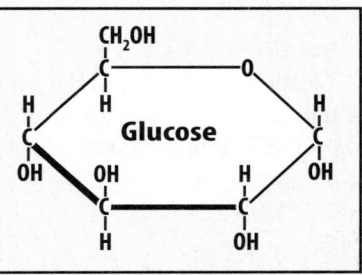
Chemistry
INTEGRATION

Energy for life is stored in the bonds of organic molecules such as glucose. A molecule of glucose is made of 6 carbons, 12 hydrogens, and 6 oxygens atoms ($C_6H_{12}O_6$). The structure is as follows.

CH$_2$OH — Glucose

✔ **Reading Check**

Answer A producer can make its own energy-rich molecules; a consumer must obtain energy-rich molecules from other organisms.

Use Science Words
Word Origin Types of consumers are described by words derived from Latin. *Vorare* means "to devour," *herba* means "grass," *caro* means "flesh," and *omnis* means "all." Present this information to students and have them use it to explain the terms *herbivore, carnivore,* and *omnivore.*

Discussion
  Most humans are omnivores. Are humans suited for this type of diet? Possible responses: Humans have canine teeth, which carnivores have, as well as molars, which herbivores have. Herbivores have long digestive tracts; carnivores have shorter tracts. Humans have digestive tracts of intermediate length.

Symbiotic Relationships

Activity

Bring in stones or pieces of tree bark with lichens growing on them. Have students look at the lichens using hand lenses. Then have them prepare wet-mount slides of lichen pieces and observe them using microscopes. **How do the algae and fungus benefit each other?** Algae make food for the fungus, and the fungus provides a habitat and moisture for the algae. L2 LS **Visual-Spatial**

Use an Analogy

Challenge students to describe a human interaction that is analogous to commensalism. Possible example: A person may go through another's trash and find something useful. This is analogous to commensalism because one person benefits, while the other is neither helped nor harmed.

Figure 15
Many examples of symbiotic relationships exist in nature.

A Lichens are a result of mutualism.

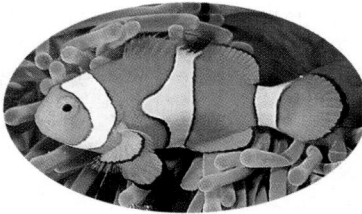

B Clown fish and sea anemones have a commensal relationship.

Magnification: 128×

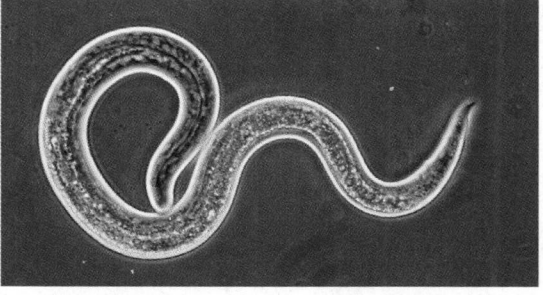

C Some roundworms are parasites that rob nutrients from their hosts.

Symbiotic Relationships

Not all relationships among organisms involve food. Many organisms live together and share resources in other ways. Any close relationship between species is called **symbiosis.**

Mutualism You may have noticed crusty lichens growing on fences, trees, or rocks. Lichens, like those shown in **Figure 15A,** are made up of an alga or a cyanobacterium that lives within the tissues of a fungus. Through photosynthesis, the cyanobacterium or alga supplies energy to itself and the fungus. The fungus provides a protected space in which the cyanobacterium or alga can live. Both organisms benefit from this association. A symbiotic relationship in which both species benefit is called **mutualism** (MYEW chuh wuh lih zum).

Commensalism If you've ever visited a marine aquarium, you might have seen the ocean organisms shown in **Figure 15B.** The creature with gently waving, tubelike tentacles is a sea anemone. The tentacles contain a mild poison. Anemones use their tentacles to capture shrimp, fish, and other small animals to eat. The striped clown fish can swim among the tentacles without being harmed. The anemone's tentacles protect the clown fish from predators. In this relationship, the clown fish benefits but the sea anemone is not helped or hurt. A symbiotic relationship in which one organism benefits and the other is not affected is called **commensalism** (kuh MEN suh lih zum).

Parasitism Pet cats or dogs sometimes have to be treated for worms. Roundworms, like the one shown in **Figure 15C,** are common in puppies. This roundworm attaches itself to the inside of the puppy's intestine and feeds on nutrients in the puppy's blood. The puppy may have abdominal pain, bloating, and diarrhea. If the infection is severe, the puppy might die. A symbiotic relationship in which one organism benefits but the other is harmed is called **parasitism** (PER uh suh tih zum).

Inclusion Strategies

Learning Disabled Help make the differences between the types of symbiotic relationships more clear by asking students to categorize these examples: a bee gets nectar from a flower and pollinates the flower *(mutualism)*; an orchid, which gets it moisture and nutrients from the air, grows on a tall tree *(commensalism)*; a tick attaches to a deer and sucks its blood *(parasitism)*.

Niches

One habitat might contain hundreds or even thousands of species. Look at the rotting log habitat shown in **Figure 16.** A rotting log in a forest can be home to many species of insects, including termites that eat decaying wood and ants that feed on the termites. Other species that live on or under the rotting log include millipedes, centipedes, spiders, and worms. You might think that competition for resources would make it impossible for so many species to live in the same habitat. However, each species has different requirements for its survival. As a result, each species has its own niche (NIHCH). A **niche** refers to how an organism survives, how it obtains food and shelter, how it finds a mate and cares for its young, and how it avoids danger.

✓ **Reading Check** *Why does each species have its own niche?*

Special adaptations that improve survival are often part of an organism's niche. Milkweed plants contain a poison that prevents many insects from feeding on them. Monarch butterfly caterpillars have an adaptation that allows them to eat milkweed. Monarchs can take advantage of a food resource that other species cannot use. Milkweed poison also helps protect monarchs from predators. When the caterpillars eat milkweed, they become slightly poisonous. Birds avoid eating monarchs because they learn that the caterpillars and adult butterflies have an awful taste and can make them sick.

Health
INTEGRATION

The poison in milkweed is similar to the drug digitalis. Small amounts of digitalis are used to treat heart ailments in humans, but it is poisonous in large doses. Look up digitalis and explain in your Science Journal how it affects the human body.

Figure 16
Different adaptations enable each species living in this rotting log to have its own niche.
A Termites eat wood. They make tunnels inside the log.
B Millipedes feed on plant matter and find shelter beneath the log. **C** Wolf spiders capture insects living in and around the log.

347

Niches

Discussion

The term *niche* is sometimes described as an activity that one person is good at, but others find difficult. **How is this similar to the biological definition?** Organisms with a particular niche often have adaptations that give them an advantage in their environment.

Health
INTEGRATION

Digitalis and similar drugs control heart rate. They tend to increase the force but decrease the frequency of heartbeats. Very small doses are used in medicine because larger amounts can cause death.

✓ **Reading Check**

Answer Each species has different requirements for its survival.

IDENTIFYING
Misconceptions

Students may think that plants do not depend on other organisms. Refer to page 330F for teaching strategies that address this misconception.

Resource Manager

Chapter Resources Booklet
  Reinforcement, p. 29
Reading and Writing Skill Activities, p. 49
Cultural Diversity, p. 13

Science Journal

Local Niches Have students identify organisms in local habitats that have different niches. Encourage them to research one organism and to write descriptive paragraphs in their science journals about how the organism survives, obtains food and shelter, finds a mate, cares for young, and avoids danger. **P**

Figure 17
The alligator is a predator. The turtle is its prey.

Predator and Prey When you think of survival in the wild, you might imagine an antelope running away from a lion. An organism's niche includes how it avoids being eaten and how it finds or captures its food. Predators, like the one shown in **Figure 17,** are consumers that capture and eat other consumers. The prey is the organism that is captured by the predator. The presence of predators usually increases the number of different species that can live in an ecosystem. Predators limit the size of prey populations. As a result, food and other resources are less likely to become scarce, and competition between species is reduced.

Cooperation Individual organisms often cooperate in ways that improve survival. For example, a white-tailed deer that detects the presence of wolves or coyotes will alert the other deer in the herd. Many insects, such as ants and honeybees, live in social groups. Different individuals perform different tasks required for the survival of the entire nest. Soldier ants protect workers that go out of the nest to gather food. Worker ants feed and care for ant larvae that hatch from eggs laid by the queen. These cooperative actions improve survival and are a part of the species' niche.

Section 3 Assessment

1. Explain why all consumers ultimately depend on producers for food.
2. Draw a food chain that models the feeding relationships of three species in a community. Choose a food chain other than the one shown in **Figure 14.**
3. Make up two imaginary organisms that have a mutualistic relationship. Give them names and explain how they benefit from the association.
4. What is the difference between a habitat and a niche?
5. **Think Critically** A parasite can obtain food only from a host organism. Most parasites weaken but do not kill their hosts. Why?

Skill Builder Activities

6. **Manipulating Variables and Controls** You are sure that Animal A benefits from a relationship with Plant B, but you are not sure if Plant B benefits, is harmed, or is unaffected by the relationship. Design an experiment to compare how well Plant B grows on its own and when Animal A is present. **For more help, refer to the Science Skill Handbook.**
7. **Using Graphics Software** Use graphics software to make three different food chains. Represent each organism with a shape that resembles it. For example, you could use a leaf shape to represent a plant. Label each shape. **For more help, refer to the** Technology Skill Handbook.

Activity

Feeding Habits of Planaria

You probably have watched minnows darting about in a stream. It is not as easy to observe organisms that live at the bottom of a stream, beneath rocks, logs, and dead leaves. Countless stream organisms, including insect larvae, worms, and microscopic organisms, live out of your view. One such organism is a type of flatworm called a planarian. In this activity, you will find out about the eating habits of planarians.

What You'll Investigate
What food items do planarians prefer to eat?

Materials
small bowl
planarians (several)
lettuce leaf
raw liver or meat
guppies (several)
pond or stream water
magnifying lens

Goals
- ■ **Observe** the food preference of planarians.
- ■ **Infer** what planarians eat in the wild.

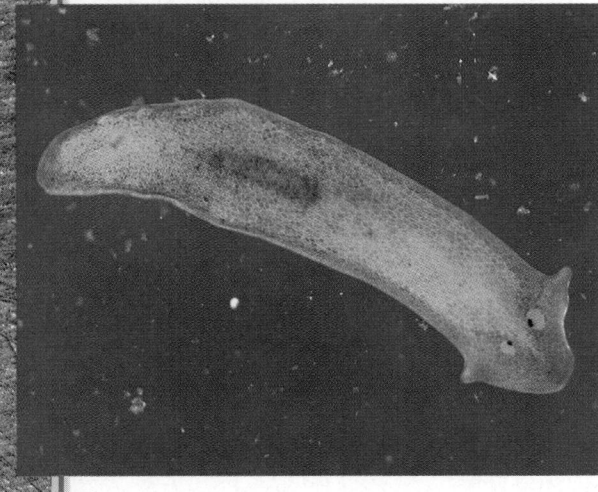

Safety Precautions

Procedure
1. Fill the bowl with stream water.
2. Place a lettuce leaf, piece of raw liver, and several guppies in the bowl. Add the planarians. Wash your hands.
3. **Observe** what happens inside the bowl for at least 20 minutes. Do not disturb the bowl or its contents. Use a magnifying lens to look at the planarians.
4. **Record** all of your observations in your Science Journal.

Conclude and Apply
1. Which food did the planarians prefer?
2. **Infer** what planarians might eat when in their natural environment.
3. Based on your observations during this activity, what is a planarian's niche in a stream ecosystem?
4. **Predict** where in a stream you might find planarians. Use references to find out whether your prediction is correct.

𝒞ommunicating
Your Data
Share your results with other students in your class. Plan an adult-supervised trip with several classmates to a local stream to search for planarians in their native habitat. **For more help, refer to the** Science Skill Handbook.

ACTIVITY 349

𝒞ommunicating
Your Data
Have students write a paragraph describing their results. They can exchange papers with a classmate to see their results.

Activity

Purpose Students observe the eating habits of planarians and infer what wild planarians eat.
L2 IS **Visual-Spatial**

Process Skills observing, predicting, inferring

Time Required 30 minutes

Safety Precautions Instruct students to handle planarians with care and to wash their hands after the lab.

Teaching Strategies To house the planarians for an extended period of time, change the water of their bowls every other day and keep a small piece of liver in the bowl.

Troubleshooting
- Set up a bowl of planarians to serve as a reference.
- The piece of liver should be about the size of a quarter.
- Tell students to cover their dishes for a few minutes; planaria do not like light.

Answers to Questions
1. liver
2. Most planaria are carnivorous night feeders. They eat protozoans, tiny snails, worms, and dead animals.
3. Although planarians prey on slow-moving animals, they primarily scavenge dead organisms from the bottom of streams.
4. Planarians live in slow-moving or still portions of a stream where dead organisms settle to the stream bottom. They are found beneath rotting leaves or rocks.

✓Assessment

Performance Ask students to infer how their results might have differed had they used tap water instead of stream water. Tap water contains chemicals toxic to soft bodied animals and could kill the planarians. Use **PASC,** p. 89.

Activity

Recognize the Problem

Purpose

Students will test the effect of a change in one environmental factor on the rate of growth of a fruit fly population.

Process Skills

identifying a question, forming hypotheses, testing a hypothesis, identifying and manipulating variables, collecting data, making and using tables, recording data, recording observations, analyzing results, forming operational definitions, evaluating other's data and conclusions, communicating, making and using graphs

Time

two 45–minute periods and once weekly observations for one to two months

Materials

Standard fruit fly culture kits are available from biological supply houses. Possible culture containers include mayonnaise jars or other empty, sanitized food jars.

Safety Precautions

- Students should take care not to release their fruit flies within the school building.
- Used fruit fly culture containers can contain bacteria and mold, and should not be reused for other purposes.

Activity — *Design Your Own Experiment*

Population Growth in Fruit Flies

Populations can grow at an exponential rate only if the environment provides the right amount of food, shelter, air, moisture, heat, living space, and other factors. You probably have seen fruit flies hovering near ripe bananas or other fruit. Fruit flies are fast-growing organisms often raised in science laboratories. The flies are kept in culture tubes and fed a diet of specially prepared food flakes. Can you improve on this standard growing method to achieve faster population growth?

Recognize the Problem

Will a change in one environmental factor affect the growth of a fruit fly population?

Form a Hypothesis

Based on your reading about fruit flies, state a hypothesis about how changing one environmental factor will affect the rate of growth of a fruit fly population.

Goals

- **Identify** the environmental factors needed by a population of fruit flies.
- **Design** an experiment to investigate how a change in one environmental factor affects in any way the size of a fruit fly population.
- **Observe** and **measure** changes in population size.

Possible Materials

fruit flies
standard fruit fly culture kit
food items (banana, orange peel, or other fruit)
water
heating or cooling source
culture containers
cloth, plastic, or other tops for culture containers
hand lens

Safety Precautions

Data Table:

Fruit Fly Population				
Culture number	Number of Flies			
	Date	Date	Date	Date
1				
2				
3				

Form a Hypothesis

Students' hypotheses should reflect a change in one environmental factor, such as type of food, amount of water, or size of container, and its possible effect on the rate of growth of the fruit fly population. For example: A larger living space will result in a faster-growing fruit fly population.

Test Your Hypothesis

Plan

1. As a group, decide on one environmental factor to investigate. Agree on a hypothesis about how a change in this factor will affect population growth. Decide how you will test your hypothesis, and identify the experimental results that would support your hypothesis.

2. **List** the steps you will need to take to test your hypothesis. Describe exactly what you will do. List your materials.

3. **Determine** the method you will use to measure changes in the size of your fruit fly populations.

4. Prepare a data table in your Science Journal to record weekly measurements of your fruit fly populations.

5. Read the entire experiment and make sure all of the steps are in a logical order.

6. **Research** the standard method used to raise fruit flies in the laboratory. Use this method as the control in your experiment.

7. **Identify** all constants, variables, and controls in your experiment.

Do

1. Make sure your teacher approves your plan before you start.

2. Carry out your experiment.

3. **Measure** the growth of your fruit fly populations weekly and record the data in your data table.

Analyze Your Data

1. What were the constants in your experiment? The variables?

2. **Compare** changes in the size of your control population with changes in your experimental population. Which population grew faster?

3. Using the information in your data table, make a line graph that shows how the sizes of your two fruit fly populations changed over time. Use a different colored pencil for each population's line on the graph.

Draw Conclusions

1. Did the results support your hypothesis? Explain.

2. **Compare** the growth of your control and experimental populations. Did either population reach exponential growth? How do you know?

Communicating Your Data

Compare the results of your experiment with those of other students in your class. **For more help, refer to the** Science Skill Handbook.

ACTIVITY 351

Assessment

Oral Have students explain the relationship between environmental conditions and population growth in fruit flies. Flies achieve the fastest rate of growth when all the conditions in their environment are at optimal levels. Any change in these conditions will result in a decrease in population growth rates. Use **Performance Assessment in the Science Classroom,** p. 89.

Communicating Your Data

Students can make an electronic spreadsheet that allows comparison of data about different environmental factors that affect the rate of growth of the fruit fly population.

Test Your Hypothesis

Possible Procedures

Provide two equal-sized populations of fruit flies with the same amount of food and moisture and the same temperature, but two different sized containers to test the effect of living area on fruit fly population growth. Make observations of the fly populations over the next one to two months. The life cycle of a fruit fly takes approximately two weeks, so students should see rapid changes in population size.

Teaching Strategy

Most students are familiar with fruit flies "appearing" near ripe fruit. Have students consider the source of these flies. Sometimes the eggs were already present on the fruit; other times flies have used their great sense of smell to locate the ripe fruit.

Expected Outcome

Most results will show that any extreme change from the standard method of maintaining fruit flies will result in a decreased rate of population growth.

Analyze Your Data

1. Answers will vary.
2. Answers will vary.
3. Student graphs will vary. Check students' work.

Error Analysis

Have students compare their results and their hypotheses and explain why differences occurred.

Draw Conclusions

1. Answers will be determined by student's hypotheses.

2. A population shows exponential growth if it increases at a fixed percentage per time period. Student answers will depend on results.

TIME
SCIENCE AND
HISTORY

TIME

SCIENCE AND
HISTORY

SCIENCE
CAN CHANGE
THE COURSE
OF HISTORY!

Content Background

The election year 2000 raised a number of questions concerning electors in the Electoral College. For perhaps the first time in recent U.S. history, a large number of people began to wonder how electors are chosen and how many are apportioned for each state.

The answer to these questions lies in the process of census taking. The census affects not only the number and distribution of congressional candidates, but also the number of electors to the Electoral College. Each state has as many electors as it has members of Congress, and every state must have at least one representative and two senators. Every 10 years the census results are used to determine the number of congressional seats of each state. The number of U.S. Representatives gained or lost in the year 1990 as a result of the census affected 21 states. For example, California gained seven seats to the 103rd Congress and New York lost three. Regionally, the South and the West gained 15 seats between 1980 and 1990 and the Northeast and the Midwest lost 15. In the year 2000, the Sun belt won 12 seats at the expense of the Rust belt.

Even though the number of Representatives remains at 435, reapportionment of seats to Congress can have significant impact.

Reapportionment of seats within states necessitates redistricting within those states so that the Representatives stand for equal numbers of people in that state.

YOU CAN COUNT

The Census gives a snapshot of the people of the United States

The doorbell rings and you hear someone at the door say to your mom, "I'm working for the U.S. Census Bureau, doing follow-up interviews. Do you have a few minutes to answer some questions?" What does this person—and the U.S. government—want to know about your family?

Counting people is important to the United States and to many other countries around the world. It helps governments determine the distribution of people in the various regions of a nation. To obtain this information, the government takes a census—a count of how many people are living in their country on a particular day at a particular time, and in a particular place. A census is a snapshot of a country's population. The time at which the count occurs is called the "census moment." Some countries close their borders for a day or two so everyone will "sit still" for the census camera at the census moment, as was done in Nigeria in 1991.

Counting on the Count

When the United States government was formed, its founders set up the House of Representatives based on population. Areas with more people had more government representatives, and areas with fewer people had fewer representatives. In 1787, the requirement for a census became part of the Constitution. A census must be taken every ten years so the proper number of representatives for each state can be calculated.

Over the years, the U.S. Census Bureau has added questions to obtain more information than just a population count. In 1810, questions about manufacturing were added. In 1850, as more immigrants began coming to the United States, a new question about where people were born was added. In 1880, census takers asked people whether or not they were married. And in 1950, the first electronic computers were used to add up the census results.

 Next, read on to find out more about the census.

352

Resources for Teachers and Students

The American Census: A Social History by Margo J. Anderson. Yale University Press, New Haven, CT. 1988.

"The History of Census Tabulation" by Keith S. Reid-Green. *Scientific American* 260 (February 1989): 98-103.

Understanding the Census by Michael R. Lavin. Epic Books, New York. 1996.

Who Counts? The Politics of Census-Taking in Contemporary America by Margo J. Anderson and Stephen E. Fienberg. Russell Sage Foundation, New York. 1999.

ON IT

Chances are you just blinked your eyes. While you did it, three people were added to the world's population. There, you blinked again—that's another three people! It may seem impossible, but that's how quickly the world's population is growing. It adds up to 184 people every minute, 11,040 every hour, 264,960 every day, and 97 million every year! On October 12, 1999, the official number of people on the planet reached a record 6 billion.

The Short Form

Before 1970, United States census data was collected by field workers. They went door to door to count the number of people living in each household. Since then, the census has been done mostly by mail. People are sent a form they must fill out. The form asks for the number of people living at an address and their names, races, ages, and relationships. Answers to these and other questions are confidential. Census workers visit some homes to check on the accuracy of the information. The census helps the government to figure out how the population is aging. Census data are also important in deciding how to distribute government services and funding.

The 2000 Snapshot

One of the findings of the 2000 Census is that the U.S. population is becoming more equally spread out across age groups. By analyzing the data from the census, officials estimate that by 2020 the population of children, middle-aged people, and senior citizens will be about equal. It's predicted also that there will be more people who are over 100 years old than ever before.

Martha F. Riche researches population changes in the United States. She was also a director of the Census Bureau. Riche thinks that the more equal distribution in age will lead to challenges for the nation. How will we meet the demands of more people who are living longer? Will we need to build more hospitals to care for them? Will more children mean a need to build more schools? Federal, state, and local governments will be using the results of the 2000 Census for years to come as they plan our future.

Martha F. Riche studies population changes.

CONNECTIONS Census Develop a school census. What questions will you ask? (Don't ask questions that are too personal.) Who will ask them? How will you make sure you counted everyone? Using the results, can you make any predictions about your school's future or its current students?

SCIENCE Online

For more information, visit science.glencoe.com

CONNECTIONS Today, the entire census is taken using a mail-in form. Have students develop a short mail-in form to take a school census. Have groups write questions to include on the forms. Challenge students to design the form so that it is understandable. After the census is taken, have students discuss challenges they encountered.

SCIENCE Online

Internet Addresses

_____

_____

_____

_____

Explore the Glencoe Science Web site at **science.glencoe.com** to find out more about topics in this feature.

Discussion

What do you think accounts for the U.S. population becoming more spread out across age groups? Remind students that from the 1940s through the 1960s there was a sharp increase in the number of babies being born. This created what is popularly known as a "baby boom," which has accounted for the disproportionate number of people in a certain age bracket. Possible answer: The population is becoming more equal in number across age groups because the population in general is declining. People are having smaller families. Seniors are living longer, so their numbers are rising to meet the numbers of middle-aged people.

Historical Significance

Explain to students that census data can have a direct affect on electing our President and Congressmen and Congresswomen. Explain to students that the Electoral College is made up of selected representatives in each state that cast their vote for the President. Tell students that the number of Electoral College votes, not popular votes, elects the President. States with large populations have more electors than do states with small populations. Explain that the number of electors gained or lost in a given state is a direct result of the U.S. Census. Tell students that in the 1990 census, the South and the West gained 15 electors and the Northeast and the Midwest lost 15. Ask students what they think accounts for the shift. Do they think that this shift had an affect on the 2000 election?

Chapter 12 Study Guide

Preview

Students can answer the questions in their Science Journals. Discuss the answers as you go through the chapter. **IS Linguistic**

Review

Students can write their answers, then compare them with those of other students. **IS Interpersonal**

Reteach

Students can look at the illustrations and describe details that support the main ideas of the chapter. **IS Visual-Spatial**

Answers to Chapter Review

SECTION 1

1. Yes, because it is part of the upper layer of crust and supports life.

SECTION 2

2. Answers may include the availability of food, water, and choice nesting places. Predators can also be a limiting factor.

SECTION 3

4. The monarch caterpillar has an adaptation that allows it to feed on the poisonous milkweed plants. This causes the adult monarch to be poisonous to its predators.

Reviewing Main Ideas

Section 1   Living Earth

1. Ecology is the study of interactions that take place in the biosphere. *Is ice-covered Antarctica a part of Earth's biosphere? Why or why not?*

2. Populations are made up of all organisms of the same species living in an area.

3. Communities are made up of all the populations of different species of organisms living in one ecosystem.

4. Living and nonliving factors affect an organism's ability to survive in its habitat.

Section 2   Populations

1. Population size can be estimated by counting a sample of a total population.

2. Competition for limiting factors can restrict the size of a population. *What limiting factors might influence the size of a rabbit population?*

3. Population growth is affected by birthrate, death rate, and the movement of individuals into or out of a community.

4. Exponential population growth can occur in environments that provide a species with plenty of food, shelter, and other resources.

Section 3   Interactions Within Communities

1. All life requires energy.

2. Most producers use the Sun's energy to make food in the form of energy-rich molecules. Consumers obtain their food by eating other organisms.

3. Mutualism, commensalism, and parasitism are the three kinds of symbiosis.

4. Every species has its own niche, which includes adaptations for survival. *What adaptations are involved in the relationship between the milkweed plant and the caterpillar of the monarch butterfly?*

 **FOLDABLES Reading & Study Skills**

After You Read

Under the population tab of your Concept Map Study Fold, write what would happen if there were an increase in the population of your animal.

FOLDABLES Reading & Study Skills

After You Read

After students have read the chapter and completed the Foldable described in Before You Read, have them do the activity on the student page.

Dinah Zike

Visualizing Main Ideas

Complete the following concept map on communities.

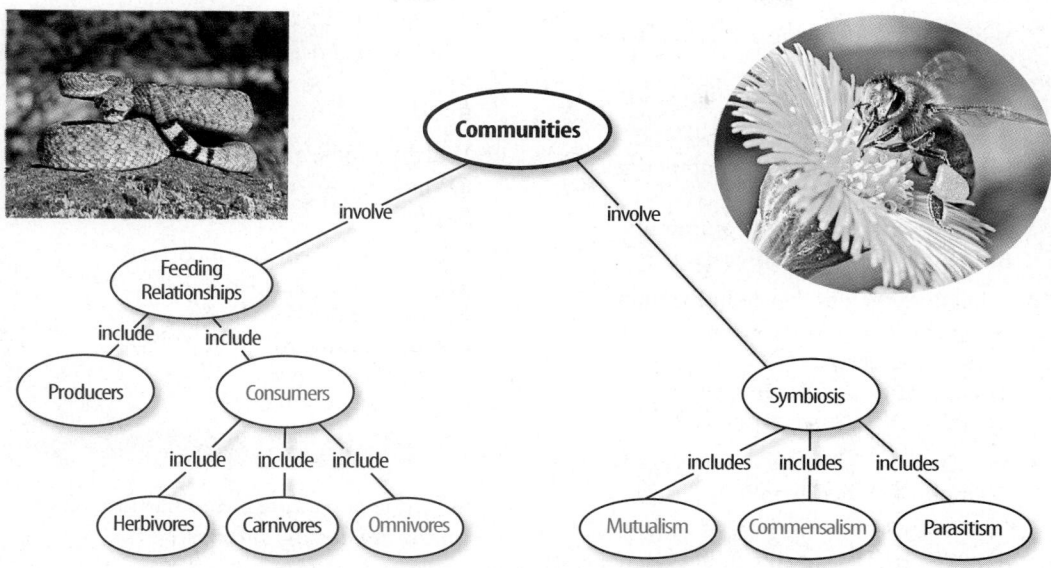

Communities
— involve → Feeding Relationships
— involve → Symbiosis

Feeding Relationships
— include → Producers
— include → Consumers

Consumers
— include → Herbivores
— include → Carnivores
— include → Omnivores

Symbiosis
— includes → Mutualism
— includes → Commensalism
— includes → Parasitism

Vocabulary Review

Vocabulary Words

a. biosphere
b. carrying capacity
c. commensalism
d. community
e. consumer
f. ecology
g. ecosystem
h. habitat

i. limiting factor
j. mutualism
k. niche
l. parasitism
m. population
n. producer
o. symbiosis

THE PRINCETON REVIEW

Study Tip

Get together with a friend to study. Quiz each other about specific topics from your textbook and class material to prepare for a test.

Using Vocabulary

Explain the difference between the vocabulary words in each of the following sets.

1. niche, habitat
2. mutualism, commensalism
3. limiting factor, carrying capacity
4. biosphere, ecosystem
5. producer, consumer
6. population, ecosystem
7. community, population
8. parasitism, symbiosis
9. ecosystem, ecology
10. parasitism, commensalism

CHAPTER STUDY GUIDE   355

Vocabulary Review

Using Vocabulary

1. Habitat is the place an organism lives. Niche refers to adaptations that help an organism survive.
2. Both describe symbiotic relationships. In mutualism both organisms benefit. In commensalism, one organism benefits, and the other neither benefits nor is harmed.
3. Carrying capacity is the largest number of individuals of one species that an ecosystem can support. Limiting factors restrict carrying capacity.
4. An ecosystem is all the living and nonliving components of an area. The biosphere is the part of Earth that supports life. It is made up of many ecosystems.
5. Producers make their own nutrients. Consumers eat producers or other consumers for nutrients.
6. An ecosystem is all the living and nonliving components of an area. A population is all the individuals of one species living in an area.
7. A community is all the different species in an area. A population refers to one species in an area.
8. Symbiosis describes a close relationship between species. Parasitism is a type of symbiosis in which one species benefits and the other species is harmed.
9. An ecosystem is all the living and nonliving components of an area. Ecology is the study of interactions between these components.
10. Both are types of symbiosis. In parasitism, one species benefits, and the other is harmed. In commensalism, one organism benefits, and the other neither benefits nor is harmed.

IDENTIFYING Misconceptions

Assess

Use the assessment as follow-up to page 330F after students have completed the chapter.

Activity After completing the activity in which students find and label interactions outdoors, have students again draw a picture of a natural community. Have students describe the interactions in the picture.

Expected Outcome In this second drawing, students should be able to identify more relationships between organisms than they did in the first drawing. The interactions they depict should include not only predation, but also various types of symbiosis. Students should also recognize that each organism interacts with many other organisms, not just a single predator or prey species.

Checking Concepts

1. A
2. C
3. D
4. D
5. B
6. A
7. C
8. C
9. D
10. A

Thinking Critically

11. It may absorb nutrients from the organism, as does a tapeworm living inside a human's intestine, or it may slowly feed on the tissue of an organism, as does a tick feeding on the blood of a deer.
12. Possible answers: food, water, shelter, space, birthrates and death rates, immigration, emigration
13. Description of habitat should include where the student lives. Description of niche should include adaptations and behaviors that enhance the student's survival.
14. commensalism
15. Organisms are adapted to feed on different foods, hunt at different times, and nest in different places. Therefore many niches can exist in the same habitat.

Chapter 12 Assessment

Checking Concepts

Choose the word or phrase that best answers the question.

1. Which of the following is a living factor in the environment?
   - A) animals
   - B) air
   - C) sunlight
   - D) soil

2. What is made up of all the populations in an area?
   - A) niches
   - B) habitats
   - C) community
   - D) ecosystem

3. What does the number of individuals in a population that occupies an area of a specific size describe?
   - A) clumping
   - B) size
   - C) spacing
   - D) density

4. Which of the following animals is an example of an herbivore?
   - A) wolf
   - B) moss
   - C) tree
   - D) rabbit

5. What term best describes a symbiotic relationship in which one species is helped and the other is harmed?
   - A) mutualism
   - B) parasitism
   - C) commensalism
   - D) consumerism

6. Which of the following conditions tends to increase the size of a population?
   - A) births exceed deaths
   - B) population size exceeds the carrying capacity
   - C) movements out of an area exceed movements into the area
   - D) severe drought

7. Which of the following is most likely to be a limiting factor in a population of fish living in the shallow water of a large lake?
   - A) sunlight
   - B) water
   - C) food
   - D) soil

8. An ecologist wants to know the size of a population of wild daisy plants growing in a meadow. The meadow measures 1,000 m². The ecologist counts 30 daisy plants in a sample area that is 100 m². What is the estimated population of daisies in the entire meadow?
   - A) 3
   - B) 30
   - C) 300
   - D) 3,000

9. Which of these organisms is a producer?
   - A) mole
   - B) owl
   - C) whale
   - D) oak tree

10. Which pair of words is incorrect?
    - A) black bear—carnivore
    - B) grasshopper—herbivore
    - C) pig—omnivore
    - D) lion—carnivore

Thinking Critically

11. Why does a parasite have a harmful effect on the organism it infects?
12. What factors affect carrying capacity?
13. Describe your own habitat and niche.
14. The female cowbird lays eggs in the nest of another bird. The other birds care for and feed the cowbird chicks when they hatch. Which type of symbiosis is this?
15. Explain how several different niches can exist in the same habitat.

Developing Skills

16. **Making Models** Place the following organisms in the correct sequence to model a food chain: grass, snake, mouse, and hawk.

Chapter ✔Assessment Planner

Portfolio Encourage students to place in their portfolios one or two items of what they consider to be their best work. Examples include:
- Activity, p. 334
- Curriculum Connection, p. 339
- Science Journal, p. 347

Performance Additional performance assessments, Performance Task Assessment Lists, and rubrics for evaluating these activities can be found in Glencoe's **Performance Assessment in the Science Classroom.**

17. Predicting Dandelion seeds can float great distances on the wind with the help of white, featherlike attachments. Predict how a dandelion seed's ability to be carried on the wind helps reduce competition among dandelion plants.

18. Classifying Classify the following relationships as parasitism, commensalism, or mutualism: a shark and a remora fish that cleans and eats parasites from the shark's gills; head lice and a human; a spiny sea urchin and a tiny fish that hides from predators by floating among the sea urchin's spines.

19. Comparing and Contrasting Compare and contrast the diets of omnivores and herbivores. Give examples of each.

20. Making and Using Tables Complete the following table.

Types of Symbiosis		
Organism A	**Organism B**	**Relationship**
Gains	Doesn't gain or lose	Commensalism
Gains	Gains	Mutualism
Gains	Loses	Parasitism

21. Poster Use photographs from old magazines to create a poster that shows at least three different food chains. Display your poster for your classmates.

TECHNOLOGY

Go to the Glencoe Science Web site at **science.glencoe.com** or use the **Glencoe Science CD-ROM** for additional chapter assessment.

THE PRINCETON REVIEW — Test Practice

A food web shows how organisms in a particular ecosystem depend on each other for food. The food web below shows how the plants and animals in a grassland ecosystem obtain energy from each other.

Study the picture and answer the following questions.

1. Other organisms also live in this habitat. Which of the following organisms could fill in the blank space in this food web?
   A) tree
   B) bison
   C) alligator
   D) hawk

2. Suppose all the snakes were removed from this ecosystem. Which of the following statements represents the most reasonable prediction of what could happen in this ecosystem?
   F) The plants would die.
   G) The owls would start eating foxes.
   H) There would be no more predators to eat the mice.
   J) The eagles would start eating more mice.

CHAPTER ASSESSMENT   357

THE PRINCETON REVIEW — Test Practice

The Test-Taking Tip was written by The Princeton Review, the nation's leader in test preparation.
1. B
2. J

Developing Skills

16. grass, mouse, snake, hawk
17. Individual seeds are able to float far from the parent plant, which helps reduce population density.
18. mutualism; parasitism; commensalism
19. Both eat plants. Omnivores, such as pigs and humans, eat both plants and animals. Herbivores, such as goats, eat only plants.
20. See student page.

Performance Assessment

21. Posters should show photographs in the correct order of energy flow. All food chains should start with a producer and then move to consumers. Use **Performance Assessment in the Science Classroom**, p. 145.

✓Assessment Resources

 **Reproducible Masters**

Chapter Resources Booklet
   Chapter Review, pp. 37–38
   Chapter Tests, pp. 39–42
   Assessment Transparency Activity, p. 49

Glencoe Science Web site
   Interactive Tutor
   Chapter Quizzes

Glencoe Technology
   🔖 Assessment Transparency
   💿 Interactive CD-ROM Chapter Quizzes
   💿 ExamView Pro Test Bank
   💿 Vocabulary PuzzleMaker Software
   📼 MindJogger Videoquiz

Section/Objectives	Standards		Activities/Features
Chapter Opener	**National**	**State/Local**	**Explore Activity:** Compare climate differences, p. 359 **Before You Read,** p. 359
	See p. 5T for a Key to Standards.		
Section 1 Abiotic Factors 🕐 2 sessions 📦 1 block 1. **Identify** common abiotic factors in most ecosystems. 2. **List** the components of air that are needed for life. 3. **Explain** how climate influences life in an ecosystem.	National Content Standards: UPC1, A1, C1, C4, D1, F2		**MiniLAB:** Determining Soil Makeup, p. 362 **Math Skills Activity:** Graphing Temperature Versus Elevation, p. 364 **Physics Integration,** p. 365 **Science Online,** p. 365 **Activity:** Humus Farm, p. 367
Section 2 Cycles of Nature 🕐 2 sessions 📦 1 block 1. **Explain** the importance of Earth's water cycle. 2. **Diagram** the carbon cycle. 3. **Recognize** the role of nitrogen in life on Earth.	National Content Standards: UPC1, A1, B1, C1, C4, D1, F2		**MiniLAB:** Comparing Fertilizers, p. 371 **Visualizing the Carbon Cycle,** p. 372 **Science Online,** p. 373
Section 3 Energy Flow 🕐 3 sessions 📦 1.5 blocks 1. **Explain** how organisms produce energy-rich compounds. 2. **Describe** how energy flows through ecosystems. 3. **Recognize** how much energy is available at different levels in a food chain.	National Content Standards: UPC1, A1, B1, B3, C1, C4, D1, F2		**Earth Science Integration,** p. 375 **Activity:** Where does the mass of a plant come from?, pp. 378–379 **Science Stats:** Extreme Climates, pp. 380–381

Activity Materials	Reproducible Resources	Section Assessment	Technology
Explore Activity: globe or world map, weather references	**Chapter Resources Booklet** Foldables Worksheet, p. 17 Directed Reading Overview, p. 19 Note-taking Worksheets, pp. 33–34	GLENCOE'S ASSESSMENT ADVANTAGE	
MiniLAB: soil (2 cups), quart jar with lid, water, dishwashing liquid (1 teaspoon), watch or clock, metric ruler **Activity:** widemouth jar, soil, grass clippings or green leaves, water, marker, metric ruler, graduated cylinder	**Chapter Resources Booklet** Transparency Activity, p. 44 MiniLAB, p. 3 Enrichment, p. 30 Reinforcement, p. 27 Directed Reading, p. 20 Lab Activity, pp. 9–12 Activity Worksheet, pp. 5–6 **Cultural Diversity,** p. 33 **Reading and Writing Skill Activities,** p. 3 **Science Inquiry Labs,** p. 7	**Portfolio** Assessment, p. 366 **Performance** MiniLAB, p. 362 Math Skills Activity, p. 364 Skill Builder Activities, p. 366 **Content** Section Assessment, p. 366	♪ Section Focus Transparency ◉ Interactive CD-ROM 🎧 Guided Reading Audio Program
MiniLAB: labels (and prices) of 3 brands of houseplant fertilizer *Need materials?* Contact Science Kit at 1-800-828-7777 or www.sciencekit.com on the Internet.	**Chapter Resources Booklet** Transparency Activity, p. 45 MiniLAB, p. 4 Enrichment, p. 31 Reinforcement, p. 28 Directed Reading, p. 21 Lab Activity, pp. 13–16 **Science Inquiry Labs,** pp. 29, 39	**Portfolio** Activity, p. 372 **Performance** MiniLAB, p. 371 Skill Builder Activities, p. 373 **Content** Section Assessment, p. 373	♪ Section Focus Transparency ◉ Interactive CD-ROM 🎧 Guided Reading Audio Program
Activity: 8 oz. plastic or paper cup, potting soil to fill cup, scale or balance, 4 radish seeds, water, paper towels	**Chapter Resources Booklet** Transparency Activity, p. 46 Enrichment, p. 32 Reinforcement, p. 29 Directed Reading, pp. 21, 22 Transparency Activity, pp. 47–48 Activity Worksheet, pp. 7–8 **Lab Management and Safety,** p. 38	**Portfolio** Activity, p. 375 **Performance** Skill Builder Activities, p. 377 **Content** Section Assessment, p. 377	♪ Section Focus Transparency ♪ Teaching Transparency ◉ Interactive CD-ROM 🎧 Guided Reading Audio Program

End of Chapter Assessment

GLENCOE'S ASSESSMENT ADVANTAGE

Blackline Masters	Technology	Professional Series
Chapter Resources Booklet Chapter Review, pp. 37–38 Chapter Tests, pp. 39–42 **Standardized Test Practice by The Princeton Review,** pp. 107–110	📼 MindJogger Videoquiz ◉ Interactive CD-ROM ◉ Vocabulary PuzzleMakers ◉ ExamView Pro Test Bank ◉ Interactive Lesson Planner ◉ Interactive Teacher Edition	Performance Assessment in the Science Classroom (PASC)

Transparencies

Section Focus

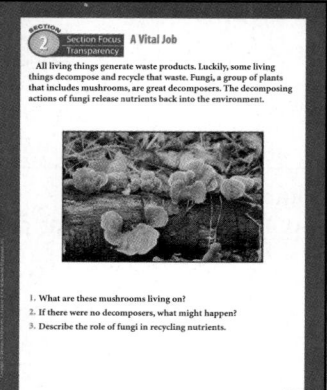

Assessment

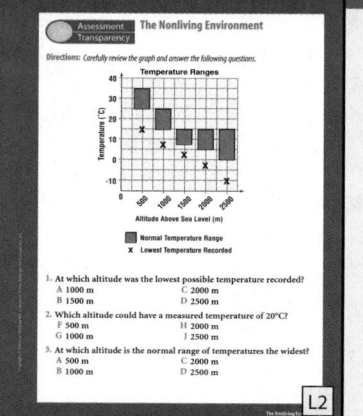

Teaching

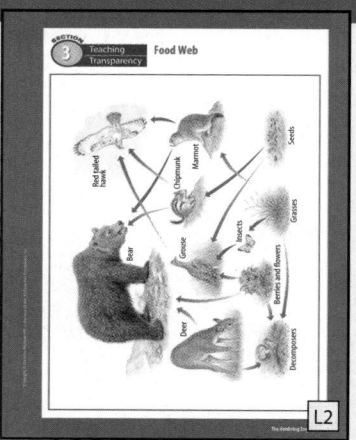

This is a representation of key blackline masters available in the Teacher Classroom Resources. See Resource Manager boxes within the chapter for additional information.

Key to Teaching Strategies

The following designations will help you decide which activities are appropriate for your students.

L1 Level 1 activities should be appropriate for students with learning difficulties.

L2 Level 2 activities should be within the ability range of all students.

L3 Level 3 activities are designed for above-average students.

ELL ELL activities should be within the ability range of English Language Learners.

COOP LEARN Cooperative Learning activities are designed for small group work.

LS Multiple Learning Styles logos, as described on page 22T, are used throughout to indicate strategies that address different learning styles.

P These strategies represent student products that can be placed into a best-work portfolio.

Hands-on Activities

Activity Worksheets

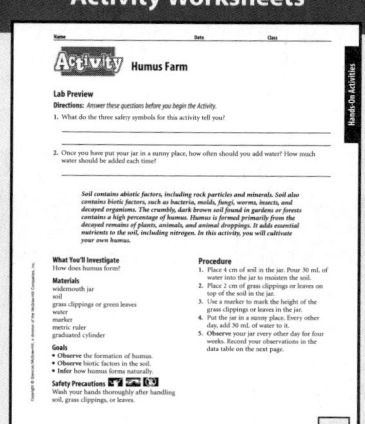

Laboratory Activities

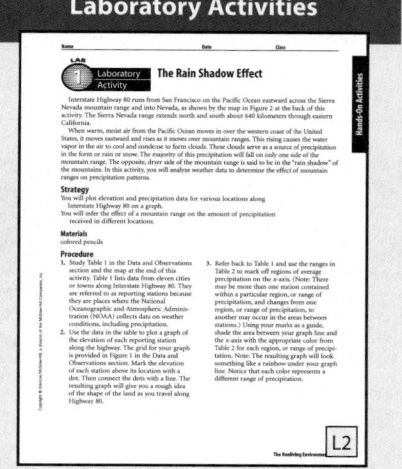

Meeting Different Ability Levels

Content Outline

Note-taking Worksheet — **The Nonliving Environment**

Section 1 Abiotic Factors

A. Living or once-living environmental features are called **biotic factors**; _____ factors are nonliving physical features.

B. **Atmosphere**—the _____ that surrounds Earth

C. _____—the major ingredient of the fluid inside the cells of all organisms

D. _____—a mixture of mineral and rock particles, the remains of dead organisms, water, and air

E. _____—the source of energy for most life on Earth

F. Most organisms' body _____ should stay within the range of 0°C to 50°C for survival.

1. Temperature is affected by _____; areas closer to the equator are warmer than areas farther from the equator.

2. _____—distance above sea level that affects temperature, wind, and soil

G. **Climate**—an area's average _____ conditions over time, including temperature, precipitation, and wind

1. For most living things, _____ and _____ are the two most important components of climate.

2. Heat energy from the Sun creates air currents called _____

Section 2 Cycles in Nature

A. Earth's biosphere contains a fixed amount of water, carbon, nitrogen, oxygen, and other materials that _____ through the environment and are reused by different organisms.

B. **Water cycle**—how water moves from the Earth's surface to the _____ and back to the surface again

1. **Evaporation**—when liquid water changes into water _____ and enters the atmosphere

2. _____—the process of changing water from a gas to a liquid

L2 The Nonliving Environment

Reinforcement

Reinforcement — **Abiotic Factors**

Directions: *Classify the factors in the picture as either* **biotic factors** *or* **abiotic factors** *by listing them under the correct heading. A factor might fall into both categories.*

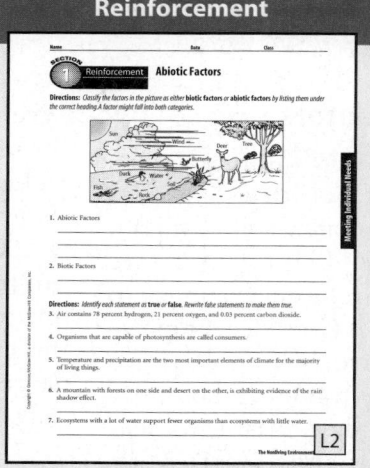

1. Abiotic Factors

_____

_____

2. Biotic Factors

_____

_____

Directions: *Identify each statement as* **true** *or* **false***. Rewrite false statements to make them true.*

3. Air contains 78 percent hydrogen, 21 percent oxygen, and 0.03 percent carbon dioxide.

4. Organisms that are capable of photosynthesis are called consumers.

5. Temperature and precipitation are the two most important elements of climate for the majority of living things.

6. A mountain with forests on one side and desert on the other, is exhibiting evidence of the rain shadow effect.

7. Ecosystems with a lot of water support fewer organisms than ecosystems with little water.

L2 The Nonliving Environment

Directed Reading

Directed Reading for Content Mastery — *Overview* **The Nonliving Environment**

Directions: *Complete the concept map using the terms in the list below.*

temperature   soil   water
food chains   biotic factors   abiotic factors

[concept map]

Directions: *Answer the following questions on the lines provided.*

7. What is the name of the process that involves water vapor in the atmosphere becoming liquid water?

8. What are the two methods producers use to make their own energy-rich molecules?

L1 The Nonliving Environment

Enrichment

Enrichment — **Desert Plants**

Think back to the hottest summer day you've ever experienced. Remember how the sweltering Sun beat down on you? Remember how thirsty you were? Now imagine that every day is like that—only you have to wait and wait and wait before getting a nice, cold drink. Perhaps you'd have to wait days, weeks, or even months. Such is the life of some desert plants.

Deserts, which make up five percent of Earth's surface, can be hot, cold, sandy, or rocky. Lack of precipitation makes an area a desert. By definition, deserts get less than 250 mm of rain each year. Every desert is different. For example, the Chihuahuan Desert in New Mexico has two rainy seasons each year, while the Atacama Desert in Chile is one of the driest places on the planet.

Plant Adaptation

Each desert is home to some kind of plant population. In fact, up to ten percent of desert land can be covered by plantlife. Desert plants can survive long periods without water because they've adapted to the very dry conditions. The kinds of plants vary by desert, but most desert plants are low-growing, thorny, leafless, or small-leaved, and are light green or gray in color. These typically include cacti, yuccas, creosote or other shrubs, and short grasses.

Some desert plants have very short life cycles, living only days or weeks. Plants with fine, shallow root systems, like most cacti, efficiently and quickly absorb large amounts of surface water.

Surface water comes from the rainfall that the desert receives each year or from permanent rivers that can flow down from mountain areas that may be nearby.

Plants with long, deep roots draw upon subsurface water; the mesquite, for example, has been documented to have roots as long as 24 m! Subsurface water comes from seepage that collects underground over a long period of time.

Ways to Preserve Water

Desert plants' leaves, or lack of them, also help in preserving water. Small leaves and thorny spines are adaptations that help desert plants maximize water conservation. Larger leaves can cause a plant to overheat and lose water through their "pores" (a process known as transpiration). Since desert plants have small leaves, spines, or no leaves at all, they lose less water through transpiration. The ocotillo will drop its small leaves when necessary, just to prevent even more water loss.

Succulent plants like the saguaro hold water in the tissues of their leaves and stems. Others go dormant or "sleep" during the dry season and thrive only when water is plentiful. These plants, known as ephemerals, grow fast, bloom, produce seeds, and then are quickly gone. (Ephemeral means "to last just a short time.") The desert lily is an ephemeral that can stay dormant for years, waiting for the right amount of water before it blooms.

1. Which abiotic factor affects all desert plants? Explain.

2. How are the spiny needles on a cactus an adaptation to desert conditions?

3. Which type of desert plant stores water in the tissues of its leaves and stems? Which type remains dormant until after the rainy season? Give an example of each.

30 The Nonliving Environment **L3**

Spanish Directed Reading

Lectura dirigida para Dominio del contenido — *Sinopsis* **El ambiente inanimado**

Instrucciones: *Completa los mapas conceptuales usando los siguientes términos.*

temperatura   tierra   agua
cadenas alimenticias   factores bióticos   factores abióticos

[mapa conceptual]

Instrucciones: *Responde las siguientes preguntas.*

7. ¿Cómo se llama el proceso que involucra el vapor de agua en la atmósfera cuando se convierte en agua líquida?

8. Menciona dos métodos que usan los productores para elaborar sus propias moléculas ricas en energía.

L1 El ambiente inanimado

Assessment

Chapter Tests

Chapter Test — **The Nonliving Environment**

I. Testing Concepts

Directions: *Match the description in the first column with the item in the second column by writing the correct letter in the space provided. Some items in the second column may not be used.*

____ 1. gases are mostly this compound
____ 2. distance from the equator
____ 3. high energy molecules made from photosynthesis
____ 4. living ecosystem components
____ 5. changing nitrogen gas to usable nitrogen in the soil
____ 6. distance above sea level
____ 7. required for recycling matter
____ 8. the first level of the food chain
____ 9. applied to replace soil nitrogen in crop fields, lawns, and gardens
____ 10. average weather over time

a. latitude
b. elevation
c. climate
d. producers
e. nitrogen fixation
f. energy
g. biotic factors
h. fertilizers
i. air
j. abiotic factors
k. sugar
l. water
m. consumers

Directions: *Identify each statement as* **true** *or* **false***. Rewrite false statements to make them correct.*

11. The atmosphere is mostly oxygen.

12. Light energy is used for photosynthesis.

13. Respiration occurs when temperatures cool water vapor in the atmosphere.

14. The nitrogen cycle involves photosynthesis and respiration.

15. Sugar molecules are broken down for energy or stored in fats, proteins, and carbohydrates.

L2 The Nonliving Environment

Test Practice Workbook

Standardized Test Practice
Teacher Edition

Glencoe **Science**

LEVEL GREEN

L2

Chapter Review

Chapter Review — **The Nonliving Environment**

Part A. Vocabulary Review

Directions: *Write the correct term in the spaces beside each definition. Unscramble the boxed letters to find a word that describes a biological process discussed in the chapter.*

1. average weather conditions over time

2. environmental factors that include soil, sunlight, and air

3. organisms that are not capable of photosynthesis

4. made of overlapping food chains

5. gas used during photosynthesis

6. decaying matter found in soil

7. bacteria in hydrothermal vent communities use this to produce food

8. the air that surrounds Earth

9. a model that shows comparative energy levels for different feeding levels

10. place where humus is found

11. An important biological process:

Part B. Concept Review

1. Number these food chain steps in the correct order using the blanks provided.
____ a. omnivores and carnivores
____ b. producers
____ c. herbivores

2. Number these gases in order from the one with the greatest amount in the atmosphere to the one with the least amount in the atmosphere.
____ a. oxygen
____ b. nitrogen
____ c. other gases
____ d. carbon dioxide

L2 The Nonliving Environment

Science Content Background

SECTION
1

Abiotic Factors

Importance to Life

Important abiotic factors include air, water, soil, sunlight, temperature, and climate. These factors are interrelated and can vary from environment to environment and over time. Consider temperature, which changes from hour to hour, day to day, season to season, and year to year. Abiotic and biotic factors are not independent. Lack of rainfall can cause a drought in a grassland. The animals that depend on plants for food would find it hard to survive. Many of the factors are predictable and cyclic, but may have extreme variations. Some can be influenced by other factors such as pollution in air, water, and soil.

Fun Fact

According to the *Guinness Book of Records,* the greatest temperature variation in one day in the United States was 100°F. This occurred in Browning, Montana on January 23–24, 1916, when the temperature dropped from 44°F to –56°F.

SECTION
2

Cycles of Nature

Natural Recycling

Matter, in the form of nutrients, moves through the organisms at each trophic level in an ecosystem. But matter cannot be replenished like the energy from sunlight. The atoms of carbon, nitrogen, and other elements that make up the bodies of organisms alive today are the same atoms that have been on Earth since life began. Matter is constantly being recycled.

Water Cycle

The amount of water on Earth remains fairly constant. While some of the water on Earth cycles, much of it is held in oceans or as ice and does not enter the cycle. At a given time, the atmosphere holds about 12,000 cubic kilometers of water, while all the freshwater rivers and lakes hold 120,000 cubic kilometers. Every day about 1,200 cubic kilometers of water evaporates from the ground or transpires from plants and about the same amount falls back to the surface as rain.

Fun Fact

If evaporation did not replenish the water in the atmosphere, it would dry out in ten days.

Nitrogen Cycle

Nitrogen gas makes up about 79 percent of the atmosphere, but cannot be utilized by plants in this form. In addition to fixation in the soil by bacteria, the high energy of lightning and cosmic radiation combines nitrogen with oxygen into usable nitrates that are carried to Earth with precipitation. The nitrogen in fertilizers is artificially fixed in processing plants. Nitrogen, which is taken up directly by plants and incorporated into plant tissue, enters the food web when plants are consumed.

Carbon Cycle

In 1994, it was reported that the total amount of carbon available on Earth was about 47,000 gigatons (1 gigaton=1 billion metric tons). About 83 percent of the available carbon was in the oceans, 22 percent in fossil fuels, and four percent in dead organic matter, living organisism, and soils. Only two percent was in the atmosphere. Many scientist believe the accelerated greenhouse effect is caused by an increased amount of carbon dioxide in the atmosphere, due largely to the burning of fossil fuels.

SCIENCE *Online*

For additional content background on this topic, go to the Glencoe Science Web site at science.glencoe.com.

SECTION 3

Energy Flow

Food Chains

The law of conservation of energy states that energy cannot be created or destroyed, but can change from one form to another. The energy in an ecosystem is passed from one organism to another through a series of interactions called a food chain. Food chains, food webs and ecological pyramids show how energy moves in only one direction through the trophic levels of an ecosystem and how energy is lost at each transition, from one trophic level to the next. The energy is lost to the environment in the form of heat generated by the body processes of organisms. Although the heat is ultimately lost to the environment, it also serves the purpose of maintaining the body temperature of the organism. Sunlight is the source of most energy, so energy is constantly being replaced.

Food Webs

Some food webs are terrestrial, some are aquatic, and some are combinations. Two types of food webs are grazing and detrital. Detritivores are organisms such as crabs and earthworms that consume dead or decomposing organic matter. The largest amount of energy passes through detrital food webs.

Fun Fact

Animal muscle yields only about one calorie of work for every four given up as heat.

Fritz Polking/Peter Arnold, Inc.

The Nonliving Environment

Chapter Vocabulary

What do you think?

Science Journal The photograph shows a chloroplast. Chlorophyll within chloroplasts traps light energy and converts it to carbohydrates. Almost all living things on Earth depend on this process to provide the energy they need to live.

CHAPTER 13

The Nonliving Environment

Could you write a story about what would happen if the Sun stopped shining? Most life on Earth depends on the Sun's energy. In this chapter, you'll learn about how organisms called producers use energy to make food and how other organisms called consumers take in that food. You'll also read about cycles in nature such as the water, carbon, and nitrogen cycles, and many other nonliving factors that affect your life.

What do you think?

Science Journal Look at the picture below with a classmate. Discuss what this might be. Here's a hint: *It's a factory that relies on sunlight for its energy supply.* Write your answer or best guess in your Science Journal.

358

Theme Connection

Systems and Interactions The ingredients for life are a part of the nonliving environment. Organisms can't exist without interaction with nonliving systems.

Do you live in a dry, sandy region covered with cactus plants or desert scrub? Is your home in the mountains? Does snow fall during the winter? Perhaps you live near the coast, where flowers bloom year-round. Earth has many ecosystems. In this chapter, you'll learn why the nonliving factors in each ecosystem are different. The following activity will get you started.

Compare climate differences

1. Locate your city or town on a globe or world map. Find your latitude. Latitude shows your distance from the equator and is expressed in degrees, minutes, and seconds.

2. Locate another city with the same latitude as your city but on a different continent.

3. Locate a third city with latitude close to the equator.

4. Using references, compare average annual precipitation and average high and low temperatures for all three cities.

Observe

In your Science Journal, hypothesize how latitude affects average temperatures and rainfall.

FOLDABLES
Reading & Study Skills

Before You Read

Making a Cause and Effect Study Fold Make the following Foldable to help you understand the cause and effect relationship of the nonliving environment.

1. Place a sheet of paper in front of you so the long side is at the top. Fold the left and right sides in to divide the paper into thirds. Then fold it in half from left to right. Unfold all the folds.

Nonliving
Water
Soil
Wind
Temperature
Elevation

2. Using the fold lines as a guide, refold the paper into a fan. Unfold all the folds again.

3. Before you read the chapter, draw a picture of a familiar ecosystem on one side of the paper. On the other side, label the folds *Nonliving, Water, Soil, Wind, Temperature,* and *Elevation* as shown.

4. As you read the chapter, write on the folds how each nonliving factor affects the environment you drew.

359

Abiotic Factors

SECTION

Abiotic Factors

Bellringer Transparency

Display the Section Focus Transparency for Section 1. Use the accompanying Transparency Activity Master. L2 ELL

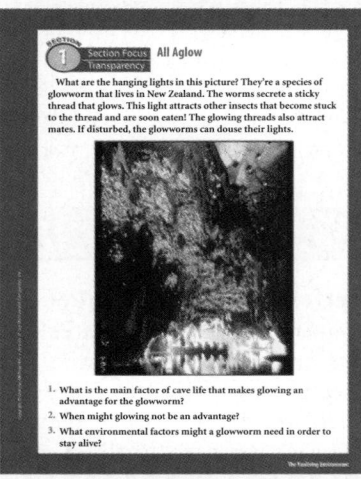

Tie to Prior Knowledge

Have students examine a fish tank or a scene from nature. Ask them to identify nonliving things that are important for living things to survive.

As You Read

What You'll Learn
- **Identify** common abiotic factors in most ecosystems.
- **List** the components of air that are needed for life.
- **Explain** how climate influences life in an ecosystem.

Vocabulary

biotic	soil
abiotic	climate
atmosphere	

Why It's Important
Knowing how organisms depend on the nonliving world can help humans maintain a healthy environment.

Figure 1
Abiotic factors—air, water, soil, sunlight, temperature, and climate—influence all life on Earth.

Environmental Factors

Living organisms depend on one another for food and shelter. The leaves of plants provide food and a home for grasshoppers, caterpillars, and other insects. Many birds depend on insects for food. Dead plants and animals decay and become part of the soil. The features of the environment that are alive, or were once alive, are called **biotic** (bi AH tihk) factors. The term *biotic* means "living."

Biotic factors are not the only things in an environment that are important to life. Most plants cannot grow without sunlight, air, water, and soil. Animals cannot survive without air, water, or the warmth that sunlight provides. The nonliving, physical features of the environment are called **abiotic** (ay bi AH tihk) factors. The prefix *a* means "not." The term *abiotic* means "not living." Abiotic factors include air, water, soil, sunlight, temperature, and climate. The abiotic factors in an environment often determine which kinds of organisms can live there. For example, water is an important abiotic factor in the environment, as shown in **Figure 1.**

Section ✓Assessment Planner

PORTFOLIO
Assessment, p. 366
PERFORMANCE ASSESSMENT
Try at Home MiniLAB, p. 362
Math Skills Activity, p. 364
Skill Builder Activities, p. 366
See page 384 for more options.

CONTENT ASSESSMENT
Section, p. 366
Challenge, p. 366
Chapter, pp. 384–385

Air

Air is invisible and plentiful, so it is easily overlooked as an abiotic factor of the environment. The air that surrounds Earth is called the **atmosphere.** Air contains 78 percent nitrogen, 21 percent oxygen, 0.94 percent argon, 0.03 percent carbon dioxide, and trace amounts of other gases. Some of these gases provide substances that support life.

Carbon dioxide (CO_2) is required for photosynthesis. Photosynthesis—a series of chemical reactions—uses CO_2, water, and energy from sunlight to produce sugar molecules. Organisms like plants that can use photosynthesis are called producers because they produce their own food. During photosynthesis, oxygen is released into the atmosphere.

When a candle burns, oxygen from the air chemically combines with the molecules of candle wax. Chemical energy stored in the wax is converted and released as heat and light energy. In a similar way, cells use oxygen to release the chemical energy stored in sugar molecules. This process is called respiration. Through respiration, cells obtain the energy needed for all life processes. Air-breathing animals aren't the only organisms that need oxygen. Plants, some bacteria, algae, fish, and most other organisms also need oxygen for respiration.

Water

Water is essential to life on Earth. It is a major ingredient of the fluid inside the cells of all organisms. In fact, most organisms are 50 percent to 95 percent water. Respiration, digestion, photosynthesis, and many other important life processes can take place only in the presence of water. As **Figure 2** shows, environments that have plenty of water usually support a greater diversity of and a larger number of organisms than environments that have little water.

Figure 2
Water is an important abiotic factor in deserts and rain forests.

A Life in deserts is limited to species that can survive for long periods without water.

B Thousands of species can live in lush rain forests where rain falls almost every day.

SECTION 1 Abiotic Factors **361**

Inclusion Strategies

Learning Disabled Ask students to comment on this question: **We can't see air, so how do we know it exists?** A variety of evidence can be discussed. We can feel the air when we move our hands very fast. We can see the effect of air when we blow it into a balloon. L1 IS **Naturalist**

---

2 Teach

Environmental Factors

Use Science Words

Word Origin Write the words *biotic* and *abiotic* on the board. Ask students to find the meanings of *bio-, sphere,* and *a-. bio:* life; *sphere:* area; *a:* without, or not

Activity

Have students make a list of the biotic and abiotic factors that would affect the population growth of frogs near a pond. L2 IS **Naturalist**

Air

Quick Demo

Light a candle and explain that oxygen helps release heat and light energy from the wax. In a similar way, oxygen in living things helps release the energy from food. Put a bell jar over the candle and direct students to observe. As the flame goes out, explain that without oxygen, energy cannot be released. IS **Visual-Spatial**

Water

Extension

Refer to a world map of biomes. Have students compare areas of similar latitude that have different biomes. Varying amounts of precipitation is most likely the primary difference between these areas. L2 IS **Visual-Spatial**

Soil

TRY AT HOME Mini LAB

Purpose Students investigate the components that make up soil. L2 IS **Kinesthetic**

Materials two cups soil, large jar with lid, water, alum or dishwashing liquid, spoon, metric ruler

Teaching Strategy Review the components of soil before students carry out the activity.

Analysis
1. Clay is likely suspended in the water.
2. Answers will vary. It is likely that silt will form the greatest component.

Assessment

Oral Why did you examine the sample at different times? Different-sized particles settle at different rates. Use **Performance Assessment in the Science Classroom,** p. 89.

TRY AT HOME Mini LAB

Determining Soil Makeup

Procedure
1. Collect 2 cups of **soil.** Remove large pieces of debris and break up clods.
2. Put the soil in a **quart jar or similar container that has a lid.**
3. Fill the container with **water** and add 1 teaspoon of **dishwashing liquid.**
4. Put the lid on tightly and shake the container.
5. After 1 min, measure and record the depth of sand that settled on the bottom.
6. After 2 h, measure and record the depth of silt that settles on top of the sand.
7. After 24 h, measure and record the depth of the layer between the silt and the floating organic matter.

Analysis
1. Clay particles are so small that they can remain suspended in water. Where is the clay in your sample?
2. Is sand, silt, or clay the greatest part of your soil sample?

Soil

Soil is a mixture of mineral and rock particles, the remains of dead organisms, water, and air. It is the topmost layer of Earth's crust, and it supports plant growth. Soil is formed, in part, of rock that has been broken down into tiny particles.

Soil is considered an abiotic factor because most of it is made up of nonliving rock and mineral particles. However, soil also contains living organisms and the decaying remains of dead organisms. Soil life includes bacteria, fungi, insects, and worms. The decaying matter found in soil is called humus. Soils contain different combinations of sand, clay, and humus. The type of soil present in a region has an important influence on the kinds of plant life that grow there.

Sunlight

All life requires energy, and sunlight is the energy source for almost all life on Earth. During photosynthesis, producers convert light energy into chemical energy that is stored in sugar molecules. Consumers are organisms that cannot make their own food. Energy is passed to consumers when they eat producers or other consumers. As shown in **Figure 3,** photosynthesis cannot take place if light is never available.

Figure 3
Photosynthesis requires light. **A** Little sunlight reaches the shady forest floor, so plant growth beneath trees is limited. **B** Sunlight does not reach into deep lake or ocean waters. Photosynthesis can take place only in shallow water or near the water's surface. *How do fish that live at the bottom of the deep ocean obtain energy?*

LAB DEMONSTRATION

Purpose to determine the amount of humus in soil

Materials Bunsen burner, crucible, topsoil rich in humus, goggles, scale

Preparation Obtain and dry topsoil before class. Explain to students that humus can burn, but the rest of soil cannot.

Procedure Fill a crucible with soil, pour it out, and weigh it. Return soil to the crucible and heat on high for 10 min. Allow to cool. Pour out the soil and reweigh it. Determine the mass of the humus, and its percentage of the original soil.

Expected Outcome Topsoils are 2–15% humus.

Assessment

Give students the following measurements and have them calculate the mass and percentage of humus in soil.

initial mass = 10 grams

final mass = 9 grams

mass of humus = 1 gram; 10% of original soil

Figure 4
Temperature is an abiotic factor that can affect an organism's survival.

A The penguin has a thick layer of fat to hold in heat and keep the bird from freezing. These emperor penguins huddle together for added warmth.

B The Arabian camel stores fat only in its hump. This way, the camel loses heat from other parts of its body, which helps it stay cool in the hot desert.

Temperature

Sunlight supplies life on Earth with light energy for photosynthesis and heat energy for warmth. Most organisms can survive only if their body temperatures stay within the range of 0°C to 50°C. Water freezes at 0°C. The penguins in **Figure 4** are adapted for survival in the freezing Antarctic. Camels can survive the hot temperatures of the Arabian Desert because their bodies are adapted for staying cool. The temperature of a region depends in part on the amount of sunlight it receives. The amount of sunlight depends on the land's latitude and elevation.

✔ Reading Check *What does sunlight provide for life on Earth?*

Latitude In this chapter's Explore Activity, you discovered that temperature is affected by latitude. You found that cities located at latitudes farther from the equator tend to have colder temperatures than cities at latitudes nearer to the equator. As **Figure 5** shows, polar regions receive less of the Sun's energy than equatorial regions. Near the equator, sunlight strikes Earth directly. Near the poles, sunlight strikes Earth at an angle, which spreads the energy over a larger area.

Figure 5
Because Earth is curved, latitudes farther from the equator are colder than latitudes near the equator.

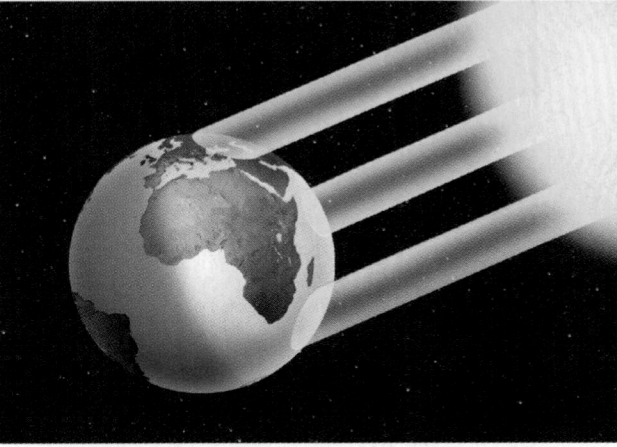

Resource Manager

Chapter Resources Booklet
MiniLAB, p. 3
Lab Activity, pp. 9–12
Science Inquiry Labs, p. 7
Cultural Diversity, p. 33

Curriculum Connection

Health Children in orphanages and hospitals often used to get rickets. Eventually, scientists discovered that sunlight prevented rickets, because it enables the skin to produce vitamin D. Ingesting vitamin D will also prevent rickets. Have students research which foods are good sources of vitamin D. Foods rich in vitamin D include milk, eggs, fortified breakfast cereals, sardines, salmon, beef, and margarine.

Sunlight

Caption Answer
Figure 3B These fish often depend on biotic materials that fall from above.

Temperature

Visual Learning ____

Figure 4B Have students identify other adaptations camels have to their native desert environment. Possible answers: Their feet are widespread to enable them to walk easily on sand; to protect them from blowing sand, they have a double row of eyelashes, haired ear openings, and the ability to close their nostrils; they also have keen senses of sight and smell.

✔ Reading Check

Answer Sunlight provides light and heat. Students may also say that, through the process of photosynthesis, sunlight provides energy for life processes.

Temperature, continued

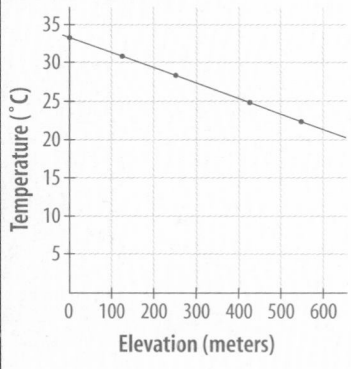

Figure 6
The stunted growth of these trees is a result of abiotic factors.

Elevation If you have climbed or driven up a mountain, you probably noticed that the temperature got cooler as you went higher. A region's elevation, or distance above sea level, affects its temperature. Earth's atmosphere acts as insulation that traps the Sun's heat. At higher elevations, the atmosphere is thinner than it is at lower elevations. Air becomes warmer when sunlight heats the air molecules. Because there are fewer air molecules at higher elevations, air temperatures there tend to be cooler.

Figure 6 shows how elevation affects other abiotic conditions, including soil and wind. At higher elevations, trees are shorter and the ground is rocky. Above the timberline—the elevation beyond which trees do not grow—plant life is limited to low-growing plants. The tops of some mountains are so cold that no plants can survive. Some mountain peaks are covered with snow year-round.

Math Skills Activity

Graphing Temperature Versus Elevation

Example Problem

You climb a mountain and record the temperature every 1,000 m of elevation. The temperature is 30°C at 304.8 m, 25°C at 609.6 m, 20°C at 914.4 m, 15°C at 1,219.2 m, and 5°C at 1,828.8 m. Make a graph of the data. Use your graph to predict the temperature at an altitude of 2,133.6 m.

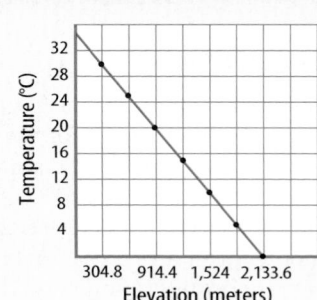

Solution

1. *This is what you know:*
   The data can be written as ordered pairs (elevation, temperature). The ordered pairs for these data are (304.8, 30), (609.6, 25), (914.4, 20), (1,219.2, 15), (1,828.8, 5).

2. *This is what you want to find:*
   Predict the temperature at an elevation of 2,133.6 m.

3. *This is what you need to do:*
   Graph the data by plotting elevation on the *x*-axis and temperature on the *y*-axis. Draw a line to connect the data points on your graph.

4. *Predict the temperature at 2,133.6 m:*
   Extend the graph line to predict the temperature at 2,133.6 m.

Practice Problem

Temperatures on another mountain are 33°C at sea level, 31°C at 125 m, 29°C at 250 m, and 26°C at 425 m. Graph the data and predict the temperature at 550 m.

For more help, refer to the Math Skill Handbook.

Cultural Diversity

Kenyan Runners Many great long distance runners are from the Kalenjin tribe in a high-altitude area of Kenya. **Why might great runners come from this area?** Possible answers: Because of lower oxygen levels at high altitudes, these Kenyans may have adaptations for increased cardiovascular efficiency; their high-altitude training may help them produce more red blood cells; there may also be social reasons.

✓ Active Reading

Quickwrites This strategy, sometimes called freewrites, lets students use spontaneous writing to discover what they already know. Have students write a list of ideas about a topic, then share these ideas with the class. Next, have students write their ideas without worrying about punctuation, spelling, and grammar. Have students use a Quickwrite to share ideas about abiotic factors.

Climate

In Fairbanks, Alaska, winter temperatures may be as low as −52°C, and more than a meter of snow might fall in one month. In Key West, Florida, snow never falls and winter temperatures rarely dip below 5°C. These two cities have different climates. **Climate** refers to an area's average weather conditions over time, including temperature, rainfall or other precipitation, and wind.

For the majority of living things, temperature and precipitation are the two most important components of climate. The average temperature and rainfall in an area influence the type of life found there. Suppose a region has an average temperature of 25°C and receives an average of less than 25 cm of rain every year. It is likely to be the home of cactus plants and other desert life. A region with similar temperatures that receives more than 300 cm of rain every year is probably a tropical rain forest.

Wind Heat energy from the Sun not only determines temperature, but also is responsible for the wind. The air is made up of molecules of gas. As the temperature increases, the molecules spread farther apart. As a result, warm air is lighter than cold air. Colder air sinks below warmer air and pushes it upward, as shown in **Figure 7.** These motions create air currents that are called wind.

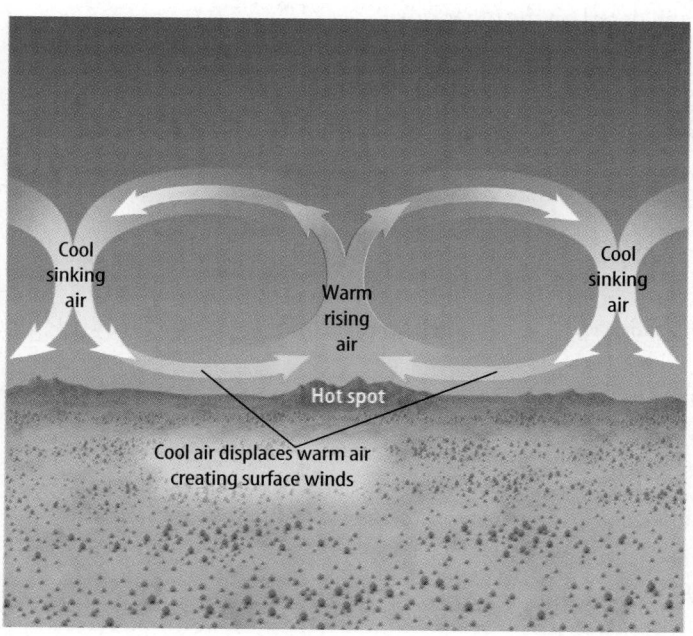

Figure 7
Winds are created when sunlight heats some portions of Earth's surface more than others. In areas that receive more heat, the air becomes warmer. Cold air sinks beneath the warm air, forcing the warm air upward.

Physics
INTEGRATION

Gravity pulls the gases of the atmosphere toward Earth's surface. Also, the weight of the air at the top of the atmosphere presses down on the air below it. In your Science Journal, explain why air at sea level is thicker than air at the top of a mountain.

Data Update Visit the Glencoe Science Web site at **science.glencoe.com** to look up recent weather data for your area. In your Science Journal, describe how these weather conditions affect plants or animals that live in your area.

Climate

Teacher FYI

Weather refers to the day-to-day atmospheric conditions in an area. Climate takes a long-term view and describes the general weather conditions associated with an area.

Physics
INTEGRATION

Imagine the air as columns in the atmosphere. A column reaching a mountaintop would be shorter than one reaching land at sea level. The taller column of air presses down, making the air at the bottom of the column at sea level denser.

Quick Demo

Show the rain shadow effect by moving a damp sponge over an imaginary mountain. As it rises up, explain that the air cools and water condenses into rain. Squeeze the sponge to show rain. As air decends on the other side of the moutain, it warms. Any remaining water in the air changes back to water vapor. L2 ELL IS **Visual-Spatial**

Internet Addresses
_____
_____
_____
_____

Explore the Glencoe Science Web site at science.glencoe.com to find out more about topics in this section.

Resource Manager

Chapter Resources Booklet
  Enrichment, p. 30
  Reinforcement, p. 27
Reading and Writing Skill Activities, p. 3
Earth Science Critical Thinking/Problem Solving, pp. 6, 22

Inclusion Strategies

Learning Disabled Show a globe and explain that since areas near the equator receive more direct sunshine, they are much warmer than areas toward the poles. As hot air is pushed aloft near the equator, cooler air rushes in to take its place. This causes wind, which is responsible for precipitation patterns. L1 IS **Visual-Spatial**

Teacher FYI

The Cascade Mountains, part of the Pacific mountain system, extend from California to Canada. The tallest peak in this range is Mt. Ranier, which reaches 4,392 m (14,410 ft). Most of the peaks are extinct volcanoes, although some have erupted in the recent past. Mount St. Helens is one of these, with eruptions in 1980 and 1981.

3 Assess

Reteach

Have students explain how water, air, and temperature can affect life. [L1] IS **Naturalist**

Challenge

Have students investigate how professional greenhouses increase the levels of carbon dioxide and the temperature to achieve an optimal plant growing environment.

✓Assessment

Portfolio Have students cut out pictures from magazines that illustrate abiotic factors in an ecosystem and use the pictures to make posters. Direct students to label each abiotic factor. Use **Performance Assessment in the Science Classroom,** p. 145.
P

Figure 8
In Washington State, the western side of the Cascade Mountains receives an average of 101 cm of rain each year. The eastern side of the Cascades is in a rain shadow that receives only about 25 cm of rain per year.

 **Earth Science INTEGRATION**

The Rain Shadow Effect The presence of mountains can affect rainfall patterns. As **Figure 8** shows, wind blowing toward one side of a mountain is forced upward by the mountain's shape. As the air nears the top of the mountain, it cools. When air cools, the moisture it contains falls as rain or snow. By the time the cool air crosses over the top of the mountain, it has lost most of its moisture. The other side of the mountain range receives much less precipitation. It is not uncommon to find lush forests on one side of a mountain range and desert on the other side.

Section 1 Assessment

1. What is the difference between biotic and abiotic factors?
2. What substances in the air are required for life on Earth?
3. Why is soil considered an abiotic factor and a biotic factor?
4. Why is climate an important abiotic factor?
5. **Think Critically** On day 1 of a hiking trip, you walk in shade under tall trees. On day 2, the trees are shorter and farther apart. On day 3, you see small plants but no trees. On day 4, you see snow. What abiotic factors might contribute to these changes?

Skill Builder Activities

6. **Identifying and Manipulating Variables and Controls** Describe an experiment to find out how much water different types of dry soil can hold. **For more help, refer to the** Science Skill Handbook.

7. **Using an Electronic Spreadsheet** Obtain two months of temperature and precipitation data for two cities in your state. Enter the data in a spreadsheet and calculate average daily temperature and rainfall. Use your calculations to compare the two climates. **For more help, refer to the** Technology Skill Handbook.

366 CHAPTER 13 The Nonliving Environment

Answers to Section Assessment

1. Biotic factors are, or once were, living. Abiotic factors are nonliving.
2. carbon dioxide, nitrogen, oxygen
3. While it is mostly nonliving material, there are many things living in soil, as well as decaying organic matter called humus.
4. Climate refers to an area's temperature, amount of precipitation, and wind. These are physical features of the environment that affect the life found there.
5. Changes in elevation, which influence temperature, are probably responsible. This could occur on a mountain, as you reach and surpass the timberline.
6. Answers will vary. Possible answer: Put soil into a funnel. Then, pour measured amounts of water into the funnel until water flows through the soil and comes out the funnel.
7. Spreadsheets should result in average temperature and rainfall for two different cities.

Activity

Humus Farm

Soil contains abiotic factors, including rock particles and minerals. Soil also contains biotic factors, such as bacteria, molds, fungi, worms, insects, and decayed organisms. The crumbly, dark brown soil found in gardens or forests contains a high percentage of humus. Humus is formed primarily from the decayed remains of plants, animals, and animal droppings. It adds essential nutrients to the soil, including nitrogen. In this activity, you will cultivate your own humus.

What You'll Investigate
How does humus form?

Materials
widemouth jar	water
soil	marker
grass clippings	metric ruler
or green leaves	graduated cylinder

Goals
- **Observe** the formation of humus.
- **Observe** biotic factors in the soil.
- **Infer** how humus forms naturally.

Safety Precautions 🖐 👓 ⊘
Wash your hands thoroughly after handling soil, grass clippings, or leaves.

Humus Formation	
Date	**Observations**
	Answers will vary

Procedure

1. Copy the data table below into your Science Journal.
2. Place 4 cm of soil in the jar. Pour 30 mL of water into the jar to moisten the soil.
3. Place 2 cm of grass clippings or green leaves on top of the soil in the jar.
4. Use a marker to mark the height of the grass clippings or green leaves in the jar.
5. Put the jar in a sunny place. Every other day, add 30 mL of water to it. In your Science Journal, write a prediction of what you think will happen in your jar.
6. **Observe** your jar every other day for four weeks. Record your observations in your data table.

Conclude and Apply

1. **Describe** what happened during your investigation.
2. **Infer** how molds and bacteria help the process of humus formation.
3. **Infer** how humus forms on forest floors or in grasslands.

Communicating Your Data

Compare your humus farm with those of your classmates. With several classmates, write a recipe for creating the richest humus. Ask your teacher to post your recipe in the classroom. **For more help, refer to the Science Skill Handbook.**

ACTIVITY 367

Communicating Your Data

Students may want to consult cookbooks to see how the ingredients for recipes are written and arranged.

SECTION

2

Cycles in Nature

As You Read

What You'll Learn

- **Explain** the importance of Earth's water cycle.
- **Diagram** the carbon cycle.
- **Recognize** the role of nitrogen in life on Earth.

Vocabulary

evaporation
condensation
water cycle

nitrogen fixation
nitrogen cycle
carbon cycle

Why It's Important

The recycling of matter on Earth demonstrates natural processes.

The Cycles of Matter

Imagine an aquarium tank containing water, fish, snails, plants, algae, and bacteria. The tank is sealed so that only light can enter. Food, water, and air cannot be added. Will the organisms in this environment survive? Through photosynthesis, plants and algae produce their own food. They also supply oxygen to the tank. Fish and snails take in oxygen and eat plants and algae. Wastes from fish and snails fertilize plants and algae. Organisms that die are decomposed by the bacteria. The organisms in this closed environment can survive because the materials are recycled. A constant supply of light energy is the only requirement. Earth's biosphere also contains a fixed amount of water, carbon, nitrogen, oxygen, and other materials required for life. These materials cycle through the environment and are reused by different organisms.

Water Cycle

If you leave a glass of water on a sunny windowsill, the water will disappear. It evaporates. **Evaporation** takes place when liquid water changes into water vapor, which is a gas, and enters the atmosphere, as shown in **Figure 9.** Water evaporates from the surfaces of lakes, streams, puddles, and oceans. Water vapor enters the atmosphere from plant leaves in a process known as transpiration (trans puh RAY shun). Animals release water vapor into the air when they exhale. Water also returns to the environment from animal wastes.

Figure 9
Water vapor is a gas that is present in the atmosphere.

A **Water evaporates after a summer rain.**

B **Water also evaporates from the ocean.**

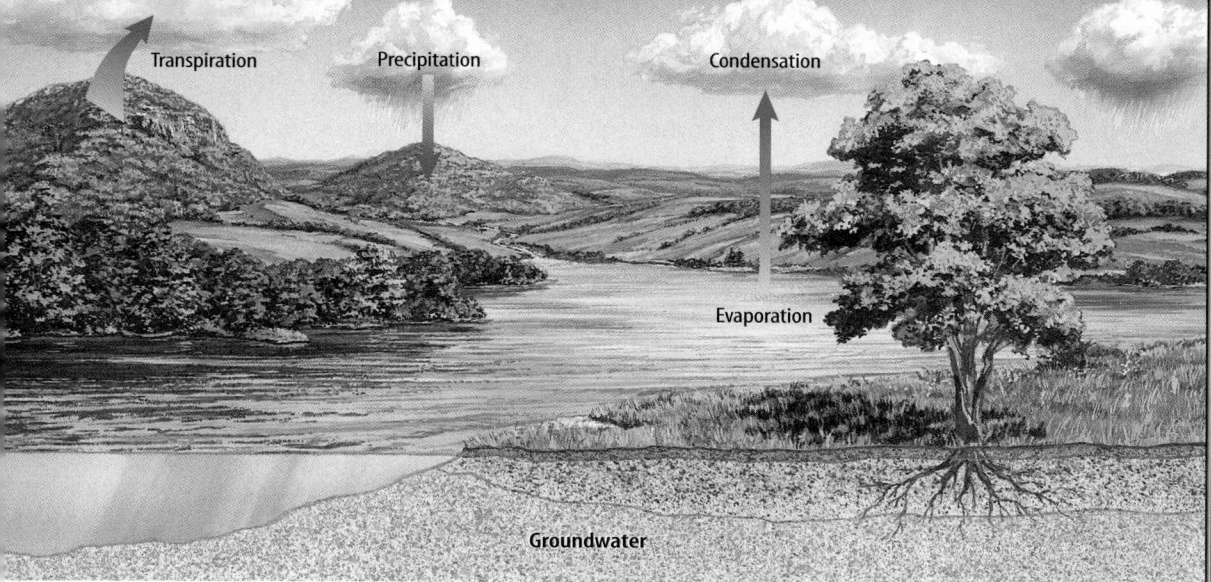

Transpiration   Precipitation   Condensation

Evaporation

Groundwater

Condensation Water vapor that has been released into the atmosphere eventually comes into contact with colder air. The temperature of the water vapor drops. Over time, the water vapor cools enough to change back into liquid water. The process of changing from a gas to a liquid is called **condensation.** Water vapor condenses on particles of dust in the air, forming tiny droplets. At first, the droplets clump together to form clouds. When they become large and heavy enough, they fall to the ground as rain or other precipitation. As the diagram in **Figure 10** shows, the **water cycle** is a model that describes how water moves from the surface of Earth to the atmosphere and back to the surface again.

Figure 10
The water cycle involves evaporation, condensation, and precipitation. Water molecules can follow several pathways through the water cycle. *How many water cycle pathways can you identify from this diagram?*

Water Use **Table 1** gives data on the amount of water people take from reservoirs, rivers, and lakes for use in households, businesses, agriculture, and power production. These actions can reduce the amount of water that evaporates into the atmosphere. They also can influence how much water returns to the atmosphere by limiting the amount of water available to plants and animals.

Table 1   U.S. Estimated Water Use in 1990

Water Use	Millions of Gallons per Day	Percent of Total
Homes and Businesses	39,100	11.5
Industry and Mining	27,800	8.2
Farms and Ranches	141,000	41.5
Electricity Production	131,800	38.6

Resource Manager

Chapter Resources Booklet
   Transparency Activity, p. 45
   Directed Reading for Content Mastery, p. 21

Reading and Writing Skill Activities, p. 29

Science Journal

Water Stories Have students imagine they are molecules of water. They should each make up a story as to how they travel and what they encounter as they go through one complete cycle of the water cycle. L2 ᴵˢ **Linguistic**

2 Teach

The Cycles of Matter

Teacher FYI

Although it is possible to achieve a closed aquarium system, it is not easy. The system must be perfectly balanced between producer and consumer, and this balance must remain constant over time.

Water Cycle

IDENTIFYING Misconceptions

Students may think that the same water falls in a given area again and again. Emphasize that water vapor moves great distances in the air all over Earth; that water in lakes, rivers, and streams is always moving; that currents in the ocean are constantly moving; and that groundwater may move great distances.

Caption Answer

Figure 10 Pathways include precipitation, evaporation, transpiration, seeping into groundwater, and runoff from the ground into other bodies of water.

Visual Learning

Table 1 Which type of water use consumes the most water? farms and ranches **Suggest a reason why.** Possible answers: irrigation of crops or grasses, watering of livestock

Nitrogen Cycle

Extension

Ask students to use the internet to find photographs of plants with a nitrogen deficiency. Have them describe some symptoms. Possible answers: yellow leaves, stunted growth L2

IS **Visual-Spatial**

Use an Analogy

What would happen to a student who ate only candy? They would ingest a lot of sugar but not enough protein. Sugar provides energy but no protein to build or repair tissues. In a similar way, if a plant did not have enough nitrogen it could make sugars, but its growth and functioning would be impaired because it could not make enough proteins.

IS **Logical-Mathematical**

✔ Reading Check

Answer the changing of atmospheric nitrogen into nitrogen compounds that plants can use

Visual Learning

Figure 11 Ask students to use the diagram as a basis for suggesting to farmers one thing they can do to increase the nitrogen in their soil. Add decaying organic matter (compost).

Nitrogen Cycle

The element nitrogen is important to all living things. Nitrogen is a necessary ingredient of proteins. Proteins are required for the life processes that take place in the cells of all organisms. Nitrogen is also an essential part of the DNA of all organisms. Although nitrogen is the most plentiful gas in the atmosphere, most organisms cannot use nitrogen directly from the air. Plants need nitrogen that has been combined with other elements to form nitrogen compounds. Through a process called **nitrogen fixation,** some types of soil bacteria can form the nitrogen compounds that plants need. Plants absorb these nitrogen compounds through their roots. Animals obtain the nitrogen they need by eating plants or other animals. When dead organisms decay, the nitrogen in their bodies returns to the soil or to the atmosphere. This transfer of nitrogen from the atmosphere to the soil, to living organisms, and back to the atmosphere is called the **nitrogen cycle,** shown in **Figure 11.**

✔ Reading Check   *What is nitrogen fixation?*

Figure 11
During the nitrogen cycle, nitrogen gas from the atmosphere is converted to a soil compound that plants can use.

Nitrogen gas is changed into usable compounds by lightning or by nitrogen-fixing bacteria that live on the roots of certain plants.

Plants use nitrogen compounds to build cells.

Animals eat plants. Animal wastes return some nitrogen compounds to the soil.

Animals and plants die and decompose, releasing nitrogen compounds back into the soil.

Inclusion Strategies

Gifted Have students research how ammonia wastes are converted to less toxic forms by bacteria in aquariums. Ammonia is oxidized by bacteria to form nitrates and nitrites. L3 IS **Naturalist**

Learning Disabled Help students realize that as plants grow, they use minerals from the soil. As plants die or drop leaves, these minerals are restored. In farming, however, the nutrients are taken away from the soil. If this is ongoing, the soil will become less fertile. In organic farming, humus and animal wastes are added to the soil to restore fertility. Other farmers also use chemical fertilizers. L1 IS **Naturalist**

Figure 12
Nitrogen fixation is important to plant growth.

A Soybeans can help restore nitrogen to the soil.

B The swollen nodules on the roots of the soybean plants contain colonies of nitrogen-fixing bacteria.

C The bacteria depend on the plant for food. The plant depends on the bacteria to form the nitrogen compounds the plant needs.

Magnification: 1,000×

Soil Nitrogen Human activities can affect the part of the nitrogen cycle that takes place in the soil. If a farmer grows a crop, such as corn or wheat, most of the plant material is taken away when the crop is harvested. The plants are not left in the field to decay and return their nitrogen compounds to the soil. If these nitrogen compounds are not replaced, the soil could become infertile. You might have noticed that adding fertilizer to soil can make plants grow greener, bushier, or taller. Most fertilizers contain the kinds of nitrogen compounds that plants need for growth. Fertilizers can be used to replace soil nitrogen in crop fields, lawns, and gardens. Compost and animal manure also contain nitrogen compounds that plants can use. They also can be added to soil to improve fertility.

Another method farmers use to replace soil nitrogen is to grow nitrogen-fixing crops. Most nitrogen-fixing bacteria live on or in the roots of certain plants. Some plants, such as peas, clover, and beans including the soybeans shown in **Figure 12,** have roots with swollen nodules that contain nitrogen-fixing bacteria. These bacteria supply nitrogen compounds to the soybean plants and add nitrogen compounds to the soil.

Visualizing the Carbon Cycle

Have students examine the pictures and read the captions. Then ask the following questions.

What activities release carbon dioxide into the atmosphere? The burning of fossil fuels, the decomposition of carbon-containing molecules by decomposers, and the break down of sugar molecules in plants and by other organisms releases carbon dioxide into the atmosphere.

Why is this process called a cycle? Possible answer: Plants use carbon dioxide from the atmosphere to make sugars. The plants then are consumed by other organisms and the carbon dioxide is released back into the atmosphere as a waste product.

Activity

Have students make their own diagram of the carbon cycle, without looking at this page, and label each part. **LS Visual-Spatial**

Extension

Have students review or research photosynthesis and how plants use carbon dioxide to make food. Then have them write a report on how photosynthesis ties into the carbon cycle. **LS Naturalist**

GEOGRAPHIC VISUALIZING THE CARBON CYCLE

Figure 13

Carbon—in the form of different kinds of carbon-containing molecules—moves through an endless cycle. The diagram below shows several stages of the carbon cycle. It begins when plants and algae remove carbon from the environment during photosynthesis. This carbon returns to the atmosphere via several carbon-cycle pathways.

A Air contains carbon in the form of carbon dioxide gas. Plants and algae use carbon dioxide to make sugars, which are energy-rich, carbon-containing compounds.

B Organisms break down sugar molecules made by plants and algae to obtain energy for life and growth. Carbon dioxide is released as a waste.

C Burning fossil fuels and wood releases carbon dioxide into the atmosphere.

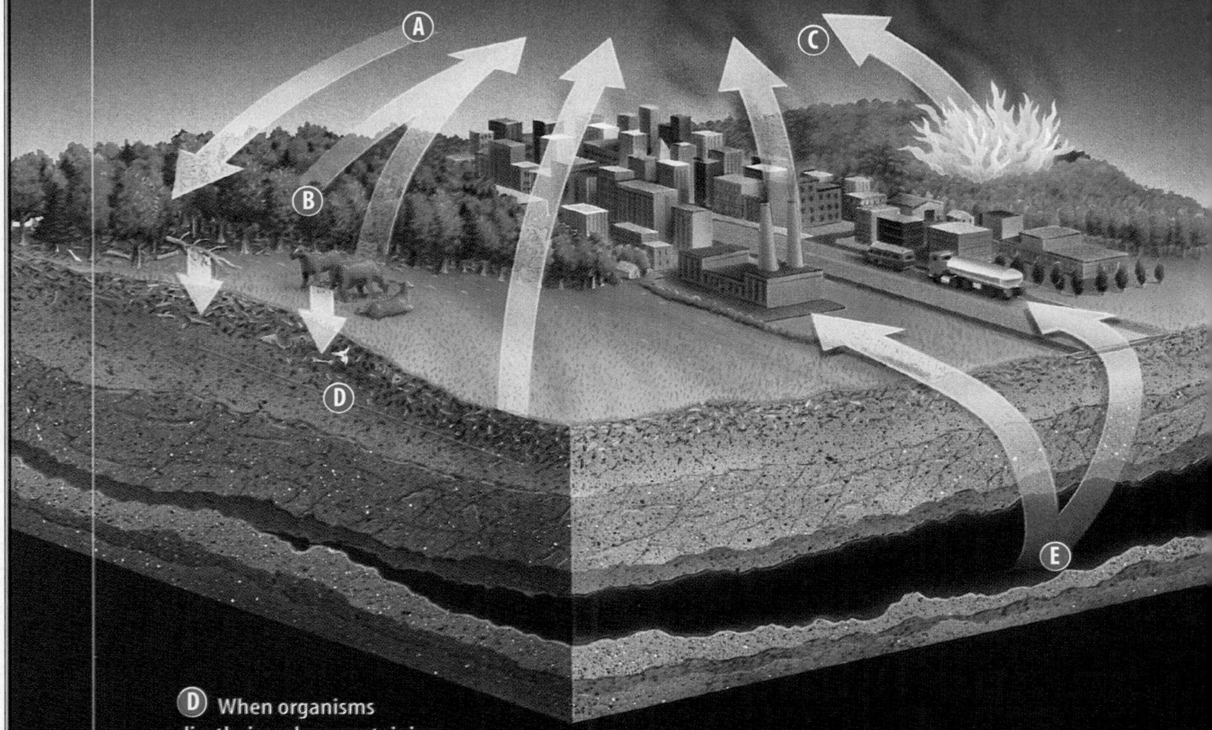

D When organisms die, their carbon-containing molecules become part of the soil. The molecules are broken down by fungi, bacteria, and other decomposers. During this decay process, carbon dioxide is released into the air.

E Under certain conditions, the remains of some dead organisms may gradually be changed into fossil fuels such as coal, gas, and oil. These carbon compounds are energy rich.

372 CHAPTER 13 The Nonliving Environment

Resource Manager

Chapter Resources Booklet
 Enrichment, p. 31
 Reinforcement, p. 28
Life Science Critical Thinking/Problem Solving, pp. 12, 22

Inclusion Strategies

Learning Disabled Have students work in groups to prepare a concept map that describes the carbon cycle. Include terms such as *consumers, photosynthesis, respiration,* and *producers.* L2 ELL COOP LEARN **LS Visual-Spatial**

The Carbon Cycle

Carbon atoms are found in the molecules that make up living organisms. Carbon is an important part of soil humus, which is formed when dead organisms decay, and it is found in the atmosphere as carbon dioxide gas (CO_2). The **carbon cycle** describes how carbon molecules move between the living and nonliving world, as shown in **Figure 13.**

The carbon cycle begins when producers remove CO_2 from the air during photosynthesis. They use CO_2, water, and sunlight to produce energy-rich sugar molecules. Energy is released from these molecules during respiration—the chemical process that provides energy for cells. Respiration uses oxygen and releases CO_2. Photosynthesis uses CO_2 and releases oxygen. These two processes help recycle carbon on Earth.

 Reading Check   *How does carbon dioxide enter the atmosphere?*

Human activities also release CO_2 into the atmosphere. Fossil fuels such as gasoline, coal, and heating oil are the remains of organisms that lived millions of years ago. These fuels are made of energy-rich, carbon-based molecules. When people burn these fuels, CO_2 is released into the atmosphere as a waste product. People also use wood for building and for fuel. Trees that are harvested for these purposes no longer remove CO_2 from the atmosphere during photosynthesis. The amount of CO_2 in the atmosphere is increasing. Extra CO_2 could trap more heat from the Sun and cause average temperatures on Earth to rise.

Research Visit the Glencoe Science Web site at **science.glencoe.com** for the chemical equations that describe photosynthesis and respiration. In your Science Journal, write these equations and use them to explain how respiration is the reverse of photosynthesis.

Section 2 Assessment

1. Describe the water cycle.
2. Explain how respiration can be considered the reverse of photosynthesis.
3. How might burning fossil fuels affect the composition of gases in the atmosphere?
4. Why do plants, animals, and other organisms need nitrogen?
5. **Think Critically** Most chemical fertilizers contain nitrogen, phosphorus, and potassium. Why don't they contain carbon? How do plants obtain carbon?

Skill Builder Activities

6. **Identifying and Manipulating Variables and Controls** Describe an experiment that would determine whether extra carbon dioxide enhances the growth of tomato plants. **For more help, refer to the** Science Skill Handbook.
7. **Communicating** Pretend you are a carbon molecule. Write a fictional account of your travels from the atmosphere, through at least two organisms, and back to the atmosphere. **For more help, refer to the** Science Skill Handbook.

Answers to Section Assessment

1. Cycles should include evaporation, condensation, and precipitation.
2. Respiration usually requires oxygen to break down substances and to obtain energy. The process releases CO_2 and water vapor. Photosynthesis requires CO_2, water, and light energy to make sugars. The process gives off oxygen as a waste.
3. It could result in an increase in the concentration of carbon dioxide.
4. to make amino acids for proteins and nucleic acids
5. Plants can get carbon from the atmosphere.
6. Answers will vary, but should include one group with normal CO_2 and one with extra CO_2. An operational definition of the growth of the tomato plants should be given, along with plans for taking measurements.
7. Answers will vary, but the first step should be photosynthesis.

The Carbon Cycle

Internet Addresses

_____

_____

_____

_____

Explore the Glencoe Science Web site at **science.glencoe.com** to find out more about topics in this section.

Reading Check

Answer as a by product of cellular respiration

 **Assess**

Reteach

Ask students to explain the different paths water vapor, carbon, and nitrogen in the air would follow before they could enter a plant. L2 **Naturalist**

Challenge

Suppose you covered all the bodies of water on Earth with oil. **How would this affect the water cycle?** Possible answers: water could not evaporate; the water cycle would be disrupted; a drought may result.

Assessment

Portfolio Have students draw a diagram of the nitrogen cycle. Use **Performance Assessment in the Science Classroom,** p. 127.

SECTION
3
Energy Flow

1 Motivate

Bellringer Transparency

Display the Section Focus Transparency for Section 3. Use the accompanying Transparency Activity Master. L2 ELL

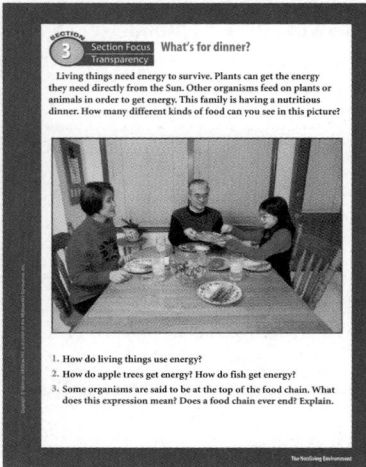

Tie to Prior Knowledge

Students may have seen athletes "hit the wall." Ask why this happens, and if they have ever "run out of energy." Explain that energy is necessary to fuel life.

Energy Flow

As You Read

What You'll Learn

■ **Explain** how organisms produce energy-rich compounds.
■ **Describe** how energy flows through ecosystems.
■ **Recognize** how much energy is available at different levels in a food chain.

Vocabulary

chemosynthesis   energy pyramid
food web

Why It's Important

All living things, including people, need a constant supply of energy.

Figure 14

A Chemicals in the water that flows from hydrothermal vents provide bacteria with a source of energy. **B** The bacterial producers use this energy to make nutrients through the process of chemosynthesis. Consumers, such as tubeworms, feed on the bacteria.

374

Magnification: 38,000×

Converting Energy

All living things are made of matter, and all living things need energy. Matter and energy move through the natural world in different ways. Matter can be recycled over and over again. The recycling of matter requires energy. Energy is not recycled, but it is converted from one form to another. The conversion of energy is important to all life on Earth.

Photosynthesis During photosynthesis, producers convert light energy into the chemical energy in sugar molecules. Some of these sugar molecules are broken down as energy is needed. Others are used to build complex carbohydrate molecules that become part of the producer's body. Fats and proteins also contain stored energy.

Chemosynthesis Not all producers rely on light for energy. During the 1970s, scientists exploring the ocean floor were amazed to find communities teeming with life. These communities were at a depth of almost 3.2 km and living in total darkness. They were found near powerful hydrothermal vents like the one shown in **Figure 14.**

Section ✓ Assessment Planner

PORTFOLIO
Activity, p. 375

PERFORMANCE ASSESSMENT
Skill Builder Activities, p. 377
See page 384 for more options.

CONTENT ASSESSMENT
Section, p. 377
Challenge, p. 377
Chapter, pp. 384–385

Hydrothermal Vents A hydrothermal vent is a deep crack in the ocean floor through which the heat of molten magma can escape. The water from hydrothermal vents is extremely hot from contact with molten rock that lies deep in Earth's crust.

Because no sunlight reaches these deep ocean regions, plants or algae cannot grow there. How do the organisms living in this community obtain energy? Scientists learned that the hot water contains nutrients such as sulfur molecules that bacteria use to produce their own food. The production of energy-rich nutrient molecules from chemicals is called **chemosynthesis** (kee moh SIN thuh sus). Consumers living in the hydrothermal vent communities rely on chemosynthetic bacteria for nutrients and energy. Chemosynthesis and photosynthesis allow producers to make their own energy-rich molecules.

✔ **Reading Check** *What is chemosynthesis?*

Energy Transfer

Energy can be converted from one form to another. It also can be transferred from one organism to another. Consumers cannot make their own food. Instead, they obtain energy by eating producers or other consumers. This way, energy stored in the molecules of one organism is transferred to another organism. At the same time, the matter that makes up those molecules is transferred from one organism to another. Throughout nature, energy and matter move from organism to organism when one organism becomes food for another organism.

Food Chains A food chain is a way of showing how matter and energy pass from one organism to another. Producers—plants, algae, and other organisms that are capable of photosynthesis or chemosynthesis—are always the first step in a food chain. Animals that consume producers such as herbivores are the second step. Carnivores and omnivores—animals that eat other consumers—are the third and higher steps of food chains. One example of a food chain is shown in **Figure 15.**

Earth Science
INTEGRATION

The first hydrothermal vent community discovered was found along the Galápagos rift zone. A rift zone forms where two plates of Earth's crust are spreading apart. In your Science Journal, describe the energy source that heats the water in the hydrothermal vents of the Galápagos rift zone.

Figure 15
In this food chain, grasses are producers, marmots are herbivores that eat the grasses, and grizzly bears are consumers that eat marmots. The arrows show the direction in which matter and energy flow.

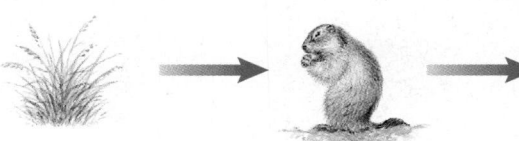

Earth Science
INTEGRATION

The source of heat in vents is geothermal energy. The hot magna heats the water to 400°C but it does not boil because of the pressure at these depths. The water quickly cools to about 2°C.

✔ **Reading Check**

Answer Chemosynthesis is the production of energy-rich food molecules from chemical energy.

Energy Transfer

Discussion

What do the arrows in food chains represent? the flow of matter and energy from one organism to another Ask students to generate other food chains. Answers will vary.

Activity

Have students make a food chain for a deep sea community. Food chains should be similar to that of a simple aquatic system, except that chemosynthetic bacteria will replace aquatic plants as producers. L2
ℕ **Visual-Spatial** P

Resource Manager

Chapter Resources Booklet
  Transparency Activity, p. 46
  Directed Reading for Content Mastery, pp. 21, 22
  Transparency Activity, pp. 47–48
Mathematics Skill Activities, p. 9

Inclusion Strategies

Learning Disabled Have students who understand the concepts of producer and consumer work with students who are having difficulty. Have partners group the terms *producer, photosynthesis, plants, consumer,* and *animal.*

L1 COOP LEARN ℕ **Interpersonal**

Energy Transfer,
continued

Visual Learning

Figure 16 Have students draw three different food chains based on the food web. Then have students assess the impact on other organisms if one organism from the food web were removed. The impact varies, depending upon many factors, such as how much one organism relies only on another organism for its food. If species X feeds only on species Y, when species Y dies out, so will species X. However, if species X feeds on many species, the loss of one will not cause species X to die out.

Energy Pyramids

Make a Model

Find a grasshopper or cricket and weigh it. Then have students collect ten times the weight of the insect in grass. For example, if the insect weighs 1 g, they should gather 10 g of grass. Place the insect on top of the pile of grass to make a model of a biomass pyramid. L1 **IS** **Logical-Mathematical**

Use an Analogy

Help students understand why so much energy is lost from one level to another. If they raised a cat from a kitten, ask them to imagine how much food the cat has eaten in its life. It is far more than the weight of the cat. Most of the food was used for energy. If a coyote ate their cat, it would not get all the food the cat ate, just the caloric value of the cat.

Resource Manager

Chapter Resources Booklet
Enrichment, p. 32
Reinforcement, p. 29

Food Webs A forest community includes many feeding relationships. These relationships can be too complex to show with a food chain. For example, grizzly bears eat many different organisms, including berries, insects, chipmunks, and fish. Berries are eaten by bears, birds, insects, and other animals. A bear carcass might be eaten by wolves, birds, or insects. A **food web** is a model that shows all the possible feeding relationships among the organisms in a community. A food web is made up of many different food chains, as shown in **Figure 16.**

Energy Pyramids

Food chains usually have at least three links, but rarely more than five. This limit exists because the amount of available energy is reduced as you move from one level to the next in a food chain. Imagine a grass plant that absorbs energy from the Sun. The plant uses some of this energy to grow and produce seeds. Some of the energy is stored in the seeds.

Figure 16
Compared to a food chain, a food web provides a more complete model of the feeding relationships in a community.

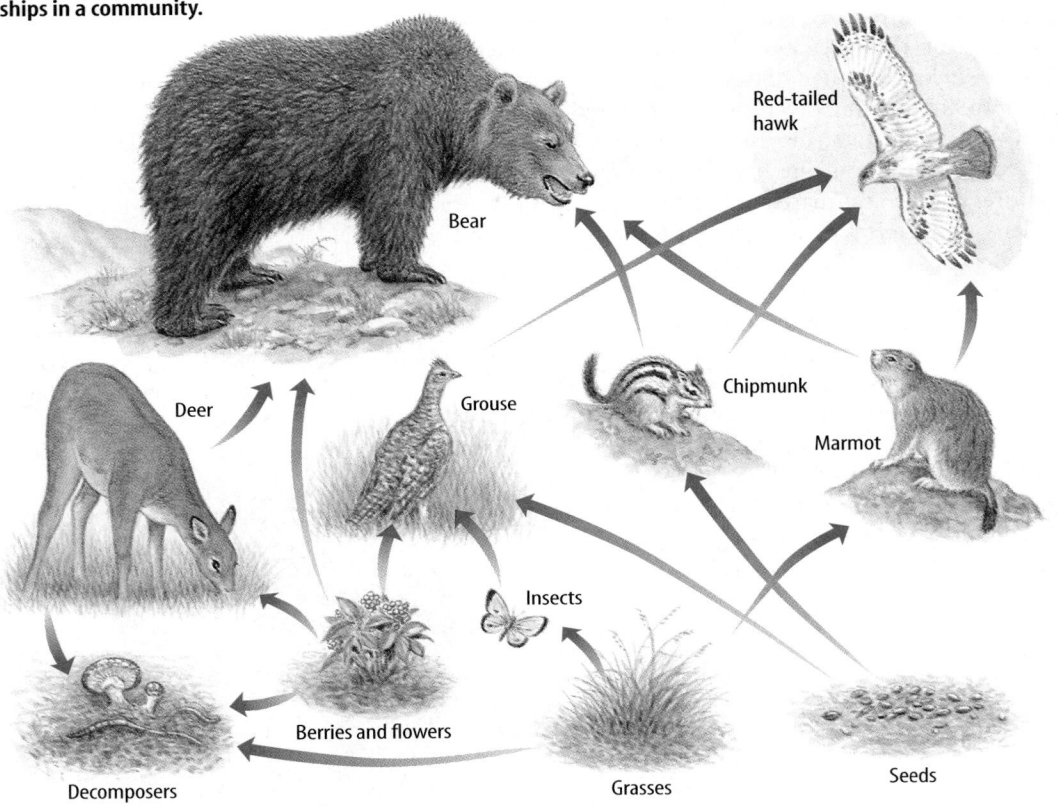

Red-tailed hawk

Bear

Deer

Grouse

Chipmunk

Marmot

Insects

Berries and flowers

Decomposers

Grasses

Seeds

Teacher FYI

The law of conservation of energy states that energy is not created or destroyed, but only converted into other forms of energy. In most ecosystems the energy starts as light energy, which is converted through photosynthesis into chemical energy.

Inclusion Strategies

Visually Impaired Obtain or make a pyramid-shaped object. Allow students to handle the model to identify its shape. Explain that the model depicts the relative amount of energy available as one moves up feeding levels in a food web. **IS** **Kinesthetic**

Available Energy When a mouse eats grass seeds, energy stored in the seeds is transferred to the mouse. However, most of the energy the plant absorbed from the Sun was used for the plant's growth. Much less energy is stored in the seeds eaten by the mouse. The mouse uses much of the energy remaining in the seeds for its own life processes, including respiration, digestion, and growth. A hawk that eats the mouse obtains even less energy.

The same thing happens at every feeding level of a food chain. The amount of available energy is reduced from one feeding level to another. An **energy pyramid**, like the one in **Figure 17,** shows the amount of energy available at each feeding level in an ecosystem. The bottom layer of the pyramid, which represents all of the producers, is the first feeding level. It is the largest level because it contains the most energy and the largest number of organisms. As you move up the pyramid, each level becomes smaller. Only about ten percent of the energy available at each feeding level of an energy pyramid is transferred to the next higher level.

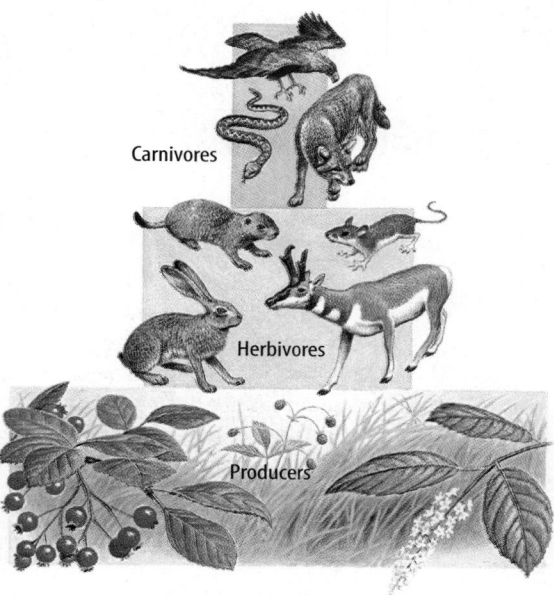

Carnivores

Herbivores

Producers

Figure 17
This energy pyramid shows that each feeding level contains less energy than the level below it.
What would happen if the hawks and snakes outnumbered the rabbits and mice in this ecosystem?

 Reading Check *Why does the first feeding level of an energy pyramid contain the most energy?*

Section 3 Assessment

1. Compare and contrast photosynthesis and chemosynthesis.
2. Explain how your three favorite foods provide you with energy from the Sun.
3. What is the difference between a food web and an energy pyramid?
4. Why is there a limit to the number of links in a food chain?
5. **Think Critically** Use your knowledge of food chains and the energy pyramid to explain why the number of mice in a grassland ecosystem is greater than the number of hawks.

Skill Builder Activities

6. **Classifying** Classify each species as photosynthetic or chemosynthetic: *Red hattus* uses red light to make its food; *Selen dion* makes food if the element selenium is present. **For more help, refer to the** Science Skill Handbook.

7. **Solving One-Step Equations** A forest has 24,055,000 kilocalories (kcals) of producers, 2,515,000 kcals of herbivores, and 235,000 kcals of carnivores. How much energy is lost between producers and herbivores? Between herbivores and carnivores? **For more help, refer to the** Math Skill Handbook.

Caption Answer

Figure 17 Less energy would be available to hawks and snakes. Eventually they would begin to die off until a balance was achieved or move out of the ecosystem.

✓ Reading Check

Answer because little energy has been lost in maintaining body systems

3 Assess

Reteach
Write the word *humans* on the board. Have students write the names of all the animals we eat below this word. Below this write all the plants that we eat or that are eaten by the animals we eat. Connect lines to make food chains. Then draw more lines to show a food web. [L1] **LS Visual-Spatial**

Challenge
Ask students to research the following organisms and design a food web that shows their relationships: *corn, rabbit, hawk, grass, wheat, rat, fox, human,* and *cow.*

✓ Assessment

Performance Use the overhead projector to project a scene from nature. Help students identify the organisms in the picture. Then have them design food chains based on the picture and their knowledge of the organisms. Use **Performance Assessment in the Science Classroom,** p. 127.

Answers to Section Assessment

1. Both involve nutrient production; photosynthesis uses energy from the Sun to produce nutrients, while chemosynthesis uses energy from chemicals.
2. All of the foods we eat provide us with energy from the Sun, either directly (producers) or indirectly (consumers).
3. A food web shows the path of energy and matter in an ecosystem. An energy pyramid shows the amount of energy available at each level.
4. because a significant amount of energy is lost at each level
5. Hawks eat mice. For the mice to support the hawk population, there must be far more energy at the mouse level than at the hawk level. Since mice are smaller than hawks, this means that there must be many more mice than hawks.
6. *Red hattus* is photosynthetic; *Selen dion* is chemosynthetic.
7. producers and herbivores: 21,540,000 kcal; herbivores and carnivores: 2,280,000 kcal

Activity

BENCH TESTED

What You'll Investigate

Purpose

Students perform a variation of Johannes Baptista Van Helmont's famous experiment to determine if plants get their mass from the soil. L2 [IS] **Logical-Mathematical**

Process Skills

observing, measuring, predicting, interpreting data, using numbers

Time Required

45 minutes to set up; three weeks for the plants to grow; 1 hour for the final measurements, calculations, and cleanup

Safety Precautions

Caution students to wash their hands after handling plants and soil.

Activity

Where does the mass of a plant come from?

An enormous oak tree starts out as a tiny acorn. The acorn sprouts in dark, moist soil. Roots grow down through the soil. Its stem and leaves grow up toward the light and air. Year after year, the tree grows taller, its trunk grows thicker, and its roots grow deeper. It becomes a towering oak that produces thousands of acorns of its own. An oak tree has much more mass than an acorn. Where does this mass come from? The soil? The air? In this activity, you'll find out by conducting an experiment with radish plants.

What You'll Investigate

Does all of the matter in a radish plant come from the soil?

Goals

- **Measure** the mass of soil before and after radish plants have been grown in it.
- **Measure** the mass of radish plants grown in the soil.
- **Analyze** the data to determine whether the mass gained by the plants equals the mass lost by the soil.

Materials

8-oz plastic or paper cup
potting soil to fill cup
scale or balance
radish seeds (4)
water
paper towels

Safety Precautions

378

Inclusion Strategies

Learning Disabled Help students understand the purpose of the investigation. Hand students a piece of two-by-four lumber so they can feel how heavy it is. Ask them where the weight of the tree came from. The weight came from the food the tree produced and utilized to build its body.

Resource Manager

Chapter Resources Booklet
  Activity Worksheet, pp. 7–8

Lab Management and Safety, p. 38

Procedure

1. Copy the data table into your Science Journal.

2. Fill the cup with dry soil.

3. Find the mass of the cup of soil and record this value in your data table.

4. Moisten the soil in the cup. Plant four radish seeds 2 cm deep in the soil. Space the seeds an equal distance apart. Wash your hands.

5. Add water to keep the soil barely moist as the seeds sprout and grow.

6. When the plants have developed four to six true leaves, usually after two to three weeks, carefully remove the plants from the soil. Gently brush the soil off the roots. Make sure all the soil remains in the cup.

7. Spread the plants out on a paper towel. Place the plants and the cup of soil in a warm area to dry out.

8. When the plants are dry, measure their mass and record this value in your data table. Write this number with a plus sign in the Gain or Loss column.

9. When the soil is dry, find the mass of the cup of soil. Record this value in your data table. Subtract the End mass from the Start mass and record this number with a minus sign in the Gain or Loss column.

Sample Data

Mass of Soil and Radish Plants			
	Start	End	Gain (+) or Loss (−)
Mass of dry soil and cup	75.8 g	75.7 g	0.1 g −
Mass of dried radish plants	0 g	2.1 g	2.1 g +

Conclude and Apply

1. In the early 1600s, a Belgian scientist named J. B. van Helmont conducted this experiment with a willow tree. What is the advantage of using radishes instead of a tree?

2. How much mass was gained or lost by the soil? By the radish plants?

3. Did the mass of the plants come completely from the soil? How do you know?

4. If all of the mass gained by the plants did not come from the soil, where could it have come from?

Compare your conclusions with those of other students in your class. **For more help, refer to the** Science Skill Handbook.

ACTIVITY 379

Procedure

Teaching Strategy

This experiment helps uncover and correct the misconception that the material for a mass increase in a plant comes from the soil. Prior to getting results, ask students if most of the mass gained by the radish plants will come from the soil. If they don't think it will come from the soil, ask where they think it will come from.

Expected Outcome

The radish plants' mass gain will be more than the soil's mass loss.

Conclude and Apply

1. Radishes grow faster and use less space. You can get a quantitative amount of mass gained and lost.

2. Answers will vary, but the soil will have a very small mass loss and the plants will have a much larger mass gain.

3. No, because the mass loss of the soil is smaller than the mass gain of the plants.

4. Answers will vary, but should include carbon dioxide from the air and water from the soil.

Error Analysis

Some errors may occur because the plants and soil are not completely dry. However, this usually does not affect the conclusion.

✔Assessment

Content Pretend that you grew a willow tree for five years like Van Helmont. Write down how much mass the tree might have gained and how much mass the soil might have lost. Use **Performance Assessment in the Science Classroom,** p. 89.

Have students post their data tables on a bulletin board for other students to see.

Content Background

The term *climate* refers to the average weather of a region over a period of time. Earth has a huge variety of climates and the climate of any region can change over time. The following list explains the main influences on the climate of a region.

1. Wind, which distributes moisture and heat
2. Distance of the region from the equator, which determines how much solar radiation reaches the area
3. Presence of large bodies of water, which decrease temperature variation in the surrounding regions
4. Altitude, which affects the temperature
5. Presence of mountains and other surface features, which influence cloud formation and precipitation

Discussion

What type of weather would you expect the south pole to have while it is pointed away from the Sun? Students should infer that the South Pole would have low temperatures and cold weather during the time it is pointed away from the Sun.

Activity

Have students work as a class to record and graph daily high and low temperatures each day for a month.

IS Logical-Mathematical

Science Stats

Extreme Climates

Did you know...

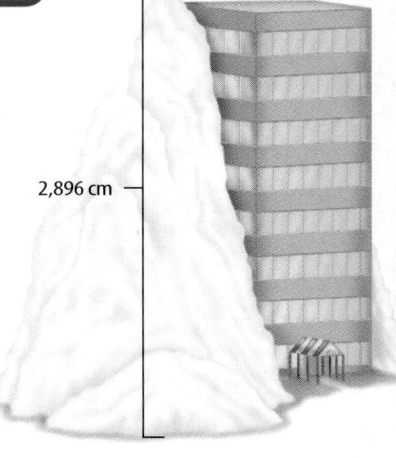

2,896 cm

... The greatest snowfall in one year occurred at Mount Baker in Washington State. Approximately 2,896 cm of snow fell on Mount Baker during the 1998-99, 12-month snowfall season. That's enough snow to bury an eight-story building.

... The hottest climate in the United States is found in Death Valley, California. In July 1913, Death Valley reached approximately 57°C. This is the hottest officially recognized temperature on Earth. As a comparison, a comfortable room temperature is about 20°C.

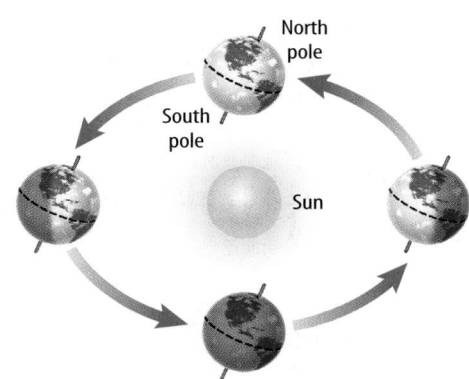

North pole

South pole

Sun

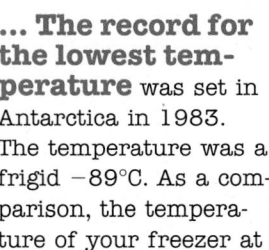

... The record for the lowest temperature was set in Antarctica in 1983. The temperature was a frigid −89°C. As a comparison, the temperature of your freezer at home is about −15°C.

... The south pole receives sunshine for less than 50 percent of the days in a year. Because Earth is tilted, the south pole is pointed away from the Sun for about half the year and receives very little during that time.

SCIENCE *Online*
Internet Addresses
_____
_____
_____
_____

Explore the Glencoe Science Web site at **science.glencoe.com** to find out more about topics in this feature.

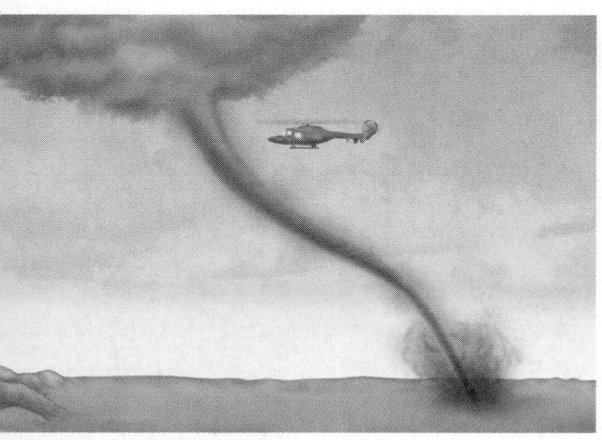

... The fastest tornado winds have been measured at a speed of about 512 km/h. That's faster than the blades of some helicopters, which can rotate at about 450 km/h.

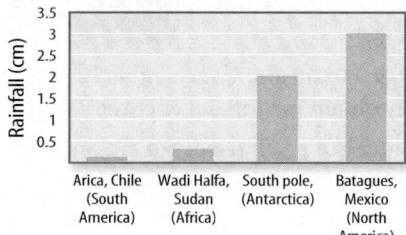

Lowest Average Annual Rainfall

Rainfall (cm)

Arica, Chile (South America) | Wadi Halfa, Sudan (Africa) | South pole, (Antarctica) | Batagues, Mexico (North America)

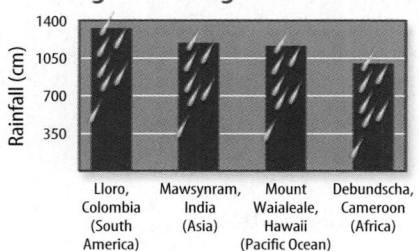

Highest Average Annual Rainfall

Rainfall (cm)

Lloro, Colombia (South America) | Mawsynram, India (Asia) | Mount Waialeale, Hawaii (Pacific Ocean) | Debundscha, Cameroon (Africa)

Do the Math

1. Look at the graph above. How many years of average south pole precipitation would it take to equal a single year of average precipitation in Lloro, Colombia?
2. What is the difference in degrees Celsius between the world record low temperature and the world record high temperature?
3. What was the average monthly snowfall at Mount Baker during the 1998-99 snowfall season?

Go Further

Go to **science.glencoe.com** and find out the average monthly rainfall in a tropical rain forest. Make a line graph to show how the amount of precipitation changes during the 12 months of the year.

Visual Learning

Lowest Average Annual Rainfall, Highest Average Annual Rainfall Have each student choose one location represented on each graph and use the annual rainfall number to calculate an average monthly rainfall number for each location.

Then, have students cut a strip of paper the same height as the average amount of monthly rainfall in each of the locations they have chosen. Use the paper strips for comparison.
LS Visual-Spatial

Do the Math

Teaching Strategies

- Remind students to use the label on each graph to determine the value represented by each bar. Also remind students to include the unit (years) with their answer.
- Use a number line to demonstrate the relative position of −89°C and +57°C. Remind students that the difference between these two values will be larger than either of the numbers.
- Inform students that the snowfall season on Mount Baker is 12 months long. The average monthly snowfall can be calculated by dividing the total snowfall by 12.

Answers

1. approximately 650 years
2. 146°C
3. 241.3 cm

Go Further

Have students add lines to their graphs to represent the average monthly rainfall in your area. Compare the amount of precipitation received in your location to that received in a tropical rain forest. Ask students to predict how the local environment would change if the amount of precipitation increased.

Reviewing Main Ideas

Preview

Students can answer the questions in their Science Journals. Discuss the answers as you go through the chapter. LS **Linguistic**

Review

Students can write their answers, then compare them with those of other students. LS **Interpersonal**

Reteach

Students can look at the illustrations and describe details that support the main ideas of the chapter. LS **Visual-Spatial**

Answers to Chapter Review

SECTION 1

1. Possible answers: proper temperatures, sufficient water and oxygen, sunlight and soil minerals for trees to make nuts

SECTION 2

1. They produce oxygen as a waste product of photosynthesis.

SECTION 3

1. through photosynthesis

5. Most of the apple's energy is converted into energy for your life functions.

Reviewing Main Ideas

Section 1 Abiotic Factors

1. Abiotic factors include air, water, soil, sunlight, temperature, and climate. *What abiotic factors are required for this squirrel's survival? Explain.*

2. The availability of water and light influences where life exists on Earth.

3. Soil and climate have an important influence on the types of organisms that can survive in different environments.

4. High latitudes and elevations generally have lower average temperatures.

Section 2 Cycles in Nature

1. Matter is limited on Earth and is recycled through the environment. *How do green plants help recycle oxygen?*

2. The water cycle involves evaporation, condensation, and precipitation.

3. The carbon cycle involves photosynthesis and respiration.

4. Nitrogen in the form of soil compounds enters plants, which are then consumed by other organisms.

Section 3 Energy Flow

1. Producers make energy-rich molecules through photosynthesis or chemosynthesis. *How do seaweeds in shallow water obtain energy?*

2. When organisms feed on other organisms, they obtain matter and energy.

3. Matter can be recycled, but energy cannot.

4. Food webs are models of the complex feeding relationships in communities.

5. Available energy decreases as you go to higher feeding levels in an energy pyramid. *What happens to most of the energy in an apple that you eat?*

FOLDABLES
Reading & Study Skills

After You Read

Find a student who drew a different ecosystem on his or her Cause and Effect Study Fold. Then, compare and contrast the information on your two Foldables.

FOLDABLES
Reading & Study Skills

After You Read

After students have read the chapter and completed the Foldable described in Before You Read, have them do the activity on the student page.

Dinah Zike

Visualizing Main Ideas

This diagram shows photosynthesis in a leaf. Fill in the blank lines with the terms light, carbon dioxide, *and* oxygen.

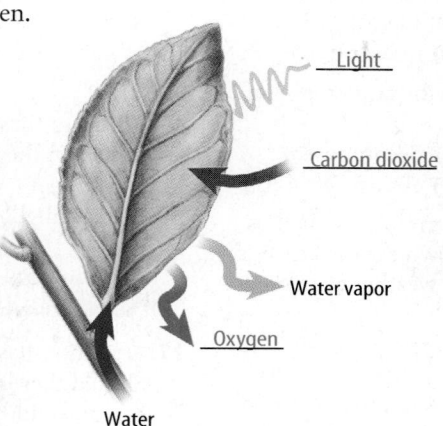

Light

Carbon dioxide

Water vapor

Oxygen

Water

Vocabulary Review

Vocabulary Words

a. abiotic
b. atmosphere
c. biotic
d. carbon cycle
e. chemosynthesis
f. climate
g. condensation
h. energy pyramid
i. evaporation
j. food web
k. nitrogen cycle
l. nitrogen fixation
m. soil
n. water cycle

THE PRINCETON REVIEW **Study Tip**

Write out the full questions and answers to end-of-chapter quizzes, not just the answers. This will help you form complete responses to important questions.

Using Vocabulary

Which vocabulary word best corresponds to each of the following events?

1. A liquid changes to a gas.

2. Some types of bacteria form nitrogen compounds in the soil.

3. Decaying plants add nitrogen to the soil.

4. Chemical energy is used to make energy-rich molecules.

5. Decaying plants add carbon to the soil.

6. A gas changes to a liquid.

7. Water flows downhill into a stream. The stream flows into a lake, and water evaporates from the lake.

8. Burning coal and exhaust from automobiles release carbon into the air.

Visualizing Main Ideas

See student page.

Vocabulary Review

Using Vocabulary

1. evaporation
2. nitrogen fixation
3. nitrogen cycle
4. chemosynthesis
5. carbon cycle
6. condensation
7. water cycle
8. carbon cycle

Chapter 13 Assessment

Checking Concepts

1. B
2. B
3. A
4. D
5. A
6. A
7. B
8. B
9. A
10. C

Thinking Critically

11. The country should grow corn and other vegetables for the people to eat. If they grow corn to feed cattle, most of the energy of the corn will be lost.

12. Webs show complex interactions rather than the simple interactions of a chain.

13. Yes; nitrogen is an important component of DNA and proteins.

14. In the mature forest, the tall trees block most of the sunlight from reaching the floor. There is therefore little plant growth, making it easy to walk.

15. As the air blows over the mountains from the ocean on the west side, it cools and loses moisture. Thus there is a forest on one side, but a desert on the other.

Checking Concepts

Choose the word or phrase that best answers the question.

1. Which of the following is an abiotic factor?
  A) penguins
  B) rain
  C) soil bacteria
  D) redwood trees

2. Which group makes up the largest level of an energy pyramid?
  A) herbivores
  B) producers
  C) decomposers
  D) carnivores

3. You climb up the western slope of the Cascade Mountains and down the eastern side. Which of the following weather changes do you observe?
  A) Warm and wet changes to cold and wet, then cold and dry, then warm and dry.
  B) Cold and wet changes to warm and wet, then warm and dry, then cold and dry.
  C) Warm and wet changes to cold and wet, then cold and dry, then warm and wet.
  D) Warm and dry changes to cold and dry, then warm and dry, then cold and dry.

4. Which of the following applies to latitudes farther from the equator?
  A) higher elevations
  B) higher temperatures
  C) higher precipitation levels
  D) lower temperatures

5. Water vapor forming droplets that form clouds directly involves which process?
  A) condensation
  B) respiration
  C) evaporation
  D) transpiration

6. Which one of the following components of air is least necessary for life on Earth?
  A) argon
  B) nitrogen
  C) carbon dioxide
  D) oxygen

7. What do plants make that requires nitrogen?
  A) sugars
  B) proteins
  C) fats
  D) carbohydrates

8. Which of the following processes removes carbon dioxide from the air?
  A) condensation
  B) photosynthesis
  C) burning
  D) respiration

9. Earth receives a constant supply of which of the following items?
  A) light energy
  B) carbon
  C) nitrogen
  D) water

10. Which of these is an energy source for chemosynthesis?
  A) sunlight
  B) moonlight
  C) sulfur molecules
  D) carnivores

Thinking Critically

11. A country has many starving people. Should they grow vegetables and corn to eat, or should they grow corn to feed cattle so they can eat beef? Explain.

12. Why is a food web a better model than a food chain?

13. Do bacteria need nitrogen? Why or why not?

14. It is often easier to walk through an old, mature forest of tall trees than through a young forest that is full of small trees. Why?

15. The Inyo Mountains are located in central California. Explain why giant sequoia trees grow on the west side of the mountains and Death Valley, a desert, is on the east side.

Developing Skills

16. Classifying Classify each of the following environmental concerns according to the cycle it affects—carbon, nitrogen, or water.
  a. algal blooms caused by excess fertilizer
  b. acid rain damage to pine trees
  c. the unnatural warming of Earth

Chapter ✓Assessment Planner

Portfolio Encourage students to place in their portfolios one or two items of what they consider to be their best work. Examples include:

• Assessment, p. 366
• Activity, p. 372
• Activity, p. 375

Performance Additional performance assessments, Performance Task Assessment Lists, and rubrics for evaluating these activities can be found in Glencoe's **Performance Assessment in the Science Classroom.**

17. Recognizing Cause and Effect A lake in Kenya has been taken over by a floating weed. What could you do to determine if nitrogen fertilizer runoff from farms is causing the problem?

18. Making and Using Graphs Abiotic factors, such as climate, cause populations to move from place to place. Make a bar graph of the following migration distances.

Mighty Migrators	
Species	**Distance (km)**
Desert locust	4,800
Caribou	800
Green turtle	1,900
Arctic tern	35,000
Gray whale	19,000

19. Forming Hypotheses For each hectare of land, ecologists found 10,000 kcals of producers, 10,000 kcals of herbivores, and 2,000 kcals of carnivores. Suggest a reason why producer and herbivore levels are equal.

20. Concept Mapping Draw a food web of these organisms: *caterpillars and rabbits eat grasses, raccoons eat rabbits and mice, mice eat grass seeds,* and *birds eat caterpillars.*

Performance Assessment

21. Poster Use magazine photographs to make a visual representation of the water cycle.

TECHNOLOGY
Go to the Glencoe Science Web site at **science.glencoe.com** or use the **Glencoe Science CD-ROM** for additional chapter assessment.

Test Practice

Food chains model how energy is transferred from one organism to another organism in the environment. The diagram below shows a food chain that includes aquatic plants and animals and a land animal.

Study the diagram and answer the following questions.

1. Which of the following statements is true based on the order of the food chain shown above?
  A) Algae eat plankton.
  B) Plankton eat salmon.
  C) Herring eat plankton.
  D) Salmon eat algae.

2. If the supply of salmon were suddenly depleted, the numbers of which of the following might also be depleted?
  F) algae   **H)** herring
  G) plankton   **J)** eagles

Test Practice

The Test-Taking Tip was written by The Princeton Review, the nation's leader in test preparation.
1. C
2. J

Developing Skills

16. a. nitrogen cycle
   b. water cycle
   c. carbon cycle
17. Possible answer: Ask farmers to restrict their use of nitrogen fertilizer and see if this clears up the lake.
18. From highest bar to lowest: Arctic tern, gray whale, desert locust, green turtle, caribou
19. Reasons may include a poor growth year for plants or a very good year for herbivore reproduction.
20. Check student food webs to ensure correct relationships are in place.

Performance Assessment

21. Posters will vary, but should show how the cycle continues. Use **PASC**, p. 145.

Assessment Resources

 Reproducible Masters

Chapter Resources Booklet
  Chapter Review, pp. 37–38
  Chapter Tests, pp. 39–42
  Assessment Transparency Activity, p. 49

Glencoe Science Web site
  Interactive Tutor
  Chapter Quizzes

Glencoe Technology
  Assessment Transparency
  Interactive CD-ROM Chapter Quizzes
  ExamView Pro Test Bank
  Vocabulary PuzzleMaker Software
  MindJogger Videoquiz

Reading Comprehension

QUESTION 1: B

Students must use information from the passage to identify the best supported answer choice.

- **Choice A** No; this is the reverse order of the food chain described in the reading passage.
- **Choice B** Yes; this is the food chain described in the reading passage.
- **Choice C** No; this is not the food chain described in the passage.
- **Choice D** No; this is not the food chain described in the passage.

QUESTION 2: J

Students must use information from the passage to identify the best supported answer choice.

- **Choice F** No; this choice is a producer.
- **Choice G** No; this choice is an herbivore.
- **Choice H** No; this is a source of energy.
- **Choice J** Yes; this choice is a predator.

THE PRINCETON REVIEW — All questions written and validated by The Princeton Review.

Reading Comprehension

Read the passage. Then read each question that follows the passage. Decide which is the best answer to each question.

Interactions in Ecosystems

Fearing for their safety and the safety of their livestock, early settlers of northern Wisconsin killed the native timberwolves. Timberwolves are a natural predator of white-tailed deer. Over time the deer population increased in size. The available vegetation could not support the deer population. Even though emergency feeding stations were set up, thousands of deer died of starvation. The deer population now is kept down by controlled hunting seasons. In some areas wolves have been reintroduced.

An ecosystem consists of organisms, from many different species, living together and connected by the flow of energy, nutrients and matter. Organisms in an ecosystem can be classified as either producers or consumers. Most producers use the Sun's radiant energy and convert it into chemical energy through photo-

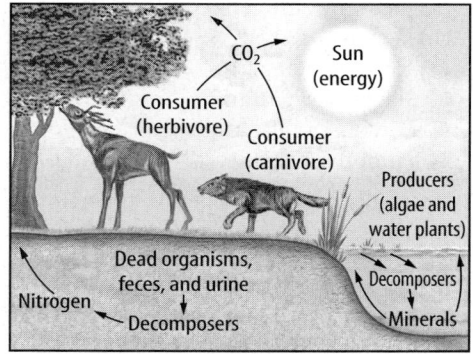

The major biotic components of an ecosystem

synthesis. Consumers take in and use this chemical energy. Herbivores eat producers, carnivores eat other consumers, and omnivores eat both producers and consumers. As organisms die, decomposers take in and use the energy in the dead organisms. In doing so, they release nutrients into the soil and carbon dioxide into the air that are used by producers again.

The loss of one species from an ecosystem may lead to the overpopulation or extinction of other species. This loss degrades the ecosystem upon which humans and other organisms depend for clean air, water, and food.

Test-Taking Tip Use the figure to help you visualize the ecosystem that is being described in the passage.

1. Food chains are a way of showing how energy, nutrients and matter flow through an ecosystem. Which of the following is a food chain of the ecosystem described in the passage?
   A) carnivore, producer, herbivore
   B) producer, herbivore, carnivore
   C) carnivore, producer, decomposer
   D) decomposer, carnivore, herbivore

2. Predators are consumers that capture and eat other consumers. The presence of a predator limits the size of the prey population. This means that food and other resources are less likely to become scarce. What is the predator in this passage?
   F) vegetation
   G) deer
   H) Sun
   J) timberwolf

Reasoning and Skills

Read each question and choose the best answer.

1. Within an ecosystem there are many populations as well as abiotic factors. Groups of populations that interact within a specific area of an ecosystem are referred to as which of the following?
   A) a habitat
   B) a community
   C) a species
   D) an atmosphere

Test-Taking Tip Think about the levels of an ecosystem and how they relate to each other.

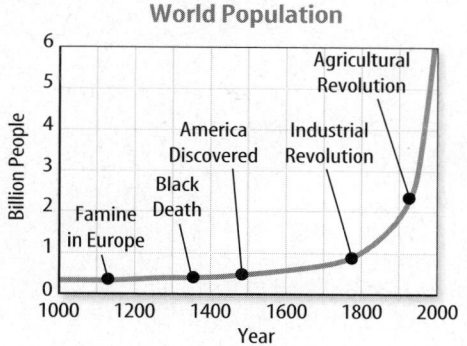

World Population

2. Refer to the Population Growth graph. In which of the following years were the birth rate and the death rate nearly equal?
   F) 1,800
   G) 2,000
   H) 1,200
   J) 1,600

Test-Taking Tip Consider what you know about the effects of birth and death rates on population size.

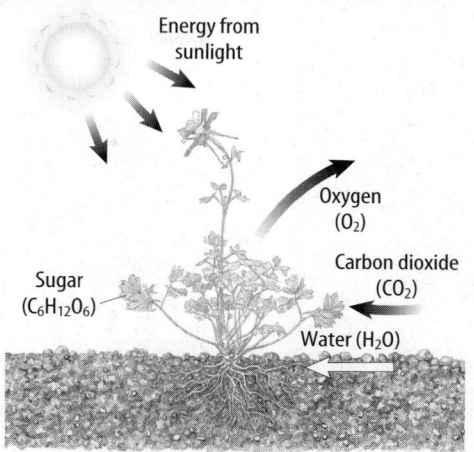

Energy from sunlight

Oxygen (O_2)

Carbon dioxide (CO_2)

Sugar ($C_6H_{12}O_6$)

Water (H_2O)

3. The conversion of energy is important to all life on Earth. Some producers use sunlight as an energy source, converting it into chemical energy through photosynthesis. Other producers that live where sunlight does not reach them, can use which of the following as an energy source?
   A) water
   C) soil
   B) air
   D) chemicals

Test-Taking Tip Read about converting energy before answering the question.

Consider this question carefully before writing your answer on a separate sheet of paper.

4. Consider what you have learned about ecosystems. Compare and contrast biotic and abiotic factors of the environment. List some abiotic factors and describe why each is important to life.

Test-Taking Tip Make a concept map of the environmental factors of an ecosystem to help answer the question.

Reasoning and Skills

QUESTION 1: B
Students must understand populations and ecosystems. Only answer choice B, *a community*, is correct.

QUESTION 2: H
Students must understand that if birth rate and death rate are equal, then there is no population growth. Only choice H, *1,200*, notes a year on the graph in which the growth rate is nearly zero.

QUESTION 3: D
Students must understand producers and energy conversion to identify choice D, *chemicals*, as the correct choice. Choices A, B, and C are used whether or not the producer receives sunlight.

QUESTION 4: Answers will vary.
Students should write a thorough response based upon information from this unit.

Teaching Tip

Suggest students brainstorm a list of ideas and then organize these ideas before writing a response.

UNIT 5

Earth and the Solar System

Unit Contents

✓ Pre-Reading Activity

Have students look for pictures of the effects of earthquakes and volcanoes and compare and contrast them.

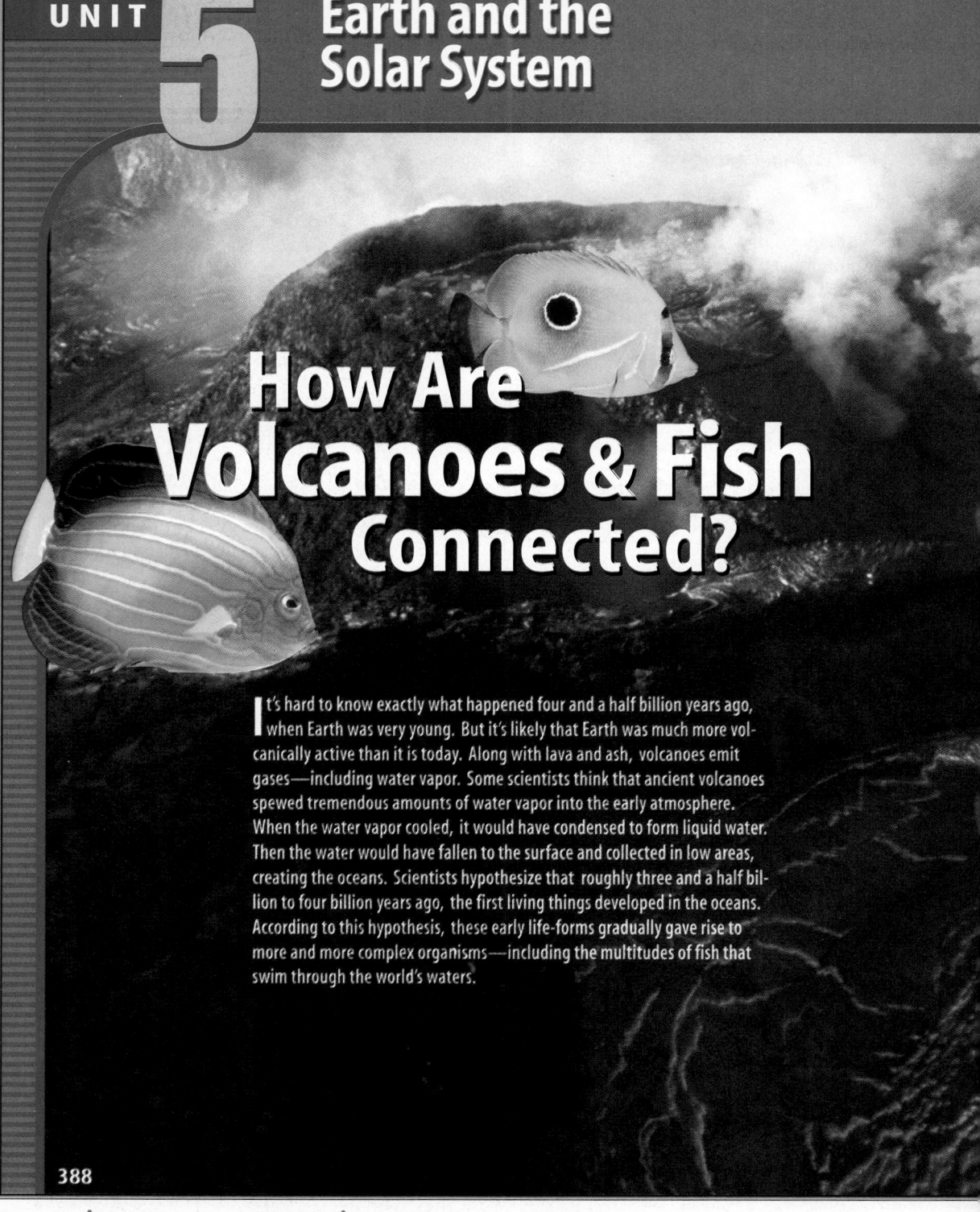

How Are Volcanoes & Fish Connected?

It's hard to know exactly what happened four and a half billion years ago, when Earth was very young. But it's likely that Earth was much more volcanically active than it is today. Along with lava and ash, volcanoes emit gases—including water vapor. Some scientists think that ancient volcanoes spewed tremendous amounts of water vapor into the early atmosphere. When the water vapor cooled, it would have condensed to form liquid water. Then the water would have fallen to the surface and collected in low areas, creating the oceans. Scientists hypothesize that roughly three and a half billion to four billion years ago, the first living things developed in the oceans. According to this hypothesis, these early life-forms gradually gave rise to more and more complex organisms—including the multitudes of fish that swim through the world's waters.

388

Teacher to Teacher

"The geographic locations of volcanos is an important part of understanding plate tectonics. Have students plot the locations of volcanoes on a class map. This activity helps to either introduce or reinforce the concept of plates and plate boundaries."

Kevin Finnegan, Teacher
McCord Middle School
Worthington, OH

Introducing the Unit

How Are Volcanoes & Fish Connected?

The surface of Earth is constantly changing. New material is formed as older material is reincorporated into Earth's interior. The crust, the surface on which we live, is broken into sections called plates. These plates are constantly moving and interacting with each other, altering the shape of the planet. Convection of the material in Earth's interior provides the force to move these plates. The appearance of Earth is further changed by volcanic and earthquake activity caused largely by the motion of the plates.

The material making up the plates also undergoes changes due to weathering, heat, and pressure. Volcanoes form new rock as older rock is eroded away. Seas were once found far inland from today's ocean boundaries. This explains the existence of marine fossils in areas miles away from the ocean's shorelines. Examining these fossils gives scientists clues about what life was like earlier in Earth's history.

SCIENCE CONNECTION

VOLCANOES AND COMETS Not all scientists agree with the hypothesis that Earth's oceans were formed primarily by emissions from ancient volcanoes. For example, some researchers suggest that the water may have come largely from comets. Divide the class into two teams. Have one team investigate the volcano hypothesis, while the other team researches the comet hypothesis. Then hold a class debate, with each team presenting evidence in support of its hypothesis.

SCIENCE CONNECTION
Activity

Ask students to brainstorm about the environmental effects created by an asteroid impact on Earth. After listing their ideas, ask them to brainstorm about the effects of a large volcanic explosion. Include their ideas in a separate list. Ask students to compare the two lists and determine how the two events are similar and different.

SCIENCE Online
Internet Addresses
_____
_____
_____
_____

Explore the Glencoe Science Web site at **science.glencoe.com** to find out more about topics in this unit.

Section/Objectives	Standards		Activities/Features
	National	State/Local	
Chapter Opener	See p. 5T for a Key to Standards.		**Explore Activity:** Reassemble an image, p. 391 **Before You Read,** p. 391
Section 1 Continental Drift 🕐 2 sessions 📦 1 block 1. **Describe** the hypothesis of continental drift. 2. **Identify** evidence supporting continental drift.	National Content Standards: UCP2, UCP3, A1, A2, D1, D2, G1, G3		**Science Online,** p. 393 **MiniLAB:** Interpreting Fossil Data, p. 394
Section 2 Seafloor Spreading 🕐 2 sessions 📦 1 block 1. **Explain** seafloor spreading. 2. **Recognize** how age and magnetic clues support seafloor spreading.	National Content Standards: UCP2, UCP3, A1, D1, D2, G1, G3		**Chemistry Integration,** p. 397 **Activity:** Seafloor Spreading Rates, p. 399
Section 3 Theory of Plate Tectonics 🕐 4 sessions 📦 2 blocks 1. **Compare and contrast** different types of plate boundaries. 2. **Explain** how heat inside Earth causes plate tectonics. 3. **Recognize** features caused by plate tectonics.	National Content Standards: UCP2, UCP3, A1, A2, D1, D2, G1, G3		**Science Online,** p. 402 **Problem-Solving Activity:** How well do the continents fit together?, p. 402 **Visualizing Plate Boundaries,** p. 403 **MiniLAB:** Modeling Convection Currents, p. 405 **Physics Integration,** p. 408 **Activity:** Predicting Tectonic Activity, pp. 410–411 **Science and Language Arts:** Listening In, pp. 412–413

NATIONAL GEOGRAPHIC

Teacher's Corner

PRODUCTS AVAILABLE FROM GLENCOE
To order call 1-800-334-7344:
CD-ROM
NGS PictureShow: Dynamic Earth
Curriculum Kit
GeoKit: Dynamic Earth
Geokit: Earth's Crust

Transparency Set
NGS PicturePack: Dynamic Earth
Videodisc
STV: Restless Earth

PRODUCTS AVAILABLE FROM NATIONAL GEOGRAPHIC SOCIETY
To order call 1-800-368-2728:
Videos
Changing Earth: Forces that Create, Forces that Destroy; Living on Our Changing Planet; Oceans in Motion

Activity Materials	Reproducible Resources	Section Assessment	Technology
Explore Activity: photographs from discarded magazines, scissors	**Chapter Resources Booklet** Foldables Worksheet, p.17 Directed Reading Overview, p. 19 Note–taking Worksheets, pp. 33–35	*GLENCOE'S* **ASSESSMENT** *ADVANTAGE*	
MiniLAB: clay or modeling dough; objects for "fossils," such as macaroni, small buttons or peanuts; spatula	**Chapter Resources Booklet** Transparency Activity, p. 44 MiniLAB, p. 3 Enrichment, p. 30 Reinforcement, p. 27 Directed Reading, p. 20 Lab Activity, pp. 9–11	**Portfolio** Challenge, p. 395 **Performance** MiniLAB, p. 394 Skill Builder Activities, p. 395 **Content** Section Assessment, p. 395	Section Focus Transparency Interactive CD-ROM Guided Reading Audio Program
Activity: metric ruler, pencil *Need materials?* Contact Science Kit at 1-800-828-7777 or www.sciencekit.com on the Internet.	**Chapter Resources Booklet** Transparency Activity, p. 45 Enrichment, p. 31 Reinforcement, p. 28 Directed Reading, p. 20 Activity Worksheet, pp. 5–6 **Mathematics Skill Activities,** p. 5	**Portfolio** Chemistry Integration, p. 397 **Performance** Skill Builder Activities, p. 398 **Content** Section Assessment, p. 398	Section Focus Transparency Interactive CD-ROM Guided Reading Audio Program
MiniLAB: water; clear, colorless casserole dish; hot plate; thermal mitts; food coloring **Activity:** Internet sites and other resources on earthquake and volcanic activity, world map	**Chapter Resources Booklet** Transparency Activity, p. 46 MiniLAB, p. 4 Enrichment, p. 32 Reinforcement, p. 29 Directed Reading, pp. 21, 22 Lab Activity, pp. 13–15 Activity Worksheet, pp. 7–8 Transparency Activity, pp. 47–48 **Lab Management and Safety,** p. 65 **Reading and Writing Skill Activities,** p. 27	**Portfolio** Science Journal, p. 401 Extension, p. 403 **Performance** Problem-Solving Activity, p. 402 MiniLAB, p. 405 Skill Builder Activities, p. 409 **Content** Section Assessment, p. 409	Section Focus Transparency Teaching Transparency Interactive CD-ROM Guided Reading Audio Program

End of Chapter Assessment

GLENCOE'S **ASSESSMENT** *ADVANTAGE*

Blackline Masters	Technology	Professional Series
Chapter Resources Booklet Chapter Review, pp. 37–38 Chapter Tests, pp. 39–42 **Standardized Test Practice by The Princeton Review,** pp. 47–50	MindJogger Videoquiz Interactive CD-ROM Vocabulary PuzzleMakers ExamView Pro Test Bank Interactive Lesson Planner Interactive Teacher Edition	Performance Assessment in the Science Classroom (PASC)

Transparencies

Section Focus

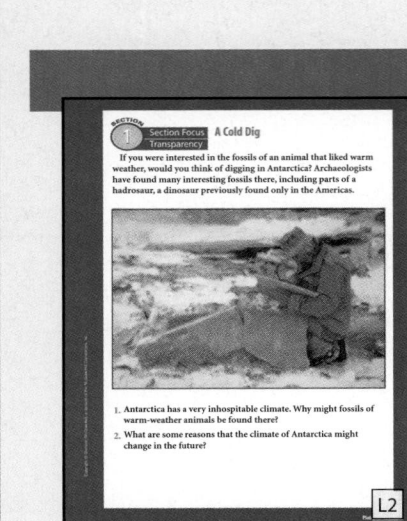

A Cold Dig

If you were interested in the fossils of an animal that liked warm weather, would you think of digging in Antarctica? Archaeologists have found many interesting fossils there, including parts of a hadrosaur, a dinosaur previously found only in the Americas.

1. Antarctica has a very inhospitable climate. Why might fossils of warm-weather animals be found there?
2. What are some reasons that the climate of Antarctica might change in the future?

L2

The Main Event

Until recently, the bottom of the sea was impossible to see. New technology has improved the view, and today we have a better idea of what is going on there. This photo shows one feature of the ocean floor—a deep-sea vent.

1. What is occurring in the photograph?
2. What features on land are similar to this deep-sea vent?
3. Judging from the photo, what do you think conditions around this vent are like?

L2

Valley of Ten Thousand Smokes

One of the most massive volcanic eruptions ever investigated occurred in a valley in southern Alaska in 1912. The eruption covered over forty square miles with ash as deep as 210 meters and left thousands of vents (called fumaroles) in the valley spewing steam and gas.

1. How did this valley get its name, the Valley of Ten Thousand Smokes?
2. Why don't you see any smoke in the photograph?
3. Name some other places where there are volcanoes.

L2

This is a representation of key blackline masters available in the Teacher Classroom Resources. See Resource Manager boxes within the chapter for additional information.

Assessment

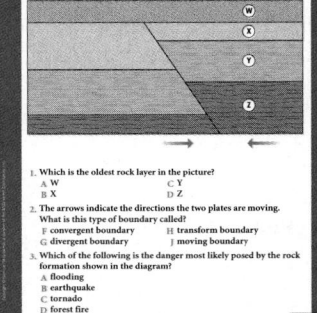

Plate Tectonics

Directions: Carefully review the diagram and answer the following questions.

1. Which is the oldest rock layer in the picture?
   A W   C Y
   B X   D Z
2. The arrows indicate the directions the two plates are moving. What is this type of boundary called?
   F convergent boundary   H transform boundary
   G divergent boundary   J moving boundary
3. Which of the following is the danger most likely posed by the rock formation shown in the diagram?
   A flooding
   B earthquake
   C tornado
   D forest fire

L2

Teaching

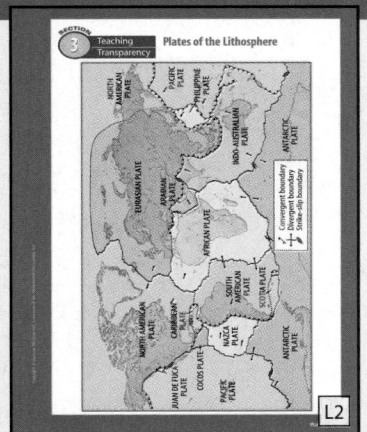

Plates of the Lithosphere

L2

Key to Teaching Strategies

The following designations will help you decide which activities are appropriate for your students.

L1 Level 1 activities should be appropriate for students with learning difficulties.

L2 Level 2 activities should be within the ability range of all students.

L3 Level 3 activities are designed for above-average students.

ELL ELL activities should be within the ability range of English Language Learners.

COOP LEARN Cooperative Learning activities are designed for small group work.

LS Multiple Learning Styles logos, as described on page 22T, are used throughout to indicate strategies that address different learning styles.

P These strategies represent student products that can be placed into a best-work portfolio.

Hands-on Activities

Activity Worksheets

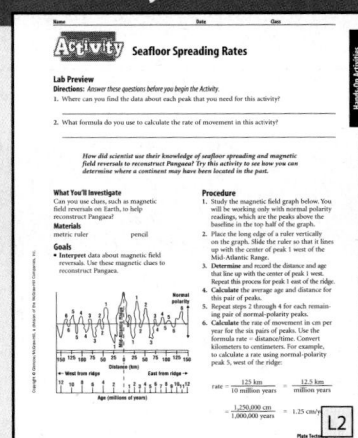

Seafloor Spreading Rates

L2

Laboratory Activities

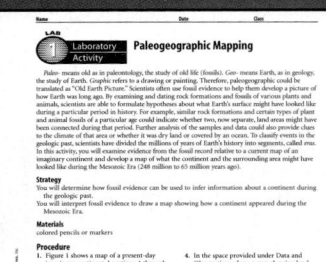

Paleogeographic Mapping

L2

Meeting Different Ability Levels

Content Outline

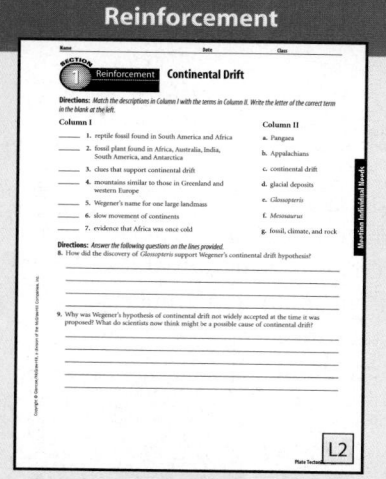

Reinforcement

Directed Reading

Assessment

Chapter Tests

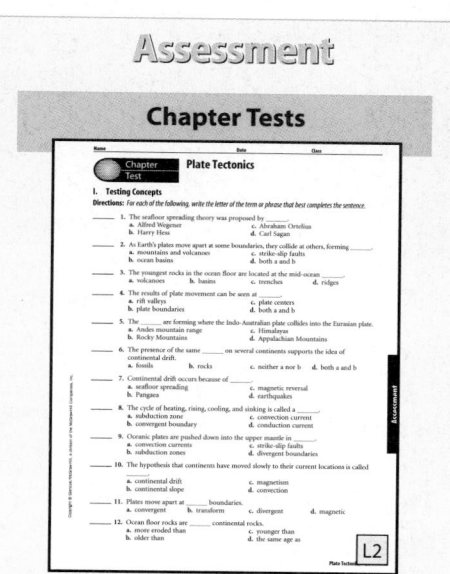

Enrichment

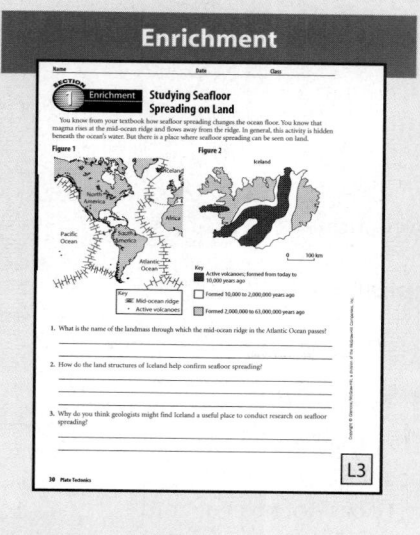

Spanish Directed Reading

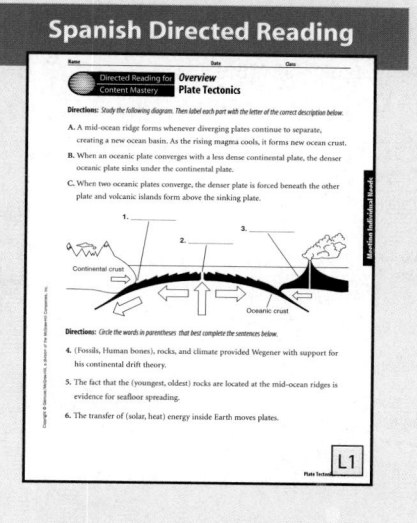

Test Practice Workbook

Chapter Review

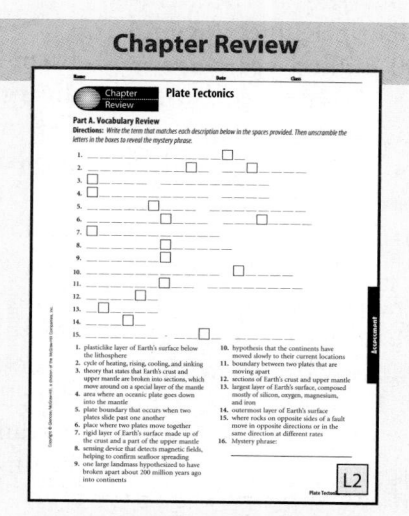

Science Content Background

SECTION 1

Continental Drift

Pangaea

About 200 million years ago, Pangaea covered around 30% of Earth's surface, while a large ocean, Panthalassa, covered the rest of the planet. Pangaea broke up to form Laurasia and Gondwana, which were separated by the Tethys Sea.

Climate Clues

The study of ancient climates is called paleoclimatology. Alfred Wegener, a meteorologist, collected data about ancient climates in hopes of finding supporting evidence for his hypothesis. During his study of paleoclimates, he noted that glaciers covered much of the southern hemisphere. This occurred between 320 million and 290 million years ago.

SECTION 2

Seafloor Spreading

The Seafloor Moves

As the ocean floor slowly separates, new rocks form at a mid-ocean ridge. It is estimated that the Atlantic Ocean grows about 2.5 cm wider every year as a result of new rock forming at the Mid-Atlantic Ridge. Around 200 million years ago, a rift began to form between Greenland and Scotland. This rift led to the formation of the North Atlantic, which appeared only 65 million years ago, and continued spreading to form the modern Atlantic Ocean.

Fun Fact

Certain species of green turtles swim from South America to Ascension Island in the South Atlantic to lay their eggs. The turtles may have started this trip when these land masses were much closer. As the seafloor spread, the instinctive trip became longer.

Magnetic Time Scale

Paleomagnetism is the study of the magnetic properties of ancient rocks. When rock material is heated above the Curie point, magnetic minerals lose their magnetic properties. As they cool they align with the current magnetic field.

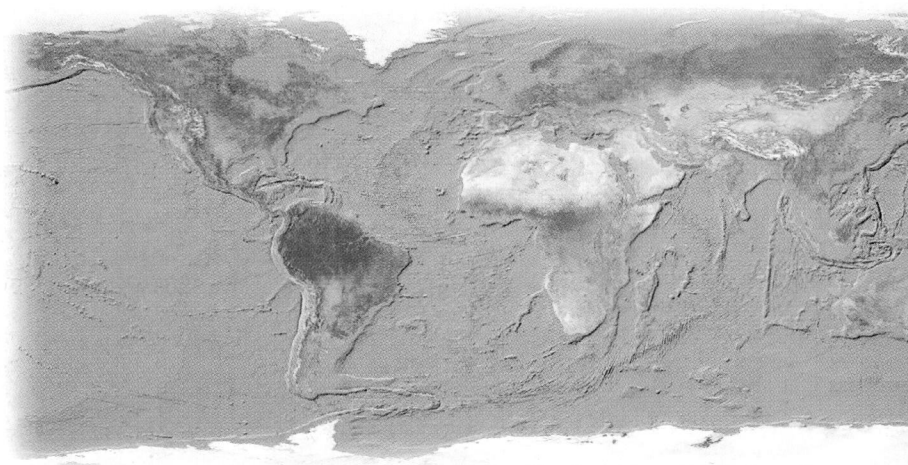

Tom Van Sant/Photo Researchers, Inc.

Thus the record of the reversals of Earth's magnetic field is recorded in the magnetic characteristics of rocks formed at that time.

SECTION 3

Theory of Plate Tectonics

Plate Boundaries

Motion of Earth's plates is accommodated at plate edges. Boundaries between lithospheric plates may be divergent, convergent, or transform. The intersection of any three plate boundaries is called a triple junction.

Divergent plate boundaries often begin as continental rifts such as the modern-day African Rift Valley. Tensional forces may stretch and thin the continental crust, forming a depression that fills with ocean water. Tensional forces continue to act on the area until a mid-ocean ridge develops. At this point, full-fledged seafloor spreading begins and the continental fragments begin to separate.

In order for Earth to maintain a constant size, lithosphere produced at mid-ocean ridges must be consumed elsewhere. This occurs at convergent boundaries. At these boundaries, older, cooler, and denser oceanic plates sink beneath less-dense plates in subduction zones. The denser plate descends into the mantle along a plane that may dip at angles ranging from 30° to 90°. This plane is defined by the foci of earthquakes associated with the subducting slab.

Transform boundaries may occur on land or on the seafloor. These faults most commonly connect offset segments of mid-ocean ridges. These ridge-to-ridge transform faults are a conspicuous feature of any mid-ocean ridge system. Transform faults also may connect a ridge to a trench or a trench to another trench.

Mountains and Volcanoes

Most of the world's spectacular mountain ranges were formed at collision-type convergent plate boundaries. When two plates carrying continents collide, rocks are folded and faulted, which results in a thickened and uplifted continental crust. The Himalaya are a classic example of a collision-type mountain range. This range started to form about 50 million years ago when India began colliding with Tibet and the Eurasian plate. Even today, India is pushing northward into Tibet and the Himalaya continue to rise. To illustrate the magnitude of the uplift that has occurred during this collision, consider that marine fossils have been found in sandstone layers near Lhasa, Tibet, which has an altitude of 12,500 feet!

Mountains also can form along ocean–continent convergent boundaries. The Andes Mountains of South America have formed as a result of rock deformation and volcanism caused by the subduction of the Nazca Plate under the South American Plate. The ocean trench marking the subduction zone is named the Peru-Chile Trench after the two countries most strongly affected by this plate boundary. When one oceanic plate descends beneath another at an ocean-ocean convergent plate boundary, a volcanic island arc forms behind the ocean trench. Volcanic arcs form as a result of partial melting of the subducting plate and mantle rock above the descending plate. The Japanese and Philippine Islands are examples of volcanic island arcs.

Fun Fact

The Indian Plate, which collided with Asia to form the Himalaya, continues to move at a rate of almost 5 cm per year. This massive plate is moving twice as fast as your fingernails grow!

SCIENCE Online

For additional content background on this topic, go to the Glencoe Science Web site at science.glencoe.com.

Nicholas Parfitt/Stone

Plate Tectonics

Chapter Vocabulary

continental drift, p. 392
Pangaea, p. 392
seafloor spreading, p. 397
plate tectonics, p. 400
plate, p. 400
lithosphere, p. 400
asthenosphere, p. 400
convection current, p. 405

What do you think?

Science Journal This is an aerial photograph of a strike-slip fault. Its movement has formed a "dog leg" in the river that flows over it. A dog leg is a sharp angle or bend.

CHAPTER 14

Plate Tectonics

Characterized by volcanoes and scenic vistas, the East African Rift Valley marks a place where Earth's crust is being pulled apart. If the pulling continues over millions of years, Africa will separate into two landmasses. In this chapter, you'll learn about Rift Valleys and other features explained by the theory of plate tectonics. You'll also learn about the fossil, climate, and rock clues that indicate that Earth's continents have drifted over time.

What do you think?

Science Journal Look at the picture below with a classmate. Discuss what you think this might be or what is happening. Here's a hint: *A river runs through this dog leg.* Write your answer or best guess in your Science Journal.

390

Theme Connection

Energy The transfer of energy in Earth's interior sets up massive convection currents in the mantle. These currents are thought to be the driving force that causes movement of Earth's plates.

Can you imagine a giant landmass that broke into many separate continents and Earth scientists working to reconstruct Earth's past? Do this activity to learn about clues that can be used to reassemble a supercontinent.

Reassemble an image

1. Collect interesting photographs from an old magazine.
2. You and a partner each select one photo, but don't show them to each other. Then each of you cut your photos into pieces no smaller than about 5 cm or 6 cm.
3. Trade your cut-up photo for your partner's.
4. Observe the pieces, and reassemble the photograph your partner has cut up.

Observe

In your Science Journal, describe the characteristics of the cut-up photograph that helped you put the image back together. Think of other examples in which characteristics of objects are used to match them up with other objects.

Before You Read

FOLDABLES
Reading & Study Skills

Making a Know-Want-Learn Study Fold It would be helpful to identify what you already know and what you want to know. Make the following Foldable to help you focus on reading about plate tectonics.

1. Place a sheet of paper in front of you so the long side is at the top. Fold the paper in half from top to bottom.
2. Fold both sides in to divide the paper into thirds. Unfold the paper so three sections show.
3. Through the top thickness of paper, cut along each of the fold lines to the topfold, forming three tabs. Label the tabs *Know, Want,* and *Learn,* as shown.
4. Before you read the chapter, write what you know about plate tectonics under the left tab and what you want to know under the middle tab.
5. As you read the chapter, write what you learn about plate tectonics under the right tab.

| Know | Want | Learn |

391

EXPLORE ACTIVITY

Purpose Use the Explore Activity to introduce students to the idea that Earth's continents may have once been connected. L2
ELL COOP LEARN IS **Linguistic**

Preparation Ask students to bring in old magazines.

Materials photos from discarded magazines, scissors

Teaching Strategy Have students compare their results with those of other students. Discuss differences and similarities.

Safety Precautions Students should handle scissors with care.

Observe

The shape and content of the pieces enable students to see how they fit together. Students may suggest jigsaw puzzles or broken artifacts.

✓Assessment

Process Ask students to write in their Science Journals the characteristics that make some photographs easier to fit together than others. Use **Performance Assessment in the Science Classroom,** p. 99.

Before You Read

FOLDABLES
Reading & Study Skills

Dinah Zike Study Fold

Purpose Use this activity to determine what students know about plate tectonics before reading the chapter. Have students list what they know, and what they want to learn. As they read the chapter, students can list what they learn, and compare it to what they wanted to learn.

📁 For additional help, see Foldables Worksheet, p. 17 in **Chapter Resources Booklet,** or go to the Glencoe Science Web site at **science.glencoe.com.** See After You Read in the Study Guide at the end of this chapter.

SECTION

1 Continental Drift

1 Motivate

Bellringer Transparency

Display the Section Focus Transparency for Section 1. Use the accompanying Transparency Activity Master. L2
ELL

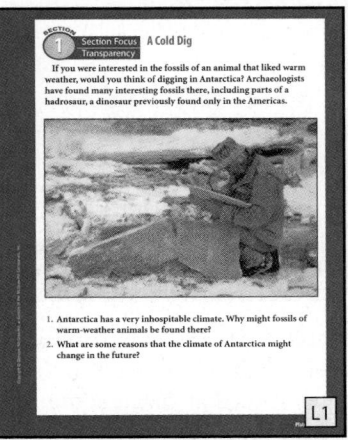

Section Focus
Transparency
A Cold Dig

If you were interested in the fossils of an animal that liked warm weather, would you think of digging in Antarctica? Archaeologists have found many interesting fossils there, including parts of a hadrosaur, a dinosaur previously found only in the Americas.

1. Antarctica has a very inhospitable climate. Why might fossils of warm-weather animals be found there?

2. What are some reasons that the climate of Antarctica might change in the future?

L1

Tie to Prior Knowledge

Have students recall the general shapes of Africa and South America. Ask if they can recall how the eastern coast of South America seems to fit into the western coast of Africa. Display a world map, asking again if students can make the connection.

✔ Reading Check

Answer Alfred Wegener

What You'll Learn

- **Describe** the hypothesis of continental drift.
- **Identify** evidence supporting continental drift.

Vocabulary
continental drift
Pangaea

Why It's Important

The hypothesis of continental drift led to plate tectonics—a theory that explains many processes in Earth.

Figure 1
This illustration represents how the continents once were joined to form Pangaea. This fitting together of continents according to shape is not the only evidence supporting the past existence of Pangaea.

Evidence for Continental Drift

If you look at a map of Earth's surface, you can see that the edges of some continents look as though they could fit together like a puzzle. Other people also have noticed this fact. For example, Dutch mapmaker Abraham Ortelius noted the fit between the coastlines of South America and Africa more than 400 years ago.

Pangaea German meteorologist Alfred Wegener (VEG nur) thought that the fit of the continents wasn't just a coincidence. He suggested that all the continents were joined together at some time in the past. In a 1912 lecture, he proposed the hypothesis of continental drift. According to the hypothesis of **continental drift,** continents have moved slowly to their current locations. Wegener suggested that all continents once were connected as one large landmass, shown in **Figure 1,** that broke apart about 200 million years ago. He called this large landmass **Pangaea** (pan JEE uh), which means "all land."

✔ Reading Check   *Who proposed continental drift?*

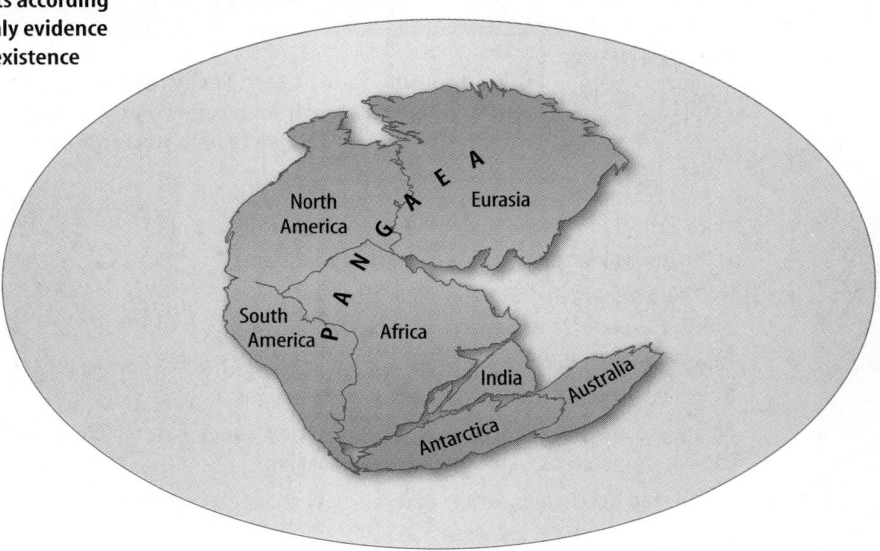

Section ✔*Assessment* Planner

PORTFOLIO
Challenge, p. 395
PERFORMANCE ASSESSMENT
Try at Home MiniLAB, p. 394
Skill Builder Activities, p. 395
See page 416 for more options.

CONTENT ASSESSMENT
Section, p. 395
Challenge, p. 395
Chapter, pp. 416–417

A Controversial Idea Wegener's ideas about continental drift were controversial. It wasn't until long after Wegener's death in 1930 that his basic hypothesis was accepted. The evidence Wegener presented hadn't been enough to convince many people during his lifetime. He was unable to explain exactly how the continents drifted apart. He proposed that the continents plowed through the ocean floor, driven by the spin of Earth. Physicists and geologists of the time strongly disagreed with Wegener's explanation. They pointed out that continental drift would not be necessary to explain many of Wegener's observations. Other important observations that came later eventually supported Wegener's earlier evidence.

Fossil Clues Besides the puzzlelike fit of the continents, fossils provided support for continental drift. Fossils of the reptile *Mesosaurus* have been found in South America and Africa, as shown in **Figure 2**. This swimming reptile lived in freshwater and on land. How could fossils of *Mesosaurus* be found on land areas separated by a large ocean of salt water? It probably couldn't swim between the continents. Wegener hypothesized that this reptile lived on both continents when they were joined.

✓ **Reading Check** *How do Mesosaurus fossils support the past existence of Pangaea?*

SCIENCE *Online*

Research Visit the Glencoe Science Web site at **science.glencoe.com** for more information about the continental drift hypothesis. Communicate to your class what you learn.

Figure 2
Fossil remains of plants and animals that lived in Pangaea have been found on more than one continent. *How do the locations of* Glossopteris, Mesosaurus, Kannemeyerid, Labyrinthodont, *and other fossils support Wegener's hypothesis of continental drift?*

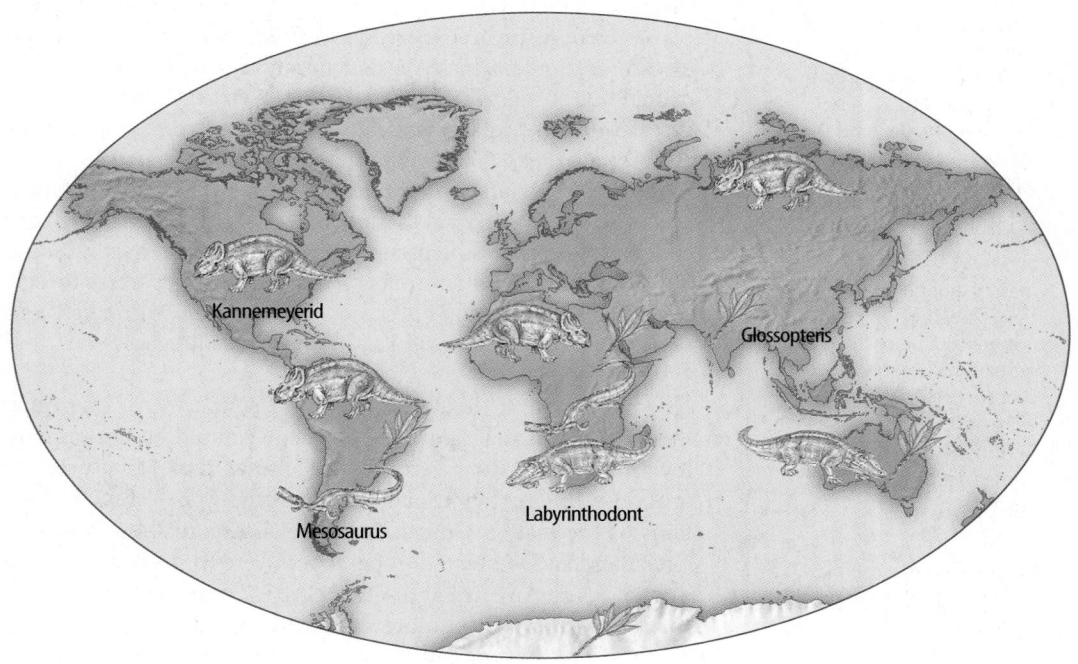

Kannemeyerid

Glossopteris

Mesosaurus

Labyrinthodont

---

2 Teach

Evidence for Continental Drift

Use an Analogy
Have students recall that when putting together a jigsaw puzzle, they use the shapes of the puzzle pieces and the picture on the box as clues. When thinking about evidence of continental drift, the puzzle pieces are analogous to the shapes of the continents, and the picture clues are analogous to evidence found on each continent.

Discussion
Why was Wegener's idea of continental drift rejected? Scientists at the time thought Wegener's observations could be explained by something other than continental drift. Also, Wegener failed to provide a reasonable or believable mechanism to explain how continental drift might occur.

✓ **Reading Check**

Answer Fossils of *Mesosaurus,* a freshwater and land animal, have been found in widespread areas separated by oceans of salt water, through which they could not swim.

Caption Answer
Figure 2 Matching fossils on widely separated continents provide evidence that these land masses were once joined.

SCIENCE *Online*
Internet Addresses
_____
_____
_____
_____

Explore the Glencoe Science Web site at **science.glencoe.com** to find out more about topics in this section.

Resource Manager

Chapter Resources Booklet
Transparency Activity, p. 44
Note-taking Worksheets, pp. 33–35
Directed Reading for Content Mastery, pp. 19, 20

Inclusion Strategies

Visually Impaired In order to help visually impaired students better understand how shapes that fit together can be used to help reconstruct Pangaea, make clay models of the continental masses that formed the supercontinent. Make sure the edges of the continents clearly match. Have students work with a partner to reconstruct the clay "Pangaea."

Fun Fact

Fossils of *Lystrosaurus,* a small reptile that lived about 200 million years ago, have been found in South Africa, Antarctica, and India.

TRY AT HOME
Mini LAB

Purpose Students reaffirm that geologic clues can be used to show how continents that are now separate were once joined.

L2 ELL IS **Kinesthetic**

Materials three colors of modeling clay or modeling dough; objects such as macaroni, small buttons, or peanuts to use as fossils; spatula for cutting landmasses apart

Teaching Strategy Review the procedure for making the landmasses with students in class before having them complete the activity at home.

Analysis

1. Possible answer: I looked for clues in the pattern of fossils and "mountain ranges."

✔ Assessment

Oral Have students describe the characteristics they used to reconstruct the original landmass. Use **Performance Assessment in the Science Classroom,** p. 143.

Figure 3
This fossil plant, *Glossopteris,* grew in a temperate climate.

TRY AT HOME
Mini LAB

Interpreting Fossil Data

Procedure

1. Build a three-layer landmass using **clay or modeling dough.**
2. Mold the clay into mountain ranges.
3. Place similar "fossils" into the clay at various locations around the landmass.
4. Form five continents from the one landmass. Also, form two smaller landmasses out of different clay with different mountain ranges and fossils.
5. Place the five continents and two smaller landmasses around the room.
6. Have someone who did not make or place the landmasses make a model that shows how they once were positioned.
7. Return the clay to its container so it can be used again.

Analysis
What clues were useful in reconstructing the original landmass?

Resource Manager

Chapter Resources Booklet
MiniLAB, p. 3
Enrichment, p. 30
Reinforcement, p. 27
Lab Activity, pp. 9–11

A Widespread Plant Another fossil that supports the hypothesis of continental drift is *Glossopteris* (glahs AHP tur us). **Figure 3** shows this fossil plant, which has been found in Africa, Australia, India, South America, and Antarctica. The presence of *Glossopteris* in so many areas also supported Wegener's idea that all of these regions once were connected and had similar climates.

Climate Clues Wegener used continental drift to explain evidence of changing climates. For example, fossils of warm-weather plants were found on the island of Spitsbergen in the Arctic Ocean. To explain this, Wegener hypothesized that Spitsbergen drifted from tropical regions to the arctic. Wegener also used continental drift to explain evidence of glaciers found in temperate and tropical areas. Glacial deposits and rock surfaces scoured and polished by glaciers are found in South America, Africa, India, and Australia. This shows that parts of these continents were covered with glaciers in the past. How could you explain why glacial deposits are found in areas where no glaciers exist today? Wegener thought that these continents were connected and partly covered with ice near Earth's south pole long ago.

Rock Clues If the continents were connected at one time, then rocks that make up the continents should be the same in locations where they were joined. Similar rock structures are found on different continents. Parts of the Appalachian Mountains of the eastern United States are similar to those found in Greenland and western Europe. If you were to study rocks from eastern South America and western Africa, you would find other rock structures that also are similar. Rock clues like these support the idea that the continents were connected in the past.

Teacher FYI

In the 1960s, evidence was found in Antarctica that indicated a warm climate existed there 200 million years ago. *Glossopteris* fossils and rocks containing coal were found only 200 miles from the south pole.

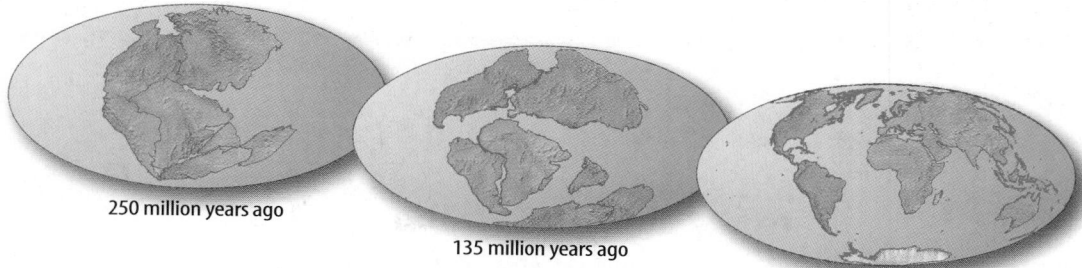

250 million years ago

135 million years ago

Present day

How could continents drift?

Although Wegener provided evidence to support his hypothesis of continental drift, he couldn't explain how, when, or why these changes, shown in **Figure 4,** took place. The idea suggested that lower-density, continental material somehow had to plow through higher-density, ocean-floor material. The force behind this plowing was thought to be the spin of Earth on its axis—a notion that was quickly rejected by physicists. Because other scientists could not provide explanations either, Wegener's idea of continental drift was initially rejected. The idea was so radically different at that time that most people closed their minds to it.

Rock, fossil, and climate clues were the main types of evidence for continental drift. After Wegener's death, more clues were found, largely because of advances in technology, and new ideas that related to continental drift were developed. You'll learn about one of these new ideas, seafloor spreading, in the next section. Seafloor spreading helped provide an explanation of how the continents could move.

Figure 4
These computer models show the probable course the continents have taken. On the far left is their position 250 million years ago. In the middle is their position 135 million years ago. At right is their current position.

Visual Learning ——o
Figure 4 **What is happening to eastern Africa at present?** It is splitting apart.

3 Assess

Reteach
Have students outline the section, including all of the important points. Have pairs exchange outlines and then use the outlines to quiz one another. [L1]
IS Interpersonal

Challenge
New evidence suggests that mountains in southwest South America match up with the Appalachians. Have students research and write a report about how this came about. Possible answer: Before colliding with the African Plate, the North American Plate may have been positioned west of South America. [L3] [P]

✔Assessment

Content Have groups of students write and perform skits in which one student plays Wegener introducing his theory, and others play scientists debunking it. Encourage students to use visual props. Use **Performance Assessment in the Science Classroom,** p. 147.

Section 1 Assessment

1. Why were Wegener's ideas about continental drift initially rejected?

2. How did Wegener use climate clues to support his hypothesis of continental drift?

3. What rock clues were used to support the hypothesis of continental drift?

4. In what ways do fossils help support the hypothesis of continental drift?

5. **Think Critically** Why would you expect to see similar rocks and rock structures on two landmasses that were connected at one time?

Skill Builder Activities

6. **Comparing and Contrasting** Compare and contrast the locations of fossils of the temperate plant *Glossopteris,* as shown in **Figure 2,** with the climate that exists at each location today. **For more help, refer to the** Science Skill Handbook.

7. **Communicating** Imagine that you are Alfred Wegener in the year 1912. In your Science Journal, write a letter to another scientist explaining your idea about continental drift. Try to convince this scientist that your hypothesis is correct. **For more help, refer to the** Science Skill Handbook.

Answers to Section Assessment

1. Wegener could not explain how the continents drifted apart. There were also other ways to explain his observations.

2. Fossils of warm-weather plants found on islands in the Arctic Ocean and glacial features found in places such as Africa supported the idea that continents drift.

3. Rock structures on different continents are similar.

4. Fossils of the same terrestrial organism were found on widely separated continents.

5. The same rock structure they shared when attached would appear on both halves after the landmass split apart.

6. Possible answer: compare—all locations are on landmasses; contrast—some locations are in temperate climates, others are in arid, semiarid, or polar climates.

7. Letters should include his evidence: continent shape and matching fossils and climate on widely separated continents.

SECTION

Seafloor Spreading

Bellringer Transparency

Display the Section Focus Transparency for Section 2. Use the accompanying Transparency Activity Master. L2

ELL

Tie to Prior Knowledge

Ask students if they ever have walked into an ocean, lake, or river. Have them describe how the floor of the body of water felt. Students may mention steep and gentle slopes, rocks, bars or ridges of sand, and depressions. Explain that the entire ocean floor has such features, and it took special tools to map it.

✔ Reading Check

Answer using sound waves

As You Read

What **You'll Learn**
- **Explain** seafloor spreading.
- **Recognize** how age and magnetic clues support seafloor spreading.

Vocabulary
seafloor spreading

Why **It's Important**
Seafloor spreading helps explain how continents moved apart.

Figure 5
As the seafloor spreads apart at a mid-ocean ridge, new seafloor is created. The older seafloor moves away from the ridge in opposite directions.

Mapping the Ocean Floor

If you were to lower a rope from a boat until it reached the seafloor, you could record the depth of the ocean at that particular point. In how many different locations would you have to do this to create an accurate map of the seafloor? This is exactly how it was done until World War I, when the use of sound waves was introduced to detect submarines. During the 1940s and 1950s, scientists began using sound waves on moving ships to map large areas of the ocean floor in detail. Sound waves echo off the ocean bottom—the longer the sound waves take to return to the ship, the deeper the water is.

Using sound waves, researchers discovered an underwater system of ridges, or mountains, and valleys like those found on the continents. In the Atlantic, the Pacific, and in other oceans around the world, a system of ridges, called the mid-ocean ridges, is present. These underwater mountain ranges, shown in **Figure 5,** stretch along the center of much of Earth's ocean floor. This discovery raised the curiosity of many scientists. What formed these mid-ocean ridges?

✔ Reading Check *How were mid-ocean ridges discovered?*

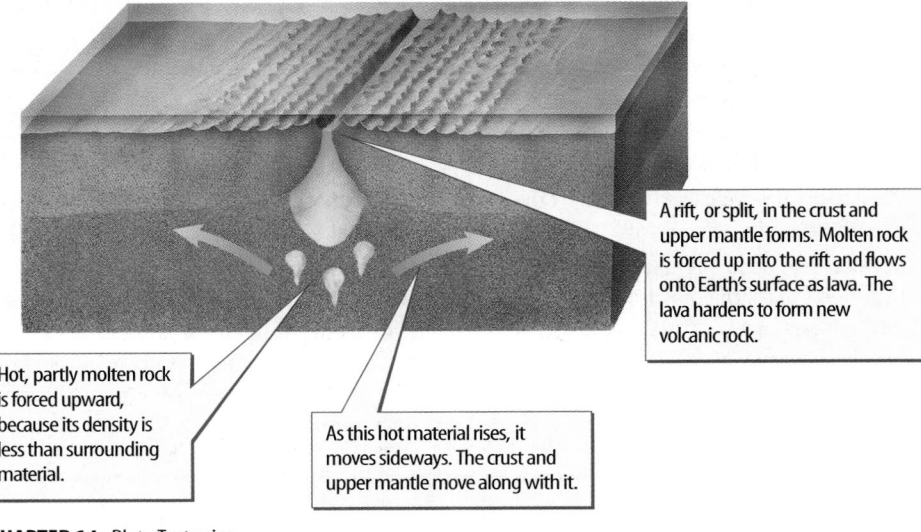

A rift, or split, in the crust and upper mantle forms. Molten rock is forced up into the rift and flows onto Earth's surface as lava. The lava hardens to form new volcanic rock.

Hot, partly molten rock is forced upward, because its density is less than surrounding material.

As this hot material rises, it moves sideways. The crust and upper mantle move along with it.

396 CHAPTER 14 Plate Tectonics

Section ✔ *Assessment* Planner

PORTFOLIO
Chemistry Integration, p. 397
PERFORMANCE ASSESSMENT
Skill Builder Activities, p. 398
See page 416 for more options.

CONTENT ASSESSMENT
Section, p. 398
Challenge, p. 398
Chapter, pp. 416–417

The Seafloor Moves In the early 1960s, Princeton University scientist Harry Hess suggested an explanation. His now-famous theory is known as **seafloor spreading.** Hess proposed that hot, less dense material below Earth's crust rises toward the surface at the mid-ocean ridges. Then, it flows sideways, carrying the seafloor away from the ridge in both directions, as seen in **Figure 5.**

As the seafloor spreads apart, magma moves upward and flows from the cracks. It becomes solid as it cools and forms new seafloor. As new seafloor moves away from the mid-ocean ridge, it cools, contracts, and becomes denser. This denser, colder seafloor sinks, helping to form the ridge. The theory of seafloor spreading was later supported by the following observations.

Reading Check *How does new seafloor form at mid-ocean ridges?*

Evidence for Spreading In 1968, scientists aboard the research ship *Glomar Challenger* began gathering information about the rocks on the seafloor. *Glomar Challenger* was equipped with a drilling rig that allowed scientists to drill into the seafloor to obtain rock samples. They made a remarkable discovery as they studied the ages of the rocks. Scientists found that the youngest rocks are located at the mid-ocean ridges. The ages of the rocks become increasingly older in samples obtained farther from the ridges, adding to the evidence for seafloor spreading.

Using submersibles along mid-ocean ridges, new seafloor features and life-forms also were discovered there, as shown in **Figure 6.** As molten material rises along the ridges, it brings heat and chemicals that support exotic life-forms in deep, ocean water. Among these are giant clams, mussels, and tube worms.

Physics
INTEGRATION

Magnetic Clues Earth's magnetic field has a north and a south pole. Magnetic lines, or directions, of force leave Earth near the south pole and enter Earth near the north pole. During a magnetic reversal, the lines of magnetic force run the opposite way. Scientists have determined that Earth's magnetic field has reversed itself many times in the past. These reversals occur over intervals of thousands or even millions of years. The reversals are recorded in rocks forming along mid-ocean ridges.

Figure 6
Many new discoveries have been made on the seafloor. These giant tube worms inhabit areas near hot water vents along mid-ocean ridges.

Chemistry
INTEGRATION

Find out what the Curie point is and describe in your Science Journal what happens to iron-bearing minerals when they are heated to the Curie point. Explain how this is important to studies of seafloor spreading.

SECTION 2 Seafloor Spreading **397**

Section 2 Seafloor Spreading **397**

Teach

Mapping the Ocean Floor

Reading Check

Answer Magma moves upward and out of cracks in seafloor. As it solidifies on the surface, new seafloor forms. Older seafloor moves away from the ridge.

Chemistry
INTEGRATION

The Curie point is the temperature above which iron-bearing minerals lose their magnetism. As lava cools into rock on the ocean floor, the rock acquires a magnetic field like that of Earth's. If these rocks are reheated beyond the Curie point, the magnetic signature they acquired at the time they formed is lost. **As an extension, have students research and write about the scientist for whom the Curie point is named.** French physicist Pierre Curie P

Teacher FYI

Harry Hess (1906–1969) was a geologist who collected important data about the seafloor during World War II, when he was captain of a navy transport vessel. His ship was fitted with a new device called a Fathometer, an echo sounder that showed ocean floor depth under the ship. The data was meant to allow troop ships to get close to shore, but Hess used it to map the floor of the Pacific Ocean.

Resource Manager

Chapter Resources Booklet
   Transparency Activity, p. 45
   Enrichment, p. 31
   Directed Reading for Content Mastery, p. 20

Mapping the Ocean Floor, continued

Caption Answer
Figure 7 It shows the rock continually formed and moved away from the ridge over time.

③ Assess

Reteach
Have pairs of students construct three-dimensional models of the seafloor at a mid-ocean ridge. L1 ELL COOP LEARN
 **Kinesthetic**

Challenge
Have students research the scientific and technological advances that led to the theory of seafloor spreading. Have students display their discoveries on a timeline. L3 ☒ **Logical-Mathematical**

✓*Assessment*

Performance Assess students' understanding by challenging them to draw concept maps that contain the main ideas in this section. Use **Performance Assessment in the Science Classroom,** p. 161.

Resource Manager

Chapter Resources Booklet
Reinforcement, p. 28
Activity Worksheet, pp. 5–6
Mathematics Skill Activities, p. 5

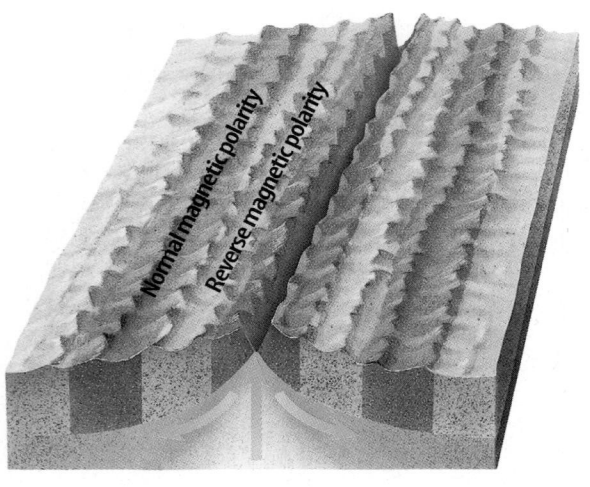

Figure 7
Changes in Earth's magnetic field are preserved in rock that forms on both sides of mid-ocean ridges. *Why is this considered to be evidence of seafloor spreading?*

Magnetic Time Scale Iron-bearing minerals, such as magnetite, that are found in the rocks of the seafloor can record Earth's magnetic field direction when they form. Whenever Earth's magnetic field reverses, newly forming iron minerals will record the magnetic reversal.

Using a sensing device called a magnetometer (mag nuh TAH muh tur) to detect magnetic fields, scientists found that rocks on the ocean floor show many periods of magnetic reversal. The magnetic alignment in the rocks reverses back and forth over time in strips parallel to the mid-ocean ridges, as shown in **Figure 7.** A strong magnetic reading is recorded when the polarity of a rock is the same as the polarity of Earth's magnetic field today. Because of this, normal polarities in rocks show up as large peaks. This discovery provided strong support that seafloor spreading was indeed occurring. The magnetic reversals showed that new rock was being formed at the mid-ocean ridges. This helped explain how the crust could move—something that the continental drift hypothesis could not do.

Section ② Assessment

1. What properties of iron-bearing minerals on the seafloor support the theory of seafloor spreading?
2. How do the ages of the rocks on the ocean floor support the theory of seafloor spreading?
3. How did Harry Hess's hypothesis explain seafloor movement?
4. Why does some partly molten material rise toward Earth's surface?
5. **Think Critically** The ideas of Hess, Wegener, and others emphasize that Earth is a dynamic planet. How is seafloor spreading different from continental drift?

Skill Builder Activities

6. **Concept Mapping** Make a concept map that includes evidence for seafloor spreading using the following phrases: *ages increase away from ridge, pattern of magnetic field reversals, mid-ocean ridge, pattern of ages,* and *reverses back and forth.* **For more help, refer to the** Science Skill Handbook.

7. **Solving One-Step Equations** North America is moving about 1.25 cm per year away from a ridge in the middle of the Atlantic Ocean. Using this rate, how much farther apart will North America and the ridge be in 200 million years? **For more help, refer to the** Math Skill Handbook.

Answers to Section Assessment

1. Magnetic reversals recorded in iron-bearing minerals show that new rock was being formed at the ridges over time.
2. The rocks get older as you move farther from the mid-ocean ridge.
3. Hot, dense material is forced upward at mid-ocean ridges. It then moves sideways, carrying the seafloor away from the ridge in both directions.
4. The molten material is less dense than the surrounding rock. So it is forced upward toward the surface.
5. Continental drift hypothesis provided no mechanism for movement; seafloor spreading explained how continents have separated over time as ocean basins enlarged.
6. *Pattern of magnetic field reversals* and *pattern of ages around ridge* branch from *mid-ocean ridge. Reverses back and forth* branches from *pattern of magnetic field reversals,* and *ages increase away from ridges* branches from *pattern of ages around ridge.*
7. If North America continues to move away from the Mid-Atlantic Ridge at 1.25 cm/y, these two features will separate an additional 250 million centimeters or 2,500 kilometers in 200 million years.

Activity

Seafloor Spreading Rates

How did scientists use their knowledge of seafloor spreading and magnetic field reversals to reconstruct Pangaea? Try this activity to see how you can determine where a continent may have been located in the past.

What You'll Investigate
Can you use clues, such as magnetic field reversals on Earth, to help reconstruct Pangaea?

Materials
metric ruler
pencil

Goals
■ **Interpret** data about magnetic field reversals. Use these magnetic clues to reconstruct Pangaea.

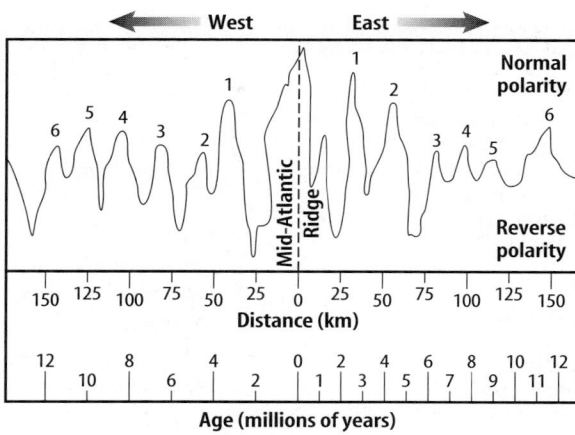

Procedure

1. Study the magnetic field graph above. You will be working only with normal polarity readings, which are the peaks above the baseline in the top half of the graph.

2. Place the long edge of a ruler vertically on the graph. Slide the ruler so that it lines up with the center of peak 1 west of the Mid-Atlantic Ridge.

3. **Determine** and record the distance and age that line up with the center of peak 1 west. Repeat this process for peak 1 east of the ridge.

4. **Calculate** the average age and distance for this pair of peaks.

5. Repeat steps 2 through 4 for the remaining pairs of normal-polarity peaks.

6. **Calculate** the rate of movement in cm per year for the six pairs of peaks. Use the formula rate = distance/time. Convert kilometers to centimeters. For example, to calculate a rate using normal-polarity peak 5, west of the ridge:

$$\text{rate} = \frac{125 \text{ km}}{10 \text{ million years}} = \frac{12.5 \text{ km}}{\text{million years}} =$$
$$\frac{1{,}250{,}000 \text{ cm}}{1{,}000{,}000 \text{ years}} = 1.25 \text{ cm/year}$$

Conclude and Apply

1. **Compare** the age of igneous rock found near the mid-ocean ridge with that of igneous rock found farther away from the ridge.

2. If the distance from a point on the coast of Africa to the Mid-Atlantic Ridge is approximately 2,400 km, calculate how long ago that point in Africa was at or near the Mid-Atlantic Ridge.

3. How could you use this method to reconstruct Pangaea?

ACTIVITY 399

Activity

BENCH TESTED

Purpose Students interpret magnetic field reversals in rock to determine the rate of seafloor spreading. L2
IS Logical-Mathematical
Process Skills making tables, using graphs, predicting, observing, inferring, using numbers, interpreting data
Time Required 50 to 60 minutes
Teaching Strategy Note that the rate of movement (half the spreading rate) is about 1.25 cm/yr.

Answers to Questions
1. The nearer rock is to the ridge, the younger it is.
2. About 192 million years ago, assuming a relatively constant rate of spreading
3. Students could determine when points on both coasts were at the ridge. This would mark when at least part of Pangaea was intact.

Assessment

Performance Have students measure the distance between a point on the east coast of the United States and the Mid-Atlantic Ridge. Have them determine when that point was near the mid-ocean ridge. Use **Performance Assessment in the Science Classroom,** p. 99.

Communicating Your Data

Students can use a table such as this to record data.

Sample Data Table:

Peak	1	2	3	4	5	6
Distance west normal polarity	40	60	75	100	125	140
Distance east normal polarity	36	60	80	100	118	145
Average distance	38	60	78	100	122	142
Age from scale (millions of years)	3.5	4.5	6.7	8.0	9.0	10.5
Rate of movement (cm/yr)	1.1	1.2	1.2	1.3	1.3	1.4

① Motivate

Bellringer Transparency

Display the Section Focus Transparency for Section 3. Use the accompanying Transparency Activity Master. L2
ELL

Tie to Prior Knowledge

Ask if anyone has ever experienced an earthquake. If so, have these students explain what happened. If no one has, explain that earthquakes cause the ground to shake, often causing great damage. Tell students that earthquakes often happen because of the movement of plates.

As You Read

What You'll Learn

- **Compare and contrast** different types of plate boundaries.
- **Explain** how heat inside Earth causes plate tectonics.
- **Recognize** features caused by plate tectonics.

Vocabulary

plate tectonics
plate
lithosphere
asthenosphere
convection current

Why It's Important

Plate tectonics explains how many of Earth's features form.

Plate Tectonics

The idea of seafloor spreading showed that more than just continents were moving, as Wegener had thought. It was now clear to scientists that sections of the seafloor and continents move in relation to one another.

Plate Movements In the 1960s, scientists developed a new theory that combined continental drift and seafloor spreading. According to the theory of **plate tectonics,** Earth's crust and part of the upper mantle are broken into sections. These sections, called **plates,** move on a plasticlike layer of the mantle. The plates can be thought of as rafts that float and move on this layer.

Composition of Earth's Plates Plates are made of the crust and a part of the upper mantle, as shown in **Figure 8.** These two parts combined are the **lithosphere** (LIH thuh sfihr). This rigid layer is about 100 km thick and generally is less dense than material underneath. The plasticlike layer below the lithosphere is called the **asthenosphere** (as THE nuh sfihr). The rigid plates of the lithosphere float and move around on the asthenosphere.

Figure 8
Plates of the lithosphere are composed of oceanic crust, continental crust, and rigid upper mantle.

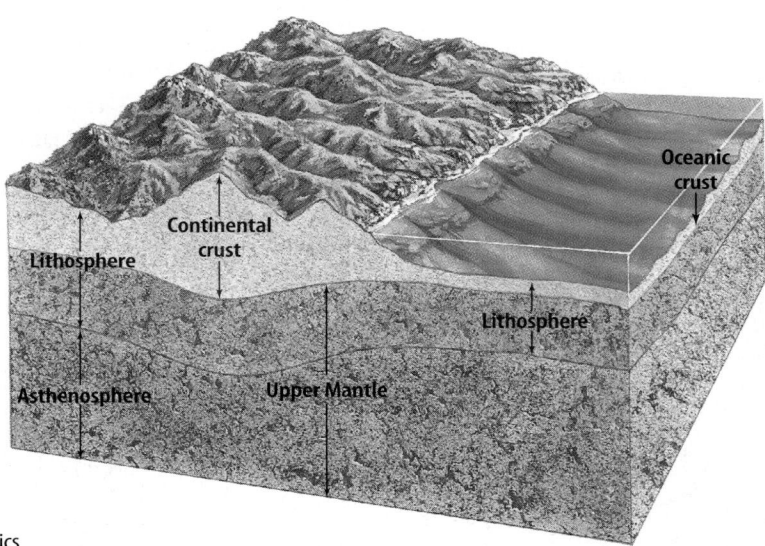

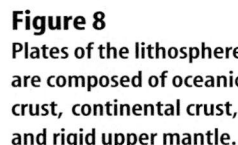

Section ✓ *Assessment* Planner

PORTFOLIO
Science Journal, p. 401
Extension, p. 403
PERFORMANCE ASSESSMENT
Problem-Solving Activity, p. 402
MiniLAB, p. 405

Skill Builder Activities, p. 409
See page 416 for more options.
CONTENT ASSESSMENT
Section, p. 409
Challenge, p. 409
Chapter, pp. 416–417

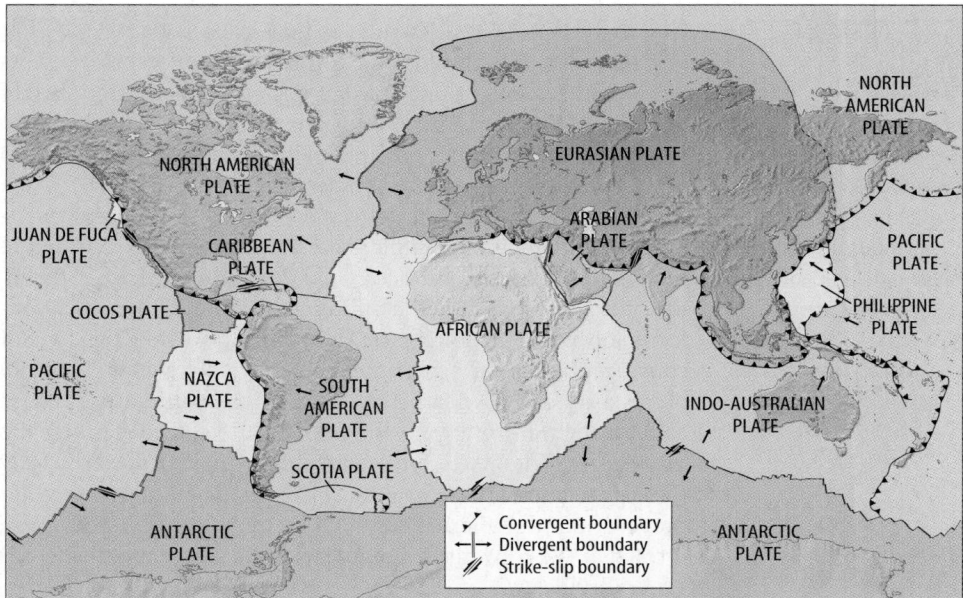

Plate Boundaries

When plates move, they can interact in several ways. They can move toward each other and converge, or collide. They also can pull apart or slide alongside one another. When the plates interact, the result of their movement is seen at the plate boundaries, as in **Figure 9.**

☑ **Reading Check**   *What are the general ways that plates interact?*

Movement along any plate boundary means that changes must happen at other boundaries. What is happening to the Atlantic Ocean floor between the North American and African Plates? Compare this with what is happening along the western margin of South America.

Plates Moving Apart   The boundary between two plates that are moving apart is called a divergent boundary. You learned about divergent boundaries when you read about seafloor spreading. In the Atlantic Ocean, the North American Plate is moving away from the Eurasian and the African Plates, as shown in **Figure 9.** That divergent boundary is called the Mid-Atlantic Ridge. The Great Rift Valley in eastern Africa might become a divergent plate boundary. There, a valley has formed where a continental plate is being pulled apart. **Figure 10** shows a side view of what a rift valley might look like and illustrates how the hot material rises up where plates separate.

Figure 9
This diagram shows the major plates of the lithosphere, their direction of movement, and the type of boundary between them. *Based on what is shown in this figure, what is happening where the Nazca Plate meets the Pacific Plate?*

Theory Development   Many scientists contributed ideas that led to plate tectonics theory. Have students select from A.L. Du Toit, S.K. Runcorn, Bruce Heezen, Arthur Holmes, J. Tuzo Wilson, Jack Oliver, Lynn R. Sykes, Fred Vine, D.H. Matthews, and L.W. Morley and write a one-page report in their Science Journals about his contributions. L2 P

Plate Tectonics

Quick Demo

Obtain a globe or make a map on which you can move continent pieces from a child's puzzle map. Use the globe or map to demonstrate continental movement.

Plate Boundaries

Caption Answer

Figure 9 These plates are moving away from each other.

☑ **Reading Check**

Answer Plates can collide, pull apart, or move past one another.

Extension

Have students research the geologic history of Iceland, concentrating on volcanic activity and its relationship to the Mid-Atlantic Ridge. Ask students to pinpoint on a map the location of the rift through the island and to indicate in which direction each section of the island is moving. L2 LS **Visual Spatial**

Plate Boundaries, continued

Activity

Show students a map with the location of volcanoes indicated. Have students use it to determine subduction areas. L2

VS Visual-Spatial

Use Science Words

Word Use Have students look up the words *diverge* and *converge* and use each word in a sentence. Then discuss how these meanings relate to plate boundaries. Possible answers: Two paths diverge at a fork in the road; traffic will converge in the center of the intersection. Plates converge, or come together, at some boundaries and diverge, or move apart, at others.

SCIENCE *Online*

Internet Addresses

Explore the Glencoe Science Web site at **science.glencoe.com** to find out more about topics in this section.

Problem-Solving Activity

National Math Standards
Correlation to Mathematics Objectives
6, 7, 8, 9

Answers

1. Yes, most fit together when continental shelves are included.
2. The continental shelves are the edges of continents. Present-day coastlines result from sea level changes.

SCIENCE *Online*

Research Visit the Glencoe Science Web site at **science.glencoe.com** for recent news or magazine articles about earthquakes and volcanic activity related to plate tectonics. Communicate to your class what you learned.

Plates Moving Together If new crust is being added at one location, why doesn't Earth's surface keep expanding? As new crust is added in one place, it disappears below the surface at another. The disappearance of crust can occur when seafloor cools, becomes denser, and sinks. This occurs where two plates move together at a convergent boundary.

When an oceanic plate converges with a less dense continental plate, the denser oceanic plate sinks under the continental plate. The area where an oceanic plate subducts, or goes down, into the mantle is called a subduction zone. Some volcanoes form above subduction zones. **Figure 10** shows how this type of convergent boundary creates a deep-sea trench where one plate bends and sinks beneath the other. High temperatures cause rock to melt around the subducting slab as it goes under the other plate. The newly formed magma is forced upward along these plate boundaries, forming volcanoes. The Andes mountain range of South America contains many volcanoes. They were formed at the convergent boundary of the Nazca and the South American Plates.

Problem-Solving Activity

How well do the continents fit together?

Recall the Explore Activity you performed at the beginning of this chapter. While you were trying to fit pieces of a cut-up photograph together, what clues did you use?

Identifying the Problem

Take a copy of a map of the world and cut out each continent. Lay them on a  tabletop and try to fit them together, using techniques you used in the Explore Activity. You will find that the pieces of your Earth puzzle—the continents—do not fit together well. Yet, several of the areas on some continents fit together extremely well.

Take out another world map—one that shows the continental shelves as well as the continents. Copy it and cut out the continents, this time including the continental shelves.

Solving the Problem

1. Does including the continental shelves solve the problem of fitting the continents together?
2. Why should continental shelves be included with maps of the continents?

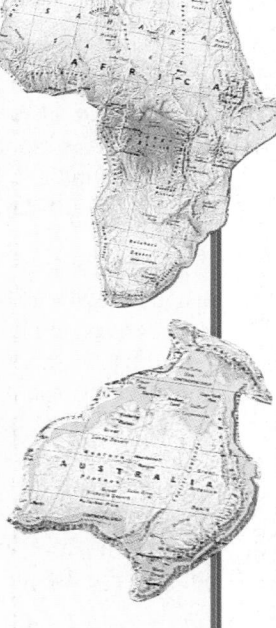

LAB DEMONSTRATION

Purpose to demonstrate compression forces that can form folded mountains

Materials two slabs of clay (5 cm thick and about 30 cm long), wax paper

Preparation Place the clay slabs on wax paper to make them easier to slide.

Procedure Lay the two clay pieces flat on a table. Have students predict what will happen when they are forced together. Push the two pieces together.

Expected Outcome Students will see folds and breaks form as the pieces of clay are pushed together.

✓Assessment

What landforms are the folds in the clay analogous to on Earth's surface? folded mountains

Figure 10

By diverging at some boundaries and converging at others, Earth's plates are continually—but gradually—reshaping the landscape around you. The Mid-Atlantic Ridge, for example, was formed when the North and South American Plates pulled apart from the Eurasian and African Plates (see globe). Some features that occur along plate boundaries—rift valleys, volcanoes, and mountain ranges—are shown on the right and below.

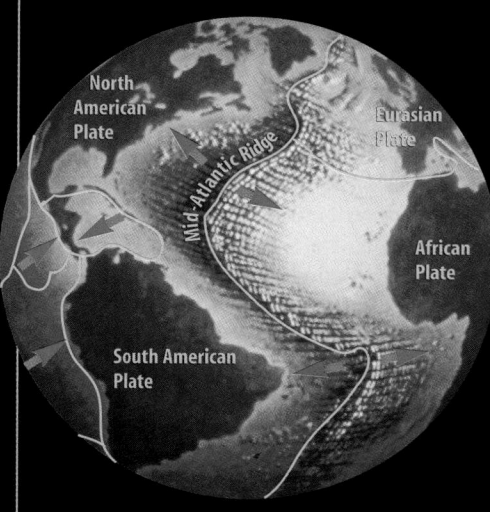

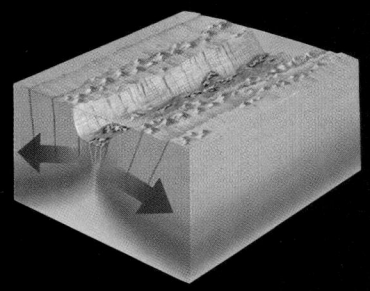

A RIFT VALLEY When continental plates pull apart, they can form rift valleys. The African continent is separating now along the East African Rift Valley.

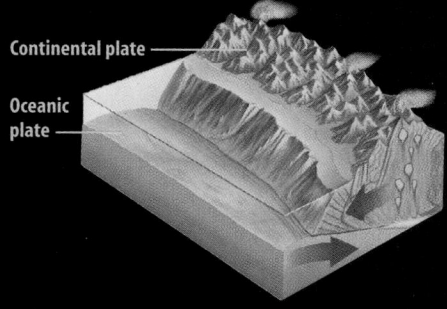

Continental plate

Oceanic plate

SUBDUCTION Where oceanic and continental plates collide, the oceanic plate plunges beneath the less dense continental plate. As the plate descends, molten rock (yellow) forms and rises toward the surface, creating volcanoes.

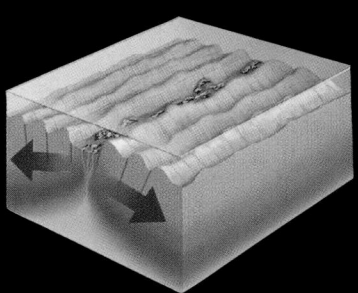

SEA-FLOOR SPREADING A mid-ocean ridge, like the Mid-Atlantic Ridge, forms where oceanic plates continue to separate. As rising magma (yellow) cools, it forms new oceanic crust.

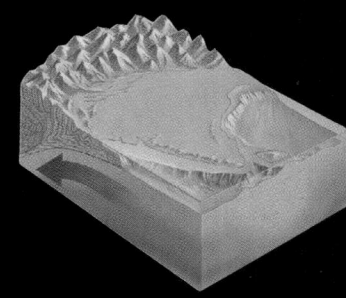

CONTINENTAL COLLISION Where two continental plates collide, they push up the crust to form mountain ranges such as the Himalaya.

403

Visualizing Plate Boundaries

Have students examine the pictures and read the captions. Then ask the following questions.

How would you predict the size of the Atlantic Ocean will change over the next 100 million years? Why? The Atlantic Ocean will become larger because sea-floor spreading is occurring along the Mid-Atlantic Ridge.

The Andes Mountains are found along the west coast of South America. How did this mountain chain form? The plate boundary along the west coast of South America is a convergent boundary, which results in the formation of mountains and volcanoes.

Activity

Have small groups research the history of Surtsey, a small island in the North Atlantic Ocean. Ask them to draw a map of the island's location and write a summary of how the island formed, describing the type of plate boundary and the volcanic activity involved. L2 ELL COOP LEARN IS **Interpersonal**

Extension

Challenge students to research how lasers and other instruments are used to monitor plate movements. Have students report their findings in brief written reports. L2 IS **Linguistic** P

Resource Manager

Chapter Resources Booklet
Transparency Activity, pp. 48–49
Lab Activity, pp. 13–15
Home and Community Involvement, p. 31

Plate Boundaries,
continued

Extension

Have students write reports in their Science Journals about the history of the study of the ocean floor. Reports should compare and contrast the work of crews aboard the *Glomar Challenger* and *JOIDES Resolution*. [L3]
LS Linguistic

Visual Learning

Figure 11B Have students study the photograph of the San Andreas Fault and then describe evidence that shows the plates on either side of the fault are moving. Students should see that streams and other features that cross the fault are offset because of movement.

Caption Answer

Figure 11A The western side (Pacific Plate) of the fault is moving faster than the eastern side (North American Plate).

Where Plates Collide A subduction zone also can form where two oceanic plates converge. In this case, the colder, older, denser oceanic plate bends and sinks down into the mantle. The Mariana Islands in the western Pacific are a chain of volcanic islands formed where two oceanic plates collide.

Usually, no subduction occurs when two continental plates collide, as shown in **Figure 10.** Because both of these plates are less dense than the material in the asthenosphere, the two plates collide and crumple up, forming mountain ranges. Earthquakes are common at these convergent boundaries. However, volcanoes do not form because there is no, or little, subduction. The Himalaya in Asia are forming where the Indo-Australian Plate collides with the Eurasian Plate.

Where Plates Slide Past Each Other The third type of plate boundary is called a transform boundary. Transform boundaries occur where two plates slide past one another. They move in opposite directions or in the same direction at different rates. When one plate slips past another suddenly, earthquakes occur. The Pacific Plate is sliding past the North American Plate, forming the famous San Andreas Fault in California, as seen in **Figure 11.** The San Andreas Fault is part of a transform plate boundary. It has been the site of many earthquakes.

Figure 11
The San Andreas Fault in California occurs along the transform plate boundary where the Pacific Plate is sliding past the North American Plate.

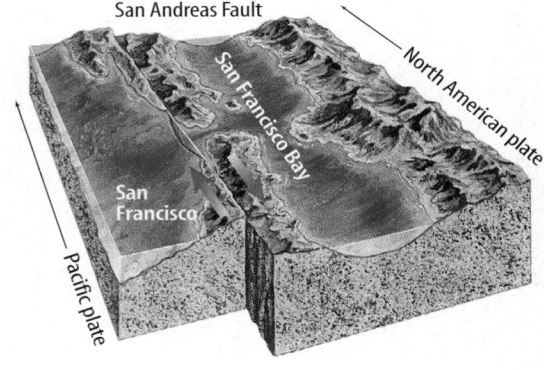

A Overall, the two plates are moving in roughly the same direction. *Why, then, do the red arrows show movement in opposite directions?*

San Andreas Fault

San Francisco Bay

North American plate

San Francisco

Pacific plate

 **B** This photograph shows an aerial view of the San Andreas Fault.

Curriculum Connection

Mathematics The deepest point on Earth's surface is the bottom of the Mariana Trench, 11.2 km below sea level. Have students find Earth's highest point. Mt. Everest is 8.8 km above sea level. After students determine which is bigger, have them draw a scale diagram showing Mt. Everest in the trench. Their drawings should show how many kilometers Mt. Everest's top would be below sea level. 2.4 km

Resource Manager

Chapter Resources Booklet
   MiniLAB, p. 4

Earth Science Critical Thinking/Problem Solving, p. 8

Reading and Writing Skill Activities,
   p. 27

Causes of Plate Tectonics

Many new discoveries have been made about Earth's crust since Wegener's day, but one question still remains. What causes the plates to move? Scientists now think they have a good idea. They think that plates move by the same basic process that occurs when you heat soup.

Convection Inside Earth Soup that is cooking in a pan on the stove contains currents caused by an unequal distribution of heat in the pan. Hot, less dense soup is forced upward by the surrounding, cooler soup. As the hot soup reaches the surface, it cools and sinks back down into the pan. This entire cycle of heating, rising, cooling, and sinking is called a **convection current**. A version of this same process, occurring in the mantle, is thought to be the force behind plate tectonics. Scientists suggest that differences in density cause hot, plasticlike rock to be forced upward toward the surface.

Moving Mantle Material Wegener wasn't able to come up with an explanation for why plates move. Today, researchers who study the movement of heat in Earth's interior have proposed several possible explanations. All of the hypotheses use convection in one way or another. It is, therefore, the transfer of heat inside Earth that provides the energy to move plates and causes many of Earth's surface features. One hypothesis is shown in **Figure 12.** It relates plate motion directly to the movement of convection currents. According to this hypothesis, convection currents cause the movements of plates.

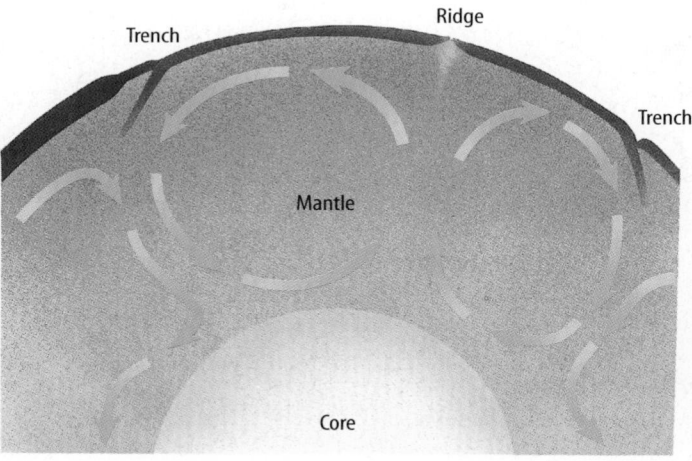

Trench
Ridge
Trench
Mantle
Core

Figure 12
In one hypothesis, convection currents occur throughout the mantle. Such convection currents (see arrows) are the driving force of plate tectonics.

Mini LAB

Modeling Convection Currents

Procedure
1. Pour **water** into a **clear, colorless casserole dish** until it is 5 cm from the top.
2. Center the dish on a **hot plate** and heat it. **WARNING:** *Wear **thermal mitts** to protect your hands.*
3. Add a few drops of **food coloring** to the water above the center of the hot plate.
4. Looking from the side of the dish, observe what happens in the water.
5. Illustrate your observations in your **Science Journal.**

Analysis
1. Determine whether any currents form in the water.
2. Infer what causes the currents to form.

Mini LAB

Purpose Students model and observe currents. L2 ELL IS **Visual-Spatial**

Materials clear glass casserole dish, water, hot plate, food coloring, thermal mitts

Teaching Strategy Have students note any movement in the water.

Safety Precautions Students must wear thermal mitts. Be sure the dish is stove-top safe.

Analysis
1. Some students will observe currents; others won't.
2. The transfer of thermal energy from the burner to the dish warms the water near the bottom of the dish. The cooler, denser water at the top of the dish sinks, displacing the warmer, less dense water, which then moves toward the top of the dish. As the warmer water cools, it becomes denser and sinks to start the cycle again.

✓ Assessment

Process Direct students to add informative labels to the drawings they made of their observations. The labels should be numbered and in sequence, explaining the steps in the formation and movement of convection currents. Use **PASC,** p. 127.

✔ Active Reading

Write-Draw-Discuss This strategy encourages students to actively participate in reading and lectures, assimilating content creatively. Have students write about an idea, clarify it, then make an illustration or drawing. Ask students to share responses with the class and display several examples. Have students Write-Draw-Discuss about the causes of plate tectonics.

Cultural Diversity

Hawaiian Terms The Hawaiian Islands are volcanoes that formed as a result of magma rising through a "hot spot" in the middle of a plate. Some volcanic rocks have names that were made common in Hawaii. *Pahoehoe* (pa-hoe-ee-hoe-ee), from the Hawaiian word meaning "rope," forms in linear ridges. *Aa* (ah-ah) forms with sharp, jagged surfaces.

Features Caused by Plate Tectonics

Discussion

Why are earthquakes "associated" with plate boundaries?
Plates do not move smoothly. Instead, they stick and catch on each other. When the plates are "stuck," strain, or potential energy, builds up in the rocks. When the plates move again, this energy is released as an earthquake.

Caption Answer

Figure 13 tension

Make a Model

Have students use paper to make a model of a divergent boundary with seafloor spreading. The model should be dynamic and show how spreading occurs. Students can draw parallel ridges on a long piece of paper and construct a mechanism for the paper to be drawn upward from both sides through a slot (the plate boundary), revealing "new" parallel ridges as it emerges. Accept any workable design. L2 ELL
LS Visual-Spatial

Activity

Organize students into four groups and assign each group one of the following topics to master and present to the class: convergent boundaries, divergent boundaries, transform boundaries, and the driving mechanism of plate tectonics. L2 COOP LEARN **LS Interpersonal**

✔ **Reading Check**

Answer earthquakes

Features Caused by Plate Tectonics

Earth is a dynamic planet with a hot interior. This heat leads to convection, which powers the movement of plates. As the plates move, they interact. The interaction of plates produces forces that build mountains, create ocean basins, and cause volcanoes. When rocks in Earth's crust break and move, energy is released in the form of seismic waves. Humans feel this release as earthquakes. You can see some of the effects of plate tectonics in mountainous regions, where volcanoes erupt, or where landscapes have changed from past earthquake or volcanic activity.

✔ **Reading Check** *What happens when seismic energy is released as rocks in Earth's crust break and move?*

Normal Faults and Rift Valleys Tension forces, which are forces that pull apart, can stretch Earth's crust. This causes large blocks of crust to break and tilt or slide down the broken surfaces of crust. When rocks break and move along surfaces, a fault forms. Faults interrupt rock layers by moving them out of place. Entire mountain ranges can form in the process, called fault-block mountains, as shown in **Figure 13.** Generally, the faults that form from pull-apart forces are normal faults—faults in which the rock layers above the fault move down when compared with rock layers below the fault.

Rift valleys and mid-ocean ridges can form where Earth's crust separates. Examples of rift valleys are the Great Rift Valley in Africa, and the valleys that occur in the middle of mid-ocean ridges. Examples of mid-ocean ridges include the Mid-Atlantic Ridge and the East Pacific Rise.

Figure 13
Fault-block mountains can form when Earth's crust is stretched by tectonic forces. The arrows indicate the directions of moving blocks. *What type of force occurs when Earth's crust is pulled in opposite directions?*

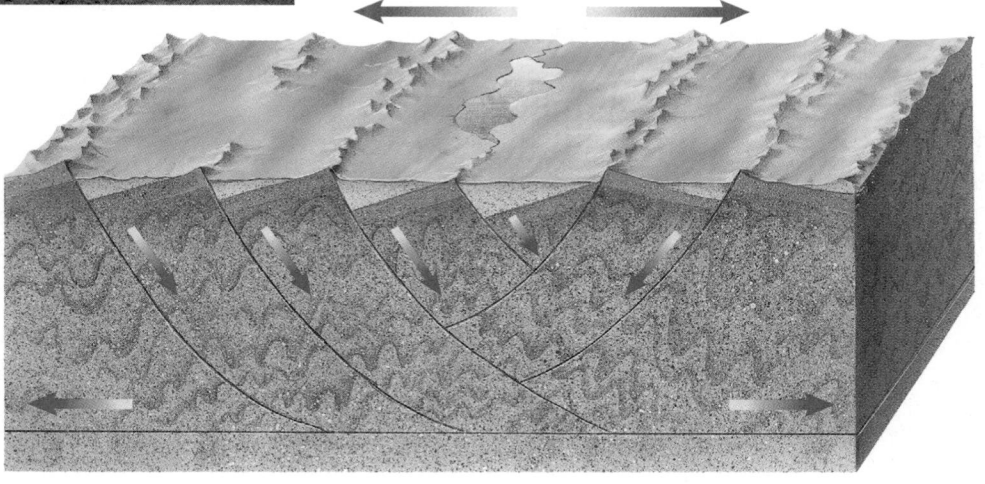

406 **CHAPTER 14** Plate Tectonics

Inclusion Strategies

Gifted Have students place a piece of long, plastic tubing into the neck of a strong balloon and secure the tube so no air can escape from the balloon. Have them place the balloon at the bottom of an aquarium tank, with the tubing extending over the top of the tank. Then have students add alternating 2-mm layers of moist sand and dry sand to the bottom of the tank, covering the balloon. If they wish, students can build a small city on the top sand layer. Then have one student slowly blow up the balloon until the sand begins to crack to simulate an earthquake. Another student can videotape the "earthquake," and students can prepare a documentary showing how the quake affected the "city." L3 COOP LEARN **LS Kinesthetic**

Mountains and Volcanoes Compression forces squeeze objects together. Where plates come together, compression forces produce several effects. As continental plates collide, the forces that are generated cause massive folding and faulting of rock layers into mountain ranges such as the Himalaya, shown in **Figure 14,** or the Appalachian Mountains. The type of faulting produced is generally reverse faulting. Along a reverse fault, the rock layers above the fault surface move up relative to the rock layers below the fault.

☑ **Reading Check** *What features occur where plates converge?*

As you learned earlier, when two oceanic plates converge, the denser plate is forced beneath the other plate. Curved chains of volcanic islands called island arcs form above the sinking plate. If an oceanic plate converges with a continental plate, the denser oceanic plate slides under the continental plate. Folding and faulting at the continental plate margin can thicken the continental crust to produce mountain ranges. Volcanoes also typically are formed at this type of convergent boundary.

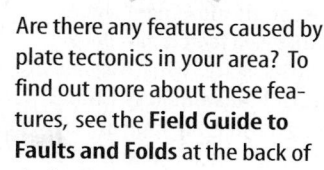

Are there any features caused by plate tectonics in your area? To find out more about these features, see the **Field Guide to Faults and Folds** at the back of the book.

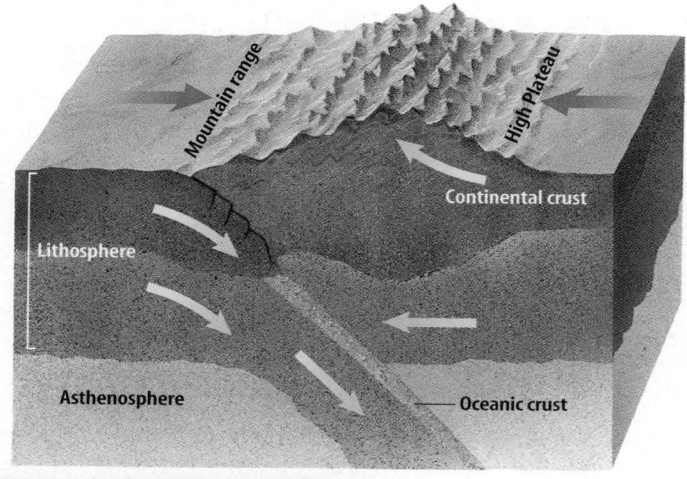

Figure 14
The Himalaya still are forming today as the Indo-Australian Plate collides with the Eurasian Plate.

☑ **Reading Check**

Answer continental–continental: high mountain ranges; oceanic–oceanic: island arcs; oceanic–continental: mountains and volcanoes

Teacher FYI

As the Indo-Australian Plate continues to push into and under the Eurasian Plate, the Eurasian Plate is thrust up over it. India moves into Asia at a rate of 3.7 to 5.4 cm/yr, thrusting the Himalaya about 1 cm higher each year. But because forces of erosion wear down the mountains by about the same amount annually, they remain about the same height.

Make a Model

Provide clay with which students can make models to show the movement of plates at a strike-slip fault. Have them include surface features offset by the movement. L1 IS **Kinesthetic**

Resource Manager

Chapter Resources Booklet
  Enrichment, p. 32

Performance Assessment in the Science Classroom, p. 42

Curriculum Connection

Geography Have students search the Internet, newspapers, and magazines for stories about earthquakes and volcanic eruptions that have occurred as a result of plate movements along faults. Have students summarize their findings in written paragraphs to share in class. Have students make a bulletin board display that includes a map showing the location of these tectonic events. L2 IS **Visual-Spatial**

Features Caused by Plate Tectonics, continued

Discussion

Would you live or construct a building along a strike-slip fault? Explain. Most would not because of the danger of earthquakes and the likelihood of destruction. **Why might so many people live along the San Andreas Fault?** Possible answers: Some people were there before the danger was known; some think the danger is minimal, some might be unable to relocate; some may think that other factors (climate, economic advantages) outweigh the negatives of earthquake danger.

Testing for Plate Tectonics

Physics
INTEGRATION

Convergent: toward each other; divergent: away from each other; transform: sliding past each other.

Teacher FYI

Creepmeters, lasers, and satellites are used to measure plate movements. They have shown that the Pacific Plate has been sliding past the North American Plate along the San Andreas Fault at a rate of 1.2 to 3.3 cm/yr. If that continues, the Pacific Plate will continue to move north relative to the North American Plate, bringing Los Angeles up next to San Francisco in about 27 million years.

Figure 15
Most of the movement along a strike-slip fault is parallel to Earth's surface. When movement occurs, human-built structures along a strike-slip fault are offset, as shown here in this road.

Physics
INTEGRATION

In which directions do forces act at convergent, divergent, and transform boundaries? Demonstrate these forces using wooden blocks or your hands.

Strike-Slip Faults At transform boundaries, two plates slide past one another without converging or diverging. The plates stick and then slide, mostly in a horizontal direction, along large strike-slip faults. In a strike-slip fault, rocks on opposite sides of the fault move in opposite directions, or in the same direction at different rates. This type of fault movement is shown in **Figure 15.** One such example is the San Andreas Fault. When plates move suddenly, vibrations are generated inside Earth that are felt as an earthquake.

Earthquakes, volcanoes, and mountain ranges are evidence of plate motion. Plate tectonics explains how activity inside Earth can affect Earth's crust differently in different locations. You've seen how plates have moved since Pangaea separated. Is it possible to measure how far plates move each year?

Testing for Plate Tectonics

Until recently, the only tests scientists could use to check for plate movement were indirect. They could study the magnetic characteristics of rocks on the seafloor. They could study volcanoes and earthquakes. These methods supported the theory that the plates have moved and still are moving. However, they did not provide proof—only support—of the idea.

New methods had to be discovered to be able to measure the small amounts of movement of Earth's plates. One method, shown in **Figure 16,** uses lasers and a satellite. Now, scientists can measure exact movements of Earth's plates of as little as 1 cm per year.

408 CHAPTER 14 Plate Tectonics

Resource Manager

Chapter Resources Booklet
Activity Worksheet, pp. 7–8
Reinforcement, p. 29
Lab Management and Safety, p. 65

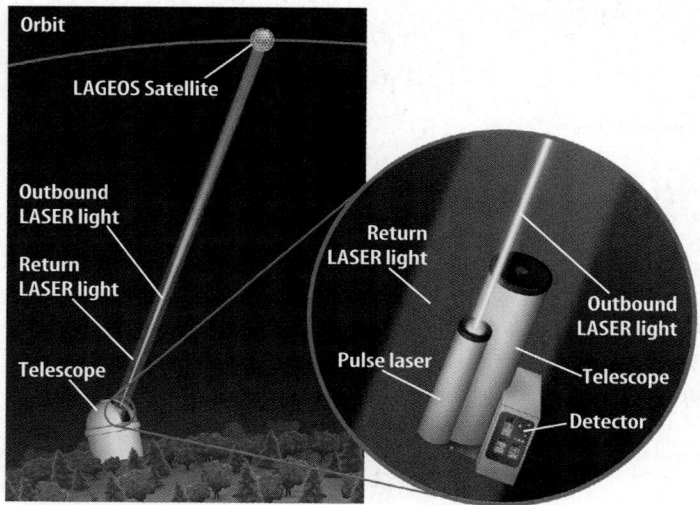

Orbit
LAGEOS Satellite
Outbound LASER light
Return LASER light
Telescope

Return LASER light
Outbound LASER light
Pulse laser
Telescope
Detector

Figure 16
When using the Satellite Laser Ranging System, scientists on the ground aim laser pulses at a satellite. The pulses reflect off the satellite and are used to determine a precise location on the ground.

Current Data Satellite data show that Hawaii is moving toward Japan at a rate of about 8.3 cm per year. Maryland is moving away from England at a rate of 1.7 cm per year. Using such methods, scientists have observed that the plates move at rates ranging from about 1 cm to 12 cm per year.

Section 3 Assessment

1. What happens to plates at a transform plate boundary?

2. What occurs at plate boundaries that are associated with seafloor spreading?

3. Describe three types of plate boundaries where volcanic eruptions can occur.

4. How are convection currents related to plate tectonics?

5. **Think Critically** Using **Figure 9** and a world map, determine what natural disasters might occur in Iceland. Also determine what disasters might occur in Tibet. Explain why some Icelandic disasters are not expected to occur in Tibet.

Skill Builder Activities

6. **Predicting** Plate tectonic activity causes many events that can be dangerous to humans. One of these events is a seismic sea wave, or tsunami. Learn how scientists predict the arrival time of a tsunami in a coastal area. **For more help, refer to the** Science Skill Handbook.

7. **Using a Word Processor** Write three separate descriptions of the three basic types of plate boundaries—divergent boundaries, convergent boundaries, and transform boundaries. Then draw a sketch of an example of each boundary next to your description. **For more help, refer to the** Technology Skill Handbook.

SECTION 3 Theory of Plate Tectonics **409**

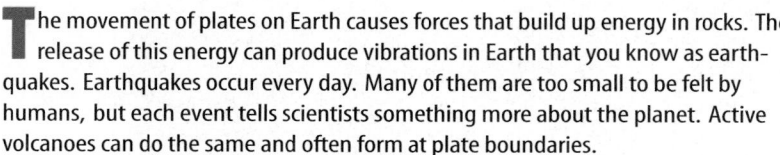

Recognize the Problem

Internet Students will obtain the latitudes and longitudes of recent earthquakes and volcanic eruptions. Data can be accessed through the Glencoe Science Web site at **science.glencoe.com.** They will plot these locations on a map of the world. Once plotted, students will use the locations to determine tectonically active areas of Earth.

Non-Internet Sources Students will obtain maps of the world on which they will make their plots. They will use the plotted locations on the map to determine tectonically active areas of Earth.

Time Required

two 35- to 40-minute class periods or one block of 70 to 80 minutes

Preparation

Internet Access the Glencoe Science Web site at **science. glencoe.com** to run through the steps that students will follow.

Non-Internet Sources If the Internet is not used, obtain tissue paper or sheets of plastic for students to use to draw copies of maps showing the locations of recent earthquakes and volcanic eruptions. The locations of earthquake epicenters and erupting volcanoes can be obtained from the U.S. Geological Survey or from local newspapers.

Predicting Tectonic Activity

The movement of plates on Earth causes forces that build up energy in rocks. The release of this energy can produce vibrations in Earth that you know as earthquakes. Earthquakes occur every day. Many of them are too small to be felt by humans, but each event tells scientists something more about the planet. Active volcanoes can do the same and often form at plate boundaries.

Recognize the Problem

Can you predict tectonically active areas by plotting locations of earthquake epicenters and volcanic eruptions?

Form a Hypothesis

Think about where earthquakes and volcanoes have occurred in the past. Make a hypothesis about whether the locations of earthquake epicenters and active volcanoes can be used to predict tectonically active areas.

Goals

- **Research** the locations of earthquakes and volcanic eruptions around the world.
- **Plot** earthquake epicenters and the locations of volcanic eruptions obtained from the Glencoe Science Web site.
- **Predict** locations that are tectonically active based on a plot of the locations of earthquake epicenters and active volcanoes.

Data Sources

SCIENCE *Online* Go to the Glencoe Science Web site at **science.glencoe.com** for more information about earthquake and volcano sites, hints about earthquake and volcano sites, and data from other students.

Inclusion Strategies

Learning Disabled Pair learning disabled students with other students who can assist them with working on the computer. Encourage learning disabled students to take the lead in recording data, with the assistance of their partners.

Test Your Hypothesis

Plan

1. Make a data table in your Science Journal like the one shown.

2. Collect data for earthquake epicenters and volcanic eruptions for at least the past two weeks. Your data should include the longitude and latitude for each location. For help, refer to the data sources given on the opposite page.

Do

1. Make sure your teacher approves your plan before you start.

2. **Plot** the locations of earthquake epicenters and volcanic eruptions on a map of the world. Use an overlay of tissue paper or plastic.

Locations of Epicenters and Eruptions		
Earthquake Epicenter/ Volcanic Eruption	Longitude	Latitude
Answers will vary.		

3. After you have collected the necessary data, predict where the tectonically active areas on Earth are.

4. **Compare and contrast** the areas that you predicted to be tectonically active with the plate boundary map shown in **Figure 9.**

Analyze Your Data

1. What areas on Earth do you predict to be the locations of tectonic activity?

2. How close did your prediction come to the actual location of tectonically active areas?

Draw Conclusions

1. How could you make your predictions closer to the locations of actual tectonic activity?

2. Would data from a longer period of time help? Explain.

3. What types of plate boundaries were close to your locations of earthquake epicenters? Volcanic eruptions?

4. **Explain** which types of plate boundaries produce volcanic eruptions. Be specific.

Communicating Your Data

SCIENCE *Online* Find this Internet activity on the Glencoe Science Web site at **science.glencoe.com.** **Post** your data in the table provided. **Compare** your data to those of other students. Combine your data with those of other students and **plot** these combined data on a map to **recognize** the relationship between plate boundaries, volcanic eruptions, and earthquake epicenters.

✓Assessment

Oral Have pairs of students form a hypothesis that could explain the relationship between the locations of earthquake epicenters and active volcanoes and Earth's tectonic activity. Have each pair of students report to the class. Use **Performance Assessment in the Science Classroom,** p. 93.

Communicating Your Data

Plot all data from each student in the class on one large map. Lead students to the realization that as more and more data are placed on the map, the relationship of these data to the location of tectonically active areas on Earth becomes much more evident.

Form a Hypothesis

Possible Hypothesis

Most student hypotheses will reflect that earthquake and volcanic activity are good predictors of tectonically active areas.

Test Your Hypothesis

Teaching Strategy Encourage students to look for clusters of earthquake and volcanic activity, or for events that occur in a linear pattern.

Expected Outcome

Students should see patterns in the locations of earthquake and volcanic activity.

Analyze Your Data

1. Predictions will likely match the locations of plate boundaries.

2. Answers will depend on data collected. Most occur along plate boundaries. Hot spot eruptions may not coincide with plate boundaries.

Draw Conclusions

1. by collecting more data points

2. Yes; it would provide more data, which would help to more closely pinpoint these areas.

3. Earthquakes: near any type with many near convergent and transform boundaries; volcanoes: near divergent boundaries and subduction zones

4. Convergent ocean-ocean and ocean-continental boundaries where one plate is subducted under the other produce magma that rises and forms volcanoes. Volcanoes also form along divergent boundaries where magma rises through cracks in the crust, either at mid-ocean ridges or on land in rift valleys.

Science and Language Arts

Listening In
by Gordon Judge

Ask students to think of a time when they listened to or overheard someone else's conversation. What happens when they can't hear everything that is being said? Tell students to keep this question in mind as they read the selection.

Respond to the Reading

Active Reading Strategies

Evaluate Titles are often important aspects of stories and poems. They help give the reader insight into the passage that he or she might not otherwise have. **What significance does this title have to the poem?**

Respond Consider the rhyme scheme of this poem. Ask yourself what affect the song-like quality of this poem has on you. **Does it remind you of other poems you've read?**

Question Reread the lines in the poem that discuss plate tectonics and other theories relating to the formation of volcanoes. Check these against relevant passages in this chapter to make sure you understand them.

Answers to Questions
1. a piece of seafloor on a plate in the Atlantic Ocean
2. Because the movement of plates is so slow.
3. a seafloor in the Pacific Ocean

Respond to the Reading

1. Who is narrating the poem?
2. Why might the narrator think he or she hasn't "moved for ages"?
3. Who or what is the narrator's "best mate"?

I'm just a bit of seafloor on this mighty solid sphere.
With no mind to be broadened, I'm quite content down here.
The mantle churns below me, and the sea's in turmoil, too;
But nothing much disturbs me, I'm rock solid through and
　　through.

I do pick up occasional low-frequency vibrations –
(I think, although I can't be sure, they're sperm whales'
　　conversations).
I know I shouldn't listen in, but what else can I do?
It seems they are all studying for degrees from the OU.

They've mentioned me in passing, as their minds begin improving:
I think I've heard them say "The theory says the sea-floor's
　　moving…".
Well, that shook me, I can tell you; yes, it gave me quite a fright.
Yet I've not moved for ages, so I *know* it can't be right.

They call it "Plate Tectonics", this new theory in their noddle.
If they would only ask me, I could tell them it's all twaddle.
Apparently, I "oozed out from a mid-Atlantic split,
Solidified and cooled right down, then moved out bit by bit".

But, how can I be moving, when I know full well myself
That I'm quite firmly anchored to a continental shelf?
"Well, the continent is moving, too; you're *pushing* it, you see,"
I hear those OU whales intone, hydro-acoustically.

Now, my best mate's a sea floor in the mighty East Pacific.
He reckons life is balmy there: the summers are terrific!
He's heard the whale-talk, too, and found it pretty scary.
"Subduction" was the word he heard, which sounded rather hairy.

It was to be his fate, they claimed with undisguised great relish:
A hot and fiery end to things – it really would be hellish.
In fact, he'd end up underneath *my* continent, lengthwise,
So I would be the one to blame for my poor mate's demise.

Well, thank you very much, OU. You've upset my composure.
Next time you send your student whales to look at my exposure
I'll tell them it's a load of tosh: it's *they* who move, not me,
Those arty-smarty blobs of blubber, clogging up the sea!

The abbreviation in the poem, "OU," refers to the United Kingdom's Open University.

Reading Further

Other sources on this topic include:

Volcano Cowboys: The Rocky Evolution of a Dangerous Science, by Dick Thompson, St. Martins Press, July 2000.

Encyclopedia of Volcanoes; by Haraldur Sigurdsson (Editor), Bruce Houghton, (Editor), Stephen R. McNutt (Editor), John Stix (Editor), Hazel Rymer (Editor); Academic Press; October 1999.

Melting the Earth: The History of Ideas on Volcanic Eruptions, by Haraldur Sigurdsson, Oxford University Press, June 1999.

Understanding Literature

Point of View Point of view refers to the perspective from which an author writes. This poem begins, "I'm just a bit of sea floor…." Right away, you know that the poem, or story, is being told from the point of view of the speaker, or the "first person." Not all first-person stories are told from the point of view of a person. The narrator in this poem is a geological feature, not a person. This point of view helps give the poem a fantastic or outlandish quality. It also gives a playful tone to the poem. What other effects does the first-person narration have on the story?

Science Connection Volcanoes can occur where two plates move toward each other. In the poem, the author gives several clues that a volcano will form. First, the narrator's "best mate" is a seafloor in the Pacific Ocean. When an oceanic plate and a continental plate collide, a volcano will form. The narrator also hears the word *subduction* spoken. Subduction zones occur when one plate sinks under another plate. Rocks melt in the zones where these plates converge, causing magma to move upward and form volcanic mountains. What other clues does the author give that a volcano will form?

Linking Science and Writing

Using Point of View Using the first-person point of view, write an account from the point of view of a living or nonliving thing. You could write an account of an object, such as a pencil, that you use or encounter every day. You also could write from the point of view of a living thing, such as a family pet. Be sure to use the personal pronoun "I" in your account.

Career Connection

Volcanologist

Ed Klimasauskas is a volcanologist at the Cascades Volcano Observatory in Washington State. His job is to study volcanoes in order to predict eruptions. Volcanologists' predictions can save lives: people can be evacuated from danger areas before an eruption occurs. Klimasauskas also educates the public about the hazards of volcanic eruptions and tells people who live near active volcanoes what they can do to be safe in case a volcano erupts. Volcanologists travel all over the world to study new sites.

SCIENCE*Online* To learn more about careers in volcanology, visit the Glencoe Science Web site at **science.glencoe.com.**

Understanding Literature

Answers to Questions

Answers may vary but might include that the use of "I" gives a personal tone or human touch to otherwise technical or scientific material. Giving inanimate objects human traits personalizes science and gives it warmth.

Science Connection

There are approximately 600 active volcanoes in the world. However, active volcanoes do not appear by chance. Most occur in belts, around mountain ranges that border the Pacific Ocean. In the poem, the narrator is "overhearing" a description of how the Pacific Plate is pushing beneath the adjacent continents—a process known as subduction.

Linking Science and Writing

Teaching Strategy

Warm-up the class to write from a point of view other than their own by playing a game. Think of a common household or classroom object, such as a hairbrush. Tell students that you spend your day living in rats' nests, trying to untangle things. Give students clues until they guess what you're thinking. Have other students do the same.

Career Connection

Because volcanoes are complex phenomena, it helps to get an early start if students are interested in the field. Students can take courses in high school such as biology, chemistry, physics, and Earth sciences. Because of the specialized nature of volcanology, volcanologists usually have a Ph.D. degree in geology.

SCIENCE *Online*
Internet Addresses

_____

_____

_____

Explore the Glencoe Science Web site at **science.glencoe.com** to find out more about topics in this feature.

Reviewing Main Ideas

Preview

Students can answer the questions in their Science Journals. Discuss the answers as you go through the chapter. **Linguistic**

Review

Students can write their answers, then compare them with those of other students. **Interpersonal**

Reteach

Students can look at the illustrations and describe details that support the main ideas of the chapter. **Visual-Spatial**

Answers to Chapter Review

SECTION 1

2. Fossils of the same types of land and fresh water organisms on widely separated landmasses indicate that the landmasses were once joined.

SECTION 2

2. Seafloor basalt contains magnetic minerals that "lock in" Earth's magnetic field as they solidify.

SECTION 3

3. The crust on converging continental plates deforms into high mountains. At other converging boundaries, crust that sinks into the mantle melts and magma is forced upward to form volcanic mountains.

Reviewing Main Ideas

Section 1 Continental Drift

1. Alfred Wegener suggested that the continents were joined together at some point in the past in a large landmass he called Pangaea. Wegener proposed that continents have moved slowly, over millions of years, to their current locations.

2. The puzzlelike fit of the continents, fossils, climatic evidence, and similar rock structures support Wegener's idea of continental drift. However, Wegener could not explain what process could cause the movement of the landmasses. *How do fossils support the hypothesis of continental drift?*

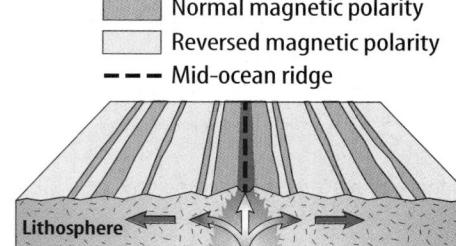

Section 2 Seafloor Spreading

1. Detailed mapping of the ocean floor in the 1950s showed underwater mountains and rift valleys.

2. In the 1960s, Harry Hess suggested seafloor spreading as an explanation for the formation of mid-ocean ridges. *How is magnetic evidence preserved in rocks forming along a mid-ocean ridge?*

■ Normal magnetic polarity
□ Reversed magnetic polarity
- - - Mid-ocean ridge

Lithosphere

3. The theory of seafloor spreading is supported by magnetic evidence in rocks and by the ages of rocks on the ocean floor.

Section 3 Theory of Plate Tectonics

1. In the 1960s, scientists combined the ideas of continental drift and seafloor spreading to develop the theory of plate tectonics. The theory states that the surface of Earth is broken into sections called plates that move around on the asthenosphere.

2. Currents in Earth's mantle called convection currents transfer heat in Earth's interior. It is thought that this transfer of heat energy moves plates.

3. Earth is a dynamic planet. As the plates move, they interact, resulting in many of the features of Earth's surface. *How do converging plates form mountains?*

FOLDABLES
Reading & Study Skills

After You Read

To help you review what you learned about plate tectonics, use the Foldable you made at the beginning of the chapter.

FOLDABLES
Reading & Study Skills

After You Read

After students have read the chapter and completed the Foldable described in Before You Read, have them do the activity on the student page.

Dinah Zike

Visualizing Main Ideas

Complete the concept map below about continental drift, seafloor spreading, and plate tectonics.

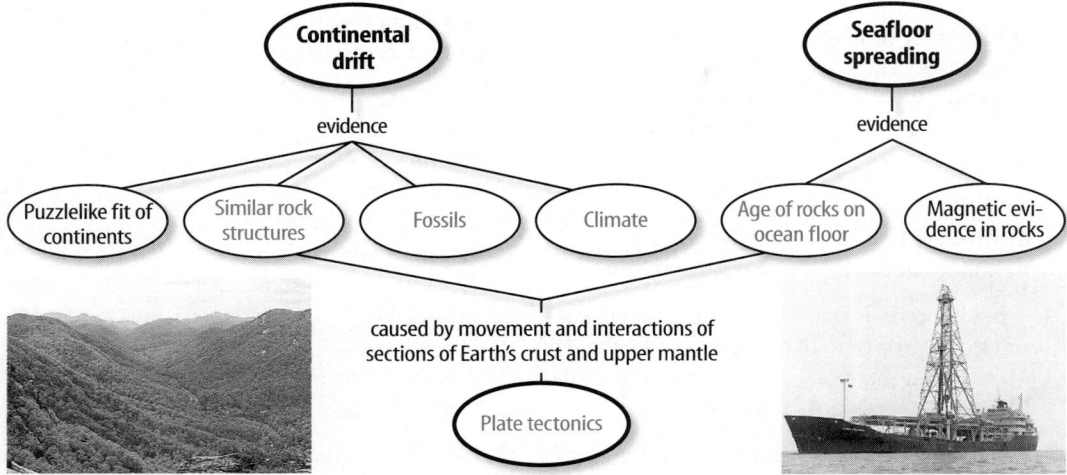

Visualizing Main Ideas

See student page.

Vocabulary Review

Vocabulary Words

1. asthenosphere
2. continental drift
3. Pangaea
4. seafloor spreading
5. convection current
6. lithosphere
7. plate tectonics
8. plate
9. seafloor spreading
10. convection current

Vocabulary Review

Vocabulary Words

a. asthenosphere
b. continental drift
c. convection current
d. lithosphere
e. Pangaea
f. plate
g. plate tectonics
h. seafloor spreading

Using Vocabulary

Each phrase below describes a vocabulary term from the list. Write the term that matches the phrase describing it.

1. plasticlike layer below the lithosphere

2. idea that continents move slowly across Earth's surface

3. large, ancient landmass that consisted of all the continents on Earth

4. process that forms new seafloor as hot material is forced upward

5. driving force for plate movement

6. composed of oceanic or continental crust and upper mantle

7. explains locations of mountains, trenches, and volcanoes

8. piece of the lithosphere that moves over a plasticlike layer

9. theory proposed by Harry Hess that includes processes along mid-ocean ridges

10. forms as warm material rises and cold material sinks

THE PRINCETON REVIEW **Study Tip**

Make a note of anything you don't understand so that you'll remember to ask your teacher about it.

Checking Concepts

1. B
2. D
3. C
4. D
5. A
6. B
7. B
8. D
9. A
10. B

Thinking Critically

11. The colliding continental plates cause earthquakes, but neither plate is forced deep into Earth, which would allow melting to occur and magma to rise through any cracks to form volcanoes.
12. Africa was located near the South Pole when all the continents were joined.
13. When molten material rises and cools at a ridge, magnetic rocks take on the orientation of Earth's magnetic field. Each time Earth's magnetic field reverses, new materials that form close to the ridge take on the new orientation.
14. It is a transform boundary. Without subduction no melting occurs and no magma is produced.
15. The fish could have moved through the oceans between continents.

Chapter 14 Assessment

Checking Concepts

Choose the word or phrase that best answers the question.

1. Which layer of Earth contains the asthenosphere?
   A) crust C) outer core
   B) mantle D) inner core

2. What type of plate boundary is the San Andreas Fault part of?
   A) divergent C) convergent
   B) subduction D) transform

3. What hypothesis states that continents slowly moved to their present positions on Earth?
   A) subduction C) continental drift
   B) seafloor spreading D) erosion

4. Which plate is subducting beneath the South American Plate to form the Andes mountain range?
   A) North American C) Indo-Australian
   B) African D) Nazca

5. Which of the following features indicates that many continents were once near Earth's south pole?
   A) glacial deposits C) volcanoes
   B) mid-ocean ridges D) earthquakes

6. What evidence in rocks supports the theory of seafloor spreading?
   A) plate movement C) subduction
   B) magnetic reversals D) convergence

7. Which type of plate boundary is the Mid-Atlantic Ridge a part of?
   A) convergent C) transform
   B) divergent D) lithosphere

8. What theory states that plates move around on the asthenosphere?
   A) continental drift C) subduction
   B) seafloor spreading D) plate tectonics

9. What forms when one plate slides past another plate?
   A) transform boundary
   B) divergent boundary
   C) subduction zone
   D) mid-ocean ridge

10. When oceanic plates collide, what volcanic landforms are made?
    A) folded mountains
    B) island arcs
    C) strike-slip faults
    D) mid-ocean ridges

Thinking Critically

11. Why do many earthquakes but few volcanic eruptions occur in the Himalaya?

12. Glacial deposits often form at high latitudes near the poles. Explain why glacial deposits have been found in Africa.

13. How is magnetism used to support the theory of seafloor spreading?

14. Explain why volcanoes do not form along the San Andreas Fault.

15. Explain why the fossil of an ocean fish found on two different continents would not be good evidence of continental drift.

Developing Skills

16. **Forming Hypotheses** Mount St. Helens in the Cascade Range is a volcano. Use **Figure 9** and a U.S. map to hypothesize how it might have formed.

17. **Measuring in SI** Movement along the African Rift Valley is about 2.1 cm per year. If plates continue to move apart at this rate, how much larger will the rift be (in meters) in 1,000 years? In 15,500 years?

Chapter ✓Assessment Planner

Portfolio Encourage students to place in their portfolios one or two items of what they consider to be their best work. Examples include:
- Challenge, p. 395
- Chemistry Integration, p. 397
- Science Journal, p. 401
- Extension, p. 403

Performance Additional performance assessments, Performance Task Assessment Lists, and rubrics for evaluating these activities can be found in Glencoe's **Performance Assessment in the Science Classroom.**

18. Concept Mapping Make an events chain concept map that describes seafloor spreading along a divergent plate boundary. Choose from the following phrases: *magma cools to form new seafloor, convection currents circulate hot material along divergent boundary,* and *older seafloor is forced apart.*

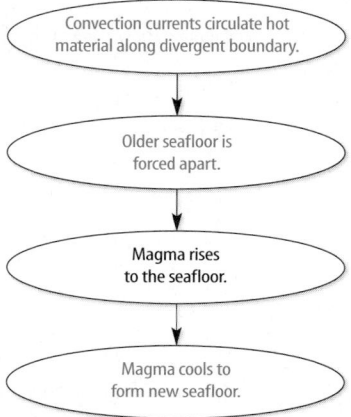

Performance Assessment

19. Observe and Infer In the MiniLab Modeling Convection Currents, you observed convection currents produced in water as it was heated. Repeat the experiment, placing sequins, pieces of wood, or pieces of rubber bands into the water. How do their movements support your observations and inferences from the MiniLab?

TECHNOLOGY

Go to the Glencoe Science Web site at **science.glencoe.com** or use the **Glencoe Science CD-ROM** for additional chapter assessment.

Test Practice

Ms. Fernandez was leading a class discussion on plate tectonics and Earth's interior.
Study the diagram below and then answer the following questions.

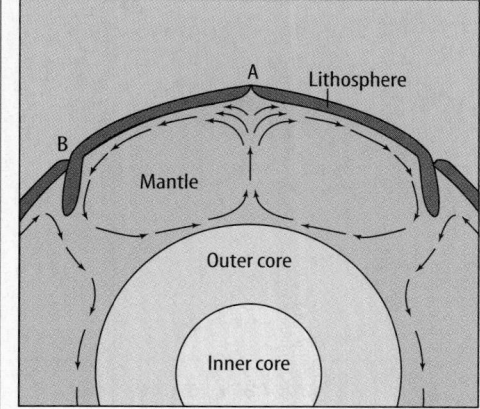

1. Suppose that the arrows in the diagram represent patterns of convection in Earth's mantle. Which type of plate boundary is most likely to form along the region labeled "A"?
 A) transform
 B) reverse
 C) convergent
 D) divergent

2. Which statement is true of the region marked "B" on the diagram?
 F) Plates separate and slip past one another sideways.
 G) Plates diverge and volcanoes form.
 H) Plates converge and volcanoes form.
 J) Plates collapse and form a strike-slip boundary.

CHAPTER ASSESSMENT 417

Test Practice

The Test-Taking Tip was written by The Princeton Review, the nation's leader in test preparation.
 1. D
 2. H

Developing Skills

16. The volcanoes of the Cascade Range formed as the Juan de Fuca Plate subducted beneath the North American Plate.
17. 21 m; 325.5 m
18. See student page.

Performance Assessment

19. The objects move around because of convection processes going on inside the water. Use **PASC**, p. 89.

✓ Assessment Resources

📁 Reproducible Masters
Chapter Resources Booklet
 Chapter Review, pp. 37–38
 Chapter Tests, pp. 39–42
 Assessment Transparency Activity, p. 49
Glencoe Science Web site
 Interactive Tutor
 Chapter Quizzes

Glencoe Technology
 Assessment Transparency
 Interactive CD-ROM Chapter Quizzes
 ExamView Pro Test Bank
 Vocabulary PuzzleMaker Software
 MindJogger Videoquiz

Section/Objectives	Standards		Activities/Features
Chapter Opener	**National**	**State/Local**	**Explore Activity:** Construct with Strength, p. 419 **Before You Read,** p. 419
	See p. 7T for a Key to Standards.		
Section 1 Earthquakes 🕐 2 sessions 📦 1 block 1. **Explain** how earthquakes are caused by a buildup of strain in Earth's crust. 2. **Compare and contrast** primary, secondary, and surface waves. 3. **Recognize** earthquake hazards and how to prepare for them.	National Content Standards: UCP2, A1, D1, E1, F3, F5		**MiniLAB:** Observing Deformation, p. 421 **Science Online,** p. 425 **Visualizing Tsunamis,** p. 426
Section 2 Volcanoes 🕐 2 sessions 📦 1 block 1. **Explain** how volcanoes can affect people. 2. **Describe** how types of materials are produced by volcanoes. 3. **Compare** how three different volcano forms develop.	National Content Standards: UCP2, A1, D1, F3		**MiniLAB:** Modeling an Eruption, p. 430 **Science Online,** p. 431 **Activity:** Disruptive Eruptions, p. 435
Section 3 Earthquakes, Volcanoes, and Plate Tectonics 🕐 4 sessions 📦 2 blocks 1. **Explain** how the locations of volcanoes and earthquake epicenters are related to tectonic plate boundaries. 2. **Explain** how heat within Earth causes Earth's plates to move.	National Content Standards: UCP2, A1, B2, D1, F3, G3		**Chemistry Integration,** p. 438 **Physics Integration,** p. 439 **Math Skills Activity:** Calculating Time Traveled by Waves, p. 440 **Activity:** Seismic Waves, p. 442 **Science and History:** Quake, pp. 444–445

NATIONAL GEOGRAPHIC

Teacher's Corner

PRODUCTS AVAILABLE FROM GLENCOE
To order call 1-800-334-7344:
CD-ROM
NGS PictureShow: Dynamic Earth
Curriculum Kit
GeoKit: Dynamic Earth
GeoKit: Earth's Crust

Transparency Set
NGS PicturePack: Dynamic Earth
Videodisc
STV: Restless Earth
PRODUCTS AVAILABLE FROM NATIONAL GEOGRAPHIC SOCIETY
To order call 1-800-368-2728:

Videos
Changing Earth: Forces That Create, Forces That Destroy
Living on Our Changing Planet
Our Dynamic Earth
Volcano!

Activity Materials	Reproducible Resources	Section Assessment	Technology
Explore Activity: 4 wooden blocks, sheet of cardboard, larger rubber bands	**Chapter Resources Booklet** Foldables Worksheet, p. 15 Directed Reading Overview, p. 17 Note-taking Worksheets, pp. 31–33	*GLENCOE'S* **ASSESSMENT** *ADVANTAGE*	
MiniLAB: 3 bars of taffy *Need materials?* Contact Science Kit at 1-800-828-7777 or www.sciencekit.com on the Internet.	**Chapter Resources Booklet** Transparency Activity, p. 42 MiniLAB, p. 3 Enrichment, p. 28 Reinforcement, p. 25 Directed Reading, p. 18 Transparency Activity, pp. 45–46 Lab Activity, pp. 9–10 **Cultural Diversity,** p. 46	Portfolio Science Journal, p. 423 Performance MiniLAB, p. 421 Skill Builder Activities, p. 428 Content Section Assessment, p. 428	Section Focus Transparency Teaching Transparency Interactive CD-ROM Guided Reading Audio Program
MiniLAB: red-colored gelatin, self-sealing plastic bag, pin **Activity:** plastic film canisters, baking soda, vinegar, 50-ml graduated cylinder, teaspoon	**Chapter Resources Booklet** Transparency Activity, p. 43 MiniLAB, p. 4 Enrichment, p. 29 Reinforcement, p. 26 Directed Reading, p. 19 Activity Worksheet, pp. 5–6 Lab Activity, pp. 11–14	Portfolio Extension, p. 431 Performance MiniLAB, p. 430 Skill Builder Activities, p. 434 Content Section Assessment, p. 434	Section Focus Transparency Interactive CD-ROM Guided Reading Audio Program
Activity: coiled spring toy, yarn or string, metric ruler	**Chapter Resources Booklet** Transparency Activity, p. 44 Enrichment, p. 30 Reinforcement, p. 27 Directed Reading, pp. 19, 20 Activity Worksheet, pp. 7–8 **Lab Management and Safety,** p. 38 **Mathematics Skill Activities,** p. 11	Portfolio Extension, p. 437 Performance Math Skills Activity, p. 440 Skill Builder Activities, p. 441 Content Section Assessment, p. 441	Section Focus Transparency Interactive CD-ROM Guided Reading Audio Program

End of Chapter Assessment

GLENCOE'S ASSESSMENT ADVANTAGE Blackline Masters	Technology	Professional Series
Chapter Resources Booklet Chapter Review, pp. 35–36 Chapter Tests, pp. 37–40 **Standardized Test Practice by The Princeton Review,** pp. 65–68	MindJogger Videoquiz Interactive CD-ROM Vocabulary PuzzleMakers ExamView Pro Test Bank Interactive Lesson Planner Interactive Teacher Edition	Performance Assessment in the Science Classroom (PASC)

Transparencies

Section Focus

Section 1 Focus Transparency — Nobody's Fault at All

The Richter scale was first used to rate the strength of earthquakes in 1935. Since then, we've learned a great deal about the causes of earthquakes, but predicting when an earthquake will strike remains tricky.

1. What happens during an earthquake?
2. What parts of an earthquake can be measured?
3. Why is it easier to predict where an earthquake will strike than when it will strike?

L2

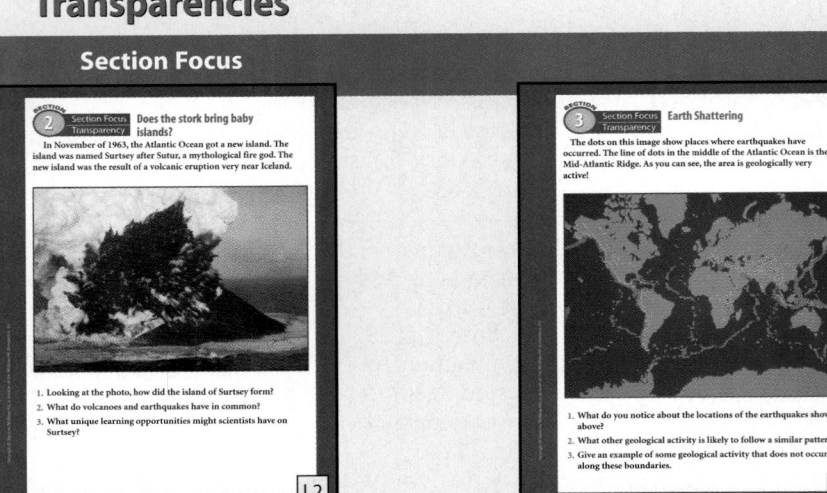

Section 2 Focus Transparency — Does the stork bring baby islands?

In November of 1963, the Atlantic Ocean got a new island. The island was named Surtsey after Sutur, a mythological fire god. The new island was the result of a volcanic eruption very near Iceland.

1. Looking at the photo, how did the island of Surtsey form?
2. What do volcanoes and earthquakes have in common?
3. What unique learning opportunities might scientists have on Surtsey?

L2

Section 3 Focus Transparency — Earth Shattering

The dots on this image show places where earthquakes have occurred. The line of dots in the middle of the Atlantic Ocean is the Mid-Atlantic Ridge. As you can see, the area is geologically very active!

1. What do you notice about the locations of the earthquakes shown above?
2. What other geological activity is likely to follow a similar pattern?
3. Give an example of some geological activity that does not occur along these boundaries.

L2

This is a representation of key blackline masters available in the Teacher Classroom Resources. See Resource Manager boxes within the chapter for additional information.

Key to Teaching Strategies

The following designations will help you decide which activities are appropriate for your students.

L1 Level 1 activities should be appropriate for students with learning difficulties.

L2 Level 2 activities should be within the ability range of all students.

L3 Level 3 activities are designed for above-average students.

ELL ELL activities should be within the ability range of English Language Learners.

COOP LEARN Cooperative Learning activities are designed for small group work.

LS Multiple Learning Styles logos, as described on page 22T, are used throughout to indicate strategies that address different learning styles.

P These strategies represent student products that can be placed into a best-work portfolio.

Assessment

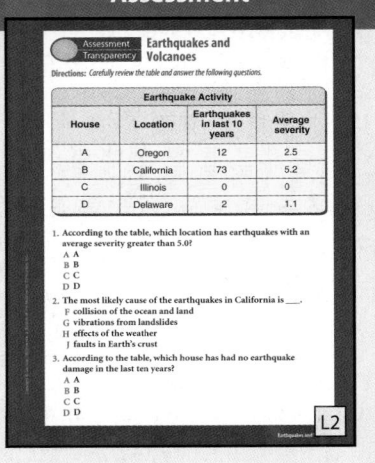

Assessment Transparency — Earthquakes and Volcanoes

Directions: Carefully review the table and answer the following questions.

Earthquake Activity

House	Location	Earthquakes in last 10 years	Average severity
A	Oregon	12	2.5
B	California	73	5.2
C	Illinois	0	0
D	Delaware	2	1.1

1. According to the table, which location has earthquakes with an average severity greater than 5.0?
   A A
   B B
   C C
   D D
2. The most likely cause of the earthquakes in California is ___.
   F collision of the ocean and land
   G vibrations from landslides
   H effects of the weather
   J faults in Earth's crust
3. According to the table, which house has had no earthquake damage in the last ten years?
   A A
   B B
   C C
   D D

L2

Teaching

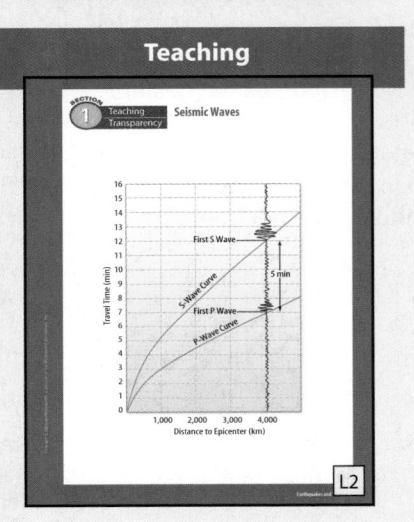

Section 1 Teaching Activity — Seismic Waves

L2

Hands-on Activities

Activity Worksheets

Laboratory Activities

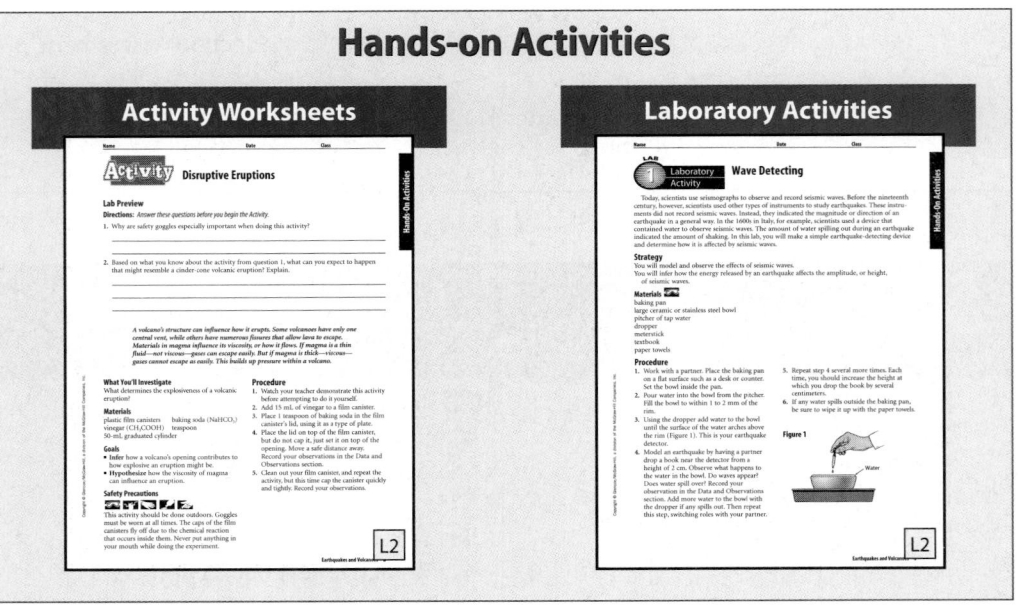

Activity — Disruptive Eruptions

Lab Preview
Directions: Answer these questions before you begin the Activity.
1. Why are safety goggles especially important when doing this activity?

2. Based on what you know about the activity from question 1, what can you expect to happen that might resemble a cinder-cone volcanic eruption? Explain.

A volcano's structure can influence how it erupts. Some volcanoes have only one central vent, while others have numerous fissures that allow lava to escape. Materials in magma influence its viscosity, or how it flows. If magma is a thin fluid—not viscous—gases can escape easily. But if magma is thick—viscous—gases cannot escape as easily. This builds up pressure within a volcano.

What You'll Investigate
What determines the explosiveness of a volcanic eruption?

Materials
plastic film canisters baking soda (NaHCO₃)
vinegar (CH₃COOH) teaspoon
50-mL graduated cylinder

Goals
• Infer how a volcano's opening contributes to how explosive an eruption might be.
• Hypothesize how the viscosity of magma can influence an eruption.

Safety Precautions
This activity should be done outdoors. Goggles must be worn at all times. The caps of the film canisters fly off due to the chemical reaction that occurs inside them. Never put anything in your mouth while doing the experiment.

Procedure
1. Watch your teacher demonstrate this activity before attempting to do it yourself.
2. Add 15 mL of vinegar to a film canister.
3. Place 1 teaspoon of baking soda in the film canister's lid, using it as a type of plate.
4. Place the lid on top of the film canister, but do not cap it, just set it on top of the opening. Move a safe distance away. Record your observations in the Data and Observations section.
5. Clean out your film canister, and repeat the activity, but this time cap the canister quickly and tightly. Record your observations.

L2

Laboratory Activity 1 — Wave Detecting

Today, scientists use seismographs to observe and record seismic waves. Before the nineteenth century, however, scientists used other types of instruments to study earthquakes. These instruments did not record seismic waves. Instead, they indicated the magnitude or direction of an earthquake in a general way. In the 1600s in Italy, for example, scientists used a device that contained water to observe seismic waves. The amount of water spilling out during an earthquake indicated the amount of shaking. In this lab, you will make a simple earthquake-detecting device and determine how it is affected by seismic waves.

Strategy
You will model and observe the effects of seismic waves.
You will infer how the energy released by an earthquake affects the amplitude, or height, of seismic waves.

Materials
baking pan
large ceramic or stainless steel bowl
pitcher of tap water
dropper
meterstick
textbook
paper towels

Procedure
1. Work with a partner. Place the baking pan on a flat surface such as a desk or counter. Set the bowl inside the pan.
2. Pour water into the bowl from the pitcher. Fill the bowl to within 1 to 2 mm of the rim.
3. Using the dropper add water to the bowl until the surface of the water arches above the rim (Figure 1). This is your earthquake detector.
4. Model an earthquake by having a partner drop a book near the detector from a height of 2 cm. Observe what happens to the water in the bowl. Does water spill over? Record your observation in the Data and Observations section. Add more water to the bowl with the dropper if any spills out. Then repeat this step, switching roles with your partner.
5. Repeat step 4 several more times. Each time, you should increase the height at which you drop the book by several centimeters.
6. If any water spills outside the baking pan, be sure to wipe it up with the paper towels.

Figure 1

L2

Meeting Different Ability Levels

Content Outline

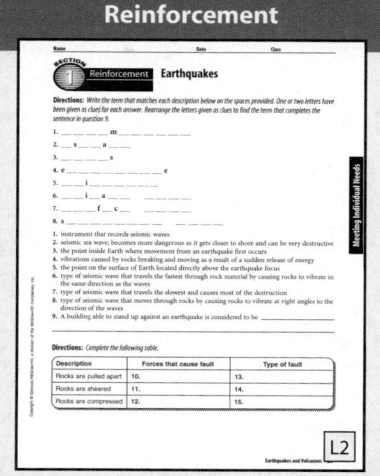

Reinforcement

Directed Reading

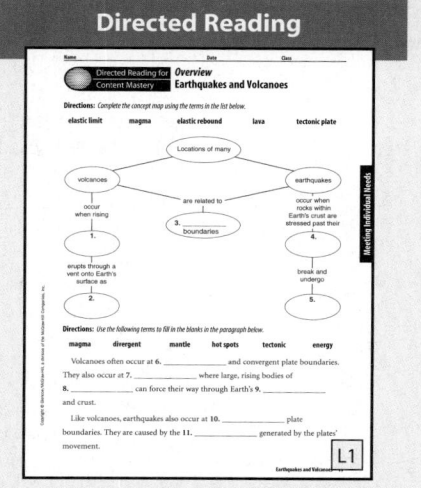

Assessment

Chapter Tests

Enrichment

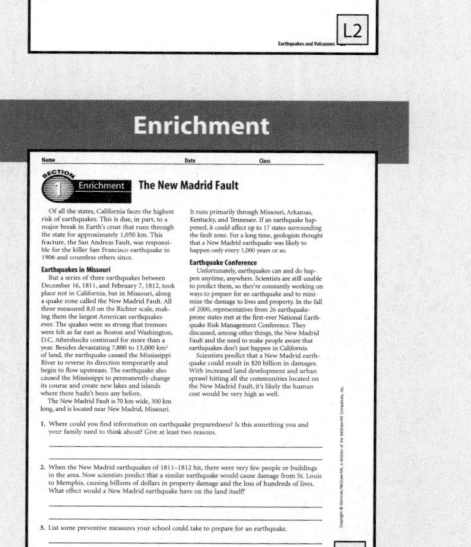

Spanish Directed Reading

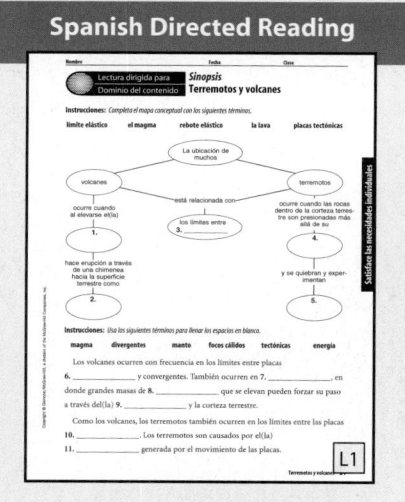

Test Practice Workbook

Chapter Review

Science Content Background

Earthquakes

Types of Faults

Normal faults, created by tension forces pulling rocks apart, are associated with areas of extension such as mid-ocean ridges. Compression forces, from which reverse faults result, also are the forces that are usually responsible for building mountains. Faults can be very evident in the structure of Earth's surface, even to the untrained eye. The San Andreas Fault, a 1,300-km long, 16-km deep strike-slip fault network that separates the North American and Pacific Plates, is so large it can be seen from the air.

Measuring Earthquake Strength

Seismologists today also measure the moment magnitude of an earthquake. This measurement is based on the total amount of energy released by the earthquake, rather than just the amplitudes of seismic waves. Measuring the moment magnitude is particularly important for larger earthquakes, which cannot always be measured with accuracy by the traditional Richter scale. For example, the 1906 San Francisco earthquake is now estimated to have had a magnitude of 7.7–7.9. On the Richter scale it was measured at 8.3. The 1995 Kobe, Japan, earthquake had a moment magnitude of 7.2 and a 6.9 magnitude on the Richter scale.

> **Fun Fact**
>
> Almost 2000 years ago in China, the first earthquake detector was created. An elaborately decorated vase had dragon heads, each with a ball in its mouth, that extended out near the top of the vase. If the vase moved, presumably as a result of seismic activity, the balls would drop from the dragons' mouths.

Earthquake Safety

Earthquake safety also means being aware of the potential for aftershocks. Aftershocks are earthquakes created by further movements along a fault after a main earthquake event has occurred. Although aftershocks usually are not as strong as the main earthquake, they can continue to cause destruction to structures already weakened or damaged by the earthquake. Aftershocks can occur for several days to several months following a quake.

Aside from more obvious dangers, such as those posed by tsunamis, earthquakes can set off other events, the effects of which can be as disastrous as the earthquake itself. Fire can result

Corbis

from broken gas and power lines. In a severe earthquake water mains can also be broken, which leaves people virtually powerless to fight the fires. In some cases, out of control fires have caused as much, if not more damage than the earthquake itself.

Some communities have taken the safety measure of installing valves in gas and water lines so that individual lines will remain unaffected by other ruptures. Landslides, in the form of mudslides, rock slides and avalanches, can also be triggered by the intense seismic activity of earthquakes. A 1959 earthquake in Montana triggered a landslide so large that it blocked off a river, forming a dam, and a lake was created.

Predicting Earthquakes

Seismologists have shown that detectable changes, both on Earth's surface and below, can occur before an earthquake takes place. Some of these changes may result from a change in the porosity of the rock. Small cracks in rock are created as forces act on it, and water subsequently flows into the cracks. Differences in the elevation and tilt of land that occur on either side of a fault also have been observed just before an earthquake.

The influx of water to the rock is thought to account for local changes of water level in wells and groundwater, changes that have also been noted to occur before some earthquakes. The presence of water in the rock also changes the electrical properties of the rock and the ground.

Other changes that have been recorded before an earthquake include an increase in the emission of radon gas from water wells, and a change in the speed of seismic waves.

SCIENCE *Online*

For additional content background on this topic, go to the Glencoe Science Web site at **science.glencoe.com.**

SECTION 2 Volcanoes
Predicting Volcanic Eruptions

Subtle changes can be detected before a volcano erupts. These changes have been successfully used to forecast a volcanic event. Magma rising into the chamber directly beneath a volcano can be associated with low to moderate seismic activity. This phenomenon also can cause the chamber to become inflated, a change that can be measured relative to sea level on Earth's surface. The new magma mixing with existing magma in the chamber can cause changes in the gases, including carbon dioxide, sulfur dioxide, and hydrochloric acid, released by the volcano. Monitoring these changes led to the successful prediction of the 1991 eruption of Mount Pinatubo in the Philippines, which saved thousands of lives.

> **Fun Fact**
>
> Only two other bodies in Earth's solar system are known to have active volcanoes: the planet Venus and Io, a moon of Jupiter.

SECTION 3 Earthquakes, Volcanoes, and Plate Tectonics
Where Volcanoes Form

Much of Earth's volcanic activity occurs unobserved at divergent plate boundaries in the ocean. The only above-sea volcanoes formed along divergent plate boundaries are in Iceland and East Africa. Most of Earth's active above-sea volcanoes occur along convergent plate boundaries including Mount St. Helen's in the state of Washington. Islands formed by hot spots include Easter Island and the Galápagos Islands in the Pacific Ocean, and the Azores and the Canary Islands in the Atlantic.

Earthquakes and Volcanoes

Chapter Vocabulary

What do you think?

Science Journal This is a satellite image of a volcano. Scientists use images of Earth taken from space to learn more about Earth's surface. Pictures such as these help scientists study lava flow.

Earthquakes and Volcanoes

The ground shook violently and the bridge came tumbling down. The Loma Prieta earthquake of 1989 hit San Francisco hard. The Cypress freeway in Oakland was one of its many victims. You might be wondering what caused this disaster and what could have been done to prevent it. In this chapter, you'll begin to answer these questions as you read about earthquakes, volcanoes, and Earth's moving plates.

What do you think?

Science Journal Look at the picture below with a classmate. Discuss what this might be. Here's a hint: *It's a far-out view of something that starts very deep down.* Write your answer or best guess in your Science Journal.

Theme Connection

Energy Energy generated by forces inside Earth is released as seismic waves during an earthquake. Energy is involved in the formation of magma and the eruption of volcanoes.

EXPLORE ACTIVITY

One of the greatest dangers associated with an earthquake occurs when people are inside buildings during the event. If buildings were constructed so they would not fall down as easily when shaken by an earthquake, the number of deaths and the amount of destruction could be reduced. In the following activity, you will see how construction materials can be used to help strengthen a building.

Construct with strength 👓

1. Using wooden blocks, construct a building with four walls. Place a piece of cardboard over the four walls as a ceiling.
2. Gently shake the table under your building. Describe what happens.
3. Reconstruct the building. Wrap large rubber bands around each section, or wall, of blocks. Then wrap large rubber bands around the entire building.
4. Gently shake the table again.

Observe
In your Science Journal, note any differences you observed as the two buildings were shaken. Hypothesize how the construction methods you used in this activity might be applied to the construction of real buildings.

Before You Read

FOLDABLES
Reading & Study Skills

Making a Compare and Contrast Study Fold Make the following Foldable to help you see how earthquakes and volcanoes are similar and different.

1. Place a sheet of paper in front of you so the long side is at the top. Fold the paper in half from the left side to the right side and then unfold.
2. Fold each side in to the centerfold line to divide the paper into fourths.
3. Draw a volcano on one flap and label the flap *Volcanoes*. Draw an earthquake on the other flap and label it *Earthquakes*.
4. Before you read the chapter, write what you know about earthquakes and volcanoes on the back of each flap. As you read the chapter, add to your information.

419

EXPLORE ACTIVITY

Purpose Use the Explore Activity to introduce students to the power of earthquakes. Explain that reinforcing structures provides support that helps buildings withstand the enormous power of an earthquake. L1 ELL COOP LEARN I.S Kinesthetic

Materials wooden blocks, large rubber bands, cardboard

Teaching Strategy Have students compare their structures with those of others. Discuss similarities and differences in how vibrations affected their structures.

Observe
Students will likely note that motion had a greater effect on the first building than the second. The rubber bands acted as reinforcements that supported the blocks. This demonstrates the need to provide buildings with additional support to withstand earthquakes.

✓**Assessment**

Performance Show students pictures of highway supports and building reinforcements. Ask whether these structures will increase or decrease an earthquake's effects. decrease Use **Performance Assessment in the Science Classroom,** p. 89.

Before You Read

FOLDABLES
Reading & Study Skills

Dinah Zike Study Fold

Purpose Students use this Foldable to diagram and describe volcanoes and earthquakes, and then use what they have learned to compare and contrast them.

📁 For additional help, see Foldables Worksheet, p. 15 in **Chapter Resources Booklet,** or go to the Glencoe Science Web site at **science.glencoe.com.** See After You Read in the Study Guide at the end of this chapter.

SECTION
1
Earthquakes

1 Motivate

Bellringer Transparency

Display the Section Focus Transparency for Section 1. Use the accompanying Transparency Activity Master. L2

ELL

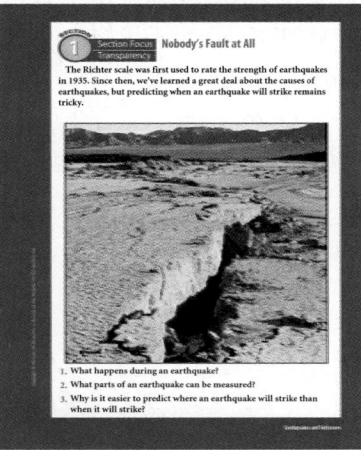

Section Focus Transparency — Nobody's Fault at All

The Richter scale was first used to rate the strength of earthquakes in 1935. Since then, we've learned a great deal about the causes of earthquakes, but predicting when an earthquake will strike remains tricky.

1. What happens during an earthquake?
2. What parts of an earthquake can be measured?
3. Why is it easier to predict where an earthquake will strike than when it will strike?

Tie to Prior Knowledge

Ask students to name locations struck by recent earthquakes. Display photographs that illustrate the damage these or other quakes caused. Guide students in realizing that it often takes a community many years to recover from the devastating effects of an earthquake.

SECTION

1
Earthquakes

■ As You Read

What You'll Learn

- **Explain** how earthquakes are caused by a buildup of strain in Earth's crust.
- **Compare and contrast** primary, secondary, and surface waves.
- **Recognize** earthquake hazards and how to prepare for them.

Vocabulary

earthquake	seismograph
fault	magnitude
seismic wave	tsunami
focus	seismic safe
epicenter	

Why It's Important

Studying earthquakes will help you learn where they might occur and how you can prepare for their hazards.

What causes earthquakes?

If you've gone for a walk in the woods lately, maybe you picked up a stick along the way. If so, did you try to bend or break it? If you've ever bent a stick slowly, you might have noticed that it changes shape but usually springs back to normal form when you stop bending it. If you continue to bend the stick, you can do it for only so long before it changes permanently. When this elastic limit is passed, the stick may break, as shown in **Figure 1.** When the stick snaps, you can feel vibrations in the stick.

Elastic Rebound As hard as they seem, rocks act in much the same way when forces push or pull on them. If enough force is applied, rocks become strained, which means they change shape. They may even break, and the ends of the broken pieces may snap back. This snapping back is called elastic rebound.

Rocks usually change shape, or deform, slowly over long periods of time. As they are strained, potential energy builds up in them. This energy is released suddenly by the action of rocks breaking and moving. Such breaking, and the movement that follows, causes vibrations that move through rock or other earth materials. If they are large enough, these vibrations are felt as **earthquakes.**

✓ **Reading Check** *What is an earthquake?*

A

B

Figure 1
A stick can bend only so far before it breaks. **A** When a stick is bent, potential energy is stored in the stick. **B** The energy is released as vibrations when the stick breaks.

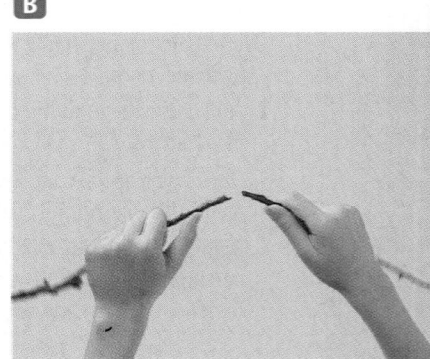

Section ✓ *Assessment* Planner

PORTFOLIO
Science Journal, p. 423
PERFORMANCE ASSESSMENT
MiniLAB, p. 421
Skill Builder Activities, p. 428
See page 448 for more options.

CONTENT ASSESSMENT
Section, p. 428
Challenge, p. 428
Chapter, pp. 448–449

Figure 2
When rocks change shape by breaking, faults form. The type of fault formed depends on the type of stress exerted on the rock.

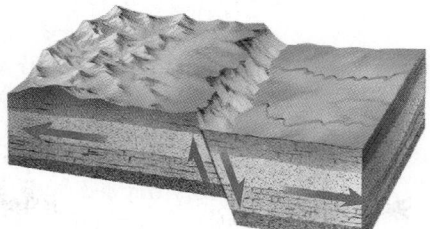

A When rocks are pulled apart, a normal fault may form.

B When rocks are compressed, a reverse fault may form.

C When rocks are sheared, a strike-slip fault may form.

Types of Faults When a section of rock breaks, rocks on either side of the break might move because of elastic rebound. The surface of such a break is called a **fault**. Several types of faults exist. The type that forms depends on how forces were applied to the rocks.

When rocks are pulled apart under tension forces, normal faults form, as shown in **Figure 2A.** Along a normal fault, rock above the fault moves down compared to rock below the fault. Compression forces squeeze rocks together, like an accordion. Compression might cause rock above a fault to move up compared to rock below the fault. This movement forms reverse faults, as shown in **Figure 2B.** As illustrated in **Figure 2C,** rock experiencing shear forces can break to form a strike-slip fault. Shear forces cause rock on either side of a strike-slip fault to move past one another in opposite directions along Earth's surface. You could infer the motion of a strike-slip fault while walking along and observing an offset feature, such as a displaced fence line, on Earth's surface.

Where do the forces come from that cause rocks to deform by bending or breaking? Why do faults form and why do earthquakes occur in certain areas? As you'll learn later in this chapter, forces inside Earth are caused by the constant motion of plates, or sections, of Earth's crust and upper mantle.

Mini LAB

Observing Deformation

WARNING: *Do not taste or eat any lab materials. Wash hands when finished.*

Procedure 🥽 ✋ 🚫

1. Remove the wrapper from three bars of **taffy.**
2. Hold a bar of taffy length-wise between your hands and gently push on it from opposite directions.
3. Hold another bar of taffy and pull it in opposite directions.

Analysis

1. Which of the procedures that you performed on the taffy involved applying tension? Which involved applying compression?
2. Infer how to apply a shear stress to the third bar of taffy.

SECTION 1 Earthquakes **421**

Making Waves

✔ **Reading Check**

Answer the point inside Earth where movement first occurs and energy is released

Teacher FYI

P-waves and S-waves are body waves generated at the focus of an earthquake. They travel outward through Earth's interior. P-waves, or primary waves, are compression waves. They cause the same type of movement of particles as sound waves. S-waves, or secondary waves, are transverse waves. They are the type of wave you see when you move one end of a rope from side to side.

IDENTIFYING Misconceptions

Students may think that earthquakes originate on Earth's surface. Explain that earthquakes are caused by vibrations that originate at the point where rocks break. This point, called the focus, is usually located deep inside Earth's crust or upper mantle.

Caption Answer

Figure 3 surface waves

Making Waves

Do you recall the last time you shouted for a friend to save you a seat on the bus? When you called out, energy was transmitted through the air to your friend, who interpreted the familiar sound of your voice as belonging to you. These sound waves were released by your vocal cords and were affected by your tongue and mouth. They traveled outward through the air. Earthquakes also release waves. Earthquake waves are transmitted through materials in Earth and along Earth's surface. Earthquake waves are called **seismic waves.** In the two-page activity, you'll make waves similar to seismic waves by moving a coiled spring toy.

Earthquake Focus and Epicenter Movement along a fault releases strain energy. Strain energy is potential energy that builds up in rock when it is bent. When this potential energy is released, it moves outward from the fault in the form of seismic waves. The point inside Earth where this movement first occurs and energy is released is called the **focus** of an earthquake, as shown in **Figure 3.** The point on Earth's surface located directly above the earthquake focus is called the **epicenter** of the earthquake.

✔ **Reading Check**   *What is the focus of an earthquake?*

Figure 3
During an earthquake, several types of seismic waves form. Primary and secondary waves travel in all directions from the focus and can travel through Earth's interior. Surface waves travel at shallow depths and along Earth's surface. *Which seismic waves are the most destructive?*

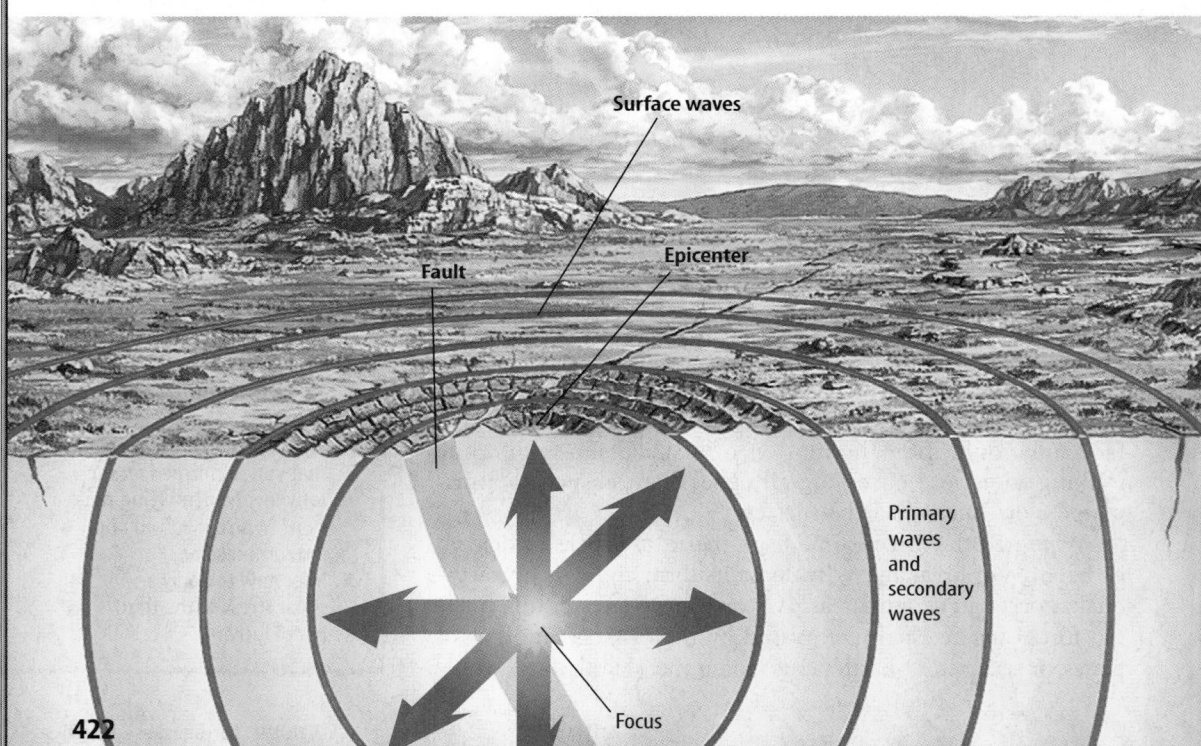

Surface waves

Fault

Epicenter

Primary waves and secondary waves

Focus

422

Inclusion Strategies

Learning Disabled Use this activity to help students understand the different motions of surface waves. First, have several students place their chairs side-by-side in a line. Have them do "the wave" as seen at sporting events, by lifting and lowering their arms, one after another. Now have them try another human "wave." Have them turn their chairs so that they are lined up one behind the other. Have students sway side to side, swaying in the same direction as, but slightly after, the person in front of them. Allow students to switch off observing and "waving," until all students have had a chance to observe both phenomena. L1 ELL COOP LEARN IS **Visual-Spatial and Kinesthetic**

Seismic Waves After they are produced at the focus, seismic waves travel away from the focus in all directions, as illustrated in **Figure 3.** Some seismic waves travel throughout Earth's interior, and others travel along Earth's surface. The surface waves cause the most damage during an earthquake event.

Primary waves, also known as P-waves, travel the fastest through rock material by causing particles in the rock to move back and forth, or vibrate, in the same direction as the waves are moving. Secondary waves, known as S-waves, move through rock material by causing particles in the rock to vibrate at right angles to the direction in which the waves are moving. P- and S-waves travel through Earth's interior. Studying them has revealed much information about Earth's interior.

Surface waves are the slowest and largest of the seismic waves, and they cause most of the destruction during an earthquake. The movements of surface waves are complex. Some surface waves move along Earth's surface in a manner that moves rock and soil in a backward rolling motion. They have been observed moving across the land like waves of water. Some surface waves vibrate in a side-to-side, or swaying, motion parallel to Earth's surface. This motion can be particularly devastating to human-built structures.

Learning from Earthquakes

On your way to lunch tomorrow, suppose you were to walk twice as fast as your friend does. What would happen to the distance between the two of you as you walked to the lunchroom? The distance between you and your friend would become greater the farther you walked, and you would arrive first. Using this same line of reasoning, scientists use the different speeds of seismic waves and their differing arrival times to calculate the distance to an earthquake epicenter.

Earthquake Measurements Seismologists are scientists who study earthquakes and seismic waves. The instrument they use to obtain a record of seismic waves from all over the world is called a **seismograph,** shown in **Figure 4A.**

One type of seismograph has a drum holding a roll of paper on a fixed frame. A pendulum with an attached pen is suspended from the frame. When seismic waves are received at the station, the drum vibrates but the pendulum remains at rest. The pen on the pendulum traces a record of the vibrations on the paper. The height of the lines traced on the paper is a measure of the energy released by the earthquake, also known as its **magnitude.**

Figure 4
Scientists study seismic waves using seismographs located around the world.

A This seismograph records incoming seismic waves using a fixed mass.

B Some seismographs collect and store data on a computer.

Learning from Earthquakes, continued

Use Science Words

Word Usage The word *epicenter* is derived from the Greek term *epi-*, which means "at" and the Latin term *centrum*, which means "center." Ask students to use the word in a sentence that illustrates its Greek and Latin derivations. Possible answer: An earthquake's epicenter is located directly above the focus or center from which surface waves originate.

How strong are earthquakes?

Visual Learning

Figure 5 What could you infer if P- and S-waves were to arrive at a seismograph station almost at the same time? The seismic station is close to the epicenter. The farther away from the epicenter, the farther apart the arrival times of the two waves.

Extension

Have students estimate how many magnitude-3.0 earthquakes would be needed to release the same energy as one magnitude-8.0 earthquake. Since the difference in magnitude is 5, the difference in released energy is 32⁵ or about 33,554,432 times. Therefore, it would take over 33.5 million magnitude-3.0 earthquakes to release the energy of one magnitude-8.0 earthquake.

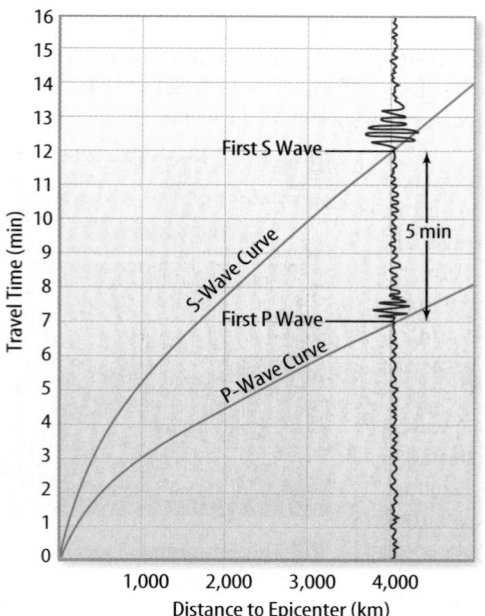

Figure 5
P- and S-waves travel at different speeds. These speeds are used to determine how close a seismograph station is to an earthquake.

Figure 6
After distances from at least three seismograph stations are determined, they are plotted as circles with radii equal to these distances on a map. The epicenter is the point at which the circles intersect.

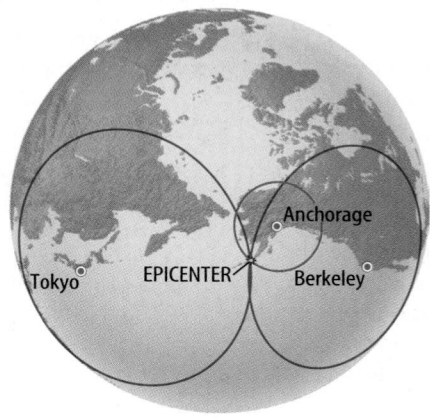

Epicenter Location When seismic-wave arrival times are recorded at a seismograph station, the distance from that station to the epicenter can be determined. The farther apart the arrival times for the different waves are, the farther away the earthquake epicenter is. This difference is shown by the graph in **Figure 5.** Using this information, scientists draw a circle with a radius equal to the distance from the earthquake for each of at least three seismograph stations, as illustrated in **Figure 6.** The point where the three circles meet is the location of the earthquake epicenter. Data from many stations normally are used to determine an epicenter location.

How strong are earthquakes?

As shown in **Table 1,** major earthquakes cause much loss of life. For example, on September 20, 1999, a major earthquake struck Taiwan, leaving more than 2,400 people dead, more than 8,700 injured, and at least 100,000 homeless. Sometimes earthquakes are felt and can cause destruction in areas hundreds of kilometers away from their epicenters. The Mexico City earthquake in 1985 is an example of this. The movement of the soft sediment underneath Mexico City caused extensive damage to this city, even though the epicenter was nearly 400 km away.

The Richter Scale Richter (RIHK tur) magnitude is based on measurements of amplitudes, or heights, of seismic waves as recorded on seismographs. Richter magnitude describes how much energy an earthquake releases. For each increase of 1.0 on the Richter scale, the amplitude of the highest recorded seismic wave increases by 10. However, about 32 times more energy is released for every increase of 1.0 on the scale. For example, an earthquake with a magnitude of 7.5 releases about 32 times more energy than one with a magnitude of 6.5, and the wave height for a 7.5-magnitude quake is ten times higher than for a quake with a magnitude of 6.5.

Resource Manager

Cultural Diversity, p. 47

Performance Assessment in the Science Classroom, p. 42

Curriculum Connection

Math Primary waves travel about 6.0 km/s through granite. Secondary waves travel about 3.5 km/s through granite. Have students calculate how much farther ahead the primary waves would be after two minutes. In 2 min (120 s) the primary waves would have traveled 720 km, and the secondary waves would have traveled 420 km. Thus, the primary waves would be 300 km ahead of the secondary waves.

Earthquake Damage

Another way to measure earthquakes is available. The modified Mercalli intensity scale measures the intensity of an earthquake. Intensity is a measure of the amount of structural and geologic damage done by an earthquake in a specific location. The range of intensities spans Roman numerals I through XII. The amount of damage done depends on several factors—the strength of the earthquake, the nature of the surface material, the design of structures, and the distance from the epicenter. An intensity-I earthquake would be felt only by a few people under ideal conditions, whereas an intensity-XII earthquake would cause major destruction to human-built structures and Earth's surface. The 1994 earthquake in Northridge, California was a Richter magnitude 6.7, and its intensity was listed at IX. An intensity-IX earthquake causes considerable damage to buildings and could cause cracks in the ground.

Tsunamis Most damage from an earthquake is caused by surface waves. Buildings can crack or fall down. Elevated bridges and highways can collapse. However, people living near the seashore must protect themselves against another hazard from earthquakes. When an earthquake occurs on the ocean floor, the sudden movement pushes against the water and powerful water waves are produced. These waves can travel outward from the earthquake thousands of kilometers in all directions.

When these seismic sea waves, or **tsunamis,** are far from shore, their energy is spread out over large distances and great water depths. The wave heights of tsunamis are less than a meter in deep water, and large ships can ride over them and not even know it. However, when tsunamis approach land, the waves slow down and their wave heights increase as they encounter the bottom of the seafloor. This creates huge tsunami waves that can be as much as 30 m in height. Just before a tsunami crashes to shore, the water near a shoreline may move rapidly out toward the sea. If this should happen, there is immediate danger that a tsunami is about to strike. **Figure 7** illustrates the behavior of a tsunami as it approaches the shore.

Table 1 Strong Earthquakes			
Year	**Location**	**Magnitude**	**Deaths**
1989	Loma Prieta, CA	7.1	62
1990	Iran	7.7	50,000
1990	Luzon, Philippines	7.8	1,621
1993	Guam	8.1	none
1993	Marharashtra, India	6.4	30,000
1994	Northridge, CA	6.7	61
1995	Kobe, Japan	6.8	5,378
1997	Iran	7.3	1,500
1998	Afghanistan-Tajikistan border	5.9	2,323
1998	Afghanistan-Tajikistan border	6.1	4,000
1999	Colombia, South America	6.2	2,000
1999	Taiwan	7.7	2,400
2000	Indonesia	7.9	103
2001	India	7.7	20,000

SCIENCE Online

Research Visit the Glencoe Science Web site at **science.glencoe.com** for information on determining earthquake magnitudes.

Teacher FYI

Seismologists increasingly use a magnitude called the moment magnitude. It is derived by multiplying the length of the fault rupture by the amount of rock movement and then again by the stiffness of the rock. This magnitude is connected directly to the strength and size of fault movement. The magnitude usually reported by seismologists is the Richter scale magnitude, modified for updated equipment. After further study, the moment magnitude can be determined and is reported.

Make a Model

Have one student hold a file folder still while another student draws a straight line across the folder. Then have the student holding the folder shake it while the second student tries to draw a straight line on the folder. Use this model of a seismograph to help students understand why a record of earthquakes is composed of wavy lines. L1 ELL

Visual-Spatial

Science Journal

Tsunamis Have students research in the library or recent earthquakes that have produced tsunamis. Instruct them to write a one-page summary describing the type of damage that was done by the tsunamis and the locations of the tsunamis relative to the earthquakes that caused them. **Linguistic**

SCIENCE Online
Internet Addresses

Explore the Glencoe Science Web site at **science.glencoe.com** to find out more about topics in this section.

Visualizing Tsunamis

Have students examine the pictures and read the captions. Then ask the following questions.

Why would it be more important to have a tsunami warning system for the Pacific Ocean than for the Atlantic Ocean? Earthquakes are much more common in and around the Pacific Ocean than they are in the Atlantic Ocean.

How long would it take for a tsunami generated by an earthquake off the coast of California to reach Hawaii? approximately 6 hours

Activity

Have small groups of students prepare a script for a TV broadcast designed to make the public more aware of what tsunamis are, the dangers of tsunamis, and what people should do if a tsunami warning is issued. Allow students to perform their broadcasts for the class.

Extension

Have students research the tsunami that struck Hawaii on April 1, 1946 and those that occurred on May 22, 1960 in Chile, Hawaii, and Japan. Ask them to prepare brief written reports that include information about the path each tsunami traveled, its maximum height, and the resulting damage.

NATIONAL GEOGRAPHIC   VISUALIZING TSUNAMIS

Figure 7

The diagram below shows stages in the development of a tsunami. A tsunami is an ocean wave that is usually generated by an earthquake and is capable of inflicting great destruction.

▶ **TSUNAMI ALERT** The red dots on this map show the tide monitoring stations that make up part of the Tsunami Warning System for the Pacific Ocean. The map shows approximately how long it would take for tsunamis that originate at different places in the Pacific to reach Hawaii. Each ring represents two hours of travel time.

TSUNAMI WARNING SYSTEM

Ⓐ The vibrations set off by a sudden movement along a fault in Earth's crust are transferred to the water's surface and spread across the ocean in a series of long waves.

Ⓑ The waves travel across the ocean at speeds ranging from about 500 to 950 kilometers per hour.

Ⓒ When a tsunami wave reaches shallow water, friction slows it down and causes it to roll up into a wall of water—sometimes 30 meters high—before it breaks against the shore.

Displacement

Tsunami Warning System buoy

Resource Manager

Chapter Resources Booklet
  Transparency Activity, pp. 45–46
  Reinforcement, p. 25
  Lab Activity, pp. 9–10

Earthquake Safety

You've just read about the destruction that earthquakes cause. Fortunately, there are ways to reduce the damage and the loss of life associated with earthquakes.

Learning the earthquake history of an area is one of the first things to do to protect yourself. If the area you are in has had earthquakes before, chances are it will again and you can prepare for that.

Is your home seismic safe? What could you do to make your home earthquake safe? As shown in **Figure 8,** it's a good idea to move all heavy objects to lower shelves so they can't fall on you. Make sure your gas hot-water heater and appliances are well secured. A new method of protecting against fire is to place sensors on your gas line that would shut off the gas when the vibrations of an earthquake are felt.

In the event of an earthquake, keep away from all windows and avoid anything that might fall on you. Watch for fallen power lines and other possible fire hazards. Collapsed buildings and piles of rubble can contain many sharp edges, so keep clear of these areas.

Seismic-Safe Structures If a building is considered **seismic safe,** it will be able to stand up against the vibrations caused by most earthquakes. Residents in earthquake-prone areas are constantly improving the way structures are built. Since 1971, stricter building codes have been enforced in California. Older buildings have been reinforced. Many high-rise office buildings now stand on huge steel-and-rubber supports that could enable them to ride out the vibrations of an earthquake. Underground water and gas pipes are replaced with pipes that will bend during an earthquake. This can help prevent broken gas lines and therefore reduce damage from fires.

Seismic-safe highways have cement pillars with spiral reinforcing rods placed within them. One structure that was severely damaged in the 1989 Loma Prieta, California earthquake was Interstate Highway 880. The collapsed highway was due to be renovated to make it seismic safe. It was built in the 1950s and did not have spiral reinforcing rods in its concrete columns. When the upper highway went in one direction, the lower one went in the opposite direction. The columns collapsed and the upper highway came down onto the lower one.

Figure 8
You can minimize your risk of getting hurt by preparing for an earthquake in advance.

Ⓐ **Placing heavy or breakable objects on lower shelves means they won't fall too far during an earthquake.**

Ⓑ **Vibration sensors on gas lines shut off the supply of gas automatically during an earthquake.** *What hazard can be prevented if the gas is turned off?*

Earthquake Safety

Discussion

Explain that the two main strategies for building earthquake-resistant structures are shock absorption and reinforcement. **How could reinforcing the walls in a structure increase earthquake safety?** It would reduce the amount of debris that might fall on victims. **How might placing shock absorbers in the foundation of a building help increase safety during an earthquake?** Shock absorbers could absorb some of the up-and-down movement within a structure, thus reducing the amount of structural failure within walls and supports.

Caption Answer
Figure 8B fire hazard

Science Journal

Safety Checklist Have students make an earthquake safety checklist in their Science Journals. Checklists should note actions people should take when an earthquake occurs. Students should include staying away from power lines, keeping clear of heavy objects that might fall on them, and using the "DUCK (get down), COVER (head), and HOLD (stay put under a sturdy piece of furniture)" safety routine.

Reteach

Show students pictures illustrating damage caused by the 1995 earthquake in Kobe, Japan, the 1989 earthquake in Loma Prieta, California, and the 1906 earthquake in San Francisco, California. Ask them to hypothesize what caused the greatest amount of damage. falling structures and fires caused by breaking gas lines L2 IS **Logical-Mathematical**

Challenge

Have small groups of students research the Tsunami Warning System (TWS) developed by the United States in 1948. Have them also determine how Geostationary Operational Environmental Satellites (GOES) are used to obtain information on impending tsunamis. The TWS was established after a tsunami hit the Aleutian and Hawaiian Islands. It was improved upon in 1964. GOES can be used to issue tsunami warnings in as quickly as two minutes after a tsunami is detected. L3 COOP LEARN IS **Linguistic**

✓ Assessment

Oral How might warning the public of an impending earthquake help save lives? People could remain outside of buildings and avoid being trapped by falling debris. **Would a warning help reduce structural damage?** No, structural damage would still occur. Use **PASC**, p. 89.

Figure 9
One way to monitor changes along a fault is to detect any movement that occurs.

Predicting Earthquakes Imagine how many lives could be saved if only the time and location of a major earthquake could be predicted. Because most injuries from earthquakes occur when structures fall on top of people, it would help if people could be warned to move outside of buildings.

Researchers try to predict earthquakes by noting changes that precede them. That way, if such changes are observed again, an earthquake warning may be issued.

For example, movement along faults is monitored using laser-equipped, distance-measuring devices, such as the one shown in **Figure 9.** Changes in groundwater level or in electrical properties of rocks under stress have been measured by some scientists. Some people even study rock layers that have been affected by ancient earthquakes. Whether any of these studies will lead to the accurate and reliable prediction of earthquakes, no one knows. A major problem is that no single change in Earth occurs for all earthquakes. Each earthquake is unique.

Long-range forecasts predict whether an earthquake of a certain magnitude is likely to occur in a given area within 30 to 100 years. Forecasts of this nature are used to update building codes to make a given area more seismic safe.

Section ① Assessment

1. What happens to rocks after their elastic limit is passed?
2. Which seismic wave arrives first at a seismograph station? Which arrives last? Which seismic waves cause most of the damage during an earthquake?
3. What improvements have been made to buildings and other structures to make them more seismic safe?
4. How can seismic waves be used to determine an earthquake's epicenter?
5. **Think Critically** Explain how a magnitude-8.0 earthquake could be classified as a low-intensity earthquake.

Skill Builder Activities

6. **Making and Using Tables** Use **Table 1** to research the earthquakes that struck Indonesia in 2000, Loma Prieta, California in 1989, and Iran in 1990. Although the three earthquakes were close in magnitude, explain why there was such a great difference in the number of deaths. **For more help, refer to the** Science Skill Handbook.

7. **Communicating** In your Science Journal, write a one-page description of how you would make your home or your classroom more seismic safe. **For more help, refer to the** Science Skill Handbook.

Answers to Section Assessment

1. Rocks undergo plastic deformation and remain bent or break.
2. P-waves arrive first; surface waves arrive last. Surface waves cause the most damage.
3. Reinforcements and shock absorbers have been added to buildings to make them safer.
4. The different speeds at which P- and S-waves travel can be used to determine distance.
5. Intensity is a measure of damage. If the earthquake occurred far from populated areas or if structures in the area had been built to withstand a large earthquake, damage, and thus intensity, might be low.
6. The structures in California were built to withstand earthquakes. Buildings in Indonesia and Iran lacked support structures and were more likely to crumble, killing people inside the buildings.
7. Possible answer: Move heavy objects to lower shelves; install pliable gas lines; secure appliances such as hot water heaters.

2 Volcanoes

How do volcanoes form?

Much like air bubbles that are forced upward toward the bottom of an overturned bottle of denser syrup, molten rock, or magma, is forced upward toward Earth's surface by denser, cooler surrounding rock. Rising magma eventually can lead to an eruption, where magma, solids, and gas are spewed out to form cone-shaped mountains called **volcanoes.** As magma flows onto Earth's surface through a vent, or opening, it is called **lava.** Volcanoes have circular holes near their summits called craters. Lava and other volcanic materials can be expelled through a volcano's crater.

Some explosive eruptions throw lava and rock thousands of meters into the air. Bits of rock or solidified lava dropped from the air are called tephra. Tephra varies in size from volcanic ash to cinders to larger rocks called bombs or blocks.

Where Plates Collide Some volcanoes form because of collision of large plates of Earth's crust and upper mantle. This process has produced a string of volcanic islands, much like those illustrated in **Figure 10,** which includes Montserrat. These islands are forming as plates made up of oceanic crust and mantle collide. The older and denser oceanic plate subducts, or sinks beneath, the less dense plate, as shown in **Figure 10.** When one plate sinks under another plate, rock in and above the sinking plate melts, forming chambers of magma. This magma is the source for volcanic eruptions that have formed the Caribbean Islands.

As You Read

What You'll Learn
- **Explain** how volcanoes can affect people.
- **Describe** how types of materials are produced by volcanoes.
- **Compare** how three different volcano forms develop.

Vocabulary
volcano
lava
shield volcano
cinder cone volcano
composite volcano

Why It's Important
Volcanic eruptions can cause serious consequences for humans and other organisms.

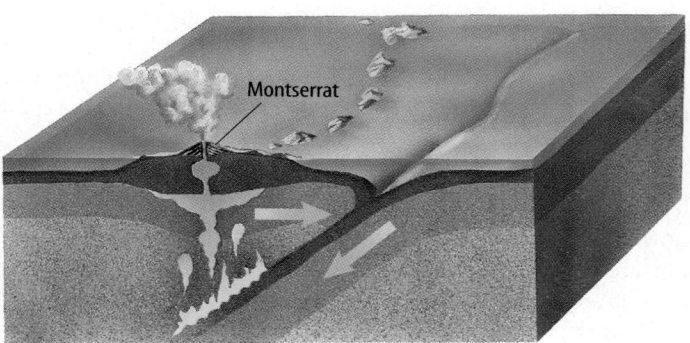

Montserrat

Figure 10
A string of Caribbean Islands known as the Lesser Antilles form because of subduction. The island of Montserrat is among these.

Section ✓*Assessment* Planner

PORTFOLIO
Extension, p. 431
PERFORMANCE ASSESSMENT
Try at Home MiniLAB, p. 430
Skill Builder Activities, p. 434
See page 448 for more options.

CONTENT ASSESSMENT
Section, p. 434
Challenge, p. 434
Chapter, pp. 448–449

2 Volcanoes

1 Motivate

Bellringer Transparency

Display the Section Focus Transparency for Section 2. Use the accompanying Transparency Activity Master. [L2] [ELL]

Tie to Prior Knowledge

Help students identify the locations of recent volcano eruptions described in the media. Ask them to name materials that are extruded from an erupting volcano. lava, tephra, gases

Resource Manager

Chapter Resources Booklet
Transparency Activity, p. 43
Directed Reading for Content Mastery, p. 19

Earth Science Critical Thinking/Problem Solving, p. 1

2 Teach

How do volcanoes form?

TRY AT HOME
Mini LAB

Purpose Students model the forces involved in a volcanic eruption. L1 ELL LS **Kinesthetic**

Materials red colored gelatin, self-sealing bag, pin

Teaching Strategy Remind students not to eat the gelatin and to be careful with the pin.

Analysis
1. Gelatin: magma; plastic bag: Earth's crust; pinhole: vent
2. pressure building within the crust
3. super-heated steam and gases

Process Infer why you used gelatin and not colored water in this activity. Gelatin more closely resembles thick, sticky silica-rich magma than does colored water. Use **Performance Assessment in the Science Classroom,** p. 89.

Teacher FYI

During eruptions, volcanoes extrude lava, gases, and tephra. Most gases released from volcanoes consist of water vapor. Scientists think that water vapor from magma was the source of Earth's early oceans and that gases released by volcanoes may have contributed to the composition of Earth's early atmosphere.

A Volcanic ash blanketing an area can cause collapse of structures or—when mixed with precipitation—mudflows.

B Objects in the path of a pyroclastic flow are subject to complete destruction.

Figure 11
Several volcanic hazards are associated with explosive activity.

TRY AT HOME
Mini LAB

Modeling an Eruption

Procedure
1. Place **red-colored gelatin** into a **self-sealing plastic bag** until the bag is half-full.
2. Seal the bag and press the gelatin to the bottom of the bag.
3. Put a hole in the bottom of the bag with a **pin**.

Analysis
1. What parts of a volcano do the gelatin, the plastic bag, and the hole represent?
2. What force in nature did you mimic as you moved the gelatin to the bottom of the bag?
3. What factors in nature cause this force to increase and lead to an eruption?

Eruptions on a Caribbean Island Soufrière (soo free UR) Hills volcano on the island of Montserrat was considered dormant until recently. However, in 1995, Soufrière Hills volcano surprised its inhabitants with explosive activity. In July 1995, plumes of ash soared to heights of more than 10,000 m. This ash covered the capital city of Plymouth and many other villages, as shown in **Figure 11A.**

Every aspect of a once-calm tropical life changed when the volcano erupted. Glowing avalanches and hot, boiling mudflows destroyed villages and shut down the main harbor of the island and its airport. During activity on July 3, 1998, volcanic ash reached heights of more than 14,000 m. This ash settled over the entire island and was followed by mudflows brought on by heavy rains.

Pyroclastic flows are another hazard for inhabitants of Montserrat. They can occur anytime on any side of the volcano. Pyroclastic flows are massive avalanches of hot, glowing rock flowing on a cushion of intensely hot gases, as shown in **Figure 11B.** Speeds at which these flows travel can reach 200 km/h.

More than one half of Montserrat has been converted to a barren wasteland by the volcano. Virtually all of the farmland is now unusable, and most of the island's business and leisure centers are gone. Many of the inhabitants of the island have been evacuated to England, surrounding islands, or northern Montserrat, which is considered safe from volcanic activity.

430 CHAPTER 15 Earthquakes and Volcanoes

Curriculum Connection

Geography Place a world map on a bulletin board. Ask each student to use the Internet or library sources to determine the location of a volcano. Have students place a pin on the map to show the location of the volcano researched. Use a piece of string to connect each pin to a card labeled with the volcano's name, latitude, and longitude.

Resource Manager

Chapter Resources Booklet
  MiniLAB, p. 4
  Enrichment, p. 29
Reading and Writing Skill Activities, p. 27

Volcanic Risks According to the volcanic-risk map shown in **Figure 12,** inactive volcanic centers exist at Silver Hill, Centre Hill, and South Soufrière Hills. The active volcano, Soufrière Hills Volcano, is located just north of South Soufrière Hills. The risk map shows different zones of the island where inhabitants still are able to stay and locations from which they have been evacuated. Twenty people who had ignored evacuation orders were killed by pyroclastic flows from the June 25, 1997, event. These are the first and only deaths that have occurred since July 1995.

Forms of Volcanoes

As you have learned, volcanoes can cause great destruction. However, volcanoes also add new rock to Earth's crust with each eruption. The way volcanoes add this new material to Earth's surface varies greatly. Different types of eruptions produce different types of volcanoes.

What determines how a volcano erupts? Some volcanic eruptions are violent, while during others lava flows out quietly around a vent. The composition of the magma plays a big part in determining the manner in which energy is released during a volcanic eruption. Lava that contains more silica, which is a compound consisting of silicon and oxygen, tends to be thicker and is more resistant to flow. Lava containing more iron and magnesium and less silica tends to flow easily. The amount of water vapor and other gases trapped in the lava also influences how lava erupts.

When you shake a bottle of carbonated soft drink before opening it, the pressure from the gas in the drink builds up and is released suddenly when the container is opened. Similarly, steam builds pressure in magma. This pressure is released as magma rises toward Earth's surface and eventually erupts. Sticky, silica-rich lava tends to trap water vapor and other gases.

Water is carried down from the surface of Earth into the mantle when one plate subducts beneath another, as in the case of the Lesser Antilles volcanoes. In hotter regions of Earth's interior, part of a descending plate and nearby rock will melt to form magma. The magma produced is more silica rich than the rock that melts to form the magma. Superheated steam produces tremendous pressure in such thick, silica-rich magmas. After enough pressure builds up, an eruption occurs. The type of lava and the gases contained in that lava determine the type of eruption that occurs.

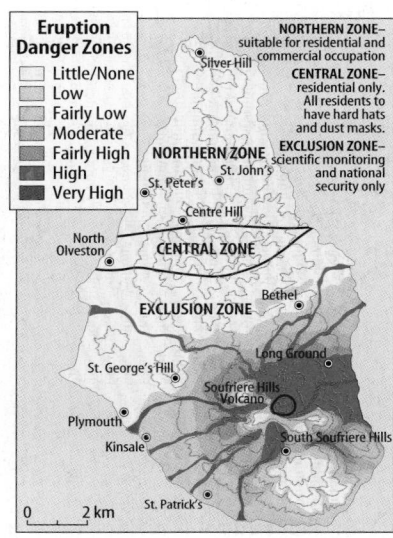

Eruption Danger Zones
- Little/None
- Low
- Fairly Low
- Moderate
- Fairly High
- High
- Very High

NORTHERN ZONE— suitable for residential and commercial occupation

CENTRAL ZONE— residential only. All residents to have hard hats and dust masks.

EXCLUSION ZONE— scientific monitoring and national security only

Silver Hill
St. Peter's
St. John's
NORTHERN ZONE
Centre Hill
North Olveston
CENTRAL ZONE
Bethel
EXCLUSION ZONE
Long Ground
St. George's Hill
Soufrière Hills Volcano
Plymouth
Kinsale
South Soufrière Hills
St. Patrick's
0   2 km

Figure 12

A volcanic risk map for Montserrat was prepared to warn inhabitants and visitors about unsafe areas on the island. *Do research and, using a computer, make your own volcanic risk map for a different volcano.*

Data Update For an online update of data on Soufrière Hills volcano on Montserrat, visit the Glencoe Science Web site at **science.glencoe.com** and select the appropriate chapter.

Forms of Volcanoes

Teacher **FYI**

When an oceanic plate subducts, part of it melts. The first minerals to melt are quartz, potassium feldspar, and other silica-rich minerals. This produces a magma that contains more silica than the original rock.

Visual Learning

Figure 12 Have students examine the map. **What area of Montserrat could you still live on?** Northern Zone **Can you still live in the Central Zone?** yes **Would life be normal there?** No; you have to wear a mask and hard hat.

Extension

Have students find out more about the recent eruptions of the Soufriére Hills Volcano on the island of Montserrat. Then have them take the role of an inhabitant of this island and write a letter to a friend describing how the volcano's eruption has affected his or her daily life. Letters should note that many inhabitants have been evacuated and property has been buried under layers of ash. L2
Linguistic P

Caption Answer

Figure 12 Answers will vary but should include eruption danger zones.

Active Reading

Synthesis Journal In this strategy, students reflect on a project, a paper, or a performance in light of their own experiences and plan for personal application. Have each student divide a sheet of paper into three sections. Have them record "What I did," "What I learned," and "How I can use it." Have students write a Synthesis Journal entry related to the MiniLAB on modeling an eruption.

Internet Addresses

_____
_____
_____

Explore the Glencoe Science Web site at **science.glencoe.com** to find out more about topics in this section.

Forms of Volcanoes,
continued

Discussion

Would the lava flowing from Kilauea Iki be hotter or cooler than lava from Mount Saint Helens? Hotter; freely flowing lava is usually rich in iron and magnesium. **How would the composition of slow moving, viscous (thick) lava compare to fast moving, runny lava?** Viscous lava is usually silica-rich and cooler, whereas fast moving lava is usually iron- and magnesium-rich and hotter.

Activity

Have students work in pairs to illustrate the three forms of volcanoes. Encourage students to use proper size ratios in their illustrations. For example, Mauna Loa (shield) is 3 times higher and 10 times wider than Mount Rainier (composite). In turn, Mount Rainier is 10 times higher and 11 times wider than Sunset Crater (cinder cone). L2
IS Visual-Spatial

✔ Reading Check

Answer basaltic lava

Figure 13
Volcanic landforms vary greatly in size and shape.

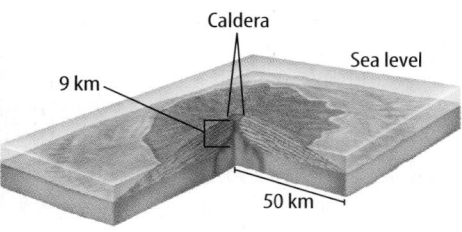

A The fluid nature of basaltic lava has produced extensive flows at Mauna Loa, Hawaii—the largest active volcano on Earth.

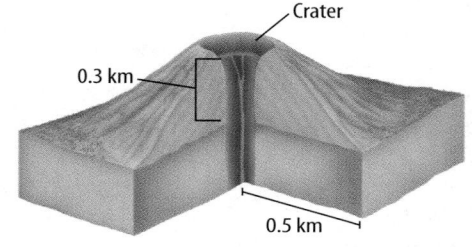

B Sunset Crater is small and steep along its flanks—typical of a cinder cone. Compare the scale given for Sunset Crater with that shown in **Figure 13A.**

Shield Volcanoes Basaltic lava, which is high in iron and magnesium and low in silica, flows in broad, flat layers. The buildup of basaltic layers forms a broad volcano with gently sloping sides called a **shield volcano.** Shield volcanoes, shown in **Figure 13A,** are the largest type of volcano to form. They form where magma is being forced up from extreme depths within Earth, or in areas where Earth's plates are moving apart. The separation of plates enables magma to be forced upward to Earth's surface.

✔ Reading Check
What materials are shield volcanoes composed of?

Cinder Cone Volcanoes Rising magma accumulates gases on its way to the surface. When the gas builds up enough pressure, it erupts. Moderate to violent eruptions throw volcanic ash, cinders, and lava high into the air. The lava cools quickly in midair and the particles of solidified lava, ash, and cinders fall back to Earth. This tephra forms a relatively small cone of volcanic material called a **cinder cone volcano.** Cinder cones are usually less than 300 m in height and often form in groups near other larger volcanoes. Because the eruption is powered by the high gas content, it usually doesn't last long. After the gas is released, the force behind the eruption is gone. Sunset Crater, an example of a cinder cone near Flagstaff, Arizona, is shown in **Figure 13B.**

Composite Volcanoes

Composite volcanoes are steep-sided mountains composed of alternating layers of lava and tephra. They sometimes erupt violently, releasing large quantities of ash and gas. This forms a tephra layer of solid materials. Then a quieter eruption forms a lava layer.

Composite volcanoes form where one plate sinks beneath another. Soufrière Hills volcano is an example of a composite volcano. Another volcanic eruption from a composite volcano was the May 1980 eruption of Mount St. Helens in the state of Washington. It erupted explosively, spewing ash that fell on regions hundreds of kilometers away from the volcano. A composite volcano is shown in **Figure 13C.**

Fissure Eruptions

Magma that is highly fluid can ooze from cracks or fissures in Earth's surface. This is the type of magma that usually is associated with fissure eruptions. The lava that erupts has a low viscosity, which means it can flow freely across the land to form flood basalts. Flood basalts that have been exposed to erosion for millions of years can become large, relatively flat landforms known as lava plateaus, as shown in **Figure 13D.** The Columbia River Plateau in the northwestern United States was formed about 15 million years ago when several fissures erupted and the flows built up layer upon layer.

C Composite cones are intermediate in size and shape compared to shield volcanoes and cinder cone volcanoes.

Mount Rainier, Washington

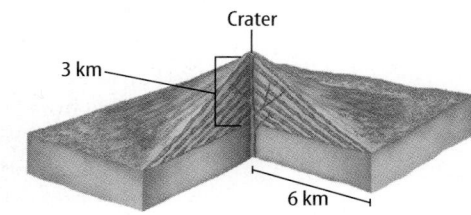
Crater
3 km
6 km

D No modern example compares with the extensive flood basalts making up the Columbia River Plateau.

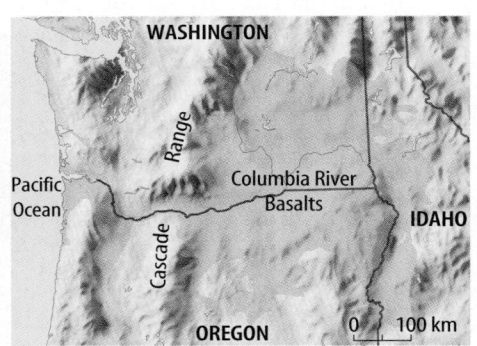
WASHINGTON
Pacific Ocean
Range
Columbia River Basalts
Cascade
IDAHO
OREGON
0   100 km

SECTION 2 Volcanoes   **433**

Draw a cross section of a subduction zone on the board. Have a student volunteer use the diagram to explain how the denser plate carries water with it as it sinks. Have a second volunteer explain that the partial melting of the sinking block and the water content of the material produce a silica-rich magma that contains water vapor and other gases. **LS** **Visual-Spatial**

Challenge

Ask students to determine how the eruption of Mount Saint Helens generated a massive mudflow that caused great destruction. The snow high on Mount Saint Helens melted when the eruption occurred. The water mixed with ash to form the mudflows, also called lahars. L3

✓ *Assessment*

Content Have students work in groups of three or four to write a song or poem about how volcanoes like those in Hawaii erupt. Poems or songs should include reference to the runny, quickly moving, basaltic lava that flows from Hawaiian volcanoes. Use **Performance Assessment in the Science Classroom,** p. 151.

Table 2 Ten Selected Eruptions in History

Volcano (Year)	Type	Eruptive Force	Silica Content	Gas Content	Eruption Products
Tambora, Indonesia (1815)	composite	high	high	high	gas, cinders, ash
Krakatau, Indonesia (1883)	composite	high	high	high	gas, cinders, ash
Pelée, Martinique (1902)	composite	high	high	high	gas, ash
Katmai, Alaska (1912)	composite	high	high	high	lava, ash, gas
Paricutín, Mexico (1943)	cinder cone	moderate	high	low	gas, cinders, ash
Helgafell, Iceland (1973)	cinder cone	moderate	low	high	gas, ash
Mount St. Helens, Washington (1980)	composite	high	high	high	gas, ash
Kilauea Iki, Hawaii (1989)	shield	low	low	low	gas, lava
Pinatubo, Philippines (1991)	composite	high	high	high	gas, ash
Soufrière Hills, Montserrat (1995–)	composite	high	high	high	gas, ash, rocks

Large Eruptions The Columbia River Plateau covers about 200,000 km² and is up to 3 km thick in places. In addition, most of Earth's crust beneath the oceans is composed of basalt that was erupted from huge fissures where plates separate.

You have read about some variables that control the type of volcanic eruption that will occur. Examine **Table 2** for a summary of these important factors. In the next section, you'll learn that the type of magma produced is associated with properties of Earth's plates and how these plates interact.

Section 2 Assessment

1. Which types of lava eruptions cover the largest area on Earth's surface?
2. Describe the processes that have led to the formation of the Soufrière Hills volcano. How have the inhabitants of Montserrat been affected by this volcano?
3. Why does a cinder cone have such steep sides?
4. What types of materials are volcanoes like Mount St. Helens made of?
5. **Think Critically** How does silica-rich magma erupt?

Skill Builder Activities

6. **Predicting** Predict what type of eruption will occur if the magma inside a volcano is low in silica, high in iron and magnesium, and contains little gas. **For more help, refer to the** Science Skill Handbook.
7. **Solving One-Step Equations** Mauna Loa in Hawaii is a shield volcano that rises 9 km above the seafloor. Sunset Crater in Arizona rises to an elevation of 300 m. How many times higher is Mauna Loa than Sunset Crater? **For more help, refer to the** Math Skill Handbook.

Answers to Section Assessment

1. fissure eruptions
2. As one plate sinks under another, rock material is melted and forced upward toward Earth's surface, where it erupts to form a volcano. Many of the inhabitants have been forced to evacuate their homes.
3. The solids extruded by a cinder cone form a steep-sided pile.
4. alternating layers of lava and tephra
5. Silica-rich magma is sticky and thick. It tends to hold in gases that cause pressure to build until finally the volcano erupts explosively.
6. The eruption will be nonexplosive, and the lava will flow easily and rapidly.
7. Mauna Loa is 30 times higher than Sunset Crater. (9,000 m ÷ 300 m = 30)

Disruptive Eruptions

A volcano's structure can influence how it erupts. Some volcanoes have only one central vent, while others have numerous fissures that allow lava to escape. Materials in magma influence its viscosity, or how it flows. If magma is a thin fluid—not viscous—gases can escape easily. But if magma is thick—viscous—gases cannot escape as easily. This builds up pressure within a volcano.

What You'll Investigate
What determines the explosiveness of a volcanic eruption?

Materials
plastic film canisters
baking soda ($NaHCO_3$)
vinegar (CH_3COOH)
50-mL graduated cylinder
teaspoon

Goals
- **Infer** how a volcano's opening contributes to how explosive an eruption might be.
- **Hypothesize** how the viscosity of magma can influence an eruption.

Safety Precautions
This activity should be done outdoors. Goggles must be worn at all times. The caps of the film canisters fly off due to the chemical reaction that occurs inside them. Never put anything in your mouth while doing the experiment.

Procedure
1. Watch your teacher demonstrate this activity before attempting to do it yourself.
2. Add 15 ml of vinegar to a film canister.

3. Place 1 teaspoon of baking soda in the film canister's lid, using it as a type of plate.
4. Place the lid on top of the film canister, but do not cap it. The baking soda will fall into the vinegar. Move a safe distance away. Record your observations in your Science Journal.

5. Clean out your film canister and repeat the activity, but this time cap the canister quickly and tightly. Record your observations.

Conclude and Apply
1. Which of the two activities models a more explosive eruption?
2. Was the pressure greater inside the canister during the first or second activity? Why?
3. What do the bubbles have to do with the explosion? How do they influence the pressure in the container?
4. If the vinegar were a more viscous substance, how would the eruption be affected?

Communicating Your Data

Research three volcanic eruptions that have occurred in the past five years. Compare each eruption to one of the eruption styles you modeled in this activity. Communicate to your class what you learn.

BENCH TESTED

Purpose Students will investigate what determines the explosiveness of a volcanic eruption.

Process Skills observing, inferring, hypothesizing

Time Required 30 minutes

Safety Precautions Be sure students move a safe distance away from the canisters.

Teaching Strategy Review with students that the reaction between vinegar and baking soda produces carbon dioxide gas.

Troubleshooting Some film canisters will not seal tightly enough to pop the top off in step 5. You may want to test the canisters ahead of time.

Answers to Questions
1. the second one
2. during the second one because the gas produced could not easily escape
3. The bubbles are carbon dioxide gas produced by the reaction. The more gas that is trapped in the canister, the greater the pressure is.
4. The gas bubbles would have a harder time escaping from a more viscous liquid so the pressure would build up more before it erupted.

✓Assessment

Oral Have students describe how they think a reaction between baking soda and vinegar mixed with ketchup would appear. Use **Performance Assessment in the Science Classroom**, p. 89

Resource Manager

Chapter Resources Booklet
Activity Worksheet, pp. 5–6

Communicating Your Data

Students should provide descriptive evidence of each eruption to support their comparisons.

SECTION
3

Earthquakes, Volcanoes, and Plate Tectonics

1 Motivate

Bellringer Transparency

 Display the Section Focus Transparency for Section 3. Use the accompanying Transparency Activity Master. L2

ELL

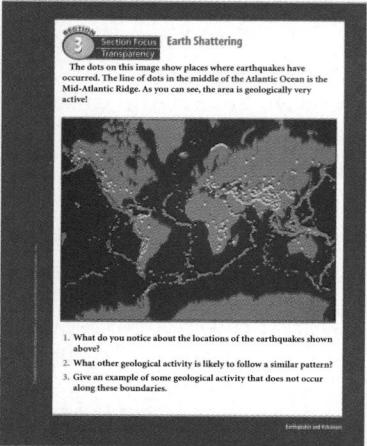

Tie to Prior Knowledge

Ask students to name recent earthquakes and volcanoes and where they were located. Record responses as a list. Then have students analyze the list for any similarities. Lists should show that most earthquakes and volcanoes occur in specific areas of the world.

SECTION 3
Earthquakes, Volcanoes, and Plate Tectonics

As You Read

What You'll Learn
- **Explain** how the locations of volcanoes and earthquake epicenters are related to tectonic plate boundaries.
- **Explain** how heat within Earth causes Earth's plates to move.

Vocabulary
rift
hot spot

Why It's Important
Most volcanoes and earthquakes are caused by the motion and interaction of Earth's plates.

Figure 14
Like the tables pictured here, Earth's plates are in contact with one another and can slide beneath each other. The way Earth's plates interact at boundaries is an important control on the locations of earthquakes and volcanoes.

Earth's Moving Plates

At the beginning of class, your teacher asks for volunteers to help set up the cafeteria for a special assembly. You and your classmates begin to move the tables carefully, like the students shown in **Figure 14.** As you move the tables, two or three of them crash into each other. Think about what could happen if the students moving those tables kept pushing on them. For a while one or two of the tables might keep another from moving. However, if enough force were used, the tables would slide past one another. One table might even slide up on top of another. It is because of this possibility that your teacher has asked that you move the tables carefully.

The movement of the tables and the possible collisions among them is like the movement of Earth's crust and uppermost mantle, called the lithosphere. Earth's lithosphere is broken into separate sections, or plates. When these plates move around, they collide, move apart, or slide past each other. The movement of these plates can cause vibrations known as earthquakes and can create conditions that cause volcanoes to form.

436 CHAPTER 15 Earthquakes and Volcanoes

Section ✓Assessment Planner

PORTFOLIO
Extension, p. 437
PERFORMANCE ASSESSMENT
Math Skills Activity, p. 440
Skill Builder Activities, p. 441
See page 448 for more options.

CONTENT ASSESSMENT
Section, p. 441
Challenge, p. 441
Chapter, pp. 448–449

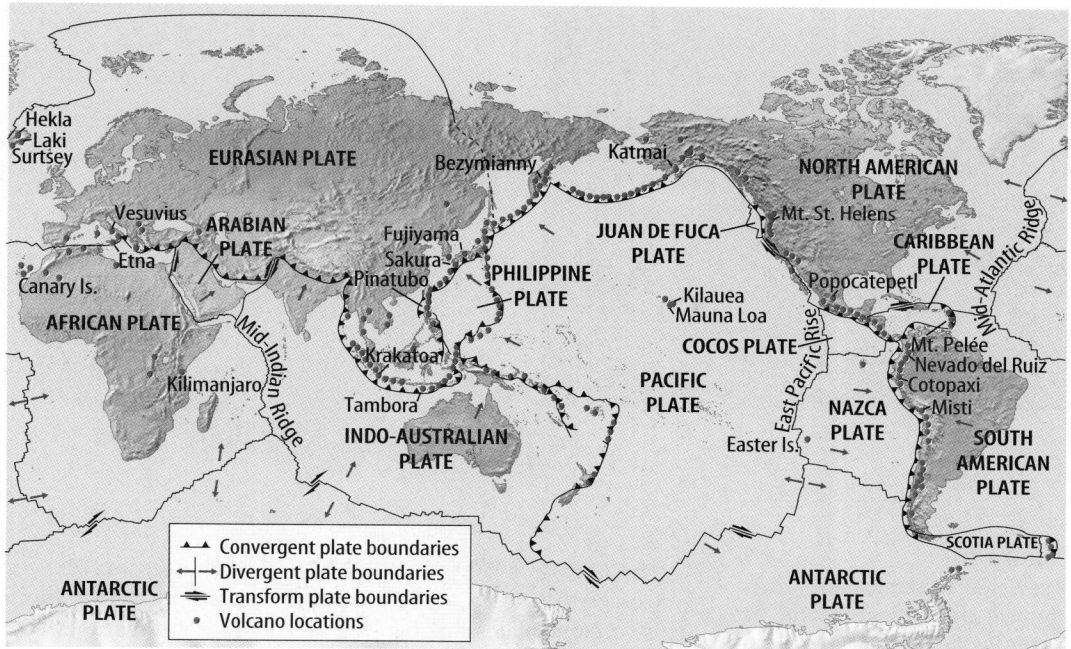

Figure 15
Earth's lithosphere is divided into about 13 major plates. Where plates collide, separate, and slip past one another at plate boundaries, interesting geological activity results.

Where Volcanoes Form

A plot of the location of plate boundaries and volcanoes on Earth shows that most volcanoes form along plate boundaries. Examine the map in **Figure 15.** Can you see how this indicates that plate tectonics and volcanic activity are related? Perhaps the energy involved in plate tectonics is causing magma to form deep under Earth's surface. You'll recall that the Soufrière Hills volcano formed where plates converge. Plate movement often explains why volcanoes form in certain areas.

Divergent Plate Boundaries Tectonic plates move apart at divergent plate boundaries. As the plates separate, long cracks called **rifts** form between them. Rifts contain fractures that serve as passageways for magma originating in the mantle. Rift zones account for most of the places where lava flows onto Earth's surface. Fissure eruptions often occur along rift zones. These eruptions form lava that cools and solidifies into basalt, the most abundant type of rock in Earth's crust.

☑ **Reading Check** *Where does magma along divergent boundaries originate?*

Earth's Moving Plates

Visual Learning

Figure 15 Explain that volcanoes occur where plates pull apart or are pushed together. **Which type of eruption is likely to occur where plates pull apart? Explain.** A fracture forms in Earth's crust where plates pull apart. Thus, fissure eruptions are likely to occur there.

Where Volcanoes Form

Extension

Have students research the geologic history of Iceland and write a report on their findings. Iceland has been built by volcanic activity along the Mid-Atlantic Ridge, a divergent plate boundary, which runs across the island. L2 **IS Linguistic** P

Make a Model

Organize the class into four groups and assign each group one of the following topics: volcanoes caused by convergence, volcanoes caused by divergence, volcanoes caused by hot spots, and different forms of volcanoes. Ask each group to make a model of their assigned topic using everyday materials. Allow groups to present their models to the class. L2 **ELL** COOP LEARN **IS Kinesthetic**

☑ **Reading Check**

Answer the mantle

Teacher FYI

Magma in the Cascades Sinking of the remaining portion of the Farallon Plate, called the Juan de Fuca Plate, has caused melting that is the source of magma for the Cascade range of volcanic mountains. These volcanoes are located in the western United States and include Mount Rainier, Mount Shasta, and Mount Saint Helens.

Resource Manager

Chapter Resources Booklet
  Enrichment, p. 30
  Transparency Activity, p. 44
Home and Community Involvement, p. 46
Earth Science Critical Thinking/Problem Solving, p. 8

Use Science Words

Word Meaning Have students find out why boundaries where plates move together are called convergent plate boundaries. *Convergent* contains the base word *converge,* which means "to approach the same point from different directions."

Activity

Show students a topographic map of the ocean floor. (Maps are available from the National Geographic Society or in an oceanography textbook.) Have students work in small groups to determine locations on the map where volcanoes caused by sinking of one plate beneath another are probably located. Volcanoes caused by subduction would be located near the edges of continents that have deep trenches just offshore. Volcanoes would also be located in island arcs near deep sea trenches. L2 COOP LEARN

 **Visual-Spatial**

Chemistry INTEGRATION

When very hot, but solid, rock from the mantle rises, the decrease in pressure allows the rock to melt.

✔ Reading Check

Answer bodies of magma rising through Earth's mantle and crust that are not necessarily part of a plate boundary

---

Fun Fact

Southeast of Hawaii's Big Island, an undersea volcano, called a seamount, rises more than 3,000 meters above the ocean floor. It has formed over the Hawaiian hot spot and will eventually become a new Hawaiian Island.

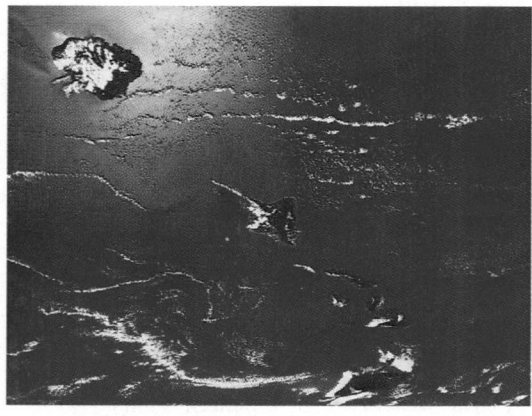

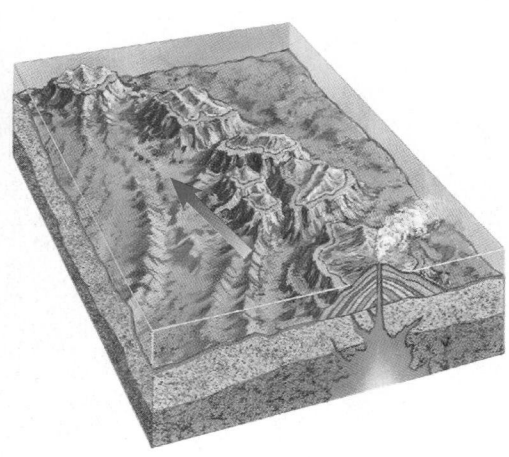

Figure 16
The Hawaiian Islands have formed, and continue to form, as the Pacific Plate moves over a hot spot. The arrow shows that the Pacific Plate is moving north-northwest.

Chemistry INTEGRATION

The melting point of a substance is the temperature at which a solid changes to a liquid. Depending on the substance, a change in pressure can raise or lower the melting point. Do research to find out how pressure affects the formation of magma in a mantle plume in a process called decompression melting.

Convergent Plate Boundaries A common location for volcanoes to form is along convergent plate boundaries. More dense oceanic plates sink beneath less dense plates that they collide with. This sets up conditions that form volcanoes.

When one plate sinks beneath another, basalt and sediment on an oceanic plate move down into the mantle. Water from the sediment and altered basalt lowers the melting point of the surrounding rock. Heat in the mantle causes part of the sinking plate and overlying mantle to melt. This melted material then is forced upward. Volcanoes have formed in this way all around the Pacific Ocean, where the Pacific Plate, among others, collides with several other plates. This belt of volcanoes surrounding the Pacific Ocean is called the Pacific Ring of Fire.

Hot Spots The Hawaiian Islands are volcanic islands that have not formed along a plate boundary. In fact, they are located well within the Pacific Plate. What process causes them to form? Large, rising bodies of magma, called **hot spots,** can force their way through Earth's mantle and crust, as shown in **Figure 16.** Scientists suggest that this is what is occurring at a hot spot that exists under the present location of Hawaii.

✔ Reading Check *What is a hot spot?*

Volcanoes on Earth usually form along rift zones, subduction zones (where one plate sinks beneath another), or over hot spots. At each of these locations, magma from deep within Earth rises toward the surface. Lava breaks through and flows out, where it piles up into layers or forms a volcanic cone.

438 **CHAPTER 15** Earthquakes and Volcanoes

Resource Manager

Chapter Resources Booklet
Reinforcement, p. 27

Earth Science Critical Thinking/Problem Solving, p. 14

Moving Plates Cause Earthquakes

Place two notebooks on your desk with the page edges facing each other. Then push them together slowly. The individual sheets of paper gradually will bend upward from the stress. If you continue to push on the notebooks, one will slip past the other suddenly. This sudden movement is like an earthquake.

Now imagine what would happen if tectonic plates were moving like the notebooks. What would happen if the plates collided and stopped moving? Forces generated by the locked-up plates would cause strain to build up. Both plates would begin to deform until the elastic limit was passed. The breaking and elastic rebound of the deformed material would produce vibrations felt as earthquakes.

Earthquakes often occur where tectonic plates come together at a convergent boundary, where tectonic plates move apart at a divergent boundary, and where tectonic plates grind past each other, called a transform boundary.

Earthquake Locations If you look at a map of earthquakes, you'll see that most occur in well-known belts. About 80 percent of them occur in the Pacific Ring of Fire—the same belt in which many of Earth's volcanoes occur. If you compare **Figure 17** with **Figure 15,** you will notice a definite relationship between earthquake epicenters and tectonic plate boundaries. Movement of the plates produces forces that generate the energy to cause earthquakes.

Physics
INTEGRATION

Friction is a force that opposes the motion of two objects in contact. Do research to find out the role of friction in plate movement and earthquakes.

Figure 17
Locations of earthquakes that have occurred between 1990 and 2000 are plotted below.

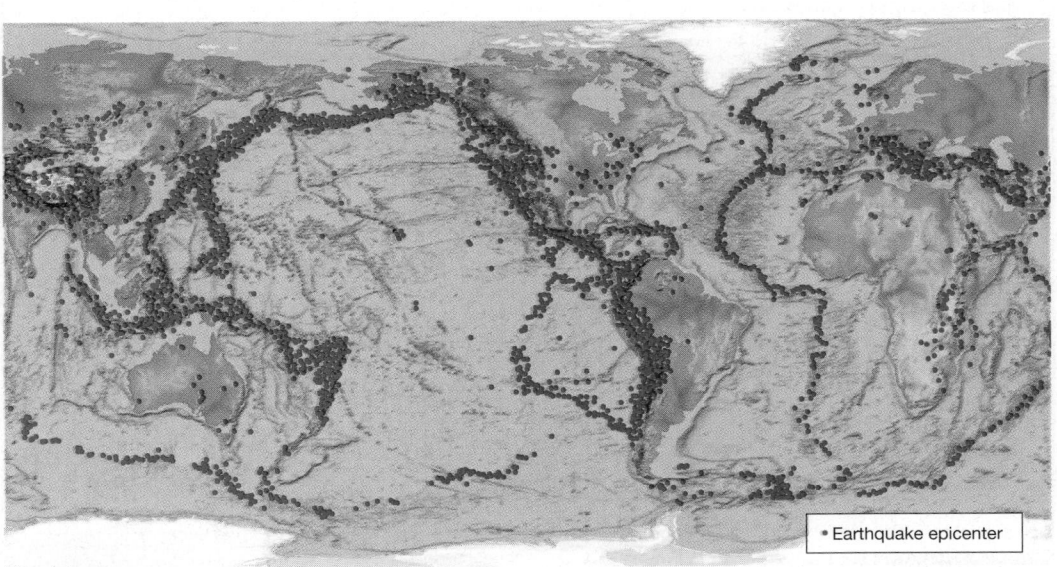

• Earthquake epicenter

Moving Plates Cause Earthquakes

Discussion

Why does a strong relationship exist between earthquakes and plate boundaries? As plates move away from, toward, or past each other, tension, compression, and shear forces are generated and build up in rocks. When energy from these forces is released, vibrations are caused, which are felt as earthquakes.

Activity

Provide blocks of wood to small groups of students. Have them use the blocks to demonstrate how the movement of plates at convergent, divergent, and transform boundaries causes earthquakes. L1 ELL COOP LEARN **Kinesthetic**

Visual Learning

Figure 17 Have students compare **Figures 17 and 15** and describe ways in which the two figures are similar. Students should note that the locations of earthquake epicenters shown in **Figure 17** align well with plate boundaries shown in **Figure 15.**

Physics
INTEGRATION

Low friction between plates would allow them to slide past one another more freely. High friction opposes this motion, causing strain energy to build up that eventually is released as earthquakes.

Science Journal

New Madrid Earthquake In 1811–1812, three of the strongest earthquakes to ever strike the United States occurred in New Madrid, Missouri. Have students research these earthquakes and write a paragraph hypothesizing how the earthquakes might be related to plate tectonics. It is thought that a failed divergent plate boundary lies under New Madrid. L2 **Linguistic**

Moving Plates Cause Earthquakes, continued

Make a Model

Use different colors of modeling clay to make a model of Earth's interior. Form a clay ball with a radius of 24 mm. Cut the ball in half and mold a 55-mm thick layer around the half ball. Continue by molding a 47-mm thick layer around the other two. Mold a final, thin layer around the other three. Display the model of Earth's inner core, outer core, mantle, and crust.

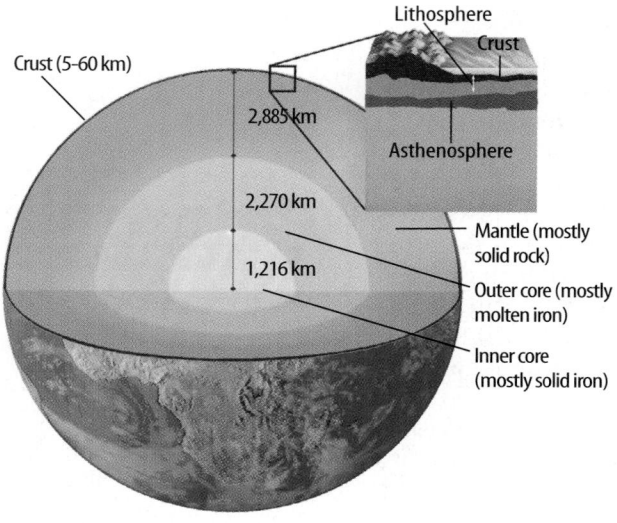

Figure 18
Seismic waves generated by earthquakes allow researchers to figure out the structure and composition of Earth's layers.

Crust (5–60 km)

Lithosphere
Crust
Asthenosphere

2,885 km

2,270 km

1,216 km

Mantle (mostly solid rock)

Outer core (mostly molten iron)

Inner core (mostly solid iron)

Earth's Plates and Interior

Researchers have learned much about Earth's interior and plate tectonics by studying seismic waves. The way in which seismic waves pass through a material depends on the properties of that material. Seismic wave speeds, and how they travel through different levels in the interior, have allowed scientists to map out the major layers of Earth, as shown in **Figure 18.**

For example, the asthenosphere was discovered when seismologists noted that seismic waves slowed when they reached the base of the lithosphere of Earth. This partially molten layer forms a warmer, softer layer over which the colder, brittle, rocky plates move.

Math Skills Activity

Calculating Time Traveled by Waves

Examine the table. What is the relationship between density of a region in Earth and the velocities of P-waves?

Example Problem

Calculate the time it would take P-waves to travel 100 km in the crust of Earth.

Density and Wave Velocity

Region	Density	P-Wave Velocity
Crust	2.8 g/cm³	6 km/s
Upper mantle	3.3 g/cm³	8 km/s

Solution

1. *This is what you know:* velocity: $v = 6$ km/s
distance: $d = 100$ km

2. *This is what you need to find:* time: t

3. *This is the equation you need to use:* $t = d/v$

4. *Solve the equation for* t *in seconds:* $t = (100 \text{ km})/(6 \text{ km/s}) = 16.7 \text{ s}$

Practice Problem

Calculate the time it takes P-waves to travel 300 km in the upper mantle.

For more help, refer to the Math Skill Handbook.

What is driving Earth's plates? There are several hypotheses about where all the energy comes from to power the movement of Earth's plates.

In one case, mantle material deep inside Earth is heated by Earth's core. This hot, less dense rock material is forced toward the surface. The hotter, rising mantle material eventually cools. The cooler material then sinks into the mantle toward Earth's core, completing the convection current. Convection currents inside Earth, shown in **Figure 19,** provide the mechanism for plate motion, which then produces the conditions that cause volcanoes and earthquakes. Sometimes magma rises up directly within a plate. Volcanic activity in Yellowstone National Park is caused by a hot spot beneath the North American Plate. Such hot spots might be related to larger-scale convection in Earth's mantle.

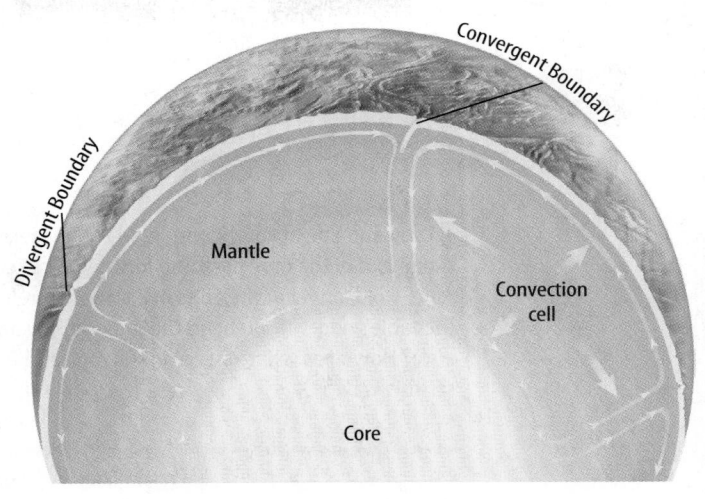

Figure 19
Convection of material in Earth's interior drives the motion of tectonic plates.

Section 3 Assessment

1. Along which type of tectonic plate boundary has the Soufrière Hills volcano formed?

2. At which type of tectonic boundary does rift-volcanism occur?

3. Explain how volcanoes in Hawaii form—even though they are located far from plate boundaries.

4. Why do most deep earthquakes occur at convergent boundaries?

5. **Think Critically** Subduction occurs where two oceanic plates or an oceanic and a continental plate converge. This causes water-rich sediment and altered rock to be forced down to great depths. Explain how water can help form a volcano.

Skill Builder Activities

6. **Forming Hypotheses** Write a hypothesis concerning the type of lava that will flow from a hot spot to form a volcano. While forming your hypothesis, consider that magma in a hot spot comes from deep inside Earth's mantle. Earth's mantle contains more iron and magnesium and less silica than the crust. **For more help, refer to the** Science Skill Handbook.

7. **Using an Electronic Spreadsheet** Research for listings of the major earthquakes over the past five years. Make a table that provides information for each of the earthquakes, including whether they are located at or near tectonic plate boundaries. **For more help, refer to the** Technology Skill Handbook.

Use an Analogy

Explain that convection currents in a warming pan of soup are similar to the convection currents located inside Earth's interior.

③ Assess

Reteach

Have students describe what is occurring in Earth's crust as you move your hands together to demonstrate converging plates, apart to demonstrate diverging plates, and past each other to demonstrate plates moving along a transform boundary. L1
ELL LS **Visual-Spatial**

Challenge

Have students hypothesize why there are a series of Hawaiian Islands instead of just one large island that grows continuously. As the Pacific Plate moves, a different part of the Plate lies above the hot spot forming the islands. L3
LS **Logical-Mathematical**

✓ Assessment

Oral Explain why magma coming from deep inside Earth's mantle is likely to be basaltic. Earth's interior is denser than the crust and it contains more iron and magnesium. Thus, magma from that area should be richer in iron and magnesium also. Use **PASC,** p. 89.

Answers to Section Assessment

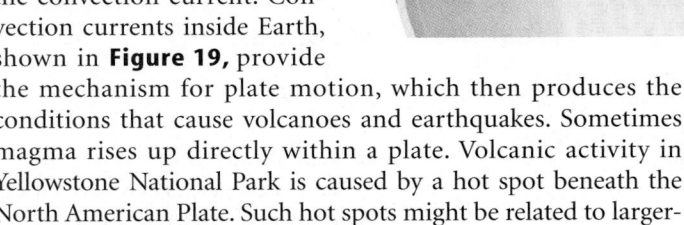

1. convergent boundary with one oceanic plate sinking beneath the other
2. divergent boundaries
3. Hot magma is forced upward through Earth's mantle and crust, forming a hot spot.
4. Deep earthquakes occur where one tectonic plate sinks beneath another.

This occurs at convergent boundaries.
5. As ocean sediment sinks into Earth's mantle, water travels along with it. The pressure of water vapor in mantle rock lowers the melting point of the rock. The lowered melting point helps to form some magma. Magma is forced upward, reaches Earth's surface, and flows out as lava.

6. Possible answer: Lava from a hot spot will be basaltic in composition and flow easily.
7. Student tables should show that most earthquake epicenters are located near current or past tectonic plate boundaries.

Section 3 Earthquakes, Volcanoes, and Plate Tectonics **441**

Activity

What You'll Investigate

Purpose

Students use a coiled spring toy to demonstrate seismic waves and to show how material is affected by the waves. L2 ELL COOP LEARN Ⓛ **Visual-Spatial**

Process Skills

observing, inferring, communicating, making and using tables, interpreting data, making models

Time Required

one class period

Safety Precautions

Caution students to wear safety goggles when manipulating the spring.

Procedure

Teaching Strategies

- Caution students not to overstretch the coiled spring.
- Keep individual coiled spring toys in separate boxes or bags to avoid tangled coils.

Troubleshooting

If students wish to measure the amount of movement in the coiled spring toy, advise them to tape the metric ruler to the desktop or floor.

Expected Outcome

The yarn or string moves perpendicular to the wave for transverse waves (S-waves). It moves parallel to the wave for compression waves (P-waves).

Activity

Seismic Waves

If you and one of your friends hold a long piece of rope between you and move one end of the rope back and forth, you can send a wave through the length of the rope. Hold a ruler at the edge of a table securely with one end of it sticking out from the table's edge. If you bend the ruler slightly and then release it, what do you experience? How does what you see in the rope and what you feel in the ruler relate to seismic waves?

What You'll Investigate

How do seismic waves differ?

Materials

coiled spring toy
yarn or string
metric ruler

Goals

- **Demonstrate** the motion of primary, secondary, and surface waves.
- **Identify** how parts of the spring move in each of the waves.

Safety Precautions 👓

Procedure

1. Copy the following data table in your Science Journal.

2. Tie a small piece of yarn or string to every tenth coil of the spring.

3. Place the spring on a smooth, flat surface. Stretch it so it is about 2 m long (1 m for shorter springs).

4. Hold your end of the spring firmly. Make a wave by having your partner snap the spring from side to side quickly.

5. Record your observations in your Science Journal and draw the wave you and your partner made in the data table.

Comparing Seismic Waves			
Observation of Wave	Observation of Yarn or String	Drawing	Wave Type
		⌇	
	Answers will vary.	▨	
		◠◡	

Inclusion Strategies

Learning Disabled Be sure each student has a specific job to do during the activity. In this way, your learning disabled students will be assured of having a role in the activity and serving as an important part of the team. Also, check with each group and see that learning disabled students observe the movements of the toy when each different type of wave is transmitted.

Seismic Waves Have students write brief paragraphs in their Science Journals explaining why P-waves and S-waves are considered body waves, but surface waves are not. P-waves and S-waves both travel outward from an earthquake focus through the body of Earth. Surface waves are generated at the surface directly above the earthquake focus at a point called the epicenter.

6. Have your lab partner hold his or her end of the spring firmly. Make a wave by quickly pushing your end of the spring toward your partner and bringing it back to its original position.

7. **Record** your observations of the wave and of the yarn or string and draw the wave in the data table.

8. Have your lab partner hold his or her end of the spring firmly. Move the spring off of the table. Gently move your end of the spring side to side while at the same time moving it in a rolling motion, first up and away and then down and toward your partner.

9. **Record** your observations and draw the wave in the data table.

Conclude and Apply

1. Based on your observations, decide which of the waves that you and your partner have generated demonstrates a primary, or pressure, wave. Record in your data table and explain why you chose the wave you did.

2. Do the same for the secondary, or shear wave, and for the surface wave. Explain why you chose the wave you did.

3. Based on your observations of wave motion, which of the waves that you and your partner generated probably would cause the most damage during an earthquake? Explain your answers.

4. What was the purpose of the yarn or string?

5. **Compare and contrast** the motion of the yarn or string when primary and secondary waves travel through the spring. Which of these waves is a compression wave? Which is a transverse wave? Explain each answer.

6. Which wave most closely resembled wave motion in a body of water? How was it different? Explain.

Compare your conclusions with those of other students in your class. **For more help, refer to the** Science Skill Handbook.

ACTIVITY 443

Resource Manager

Chapter Resources Booklet
  Activity Worksheet, pp. 7–8
Lab Management and Safety, p. 38

Fill out your data table and compare your results with those of others in the class. Comment on similarities and differences that you notice.

Conclude and Apply

1. Second wave; parts of the spring move parallel to the wave.
2. The first wave was the secondary wave; spring parts move perpendicular to the wave. The third wave was the surface wave; it causes most movement.
3. surface waves; most movement
4. to aid students in seeing how parts of the coiled spring toy moved
5. Both waves caused the yarn or string to move. Secondary waves gave the yarn perpendicular movement; primary waves gave it parallel movement. Primary waves compress the spring and so are compression waves; secondary waves move the spring sideways and so are transverse waves.
6. Surface waves cause the spring to move elliptically, as do waves in water.

Error Analysis
How did the yarn move in the first two waves your group generated? perpendicular to the wave in the first; parallel in the second **Which wave caused the most movement in the spring?** the third wave Have students explain possible causes of error. These might include improperly moving the spring or misinterpreting the spring's movement.

Performance Have two students hold a rope between them and send a transverse wave along the rope. The rope moves side to side. Use **Performance Assessment in the Science Classroom,** p. 123.

Content Background

Earth's crust and uppermost mantle are divided into segments called plates. These plates are constantly moving against one another. Some plates converge, some pull apart, and others slide past each other. While seismic activity occurs all over the planet, most of the world's volcanic regions, earthquake belts, and deep-sea trenches, are located along these plate boundaries.

The San Andreas Fault lies along two plates moving laterally against one another. This lateral movement along the fault causes buildup of strain energy along the fault. Sometimes the energy is released slowly and regularly over time in small tremors that are barely felt. But when the energy continues to build over a long period of time, the energy may be released in a sudden burst. This causes massive vibrations that travel through rock, causing a destructive earthquake. The size of the earthquake is directly related to the amount of energy released at the point of the disturbance, called the focus.

A method for measuring earthquakes, the Richter scale, was developed by Charles Richter. This system assigns a number to an earthquake according to the amount of energy released at the focus. The logarithmic scale begins at one and each increasing number indicates an earthquake that releases 32 times more energy than the next lower number.

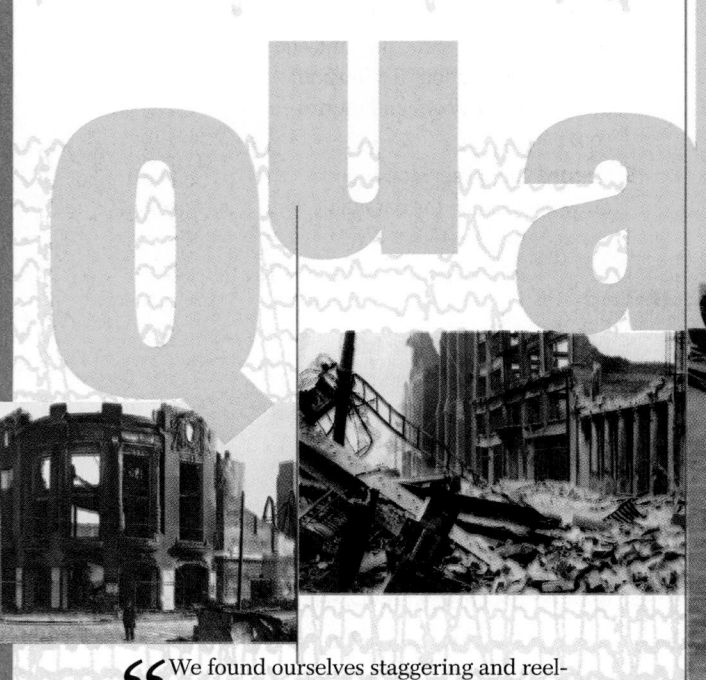

quake

The 1906 San Francisco earthquake taught people valuable lessons

"We found ourselves staggering and reeling. It was as if the earth was slipping gently from under our feet. Then came the sickening swaying of the earth that threw us flat upon our faces. We struggled in the street. We could not get on our feet. Then it seemed as though my head were split with the roar that crashed into my ears. Big buildings were crumbling as one might crush a biscuit in one's hand."

That's how survivor P. Barrett described the San Francisco earthquake of 1906. Duration of the quake on the morning of April 18—one minute. Yet, in that short time, Earth opened a gaping hole stretching more than 430 km. The tragic result was one of the worst natural disasters in U.S. history.

444

Resources for Teachers and Students

Earthquake: The World Reacts by Paul Bennett. Smart Apple Media, Mankato, MN. 1999.

Magnitude 8: Earthquakes and Life Along the San Andreas Fault by Philip L. Fradkin. Henry Holt and Company, New York 1998.

Earthquakes by Bruce A. Bolt. W.H. Freeman and Company, University of California, Berkeley 1988.

Earthquake Prediction by Haroun Tazieff. McGraw-Hill, Inc., New York 1992.

Janice VanCleave's Earthquakes by Janice Pratt Van-Cleave. John Wiley & Sons, Inc. New York 1993.

Fires caused by falling chimneys and fed by broken gas mains raged for three days. Despite the estimated 3,000 deaths and enormous devastation to San Francisco, the earthquake did have a positive effect. It led to major building changes that would help protect people and property from future quakes.

Before the 1906 earthquake, little was known about how or where earthquakes were likely to occur. And not much was known about the destructiveness of quakes. However, after the quake hit San Francisco, scientists and government workers set up a State Earthquake Investigation Commission.

The 1906 quake destroyed City Hall (above). Today, a rebuilt City Hall stands on the same site (right).

Scientists and engineers placed instruments in buildings and bridges, and nearby on the ground, to measure how structures respond to the motion of the ground during an earthquake. They found that structures built on soft, muddy clay shook worse than structures built on harder ground, like bedrock. They also discovered that buildings made from flexible materials, such as wood, are damaged less than those constructed of rigid materials, such as steel and brick. Rigid materials will snap, rather than sway, during an earthquake. These discoveries led to knowledge about quakes that is still used today to make buildings safer.

Thanks to these early findings, combined with recent developments in earthquake detection, California now has instruments tracking plate motions throughout the state. Computers analyze information from seismographs that have helped to map the San Andreas Fault—the area along which many California earthquakes take place. This information is helping scientists better understand how and when earthquakes might strike.

The 1906 quake also has led to building codes that require stronger construction materials for homes, offices, and bridges. Laws have been passed saying where hospitals, homes, and nuclear power plants can be built—away from soft ground and away from the San Andreas Fault.

Even today, scientists can't predict an earthquake. But thanks to what they learned from the 1906 quake—and others—people are safer today than ever before.

Discussion

What should be included in an emergency preparedness plan for your family? Remind students that natural disasters like earthquakes, hurricanes, floods, and tornadoes may cause homes to collapse, broken gas and water lines, injury, and loss of power. Possible answers: Learn how to protect yourself against the most common natural disasters that occur in your area. Hold regular drills with family members. Take a first aid class. Learn how to use a fire extinguisher. Store first aid supplies, food, water, battery-powered radio, fresh batteries, flashlight, and protective clothing.

Historical Significance

Explain to students that most of the buildings in San Francisco at the time of the 1906 earthquake were made of wood and brick. There was little concern about building earthquake-resistant structures. While the shaking itself devastated many of the poorly built structures, most of the damage was caused by fires that swept through the city. Broken water lines forced firefighters to haul water into the city from the ocean and reservoirs. After the 1906 earthquake, San Francisco enforced ordinances that improved buildings and plans to deal with broken water lines without compromising the safety of the city's residents.

CONNECTIONS Write Prepare a diary entry pretending to be a person who experienced the 1906 San Francisco earthquake. Possible events to include in your entry: What were you doing at 5:15 A.M.? What began to happen around you? What did you see and hear?

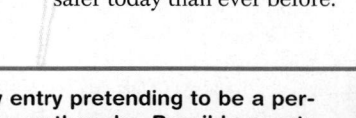

For more information, visit science.glencoe.com

CONNECTIONS

Ask students to brainstorm possible responses for their diary entries. List the answers to each question in separate columns as students suggest them. Direct the class to choose several of the ideas from each list to incorporate into their own diary entry. Encourage students to use other original ideas while composing their diaries.

SCIENCE Online

Internet Addresses

_____
_____
_____

Explore the Glencoe Science Web site at **science.glencoe.com** to find out more about topics in this feature.

Reviewing Main Ideas

Preview

Students can answer the questions in their Science Journals. Discuss the answers as you go through the chapter. **Linguistic**

Review

Students can write their answers, then compare them with those of other students. **Interpersonal**

Reteach

Students can look at the illustrations and describe details that support the main ideas of the chapter. **Visual-Spatial**

Answers to Chapter Review

SECTION 1

2. arrival times of seismic waves at a minimum of three seismograph stations

SECTION 2

2. tephra and lava

SECTION 3

3. convergent plate boundary where one oceanic plate sinks beneath another oceanic plate

---

Reviewing Main Ideas

Section 1 Earthquakes

1. Earthquakes occur whenever rocks inside Earth pass their elastic limit, break, and experience elastic rebound.

2. The precise point where an earthquake occurs is the focus. The point on Earth's surface directly above an earthquake's focus is the epicenter. *What do scientists measure on seismograms to determine an epicenter?*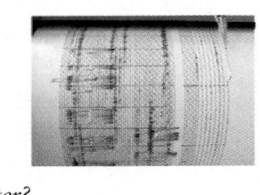

3. Seismic waves are vibrations inside Earth. P- and S-waves travel in all directions away from the earthquake focus and move throughout Earth, including the deep interior. Surface waves travel along the surface.

4. Earthquakes are measured by their magnitudes—the amount of energy they release—and by their intensity—the amount of damage they produce.

Section 2 Volcanoes

1. The Soufrière Hills volcano is a composite volcano formed by the convergence of two tectonic plates.

2. Material extruded from volcanoes varies greatly and includes lava, tephra, and gases. *What types of material erupted to form the volcano shown here?*

3. The way a volcano erupts is determined by the composition of the lava and the amount of water vapor and other gases in the lava.

4. Three different forms of volcanoes are shield volcanoes, cinder cone volcanoes, and composite volcanoes.

Section 3 Earthquakes, Volcanoes, and Plate Tectonics

1. The locations of volcanoes and earthquake epicenters are related to the locations of tectonic plate boundaries.

2. Volcanoes occur along rift zones and subduction zones, as well as at hot spots.

3. Most earthquakes occur at convergent, divergent, and transform plate boundaries, but some occur within the plates. *Which type of plate boundary is illustrated below? Be specific.*

After You Read

FOLDABLES Reading & Study Skills

Record how earthquakes and volcanoes are similar and different on the center section of your Foldable.

FOLDABLES Reading & Study Skills

After You Read

After students have read the chapter and completed the Foldable described in Before You Read, have them do the activity on the student page.

Dinah Zike

Visualizing Main Ideas

Fill in the following table comparing characteristics of shield, composite, and cinder cone volcanoes.

Volcanoes			
Characteristic	Shield Volcano	Cinder Cone Volcano	Composite Volcano
Relative size	large		
Nature of eruption	low eruptive force	high eruptive force	moderate to high eruptive force
Materials extruded	lava, gas	cinders, gas	lava, ash, gas
Composition of lava	low silica	variable	variable
Ability of lava to flow	high	low	variable

Vocabulary Review

Vocabulary Words

a. cinder cone volcano
b. composite volcano
c. earthquake
d. epicenter
e. fault
f. focus
g. hot spot
h. lava
i. magnitude
j. rift
k. seismic safe
l. seismic wave
m. seismograph
n. shield volcano
o. tsunami
p. volcano

THE PRINCETON REVIEW   Study Tip

Sit with a study partner and read aloud to each other from a chapter. Then discuss what you've been reading with each other.

Using Vocabulary

Explain the differences between the vocabulary words in each of the following sets.

1. fault, earthquake
2. seismic wave, seismic safe
3. shield volcano, composite volcano
4. focus, epicenter
5. seismic wave, seismograph
6. hot spot, focus
7. tsunami, seismic wave
8. epicenter, earthquake
9. focus, fault
10. cinder cone volcano, shield volcano

Visualizing Main Ideas

See student page.

Vocabulary Review

Using Vocabulary

1. fault—a break along which there is motion; earthquake—vibrations generated by the movement along a fault
2. seismic wave—wave caused by earthquakes; seismic safe—able to withstand vibrations
3. shield—largest type of volcano, made from basaltic lava; composite—medium-sized volcano, made from alternating lava and tephra layers
4. focus—where earthquake originates; epicenter—point on surface directly above focus
5. seismic wave—wave produced by an earthquake; seismograph—instrument used to record earthquake waves
6. hot spot—place where magma is rising through the mantle and crust; focus—point where earthquake originates
7. tsunami—seismic sea wave; seismic wave—waves caused by earthquakes
8. epicenter—point on surface directly above focus; earthquake—vibrations caused by fault movement
9. focus—point where rocks move and cause an earthquake; fault—fracture along which rock movement occurs
10. cinder cone—smallest volcano, made of tephra; shield—largest volcano, made from basaltic lava

Checking Concepts

1. D
2. A
3. B
4. C
5. D
6. B
7. A
8. D
9. B
10. B

Thinking Critically

11. The silica-rich magma contains water vapor and other gases under intense pressure in the magma, causing it to erupt explosively.

12. Tephra can erupt from both, however eruptions of composite volcanoes alternate between tephra and lava.

13. Silica-rich magma is viscous and can trap gases and build up pressure. Iron- and magnesium-rich magma is hotter and flows more easily, and allows gases to escape more readily.

14. The lava from a shield volcano is hotter and more runny, therefore it can flow long distances before cooling.

15. the amount of structural and geologic damage done

Checking Concepts

Choose the word or phrase that best answers the question.

1. Which type of plate boundary caused the formation of the Soufrière Hills volcano?
   A) divergent
   C) rift
   B) transform
   D) convergent

2. What is a cone-shaped mountain that is built from layers of lava?
   A) volcano
   C) vent
   B) lava flow
   D) crater

3. What are avalanches of hot, glowing rock flowing on a cushion of hot gases called?
   A) lava flows
   C) mudflows
   B) pyroclastic flows
   D) gas clouds

4. Which type of lava flows easily?
   A) silica-rich lava
   C) basaltic lava
   B) composite lava
   D) smooth lava

5. Which type of volcano is built from alternating layers of lava and tephra?
   A) shield volcano
   B) cinder cone volcano
   C) lava dome
   D) composite volcano

6. Which type of volcano forms a relatively small, steep-sided cone?
   A) shield volcano
   B) cinder cone volcano
   C) lava dome
   D) composite volcano

7. Which seismic wave moves through Earth at the fastest speed?
   A) primary wave
   C) surface wave
   B) secondary wave
   D) tsunami

8. Which of the following is a wave of water caused by an earthquake under the ocean?
   A) primary wave
   C) surface wave
   B) secondary wave
   D) tsunami

9. What is the point on Earth's surface directly above an earthquake's focus?
   A) earthquake center
   B) epicenter
   C) wave center
   D) focus

10. What is the cause of the volcanoes on Hawaii?
    A) rift zone
    B) hot spot
    C) divergent plate boundary
    D) convergent plate boundary

Thinking Critically

11. Why does the Soufrière Hills volcano erupt so explosively?

12. Compare and contrast composite and cinder cone volcanoes.

13. How can the composition of magma affect the way a volcano erupts?

14. Why do shield volcanoes have flatter slopes than composite volcanoes?

15. What factors determine an earthquake's intensity on the modified Mercalli scale?

Developing Skills

16. **Making and Using Tables** Use **Table 2** in Section 2 to answer the following questions. What general statement can be made about the eruptive force of composite volcanoes? What usually is erupted from shield volcanoes such as Kilauea Iki?

17. **Comparing and Contrasting** Compare and contrast magnitude and intensity.

18. **Making Models** Select one of the three forms of volcanoes and make a model, using appropriate materials.

Chapter ✓Assessment Planner

Portfolio Encourage students to place in their portfolios one or two items of what they consider to be their best work. Examples include:
- Science Journal, p. 423
- Extension, p. 431
- Extension, p. 437

Performance Additional performance assessments, Performance Task Assessment Lists, and rubrics for evaluating these activities can be found in Glencoe's **Performance Assessment in the Science Classroom.**

19. Drawing Conclusions You are flying over an area that has just experienced an earthquake. You see that most of the buildings are damaged or destroyed and much of the surrounding countryside is disrupted. What level of intensity would you conclude for this earthquake?

20. Concept Mapping Complete this concept map on examples of features produced along plate boundaries. Use the following terms: *Mid-Atlantic Ridge, Soufrière Hills volcano, divergent, San Andreas Fault, convergent,* and *transform.*

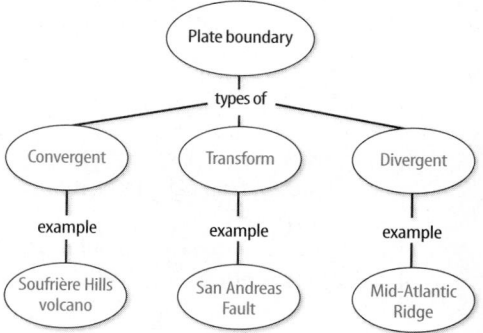

Performance Assessment

21. Oral Presentation Research the earthquake or volcano history of your state or community. Find out how long ago your area experienced earthquake- or volcano-related problems. Present your findings in a speech to your class.

TECHNOLOGY

 Go to the Glencoe Science Web site at **science.glencoe.com** or use the **Glencoe Science CD-ROM** for additional chapter assessment.

 THE PRINCETON REVIEW **Test Practice**

The table below presents data about Earth's plate boundaries.

Plate Boundaries		
Plate	**Number of convergent boundaries**	**Number of divergent boundaries**
African	1	4
Antarctic	1	2
Indo-Australian	4	2
Eurasian	4	0
North American	2	1
Pacific	6	1
South American	2	1

Study the table and answer the following questions.

1. Which plate has the most spreading boundaries?
   A) African
   B) Indo-Australian
   C) Pacific
   D) Antarctic

2. If composite volcanoes often form along convergent boundaries, which plate should be surrounded by the most composite volcanoes?
   F) Pacific
   G) Antarctic
   H) Eurasian
   J) Indo-Australian

THE PRINCETON REVIEW **Test Practice**

The Test-Taking Tip was written by The Princeton Review, the nation's leader in test preparation.
1. A
2. F

Developing Skills

16. Composite volcanoes have a high eruptive force; lava and gas.
17. Both magnitude and intensity are used to measure earthquakes. Magnitude measures energy released, and intensity measures damage done.
18. Models will vary, but should follow data presented in the text for each form.
19. Accept any answer between IX and XII.
20. See student page.

Performance Assessment

21. Answers will vary depending on your location. Use **Performance Assessment in the Science Classroom**, p. 143.

✓Assessment Resources

📁 Reproducible Masters
Chapter Resources Booklet
   Chapter Review, pp. 35–36
   Chapter Tests, pp. 37–40
   Assessment Transparency Activity, p. 47
Glencoe Science Web site
   Interactive Tutor
   Chapter Quizzes

Glencoe Technology
   🖐 Assessment Transparency
   💿 Interactive CD-ROM Chapter Quizzes
   💿 ExamView Pro Test Bank
   💿 Vocabulary PuzzleMaker Software
   📼 MindJogger Videoquiz

Section/Objectives	Standards		Activities/Features
Chapter Opener	**National**	**State/Local**	**Explore Activity:** Explore how currents work, p. 451
	See p. 5T for a Key to Standards.		**Before You Read,** p. 451
Section 1 Ocean Water ⏱ 2 sessions 📦 1 block 1. **Identify** the origin of the water in Earth's oceans. 2. **Explain** how dissolved salts and other substances get into seawater. 3. **Describe** the composition of seawater.	National Content Standards: UCP4, D1, D2		
Section 2 Ocean Currents ⏱ 2 sessions 📦 1 block 1. **Explain** how winds and the Coriolis effect influence surface currents. 2. **Discuss** the temperatures of coastal waters. 3. **Describe** density currents.	National Content Standards: UCP2, A1, B1, B3, D1		**Science Online,** p. 457 **MiniLAB:** Modeling a Density Current, p. 459 **Math Skills Activity:** Calculating Density, p. 460
Section 3 Ocean Waves and Tides ⏱ 3 sessions 📦 1.5 blocks 1. **Describe** wave formation. 2. **Distinguish** between the movement of water particles in a wave and the movement of the wave. 3. **Explain** how ocean tides form.	National Content Standards: UCP3, B1, B3, D1, D3, E2, G1, G2		**MiniLAB:** Modeling Water Particle Movement, p. 463 **Visualizing Wave Movement,** p. 464 **Science Online,** p. 465 **Life Science Integration,** p. 467 **Activity:** Making Waves, p. 469 **Activity:** Sink or Float, pp. 470–471 **Science and Language Arts:** The Jungle of Ceylon, pp. 472–473

NATIONAL GEOGRAPHIC

Teacher's Corner

PRODUCTS AVAILABLE FROM GLENCOE
To order call 1-800-334-7344:
CD-ROM
NGS PictureShow: Oceans
Curriculum Kit
GeoKit: Oceans

Transparency Set
NGS PicturePack: Oceans

PRODUCTS AVAILABLE FROM NATIONAL GEOGRAPHIC SOCIETY
To order call 1-800-368-2728:
Videos
Living Ocean
Oceans in Motion
Water: A Precious Resource

Activity Materials	Reproducible Resources	Section Assessment	Technology
Explore Activity: beaker, bowl, ice, warm water, dropper, food coloring	**Chapter Resources Booklet** Foldables Worksheet, p. 13 Directed Reading Overview, p. 15 Note-taking Worksheets, pp. 29–31	GLENCOE'S ASSESSMENT ADVANTAGE	
Need materials? Contact Science Kit at 1-800-828-7777 or www.sciencekit.com on the Internet.	**Chapter Resources Booklet** Transparency Activity, p. 40 Lab Activity, pp. 9–10 Enrichment, p. 26 Reinforcement, p. 23 Directed Reading, p. 16 **Cultural Diversity,** p. 65	**Portfolio** Assessment, p. 455 **Performance** Skill Builder Activities, p. 455 **Content** Section Assessment, p. 455	Section Focus Transparency Interactive CD-ROM Guided Reading Audio Program
MiniLAB: clear plastic storage box, water, salt, glass, food coloring, spoon	**Chapter Resources Booklet** Transparency Activity, p. 41 MiniLAB, p. 3 Lab Activity, pp. 11–12 Enrichment, p. 27 Reinforcement, p. 24 Directed Reading, p. 16 **Mathematics Skill Activities,** p. 9 **Science Inquiry Labs,** p. 31	**Portfolio** Curriculum Connection, p. 458 **Performance** MiniLAB, p. 459 Math Skills Activity, p. 460 Skill Builder Activities, p. 461 **Content** Section Assessment, p. 461	Section Focus Transparency Interactive CD-ROM Guided Reading Audio Program
MiniLAB: plastic storage box, tape, water, cork, spoon **Activity:** 11″ x 14″ white paper, 3-speed electric fan, gooseneck lamp, clock or watch, clear-plastic storage box, water, metric ruler **Activity:** small, uncooked potato; teaspoon; salt; large glass bowl; water; balance; large graduated cylinder; metric ruler	**Chapter Resources Booklet** Transparency Activity, p. 42 MiniLAB, p. 4 Enrichment, p. 28 Reinforcement, p. 25 Directed Reading, pp. 17, 18 Transparency Activity, pp. 43–44 Activity Worksheet, pp. 5–6, 7–8 **Lab Management and Safety,** p. 65	**Portfolio** Extension, p. 464 **Performance** MiniLAB, p. 463 Skill Builder Activities, p. 468 **Content** Section Assessment, p. 468	Section Focus Transparency Teaching Transparency Interactive CD-ROM Guided Reading Audio Program

End of Chapter Assessment

GLENCOE'S ASSESSMENT ADVANTAGE

Blackline Masters	Technology	Professional Series
Chapter Resources Booklet Chapter Review, pp. 33–34 Chapter Tests, pp. 35–38 **Standardized Test Practice by The Princeton Review,** pp. 79–82	MindJogger Videoquiz Interactive CD-ROM Vocabulary PuzzleMakers ExamView Pro Test Bank Interactive Lesson Planner Interactive Teacher Edition	Performance Assessment in the Science Classroom (PASC)

Transparencies

Section Focus

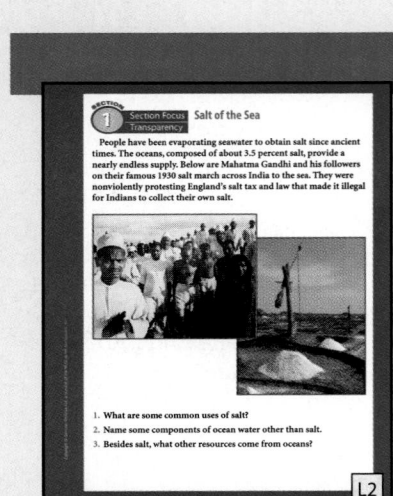

Section Focus Transparency 1 — Salt of the Sea

People have been evaporating seawater to obtain salt since ancient times. The oceans, composed of about 3.5 percent salt, provide a nearly endless supply. Below are Mahatma Gandhi and his followers on their famous 1930 salt march across India to the sea. They were nonviolently protesting England's salt tax and law that made it illegal for Indians to collect their own salt.

1. What are some common uses of salt?
2. Name some components of ocean water other than salt.
3. Besides salt, what other resources come from oceans?

L2

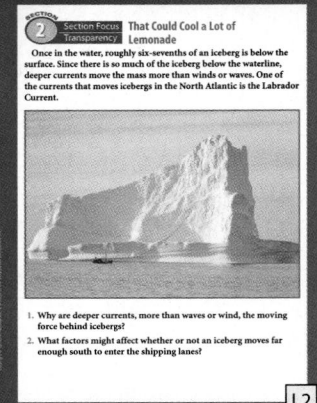

Section Focus Transparency 2 — That Could Cool a Lot of Lemonade

Once in the water, roughly six-sevenths of an iceberg is below the surface. Since there is so much of the iceberg below the waterline, deeper currents move the mass more than winds or waves. One of the currents that moves icebergs in the North Atlantic is the Labrador Current.

1. Why are deeper currents, more than waves or wind, the moving force behind icebergs?
2. What factors might affect whether or not an iceberg moves far enough south to enter the shipping lanes?

L2

Section Focus Transparency 3 — Run, Grunion, Run

Grunion are small fish that know how to take advantage of California tides. When tides are the highest, they swim with each wave as far up the beach as possible and lay their eggs, as shown below. About two weeks later, when tides are again peaking, the hatched baby grunion are carried into the ocean as waves wash over the spawning area.

1. When would be a good time to catch grunion?
2. Why do you think grunion lay their eggs in an area that is temporarily out of reach of the tides?
3. Why do sand castles built on the beach get washed away?

L2

This is a representation of key blackline masters available in the Teacher Classroom Resources. See Resource Manager boxes within the chapter for additional information.

Assessment

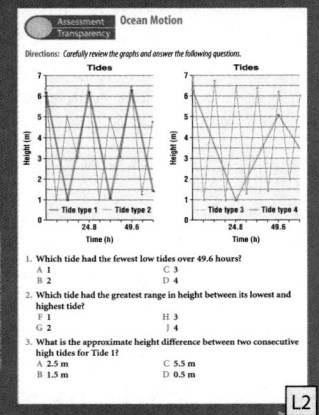

Assessment Transparency — Ocean Motion

Directions: *Carefully review the graphs and answer the following questions.*

1. Which tide had the fewest low tides over 49.6 hours?
   A 1   C 3
   B 2   D 4
2. Which tide had the greatest range in height between its lowest and highest tide?
   F 1   H 3
   G 2   J 4
3. What is the approximate height difference between two consecutive high tides for Tide 1?
   A 2.5 m   C 5.5 m
   B 1.5 m   D 0.5 m

L2

Teaching

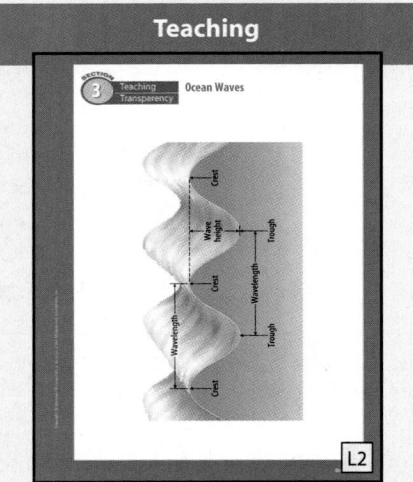

Teaching Transparency — Ocean Waves

L2

Key to Teaching Strategies

The following designations will help you decide which activities are appropriate for your students.

L1 Level 1 activities should be appropriate for students with learning difficulties.

L2 Level 2 activities should be within the ability range of all students.

L3 Level 3 activities are designed for above-average students.

ELL ELL activities should be within the ability range of English Language Learners.

COOP LEARN Cooperative Learning activities are designed for small group work.

LS Multiple Learning Styles logos, as described on page 22T, are used throughout to indicate strategies that address different learning styles.

P These strategies represent student products that can be placed into a best-work portfolio.

Hands-on Activities

Activity Worksheets

Activity — Making Waves

Lab Preview
Directions: *Answer these questions before you begin the Activity.*
1. Explain the three safety symbols.

2. Which two of the materials in the list will represent air motion and waves?

Wind generates some waves. The energy of motion is transferred from the wind to the surface water of the ocean. What factors influence the generation of waves?

What You'll Investigate
How do the speed of the wind and the length of time the wind blows affect the height of a wave?

Materials
11" x 14" white paper   rectangular, clear-plastic storage box
3-speed electric fan   water
gooseneck lamp   metric ruler
clock or watch

Goals
• Observe how wind speed and duration affect wave height.

Safety Precautions:
Do not allow any part of the light or cord to come in contact with the water.

Procedure
1. Position the box on white paper beside the lamp.
2. Fill the plastic box with water to within 3 cm of the top. Direct light from the lamp into the box.
3. Place the fan at one end of the box to create waves. Start the fan on its lowest speed. Keep the fan on during measuring.
4. After 3 min, measure the height of the waves caused by the fan. Record your observations in Table 1. Through the plastic box, observe the shadows of the waves on the white paper.
5. After 3 min, measure the wave height and record your observations.
6. Repeat steps 3 to 5 with the fan on medium, then on high.
7. Turn off the fan. Unplug it. Observe what happens.

L2

Laboratory Activities

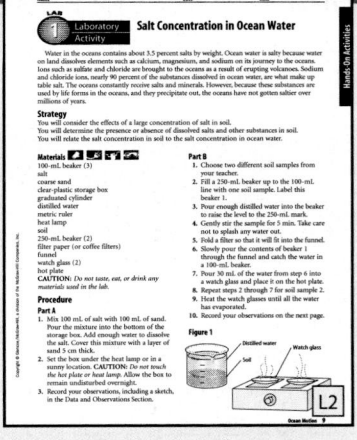

Laboratory Activity 1 — Salt Concentration in Ocean Water

Water in the oceans contains about 3.5 percent salts by weight. Ocean water is salty because water on land dissolves elements such as calcium, magnesium, and sodium on its journey to the oceans. Ions such as sulfate and chloride are brought to the ocean as a result of erupting volcanoes. Sodium and chloride ions, nearly 90 percent of the substances dissolved in ocean water, are what make up table salt. The oceans constantly receive salts and minerals. However, because these substances are used by life forms in the oceans, and they precipitate out, the oceans have not gotten saltier over millions of years.

Strategy
You will consider the effects of a large concentration of salt in soil. You will determine the presence or absence of dissolved salts and other substances in soil. You will relate the salt concentration in soil to the salt concentration in ocean water.

Materials
100-mL beaker (3)
salt
coarse sand
clear-plastic storage box
graduated cylinder
distilled water
metric ruler
heat lamp
250-mL beaker (2)
filter paper (or coffee filters)
funnel
watch glass (2)
hot plate
CAUTION: *Do not taste, eat, or drink any materials used in the lab.*

Part B
1. Choose two different soil samples from your teacher.
2. Fill a 250-mL beaker up to the 100-mL line with one soil sample. Label this beaker 1.
3. Pour enough distilled water into the beaker to raise the level to the 250-mL mark.
4. Gently stir the sample for 5 min. Take care not to splash any water out.
5. Fold a filter so that it will fit into the funnel.
6. Slowly pour the contents of beaker 1 through the funnel and catch the water in a 100-mL beaker.
7. Pour 50 mL of the water from step 6 into a watch glass and place it on the hot plate.
8. Repeat steps 2 through 7 for soil sample 2.
9. Heat the watch glasses until all the water has evaporated.
10. Record your observations on the next page.

Procedure
Part A
1. Mix 100 mL of salt with 100 mL of sand. Pour this mixture into the bottom of the storage box. Add enough water to dissolve the salt. Cover this mixture with a layer of sand 5 cm thick.
2. Set the box under the heat lamp or in a sunny location. CAUTION: *Do not touch the hot plate or heat lamp.* Allow the box to remain undisturbed overnight.
3. Record your observations, including a sketch, in the Data and Observations Section.

Figure 1

L2

Meeting Different Ability Levels

Content Outline

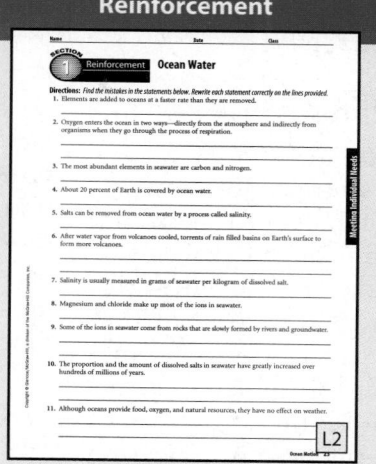

L2

Reinforcement

L2

Directed Reading

L1

Assessment

Chapter Tests

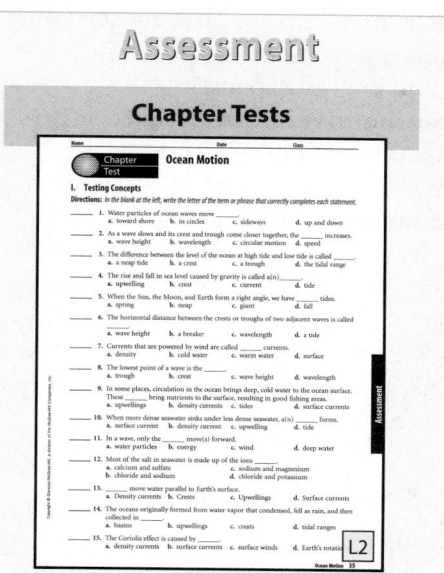

L2

Enrichment

L3

Spanish Directed Reading

L1

Test Practice Workbook

L2

Chapter Review

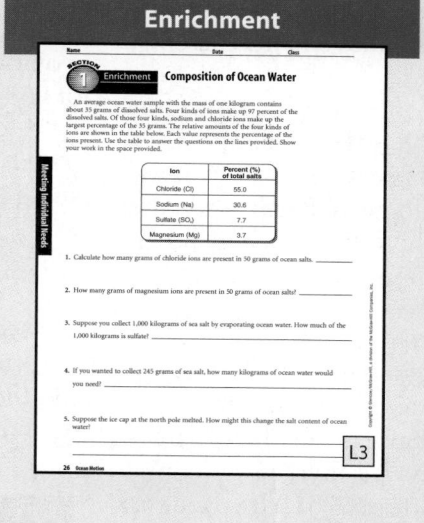

L2

Science Content Background

SECTION 1

Ocean Water

Importance of Oceans

Oceans cover 71 percent of Earth's surface—61 percent of the northern hemisphere and 81 percent of the southern hemisphere. Photosynthetic marine organisms produce 70 percent of the world's oxygen, and the oceans play a major role in determining weather and climate patterns. Physical oceanography concerns energy transmission through ocean water. It deals with wave formation and movement, currents, and tides.

Although oceans are important to life on Earth, they make up only a thin skin on its surface. Isaac Asimov made the following analogy: If Earth were the size of a billiard ball, the oceans would be an unnoticeable film of dampness.

Origin of Oceans

The locations of the ocean basins have changed throughout geologic time. Presently, all oceans connect. Geographers have given them names according to where they are divided by continents. The average depth of the oceans is 3.8 kilometers; the volume of the oceans is 1.35 billion cubic kilometers.

Composition of Oceans

Chemical oceanography is the study of the chemical properties of seawater and the causes, effects, and changes in ocean chemistry. Salinity is measured with a conductivity indicator. This instrument determines the electrical conductivity of the water when a voltage is applied. The higher the conductivity is, the higher the salinity is. If the instrument is calibrated properly, an accurate determination of salinity can be made.

Fun Fact

England has a much warmer climate than Scandinavia and Labrador, which are at similar latitudes, because heat from the warm North Atlantic Drift current warms the country.

Scientists once thought that oceans increased in salinity over time. As our understanding of oceanic processes has increased, that idea has been revised. Current models show that the overall salinity of the oceans has been roughly constant for the last several hundred million years and probably hasn't changed much since the oceans formed.

On average each cubic kilometer of ocean water contains about 50 kilograms (roughly 100 pounds) of gold. At $300 an ounce, that much gold would be worth approximately half a million dollars. Unfortunately, at present technology levels, to extract that much gold would cost much more than it's worth because of equipment and energy expenses.

Oceans can be divided into three layers based on temperature. Thermal energy in the surface layer is evenly distributed because waves mix the water and because of the turbulence caused by currents. The depth of this layer averages 200 m to 300 m. Below the surface layer is the thermocline, where the temperature drops rapidly to about 5° C. Below the thermocline, temperature decreases slightly to about 1° C.

SECTION 2

Ocean Currents

Upwelling

Most upwellings occur along the eastern shores of oceans where winds blow surface water away from the shore. From space, satellites can detect upwellings. Because the water in an upwelling is cold compared to the surrounding water, infrared cameras can spot the difference. This information is useful to fishers.

Fun Fact

The typical residence time in the ocean for a sodium ion is 260 million years.

Deep Water

North Atlantic Deep Water forms in the Norwegian and Greenland Seas. Warm water carried poleward by the North Atlantic Drift cools and sinks. After sinking, the water mixes with salty water from the Arctic Sea to become a cold, salty bottom water. This water accumulates behind a submarine plateau until it spills over into the Atlantic Ocean and spreads southward.

Antarctic Bottom Water forms around Antarctica. Regions of exposed seawater within winter ice cover, called polynyas, are thought to be important in the formation of Antarctic Bottom Water. Here sea ice forms rapidly, but is quickly blown away from the open region. The formation of relatively fresh sea ice causes the remaining water to become salty and cold. It then can sink to form Antarctic Bottom Water.

SECTION 3

Ocean Waves and Tides

Waves

The longer wind blows, the higher the waves mount until they reach a maximum height for a given wind velocity. For a given wind velocity, waves tend to be higher on large, deep bodies of water than on shallower bodies of water. Waves on the larger, deeper bodies develop without the interference of drag on the ocean bottom.

Storm waves have longer wavelengths than normal waves. Their erosional effects on the basin bottom extend relatively far from shore.

SCIENCE Online

For additional content background on this topic, go to the Glencoe Science Web site at science.glencoe.com.

Tides

The equilibrium theory of tide formation (discussed in this chapter) states that one high tide should form on the side of Earth toward the Moon and one on the opposite side. In reality, the tidal waves break up into cells in the oceans and high tides rotate around the center of each cell.

Dale E. Boyer/Photo Researchers, Inc.

Ocean Motion

Chapter Vocabulary

What do you think?

Science Journal The photo shows houses built on stilts along the Bay of Fundy, between Nova Scotia and New Brunswick, Canada. The bay has the world's highest high tides, about 15 meters above low tide. To keep houses along parts of its shore from being swamped by water at high tide, some are built on stilts. This photo shows the houses at low tide.

Ocean Motion

Surfers in Hawaii experience firsthand the enormous power of moving water. It surprises people to learn that wind causes most waves, from small ripples to the giant waves of hurricanes, some more than 30 m high. Wind also creates surface currents. Other types of currents move through the ocean, too. In this chapter, you'll learn about the composition of ocean water, the interaction between the atmosphere and the oceans, and how waves, currents, and tides are created.

What do you think?

Science Journal Look at the picture below with a classmate. Discuss what you think this might be or what is happening. Here's a hint: *Daily fluctuations make this happen.* Write your answer or best guess in your Science Journal.

450

Theme Connection

Energy Students will learn that wind provides the energy for surface currents and most ocean waves, that temperature and density power deep-ocean circulation, and that the gravitational attraction of the Sun and the Moon supply the force that sets tides in motion.

EXPLORE
ACTIVITY

Surface currents are caused by wind, but wind cannot cause currents deep in the ocean. Instead, deep-water currents are created by differences in the density of ocean water. Several factors affect water density. One is temperature. Do the activity below to see how temperature differences create these kinds of currents.

Explore how currents work

1. In a bowl, mix ice and cold water to make ice water.
2. Fill a beaker with warm tap water.
3. Add a few drops of food coloring to the ice water and stir the mixture.
4. Use a dropper to place some of this ice water on top of the warm water.

Observe

In your Science Journal, describe what happened. Did adding cold water on top produce a current? Look up the word *convection* in a dictionary. Infer why the current you created is called a convection current.

FOLDABLES
Reading & Study Skills

Before You Read

Making a Cause and Effect Study Fold Make the following Foldable to help you understand the cause and effect relationship of ocean motion.

1. Place a sheet of paper in front of you so the long side is at the top. Fold the paper in half from the left side to the right side. Fold top to bottom and crease. Then unfold.

2. Through the top thickness of paper, cut along the middle fold line to form two tabs. Label the tabs *Causes of Ocean Motion* and *Effects of Ocean Motion*.

3. As you read the chapter, write what you learn about why the ocean moves and the types of ocean motion under the top tab.

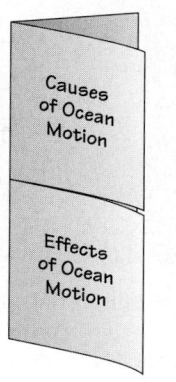
Causes of Ocean Motion

Effects of Ocean Motion

451

Purpose Use the Explore Activity to introduce students to the way deep-ocean currents work. L2 ELL COOP LEARN

IS **Visual-Spatial**

Preparation Prepare ice ahead of time.

Materials ice cubes, warm water, beaker, food coloring, dropper, bowl, cold water

Teaching Strategy Be sure that students understand the term *density.*

Observe

When ice water was placed on top of warm water, a current formed as the denser cold water sank through the warmer water, displacing and forcing the warmer water upward. Convection is defined as the movement of fluid between areas that have unequal densities caused by unequal temperatures. It's called a convection current because the difference in density and temperature drives the movement of water.

✓ *Assessment*

Oral Ask students why a current did not form when warm water was placed on top of ice water. Warm water is less dense than cold water, so it stays on top and there is no movement. Use **Performance Assessment in the Science Classroom,** p. 89.

FOLDABLES
Reading & Study Skills

Before You Read

Dinah Zike Study Fold
Purpose Students make and use a Foldable to collect information on the motion of the ocean and then use what they have learned to investigate its cause and effect.

📁 For additional help, see Foldables Worksheet, p. 13 in **Chapter Resources Booklet,** or go to the Glencoe Science Web site at **science.glencoe.com.** See After You Read in the Study Guide at the end of this chapter.

SECTION

Ocean Water

1 Motivate

Bellringer Transparency

Display the Section Focus Transparency for Section 1. Use the accompanying Transparency Activity Master. L2

ELL

Tie to Prior Knowledge

Have students quickly list three things they know about the ocean. **How many listed that the water is salty? Where did the salt come from?** Most enters the water from surrounding land. Tell students they will discover many things about the ocean in this section, including the reason its water is salty.

SECTION

Ocean Water

As You Read

What You'll Learn

- **Identify** the origin of the water in Earth's oceans.
- **Explain** how dissolved salts and other substances get into seawater.
- **Describe** the composition of seawater.

Vocabulary

basin
salinity

Why It's Important

Oceans affect weather and provide food and natural resources.

Importance of Oceans

Imagine yourself lying on a beach and listening to the waves gently roll onto shore. A warm breeze blows off the water, making it seem as if you're in a tropical paradise. It's easy to appreciate the oceans under these circumstances, but the oceans affect your life in other ways, too.

Varied Resources Oceans are important for food, minerals, transportation, and weather. Today, as shown in **Figure 1,** a huge variety of different resources comes from the oceans of the world. Oceans also allow efficient transportation. Can you think of a product you own that was transported by a ship? Energy and mineral resources also are found in oceans. Oil wells often are drilled in shallow ocean water. Oceans affect weather and climate. Hurricanes develop in some tropical waters, and moist air masses move onto land from oceans. Ocean currents keep some places warm while creating cool, foggy days elsewhere.

✓ **Reading Check** *What resources come from oceans?*

Figure 1
People depend on the oceans for many resources.

A Krill are tiny, shrimplike animals that live in the Antarctic Ocean. Some cultures use krill in noodles and rice cakes.

B Kelp is a fast-growing seaweed that is a source of algin, used in making ice cream, salad dressing, medicines, and cosmetics.

452 CHAPTER 16 Ocean Motion

Section ✓*Assessment* Planner

PORTFOLIO
Assessment, p. 455
PERFORMANCE ASSESSMENT
Skill Builder Activities, p. 455
See page 476 for more options.

CONTENT ASSESSMENT
Section, p. 455
Challenge, p. 455
Chapter, pp. 476–477

Origin of Oceans

During Earth's first billion years, its surface, shown in **Figure 2A,** was much more volcanically active than it is today. When volcanoes erupt, they spew lava and ash, and they give off water vapor, carbon dioxide, and other gases. Scientists hypothesize that about 4 billion years ago, this water vapor began to be stored in Earth's early atmosphere. Over millions of years, it cooled enough to condense into storm clouds. Torrential rains began to fall. Shown in **Figure 2B,** oceans were formed as this water filled low areas on Earth called **basins.** Today, 70 percent of Earth's surface is covered by ocean water.

Composition of Oceans

Ocean water contains dissolved gases such as oxygen, carbon dioxide, and nitrogen. Oxygen is the gas that almost all organisms need for respiration. It enters the oceans in two ways— directly from the atmosphere and from organisms that photosynthesize. Carbon dioxide enters the ocean from the atmosphere and from organisms when they respire. The atmosphere is the only important source of nitrogen gas. Bacteria combine nitrogen and oxygen to create nitrates, which are important nutrients for plants.

If you've ever tasted ocean water, you know that it is salty. Ocean water contains many dissolved salts. Chloride, sodium, sulfate, magnesium, calcium, and potassium are some of the ions in seawater. An ion is a charged atom or group of atoms. Some of these ions come from rocks that are dissolved slowly by rivers and groundwater. These include calcium, magnesium, and sodium. Rivers carry these chemicals to the oceans. Erupting volcanoes add other ions, such as sulfate and chloride.

Reading Check *How do sodium and chloride ions get into seawater?*

Figure 2
Earth's oceans formed from water vapor.

A Water vapor was released into the atmosphere by volcanoes that also gave off other gases, such as carbon dioxide and nitrogen.

B Condensed water vapor formed storm clouds. Oceans formed when basins filled with water from torrential rains.

SECTION 1 Ocean Water **453**

Inclusion Strategies

Learning Disabled Have groups of students make puzzles of Earth's oceans and landmasses. They can transfer a map of the world onto cardboard and cut it into pieces. Ocean names should be included on the puzzle pieces. Groups should then exchange puzzles and compete to see which group puts the puzzle together fastest. L2
ELL  **Kinesthetic**

Importance of Oceans

Reading Check

Answer substances that are used in foods, medicines, and cosmetics; fuels such as oil; metals such as manganese

Origin of Oceans

Make a Model

Have students model how salt gets into oceans. Make a mixture of half salt and half soil. Have pairs of students put a couple of tablespoons of the mixture into a coffee filter and place the filter inside a paper cup with five small holes punched into the bottom. Have students pour three tablespoons of water into the cup and hold it 2 cm above a sheet of black construction paper as the water drips onto the paper. When all the water has dripped out, put the paper in the Sun to dry. Students will find a dried salt residue on the paper. Have them explain their results. As water was poured through the soil, salt dissolved in it and was deposited on the paper. In the same way, runoff picks up and deposits dissolved salts from the land in the ocean.

Composition of Oceans

Reading Check

Answer Rivers and groundwater slowly dissolve rocks and carry sodium and chloride ions to oceans. Volcanoes also release chloride.

Composition of Oceans, continued

Caption Answer
Figure 3 35 g

Discussion
Why are there drinking water shortages in some places if Earth's surface is 70 percent ocean? Although oceans cover most of the planet, ocean water is too salty to drink.

Teacher FYI

In addition to organic processes, inorganic processes also remove dissolved substances from seawater. One example is the formation of manganese nodules, which are valuable mineral deposits on the ocean floor. The nodules form when manganese precipitates out of seawater.

Use Science Words
Word Meaning Have students find out why an industrial plant that removes salt from seawater is called a *desalination* plant. *De-* is a prefix meaning "away"; *saline* relates to salt.

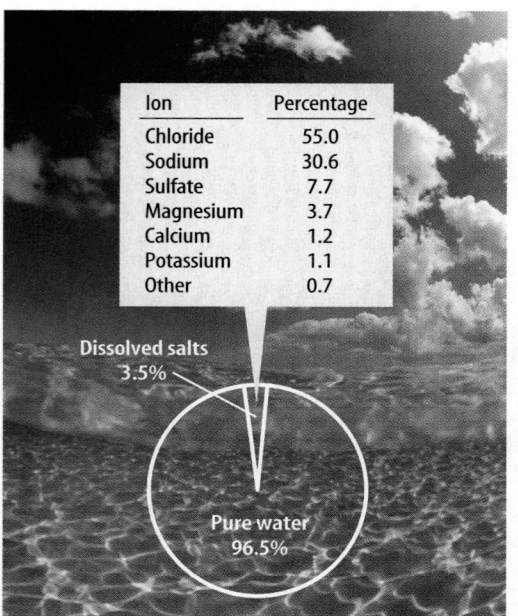

Ion	Percentage
Chloride	55.0
Sodium	30.6
Sulfate	7.7
Magnesium	3.7
Calcium	1.2
Potassium	1.1
Other	0.7

Dissolved salts 3.5%

Pure water 96.5%

Figure 3
Ocean water contains about 3.5 percent dissolved salts. *If you evaporated 1,000 g of seawater, how many grams of salt would be left?*

Salts The most abundant elements in seawater are the hydrogen and oxygen that make up water. Ions of many other elements are found dissolved in seawater. When seawater is evaporated, these ions combine to form materials called salts. Sodium and chloride make up most of the ions in seawater. If seawater evaporates, the sodium and chloride ions combine to form a salt called halite. Halite is the common table salt you use to season food. It is this dissolved salt and similar ones that give ocean water its salty taste.

Salinity (say LIH nuh tee) is a measure of the amount of salts dissolved in seawater. It usually is measured in grams of dissolved salt per kilogram of seawater. One kilogram of ocean water contains about 35 g of dissolved salts, or 3.5 percent. The chart in **Figure 3** shows the most abundant ions in ocean water. The proportion and amount of dissolved salts in seawater remain nearly constant and have stayed about the same for hundreds of millions of years. This tells you that the composition of the oceans is in balance. Evidence that scientists have gathered indicates that Earth's oceans are not growing saltier.

Life Science INTEGRATION

Removal of Elements Although rivers, volcanoes, and the atmosphere constantly add material to the oceans, the oceans are considered to be in a steady state. This means that elements are added to the oceans at about the same rate that they are removed. They are removed when ocean water evaporates, leaving salt behind, and when organisms use the dissolved salts to make shells. Some marine animals remove calcium ions from the water to form bones. Other animals, such as oysters and clams, use the dissolved calcium to form shells. Some algae, called diatoms, have silica shells. Because many organisms use calcium and silicon, these elements are removed more quickly from seawater than elements such as chlorine or sodium.

Desalination Salt can be removed from ocean water by a process called desalination (dee sa luh NAY shun). If you have ever swum in the ocean, you know what happens when your skin dries. The white, flaky substance on your skin is salt. As seawater evaporates, salt is left behind. As demand for freshwater increases throughout the world, scientists are working on technology to remove salt to make seawater drinkable.

Resource Manager

Chapter Resources Booklet
Lab Activity, pp. 9–10
Enrichment, p. 26
Reinforcement, p. 23

Cultural Diversity

Seashell Money Hundreds of years ago, the native people of eastern North America used carved and polished strings of shells, called wampum, as money. They made wampum beads from the white shells of the whelk and the purple shells of a type of clam. When Europeans came to North America, standard length strings of wampum beads became a unit of currency in their trade with coastal Native Americans.

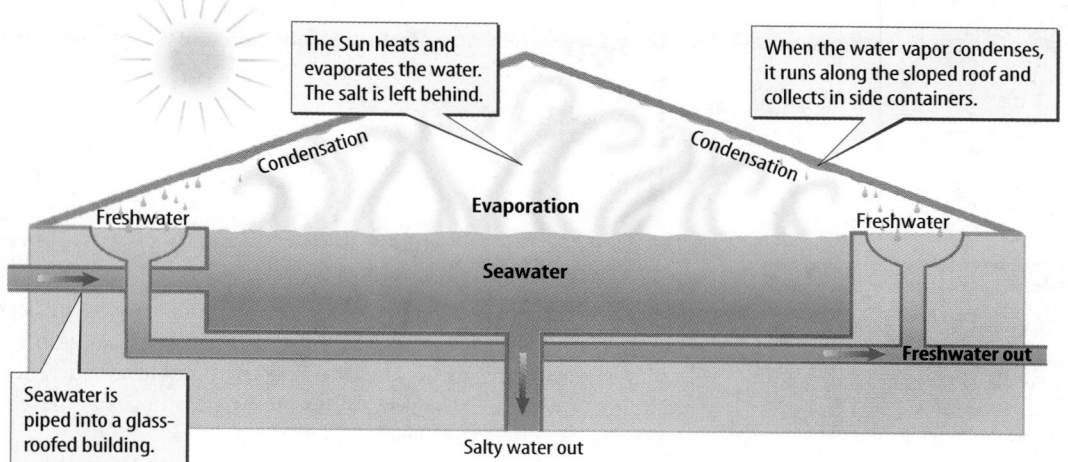

The Sun heats and evaporates the water. The salt is left behind.

When the water vapor condenses, it runs along the sloped roof and collects in side containers.

Condensation

Condensation

Evaporation

Freshwater

Freshwater

Seawater

Freshwater out

Seawater is piped into a glass-roofed building.

Salty water out

Visual Learning

Figure 4 Ask students to locate the seawater and the freshwater in the diagram.

Desalination Plants Some methods of desalination include evaporating seawater and collecting the freshwater as it condenses on a glass roof. **Figure 4** shows how a desalination plant that uses solar energy works. Other plants desalinate water by passing it through a membrane that removes the dissolved salts. Freshwater also can be obtained by melting frozen seawater. As seawater freezes, the ice crystals that form contain much less salt than the remaining water. The salty, unfrozen water then can be separated from the ice. The ice can be washed and melted to produce freshwater.

Figure 4
This desalination plant uses solar energy to produce freshwater.

3 Assess

Reteach

Direct students to write summaries containing the main points covered in the section.
L2 ELL ℕ **Linguistic**

Challenge

Challenge student teams to design and build solar desalination devices. Have each team begin with the same amount and concentration of salt water. Then have teams compete to see which one can collect the most freshwater.

Assessment

Performance Have each student make a concept map that shows how elements are naturally added to and removed from the oceans. Use **Performance Assessment in the Science Classroom,** p. 161. P

Section 1 Assessment

1. Describe at least five ways that Earth's oceans affect your life.

2. According to scientific hypothesis, how were Earth's oceans formed? When do scientists hypothesize they formed?

3. Where do the dissolved salts in ocean water come from?

4. How does oxygen get into oceans?

5. **Think Critically** Organisms in the oceans are important sources of food and medicine. What steps can humans take to ensure that these resources are available for future generations?

Skill Builder Activities

6. **Concept Mapping** Make a concept map that shows how sodium and chloride become dissolved in ocean water and what happens when the seawater evaporates. Use the terms *rivers, volcanoes, halite, source of, sodium, chloride,* and *combine to form*. **For more help, refer to the** Science Skill Handbook.

7. **Using Proportions** If the average salinity of seawater is 35 parts per thousand, how many grams of dissolved salts will 500 g of seawater contain? **For more help, refer to the** Math Skill Handbook.

Answers to Section Assessment

1. Possible answers: source of food, oxygen, minerals, medicines, and energy; means of transportation; effects on weather and climate; recreation

2. Volcanoes released water vapor that accumulated, cooled, and condensed to fall as rain that filled the basins about 4 billion years ago.

3. River water and groundwater carry dissolved salts from soil and rock on land into the ocean. Volcanoes also provide chlorine.

4. Some oxygen comes directly from the atmosphere, and other oxygen is produced when organisms photosynthesize.

5. People can conserve these resources by not overharvesting the organisms and by not polluting the oceans.

6. See concept map in side column.

7. 17.5 g (1/2 × 35)

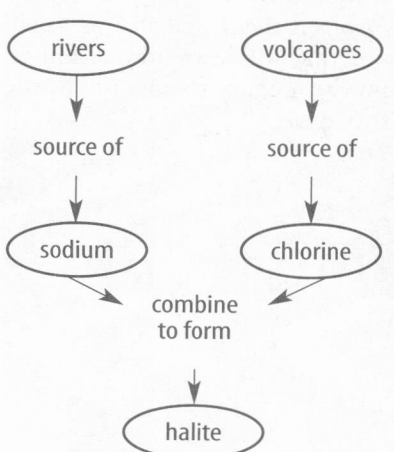

rivers

volcanoes

source of

source of

sodium

chlorine

combine to form

halite

SECTION

Ocean Currents

1 Motivate

Bellringer Transparency

Display the Section Focus Transparency for Section 2. Use the accompanying Transparency Activity Master. L2

ELL

Section Focus Transparency   That Could Cool a Lot of Lemonade

Once in the water, roughly six-sevenths of an iceberg is below the surface. Since there is so much of the iceberg below the waterline, deeper currents move the mass more than winds or waves. One of the currents that moves icebergs in the North Atlantic is the Labrador Current.

1. Why are deeper currents, more than waves or wind, the moving force behind icebergs?
2. What factors might affect whether or not an iceberg moves far enough south to enter the shipping lanes?

L2

Tie to Prior Knowledge

Ask students whether they have ever gone swimming or wading in a river, a large lake, or the ocean. Have they ever felt tugged or pulled by water moving under the surface? Tell students these were currents. Also tell them that in this section they will learn how currents in the ocean form and how they move.

As You Read

What You'll Learn

- **Explain** how winds and the Coriolis effect influence surface currents.
- **Discuss** the temperatures of coastal waters.
- **Describe** density currents.

Vocabulary

surface current
Coriolis effect
upwelling
density current

Why It's Important

Ocean currents and the atmosphere transfer heat that creates the climate you live in.

Figure 5
These are the major surface currents of Earth's oceans.

Surface Currents

When you stir chocolate into a glass of milk, do you notice the milk swirling around in the glass in a circle? If so, you've observed something similar to an ocean current. Ocean currents are a mass movement, or flow, of ocean water. An ocean current is like a river within the ocean.

Surface currents move water horizontally—parallel to Earth's surface. These currents are powered by wind. The wind forces the ocean to move in huge, circular patterns. **Figure 5** shows these major surface currents. Notice that some currents are shown with red arrows and some are shown with blue arrows. Red arrows indicate warm currents. Blue arrows indicate cold currents. The currents on the ocean's surface are related to the general circulation of winds on Earth.

Surface currents move only the upper few hundred meters of seawater. Some seeds and plants are carried between continents by surface currents. Sailors take advantage of these currents along with winds to sail more efficiently from place to place.

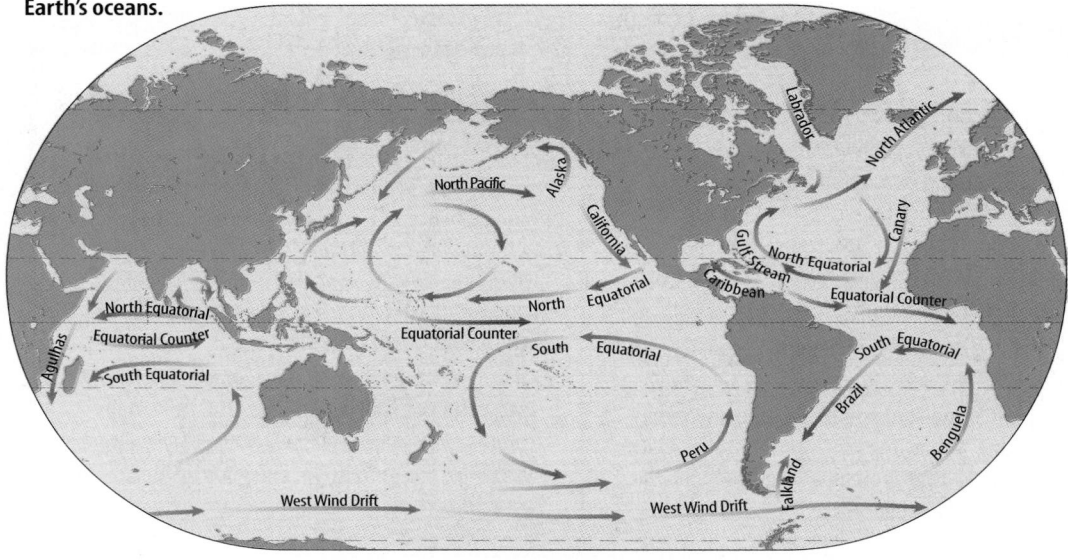

Section ✓*Assessment* Planner

PORTFOLIO
Curriculum Connection, p. 458
PERFORMANCE ASSESSMENT
Try at Home MiniLAB, p. 459
Math Skills Activity, p. 460
Skill Builder Activities, p. 461
See page 476 for more options.

CONTENT ASSESSMENT
Section, p. 461
Challenge, p. 461
Chapter, pp. 476–477

How Surface Currents

Form Surface ocean currents and surface winds are affected by the Coriolis (kor ee OH lus) effect. The **Coriolis effect** is the shifting of winds and surface currents from their expected paths that is caused by Earth's rotation. Imagine that you try to draw a line straight out from the center of a disk to the edge of the disk. You probably could do that with no problem. But what would happen if the disk were slowly spinning like the one in **Figure 6A?** As the student tried to draw a straight line, the disk rotated and, as shown in **Figure 6B,** the line curved.

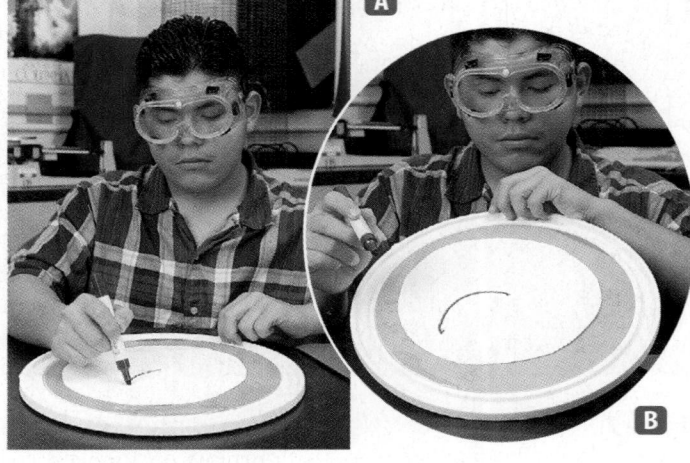

A

B

A similar thing happens to wind and surface currents. Because Earth rotates toward the east, winds appear to curve to the right in the northern hemisphere and to the left in the southern hemisphere. These surface winds can cause water to pile up in certain parts of the ocean. When gravity pulls water off the pile, the Coriolis effect turns the water. This causes surface water in the oceans to spiral around the piles of water. The Coriolis effect causes currents north of the equator to turn to the right. Currents south of the equator are turned to the left. Look again at the map of surface currents in **Figure 5** to see the results of the Coriolis effect.

The Gulf Stream Although satellites provide new information about ocean movements, much of what is known about surface currents comes from records that were kept by sailors of the nineteenth century. Sailors always have used surface currents to help them travel quickly. Sailing ships depend on some surface currents to carry them to the west and others to carry them east. During the American colonial era, ships floated on the 100-km-wide Gulf Stream current to go quickly from North America to England. Find the Gulf Stream current in the Atlantic Ocean on the map in **Figure 5.**

In the late 1700s, Deputy Postmaster General Benjamin Franklin received complaints about why it took longer to receive a letter from England than it did to send one there. Upon investigation, Franklin found that a Nantucket whaling captain's map furnished the answer. Going against the Gulf Stream delayed ships sailing west from England by up to 110 km per day.

Figure 6

A The student draws a line straight out from the center of the disk. B Because the disk was spinning, the line is curved.

SCIENCE
Online

Research Visit the Glencoe Science Web site at **science.glencoe.com** for more information about ocean currents. Communicate to your class what you learn.

2 Teach

Surface Currents

Visual Learning——

Figure 5 Tell students that a gyre refers to the circular pattern of currents that occurs in each of the major ocean basins. **Which currents make up the gyre in the South Pacific Ocean?** South Equatorial current and Peru current

Discussion

Why is the Gulf Stream current not as important to sailors today as it was 200 years ago? Sailors 200 years ago used the strength of the wind in their sails and the force of currents pushing their ships to power them across the oceans. Today, ships have motors that power them, making dependence on currents like the Gulf Stream less necessary.

SCIENCE
Online

Internet Addresses

_____

_____

_____

Explore the Glencoe Science Web site at **science.glencoe.com** to find out more about topics in this section.

SECTION 2 Ocean Currents **457**

Resource Manager

Chapter Resources Booklet
  Transparency Activity, p. 41
Science Inquiry Labs, p. 31

✓ Active Reading

Write-Draw-Discuss This strategy encourages students to actively participate in reading and lectures, assimilating content creatively. Have students write about an idea, clarify it, then make an illustration or drawing. Ask students to share responses with the class and display several examples. Have students Write-Draw-Discuss about surface currents.

Surface Currents,
continued

Discussion

Although the climate in the area is warm in summer, the waters of San Francisco Bay never get very warm. Ask students to use what they know about currents to give a possible explanation. Cold currents along the coast of California could influence the temperature of the bay.

Teacher FYI

Oceanographers track ocean currents with neutrally buoyant floats and satellites. Neutrally buoyant floats sink to a desired depth and move with the current. Satellites are equipped with devices that detect surface-current velocities using infrared, color, and microwave emissions from the sea's surface.

Figure 7
Bottles and other floating objects that enter the ocean are used to gain information about surface currents.

Figure 8
Data about ocean temperature collected by a satellite were used to make this surface-temperature image of the Atlantic Ocean.

Tracking Surface Currents Items that wash up on beaches, such as the bottle shown in **Figure 7,** provide information about ocean currents. Drift bottles containing messages and numbered cards are released from a variety of coastal locations. The bottles are carried by surface currents and might end up on a beach. The person who finds a bottle writes down the date and the location where the bottle was found. Then the card is sent back to the institution that launched the bottle. By doing this, valuable information is provided about the current that carried the bottle.

Warm and Cold Surface Currents Notice in **Figure 5** that currents on the west coasts of continents begin near the poles where the water is colder. The California Current that flows along the west coast of the United States is a cold surface current. East-coast currents originate near the equator where the water is warmer. Warm surface currents, such as the Gulf Stream, distribute heat from equatorial regions to other areas of Earth. **Figure 8** shows the warm water of the Gulf Stream in red and orange. Cooler water appears in blue and green.

As warm water flows away from the equator, heat is released to the atmosphere. The atmosphere is warmed. This transfer of heat influences climate.

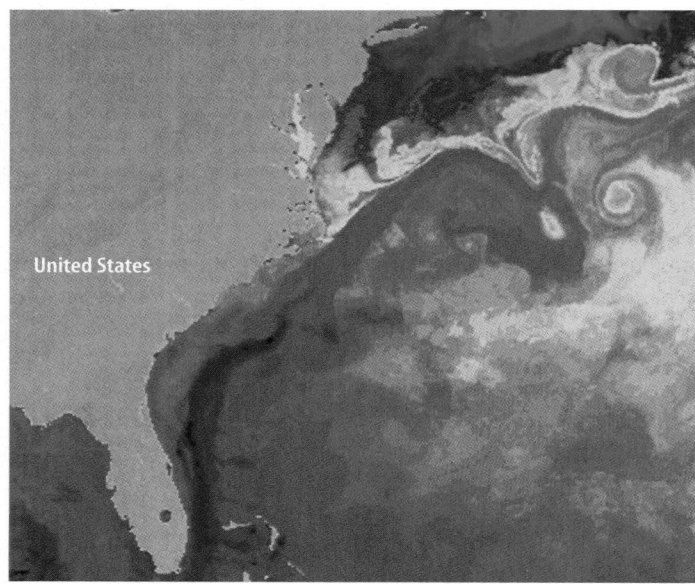

United States

Curriculum Connection

History Have students research either the way the positions of currents affected ancient trade routes, or Benjamin Franklin's study of the Gulf Stream. Have them write brief reports on what they find. L2 LS **Linguistic** P

Fun Fact

Surface currents generally affect only the upper 100 to 200 meters of ocean water.

Figure 9
Winds push surface water away from the coast of Peru, causing upwelling. This process brings colder water to the surface.

Water movement
Southerly wind
Upwelling

Upwelling

Upwelling is a circulation in the ocean that brings deep, cold water to the ocean surface. Along some coasts of continents, wind blowing parallel to the coast carries water away from the land because of the Coriolis effect, as shown in **Figure 9.** Cold, deep ocean water rises to the surface and replaces water that has moved away from shore. This water contains high concentrations of nutrients from organisms that died, sank to the bottom, and decayed. Nutrients promote plankton growth, which attracts fish. Areas of upwelling occur along the coasts of Oregon, Washington, and Peru and create important fishing grounds.

Density Currents

Deep in the ocean, waters circulate not because of wind but because of density differences. A **density current** forms when a mass of seawater becomes more dense than the surrounding water. Gravity causes more dense seawater to sink beneath less dense seawater. This deep, dense water then slowly spreads to the rest of the ocean.

The density of seawater can be increased if salinity increases, as you can see if you perform the MiniLAB on this page. It also can be increased by a decrease in temperature. In the Explore Activity, the cold water was more dense than the warm water in the beaker. The cold water sank to the bottom. This created a density current that moved the food coloring.

Changes in temperature and salinity work together to create density currents. Density currents circulate ocean water slowly—moving as little as a few meters per month.

Modeling a Density Current
Procedure 🥽 🧤
1. Fill a **clear plastic storage box** (shoe-box size) with room-temperature **water.**
2. Mix several spoonfuls of table **salt** into a **glass** of water at room temperature.
3. Add a few drops of **food coloring** to the saltwater solution. Pour the solution slowly into the freshwater in the large container.

Analysis
1. Describe what happened when you added salt water to freshwater.
2. How does this lab relate to density currents?

Density Currents

Purpose Students model a density current. L1 ELL COOP LEARN IS **Kinesthetic**

Materials clear plastic storage box, water, 8-ounce glass or beaker, 55 g table salt, food coloring, teaspoon

Teaching Strategy Review density with students before assigning the MiniLAB.

Safety Precautions Caution students not to taste, eat, or drink any lab materials.

Troubleshooting To see the current, have students look into the box from the side, not the top.

Analysis
1. The salt water sank to the bottom and spread out toward the sides of the container.
2. Higher salinity increases the density of ocean water. This can contribute to the formation of density currents.

Process Have students draw and label a diagram based on this MiniLAB that shows how density currents in the ocean work. Use **PASC**, p. 161.

Resource Manager

Chapter Resources Booklet
MiniLAB, p. 3
Lab Activity, pp. 11–12

Cultural **Diversity**

Fishing Upwelling of cold water off the coast of Peru brings large numbers of anchovies to the coast. Peruvians eat these fish and make them into fish meal, which is used to make tortillas and bread and to feed chickens. Have students research what happens during an El Niño. Wind patterns reverse, blocking the upwelling cold water, and stopping the movement of anchovies to the Peruvian coast.

Density Currents, continued

Chemistry INTEGRATION

Because of its salt concentration, ocean water has a much lower freezing point than freshwater.

Math Skills Activity

National Math Standards

Correlation to Mathematics Objectives

1, 2, 4, 6, 8, 9

Answers to Practice Problems

1. You know the volume and the mass of the sample and the equation $d = m/v$. Substituting these values into this equation gives $d = 79{,}000 \text{ g}/78{,}000 \text{ cm}^3$. This equals a density of 1.01 g/cm^3.

2. In this problem you know the density and the mass, so you must rearrange the equation $d = m/v$ to solve for v. This is $v = m/d$. Then substituting the given values gives $v = 50{,}000 \text{ g}/1.03 \text{ g/cm}^3$. Solving this gives a volume of $48{,}544 \text{ cm}^3$.

Resource Manager

Chapter Resources Booklet
Enrichment, p. 27
Reinforcement, p. 24

Chemistry INTEGRATION

When salt dissolves in water, the freezing point of the mixture is lowered. The greater the number of particles dissolved in the water is, the more the freezing point is lowered. How does this help ocean water near the poles get colder than freshwater could?

Deep Waters An important density current begins in Antarctica where the most dense ocean water forms during the winter. As ice forms, seawater freezes, but the salt is left behind in the unfrozen water. This extra salt increases the salinity and, therefore, the density of the ocean water until it is very dense. This dense water sinks and slowly spreads along the ocean bottom toward the equator, forming a density current. In the Pacific Ocean, this water could take 1,000 years to reach the equator.

In the North Atlantic Ocean, cold, dense water forms around Norway, Greenland, and Labrador. These waters sink, forming North Atlantic Deep Water. In about the northern one third to one half of the Atlantic Ocean, North Atlantic Deep Water forms the bottom layer of ocean water. In the southern part of the Atlantic Ocean, it flows at depths of about 3,000 m, just above the denser water formed near Antarctica. The dense waters circulate more quickly in the Atlantic Ocean than in the Pacific Ocean. In the Atlantic, a density current could circulate in 275 years.

Math Skills Activity

Calculating Density

Example Problem

You have an aquarium full of freshwater in which you have dissolved salt. If the mass of the salt water is 123,000 g and its volume is 120,000 cm³, what is the density of the salt water?

Solution

1 *This is what you know:*   volume: $v = 120{,}000 \text{ cm}^3$
     mass of salt water: $m = 123{,}000 \text{ g}$

2 *This is what you need to find:*   density of water: d

3 *This is the equation you need to use:* $d = m/v$

4 *Substitute the known values:* $d = 123{,}000 \text{ g}/120{,}000 \text{ cm}^3 = 1.025 \text{ g/cm}^3$

Check your answer by multiplying your answer by the volume. Do you calculate the same mass of salt water that was given?

Practice Problems

1. Calculate the density of 78,000 cm³ of salt water with a mass of 79,000 g.
2. If a sample of ocean water has a density of 1.03 g/cm³ and a mass of 50,000 g, what is the volume of the water?

For more help, refer to the Math Skill Handbook.

LAB DEMONSTRATION

Purpose to model a density current

Materials four Erlenmeyer flasks, two 2-hole stoppers, four glass tubes, water, salt, food coloring

Preparation Insert the glass tubes into the stoppers.

Procedure Fill the four flasks with water. Add food coloring to two flasks. Add 35 g of salt to the water in a third flask. Insert stoppers into the two flasks without colored water. Invert each stoppered flask over a flask of colored water. Observe.

Expected Outcome Colored water moves up into the flask with salt water, but does not move into the flask with fresh water.

What caused the density current in one set of flasks? Salty, dense water sank, forcing less dense water up. **What was the purpose of the other set of flasks?** That set was the control.

Intermediate Waters A density current also occurs in the Mediterranean Sea, a nearly enclosed body of water. The warm temperatures and dry air in the region cause large amounts of water to evaporate from the surface of the sea. This evaporation increases the salinity and density of the water. This dense water from the Mediterranean flows through the narrow Straits of Gibraltar into the Atlantic Ocean at a depth of about 320 m. When it reaches the Atlantic, it flows to depths of 1,000 m to 2,000 m because it is more dense than the water in the upper parts of the North Atlantic Ocean. However, the water from the Mediterranean is less dense than the very cold, salty water flowing from the North Atlantic Ocean around Greenland, Norway, and Labrador. Therefore, as shown in **Figure 10,** the Mediterranean water forms a middle layer of water—the Mediterranean Intermediate Water.

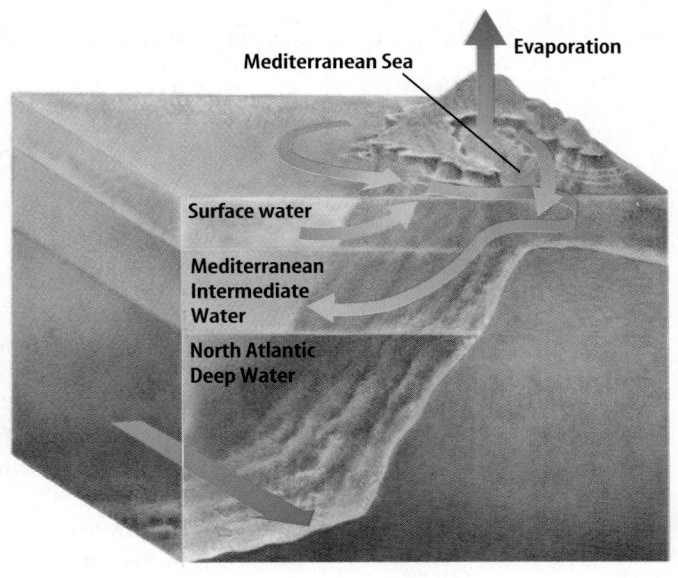

Mediterranean Sea — Evaporation

Surface water

Mediterranean Intermediate Water

North Atlantic Deep Water

Figure 10
Dense layers of North Atlantic Deep Water form in the Greenland, Labrador, and Norwegian Seas. This water flows southward along the North Atlantic seafloor. Less dense water from the Mediterranean Sea forms Mediterranean Intermediate Water.

 Reading Check *What causes the Mediterranean Intermediate Water to form?*

Reading Check

Answer Evaporation from the Mediterranean Sea produces a salty water mass that moves out into the Atlantic Ocean, where it sinks beneath the less dense surface water.

③ Assess

Reteach
Obtain a map that shows wind circulation patterns. Have students discuss how major wind patterns influence major surface currents as shown in **Figure 5**.

Challenge
Challenge students to research how the Gulf Stream affects the climate in land areas it passes close to on its trip to northwestern Europe. In general, because of prevailing wind patterns, the Gulf Stream has more of an effect on the climate in northwestern Europe, making it warmer than the climate of eastern North America.

✓ Assessment

Process Assess students' abilities to interpret scientific illustrations by having them examine **Figure 5** and speculate about how ocean circulation would be different if the southern tip of South America and the Antarctic Peninsula were connected. The Drake Passage, which separates these two continents, opened about 25 to 30 million years ago and allowed ocean circulation around Antarctica, changing its climate and possibly causing glaciers to form. Use **PASC**, p. 89.

Section ② Assessment

1. What factors create surface currents?
2. What is the Coriolis effect?
3. How do density currents circulate water?
4. What is upwelling?
5. **Think Critically** The latitudes of San Diego, California, and Charleston, South Carolina, are exactly the same. However, the average yearly water temperature in the ocean off Charleston is much higher than the water temperature off San Diego. Explain why.

Skill Builder Activities

6. **Predicting** A river flows into the ocean. Predict what will happen to this layer of freshwater. Explain your prediction. **For more help, refer to the** Science Skill Handbook.

7. **Using an Electronic Spreadsheet** Make a spreadsheet that compares surface and density currents. Focus on characteristics such as wind, horizontal and vertical movement, temperature, and density. **For more help, refer to the** Technology Skill Handbook.

Answers to Section Assessment

1. wind and the Coriolis effect
2. the shifting of winds and surface currents from their expected paths that is caused by Earth's rotation
3. Cold or very salty water is denser than warm or less salty water and sinks in the ocean. This displaces warmer or less salty water, which

moves upward. This movement drives density currents.
4. It is a circulation in the ocean that brings deep, cold water to the ocean surface.
5. Ocean water off Charleston is influenced by the warm water of the Gulf Stream current, while ocean water off

San Diego is influenced by the cold water of the California current.
6. It will flow along the surface because it is less dense than salty seawater.
7. Spreadsheets should include that surface currents are caused by winds, move horizontally on the surface, and are warm or cold. Density currents are

caused by differences in temperature and salinity, move both vertically and horizontally under the surface, have cold and warm sections, and have varying densities.

Ocean Waves and Tides

Ocean Waves and Tides

1 Motivate

Bellringer Transparency

Display the Section Focus Transparency for Section 3. Use the accompanying Transparency Activity Master. L2
ELL

Tie to Prior Knowledge

Ask students whether they have ever seen waves on a lake, a river, or the ocean. Then ask whether they know how waves form. Write students' responses on the board and allow the class to discuss them. Then tell students they will find out in this section how waves form.

As You Read

What You'll Learn

- **Describe** wave formation.
- **Distinguish** between the movement of water particles in a wave and the movement of the wave.
- **Explain** how ocean tides form.

Vocabulary

wave	breaker
crest	tide
trough	tidal range

Why It's Important

Waves and tides affect life and property in coastal areas.

Figure 11
Ocean waves carry energy through seawater.

A Identify the crests and troughs in this picture.

Waves

If you've been to the seashore or seen a beach on TV, you've watched waves roll in. There is something hypnotic about ocean waves. They keep coming and coming, one after another. But what is an ocean wave? A **wave** is a rhythmic movement that carries energy through matter or space. In the ocean, waves like those in **Figure 11A** move through seawater.

Describing Waves Several terms are used to describe waves, as shown in **Figure 11B.** Notice that waves look like hills and valleys. The **crest** is the highest point of the wave. The **trough** (TRAWF) is the lowest point of the wave. Wavelength is the horizontal distance between the crests or between the troughs of two adjacent waves. Wave height is the vertical distance between crest and trough.

Half the distance of the wave height is called the amplitude (AM pluh tewd) of the wave. The amplitude squared is proportional to the amount of energy the wave carries. For example, a wave with twice the amplitude of the wave in **Figure 11** carries four times (2 × 2 = 4) the energy. On a calm day, the amplitude of ocean waves is small. But during a storm, wave amplitude increases and the waves carry a lot more energy. Large waves can damage ships and coastal property.

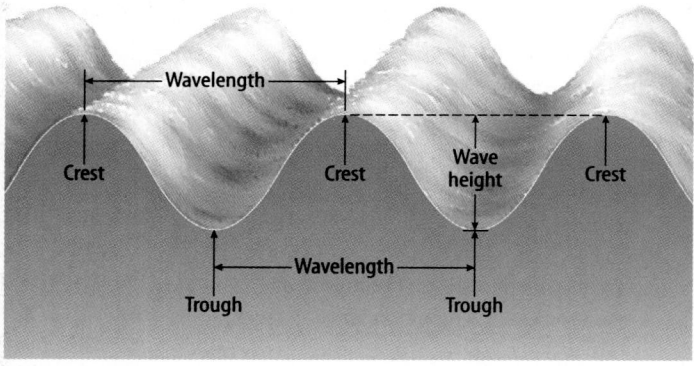

B The crest, trough, wavelength, and wave height describe a wave.

Section ✓Assessment Planner

PORTFOLIO
Extension, p. 464

PERFORMANCE ASSESSMENT
MiniLAB, p. 463
Skill Builder Activities, p. 468
See page 476 for more options.

CONTENT ASSESSMENT
Section, p. 468
Challenge, p. 468
Chapter, pp. 476–477

Wave Movement You might have noticed that if you throw a pebble into a pond, a circular wave moves outward from where the pebble entered the water, as shown in **Figure 12.** A bobber on a fishing line floating in the water will bob up and down as the wave passes, but it will not move outward with the wave. Notice that the bobber's position doesn't change.

When you watch an ocean wave, it looks as though the water is moving forward. But unless the wave is breaking onto shore, the water does not move forward. Each molecule of water stays in about the same place as the wave passes. **Figure 13** shows this. Water in a wave moves around in circles. Only the energy moves forward while the water remains in about the same place. Below a depth equal to about half the wavelength, water movement stops. Below that depth, water is not affected by waves. Submarines that travel below this level usually are not affected by surface storms.

Breakers A wave changes shape in the shallow area near shore. Near the shoreline, friction with the ocean bottom slows water at the bottom of the wave. As the wave slows, its crest and trough come closer together. The wave height increases. The top of a wave, not slowed by friction, moves faster than the bottom. Eventually, the top of the wave outruns the bottom and it collapses. The wave crest falls as water tumbles over on itself. The wave breaks onto the shore. **Figure 13** also shows this process. This collapsing wave is a **breaker.** It is the collapse of this wave that propels a surfer and surfboard onto shore. After a wave breaks onto shore, gravity pulls the water back into the sea.

 **Reading Check** *What causes an ocean wave to slow down?*

Mini LAB

Modeling Water Particle Movement

Procedure
1. Put a piece of **tape** on the outside bottom of a clear, rectangular **plastic storage box.** Fill the box with **water.**
2. Float a **cork** in the container above the piece of tape.
3. Use a **spoon** to make gentle waves in the container.
4. Observe the movement of the waves and the cork.

Analysis
1. Describe the movement of the waves and the motion of the cork.
2. Compare the movement of the cork in the water with the movement of water particles in a wave.

Waves

Mini LAB

Purpose Students make a wave model that shows water particle movement. L2 ELL COOP LEARN LS **Kinesthetic**

Materials masking tape, clear plastic storage box, water, cork, spoon

Teaching Strategy Students need to make waves, not currents. Thus they must gently tap the bowl of the spoon in one spot on the water.

Analysis
1. The wave moves across the box from the point where the spoon is generating them. The cork bobs up and down as waves pass under it.
2. The cork and the water particles move in small circles as a wave passes. They stay in about the same place, rather than moving across the body of water.

Performance Have students devise other ways of creating waves in the box and have them observe the motion of the cork. Use **PASC,** p. 123.

✔ **Reading Check**

Answer friction with the ocean bottom

Resource Manager

Chapter Resources Booklet
   Transparency Activity, p. 42
   MiniLAB, p. 4

Curriculum Connection

Language Arts Explain to students that onomatopoeia is a poetry technique that uses words with sounds that make you think about their meanings. Examples include words like buzz, hiss, plop, flop, gunk, gushy, swish, splash, zigzag, zing, and zip. Have students write poems using onomatopoeia to describe waves and wave motion. L2 LS **Linguistic**

NATIONAL GEOGRAPHIC

Visualizing Wave Movement

Have students examine the pictures and read the captions. Then ask the following questions.

How does the movement of the dominoes differ from the movement of water particles in waves? The dominoes simply fall down, while the water particles move around in circles. Both the dominoes and the water particles transfer energy in their movements. (The source of a wave's energy is usually wind.)

How does the degree of slope of the ocean floor near the beach affect the height of waves breaking on the beach? The steeper the slope, the taller the breaking waves; more gradually sloping ocean floor produces shorter waves.

Activity

Have students make diagrams of wave movement and include in their diagrams evidence that energy, not water particles, is moving forward. Offer them the example of a floating seagull bobbing up and down in the waves but not moving closer to the beach. Encourage them to brainstorm as many examples as they can.

Extension

Challenge students to find out the location of the world's most popular surfing sites and the reasons for the big waves at those sites. Have them write a report on their findings. L2

LS Linguistic P

NATIONAL GEOGRAPHIC VISUALIZING WAVE MOVEMENT

Figure 13

As ocean waves move toward the shore, they seem to be traveling in from a great distance, hurrying toward land. Actually, the water in waves moves relatively little, as shown here. It's the energy in the waves that moves across the ocean surface. Eventually that energy is transferred—in a crash of foam and spray—to the land.

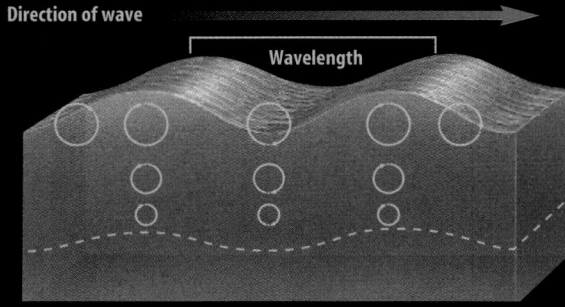

Direction of wave

Wavelength

A Particles of water move around in circles rather than forward. Near the water's surface, the circles are relatively large. Below the surface, the circles become progressively smaller. Little water movement occurs below a depth equal to about one-half of a wave's length.

B The energy in waves, however, does move forward. One way to visualize this energy movement is to imagine a line of dominoes. Knock over the first domino, and the others fall in sequence. As they fall, individual dominoes—like water particles in waves—remain close to where they started. But each transfers its energy to the next one down the line.

Wavelengths are constant

Wavelengths decrease as bottom drag increases

Waves break

C As waves approach shore, wavelength decreases and wave height increases. This causes breakers to form. Where ocean floor rises steeply to beach, incoming waves break quickly at a great height, forming huge arching waves.

464 CHAPTER 16 Ocean Motion

Resource Manager

Chapter Resources Booklet
Transparency Activity, pp. 43–44
Directed Reading for Content Mastery, pp. 17, 18

How Water Waves Form On a windy day, waves form on a lake or ocean. When wind blows across a body of water, friction causes the water to move along with the wind. If the wind speed is great enough, the water begins to pile up, forming a wave. As the wind continues to blow, the wave increases in height. Some waves reach tremendous heights, as shown in **Figure 14.** Storm winds have been known to produce waves more than 30 m high—taller than a six-story building.

The height of waves depends on the speed of the wind, the distance over which the wind blows, and the length of time the wind blows. When the wind stops blowing, waves stop forming. But once set in motion, waves continue moving for long distances, even if the wind stops. The waves you see lapping at a beach could have formed halfway around the world.

> ✓ **Reading Check** *What factors affect the height of waves?*

Tides

When you go to a beach, you probably notice the level of the sea rise and fall during the day. This rise and fall in sea level is called a **tide.** A tide is caused by a giant wave produced by the gravitational pull of the Sun and the Moon. This wave has a wave height of only 1 m or 2 m, but it has a wavelength that is thousands of kilometers long. As the crest of this wave approaches the shore, sea level appears to rise. This rise in sea level is called high tide. Later, as the trough of the wave approaches, sea level appears to drop. This drop in sea level is referred to as low tide.

Research Visit the Glencoe Science Web site at **science.glencoe.com** for more information about tides. Communicate to your class what you learn.

Waves, continued

Use an Analogy

Arrange chairs in a long row. Have a group of students sit in the chairs and quickly stand up and sit down in succession to make a human wave while other students watch. Have students compare the movement of each person in the wave to the movement of water molecules in an ocean wave. [L2] ELL COOP LEARN
[LS] **Interpersonal**

Fun Fact

The height of an average wave is 3.7 m. The largest waves occur in the West Wind Drift beneath the continuous strong winds surrounding Antarctica.

✓ **Reading Check**

Answer speed of wind, distance over which wind blows, length of time wind blows

Tides

Quick Demo

Use a model of the Sun, the Moon, and Earth to show students how all three bodies interact to produce tides in Earth's oceans. Show the arrangement of all three bodies during a new moon and full moon, when the gravity of the Moon and the Sun pull together to generate the greatest tidal range.

Teacher FYI

For a given wind velocity, waves tend to be higher on large, deep bodies of water than on shallower water bodies. Waves on the larger, deeper bodies develop without the interference of drag on the ocean bottom.

Internet Addresses

_____

_____

_____

Explore the Glencoe Science Web site at **science.glencoe.com** to find out more about topics in this section.

Visual Learning

Figure 15 Would there be any problem with walking from the mainland to Mont-Saint-Michel at low tide, without using the causeway? Explain. Yes; although it would depend on the time of the walk, the fact that the tide returns quickly would mean someone walking on the tidal flats could become trapped or be drowned by the waters as they return at high tide.

Teacher FYI

Mont-Saint-Michel is located between Normandy and Brittany in France. The island on which the buildings stand is a granite outcrop 78 m high. Great walls surround a Gothic-style Benedictine abbey that was originally built in 966. The walls and towers of the abbey were added much later, as was a causeway that connects the island to land.

Activity

If your school is located near an ocean, have students determine the times of today's low and high tides and the phase of the Moon. Have them relate the Moon's phase to the tides. If you do not live near a seacoast, tidal information can be obtained from coastal weather stations. L2

Caption Answer

Figure 16 low tide Have students note the difference between the height of the wharf and sea level. Point out the ladders that allow sailors to access the wharf during low tide.

Figure 15
A large difference between high tide and low tide can be seen at Mont-Saint-Michel off the northwestern coast of France.

A Mont-Saint-Michel lies about 1.6 km offshore and is connected to the mainland at low tide.

B Incoming tides move very quickly, making Mont-Saint-Michel an island at high tide.

Figure 16
The Bay of Fundy has the greatest tidal range in the world. *Was this picture taken at high tide or low tide?*

Tidal Range As Earth rotates, different locations on Earth's surface pass through the high and low positions. Many coastal locations, such as the Atlantic and Pacific coasts of the United States, experience two high tides and two low tides each day. One low-tide/high-tide cycle takes 12 h, 25 min. A daily cycle of two high tides and two low tides takes 24 h, 50 min—slightly more than a day. But because ocean basins vary in size and shape, some coastal locations, such as many along the Gulf of Mexico, have only one high and one low tide each day. The **tidal range** is the difference between the level of the ocean at high tide and low tide. Notice the tidal range in the photos in **Figure 15.**

Extreme Tidal Ranges The shape of the seacoast and the shape of the ocean floor affect the ranges of tides. Along a smooth, wide beach, the incoming water can spread over a large area. There the water level might rise only a few centimeters at high tide. In a narrow gulf or bay, however, the water might rise many meters at high tide.

Most shorelines have tidal ranges between 1 m and 2 m. Some places, such as those on the Mediterranean Sea, have tidal ranges of only about 30 cm. Other places have large tidal ranges. Mont-Saint-Michel, shown in **Figure 15,** lies in the Gulf of Saint-Malo off the northwestern coast of France. There the tidal range reaches about 13.5 m.

The dock shown in **Figure 16** is in Digby, Nova Scotia in the Bay of Fundy. This bay is extremely narrow, which contributes to large tidal ranges. The difference between water levels at high tide and low tide can be as much as 15 m.

466 CHAPTER 16 Ocean Motion

Science Journal

Grunion In the waters off southern California, the reproductive cycle of the grunion fish follows the tidal schedule. Have students research the egg-laying habits of the grunion and write about them in their Science Journals. On several nights after the full moon in spring and summer spawning season, grunion swim onto beaches. Females deposit their eggs in the sand and males spread their milt on top of the eggs. About ten nights later, as the tides are again increasing in height, the eggs are washed out of the sand and hatch.

Tidal Bores In some areas when a rising tide enters a shallow, narrow river from a wide area of the sea, a wave called a tidal bore forms. A tidal bore can have a breaking crest or it can be a smooth wave. Tidal bores tend to be found in places with large tidal ranges. The Amazon River in Brazil, the Tsientang River in China, and rivers that empty into the Bay of Fundy in Nova Scotia have tidal bores.

When a tidal bore enters a river, it causes surface water to reverse its flow. In the Amazon River, the tidal bore rushes 650 km upstream at speeds of 65 km/h, causing a wave more than 5 m in height. Four rivers that empty into the Bay of Fundy have tidal bores. In those rivers, bore rafting is a popular sport.

The Gravitational Effect of the Moon For the most part, tides are caused by the interaction of gravity in the Earth-Moon system. The Moon's gravity exerts a strong pull on Earth. Earth and the water in Earth's oceans respond to this pull. The water bulges outward as Earth and the Moon revolve around a common center of mass. These events are explained in **Figure 17.**

Two bulges of water form, one on the side of Earth closest to the Moon and one on the opposite side of Earth. The reason two bulges form is because the Moon's gravity pulls harder on parts of Earth closer to the Moon than on parts farther away. You can imagine this if you think about pulling a large ball of dough in the same direction but harder on one side than the other side. The ball of dough will stretch and form two bulges. Earth does the same thing. The ocean bulges are the high tides, and the areas of Earth's oceans that are not toward or away from the Moon are the low tides. As Earth rotates, different locations on its surface pass through high and low tide.

Extension

Have students write research reports about using tides and ocean waves to generate electricity.

Figure 17
The Moon and Earth revolve around a common center of mass. Because the Moon's gravity pulls harder on parts of Earth closer to the Moon, a bulge of water forms on the side of Earth facing the Moon and the side of Earth opposite the Moon.

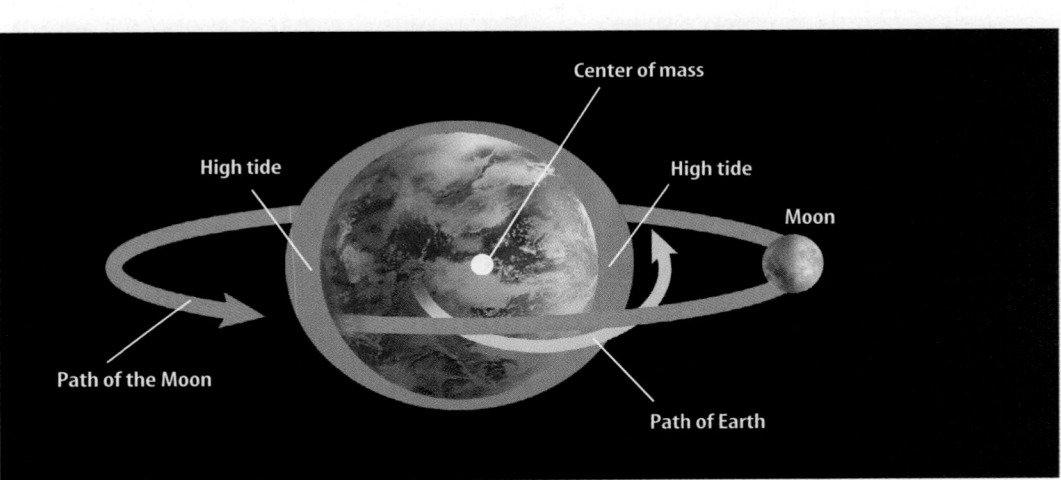

Center of mass

High tide

High tide

Moon

Path of the Moon

Path of Earth

Resource Manager

Chapter Resources Booklet
Reinforcement, p. 25
Enrichment, p. 28

Visual Learning

Figure 18 What phase of the Moon would you expect to see during a neap tide and during a spring tide? first or third quarter; full or new Moon

3 Assess

Reteach

Use a wave demonstration spring or coiled-spring toy to show how energy is transferred through a wave. Tie a piece of ribbon to the middle of the spring. Have two students create a wave while another student holds the ribbon. Have the class note that the ribbon does not move forward with the wave as energy moves through the spring. **LS Interpersonal**

Challenge

Why does the Moon have a greater gravitational effect on Earth's tides than the Sun, although the Sun is much larger? The Sun is much farther from Earth than the Moon is.

✓ Assessment

Oral Have students write questions on the content of the chapter and quiz each other aloud. Use **Performance Assessment in the Science Classroom,** p. 91.

Figure 18
The gravitational attraction of the Sun causes spring tides and neap tides.

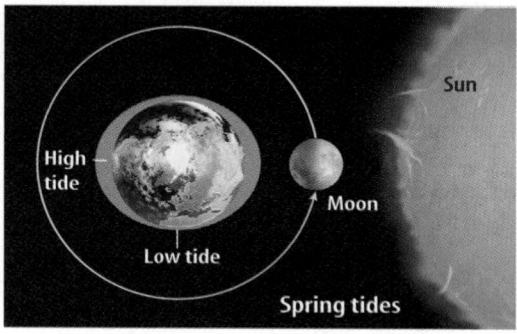

A When the Sun, the Moon, and Earth are aligned, spring tides occur.

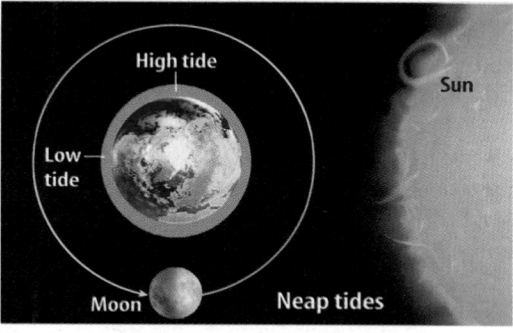

B When the Sun, Earth, and the Moon form a right angle, neap tides occur.

The Gravitational Effect of the Sun The Sun also affects tides. The Sun can strengthen or weaken the Moon's effects. When the Moon, Earth, and the Sun are lined up together, the combined pull of the Sun and the Moon causes spring tides, shown in **Figure 18A.** During spring tides, high tides are higher and low tides are lower than normal. The name *spring tide* has nothing to do with the season of spring. It comes from the German word *springen,* which means "to jump." When the Sun, Earth, and the Moon form a right angle, as shown in **Figure 18B,** high tides are lower and low tides are higher than normal. These are called neap tides.

Section 3 Assessment

1. Describe the parts of an ocean wave.
2. How does wind create water waves?
3. What causes high tides? Spring tides?
4. Compare water and wave movement.
5. **Think Critically** At the ocean, you spot a wave about 200 m from shore. A few seconds later, the wave breaks on the beach. Explain why the water in the breaker is not the same water that was in the wave 200 m away.

Skill Builder Activities

6. **Comparing and Contrasting** Compare and contrast the effects of the Sun and the Moon on Earth's tides. **For more help, refer to the** Science Skill Handbook.

7. **Communicating** Many planets have more than one moon. In your Science Journal, write a description of what tides might be like if Earth had two moons. **For more help, refer to the** Science Skill Handbook.

Answers to Section Assessment

1. crest: highest point, trough: lowest point, wave height: vertical distance between crest and trough, wavelength: horizontal distance between crests or troughs of two successive waves, amplitude: half of wave height
2. Friction pulls water along with wind.
3. Tides are caused by a giant wave that forms as the result of the gravitational

pull of the Sun and the Moon. As the wave's crest approaches the shore, the water level appears to rise in a high tide. Spring tides are caused by the combined gravitational effect when the Moon, Earth, and the Sun are in line
4. As the wave moves horizontally through the water, particles of

water are moved up, forward, down, and back.
5. Although the energy in waves moves, the water particles themselves do not.
6. Both affect tides because of gravitational attraction, but the effect of the Moon is greater because it's so much closer.

7. Answers will vary, but both moons would exert gravitational attraction that would result in tides. If both moons and the Sun lined up with Earth, the tidal range would be greater. If the two moons were at right angles to one another, tidal range would be smaller.

Making Waves

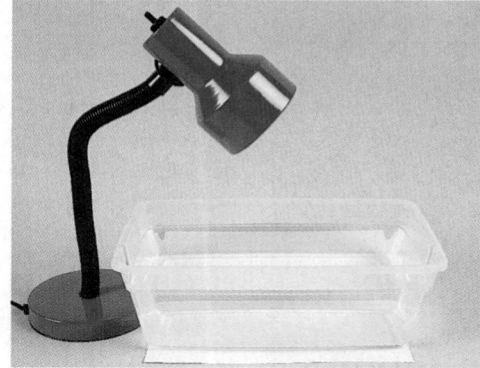

Wind generates some waves. The energy of motion is transferred from the wind to the surface water of the ocean. What factors influence the generation of waves?

What You'll Investigate
How do the speed of the wind and the length of time the wind blows affect the height of a wave?

Materials
11" × 14" white paper   water
3-speed electric fan   metric ruler
gooseneck lamp
clock or watch
rectangular, clear-plastic storage box

Goals
■ **Observe** how wind speed and duration affect wave height.

Safety Precautions 🔪 🥽 ⚡
Do not allow any part of the light or cord to come in contact with the water.

Procedure

1. Position the box on white paper beside the lamp.

2. Fill the plastic box with water to within 3 cm of the top. Direct light from the lamp onto the box.

3. Place the fan at one end of the box to create waves. Start the fan on its slowest speed. Keep the fan on during measuring.

4. After 3 min, measure the height of the waves caused by the fan. Record your observations in a table similar to the one shown. Through the plastic box, observe the shadows of the waves on the white paper.

5. After 5 min, measure the wave height and record your observations.

6. Repeat steps 3 to 5 with the fan on medium, then on high.

7. Turn off the fan. Unplug it. Observe what happens.

Wave Data

Fan Speed	Time (min)	Wave Height (mm)	Observations
Low	3	2	
Low	5	3	
Medium	3	3.5	
Medium	5	4.5	
High	3	5	
High	5	5.5	

Conclude and Apply

1. **Analyze** your data to determine whether the wave height is affected by the length of time that the wind blows. Explain.

2. **Analyze** your data to determine whether the height of the waves is affected by the speed of the wind. Explain.

ACTIVITY 469

Resource Manager

Chapter Resources Booklet
Activity Worksheet, pp. 5–6

Communicating Your Data

Use a computer graphics program to plot the data obtained from this activity. Compare your plot with those of other students in the class. Graphs should show how the length of time the wind blows and wind speed affects wave height.

BENCH TESTED

Purpose Students observe and describe the factors that affect the height of waves. [L2] [ELL] [COOP LEARN] [IS] **Visual-Spatial**

Process Skills making models, observing and inferring, relating cause and effect, interpreting data, predicting, analyzing

Time Required 35 minutes

Alternate Materials If enough table-model, three-speed fans cannot be obtained, the activity can be done by placing three or four student setups on the floor in front of a large floor fan that operates at several speeds. An overhead or filmstrip projector works well in place of the recommended light source and ring stand setup.

Safety Precautions Caution students to keep electrical cords and appliances away from water, to use care when handling the hot light source, and to keep objects away from moving fan blades.

Teaching Strategy If necessary, have students review Recognizing Cause and Effect in the Skill Handbook.

Answers to Questions
1. It is; the longer the wind blows, the higher the wave.
2. It is; the stronger the wind, the higher the wave.

✔ Assessment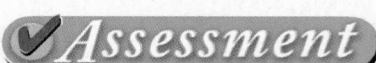

Performance To further assess students' ability to understand factors that affect the height of waves, have them design an experiment to see how the fetch (the distance over which the wind blows) affects wave height. Use **Performance Assessment in the Science Classroom**, p. 95.

Activity

BENCH TESTED

Recognize the Problem

Purpose

Students will design an experiment and data table to chart how increasing salinity affects the ability of a potato to float in water.

Process Skills

designing an experiment, forming a hypothesis, comparing, observing and inferring, communicating, interpreting data, recording data, analyzing results, making and using tables

Time Required

one class period

Form a Hypothesis

Possible Hypothesis

Students may hypothesize that with increasing salinity, the potato rises or the opposite, that it sinks with increasing salinity.

Test Your Hypothesis

Possible Procedures

Fill a large glass bowl with approximately 960 mL of water. Weigh a small potato and drop it into the bowl. Use the metric ruler to record the displacement of the water. Remove the potato and add 1 teaspoon of salt to the water. Stir the water until the salt dissolves. Drop the potato into the water and record the results. Use a metric ruler to measure the amount of water that is displaced each time. Repeat the above steps until you notice a change in the potato's ability to float. For help figuring density, refer to the Math Skills Activity in this chapter.

Activity

Design Your Own Experiment

Sink or Float

As you know, ocean water contains many dissolved salts. How does this affect objects within the oceans? Why do certain objects float on top of the ocean's waves, while others sink directly to the bottom? Density is a measurement of mass per volume. You can use density to determine whether an object will float within a certain volume of water of a specific salinity. In this activity you will investigate the effect of salinity on whether an object floats or sinks.

Recognizing the Problem

How does salinity affect whether a potato will float or sink?

Form a Hypothesis

Based on what you know so far about salinity, why things float or sink, and the density of a potato, plus what it looks and feels like, formulate a hypothesis. Do you think the salinity of water has any effect on objects that are floating in water? What kind of effect? Will they float or sink? How would a dense object like a potato be different from a less dense object like a cork?

Goals

■ **Design** an experiment to identify how increasing salinity affects the ability of a potato to float in water.

Possible Materials

small, uncooked potato
teaspoon
salt
large glass bowl
water
balance
large graduated cylinder
metric ruler

Safety

Resource Manager

Chapter Resources Booklet
  Activity Worksheet, pp. 7–8
Lab Management and Safety, p. 65

Test Your Hypothesis

Plan

1. As a group, agree upon and write your hypothesis statement.
2. Devise a method to test how salinity affects whether a potato floats in water.
3. **List** the steps you need to take to test your hypothesis. Be specific, describing exactly what you will do at each step.
4. Read over your plan for testing your hypothesis.
5. How will you determine the densities of the potato and the different water samples? How you will measure the salinity of the water? How will you change the salinity of the water? Will you add teaspoons of salt one at a time?
6. How you will measure the ability of an object to float? Could you somehow measure the displacement of

the water? Perhaps you could draw a line somewhere on your bowl and see how the position of the potato changes.

7. **Design** a data table where you can record your results. Include columns/rows for the salinity and float/sink measurements. What else should you include?

Do

1. Make sure your teacher approves your plan before you start.
2. Carry out the experiment.
3. While conducting the experiment, record your data and any observations that you or other group members make in your Science Journal.

Analyze Your Data

1. **Compare** how the potato floated in water with different salinities.
2. How does the ability of an object to float change with changing salinity?

Draw Conclusions

1. Did your experiment support the hypothesis you made?
2. A heavily loaded ship barely floats in the Gulf of Mexico. Based on what you learned, infer what might happen to the ship if it travels into the freshwater of the Mississippi River.

Communicating
Your Data

Prepare a chart showing the results of your experiment. Share the chart with members of your class. **For more help, refer to the** Science Skill Handbook.

ACTIVITY 471

Teaching Strategy

Demonstrate how to measure displacement of water using a metric ruler and bowl containing water.

Expected Outcome

The potato will float better in higher salt concentrations. It will take approximately 12–14 teaspoons of salt to float a 100 g potato.

Analyze Your Data

1. As the salinity of the water increased, the potato became more buoyant.
2. If the salinity is lowered, denser objects will not float as well. The density of the object affects whether or not it will float. For example, a bobber will float in freshwater or salt water.

Error Analysis

If students are unable to get their potato to float in the time allowed, have them review the procedure steps. How much water did they use? How much salt?

Draw Conclusions

1. Answers will vary.
2. Students might indicate that the ship will sink if it travels into freshwater.

Process Have students evaluate the data from other classmates. If their data is significantly different, have them discuss why it might be different. Use **Performance Assessment in the Science Classroom,** p. 99.

Communicating
Your Data

Student charts should show how much salt was added each time and whether or not the potato changed position with the addition of salt.

Science and Language Arts

"The Jungle of Ceylon"
from Passions and Impressions
by Pablo Neruda

Ask students whether they have ever visited a place that has a tropical climate. Ask them to write down as many adjectives as they can think of that describe a tropical environment.

Respond to the Reading

Active Reading Strategies

Visualize The author skillfully describes the coast of the island of Ceylon. Ask students to try to visualize all of the features of the island he depicts, including the reef, the birds, the tides, the trees and the boats.

Question The author describes the jungle as having "a silence like that of libraries: abstract and humid." **Why does he compare the jungle to a library?**

Listen Read the passage aloud. Have students notice how the author uses words that have the same first letter or consonant sound. This is called alliteration.

Question Ask students whether they think the author's use of alliteration helps them visualize the scene he is describing.

Answers to Questions

1. It was a gentle and happy place; he describes it as *felicitous.*
2. rippling ruff of feathers and foam
3. tropical

Respond to the Reading

1. What were his impressions of the island on arrival?
2. What words does the author choose to describe waves?
3. How would you describe the climate of Ceylon?

The following passage is part of a travel chronicle describing the Chilean poet Pablo Neruda's visit to the island of Ceylon, now called Sri Lanka, which is located southeast of India. The author considered himself so connected to Earth that he wrote in green ink.

Felicitous[1] shore! A coral reef stretches parallel to the beach; there the ocean interposes in its blues the perpetual white of a rippling ruff[2] of feathers and foam; the triangular red sails of sampans[3]; the unmarred line of the coast on which the straight trunks of the coconut palms rise like explosions, their brilliant green Spanish combs nearly touching the sky. … In the deep jungle, there is a silence like that of libraries: abstract and humid.

1 Happy
2 round collar made of layers of lace
3 East Asian boats

Reading Further

Other works by this author include:

Residence on Earth, by Pablo Neruda, New Directions, March 1973.

The Book of Questions, by Pablo Neruda, Copper Canyon Press, September 1991.

Other sources on this topic include:

Currents of Change: Impacts of El Nino and La Nina on Climate and Society, Cambridge University Press, February 2001.

Understanding Literature

Imagery Imagery is a series of words that evoke pictures to the reader. Poets use imagery to connect images to abstract concepts. The poet, here, wants to capture a particular feature of the reef and does so by describing it as a "ruff of feathers and foam," invoking the image of a gentle place, without the author saying so. Imagery also gives the reader more information about the story or chronicle. The poet further describes the shore as "happy", which helps us learn that the poet is arriving on the island on a clear, calm day.

Where else in the poem does the poet use imagery to convey a mood or feeling?

Science Connection In the poem there are several indicators that the wind, which causes waves and currents, is light and the waves are small, using imagery as discussed above.

Sri Lanka, however, often is plagued by monsoons, which affect ocean conditions and local climate. Monsoons are seasonal reversals of the regional winds. During the wet season, moist winds blow in from the sea, causing storms and producing waves. During the dry season, winds blow from the land and sunny days are common.

Linking Science and Writing

Weather Report Write a weather report for fishers and others who work at sea. Pick a geographic location to focus on. If possible, do research on wave conditions in this area. Include the times for low and high tides in your report. Add any additional weather information that you think might be important to people who work at or around the sea.

Career Connection

Oceanographer

Oceanographer Dr. Robert D. Ballard is an American oceanographer who revolutionized deep-sea archaeology. He developed several high-tech vessels that can explore ocean bottoms previously out of reach. Dr. Ballard discovered the location of the wreckage of the *Titanic, Lusitania,* and *Bismark*. He also discovered the wreckage of eight ancient ships in the Mediterranean Sea. Dr. Ballard has degrees in chemistry and geology as well as doctorate degrees in marine geology and geophysics.

SCIENCE*Online* To learn more about careers in oceanography, visit the Glencoe Science Web site at **science.glencoe.com.**

Understanding Literature

Answers to Questions

Answers may vary but might include that the author uses the word "explosion" when referring to the tops of palm trees to convey a contrast between the trees and the gentle sea. He also compares the silence of the jungle to that of a library as a way of emphasizing the jungle's stillness and solitude.

Science Connection

Ocean currents in the Atlantic Ocean and the Pacific Ocean are nearly the same throughout the year. However, surface currents in the northern part of the Indian Ocean change with the monsoon winds. This is referred to as the Monsoon Drift. When the northeast monsoons blow over Sri Lanka, the Northeast Monsoon Drift flows toward the west. When the southwest monsoon blows, the current flow reverses.

Linking Science and Writing

Teaching Strategies

Tell students to bring to class maps from the newspaper that describe area weather patterns. Have students do brief oral presentations describing the weather patterns on the map.

Career Connection

Students interested in a career in marine science should enroll in as many chemistry, Earth science, biology, physics, computer science, and mathematics classes as possible, in high school and in college. Oceanographers do not specialize until later in their education.

With a high school education or a two-year degree, students can be technicians in marine science. In order to analyze the data they collect, however, students will need to go to a 4-year college as well as get an advanced degree. About 30 U.S. schools offer specialized technical training in marine-related fields.

Reviewing Main Ideas

Preview

Students can answer the questions in their Science Journals. Discuss the answers as you go through the chapter. **Linguistic**

Review

Students can write their answers, then compare them with those of other students. **Interpersonal**

Reteach

Students can look at the illustrations and describe details that support the main ideas of the chapter. **Visual-Spatial**

Answers to Chapter Review

SECTION 1

3. halite

SECTION 2

4. The warm temperature and dry air cause large amounts of water to evaporate from the sea's surface. The remaining water contains an increased salt concentration and is more dense than the water around it. The denser water sinks and flows out of the Mediterranean Sea at the Straits of Gibraltar. Less dense water from the Atlantic Ocean flows in to replace it.

SECTION 3

3. They result when the gravitational effect of the Moon and the Sun causes a bulge, or wave, in Earth's oceans that spreads around the planet. When the crest of the wave approaches a shore, the water appears to rise on the shore as high tide. Low tide occurs when the trough of the wave approaches the shore.

Reviewing Main Ideas

Section 1 Ocean Water

1. Earth's ocean water might have originated from water vapor released from volcanoes. Over millions of years, the water condensed and rain fell, filling basins.

2. The oceans are a mixture of water, dissolved salts, and dissolved gases that are in constant motion.

3. Groundwater and rivers weather rock and dissolve some minerals to form ions. The ions are carried to the oceans where they give seawater its salty taste. *What kind of salt, shown here, makes up most of the salt left when seawater is evaporated?*

Section 2 Ocean Currents

1. Wind causes surface currents. Surface currents are affected by the Coriolis effect. The Coriolis effect turns currents north of the equator clockwise and turns currents south of the equator counterclockwise.

2. Surface currents can greatly affect climate and economic activity such as fishing. Upwelling brings deep, cold water to the ocean's surface.

3. Cool currents off western coasts originate far from the equator. Warmer currents along eastern coasts begin near the equator.

4. Differences in temperature and salinity between water masses in the oceans set up circulation patterns called density currents. *How do density currents originate in the Mediterranean Sea, shown here?*

Section 3 Ocean Waves and Tides

1. A wave is a rhythmic movement that carries energy. The crest is the highest point of a wave. The trough is the lowest point.

2. In a wave, energy moves forward while water particles move around in small circles.

3. Wind causes water to pile up and form most water waves. Tides are not caused by wind. *What causes the high and low tides shown here?*

FOLDABLES Reading & Study Skills

After You Read

Under the bottom tab of your Foldable, write about the effects of ocean motion on climate, world economics, and ocean water.

FOLDABLES Reading & Study Skills

After You Read

After students have read the chapter and completed the Foldable described in Before You Read, have them do the activity on the student page.

Dinah Zike

Visualizing Main Ideas

Complete the following concept map on ocean motions.

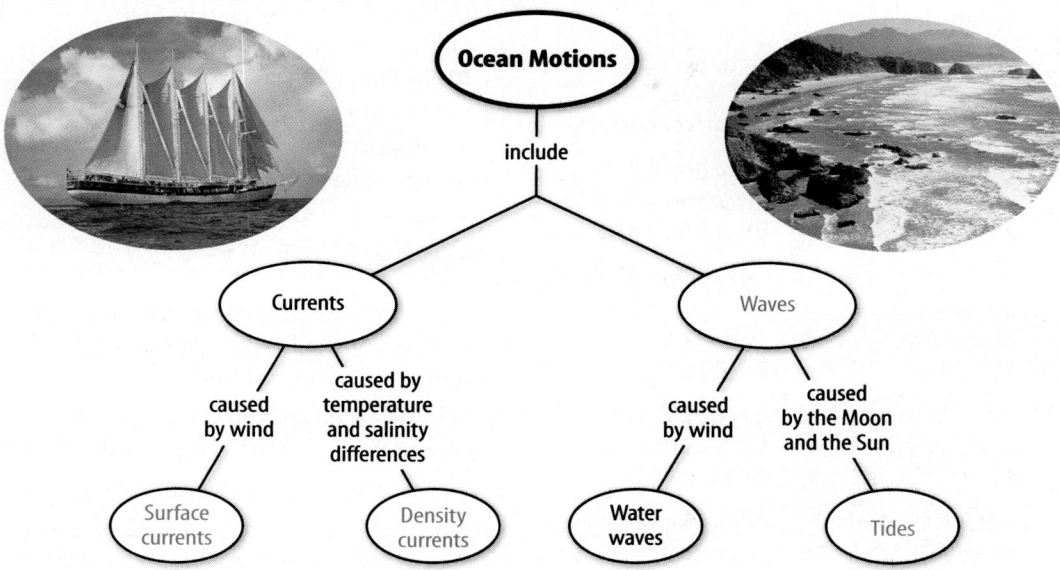

Ocean Motions

include

Currents

Waves

caused by wind

caused by temperature and salinity differences

caused by wind

caused by the Moon and the Sun

Surface currents

Density currents

Water waves

Tides

Vocabulary Review

Vocabulary Words

a. basin
b. breaker
c. Coriolis effect
d. crest
e. density current
f. salinity

g. surface current
h. tidal range
i. tide
j. trough
k. upwelling
l. wave

THE PRINCETON REVIEW — Study Tip

After you've read a chapter, go back to the beginning and speed-read through what you've just read. This will help you better remember what you have read.

Using Vocabulary

Replace the underlined words with the vocabulary words that have the same meaning.

1. The <u>amount of dissolved salts</u> in seawater has stayed about the same for hundreds of millions of years.

2. An <u>area where nutrient-rich water comes to the surface</u> is a good place to catch fish.

3. Wind creates a <u>horizontal current at the top of the ocean</u>.

4. Along most ocean beaches, a <u>rise and fall of the ocean related to gravitational pull</u> is easy to see.

5. Wind pushes on water to make a <u>movement of energy through the water</u>.

CHAPTER STUDY GUIDE 475

Visualizing Main Ideas

See student page.

Vocabulary Review

Using Vocabulary

1. The *salinity* in seawater has stayed about the same for hundreds of millions of years.
2. An *upwelling* is a good place to catch fish.
3. Wind creates a *surface current*.
4. Along most ocean beaches, a *tide* is easy to see.
5. Wind pushes on water to make a *wave*.

Checking Concepts

1. B
2. A
3. A
4. D
5. C
6. B
7. A
8. D
9. B
10. C

Thinking Critically

11. It could wash up onto a beach on the coast of western or north-western Europe because the Gulf Stream travels there from Florida.

12. Many marine organisms use these elements in their life processes, thus removing them from the ocean.

13. It forms when salt is left over as ice forms from salt water at the South Pole. The salt increases the density of the cold water, causing it to sink beneath less-dense water.

14. At the mouth of the Mississippi River the water has low salinity, while it is very salty in the Mediterranean Sea. The water is therefore denser in the Mediterranean.

15. highest high tide, day 4; lowest high tide, day 23; highest low tide, day 24; lowest low tide, day 4; spring tide, days 4 and 18; neap tide, days 13 and 24

Checking Concepts

Choose the word or phrase that best answers the question.

1. Where might ocean water have originated?
   A) salt marshes   C) basins
   B) volcanoes   D) surface currents

2. How does chlorine enter the oceans?
   A) volcanoes   C) density currents
   B) rivers   D) groundwater

3. What is the most common ion found in ocean water?
   A) chloride   C) boron
   B) calcium   D) sulfate

4. What causes most surface currents?
   A) density differences   C) salinity
   B) the Gulf Stream   D) wind

5. What is the highest point on a wave called?
   A) wave height   C) crest
   B) trough   D) wavelength

6. In the ocean, what is the rhythmic movement that carries energy through seawater?
   A) current   C) crest
   B) wave   D) upwelling

7. Which of the following causes the density of seawater to increase?
   A) a decrease in temperature
   B) a decrease in salinity
   C) an increase in temperature
   D) a decrease in pressure

8. In which direction does the Coriolis effect cause currents in the northern hemisphere to turn?
   A) east
   B) south
   C) counterclockwise
   D) clockwise

9. Tides are affected by the positions of which celestial bodies?
   A) Earth and the Moon
   B) Earth, the Moon, and the Sun
   C) Venus, Earth, and Mars
   D) the Sun, Earth, and Mars

10. What affects surface currents?
    A) crests   C) the Coriolis effect
    B) upwellings   D) tides

Thinking Critically

11. If a sealed bottle is dropped into the ocean off the coast of Florida, where do you think it might wash up? Explain.

12. Why do silicon and calcium remain in seawater for a shorter time than sodium?

13. Describe the Antarctic density current.

14. How would the density of seawater at the mouth of the Mississippi River and in the Mediterranean Sea compare? Explain.

15. Refer to the graph below. On which day is the high tide highest? Lowest? On which day(s) is the low tide lowest? Highest? On which day(s) would Earth, the Moon, and the Sun be lined up? On which day(s) would the Moon, Earth, and the Sun form a right angle?

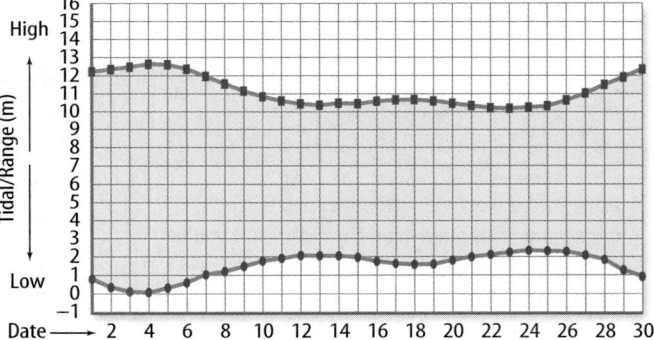

Chapter ✓Assessment Planner

Portfolio Encourage students to place in their portfolios one or two items of what they consider to be their best work. Examples include:
- Assessment, p. 455
- Curriculum Connection, p. 458
- Extension, p. 464

Performance Additional performance assessments, Performance Task Assessment Lists, and rubrics for evaluating these activities can be found in Glencoe's **Performance Assessment in the Science Classroom.**

Developing Skills

16. Recognizing Cause and Effect What causes upwelling? What effect does it have? What can happen when upwelling stops?

17. Comparing and Contrasting Compare and contrast ocean waves and ocean currents.

18. Predicting Predict how drift bottles that are dropped into the ocean at points A and B will move. Explain.

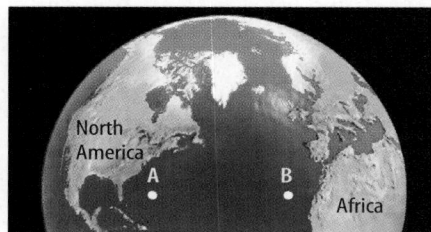

19. Recognizing Cause and Effect In the Mediterranean Sea, a density current forms because of the high rate of evaporation of water from the surface. How can evaporation cause a density current?

Performance Assessment

20. Invention Design a method for desalinating water that does not use solar energy. Draw it, and display it for your class.

21. Design and Perform an Experiment Create an experiment to test the density of water at different temperatures.

TECHNOLOGY

Go to the Glencoe Science Web site at **science.glencoe.com** or use the **Glencoe Science CD-ROM** for additional chapter assessment.

 **THE PRINCETON REVIEW** **Test Practice**

A marine scientist used the following graphic to support a lecture about ocean currents.

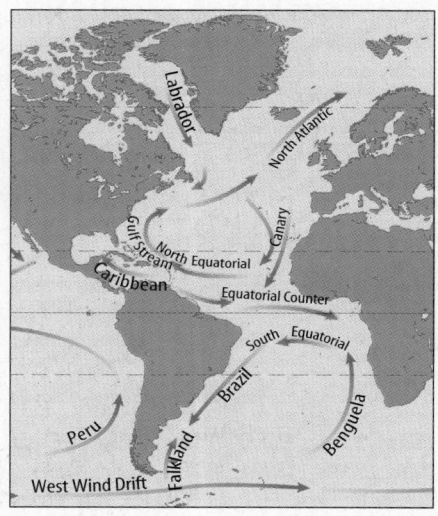

Study the graphic and answer the following questions.

1. The direction of ocean currents in the northern hemisphere is _____.
   A) counterclockwise
   B) north to south only
   C) clockwise
   D) east to west only

2. A reasonable conclusion based on the information in the graphic is that _____.
   F) the ocean's currents only flow in one direction
   G) the ocean's waters are constantly in motion
   H) the Gulf Stream flows east to west
   J) the Atlantic Ocean is deep

CHAPTER ASSESSMENT 477

 **THE PRINCETON REVIEW** **Test Practice**

The Test-Taking Tip was written by The Princeton Review, the nation's leader in test preparation.
1. C
2. G

Developing Skills

16. Surface water is pushed away from an area by wind, allowing underlying cold water to rise to the surface, and sometimes fish numbers rise as well. If upwelling stops, good fishing areas can become barren.

17. Wind causes surface currents and waves. But surface currents move water from one place to another. Energy moves laterally in waves, but the water does not.

18. North from A, following shorelines around in clockwise pattern, moving south from B. Movement would be caused by surface currents.

19. When salt water evaporates, the water left behind has a higher concentration of salt, making it denser. The denser water sinks and flows out of the Mediterranean Sea into the Atlantic Ocean. Less dense surface water from the Atlantic flows in to replace it.

Performance Assessment

20. Students can use some artificial source, such as a hot plate, to heat and evaporate water. Use **PASC**, p. 117.

21. Designs should include procedures for heating and cooling the water; ways to measure the temperature, volume, and mass of the water samples; and a method for calculating density. Hydrometers can be used to determine actual densities of samples. They can be made by students or purchased from aquarium supply stores. Use **PASC**, p. 95.

✓Assessment Resources

📁 Reproducible Masters

Chapter Resources Booklet
   Chapter Review, pp. 33–34
   Chapter Tests, pp. 35–38
   Assessment Transparency Activity, p. 45

Glencoe Science Web site
   Interactive Tutor
   Chapter Quizzes

Glencoe Technology
   🖌 Assessment Transparency
   💿 Interactive CD-ROM Chapter Quizzes
   💿 ExamView Pro Test Bank
   💿 Vocabulary PuzzleMaker Software
   📼 MindJogger Videoquiz

Section/Objectives	Standards		Activities/Features
Chapter Opener	**National**	**State/Local**	**Explore Activity:** Model Earth's shape, p. 479 **Before You Read,** p. 479
	See p. 6T for a Key to Standards.		
Section 1 Earth's Motion and Seasons 🕐 1 session 📦 0.5 block 1. **Identify** Earth's shape and other physical properties. 2. **Compare and contrast** Earth's rotation and revolution. 3. **Explain** the causes of Earth's seasons.	National Content Standards: UCP2, D3		**Science Online,** p. 483
Section 2 Earth's Moon 🕐 2 sessions 📦 1 block 1. **Identify** the Moon's surface features and interior. 2. **Explain** the Moon's phases. 3. **Explain** the causes of solar and lunar eclipses. 4. **Compare** possible origins of the Moon.	National Content Standards: UCP2, A1, D3, G2		**Life Science Integration,** p. 487 **MiniLAB:** Modeling the Moon's Rotation, p. 488 **Science Online,** p. 490 **Visualizing How the Moon Formed,** p. 493 **Activity:** Viewing the Moon, p. 495
Section 3 Our Solar System 🕐 4 sessions 📦 2 blocks 1. **List** the important characteristics of inner planets. 2. **Identify** how other inner planets compare and contrast with Earth. 3. **List** the important characteristics of outer planets.	National Content Standards: UCP1, A1, D3, F3, F5		**Chemistry Integration,** p. 498 **Problem-Solving Activity:** What influences a planet's atmosphere?, p. 499 **Science Online,** p. 500 **MiniLAB:** Interpreting Your Creature Feature, p. 501 **Activity:** The Slant of the Sun's Rays, p. 504 **Science and Society:** Collision Course, p. 504

NATIONAL GEOGRAPHIC

Teacher's Corner

PRODUCTS AVAILABLE FROM NATIONAL GEOGRAPHIC SOCIETY
To order call 1-800-368-2728:
Poster
The Earth's Moon
Videos
Sun, Earth, Moon

INDEX TO NATIONAL GEOGRAPHIC SOCIETY
The following articles may be used for research relating to this chapter:
"Physical World," by Joel L. Swerdlow, May 1998.
"Orbit: The Astronauts' View of Home," by Jay Apt, November 1996.

"The Darkness That Enlightens," by Jay M. Pasachoff, May 1992.
"The Moon's Racing Shadow," by Roger H. Ressmeyer, May 1992.
"Our Restless Planet Earth," by Rick Gore, August 1985.

Activity Materials	Reproducible Resources	Section Assessment	Technology
Explore Activity: scissors, metric ruler, cardboard, tape, basketball	**Chapter Resources Booklet** Foldables Worksheet, p. 17 Directed Reading Overview, p. 19 Note-taking Worksheets, pp. 33–36	GLENCOE'S **ASSESSMENT** ADVANTAGE	
Need materials? Contact Science Kit at 1-800-828-7777 or www.sciencekit.com on the Internet.	**Chapter Resources Booklet** Enrichment, p. 30 Reinforcement, p. 27 Directed Reading, p. 20 Transparency Activity, pp. 49–50 Transparency Activity, p. 46 **Science Inquiry Labs,** p. 41	Portfolio Cultural Diversity, p. 484 Performance Skill Builder Activities, p. 485 Content Section Assessment, p. 485	Section Focus Transparency Teaching Transparency Interactive CD-ROM Guided Reading Audio Program
MiniLAB: masking tape, basketball, 2 chairs **Activity:** telescope, drawing paper, drawing pencils	**Chapter Resources Booklet** MiniLAB, p. 3 Enrichment, p. 31 Reinforcement, p. 28 Directed Reading, p. 20 Activity Worksheet, pp. 5–6 Transparency Activity, p. 47 Lab Activity, pp. 9–11 **Cultural Diversity,** pp. 29, 31	Portfolio Life Science Integration, p. 487 Performance MiniLAB, p. 488 Skill Builder Activities, p. 494 Content Section Assessment, p. 494	Section Focus Transparency Interactive CD-ROM Guided Reading Audio Program
MiniLAB: colored pencils or crayons, drawing paper **Activity:** shallow baking pans (lined with cardboard or paper), alcohol thermometers, wood blocks, protractor, clock or stopwatch	**Chapter Resources Booklet** MiniLAB, p. 4 Enrichment, p. 32 Reinforcement, p. 29 Directed Reading, pp. 21, 22 Activity Worksheet, pp. 7–8 Transparency Activity, p. 48 Lab Activity, pp. 13–15 **Reading And Writing Skill Activities,** p. 11 **Home and Community Involvement,** p. 44 **Lab Management and Safety,** p. 73	Portfolio Science Journal, p. 498 Performance Problem-Solving Activity, p. 499 MiniLAB, p. 501 Skill Builder Activities, p. 503 Content Section Assessment, p. 503	Section Focus Transparency Interactive CD-ROM Guided Reading Audio Program

End of Chapter Assessment

GLENCOE'S **ASSESSMENT** ADVANTAGE

Blackline Masters	Technology	Professional Series
Chapter Resources Booklet Chapter Review, pp. 39–40 Chapter Tests, pp. 41–44 **Standardized Test Practice by The Princeton Review,** pp. 73–76	MindJogger Videoquiz Interactive CD-ROM Vocabulary PuzzleMakers ExamView Pro Test Bank Interactive Lesson Planner Interactive Teacher Edition	Performance Assessment in the Science Classroom (PASC)

Transparencies

Section Focus

Section Focus Transparency 1 — Turning of the Seasons

L2

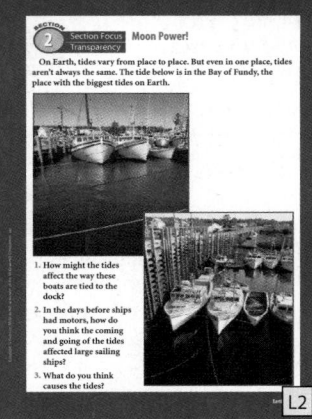

Section Focus Transparency 2 — Moon Power!

L2

Section Focus Transparency 3 — Evening Flow

L2

This is a representation of key blackline masters available in the Teacher Classroom Resources. See Resource Manager boxes within the chapter for additional information.

Key to Teaching Strategies

The following designations will help you decide which activities are appropriate for your students.

L1 Level 1 activities should be appropriate for students with learning difficulties.

L2 Level 2 activities should be within the ability range of all students.

L3 Level 3 activities are designed for above-average students.

ELL ELL activities should be within the ability range of English Language Learners.

COOP LEARN Cooperative Learning activities are designed for small group work.

LS Multiple Learning Styles logos, as described on page 22T, are used throughout to indicate strategies that address different learning styles.

P These strategies represent student products that can be placed into a best-work portfolio.

Assessment

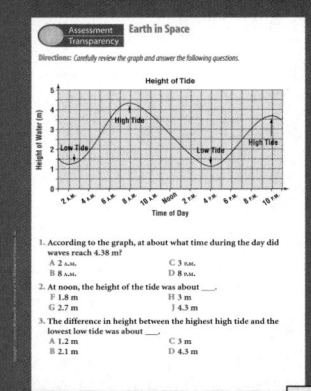

Assessment Transparency — Earth in Space

L2

Teaching

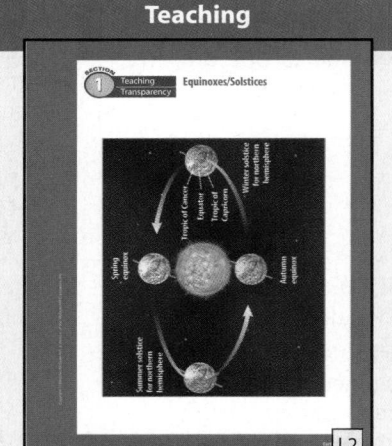

Teaching Transparency 1 — Equinoxes/Solstices

L2

Hands-on Activities

Activity Worksheets

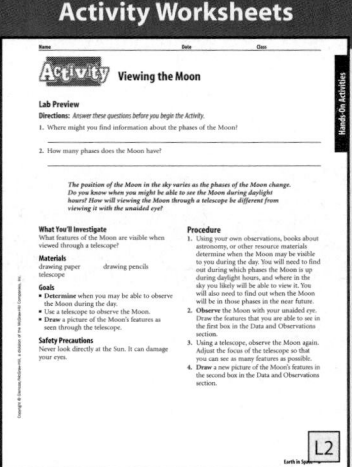

Activity — Viewing the Moon

L2

Laboratory Activities

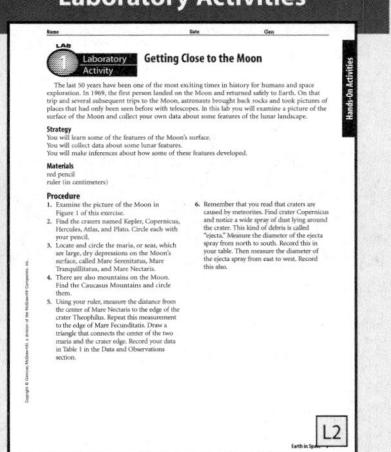

Laboratory Activity — Getting Close to the Moon

L2

RESOURCE MANAGER

Meeting Different Ability Levels

Content Outline
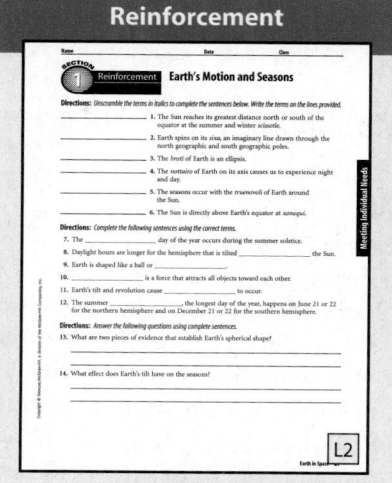

Reinforcement

Directed Reading

Assessment

Chapter Tests
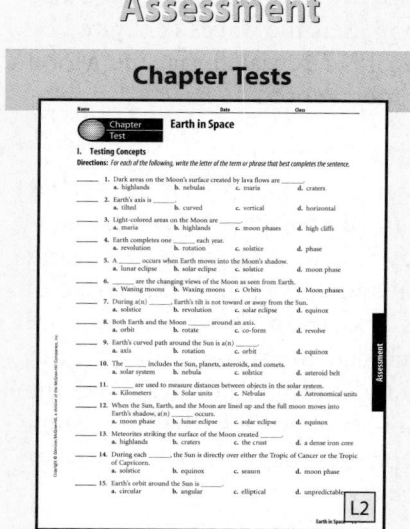

Enrichment
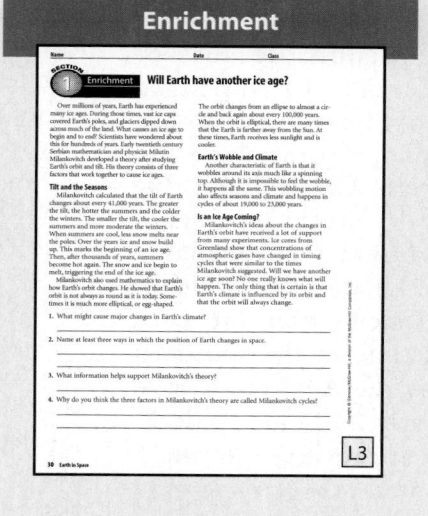

Spanish Directed Reading
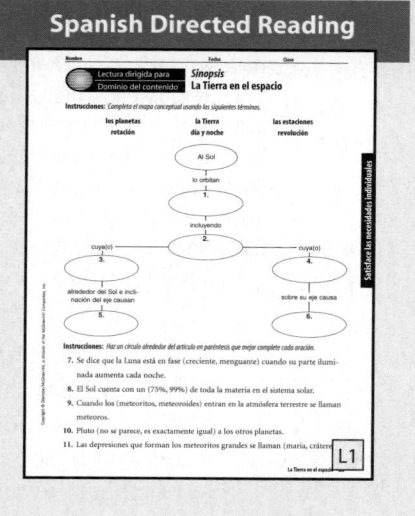

Test Practice Workbook

Chapter Review
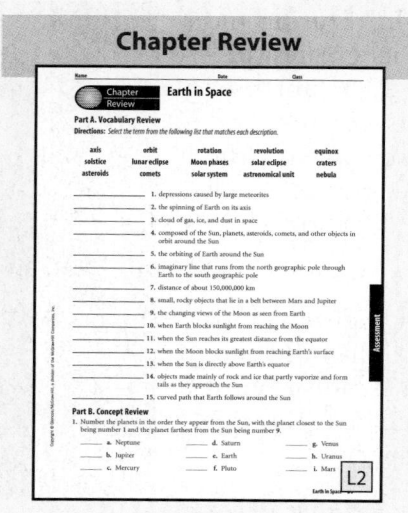

Science Content Background

SECTION 1 — Earth's Motion and Seasons

Earth's Tilt

Although it is known that Earth's tilt has fluctuated throughout geologic time, from about 21.5° to 24.5°, the exact origin of the tilt is unclear. It is a widely accepted hypothesis that soon after its formation, Earth collided with a Mars-sized body, which may have led to the formation of the Moon. It is now believed that the tilt of the Earth was also a result of this collision. Because of Earth's tilt, during a northern hemisphere summer, areas above the Arctic Circle (66.5° N) receive nearly 24 hours of daylight. The nickname "the Land of the Midnight Sun" stems from this phenomenon. During this time in the southern hemisphere, areas below the Antarctic Circle (66.5° S) experience nearly 24 hours of darkness. These conditions are reversed during a northern hemisphere winter.

> **Fun Fact**
>
> There is no air resistance on the Moon. If you were to drop a hammer and a feather at the same time on Earth, the hammer would reach the ground much sooner than the feather. If you were to do this on the Moon, they would hit the ground at the same time.

Solstices

The word *solstice* comes from Latin and means, literally, "Sun halt." During the solstices the Sun reaches its greatest distance from the equator, 23.5° north or south. Having reached its greatest progression northward or southward, the Sun "halts" and begins the progression all over again in the opposite direction.

Equinoxes

The lengths of day and night are not quite equal at an equinox. The difference occurs because the Sun is not a point source of light and because light is refracted by Earth's atmosphere.

SECTION 2 — Earth's Moon

The Moon's Interior

Much of what is known about the interior composition of both the Earth and the Moon comes from data collected during seismic events by seismographs. Moonquakes do not occur very often; however, the seismic waves produced by meteorites crashing into the surface of the Moon can be just as useful as those produced during a quake. In several instances, seismic waves have been deliberately created by crashing used rockets and lunar modules into the Moon. Much has been learned in this manner about the crust and mantle of the Moon. Seismic waves generated by a natural impact in 1972 revealed that the Moon may have a small metal core.

Observations from Stonehenge

Stonehenge is just one example of an earlier culture's success in discovering the fundamentals of astronomy. Built over three thousand years ago near Salisbury, England, this circle of standing stones was used to mark celestial events. These included the summer and winter solstices, the fall and spring equinoxes, and the phases of the Moon. It is possible that the stones were also used to predict the occurrences of solar and lunar eclipses.

Yann Arthus-Bertrand/Corbis

Our Solar System

Jupiter

Weather systems on Earth are driven by heat energy from the Sun. Because Jupiter is farther from the Sun than Earth is, its main source of heat energy is not derived from the Sun but from the interior of the planet itself. Temperatures as high as 30,000°C might exist in Jupiter's core. It is the combination of heat from the core and Jupiter's accelerated rotation rate (9 hours and 50 minutes) that forms massive storms in Jupiter's atmosphere and on its surface. Earth-sized blizzards of

Fun Fact

The order of the planets sometimes switches. Because of its elliptical orbit, Pluto is sometimes actually closer to the Sun than Neptune is. From 1977 to 1999, Pluto was the second to last planet in our solar system.

ammonia and ice crystals occur in the upper clouds of the atmosphere. Closer to the surface, thunderstorms with winds as high as 300 miles per hour and superbolts of lightning rage for years. Jupiter's most famous storm, the Great Red Spot, has been under way for over 350 years. This storm is about twice the size of Earth. It is theorized that the spot obtains its color from phosphorus and sulfur that are pulled up from the interior of the planet.

Comets

Comets are divided into three parts: the nucleus, the coma, and the tails. The nucleus of the comet is the frozen cluster of water and rock. As the comet comes close to the Sun, the vaporized gases and dust form a cloud around the nucleus, the coma. The gases and dust often trail behind as two separate tails.

For additional content background on this topic, go to the Glencoe Science Web site at science.glencoe.com.

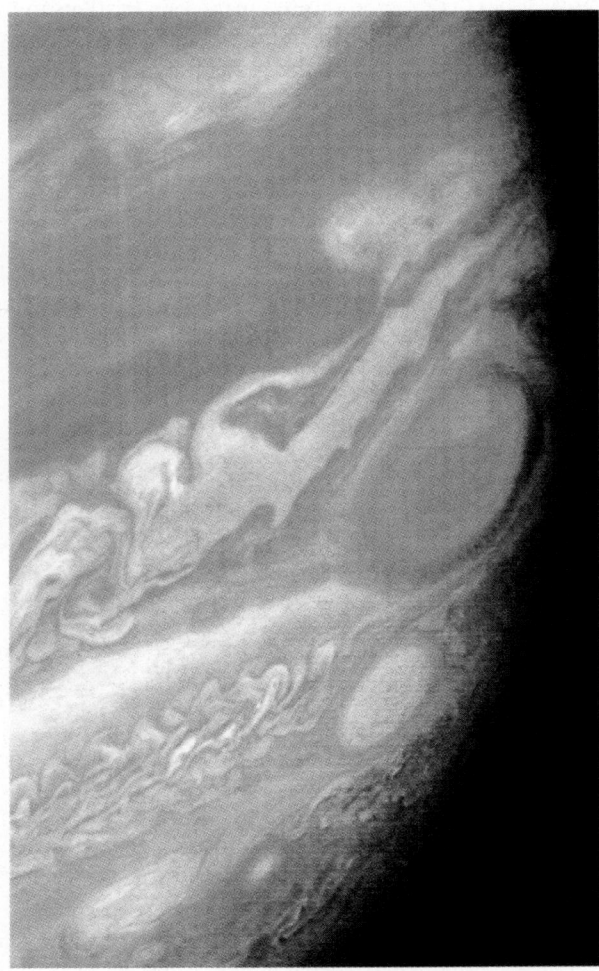

NASA/JPL/Tom Stack & Associates

Earth in Space

Chapter Vocabulary

What do you think?

Science Journal The photo shows a meteorite. Certain minerals in the meteorite are giving off light (fluorescing) because the rock is being illuminated by a black light.

Earth in Space

What do you know about Earth's shape? What do you think happens to cause the seasons? Why do you suppose *maria*, the Latin word for seas, is used to describe some parts of the mostly dry and lifeless Moon? And what do you imagine is on the "other" side—the far side—of the Moon? This chapter will help you find answers to these questions.

You'll also learn about the Sun and other planets and moons in the solar system. They formed, along with the brilliant meteor shown here, billions of years ago.

What do you think?

Science Journal Look at the picture below with a classmate. Discuss what you think this might be or what is happening. Here's a hint: *Have you ever wished upon a falling star?* Write your answer or best guess in your Science Journal.

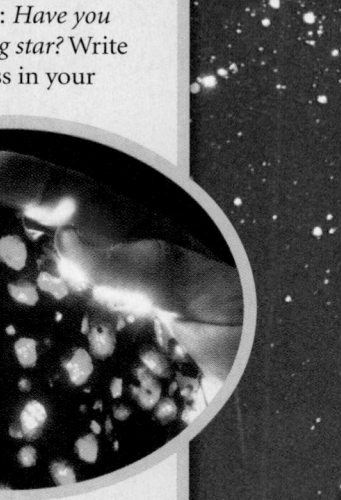

478

Theme Connection

Systems and Interactions The chapter discusses the interactions among the Sun, planets, and moons of the solar system. These interactions cause seasons, eclipses, and lunar phases.

Could you prove that Earth is round? If you look out across a field or a large body of water, Earth seems to be flat, but you know that Earth is shaped like a large ball. What can you see from Earth's surface that proves Earth is round?

Model Earth's shape

1. Cut a strip of cardboard about 8 cm long and 8 cm tall into the shape of a sailboat. Fold up about 2 cm of the cardboard at the boat's base. Tape this 2-cm section to a basketball so that the peak of the sailboat sticks straight up.

2. Roll the basketball on a table at eye level so that the sailboat sticks out horizontally, parallel to the table, and points opposite from your view. Look at the top of the ball. The curving edge of the basketball can be compared to a horizon.

3. Roll the ball toward you slowly so that the sail comes into view over the top of the ball. Stop when you can see the entire paper sailboat.

4. Record everything you observe in your Science Journal.

Observe

In your Science Journal, write a paragraph that explains how the shape of the basketball affected your view of the sailboat. Interpret how this can be considered a model of Earth's shape with you looking out over the sea.

Before You Read

FOLDABLES
Reading & Study Skills

Making a Compare and Contrast Study Fold Make the following Foldable to help you see how Earth and moon are similar and different.

1. Place a sheet of paper in front of you so the long side is at the top. Fold the paper in half from the left side to the right side. Fold top to bottom and crease. Then unfold.

2. Through the top thickness of paper, cut along the middle fold line to form two tabs as shown.

3. Label "Alike" and "Different" across the front of the paper as shown.

4. Before you read the chapter, list all the ways you think Earth and the Moon are alike and different under the tabs.

5. As you read the chapter, add to or change the information you wrote under the tabs.

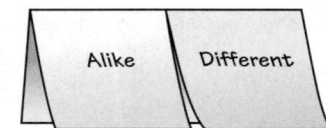

479

EXPLORE ACTIVITY

Purpose Use the Explore Activity to introduce evidence of Earth's shape as students use a model to prove that Earth is round. L2 COOP LEARN
LS Visual-Spatial

Materials basketball, cardboard, tape, scissors, metric ruler

Alternate Materials Earth globe, volleyball, kickball, soccer ball

Teaching Strategy Have students work in pairs. As one does the activity, the other records observations. Then have students switch roles.

Observe

Because of the ball's round shape, the sailboat gradually appears as the ball's curved surface turns toward you. The same thing happens on Earth. The boat comes slowly into view as it approaches over Earth's curved surface.

✓ Assessment

Oral Have students explain how an island would appear as a boat on which they are riding approaches it. Use **Performance Assessment in the Science Classroom**, p. 89.

Before You Read

FOLDABLES
Reading & Study Skills

Dinah Zike Study Fold
Purpose Determine what students know about Earth's movement in space by providing a Foldable for collecting data to compare and contrast rotation and revolution.

📁 For additional help, see Foldables Worksheet, p. 17 in **Chapter Resources Booklet,** or go to the Glencoe Science Web site at **science.glencoe.com.** See After You Read in the Study Guide at the end of this chapter.

1 Motivate

Bellringer Transparency

Display the Section Focus Transparency for Section 1. Use the accompanying Transparency Activity Master. L2 ELL

Tie to Prior Knowledge

Have students recall how the Sun changes position in the sky throughout the day. Ask them to compare its position in early morning, at midday, and in late evening. They should recall that it starts low in one part of the sky in the morning, rises high by midday, then sinks low in the opposite part of the sky by evening. Explain that the turning of Earth causes this apparent movement of the Sun.

As You Read

What **You'll Learn**

- **Identify** Earth's shape and other physical properties.
- **Compare and contrast** Earth's rotation and revolution.
- **Explain** the causes of Earth's seasons.

Vocabulary

axis	orbit
rotation	solstice
revolution	equinox

Why **It's Important**

Movements of Earth cause changes from day to night and from one season to another.

Figure 1
Earth's nearly spherical shape was first observed directly by images taken from spacecraft.
What observations on Earth's surface also suggest that it is spherical?

Earth's Physical Data

Think about the last time you saw a beautiful sunset. Late in the day, you may have noticed the Sun sinking lower and lower in the western sky. Eventually, as the Sun went below the horizon, the sky became darker. Was the Sun actually traveling out of view, or were you?

In the past, some people thought that the Sun, the Moon, and other objects in space moved around Earth each day. Now it is known that some of the motions of these objects, as observed from Earth, are really caused by Earth's movements.

Also, many people used to think that Earth was flat. They thought that if you sailed far enough out to sea, you eventually would fall off. It is now known that this is not true. What general shape does Earth have?

Spherical Earth As shown in **Figure 1,** pictures from space show that Earth is shaped like a ball, or a sphere. A sphere (SFIHR) is a three-dimensional object whose surface at all points is the same distance from its center. What other evidence can you think of that reveals Earth's shape?

Section ✔*Assessment* Planner

PORTFOLIO
Cultural Diversity, p. 484
PERFORMANCE ASSESSMENT
Skill Builder Activities, p. 485
See page 510 for more options.

CONTENT ASSESSMENT
Section, p. 485
Challenge, p. 485
Chapter, pp. 510–511

Evidence for Earth's Shape Have you ever stood on a dock and watched a sailboat come in? If so, you may have noticed that the first thing you see is the top of the boat's sail. This occurs because Earth's curved shape hides the rest of the boat from view until it is closer to you. As the boat slowly comes closer to you, more and more of its sail is visible. Finally, the entire boat is in view.

More proof of Earth's shape is that Earth casts a curved shadow on the Moon during a lunar eclipse, like the one shown in **Figure 2.** Something flat, like a book, casts a straight shadow, whereas objects with curved surfaces cast curved shadows.

✔ **Reading Check** *What object casts a shadow on the Moon during a lunar eclipse?*

Influence of Gravity The spherical shape of Earth and other planets is because of gravity. Gravity is a force that attracts all objects toward each other. The farther away the objects are, the weaker the pull of gravity is. Also, the larger an object is, the larger its gravitational pull is. A large object in space is spherical because gravity attracted particles toward its center while it was in a liquid or gaseous state. A spherical shape decreases the distance between particles in the object and its center. In this way, the potential energy due to gravity is less, and a stable shape results.

Even though Earth is round, it may seem flat to you. This is because Earth's surface is so large compared to your size.

Figure 2
Earth's spherical shape also is indicated by the curved shadow it casts on the Moon during a partial lunar eclipse.

Teacher FYI

Earth's rotation is slowing, which means our days are getting longer. Scientists hypothesize that the Moon's gravity drags on Earth, acting as a brake. Fossil evidence indicates that a day was only 22 hours long 400 million years ago. The length of day on Earth is increasing by about 16 seconds every million years.

Resource Manager

Chapter Resources Booklet
    Note-taking Worksheets, pp. 33–36
    Transparency Activity, p. 46

Earth Science Critical Thinking/Problem Solving, p. 23

② Teach

Earth's Physical Data

Caption Answer
Figure 1 the way objects slowly appear over the horizon as they get closer and slowly disappear beneath it as they move farther away; the curved shadow Earth casts on the Moon during a lunar eclipse

Activity

One proof of Earth's shape is the curved shadow it casts on the Moon during lunar eclipses. Have students demonstrate that only a spherical object would cast such a shadow. Give groups of three students a flashlight and three objects (a ball, a round flat object such as a plate, and a cylindrical object such as a can). Darken the room. Set up a screen on which students can view the shadows. Have students turn each object as they shine the light on it. Have students observe the shape of the shadow each object casts. They should find that only the spherical object always casts a curved shadow. L1 IS **Visual-Spatial**

✔ **Reading Check**

Answer Earth

Earth's Physical Data, continued

Quick Demo

Hold up a round balloon, and use your two hands to push in on it slightly at the top and bottom. Explain that Earth is shaped this way due to forces produced by the planet's rotation.

Motions of Earth

Quick Demo

Spin a top on a table in front of the class. Explain that the movement of the top is like Earth's rotation, and that the top and bottom tips of the top are like Earth's (imaginary) axis.

Extension

NOTE: This activity works best in winter or summer. Have students contact at least three friends or relatives who live in cities that are fairly far apart in latitude. These contacts should record the hours of daylight and darkness on a certain date. Have students locate the cities on a map. At each city's location, have students draw a circle graph comparing hours of daylight and darkness. Have students note the season and use the data to make a statement about how the ratio of daylight and darkness changes with latitude. L2 IS **Interpersonal**

✔ Reading Check

Answer Earth's axis

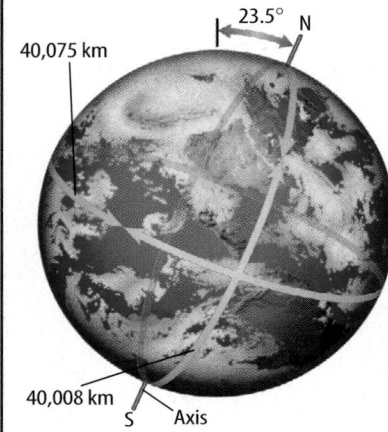

Figure 3
Earth is almost a sphere, but its circumference measurements vary slightly. The north-south circumference of Earth is smaller than the east-west circumference.

Table 1 Physical Properties of Earth

Diameter (pole to pole)	12,714 km
Diameter (equator)	12,756 km
Circumference (poles) (*distance around Earth through N and S poles*)	40,008 km
Circumference (equator) (*distance around Earth through equator*)	40,075 km
Mass	5.98×10^{24} kg
Average Density (*average mass per unit volume*)	5.52 g/cm^3
Average distance from the Sun	149,600,000 km
Period of rotation (1 day) (*spin on axis*)	23 h, 56 min
Period of revolution (1 year) (*path around the Sun*)	365 days, 6 h, 9 min

Almost a Sphere Earth is shaped like a sphere, but not a perfect one. It bulges slightly at the equator and is somewhat flattened around the poles. As shown in **Figure 3,** this causes Earth's circumference at the equator to be a bit larger than Earth's circumference as measured through the north and south poles. The circumference of Earth and some other physical properties are listed in **Table 1.**

Motions of Earth

Why the Sun appears to set each day and why the Moon and other objects in the sky appear to move from east to west is illustrated in **Figure 4.** Earth's geographic poles are located at the north and south ends of Earth's axis. Earth's **axis** is the imaginary line drawn from the north geographic pole through Earth to the south geographic pole. Earth spins around this imaginary line. The spinning of Earth on its axis, called **rotation,** causes you to experience day and night.

✔ Reading Check
What imaginary line runs through Earth's north and south geographic poles?

LAB DEMONSTRATION

Purpose to observe the cause of seasons
Materials globe, lamp with bare bulb
Safety Precautions Be careful around hot, unshielded light bulbs.

Procedure Hold the globe with its north pole tilted toward the light. Have students observe as you circle the light holding the globe in this position.

Expected Outcome Light strikes longer and more directly on the hemisphere tilted toward the light.

✔ Assessment

If this were Earth and the Sun, which part of Earth would get more light and heat? the hemisphere tilted toward the Sun **What would be the season in that hemisphere?** summer

Earth's Orbit Earth has another type of motion. As it rotates on its axis each day, Earth also moves along a path around the Sun. This motion of Earth around the Sun, shown in **Figure 4,** is called **revolution.** How many times does Earth rotate on its axis during one complete revolution around the Sun? Just as day and night are caused by rotation, what happens on Earth that is caused by its revolution?

Seasons A new year has begun. As days and weeks pass, you notice that the Sun remains in the sky later and later each day. You look forward to spring when you will be able to stay outside longer in the evening because the days become longer and longer. What is causing this change?

You learned earlier that Earth's rotation causes day and night. Earth also moves around the Sun, completing one revolution each year. Earth is really a satellite of the Sun, moving around it along a curved path called an **orbit.** The shape of Earth's orbit is an ellipse, which is rounded like a circle but somewhat flattened. As Earth moves along in its orbit, the way in which the Sun's light strikes Earth's surface changes.

Earth's elliptical orbit causes it to be closer to the Sun in January and farther from the Sun in July. But, the total amount of energy Earth receives from the Sun changes little during a year. However, the amount of energy that specific places on Earth receive varies quite a lot.

SCIENCE
Online

Research Visit the Glencoe Science Web site at **science.glencoe.com** for more information about Earth's rotation and revolution.

Figure 4
Earth's counterclockwise motions cause day and night and the seasons.

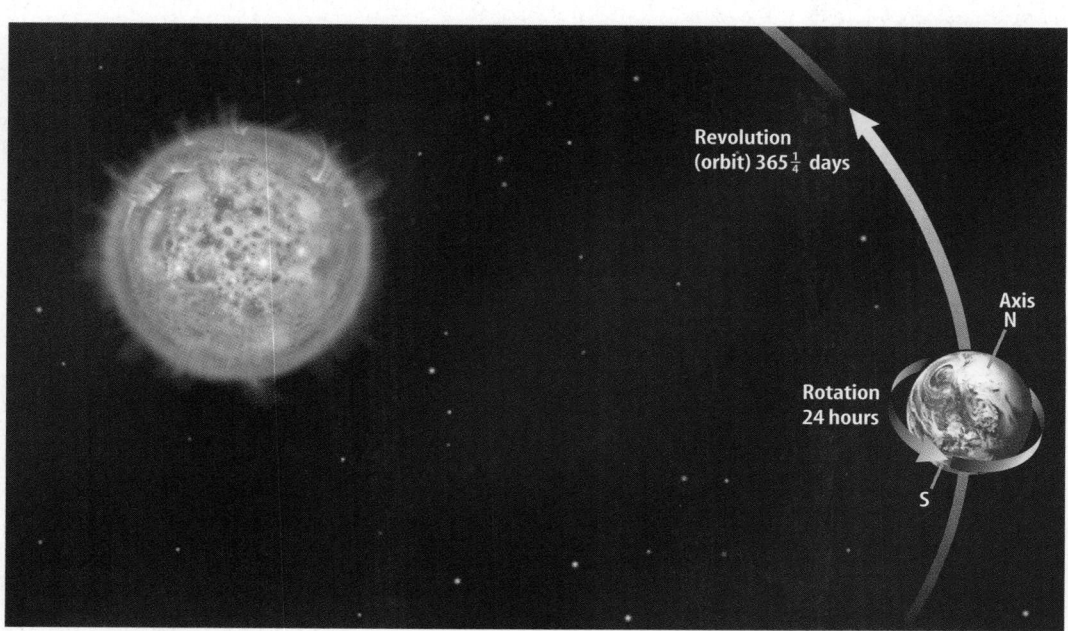

Revolution (orbit) $365\frac{1}{4}$ days

Axis N

Rotation 24 hours

S

Fun Fact

Earth travels at an average speed of 106,000 km (66,000 mi) per hour in orbit.

Text Question Answers

365; seasons and the passage of one year; Earth's tilt and revolution, which causes seasonal changes in the length of day and night

Discussion

Earth is closer to the Sun in January than in July. Does this surprise you? Why? Most students will say yes, as they would expect Earth to be closer in summer when it's warmer. **What does this tell you about the reasons for seasonal temperature changes?** Students should infer that seasonal temperature changes do not depend on Earth's distance from the Sun. Instead, Earth's tilt on its axis causes the amount of sunlight (and heat) locations get to change throughout the year, causing seasons.

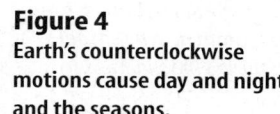
SCIENCE
Online
Internet Addresses

_____
_____
_____
_____

Explore the Glencoe Science Web site at **science.glencoe.com** to find out more about topics in this section.

Resource Manager

Chapter Resources Booklet
　　Enrichment, p. 30
　　Directed Reading for Content Mastery, pp. 19, 20

✔ **Active Reading**

Metacognition Journal In this strategy, each student analyzes his or her own thought processes. Have students divide the paper in half. On the left, have them record what they have learned about a topic. On the right, have them record the reason they learned it. Have students write a Metacognition Journal about Earth's physical data.

Use Science Words

Word Origins Share the origin of the word equinox, which comes from a Latin word meaning "equal" (aequus) "night" (nox). Have students determine the definitions of the following words that contain equi-, and write a sentence containing each one: *equidistant* (equal distance), *equilateral* (equal sides), *equiangular* (equal angles).

Visual Learning

Figure 6 When does the southern hemisphere experience summer? When it is tilted toward the Sun; this occurs during the northern hemisphere's winter.

Caption Answer

Figure 5 The part of Earth that is tilted toward the Sun stays in sunlight for a longer time as Earth rotates.

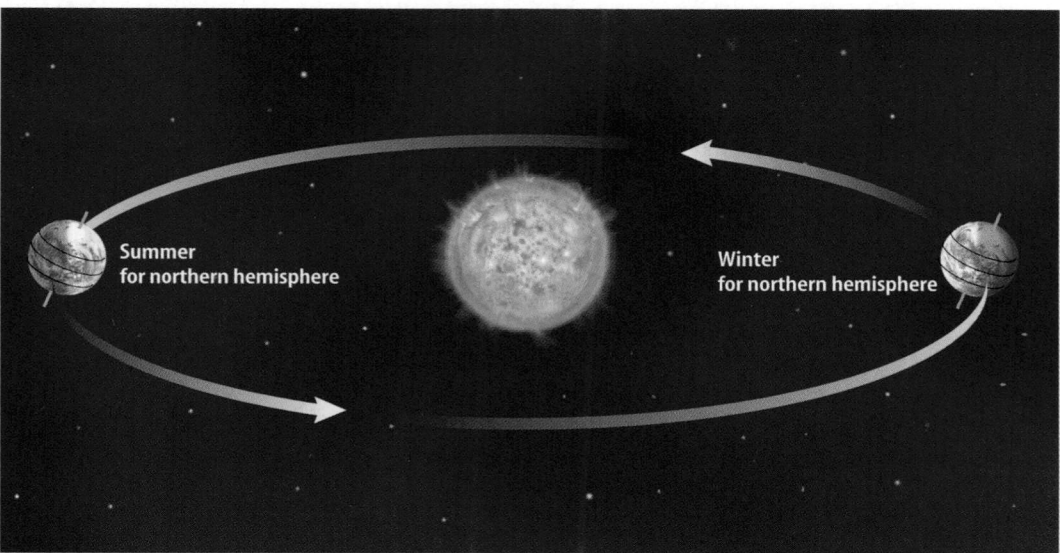

Figure 5
When the northern hemisphere is tilted toward the Sun, it experiences summer. *Why are days longer during the summer?*

Earth's Tilt You can observe one reason why the amount of energy from the Sun varies by moving a globe of Earth slowly around a light source. If you keep the globe tilted in one direction, you will see that the top half of the globe is tilted toward the light during part of its orbit and tilted away from the light during another part of its orbit.

Imagine a flat surface that contains Earth's orbit. Earth's axis forms a 23.5-degree angle with this imaginary surface, and always points to the North Star. Because of this, just as in your model, daylight hours are longer for the half of Earth, or hemisphere, tilted toward the Sun. Also, the Sun's rays hit that hemisphere more directly, at a higher angle. In other words, the Sun is higher in the sky for longer periods of time. Think again about when it gets dark outside at different times of the year. During which season do you notice longer days and shorter nights? As shown in **Figure 5,** this happens during summer.

Solstices Because of the tilt of Earth's axis, the Sun's position relative to Earth's equator changes. At two times during the year, the Sun reaches its greatest distance north or south of the equator and is directly over the Tropic of Cancer or the Tropic of Capricorn, as shown in **Figure 6.** These times are known as the summer and winter **solstices.** Summer solstice, which is about the longest day of the year, happens on June 21 or 22 for the northern hemisphere and on December 21 or 22 for the southern hemisphere. The opposite of this for each hemisphere is winter solstice, which is about the shortest day of the year.

Cultural Diversity

A Natural Calendar The Micmac tribe of Canada used natural cycles and events to mark seasons. They knew that geese returned from the south in early spring. Late fall was the time to hunt elk that had fattened up for winter. At year's end, it was possible to catch cod, which were plentiful beneath the ice. Have students list natural cycles or events that mark seasonal changes where they live. L2 P

Resource Manager

Chapter Resources Booklet
Transparency Activity, pp. 49–50
Reinforcement, p. 27
Science Inquiry Labs, p. 41

Equinoxes At **equinox,** (EE kwuh nahks) when the Sun is directly above Earth's equator, the lengths of day and night are nearly equal all over the world. During equinox, Earth's tilt is not toward or away from the Sun. In the northern hemisphere, spring equinox is March 21 or 22 and fall equinox is September 21 or 22. As you saw in **Table 1,** the time it takes for Earth to revolve around the Sun is not a whole number of days. Because of this, the dates for solstices and equinoxes change slightly over time.

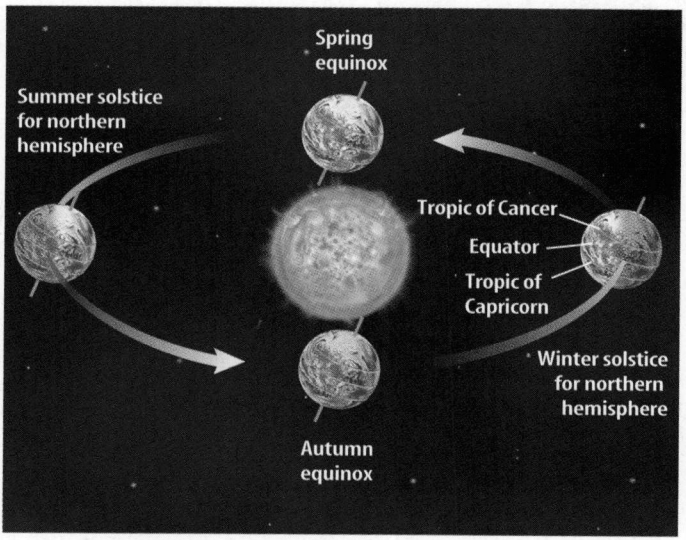

Spring equinox

Summer solstice for northern hemisphere

Tropic of Cancer
Equator
Tropic of Capricorn

Winter solstice for northern hemisphere

Autumn equinox

Figure 6
When the Sun is directly above the equator, day and night have nearly equal lengths.

Earth's Place in Space Earth is shaped much like a sphere. As Earth rotates on its axis, the Sun appears to rise and set in the sky. Earth's tilt and revolution around the Sun cause seasons to occur. In the next section, you will learn about Earth's nearest neighbor in space, the Moon. Later, you will learn about other planets in our solar system and how they compare with Earth.

Section ① Assessment

1. Which Earth motion causes a point on Earth to experience different amounts of energy from the Sun at different times of the year?

2. How many daylight hours do people in different places on Earth experience during an equinox?

3. Why is Earth's shape considered to be nearly spherical?

4. How do the rotation and revolution of Earth differ?

5. **Think Critically** In **Table 1,** why is Earth's distance from the Sun reported as an average distance?

Skill Builder Activities

6. **Making Models** Use a globe and an unshaded light source to illustrate how the tilt of the Earth on its axis, as it rotates and revolves around the Sun, causes changes in the length of a day. **For more help,** refer to the Science Skill Handbook.

7. **Communicating** Using data in **Table 1,** write a brief paragraph in your Science Journal that describes Earth's shape, size, and motions. Research the same physical properties of Venus. Write another paragraph that compares and contrasts Venus's properties with those of Earth. **For more help,** refer to the Science Skill Handbook.

Reteach

Hold a tilted Earth globe next to a lamp with a bare bulb. Be sure the tilt is neither toward nor away from the light source. Spin the globe. Explain that Earth is in this position—with neither the northern nor southern hemisphere tilted toward or away from the Sun—during an equinox. During an equinox, places on Earth (just as all places on the lit globe) receive approximately the same amount of daylight and darkness. [L1] [LS]
Visual-Spatial

Challenge

If Earth were not tilted, would it still experience seasons? Different areas of Earth would experience different climates based on latitude and topography, but there would be no seasonal changes.

Content Have students write songs with lyrics that explain the causes of changing seasons. Use **Performance Assessment in the Science Classroom,** p. 151.

Answers to Section Assessment

1. revolution
2. approximately 12 hours, because day and night are nearly equal
3. It is flattened only slightly at the poles and bulges slightly at the equator.
4. Rotation is turning on an axis; revolution is orbiting another body.
5. Earth's orbit is elliptical, so distance

from the Sun varies throughout the year.
6. Students can walk around the light source with the axis of the globe perpendicular to the floor. Then repeat with the globe tilted to illustrate that days are longer in the hemisphere tilted toward the light, shorter in the

one tilted away. Have them spin the globe to determine how the duration of day and night depends on the tilt of Earth's axis.
7. Earth is nearly spherical. Its equatorial circumference is 40,075 km. Its equatorial diameter is 12,756 km. Earth rotates once every 23 hrs, 56 mins,

making one day. It revolves once each 365-1/4 days, making one year. Venus is also nearly spherical. Its diameter is 12,104 km. Venus rotates once every 243 Earth days. It revolves once every 225 Earth days, making a day on Venus longer than its year.

1 Motivate

Bellringer Transparency

Display the Section Focus Transparency for Section 2. Use the accompanying Transparency Activity Master. L2 ELL

Tie to Prior Knowledge

How does the Moon's appearance change during a month? It appears to have different shapes as it goes through phases. **Is the Moon in the sky at the same time and place each day?** Its time of appearance and location vary.

As You Read

What You'll Learn

- **Identify** the Moon's surface features and interior.
- **Explain** the Moon's phases.
- **Explain** the causes of solar and lunar eclipses.
- **Compare** possible origins of the Moon.

Vocabulary

crater
moon phase
solar eclipse
lunar eclipse

Why It's Important

The Moon is Earth's closest neighbor in space.

The Moon's Surface and Interior

Take a good look at the surface of the Moon during the next full moon. You can see some of its large surface features, especially if you use binoculars or a small telescope. You will see dark-colored maria (MAR ee uh) and lighter-colored highland areas, as illustrated in **Figure 7.** Galileo first named the dark-colored regions *maria*, the Latin word for seas. They reminded Galileo of the oceans. Maria probably formed when lava flows from the Moon's interior flooded into large, bowl-like regions on the Moon's surface. These depressions may have formed early in the Moon's history. Collected during *Apollo* missions and then analyzed in laboratories on Earth, rocks from the maria are about 3.2 billion to 3.7 billion years old. They are the youngest rocks found on the Moon thus far.

The oldest moon rocks analyzed so far—dating to about 4.4 billion years old—were found in the lunar highlands. The lunar highlands are areas of the lunar surface with an elevation that is several kilometers higher than the maria. Some lunar highlands are located in the south-central region of the Moon.

Figure 7

On a clear night and especially during a full moon, you can observe some of the Moon's surface features. *How can you recognize the maria, lunar highlands, and craters?*

Section ✓Assessment Planner

PORTFOLIO	**CONTENT ASSESSMENT**
Life Science Integration, p. 487	Section, p. 494
PERFORMANCE ASSESSMENT	Challenge, p. 494
MiniLAB, p. 488	Chapter, pp. 510–511
Skill Builder Activities, p. 494	
See page 510 for more options.	

Craters As you look at the Moon's surface features, you will see craters. **Craters,** also shown in **Figure 7,** are depressions formed by large meteorites—space objects that strike the surface. As meteorites struck the Moon, cracks could have formed in the Moon's crust, allowing lava flows to fill in the large depressions. Craters are useful for determining how old parts of a moon's or a planet's surface are compared to other parts. The more abundant the craters are in a region, the older the surface is.

The Moon's Interior During the *Apollo* space program, astronauts left several seismographs (SIZE muh grafs) on the Moon. A seismograph is an instrument that detects tremors, or seismic vibrations. On Earth, seismographs are used to measure earthquake activity. On the Moon, they are used to study moonquakes. Based on the study of moonquakes, a model of the Moon's interior has been proposed, as illustrated in **Figure 8.** The Moon's crust is about 60 km thick on the side facing Earth and about 150 km thick on the far side. The difference in thickness is probably the reason fewer lava flows occurred on the far side of the Moon. Below the crust, a solid layer called the mantle may extend 900 km to 950 km farther down. A soft layer of mantle may continue another 500 km deeper still. Below this may be an iron-rich, solid core with a radius of about 300–450 km.

Like the Moon, Earth also has a dense, iron core. However, the Moon's core is small compared to its total volume. Compared with Earth, the Moon is most like Earth's outer two layers—the mantle and the crust—in density. This supports a hypothesis that the Moon may have formed from material ejected from Earth's mantle and crust.

Motions of the Moon

The same side of the Moon is always facing Earth. You can verify this by examining the Moon in the sky night after night. You'll see that bright and dark surface features remain in the same positions. Does this mean that the Moon doesn't turn on an axis as it moves around Earth? Next, explore why the same side of the Moon always faces Earth.

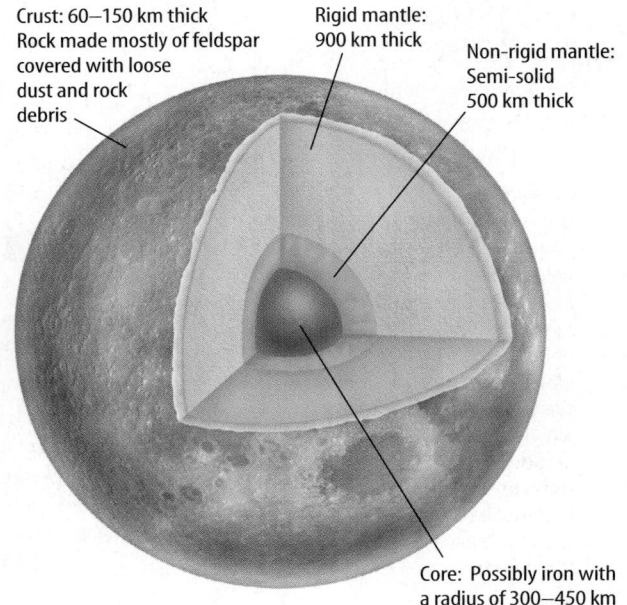

Crust: 60–150 km thick Rock made mostly of feldspar covered with loose dust and rock debris

Rigid mantle: 900 km thick

Non-rigid mantle: Semi-solid 500 km thick

Core: Possibly iron with a radius of 300–450 km

Figure 8
The small size of the Moon's core suggests it formed from a part of the crust and mantle of Earth.

Life Science
INTEGRATION

Research from space probes indicates that conditions on some areas of the Moon might make Moon colonies possible someday. In your Science Journal, write a brief summary of what might have been discovered and how it would be useful to a Moon colony.

Science Journal

Earth Craters Tell students that Earth has craters, too. Some of these craters were caused by large meteorites that hit Earth. Have students describe in their Science Journals why they think craters are less noticeable on Earth's surface than they are on the Moon's surface. Because of Earth's atmosphere, fewer meteorites hit Earth, and erosion destroys most impact craters.

The Moon's Surface and Interior

Caption Answer
Figure 7 Maria are large dark areas, lunar highlands are light areas, and craters are circular depressions.

Life Science
INTEGRATION

Recent lunar probes have found what scientists believe to be frozen water at the Moon's poles. If melted, this ice could provide a water source for Moon colonies. **Why might people want to set up Moon colonies?** Possible answers: to extract resources, to study space, as a stepping-stone to other planets

IDENTIFYING
Misconceptions

Some students may think the Moon's far side is always dark. Explain that the Moon's far side receives as much sunlight as the side we see. It just remains turned away from Earth.

Make a Model

Have students make a cross-section model of the Moon's interior with clay or cut paper, based on **Figure 8.** Students can also choose to make a clay model of a part of the Moon's surface showing craters, maria, and highlands.

Motions of the Moon

Mini LAB

Modeling the Moon's Rotation

Procedure

1. Use **masking tape** to place a large X on a **basketball** that will represent the Moon.
2. Ask two students to sit in **chairs** in the center of the room.
3. Place other students around the outer edge of the room.
4. Slowly walk completely around the two students in the center while holding the basketball so that the side with the X always faces the two students.

Analysis

1. Ask the two students in the center whether they think the basketball turned around as you circled them. Then ask several students along the outer edge of the room whether they think the basketball turned around.
2. Based on these observations, infer whether or not the Moon rotates as it moves around Earth. Explain your answer.

Revolution and Rotation of the Moon The Moon revolves around Earth at an average distance of about 384,000 km. It takes 27.3 days for the Moon to complete one orbit around Earth. The Moon also takes 27.3 days to rotate once on its axis. Because these two motions of the Moon take the same amount of time, the same side of the Moon is always facing Earth. Examine **Figure 9** to see how this works.

✓ Reading Check
Why does the same side of the Moon always face Earth?

However, these two lunar motions aren't exactly the same during the Moon's 27.3-day rotation-and-revolution period. Because the Moon's orbit is an ellipse, it moves faster when it's closer to Earth and slower when it's farther away. During one orbit, observers are able to see a little more of the eastern side of the Moon and then a little more of the western side.

Moon Phases If you ever watched the Moon for several days in a row, you probably noticed how its shape and position in the sky change. You learned that the Moon rotates on its axis and revolves around Earth. Motions of the Moon cause the regular cycle of change in the way the Moon looks to an observer on Earth.

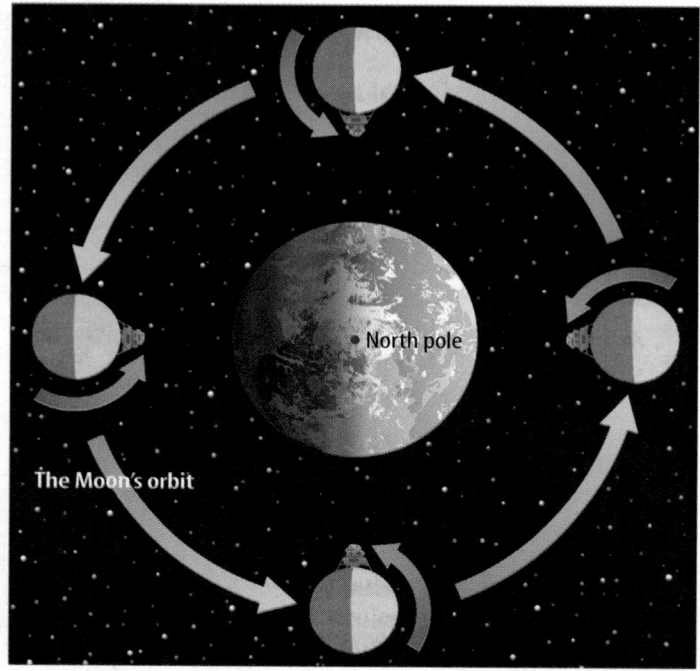

Figure 9
Observers viewing the Moon from Earth always see the same side of the Moon. This is caused by two separate motions of the Moon that take the same amount of time.

488 CHAPTER 17 Earth in Space

The Sun Lights the Moon You see the Moon because it reflects sunlight. As the Moon revolves around Earth, the Sun always lights one half of it. However, you don't always see the entire lighted part of the Moon. What you do see are phases, or different portions of the lighted part. **Moon phases,** illustrated in **Figure 10,** are the changing views of the Moon as seen from Earth.

New Moon and Waxing Phases New moon occurs when the Moon is positioned between Earth and the Sun. You can't see any of a new moon, because the lighted half of the Moon is facing the Sun. The new moon rises and sets with the Sun and never appears in the night sky.

Figure 10
The amount of the Moon's surface that looks bright to observers on Earth changes during a complete cycle of the Moon's phases. *What makes the Moon's surface appear so bright?*

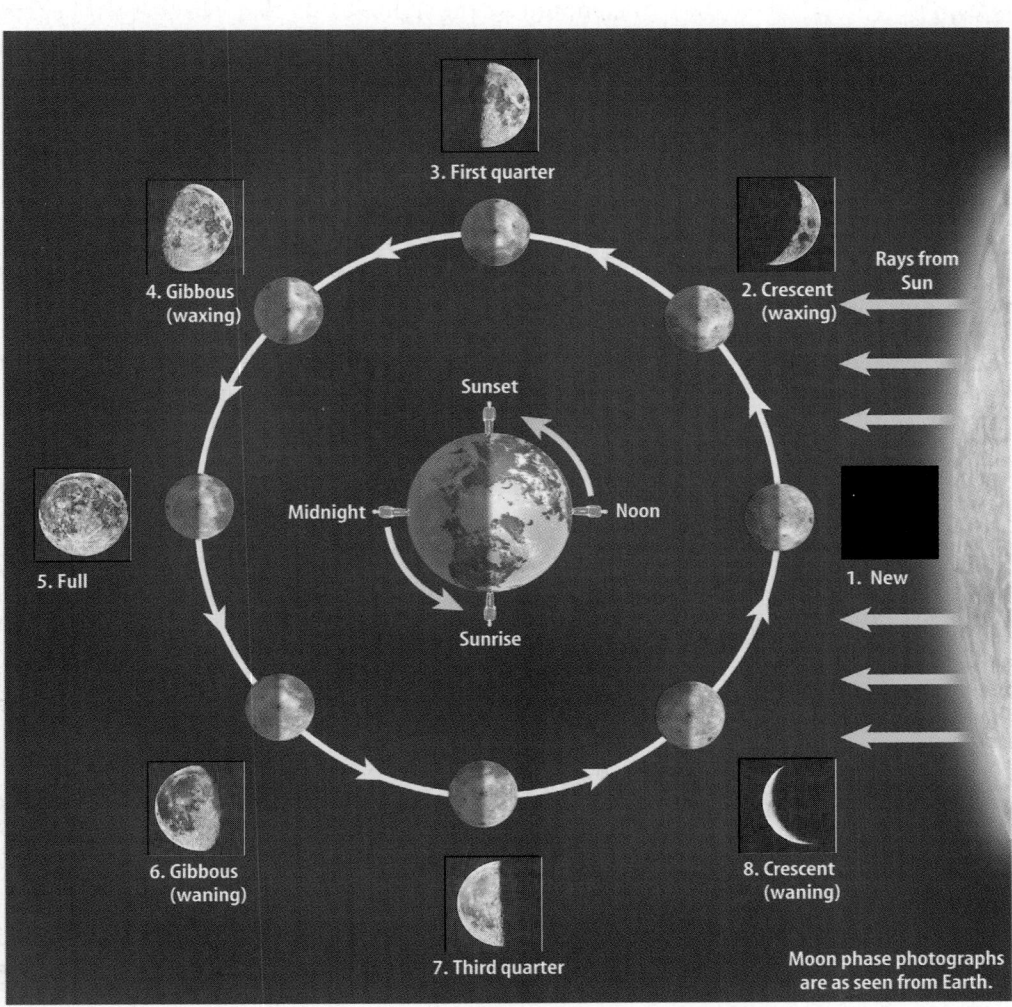

3. First quarter
4. Gibbous (waxing)
2. Crescent (waxing)
Rays from Sun
Sunset
Midnight
Noon
5. Full
1. New
Sunrise
6. Gibbous (waning)
8. Crescent (waning)
7. Third quarter

Moon phase photographs are as seen from Earth.

Activity

Have students work in pairs to make sets of flip cards showing the Moon's phases. Have them cut out 12 cards, each of which is 7.5 cm square. Direct them to draw the Moon's eight major phases **(Figure 10)** and some stages in between on one side of the cards. Have students connect the cards at the side using a heavy-duty stapler. When they flip the cards, they will see the Moon's phases change. L1
Visual-Spatial

Quick Demo

Darken the room to demonstrate why we see phases of the Moon. Put a light source at one end of the room and seat students in the center. Circle the room with a basketball representing the Moon. Students will see that although half the ball is always lighted, they see only a part of its lighted side depending on where the ball is.
Visual-Spatial

Activity

Have students collect information about the phases of the Moon by observing, sketching, and describing them for several months. Have them analyze the data in their journals to determine the pattern that emerges.

Inclusion Strategies

Behaviorally Disordered Have students research myths about the full Moon. After gathering the information, encourage students to compose a song or poem about the myths they have researched. After previewing their work, invite the students to share their songs or poems with the class. L1 **Auditory-Musical**

Curriculum Connection

Literature Have students look for poems or short stories written about the Moon and its phases. Once students have located the literature, have them write in their Science Journals a summary of their interpretation of the selection. L2 **Linguistic**

Motions of the Moon, continued

SCIENCE
Online

Internet Addresses

_____
_____
_____
_____

Explore the Glencoe Science Web site at science.glencoe.com to find out more about topics in this section.

Discussion

After full Moon, will the phases be waxing or waning? Why? Waning; the lighted portion of the Moon that we see will be getting smaller. **Which phase follows a full Moon?** waning gibbous

Fun Fact

During new Moon, the Moon's face is dimly lit by reflected light from Earth called earthshine. During other phases (except full Moon) the line between the sunlit and dark parts of the Moon's face is called the terminator.

✔ Reading Check

Answer The phases that occur as the amount of the Moon's lighted side seen from Earth decreases.

Caption Answer

The complete cycle of lunar phases takes longer. It takes about two days longer for the Earth, Moon, and Sun to line up at new moon.

SCIENCE
Online

Research Visit the Glencoe Science Web site at **science.glencoe.com** for more information about phases of the Moon.

Figure 11
It takes longer for a complete Moon phase cycle than a complete Moon revolution. The revolution of Earth and the Moon around the Sun lengthens the path needed for the Moon, Earth, and the Sun to line up again at new moon. *Which takes longer, a complete cycle of lunar phases or a complete orbit of the Moon around Earth? How does the revolution of the Earth-Moon system around the Sun cause this difference in time?*

Waxing Moon Shortly after new moon, more and more of its lighted side faces Earth and becomes visible. The phases are said to be waxing, or growing in size. About 24 hours after new moon, you can see a thin sliver of the lighted side. This phase is called waxing crescent. As the Moon continues its trip around Earth, you eventually can see half of the lighted side. This phase is first quarter and occurs about a week after new moon.

The Moon's phases continue to wax through waxing gibbous (GIHB us) and then full moon—the phase when you can see all of the lighted side. At full moon, Earth is between the Sun and the Moon.

Full Moon and Waning Phases After passing full moon, the amount of the lighted side that can be seen begins to decrease. Now the phases are said to be waning. Waning gibbous occurs just after full moon. Next comes third quarter when you can see only half of the lighted side. The phases continue to wane, and waning crescent occurs just before another new moon. Once again you see a small slice of the lighted side.

✔ Reading Check   *What are the waning phases of the Moon?*

The complete cycle of the Moon's phases takes about 29.5 days. However, you will recall that the Moon takes only 27.3 days to revolve once around Earth. **Figure 11** explains the time difference between these two lunar cycles. Earth's revolution around the Sun causes the time lag. It takes the Moon about two days longer to align itself again between Earth and the Sun at new moon.

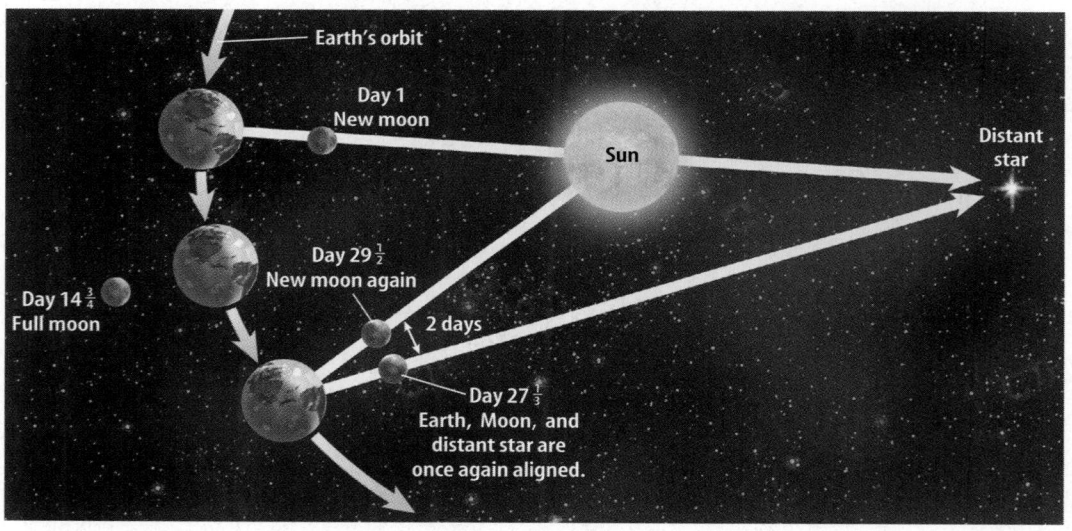

Earth's orbit

Day 1
New moon

Sun

Distant star

Day 29½
New moon again

Day 14¾
Full moon

2 days

Day 27⅓
Earth, Moon, and distant star are once again aligned.

Cultural Diversity

Astronomy in Ancient China Centuries ago, Chinese emperors employed astronomers to study the movements of the stars and planets. They created complex instruments for observing the sky and kept records of eclipses and comets. Have interested students research and report on tools used by these ancient Chinese scientists.

Resource Manager

Chapter Resources Booklet
  Directed Reading for Content Mastery, p. 20
Cultural Diversity, p. 29

Eclipses

You can see other effects of the Moon's revolution than just the changes in its phases. Sometimes during new and full moon, shadows cast by one object will fall on another. While walking along on a sunny day, have you ever noticed how a passing airplane can cast a shadow on you? On a much larger scale, the Moon can do this too, when it lines up directly with the Sun. When this happens, the Moon can cast its shadow all the way to Earth. Earth also can cast its shadow onto the Moon during a full moon. When shadows are cast in these ways, eclipses occur.

Eclipses occur only when the Sun, the Moon, and Earth are lined up perfectly. Because the Moon's orbit is tilted at a different angle than Earth's orbit, the Moon's shadow most often misses Earth, and eclipses happen only a few times each year.

Solar Eclipses During new moon, if Earth moves into the Moon's shadow, a **solar eclipse** occurs. As shown in **Figure 12,** the Moon blocks sunlight from reaching a portion of Earth's surface. Only areas on Earth in the Moon's umbra, or the darkest part of its shadow, experience a total solar eclipse. Those areas in the penumbra, or lighter part of the shadow, experience a partial solar eclipse. During a total solar eclipse, the sky becomes dark and stars can be seen easily. Because Earth rotates, a solar eclipse lasts only a few minutes in any one location.

Figure 12
A Solar eclipses occur when the Sun, the Moon, and Earth are lined up in a specific way.
B Eclipses happen because the Moon casts a shadow on Earth.
WARNING: *Never look directly at a solar eclipse. Only observe solar eclipses indirectly.*

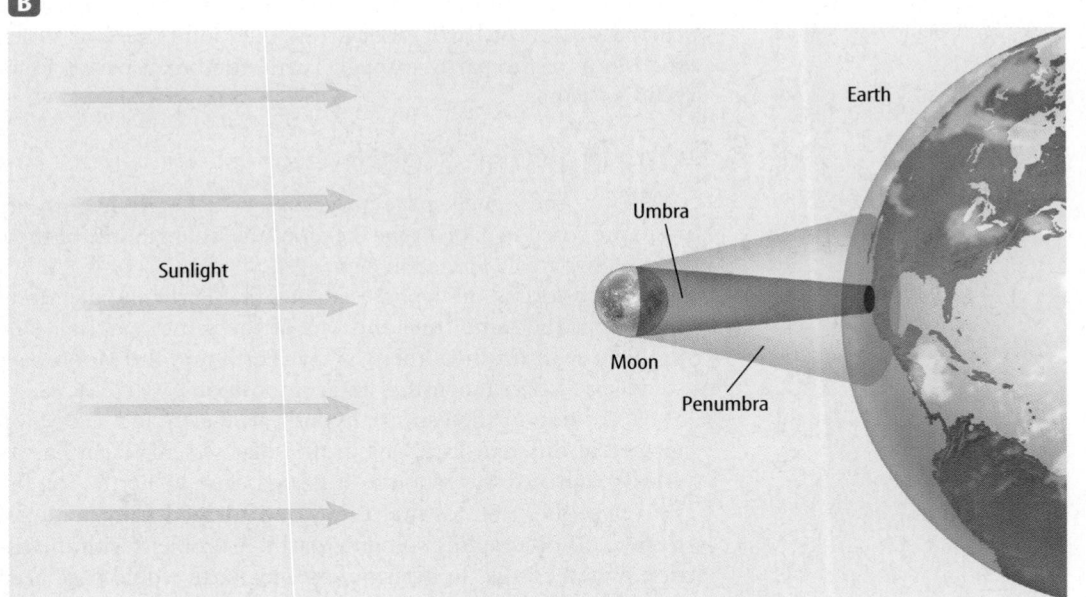

Eclipses

Use Science Words

Word Origins Eclipses can occur only if the Moon, the Sun, and Earth are in a straight line, which is a state known as *syzygy* (pronounced **sih•zuh•gee**). Have students find the origin of this word. Syzygy comes from the Greek word *syzygos*, which means "yoked together."

Quick Demo

Place a light source (the Sun), such as an unshaded lamp, at the front of the room. Hold a tennis ball (the Moon) in front of the light so its shadow falls on one student (Earth). **Which type of eclipse does this resemble?** solar Now take the ball to the back of the room and have the same student stand so that he or she blocks light falling on the tennis ball. The entire tennis ball will be in the student's shadow. **Which type of eclipse does this resemble?** lunar

Visual Learning

Figure 12 Which phase of the Moon occurs during the type of eclipse shown here? The Moon is between the Sun and Earth, with its lighted side facing away from Earth, so this is new Moon phase.

Curriculum Connection

Literature Long ago, total solar eclipses were viewed as frightening events. Have students write a short story about the occurrence of a total solar eclipse on a bright sunny day thousands of years ago. Have the story describe what people were doing when the eclipse occurred, what they observed, and how they reacted. Have students share their stories with the class.

Teacher FYI

The chances of seeing a total solar eclipse in any one spot on Earth are slim. The people in Greenland will have the chance on August 1, 2008. People in parts of the contiguous 48 states will not get the chance until August 21, 2017.

Visual Learning

Figure 13 Why are lunar eclipses only possible during a full moon? That is the only time the moon can pass through Earth's shadow. During the other phases, the Moon is either in front of or next to Earth.

Fun Fact

The full Moon often looks red during a lunar eclipse because some of the Sun's light is bent by Earth's atmosphere as the light travels toward the Moon. The red color appears because Earth's atmosphere scatters the wavelengths of other colors in sunlight more than it does red.

Origin of the Moon

Discussion

Draw students' attention to the fission hypothesis of Moon formation. Tell students that some scientists thought that the material that became the Moon could have come from the area of the Pacific Ocean. **Why might a scientist have come up with this hypothesis?** The Pacific is Earth's largest and deepest ocean, making it an area from which material might have come.

Teacher **FYI**

The diameter of Earth's Moon is about one-fourth the diameter of Earth—a much larger ratio of moon to planet than most other moons and planets in the solar system. For this reason, Earth and the Moon are sometimes considered a double planet.

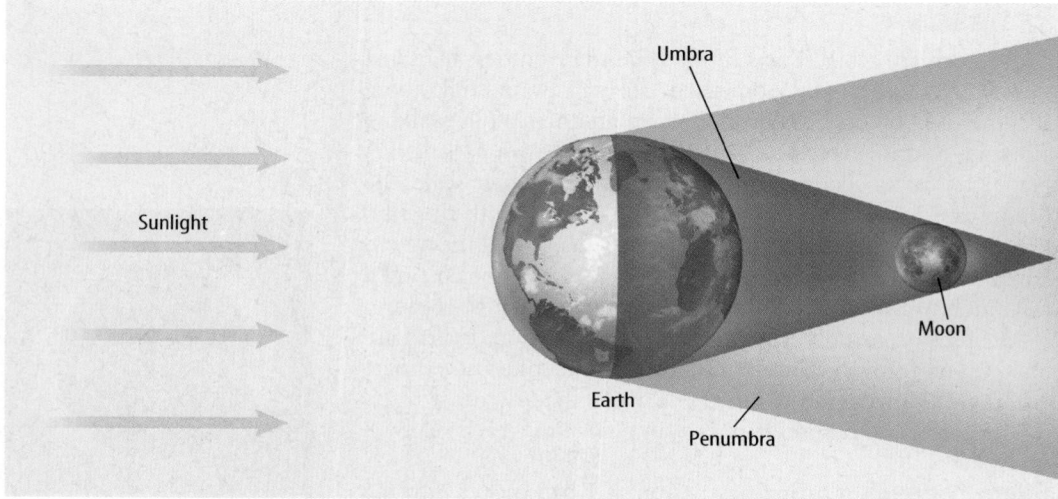

Figure 13
Lunar eclipses occur when the Sun, the Moon, and Earth line up so that Earth's shadow is cast upon a full moon. When the entire Moon is eclipsed, anyone on Earth who can see a full moon can see the lunar eclipse.

Lunar Eclipses A **lunar eclipse,** illustrated in **Figure 13,** occurs when the Sun, Earth, and the Moon are lined up such that the full moon moves into Earth's shadow. Direct sunlight is blocked from reaching the Moon. When the Moon is in the darkest part of Earth's shadow, a total lunar eclipse occurs.

During a total lunar eclipse, the full moon darkens. Because some sunlight refracts through Earth's atmosphere, the Moon appears to be deep red. As the Moon moves out of the umbra and into the penumbra, or lighter shadow, you can see the curved shadow of Earth move across the Moon's surface. When the Moon passes partly through Earth's umbra, a partial lunar eclipse occurs.

Origin of the Moon

Before the *Apollo* space program, several early hypotheses were proposed to explain the origin of the Moon. Some of these hypotheses are illustrated in **Figure 14.**

The co-formation hypothesis states that Earth and the Moon formed at the same time and out of the same material. One problem with this hypothesis is that Earth and the Moon have somewhat different densities and compositions.

According to the capture hypothesis, Earth and the Moon formed at different locations in the solar system. Then Earth's gravity captured the Moon as it passed close to Earth. The fission hypothesis states that the Moon formed from material thrown off of a rapidly spinning Earth. A problem with the fission hypothesis lies in determining why Earth would have been spinning so fast.

Science Journal

Observing the Moon Have students keep an observation log of the Moon over a two-week period. They should record in their Science Journals the Moon's phase, altitude above the horizon (a fist equals 10 degrees at arm's length), general appearance, and any special features visible. Students should also note the time and sky conditions. Students may not realize that the Moon is sometimes visible during the day. Challenge students to make some observations during daylight hours, and to record these observations in their Science Journals as well. L2 **LS** **Naturalist**

NATIONAL GEOGRAPHIC

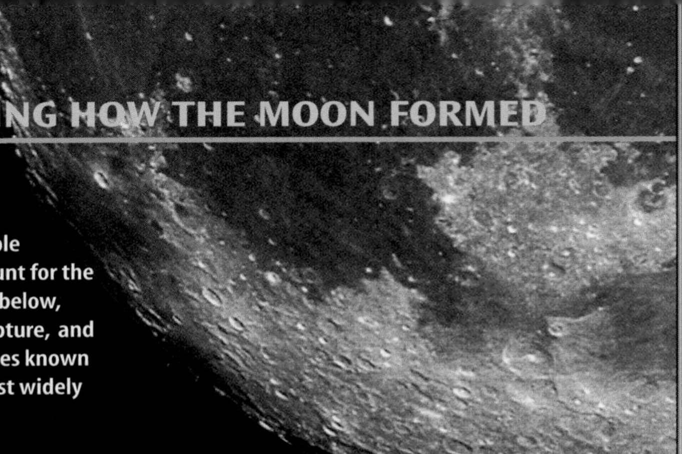

Figure 14

Scientists have proposed several possible explanations, or hypotheses, to account for the formation of Earth's Moon. As shown below, these include the co-formation, fission, capture, and collision hypotheses. The latter—sometimes known as the giant impact hypothesis—is the most widely accepted today.

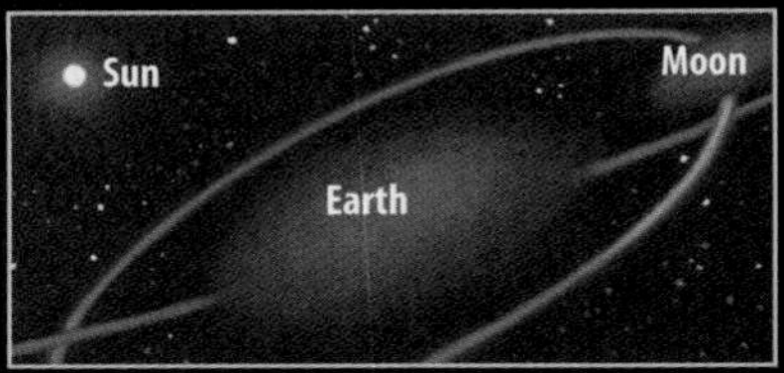

▲ **CO-FORMATION** Earth and the Moon form at the same time from a vast cloud of cosmic matter that condenses into the bodies of the solar system.

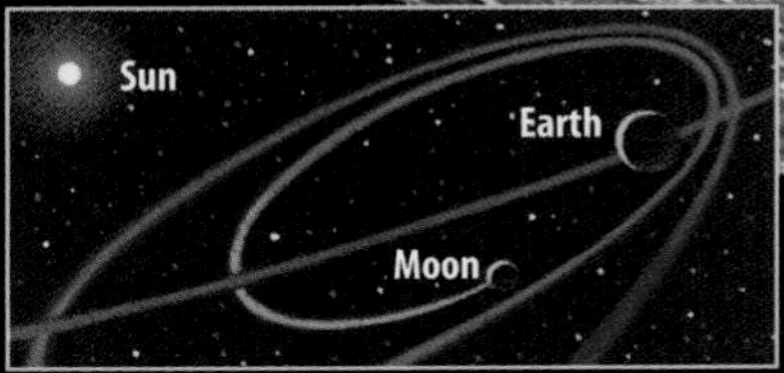

▲ **CAPTURE** Earth's gravity captures the Moon into Earth orbit as the Moon passes close to Earth.

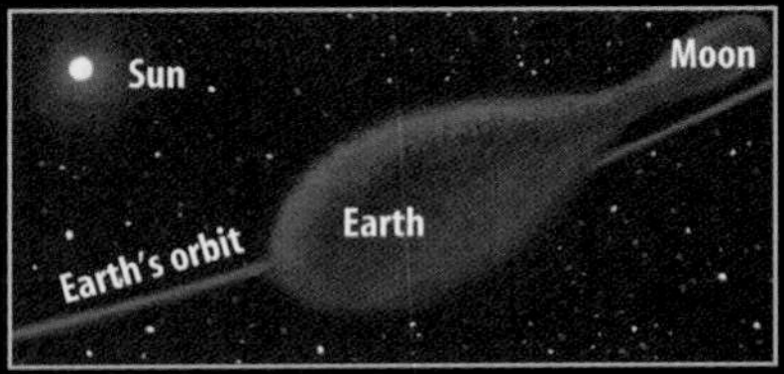

▲ **FISSION** A rapidly spinning molten Earth tears in two. The smaller blob of matter enters into orbit as the Moon.

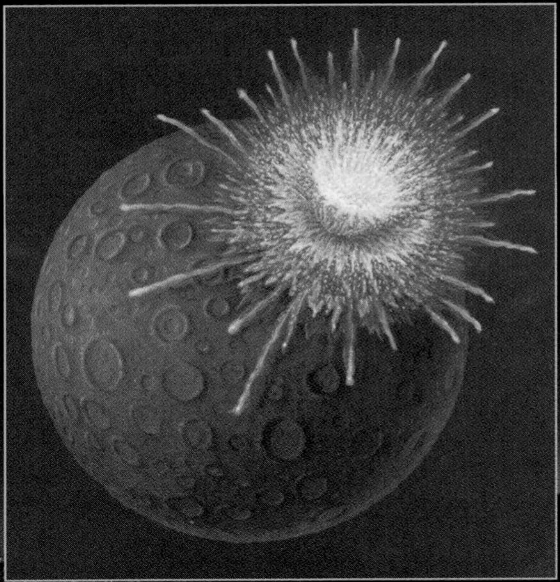

▲ **COLLISION** A Mars-sized body collides with the primordial Earth. The colossal impact smashes off sufficient debris from Earth to form the Moon.

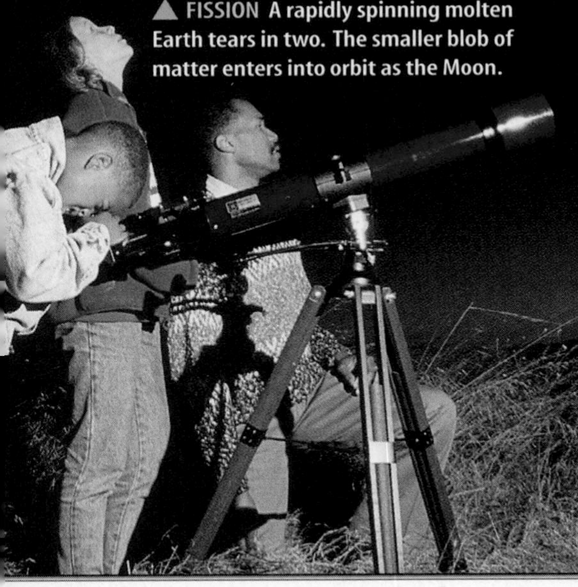

493

Visualizing How the Moon Formed

Have students examine the pictures and read the captions. Then ask the following questions.

Why have different hypotheses been proposed for the Moon's formation? Possible answer: No one existed to observe how it happened; scientists interpret information differently; hypotheses may change as new information is gathered.

Explain to students that evidence indicates the moons of Mars were once asteroids traveling through the solar system. **Which hypothesis of Earth's Moon formation is this similar to? Why?** The capture hypothesis because the asteroids would have been captured by Mars's gravity.

Activity

Organize the class into four groups. Have each group research one of the hypotheses proposed for the formation of the Moon. Each group should use clay to make three-dimensional models depicting the hypothesis. They should present the models to the class, pointing out reasons scientists accept or reject the hypothesis.

Extension

Have interested students write a science fiction story about a person who traveled back in time to witness the collision of a Mars-size body with Earth that resulted in the Moon's formation.

Resource Manager

Chapter Resources Booklet
Lab Activity, pp. 9–11

Discussion

Explain that the *Apollo* space-craft always carried three astronauts. Two would descend to the lunar surface in a landing vehicle, while the third astronaut remained in the command module in orbit around the Moon. **Why might one astronaut always have been left in orbit?** Students should infer that an astronaut was needed aboard the orbiting command module to control the spacecraft and to help the lunar module dock with the command module when it returned.

3 Assess

Reteach

Have students model solar and lunar eclipses using three different-sized balls representing the Sun, Earth, and the Moon. L1
 **Visual-Spatial**

Challenge

Astronauts who visited the Moon returned with rock samples. Tell students to find one fact that scientists who studied the samples have discovered about the Moon. Collect the facts and list them on the board. Possible answer: The rocks range in age from about 3.2 billion years in the maria to nearly 4.6 billion years in the highlands.

✓Assessment

Content Ask students why Earth did not totally break up when the Mars-sized body hit it. The collision was a glancing blow. Use **PASC,** p. 89.

Figure 15
Moon rocks collected during the *Apollo* space program provide clues about how the Moon formed.

Collision Hypothesis A lot of uncertainty still exists about the origin of the Moon. However, the collection and study of moon rocks, shown in **Figure 15,** brought evidence to support one recent hypothesis. This hypothesis, summarized in **Figure 14,** involves a great collision. When Earth was about 100 million years old, a Mars-sized space object may have collided with Earth. Such an object would have broken through Earth's crust and plunged toward the core. This collision would have thrown large amounts of gas and debris into orbit around Earth. Within about 1,000 years the gas and debris then could have condensed to form the Moon. The collision hypothesis is strengthened by the fact that Earth and the Moon have different densities. The Moon's density is similar to material that would have been thrown off Earth's mantle and crust when the object collided with Earth.

Earth is the third planet from the Sun. Along with the Moon, Earth could be considered a double planet. In the next section you will learn about other planets in the solar system. Some have properties similar to Earth's—others are different from Earth.

Section 2 Assessment

1. Which phase of the Moon occurs when Earth is located between the Moon and the Sun?

2. Describe the arrangement of the Moon, the Sun, and Earth during a solar eclipse. How is this different from the arrangement during a lunar eclipse?

3. Why are more maria found on the side of the Moon facing Earth than on the opposite side?

4. Describe evidence that supports the collision hypothesis on how the Moon formed.

5. **Think Critically** Explain why more people observe a total lunar eclipse than a total solar eclipse.

Skill Builder Activities

6. **Recognizing Cause and Effect** Answer these questions about the Moon orbiting Earth. **For more help, refer to the Science Skill Handbook.**
   a. Which type of eclipse may occur when the Moon moves between the Sun and Earth?
   b. How does the Moon's orbit around Earth cause the observed cyclical phases of the Moon? What role does the Sun play?

7. **Using an Electronic Spreadsheet** Using a spreadsheet, make a table comparing hypotheses about the origin of the Moon. Include strengths and weaknesses for each hypothesis. **For more help, refer to the Technology Skill Handbook.**

Answers to Section Assessment

1. full Moon
2. The Moon is between the Sun and Earth during a solar eclipse. Earth is between the Sun and Moon during a lunar eclipse.
3. Lunar crust is thicker on the side away from Earth. Lava would not have been able to get to the surface as easily.
4. The density of Moon material is similar to the material that would

have been thrown into orbit from Earth's crust and mantle.
5. Everyone on Earth's night side can see a lunar eclipse. You must be in the small shadow the Moon casts on Earth to see a total solar eclipse.
6. As the Moon orbits Earth the amount of the illuminated portion visible from Earth changes, causing the

phases. The light we see is sunlight reflected from the Moon's surface.
7. Possible answer: *capture:* pro–explains some of the composition differences; **con**–a collision or the flinging of the Moon into a different orbit more likely; *coformation/ double/planet:* pro–explains composition similarity, but not entirely; **con**–differences in rotation

rates and why Moon materials didn't fall back to Earth unexplained; *fission:* **pro**–explains why Moon's composition is similar to Earth's mantle; **con**–no reason for changing rotation rates; *impact:* pro–explains the way Earth spins, why Earth has a larger metallic core than the Moon; **con**–seems improbable, but best explanation so far

Activity

Viewing the Moon

The position of the Moon in the sky varies as the phases of the Moon change. Do you know when you might be able to see the Moon during daylight hours? How will viewing the Moon through a telescope be different from viewing it with the unaided eye?

What You'll Investigate
What features of the Moon are visible when viewed through a telescope?

Materials
telescope   drawing pencils
drawing paper

Goals
- **Determine** when you may be able to observe the Moon during the day.
- Use a telescope to observe the Moon.
- **Draw** a picture of the Moon's features as seen through the telescope.

Safety Precautions
Never look directly at the Sun. It can damage your eyes.

Procedure

1. Using your own observations, books about astronomy, or other resource materials, determine when the Moon may be visible to you during the day. You will need to find out during which phases the Moon is up during daylight hours, and where in the sky you likely will be able to view it. You will also need to find out when the Moon will be in those phases in the near future.
2. **Observe** the Moon with your unaided eye. Draw the features that you are able to see.

3. Using a telescope, observe the Moon again. Adjust the focus of the telescope so that you can see as many features as possible.
4. **Draw** a new picture of the Moon's features.

Conclude and Apply

1. **Describe** what you learned about when the Moon is visible in the sky. If a friend wanted to know when to try to see the Moon during the day next month, what would you say?
2. **Describe** the differences between how the Moon looked with the naked eye and through the telescope. Did the Moon appear to be the same size when you looked at it both ways?
3. What features were you able to see through the telescope that were not visible with the unaided eye?
4. Was there anything else different about the way the Moon looked through the telescope? Explain your answer.
5. **Identify** some of the types of features that you included in your drawings.

Communicating Your Data

The next time you notice the Moon when you are with your family or friends, talk about when the Moon is visible in the sky and the different features that are visible.

ACTIVITY 495

Communicating Your Data

Encourage students to create a phases of the Moon chart for reference.

Activity

BENCH TESTED

Purpose Students observe the Moon and lunar features through a telescope. L2

Process Skills Observing, identifying, inferring

Time Required One 45 minute class period for research; one 45 minute period for observation

Safety Precautions Caution students never to view the Sun with the unaided eye or a telescope.

Teaching Strategy If the Moon is visible during the morning hours host a lunar viewing party.

Conclude and Apply

1. The Moon rises 50 minutes later each night. To determine when it can be viewed during the day, a chart of Moon phases could be consulted.
2. The Moon and its features were magnified and showed more detail.
3. The flatness of the mare is better seen, and the crater covered highlands can be viewed. The terminator can be distinguished, and the long shadows formed at this line are visible. The shadows of lunar mountains can be observed throughout the field of view as well.
4. The Moon and its features are magnified, and it appears brighter.
5. Answers will vary.

Assessment

Performance Ask students to research the origin of the word *lunacy*. Lunacy meant "to be possessed by the Moon" in the belief that the Moon influenced the behavior of people. Use **PASC,** p. 175.

SECTION

Our Solar System

As You Read

What You'll Learn
- **List** the important characteristics of inner planets.
- **Identify** how other inner planets compare and contrast with Earth.
- **List** the important characteristics of outer planets.

Vocabulary
solar system   comet
astronomical unit   nebula
asteroid

Why It's Important
Learning about other planets helps you understand Earth and the formation of our solar system.

Size of the Solar System

Measurements in space are difficult to make because space is so vast. Even our own solar system is extremely large. Our **solar system,** illustrated in **Figure 16,** is composed of the Sun, planets, asteroids, comets, and other objects in orbit around the Sun. How would you begin to measure something this large? If you are measuring distance on Earth, kilometers work fine, but not for measuring huge distances in space. Earth, for example, is about 150,000,000 km from the Sun. This distance is referred to as 1 **astronomical unit,** or 1 AU. Jupiter, the largest planet in the solar system, is more than 5 AU from the Sun. Astronomical units can be used to measure distances between objects within the solar system. Even larger units are used to measure distances between stars.

Located at the center of the solar system is a star you know as the Sun. The Sun is an enormous ball of gas that produces energy by fusing hydrogen into helium in its core. More than 99 percent of all matter in the solar system is contained in the Sun.

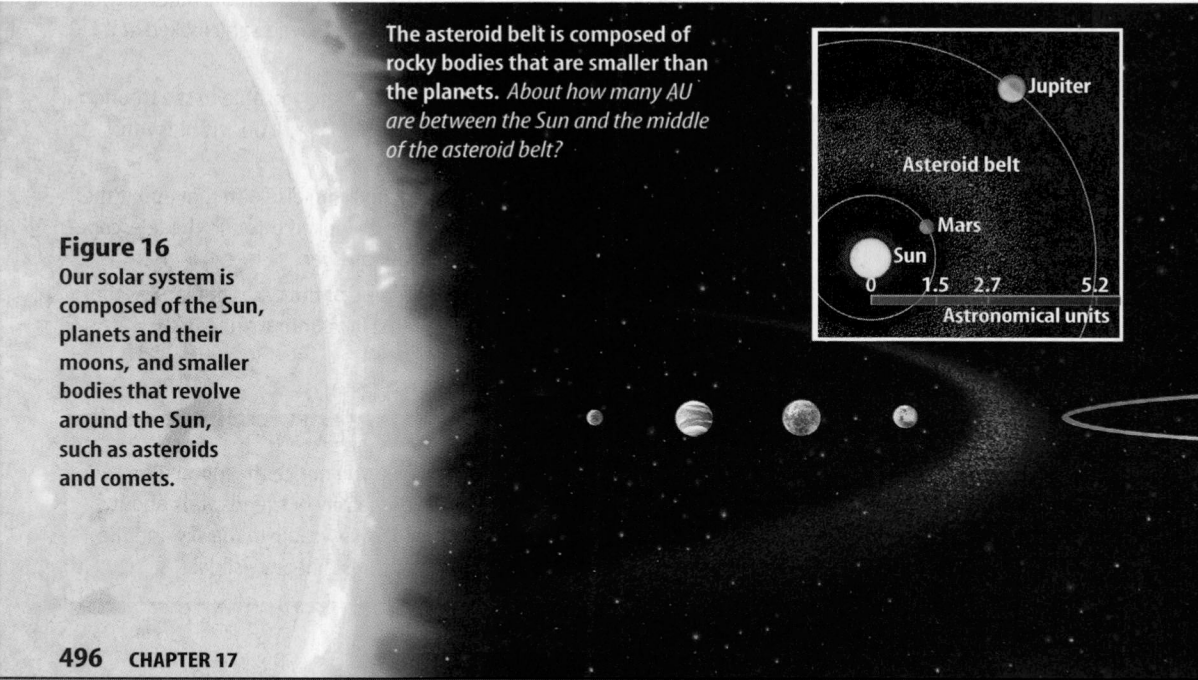

The asteroid belt is composed of rocky bodies that are smaller than the planets. *About how many AU are between the Sun and the middle of the asteroid belt?*

Jupiter

Asteroid belt

Mars

Sun

0   1.5   2.7   5.2

Astronomical units

Figure 16
Our solar system is composed of the Sun, planets and their moons, and smaller bodies that revolve around the Sun, such as asteroids and comets.

496 CHAPTER 17

Section ✓*Assessment* Planner

PORTFOLIO
Science Journal, p. 498
PERFORMANCE ASSESSMENT
Problem-Solving Activity, p. 499
Try at Home MiniLAB, p. 501
Skill Builder Activities, p. 503
See page 510 for more options.

CONTENT ASSESSMENT
Section, p. 503
Challenge, p. 503
Chapter, pp. 510–511

An Average Star Although the Sun is important to life on Earth, it is much like many other stars in the universe. The Sun is middle-aged and about average in the amount of light it gives off.

The Planets

The planets in our solar system can be classified as inner or outer planets. Inner planets have orbits that lie inside the orbit of the asteroid belt. The inner planets are mostly solid, rocky bodies with thin atmospheres compared with the atmospheres of outer planets. Outer planets have orbits that lie outside the orbit of the asteroid belt. Four of the outer planets are gaseous giants, and one is a small ice/rock planet that seems to be out of place.

Inner Planets

The inner planets are Mercury, Venus, Earth, and Mars. Known as the terrestrial planets, after the Latin word *terra*, they are similar in size to Earth and are made up mainly of rock.

Mercury Mercury is the closest planet to the Sun. It is covered by craters formed when meteorites crashed into its surface. The surface of Mercury also has cliffs, as shown in **Figure 17,** some of which are 3 km high. These cliffs may have formed when Mercury's molten, iron-rich core cooled and contracted, causing the outer solid crust to shrink. The planet seems to have shrunk about 2 km in diameter.

Figure 17
The Discovery Rupes Scarp is a huge cliff that may have formed as Mercury cooled and contracted. *How do craters on Mercury, like craters on the Moon, form?*

497

Inner Planets,
continued

Discussion

Inferior planets have an orbit that is inside Earth's orbit. Which of the inner planets can also be classified as inferior planets? Mercury and Venus

Chemistry
INTEGRATION

On Earth, iron oxide (rust) forms when iron reacts with oxygen in the presence of air or water. Ancient Mars may have had water on its surface and an atmosphere that contained oxygen. The oxygen could have combined with iron in Martian soil and rocks in the presence of water. Even without water, iron in Martian rocks still could have combined with oxygen from the atmosphere.

Visual Learning

Figure 19 Have students compare and contrast Mars' appearance with that of Earth. Mars is barren, with a landscape of reddish brown rocks and soil. Some areas on Earth look similarly barren and rocky, but Earth also includes areas of forests, bodies of water, and grasslands, any of which students can describe.

Figure 18
Clouds in Venus's atmosphere are composed partly of sulfuric acid droplets. *What are clouds on Earth composed of?*

Chemistry
INTEGRATION

The weathered rocks on Mars are reddish because of the presence of iron oxide. Research the chemical reaction that forms iron oxide on Earth and relate that to what might have happened on Mars.

Figure 19
Just as a metal toy left outside on Earth rusts, red rocks on Mars's surface show that iron in the rocks has rusted.

Venus Venus, the second inner planet from the Sun, shown in **Figure 18,** often has been referred to as Earth's twin, but only because of their similar sizes and masses. Otherwise, the surface conditions and atmospheres of Earth and Venus are extremely different. Thick clouds surround Venus and trap energy from the Sun, causing Venus's surface temperature to reach about 470°C. The process is similar to what occurs in a greenhouse.

Earth Earth is the third inner planet from the Sun. It is unique because surface temperatures enable water to exist in three states—solid, liquid, and gas. Ozone, a molecule of three oxygen atoms bound together, exists in the layer of Earth's atmosphere known as the stratosphere. This ozone protects life from the Sun's harmful ultraviolet radiation.

Mars Mars is the fourth inner planet from the Sun. It often is called the red planet. Iron oxide, the same material found in rust, exists in Mars's weathered surface rocks, giving the planet a reddish color. The Martian surface is shown in **Figure 19.** The rocks that have rusted are similar in composition to some volcanic rocks on Earth. The largest volcano in the solar system, Olympus Mons, is found on Mars.

Mars has two polar ice caps that change in size between Martian winter and summer. The northern polar cap is made up of water ice, whereas the southern polar cap is made up of frozen carbon dioxide. Mars has two Moons, Phobos (FOH bos) and Deimos (DI mos). Also, long channels exist on Mars. The channels on Mars are hypothesized to have been carved by flowing water sometime in the past. Mars's atmosphere, made up mostly of carbon dioxide with some nitrogen and argon, is much thinner than Earth's.

Curriculum Connection

Math Have students select an inner planet other than Earth and compute both its volume and Earth's using the formula $V = \frac{1}{6}\pi d^3$, where V is volume and d is diameter of the planet. (Students can find planet diameters in an encyclopedia.) Have students share data to put the planets in order from smallest to largest volume. **How does Earth compare to the other inner planets?** It is the largest.

Science Journal

Venus and Mars Have students research the surface conditions of Venus and Mars, Earth's two closest neighbors in space. Instruct them to write a paragraph in their Science Journals that compares and contrasts what it would be like on the surfaces of these two planets. L2
Linguistic P

Outer Planets

The outer planets are Jupiter, Saturn, Uranus, Neptune, and Pluto. Except for Pluto, they all are gaseous giant planets with thick atmospheres. The outer planets are mainly made up of light elements such as hydrogen and helium.

Jupiter and Saturn Jupiter, shown in **Figure 20A,** is the largest planet in the solar system. It is the fifth planet from the Sun. Jupiter's atmosphere is made mostly of hydrogen and helium and contains many huge storms. The largest and most prominent of these storms is the Great Red Spot. With its 28 moons, Jupiter is like a miniature solar system.

Problem-Solving Activity

What influences a planet's atmosphere?

The inner planets are small and dense and have thin atmospheres. The outer planets are large and gaseous. You might even say an outer planet is mostly atmosphere. Do a planet's gravity and distance from the Sun affect what kinds of gases its atmosphere contains? Use your ability to interpret a data table to find out.

Identifying the Problem

The table below lists the main gases in the atmospheres of two inner and two outer planets. Each planet's atmosphere also contains many other gases, but these are only present in small amounts.

Looking at the table, what conclusions can you draw? How do you think a planet's distance from the Sun and the size of the planet contribute to the kind of atmosphere it has?

Solving the Problem

1. What gases do the atmospheres of the inner and outer planets contain? What is special about Earth's atmosphere that makes it able to support modern life?
2. Can you think of any reasons why the outer planets have the gaseous atmospheres they do? Hint: *Hydrogen and Helium are the two lightest elements.*

Atmospheric Composition of the Planets	
Planet	**Atmosphere's Major Components**
Earth	78.1% Nitrogen (N_2); 20.9% Oxygen (O_2); Some Argon (Ar) and Carbon Dioxide (CO_2)
Mars	95.3% Carbon Dioxide (CO_2); 2.7% Nitrogen (N_2); 1.6% Argon (Ar); 0.13% Oxygen (O_2); 0.08% Carbon Monoxide (CO)
Jupiter	89.8% Molecular Hydrogen (H_2); 10.2% Helium (He)
Uranus	82.5% Molecular Hydrogen (H_2); 15.2% Helium (He); about 2.3% Methane (CH_4)

Inclusion Strategies

Learning Disabled Help students remember the order of the planets in the solar system by having them develop an easy-to-remember saying that uses the first letter of each planet name, in order from the Sun. For example, *My Very Exceptional Mother Just Served Us Nutritious Pizza.* **Musical-Auditory**

Outer Planets

Extension

Have students use the NASA website **(http://www.nasa.gov)** to research the latest discoveries on the major moons of Jupiter, Saturn, and Uranus. What are their surfaces like? Is there a possibility of life on these bodies? What are some plans for future exploration? Invite students to report their findings to the class.

Problem-Solving Activity

National Math Standards
Correlation to Mathematics Objectives
1, 5, 6, 7, 8, 9

Answers

1. Inner planets: nitrogen, carbon dioxide, oxygen, argon; outer planets: mostly hydrogen and helium; Earth's has large amounts of nitrogen and oxygen, which supports life.

2. Possible answers: Because of the Sun's heat, lighter elements (hydrogen, helium) have escaped inner planets; outer planets get less heat and can thus accumulate more of the lighter elements. Students might also suggest that the large gravitational forces of the outer planets can hold onto lighter elements better than the smaller gravitational forces of the inner planets.

Outer Planets,
continued

Teacher FYI

Astronauts may someday visit Mars, but a landing on Jupiter would be impossible. Like the rest of the outer planets (except Pluto), Jupiter has no solid surface. What we see when we look at Jupiter is the planet's clouds and thick atmosphere. About 32,000 kilometers beneath these clouds, high pressure turns the hydrogen gas into a layer of liquid metal. The only solid part of the planet is its core.

Discussion

Scientists working on the Galileo mission have speculated that Europa may have a crust of ice that is several kilometers thick and a 100-km thick ocean of water beneath it. If this is true, it raises the possibility of life existing in the ocean under the ice. Most scientists agree that water played a key role in the appearance of life on Earth. **Do you think it is important to send a probe to find out if there is life on Europa?** Accept all answers as a basis for discussion.

Text Question Answer

It increases the possibility because life as we know it requires water.

 **A** Jupiter's atmosphere is thick because of its gravity and great distance from the Sun.

B Saturn's rings are made up of seven main divisions—each of which is composed of particles of ice and rock.

Figure 20
The first four outer planets also are known as the gaseous giants.

SCIENCE Online

Collect Data For an online update of planetary data, visit the Glencoe Science Web site at **science.glencoe.com** and select the appropriate chapter.

 **Life Science INTEGRATION**

Jupiter's Moons The four largest moons of Jupiter are Io, Europa, Ganymede, and Callisto. They are called the Galilean satellites after Galileo Galilei, who discovered them in 1610. Volcanoes continually erupt on Io, the most volcanically active body in the solar system. An ocean of liquid water is hypothesized to exist beneath the cracked, frozen ice crust of Europa. Does this mean that life could exist on Europa? The National Aeronautics and Space Administration (NASA) plans to send an orbiting spacecraft that will arrive and study this moon in 2008.

Saturn The next outer planet is Saturn, shown in **Figure 20B.** The gases in Saturn's atmosphere are made up in large part of hydrogen and helium. Saturn is the sixth planet from the Sun. It often is called the ringed planet because of its striking ring system. Although all of the gaseous giant planets have ring systems, Saturn's rings are by far the most spectacular. Saturn is known to have seven major ring divisions made up of hundreds of smaller rings. Each ring is made up of pieces of ice and rock.

Saturn has at least 30 moons, the largest of which is Titan. The atmosphere surrounding Titan is denser than the atmospheres of Mercury, Earth, and Mars. The environment on Titan might be similar to the environment on Earth before oxygen became a major atmospheric gas.

500 CHAPTER 17 Earth in Space

Teacher FYI

In 1980 and 1981, the space probes *Voyager I* and *Voyager II* flew past Saturn, sending back the first detailed photos of the planet's rings. The *Cassini* space probe's mission includes orbiting Saturn and placing a lander on the Moon Titan.

SCIENCE Online
Internet Addresses

_____
_____
_____

Explore the Glencoe Science Web site at **science.glencoe.com** to find out more about topics in this section.

C The bluish-green color of Uranus is thought to be caused by methane in its atmosphere.

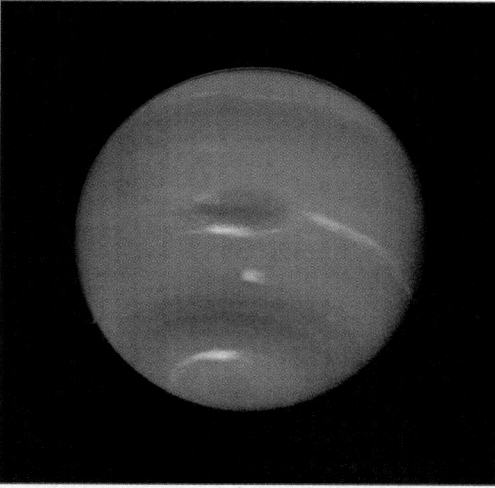

D Like Uranus, the blue color of Neptune is also thought to be caused by methane. The Great Dark Spot was a storm system similar in size to the diameter of Earth.

Uranus Shown in **Figure 20C,** the seventh planet from the Sun is Uranus. The atmosphere of Uranus, made up mostly of hydrogen, also contains helium and methane. The methane gives the planet a distinctive, bluish-green color. This is because methane gas reflects blue light and absorbs red light. Uranus is thought to have a total of 21 moons. However, additional satellites might exist.

Neptune The eighth planet from the Sun is Neptune. The precise composition of Neptune is uncertain. It is thought that Neptune's atmosphere of hydrogen, helium, and methane gradually changes into a slushlike layer, comprised partially of water and other melted ices. Toward the interior, this slushy material is thought to change into solid ice. In turn, this icy layer may surround a central, rocky core that is about the size of Earth.

As with Uranus, the methane in Neptune's atmosphere gives the planet its bluish color, as shown in **Figure 20D.** Winds in the gaseous portion of Neptune exceed speeds of 2,400 km per hour—faster than winds on any other planet.

Eight natural satellites of Neptune have been discovered so far. The largest of these, Triton, has great geysers that shoot gaseous nitrogen into space. A lack of craters on Triton's surface suggests that the surface of Triton is fairly young.

Inclusion Strategies

Behaviorally Disordered Before students carry out the activity in the MiniLAB at home, have students work with peer monitors to help them define the activity. The peer monitors could help the students choose a planet or moon, aid them in defining conditions that exist on the chosen planet or moon, and provide a few suggestions as to how a creature might be adapted to these conditions.

Discussion

Pluto is the only planet in the solar system that has not yet been visited by space probes from Earth. Why would this be the case? Students should infer that this has to do with Pluto's distance from the Sun, its location in relation to the other planets, or the lack of scientific interest in Pluto compared to other planets.

Other Objects in the Solar System

Use an Analogy

Remind students of the behavior of their hair on a windy day to help explain how the solar wind affects comet tails. When they are facing into the wind, their hair is pushed out behind them. When they have their backs to the wind, their hair is pushed from the backs of their heads towards their faces. This is analogous to the outward streaming of solar wind particles that forces the tails of a comet to point away from the Sun.

✔ **Reading Check**

Answer Meteorites are meteoroids that strike Earth.

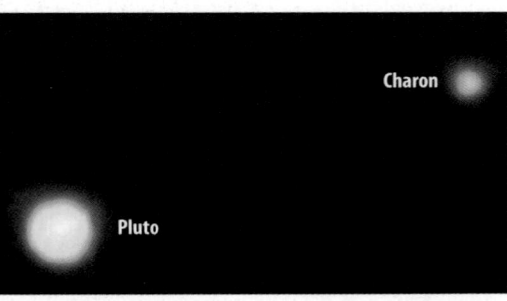

Figure 21
Pluto and its moon, Charon, are so close together that they usually can't be detected separately using ground-based telescopes. Because of this, Charon was discovered nearly 50 years after Pluto.

Pluto Pluto, shown in **Figure 21,** is so far from the Sun that it has completed less than 20 percent of one revolution around the Sun since its discovery in 1930. Pluto is totally different from the other outer planets. It is a planet that is thought to be made partly of ice and partly of rock. Apparently, a frozen layer of methane, nitrogen, and carbon monoxide sometimes covers Pluto's surface. At times, however, when Pluto is at its closest point to the Sun, these materials thaw into their gaseous states and rise, forming a temporary atmosphere. The surface of Charon, Pluto's moon, appears to be covered by water ice.

Other Objects in the Solar System

Other objects that exist in the solar system include asteroids, comets, and meteoroids. **Asteroids** are small, rocky objects that mostly lie in a belt located between the orbits of Mars and Jupiter. The asteroid belt is used by astronomers as a dividing line that separates the inner and outer planets. Jupiter's tremendous gravity probably kept a planet from forming from the matter contained in the asteroid belt.

Comets are made mainly of rocky particles and water ices. As their orbits approach the Sun, parts of comets vaporize and form tails. Comet tails, shown in **Figure 22,** always point away from the Sun. Almost all of the solar system's comets are located in the Kuiper Belt and the Oort Cloud. The Kuiper Belt is located beyond Neptune's orbit, and the Oort Cloud is located far beyond Pluto's orbit.

When comets break up, some of the resulting particles remain in their orbits. When asteroids collide, small pieces break off. Both of these processes produce small objects in the solar system known as meteoroids. If meteoroids enter Earth's atmosphere, they are called meteors, and when they fall to Earth, they are called meteorites.

✔ **Reading Check** *How are meteoroids related to meteorites?*

Figure 22
The brilliant head of a comet, called a coma, glows as its ices vaporize upon approaching the Sun.

Inclusion Strategies

Visually Impaired Provide a tactile model of a comet's tail that visually impaired students can explore. Cut out strips of paper and attach them to one side of a small ball. Pass the ball in front of a gently blowing fan, and allow visually impaired students to feel the direction in which the strips of paper are blowing. Reverse the direction of the ball, and again allow students to explore the comet.

Resource Manager

Chapter Resources Booklet
  Reinforcement, p. 29
Science Inquiry Labs, p. 39
Earth Science Critical Thinking/Problem Solving, p. 8

Origin of the Solar System

How did the solar system begin? One hypothesis is that the Sun and all the planets and other objects condensed from a large cloud of gas, ice, and dust about 5 billion years ago, as illustrated in **Figure 23.** This large **nebula** (NEB yuh luh), or cloud of material, was rotating slowly in space. Shock waves, perhaps from a nearby exploding star, might have caused the cloud to start condensing. As it condensed, it started rotating faster and flattened into a disk. Most of the condensing material was pulled toward the center to form an early Sun. The remaining gas, ice, and dust present in the outer areas of the nebula condensed, collided, and stuck together forming planets, moons, and other objects found throughout the solar system. Conditions in the inner part of the cloud caused small, solid planets to form, whereas conditions in the outer part were better for the formation of gaseous giant planets. Comets are thought to be made up of material left over from the original condensation of the cloud.

Figure 23
The solar system is thought to have formed from a cloud of rotating gases and dust particles.

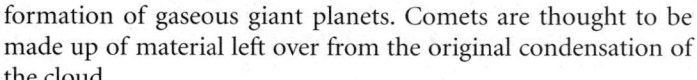

Section 3 Assessment

1. Which general class of planets is solid, rocky, and Earth-sized?

2. Why is Venus called Earth's twin planet?

3. Explain how 3-km-high cliffs could have formed on the surface of Mercury.

4. Although all gaseous giant planets have rings, why is Saturn considered to be the ringed planet more so than the others?

5. **Think Critically** How can the composition of the planets in the solar system be explained by the hypothesis described on this page? Can you think of any evidence that is not explained by this hypothesis?

Skill Builder Activities

6. **Comparing and Contrasting** Research the planets to determine their sizes. Make a model comparing planetary sizes. Select a scale for your model so that the smallest planet is visible and the largest planet is reasonable in size. **For more help, refer to the** Science Skill Handbook.

7. **Calculating Ratios** Research the equatorial diameters of Earth's Moon and the four Galilean moons of Jupiter. Calculate the ratio of each moon's diameter to Earth's Moon's diameter. **For more help, refer to the** Math Skill Handbook.

Section 3 Our Solar System **503**

Answers to Section Assessment

1. inner planets
2. They are similar in size and mass.
3. As the interior cooled, its crust cooled and shrank, possibly forming the cliffs.
4. Its rings are larger and more visible.
5. The planets are composed of the materials that were present in the nebula. The composition of individual planets was determined by conditions

where the planet formed, that is, rate of rotation, amount of heat, or amount of material present. Evidence not explained by this hypothesis depends on students' interpretation of the hypothesis. Look for depth and quality of response.
6. Models will vary depending on scale and materials used.

7. Earth's Moon = 3,476 km, Io = 3,630 km, Europa = 3,138 km, Ganymede = 5,268 km, and Callisto = 4,806 km. Earth's Moon: 1, Io: 1.04, Europa: 0.90, Ganymede: 1.52, Callisto: 1.38

Activity
Model and Invent

The Slant of the Sun's Rays

Recognize the Problem

Purpose

Students will demonstrate the relationship between the angle of the Sun's rays striking Earth and Earth's surface temperature.

Process Skills

making a model, observing, analyzing, predicting

Time Required

One 45-minute class period to make the models and at least 1 hour to perform the experiment and record results.

Thinking Critically

Discussion

Ask students to think about the differences between the seasons, particularly the length of daylight hours and the strength of the Sun's rays. Why are the Sun's rays much stronger on a sunny summer day than on a sunny winter day? How high does the Sun get in the sky during the summer compared to winter? Why are winter temperatures much colder than summer temperatures?

Planning the Model

Teaching Strategies

• Have students line bottom of baking pan, box or box lids with dark colored paper, which will better absorb solar radiation.

• Have students tape the thermometers to the lined surface in order to measure the temperature changes that occur during the experiment.

• Inspect the different angles of the students' trays to be certain they are accurate.

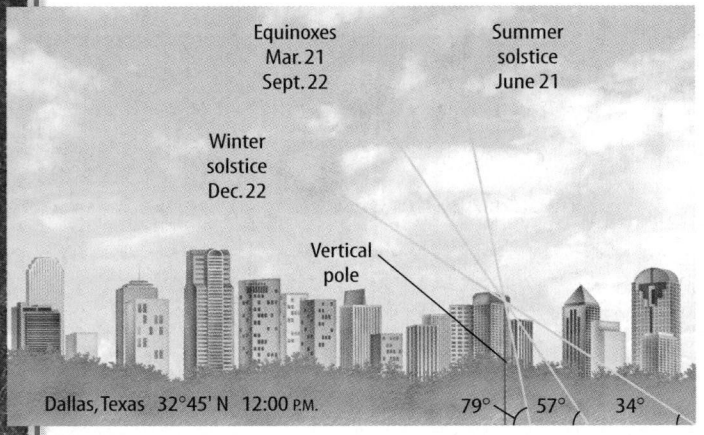

During winter in the northern hemisphere, the north pole is positioned away from the Sun. This causes the angle of the Sun's rays striking Earth to be smaller in winter than in summer, and there are fewer hours of sunlight. The reverse is true during the summer months. The Sun's rays strike Earth at higher angles—concentrating more radiation on the surface.

Recognize the Problem

How does the angle of the Sun's rays affect Earth's surface temperature?

Thinking Critically

■ How does the angle of the Sun's rays determine seasonal changes?
■ How might temperatures on Earth change if Earth were tilted at a different angle?

Angle of the Sun's Rays at Noon at Latitude 32° 45' N (Dallas)	
Date	**Angle**
December 22 (winter solstice)	34°
January 22	37°
February 22	46°
March 21 (vernal equinox)	57°
April 21	69°
May 21	77°
June 21 (summer solstice)	79°

Goals

■ **Design** a model for simulating the effect of changing angles of the Sun's rays on Earth's surface temperatures.

Possible Materials

shallow baking pans lined with cardboard
* paper, boxes, or box lids
thermometers (non-mercury)
wood blocks,
* bricks, or textbooks
protractor
clock
* stopwatch
*Alternate materials

Safety Precautions

Use thermometers as directed by teacher. Do not use "shake down" lab thermometers.

Data Source

Consult the data table providing angles of the Sun's rays for Dallas, Texas, in the northern hemisphere during different months of the year.

504   CHAPTER 17 Earth in Space

• Each tray will have to be used more than once depending on the number of different angles students decide to measure.

• Have students begin in the morning with the smallest angle. For each angle, leave tray exposed to the Sun for 20 minutes.

• Let thermometers and trays cool to room temperature before performing the experiment again with a new angle.

• If a tray is exposed for a longer time, such as 1 hour, have students readjust the angle of the surface every 15 minutes so that it remains the same as the Sun moves across the sky.

• Clear away items next to the classroom windows to provide space for students to set up their experiments.

Planning the Model

1. Design a model that will duplicate the angle of the Sun's rays during different seasons of the year.

2. Choose the materials you will need to construct your model. Be certain to provide identical conditions for each angle of the Sun's rays that you seek to duplicate.

Check Model Plans

1. Present your model design to the class in the form of diagrams, poster, slide show, or video. Ask your classmates how your group's model design could be adjusted to make it more accurate.

2. Decide on a location that will provide direct sunlight and will allow your classmates to easily observe your model.

Safety Precautions

WARNING: *Never look directly at the Sun at any time during your experiment.*

Window ——— Sun's rays

Winter solstice
34°

Equinoxes
57°

Summer solstice
79°

Making the Model

1. Create a model that demonstrates the effects different angles of the Sun's rays have on the temperature of Earth's surface.

2. Demonstrate your model during the morning, when the Sun's rays will hit the flat tray at an angle similar to the Sun's rays during winter solstice. Measure the angle of the Sun's rays by laying the protractor flat on the tray. Then sight the angle of the Sun's rays with respect to the tray.

3. Tilt other trays forward to simulate the Sun's rays striking Earth at higher angles during different times of the year.

Analyzing and Applying Results

1. Which angle had the greatest effect on the surface temperature of your trays? Which angle had the least effect?

2. Predict how each of the seasons in your area would change if Earth's axis tilt changed suddenly from 23.5 degrees to 40 degrees.

Communicating Your Data

Demonstrate your model for your class. **Explain** how your model replicated the angle of the Sun's rays for each of the four seasons in Dallas, Texas.

ACTIVITY 505

Making the Model

Expected Outcome

Exposed surface should increase in temperature as the angle of the Sun increases.

Analyzing and Applying Results

1. Students' answers may vary as to the exact measure of the angle, but generally the largest angle should have the greatest effect and the smallest angle should have the least effect on the temperature of the exposed surface.

2. Summer would become much hotter, and winter would become much colder.

✓ Assessment

Process Ask students to explain why temperatures at the equator vary little throughout the year. Equator temperatures are consistently warm because the Sun's rays strike the ground at consistently large angles. Use **Performance Assessment in the Science Classroom**, p. 89.

SCIENCE Online

Internet Addresses

_____

_____

_____

Explore the Glencoe Science Web site at **science.glencoe.com** to find out more about topics in this activity.

Resource Manager

Chapter Resources Booklet
  Activity Worksheet, pp. 7–8
Reading and Writing Skill Activities, p. 11
Lab Management and Safety, p. 73

Communicating Your Data

Encourage students to use electronically designed diagrams of their tray set-ups.

Content Background

In the early days of astronomy, asteroids were thought to be the remains of planets that exploded. New technologies have led astronomers to rethink their understanding of how these objects formed. Today astronomers believe most asteroids are pieces of space debris that are left over from the formation of solar systems.

When a very massive star dies, a tremendous explosion sends material from the star hurling through space. As this matter spreads out, it cools down and begins to rotate. At the same time, it starts to gather together. As this matter accumulates, planetesimals, small bodies of matter, are formed.

These planetesimals grow in size as they collide with each other. This process is known as accretion. Eventually, these planetesimals can grow large enough to form planets. For one reason or another, not all planetesimals are able to become planets. These leftover planetesimals are asteroids.

Several hundred asteroids are known to exist in the space between Mars and Jupiter. This region is called the "Asteroid belt." For the most part, these asteroids maintain a steady orbit within the belt.

Occasionally, an asteroid's orbit can be changed by Jupiter's gravity or a collision with another asteroid. Often these collisions give rise to meteoroids. When the new orbit involves the inner solar system, it is considered a Near Earth Asteroid (NEA).

Collision Course

Will an asteroid collide with Earth?

506

Resources for Teachers and Students

Asteroids: A History, by Curtis Peebles, Smithsonian Institute Press, 2000.

Rocks from Space, by O. Richard Norton, Mountain Press Publishing Company, 1998.

Cosmic Collisions, by Dana Desonie, Henry Holt and Company, Inc., 1996.

Asteroids—those giant rocks hurtling through space—have been the basis for several disaster movies. But are asteroids really threats? "Absolutely!" say many scientists who study space. In fact, they believe the question is not can—but when—will Earth be hit by an asteroid. Because asteroids already have hit our planet many times since it was formed, it makes sense that an asteroid collision will happen again.

Earth is scarred with about 120 recognizable craters that are visible in many parts of the world. But due to erosion, plant growth, and other processes that cover up Earth's surface features, there are sure to be many craters that have disappeared from sight. However, visitors to Meteor Crater, Arizona, can see a 1.2-km-wide depression caused by an asteroid that impacted Earth about 49,000 years ago. A much older crater lies in Mexico's Yucatan Peninsula. The depression is about 195 km wide and was created about 65 million years ago.

Some scientists believe the Yucatan asteroid created a giant dust cloud that blocked the Sun's rays from reaching Earth. This may have caused the planet to turn dark for about six months and may have led to freezing temperatures. This would have put an end to much of Earth's early plant life. And, scientists hypothesize, this was the asteroid that led to the extinction of the dinosaurs and about half of the other species that once inhabited Earth.

Rocks in Space

With space crowded with giant chunks of rock, some the size of mountains, is there anything we can do to protect ourselves from such an impact? Astronomer/geologist Eugene Shoemaker thought so and is responsible for alerting the world to the dangers of asteroid impact. In 1973, he and geologist Eleanor Helin began the first Near Earth Objects (NEO) watch at the Mount Palomar Observatory in California. Scanning the sky, they sought out objects that might be on a collision course with Earth. But to the team's disappointment, few people were concerned.

Then, in 1996, all that changed. An asteroid, about 0.5 km wide, came within 450,800 km of Earth. Scientists said this was a close call! Today, groups of scientists are working on creating systems to track NEOs. As of 2000, they recorded 1,082 NEOs. Of those, 407 were about 0.75 km in diameter or more!

Some physicists and astronomers are working on ways to defend our planet from NEOs. One idea is to send a warhead-tipped rocket to try to change a dangerous asteroid's orbit away from Earth.

Don't worry, though: A collision isn't in the foreseeable future. In fact, there is little chance of an asteroid hitting Earth anytime soon. The enormous pressures and temperatures that are generated when an asteroid hits Earth's atmosphere usually vaporize it altogether. So, you can't use the excuse, "An asteroid is coming!" to put off doing your homework or cleaning your room!

Meteor Crater, near Winslow, Arizona, was formed about 49,000 years ago. It is about 200 m deep.

CONNECTIONS Brainstorm Working in small groups, come up with as many ways as you can to blast an asteroid to pieces or make it change course before hitting Earth. Present your reports to the rest of the class.

SCIENCE Online
For more information, visit science.glencoe.com

CONNECTIONS Lasers, sound waves, or nuclear devices could be used to either change the asteroid's orbit or blow it up. Encourage students to use their imagination. Their written reports should include descriptions of how their plan would work and how they will implement it. Their oral report should include posters and other visual aids.

SCIENCE Online

Internet Addresses

_____

_____

_____

Explore the Glencoe Science Web site at **science.glencoe.com** to find out more about topics in this feature.

Discussion

Two ways to reduce the possibility of an asteroid colliding with Earth are changing the asteroid's orbit or blasting it into small pieces. Ask students to brainstorm the pros and cons of these two methods. List their responses on the board. Possible responses: Changing the asteroid's orbit requires time to develop new technologies; blasting it into pieces may result in an increase in the number of objects that could strike Earth.

Investigate the Issue

Set the stage for both *Investigate the Issue* and *Connections* with the following narrative: The Secretary General of the United Nations has asked your class to develop alternative plans for defending Earth from an asteroid expected to collide with the planet. Since the threat is global, all the world's resources are at your disposal.

Ask students to organize themselves into two groups, one group to design a plan for deflecting an asteroid and the other to design a plan for blasting the asteroid into pieces. Encourage students to use their imagination and not be restricted by today's technology. Instruct students to prepare both a written and an oral report for the Secretary General.

Reviewing Main Ideas

Preview

Students can answer the questions in their Science Journals. Discuss the answers as you go through the chapter. **Linguistic**

Review

Students can write their answers, then compare them with those of other students. **Interpersonal**

Reteach

Students can look at the illustrations and describe details that support the main ideas of the chapter. **Visual-Spatial**

Answers to Chapter Review

SECTION 1

1. photos from space, Earth's curved shadow during lunar eclipses, objects slowly appearing over the horizon as they get closer

SECTION 2

1. Maria are large dark areas, lunar highlands are light areas, and craters are circular depressions.

SECTION 3

3. asteroids

Chapter 17 Study Guide

Reviewing Main Ideas

Section 1 Earth's Motion and Seasons

1. Earth's shape is nearly spherical. *What observations confirm Earth's shape?*

2. Earth's motions include rotation, or spinning on its axis, and revolution, or movement around the Sun in its orbit.

3. Day and night are caused by Earth spinning on its axis. Earth's tilt and revolution cause seasons to occur.

Section 2 Earth's Moon

1. Surface features on the Moon include maria, craters, and lunar highlands. *How can you recognize these surface features from Earth?*

2. The Moon rotates once and revolves around Earth once in 27.3 days. The Moon's orbit is tilted with respect to Earth's orbit.

3. Phases of Earth's Moon, solar eclipses, and lunar eclipses are caused by the Moon's revolution around Earth.

4. One hypothesis concerning the origin of Earth's Moon is that a Mars-sized body collided with Earth, throwing off material that later condensed to form the Moon.

Section 3 Our Solar System

1. The solar system includes the Sun, the planets, moons, asteroids, comets, and meteoroids.

2. Planets in our solar system can be classified as inner or outer planets.

3. Inner planets are small and rocky and have thin atmospheres. Outer planets are generally large and gaseous and have thick, dense atmospheres. *What objects are concentrated in a belt between the inner and outer planets?*

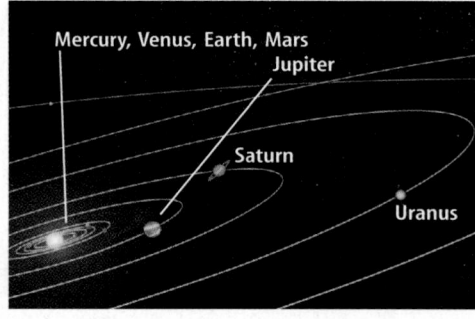

Mercury, Venus, Earth, Mars
Jupiter
Saturn
Uranus

4. One hypothesis on the origin of the solar system states that it formed by the condensation of a large cloud of gas, ice, and dust.

FOLDABLES
Reading & Study Skills

After You Read

Look at your Foldable and explain what characteristics make Earth a perfect place for life and the Moon an impossible place for life to exist.

FOLDABLES
Reading & Study Skills

After You Read

After students have read the chapter and completed the Foldable described in Before You Read, have them do the activity on the student page.

Dinah Zike

Visualizing Main Ideas

Using the following phrases, fill in the concept map below to complete the moon phase cycle: full moon, waning gibbous, waning crescent, and first quarter.

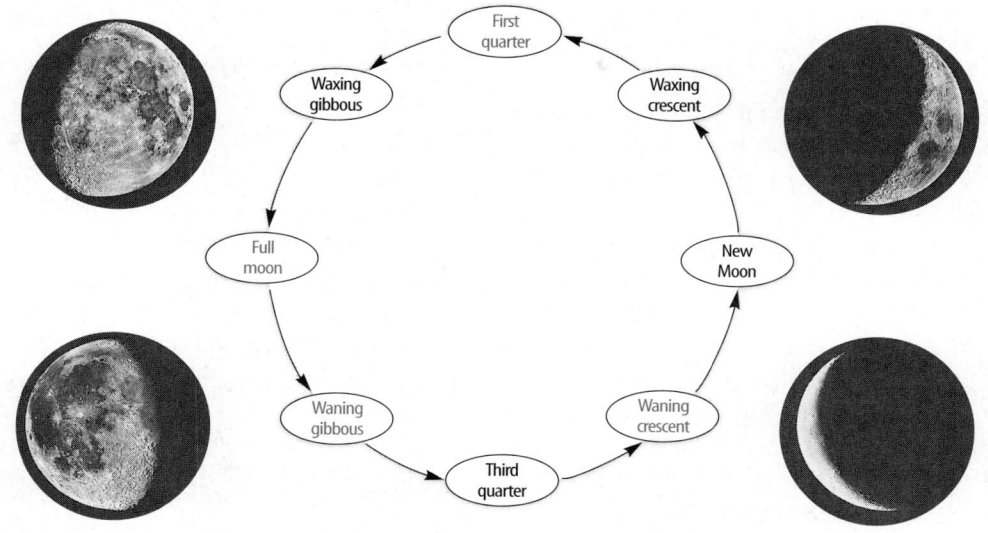

Vocabulary Review

Vocabulary Words

a. asteroid
b. astronomical unit
c. axis
d. comet
e. crater
f. equinox
g. lunar eclipse
h. moon phase

i. nebula
j. orbit
k. revolution
l. rotation
m. solar eclipse
n. solar system
o. solstice

THE PRINCETON REVIEW Study Tip

As you read, look up the definition of any prefixes you do not recognize. Once you know the meaning of a prefix, you'll be able to figure out the definition of many new words.

Using Vocabulary

Explain the difference between the vocabulary words in each of the following sets.

1. rotation, revolution
2. orbit, axis
3. solar eclipse, lunar eclipse
4. equinox, solstice
5. comets, craters
6. solar system, solar eclipse
7. Moon phases, lunar eclipse
8. rotation, orbit
9. nebula, solar system
10. asteroid, comet

CHAPTER STUDY GUIDE 509

Visualizing Main Ideas

See student page.

Vocabulary Review

Using Vocabulary

1. Rotation is the spinning of an object on its axis; revolution is movement of one object around another.
2. Orbit is the path an object takes as it revolves; axis is the imaginary line around which an object rotates.
3. A solar eclipse occurs when the Moon's shadow falls on Earth. A lunar eclipse occurs when Earth's shadow falls on the Moon.
4. Equinox: Sun is directly over Earth's equator; solstice: Sun is at its greatest distance north or south of the equator.
5. Comets: small objects made of ice and rock that orbit the Sun; craters: depressions that form when an object hits a planet or moon.
6. Solar system: planets, moons, and other objects that orbit the Sun; solar eclipse: Moon passes between Earth and Sun.
7. Phases: changing views of the Moon as seen from Earth; lunar eclipse: Earth passes directly between the Sun and the Moon.
8. Rotation is the spinning of an object on an axis. An orbit is the path an object takes as it revolves.
9. Nebula: cloud of material in space; solar system: planets and other objects that orbit the Sun.
10. An asteroid is a small, rocky object orbiting the Sun. A comet is a body of rock and ice that vaporizes when its orbit takes it near the Sun.

Checking Concepts

1. A
2. C
3. D
4. A
5. B
6. C
7. C
8. B
9. D
10. C

Thinking Critically

11. Inner planets are small, solid, rocky bodies in space. Outer planets (except Pluto) are large and gaseous.

12. The Moon's crust is thinner on the side facing Earth, making it more likely that lava would flow up from the interior and form maria there.

13. because of the likely presence of water below the crust

14. During the summer solstice in the northern hemisphere, the Sun reaches its greatest distance north of the equator and is directly over the Tropic of Cancer. During the winter solstice in the northern hemisphere, the Sun reaches its greatest distance south of the equator and is directly over the Tropic of Capricorn. During the equinox the Sun is directly over the equator.

15. Earth's shape bulges slightly at the equator and is flattened slightly at the poles.

Checking Concepts

Choose the word or phrase that best answers the question.

1. Earth's spinning on its axis is which motion?
   A) rotation
   C) revolution
   B) waxing
   D) waning

2. What occurs when the Sun reaches its greatest distance north or south of the equator?
   A) orbit
   C) solstice
   B) equinox
   D) axis

3. What is the imaginary line around which Earth spins called?
   A) orbit
   C) solstice
   B) equinox
   D) axis

4. Which moon surface feature probably formed when lava flows filled large basins?
   A) maria
   C) highlands
   B) craters
   D) volcanoes

5. Meteorites that strike the Moon's surface cause which surface feature?
   A) maria
   C) highlands
   B) craters
   D) volcanoes

6. How long is the Moon's period of revolution?
   A) 27.3 hours
   C) 27.3 days
   B) 29.5 hours
   D) 29.5 days

7. How long does it take for the Moon to rotate once on its axis?
   A) 27.3 hours
   C) 27.3 days
   B) 29.5 hours
   D) 29.5 days

8. What occurs when the Moon is directly between the Sun and Earth?
   A) lunar eclipse
   C) full moon
   B) solar eclipse
   D) waxing crescent

9. Which planet is most like Earth in size and mass?
   A) Mercury
   C) Saturn
   B) Mars
   D) Venus

10. Europa is a satellite of which planet?
    A) Uranus
    C) Jupiter
    B) Saturn
    D) Mars

Thinking Critically

11. Describe the differences between inner and outer planets.

12. Why are more maria found on the near side of the Moon than on the far side?

13. Why do scientists hypothesize that life might exist on Europa?

14. Explain the Sun's positions relative to the equator during winter and summer solstices and equinox.

15. Describe how Earth's shape is influenced by gravity.

Developing Skills

16. **Classifying** A new planet is found circling the Sun, and you are given the job of classifying it. The new planet has a thick, dense atmosphere and no apparent solid surface. It lies beyond the orbit of Pluto. How would you classify this newly discovered planet?

17. **Making and Using Tables** Complete the table of outer planets that shows how many satellites each planet has and what gases are found in each planet's atmosphere.

Planetary Facts		
Planet	**Number of Satellites**	**Major Atmospheric Gases**
Jupiter	28	H_2, He
Saturn	30	H_2, He
Uranus	21	H_2, He, CH_4
Neptune	8	H_2, He, CH_4
Pluto	1	CH_4, CO, N_2

Chapter ✓Assessment Planner

Portfolio Encourage students to place in their portfolios one or two items of what they consider to be their best work. Examples include:
- Cultural Diversity, p. 484
- Life Science Integration, p. 487
- Science Journal, p. 498

Performance Additional performance assessments, Performance Task Assessment Lists, and rubrics for evaluating these activities can be found in Glencoe's **Performance Assessment in the Science Classroom.**

18. Concept Mapping Complete the following concept maps about Mars and Neptune. Use the following words or phrases: *red, outer planet, rocky, gas giant, blue,* and *inner planet*.

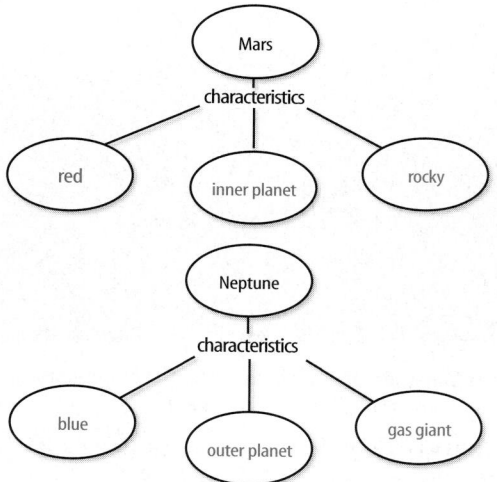

19. Making Models Make a three-dimensional model of a total solar eclipse. Be sure to include all objects involved.

20. Forming Hypotheses Research their characteristics and formulate a hypothesis explaining the origin of Pluto, Charon, and Triton.

21. Poster Use photographs or illustrations of the Sun, the Moon, and Earth. Position each object as it would be located during a lunar and a solar eclipse.

TECHNOLOGY

Go to the Glencoe Science Web site at **science.glencoe.com** or use the **Glencoe Science CD-ROM** for additional chapter assessment.

 THE PRINCETON REVIEW Test Practice

A student is beginning a study of the inner planets. These planets and some of their characteristics are listed in the table below.

The Inner Planets

Planet	Average Distance From Sun (millions of km)	Diameter (km)	Period of Revolution (Earth days)	Period of Rotation (Earth days-hours)
Mercury	58	4878	88	58-16
Venus	109	12104	225	243-0
Earth	150	12756	365	0-24
Mars	227	6794	686	0-24.5

Study the table and answer the following questions.

1. According to this information, which inner planet takes more than one Earth year to complete its journey around the Sun?
- **A)** Mercury
- **B)** Venus
- **C)** Earth
- **D)** Mars

2. A reasonable hypothesis, based on the data in the table, is that as a planet's distance from the Sun increases _____.
- **F)** the planet's period of revolution increases
- **G)** the planet's period of revolution decreases
- **H)** the planet's period of rotation increases
- **J)** the planet's period of rotation decreases

THE PRINCETON REVIEW Test Practice

The Test-Taking Tip was written by The Princeton Review, the nation's leader in test preparation.
1. D
2. F

Developing Skills

16. It has the characteristics of outer planets.
17. See student page.
18. See student page.
19. Student models should show the Moon between the Sun and Earth. All three objects should be in a straight line.
20. All three objects may have been comets.

Performance Assessment

21. Solar: Moon between Sun and Earth; Lunar: Earth between Sun and Moon. Use **PASC**, p. 145.

✓Assessment Resources

 Reproducible Masters

Chapter Resources Booklet
Chapter Review, pp. 39–40
Chapter Tests, pp. 41–44
Assessment Transparency Activity, p. 51

Glencoe Science Web site
Interactive Tutor
Chapter Quizzes

Glencoe Technology
Assessment Transparency
Interactive CD-ROM Chapter Quizzes
ExamView Pro Test Bank
Vocabulary PuzzleMaker Software
MindJogger Videoquiz

Reading Comprehension

QUESTION 1: B

Students must identify the conclusion that is best supported by information in the passage. Only answer choice B is supported by information in the passage.

Teaching Tip

Suggest to students that as they read a passage, they write a one-sentence summary of each paragraph.

QUESTION 2: F

Students must identify the answer choice that is best supported by information in the passage.

- **Choice F** Yes; this is supported by information in the passage.
- **Choice G** No; this is not supported by information in the passage.
- **Choice H** No; this is not supported by information in the passage.
- **Choice J** No; this is not supported by information in the passage.

THE PRINCETON REVIEW   All questions written and validated by The Princeton Review.

Reading Comprehension

Read the passage carefully. Then read the questions that follow the passage. Decide which is the best answer to each question.

Earthquakes and Volcanoes

Earthquakes are destructive and potentially fatal natural disasters. Geologists have been working to learn what they can about earthquakes in order to better protect property and save human lives.

Scientists know that many earthquakes occur because tectonic plates interact with one another at plate boundaries. Studies of faults have led to long-term forecasts that earthquakes should occur in certain regions. For example, a major earthquake has been forecast for an area near Parkfield, California, which is along the San Andreas Fault. However, scientists cannot predict exactly when and where an earthquake will occur.

One approach to forecasting earthquakes is known as paleoseismology. Paleoseismology involves the study of past movements of rock and sediment along faults. Motion along a fault results in an earthquake. Therefore, studying this movement is one way to study ancient earthquake occurrences.

This movement can be measured in the field by observing shifted rock and sediment along a fault. If this displaced sediment can be dated, the time at which the earthquake occurred also can be estimated. With information on several past earthquakes, scientists can estimate how long, on average, time intervals are between the earthquakes. This is one way to estimate how many earthquakes might occur along a fault over a period of time.

Although scientists are not yet able to predict earthquakes reliably, the information gained from their research advances the field.

Test-Taking Tip   Identify whether this passage is fictional or informational.

The San Andreas Fault is part of a plate boundary, and many earthquakes occur along it.

1. Based on the information in this passage, what can the reader conclude?
   A) Earthquakes always occur during heavy rainstorms.
   B) Earthquakes cannot be predicted reliably, but they can be forecast over estimated periods of time.
   C) Earthquakes are extremely rare natural occurrences.
   D) Earthquakes do not affect property and human lives much.

2. What does the information in this passage suggest?
   F) Studies of displacement along faults can provide information for forecasting earthquakes.
   G) Studying faults allows scientists to determine the time and date of the next earthquake.
   H) Paleoseismology is the study of fossils along the San Andreas Fault.
   J) Scientists do not know what causes earthquakes.

Standardized Test Practice

Reasoning and Skills

Read each question and decide which is the best answer.

1. All of the following is evidence used by Alfred Wegener to support the hypothesis of continental drift EXCEPT _____.
   A) the puzzlelike fit of the coastlines
   B) matching fossils
   C) similar rock structures
   D) mid-ocean ridges

Test-Taking Tip Think about what evidence Wegener had considered when he presented his hypothesis in 1912.

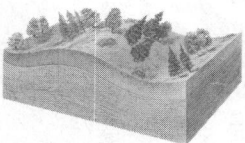

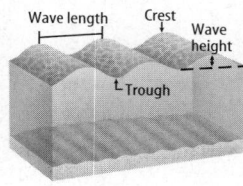

2. Refer to the diagrams above, which show earthquake waves and water waves. The waves are similar in that _____.
   F) they travel from the focus in all directions
   G) they carry energy through space
   H) the material they move through is transported
   J) only the energy moves forward; the material does not move forward

Test-Taking Tip Think about and compare the characteristics of seismic and water waves.

3. All of these statements are true about volcanoes EXCEPT _____.
   A) three basic types of volcanoes are shield, cinder cone, and composite
   B) the amount of water vapor, other gases, and silica in magma influence the kind of eruption that will take place
   C) the lower the silica content is in magma, the more explosive an eruption will be
   D) a volcano's form depends upon the type of eruption and the composition of the erupted material

Test-Taking Tip Think about the different kinds of volcanoes, how they form, and what factors influence the type of eruption.

Consider this question carefully before writing or sketching your answer on a separate sheet of paper.

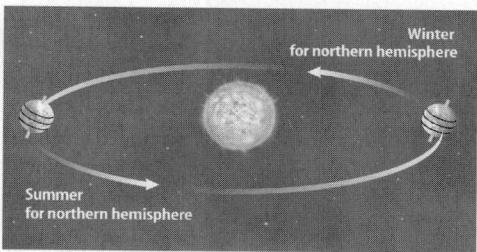

4. The diagram shows the position of Earth relative to the Sun during the northern hemisphere's winter and summer. Describe why the lengths of day and night are different during these two seasons.

Test-Taking Tip Notice that Earth's axis is tilted.

Reasoning and Skills

QUESTION 1: D

Students must know that *mid-ocean ridges* were not discovered until the 1960's—many years after Wegener developed his hypothesis—in order to identify choice D as correct.

QUESTION 2: J

Students must understand earthquake waves to identify choice J as correct. Students should know that both the water and the land return to their original locations after a wave passes.

QUESTION 3: C

Students must identify the false statement. Choice C is the only answer that is false. Choices A, B, and D are true statements.

Teaching Tip

Tell students to reread all questions that contain negative words such as "not" or "except" to be sure they understand what the question is asking.

QUESTION 4: Answers will vary.

Students should mention that the tilt of Earth's axis causes the seasons and the changing lengths of day and night.

UNIT 6

Unit Contents

Pre-Reading Activity

Have students find and compare models of atoms.

UNIT 6 **Building Blocks of Matter**

How Are Refrigerators & Frying Pans Connected?

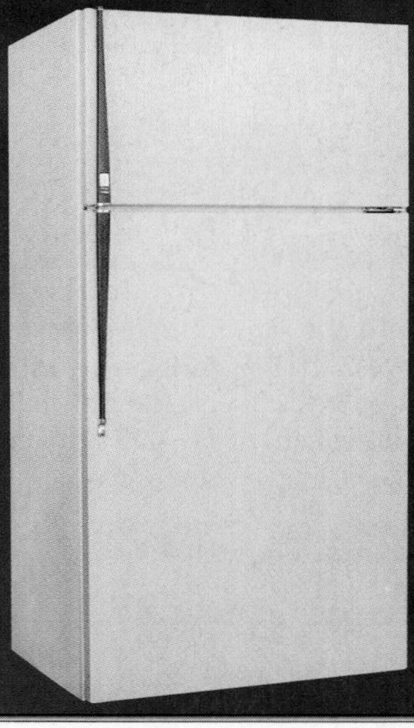

In the late 1930s, scientists were experimenting with a gas that they hoped would work as a new coolant in refrigerators. They filled several metal canisters with the gas and stored the canisters on dry ice. Later, when they opened the canisters, they were surprised to find that the gas had disappeared and that the inside of each canister was coated with a slick, powdery white solid. The gas had undergone a chemical change. That is, the chemical bonds in its molecules had broken and new bonds had formed, turning one kind of matter into a completely different kind of matter. Strangely, the mysterious white powder proved to be just about the slipperiest substance that anyone had ever encountered. Years later, a creative Frenchman obtained some of the slippery stuff and tried applying it to his fishing tackle to keep the lines from tangling. His wife noticed what he was doing and suggested putting the substance on the inside of a frying pan to keep food from sticking. He did, and nonstick cookware was born!

514

Teacher to Teacher

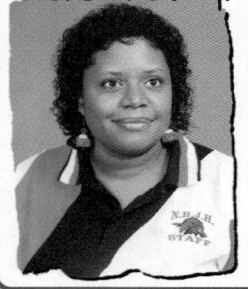

"Multicolored modeling clay is an inexpensive and reusable material for middle school students to use to visualize science concepts. Students use their creativity to make 'atoms' that have touchable protons, neutrons, and electrons."

Petrolia Moss, Teacher
North Heights Junior High
Texarkana, AK

NATIONAL GEOGRAPHIC

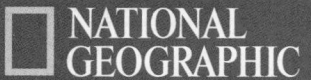

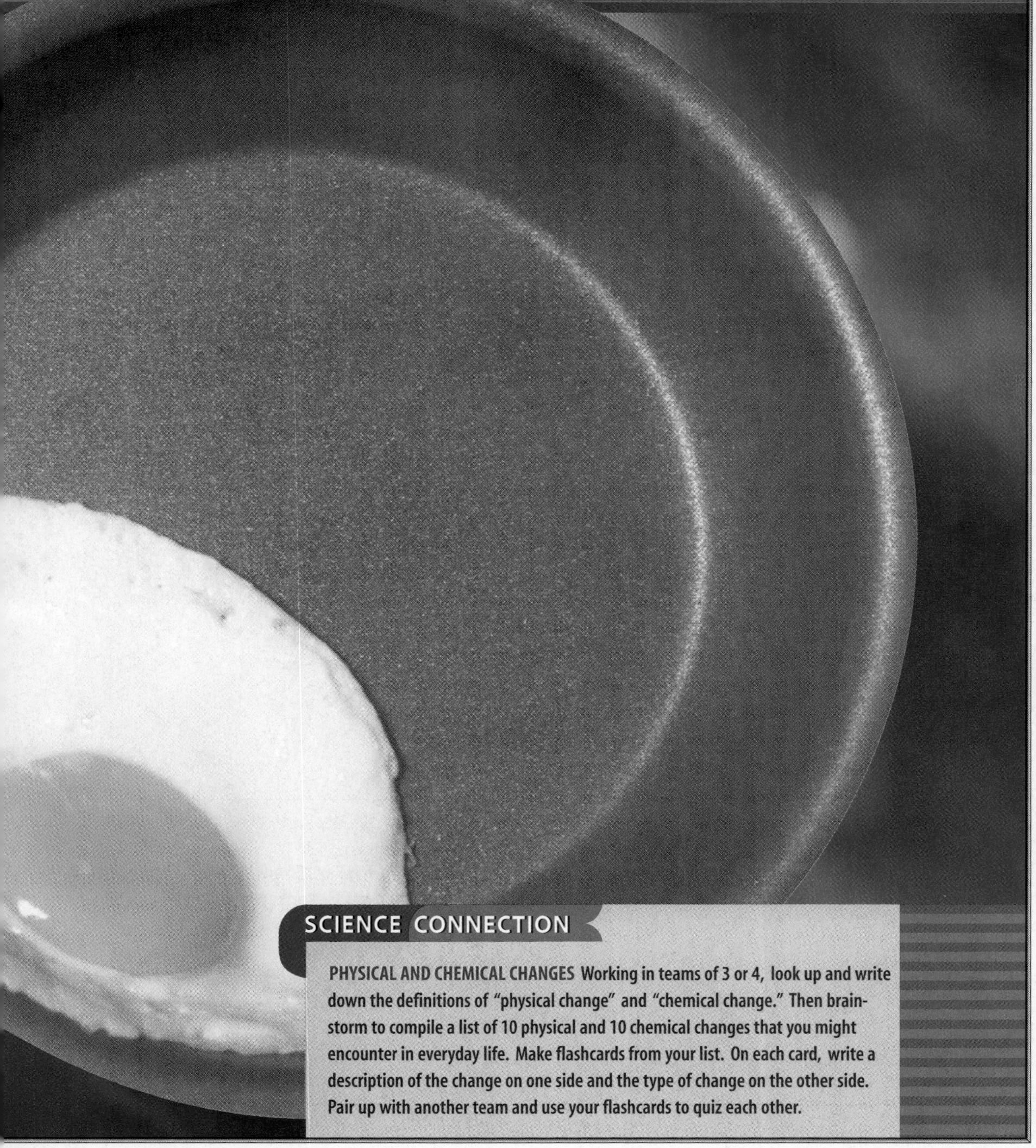

SCIENCE CONNECTION

PHYSICAL AND CHEMICAL CHANGES Working in teams of 3 or 4, look up and write down the definitions of "physical change" and "chemical change." Then brainstorm to compile a list of 10 physical and 10 chemical changes that you might encounter in everyday life. Make flashcards from your list. On each card, write a description of the change on one side and the type of change on the other side. Pair up with another team and use your flashcards to quiz each other.

SCIENCE Online

Internet Addresses

Explore the Glencoe Science Web site at **science.glencoe.com** to find out more about topics in this unit.

NATIONAL GEOGRAPHIC

Introducing the Unit

How Are Refrigerators & Frying Pans Connected?

It was Roy Plunkett who first discovered polytetrafluoroethylene (PTFE) in 1938. It was used to protect metal equipment from corrosion during World War II. It was 1960 when the first nonstick cookware was released. PTFE is an organic polymer known for its strength, toughness, and slippery surface. It is almost completely indifferent to attack by all chemicals, and retains its physical properties at high temperatures. These qualities make it ideal for use in gaskets, bearings, cooking utensils, and numerous other products.

SCIENCE CONNECTION

Activity

Ask students to further classify their physical and chemical changes from the Science Connection. Possible subcategories for physical changes might include a change in state, a change in quantity, and change in appearance. Possible sub-categories for chemical changes include reactions that release energy (exothermic) vs. reactions that absorb energy (endothermic) and slow reactions vs. fast reactions. Have students support their selections with the information presented in the unit.

Section/Objectives	Standards		Activities/Features
Chapter Opener	**National**	**State/Local**	**Explore Activity:** Change the state of water, p. 517 **Before You Read,** p. 517
	See p. 5T for a Key to Standards.		
Section 1 Atoms ⏱ 2 sessions 📦 1 block 1. **Identify** the states of matter. 2. **Describe** the internal structure of an atom. 3. **Compare** isotopes of an element.	National Content Standards: UCP1, A1, B1		**MiniLAB:** Searching for Elements, p. 519 **Health Integration,** p. 521
Section 2 Combinations of Atoms ⏱ 2 sessions 📦 1 block 1. **Describe** several ways atoms combine to form compounds. 2. **List** differences between compounds and mixtures	National Content Standards: UCP3, A1, B1		**Science Online,** p. 524 **MiniLAB:** Classifying Forms of Matter, p. 527 **Chemistry Integration,** p. 528 **Activity:** Scales of Measurement, p. 529
Section 3 Properties of Matter ⏱ 3 sessions 📦 1.5 blocks 1. **Distinguish** between chemical and physical properties. 2. **List** the four states of matter.	National Content Standards: UCP1, A1, B2, G2		**Math Skills Activity:** Calculating Density, p. 531 **Visualizing States of Matter,** p. 533 **Activity:** Determining Density, p. 536-537 **Science Stats:** Amazing Atoms, p. 538-539

Activity Materials	Reproducible Resources	Section Assessment	Technology
Explore Activity: 1,000-mL glass beaker, water, tape, hot plate, clock or watch	**Chapter Resources Booklet** Foldables Worksheet, p. 13 Directed Reading Overview, p. 15 Note-taking Worksheets, pp. 29–31	GLENCOE'S ASSESSMENT ADVANTAGE	
MiniLAB: Periodic Table of the Elements, highlighter *Need materials? Contact Science Kit at 1-800-828-7777 or www.sciencekit.com on the Internet.*	**Chapter Resources Booklet** Transparency Activity, p. 40 MiniLAB, p. 3 Enrichment, p. 26 Reinforcement, p. 23 Directed Reading, p. 16 **Cultural Diversity,** p. 55	**Portfolio** Science Journal, p. 519 **Performance** MiniLAB, p. 519 Skill Builder Activities, p. 522 **Content** Section Assessment, p. 522	Section Focus Transparency Interactive CD-ROM Guided Reading Audio Program
MiniLAB: none **Activity:** triple-beam balance, 100-mL graduated cylinder, 2 metersticks, 3 non-mercury thermometers, stick or dowel, rock sample, string, globe, water	**Chapter Resources Booklet** Transparency Activity, p. 41 MiniLAB, p. 4 Lab Activity, pp. 9–10 Enrichment, p. 27 Reinforcement, p. 24 Directed Reading, p. 16 Activity Worksheet, pp. 5–6 Transparency Activity, pp. 43–44 **Science Inquiry Labs,** p. 51	**Portfolio** Cultural diversity, p. 525 **Performance** MiniLAB, p. 527 Skill Builder Activities, p. 528 **Content** Section Assessment, p. 528	Section Focus Transparency Teaching Transparency Interactive CD-ROM Guided Reading Audio Program
Activity: pan, triple-beam balance, 100-mL beaker, 250-mL graduated cylinder, water, sponge, piece of quartz, piece of clay, small wooden block, small metal block, small cork, rock, ruler	**Chapter Resources Booklet** Transparency Activity, p. 42 Lab Activity, pp. 11–12 Enrichment, p. 28 Reinforcement, p. 25 Directed Reading, pp. 17, 18 Activity Worksheet, pp. 7–8 **Mathematics Skill Activities,** p. 9	**Portfolio** Extension, p. 533 **Performance** Math Skills Activity, p. 531 Skill Builder Activities, p. 535 **Content** Section Assessment, p. 535	Section Focus Transparency Interactive CD-ROM Guided Reading Audio Program

End of Chapter Assessment

Blackline Masters	Technology	Professional Series
Chapter Resources Booklet Chapter Review, pp. 33–34 Chapter Tests, pp. 35–38 **Standardized Test Practice by The Princeton Review,** pp. 15–18	MindJogger Videoquiz Interactive CD-ROM Vocabulary PuzzleMakers ExamView Pro Test Bank Interactive Lesson Planner Interactive Teacher Edition	Performance Assessment in the Science Classroom (PASC)

Transparencies

Section Focus

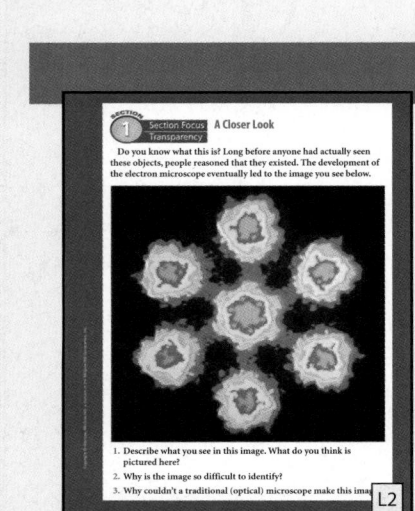

Section Focus Transparency 1 — A Closer Look

Do you know what this is? Long before anyone had actually seen these objects, people reasoned that they existed. The development of the electron microscope eventually led to the image you see below.

1. Describe what you see in this image. What do you think is pictured here?
2. Why is the image so difficult to identify?
3. Why couldn't a traditional (optical) microscope make this image? **L2**

Section Focus Transparency 2 — Oxygen-Oxygen

All matter, including everything in this scene, is composed of atoms in different combinations. Oxygen is an atom that is very important to living things. As you look at this scene, try to figure out what oxygen has to do with it all.

1. Why is oxygen important to everything in the picture?
2. How do plants and animals exchange oxygen? **L2**

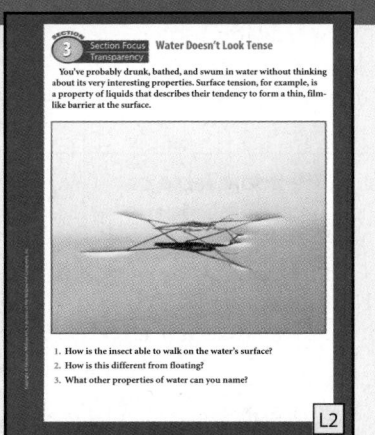

Section Focus Transparency 3 — Water Doesn't Look Tense

You've probably drunk, bathed, and swum in water without thinking about its very interesting properties. Surface tension, for example, is a property of liquids that describes their tendency to form a thin, film-like barrier at the surface.

1. How is the insect able to walk on the water's surface?
2. How is this different from floating?
3. What other properties of water can you name? **L2**

This is a representation of key blackline masters available in the Teacher Classroom Resources. See Resource Manager boxes within the chapter for additional information.

Assessment

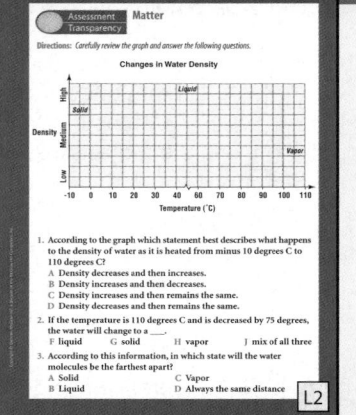

Assessment Transparency — Matter

Directions: Carefully review the graph and answer the following questions.

Changes in Water Density

1. According to the graph which statement best describes what happens to the density of water as it is heated from minus 10 degrees C to 110 degrees C?
   A Density decreases and then increases.
   B Density increases and then decreases.
   C Density increases and then remains the same.
   D Density decreases and then remains the same.
2. If the temperature is 110 degrees C and is decreased by 75 degrees, the water will change to a ____.
   F liquid   G solid   H vapor   J mix of all three
3. According to this information, in which state will the water molecules be the farthest apart?
   A Solid   C Vapor
   B Liquid   D Always the same distance **L2**

Teaching

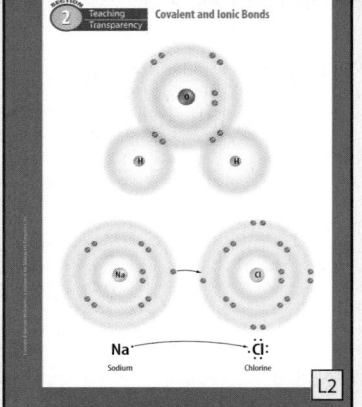

Teaching Transparency 2 — Covalent and Ionic Bonds

Na — Cl:
Sodium   Chlorine **L2**

Key to Teaching Strategies

The following designations will help you decide which activities are appropriate for your students.

L1 Level 1 activities should be appropriate for students with learning difficulties.

L2 Level 2 activities should be within the ability range of all students.

L3 Level 3 activities are designed for above-average students.

ELL ELL activities should be within the ability range of English Language Learners.

COOP LEARN Cooperative Learning activities are designed for small group work.

LS Multiple Learning Styles logos, as described on page 22T, are used throughout to indicate strategies that address different learning styles.

P These strategies represent student products that can be placed into a best-work portfolio.

Hands-on Activities

Activity Worksheets

Activity — Scales of Measurement

Lab Preview
Directions: Answer these questions before you begin the Activity.

1. What physical properties are you measuring in this activity?

2. Why is the sharp object safety symbol shown?

How would you describe some of the objects in your classroom? Perhaps your desktop is about one-half the size of a door. Measuring physical properties in a laboratory experiment will help you make better observations.

What You'll Investigate
How are physical properties of objects measured?

Materials
triple beam balance
100-mL graduated cylinder
metersticks (2)
non-mercury thermometers (3)
stick or dowel
rock sample
string
globe
water

Goals
■ **Measure** various physical properties in SI.
■ **Determine** sources of error.

Safety Precautions

Procedure
Do not "shake down" lab thermometers.
1. Go to every station and determine the measurement requested. Record your observations in the data table on the next page and list sources of error.
   a. Use a balance to determine the mass, to the nearest 0.1g, of the rock sample.
   b. Use a graduated cylinder to measure the water volume, to the nearest 0.5 mL.
   c. Use three thermometers to determine the average temperature, to the nearest 0.5°C, at a selected location in the room.
   d. Use a meterstick to measure the length, to the nearest 0.1 cm, of the stick or dowel.
   e. Use a meterstick and string to measure the circumference of the globe. Be accurate to the nearest 0.1 cm. **L2**

Laboratory Activities

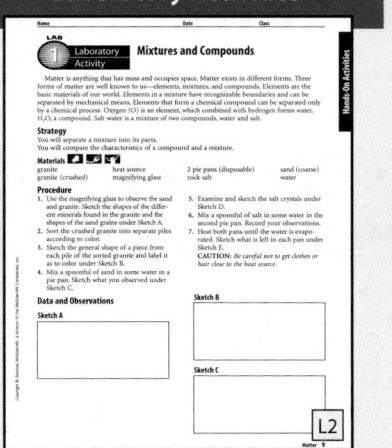

Laboratory Activity 1 — Mixtures and Compounds

Matter is anything that has mass and occupies space. Matter exists in different forms. Three forms of matter are well known to us—elements, mixtures, and compounds. Elements are the basic materials of our world. Elements in a mixture have recognizable boundaries and can be separated by mechanical means. Elements that form a chemical compound can be separated only by a chemical process. Oxygen (O) is an element, which combined with hydrogen forms water, H₂O, a compound. Salt water is a mixture of two compounds, water and salt.

Strategy
You will separate a mixture into its parts.
You will compare the characteristics of a compound and a mixture.

Materials
granite   heat source   2 pie pans (disposable)   sand (coarse)
granite (crushed)   magnifying glass   water
rock salt

Procedure
1. Use the magnifying glass to observe the sand and granite. Sketch the shapes of the different minerals found in the granite and the shapes of the sand grains under Sketch A.
2. Sort the crushed granite into separate piles according to color.
3. Sketch the general shape of a piece from each pile of the sorted granite and label it as to color under Sketch B.
4. Mix a spoonful of sand in some water in a pie pan. Sketch what you observed under Sketch C.
5. Examine and sketch the salt crystals under Sketch D.
6. Mix a spoonful of salt in some water in the second pie pan. Record your observations.
7. Heat both pans until the water is evaporated. Sketch what is left in each pan under Sketch E.
   CAUTION: Be careful not to get clothes or hair close to the heat source.

Data and Observations
Sketch A
Sketch B
Sketch C
Sketch D **L2**

Meeting Different Ability Levels

Content Outline

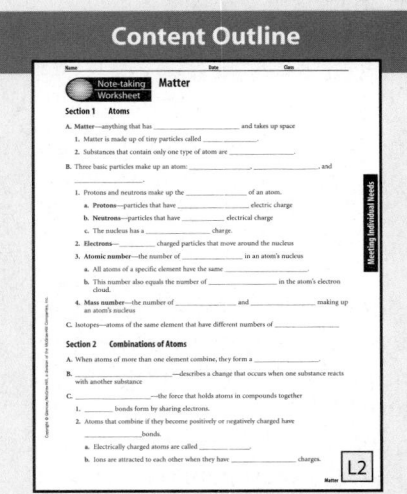

Reinforcement

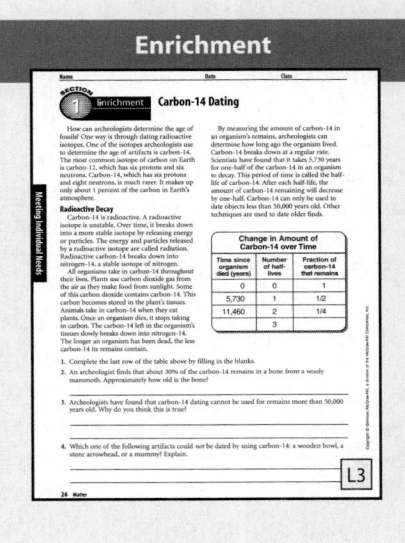

Directed Reading

Assessment

Chapter Tests

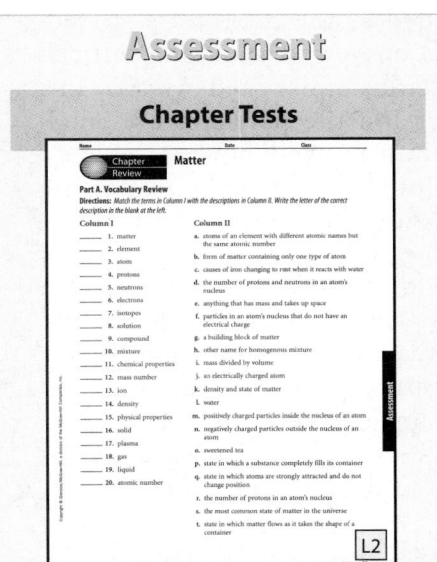

Enrichment

Spanish Directed Reading

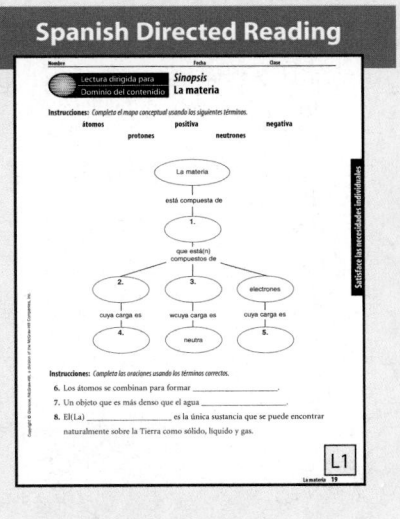

Test Practice Workbook

Chapter Review

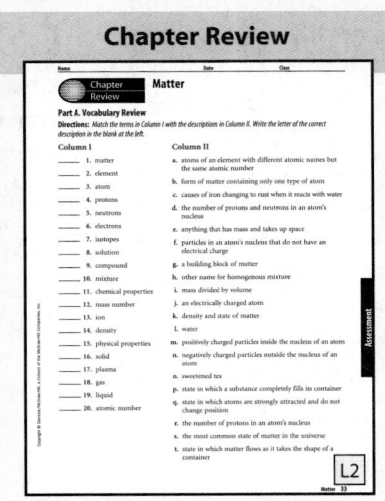

Science Content Background

SECTION 1

Atoms
Uses of Isotopes

Radon gas (Rn-222) exists naturally in the environment. It is one of several isotopes produced as radioactive uranium decays into lead. The radon itself decays, and during this process it gives off particles. Continued exposure to radon gas and its harmful particles can result in tissue damage and lung cancer in humans. In the open air, radon gas is not threatening because it exists in such small amounts. It can, however, leak from the ground into buildings and homes and accumulate to dangerously high levels. The same sequence of uranium-to-lead decay that yields the potentially deadly radon gas is one of the most common and accurate methods that scientists use to determine the age of rocks.

Fun Fact

Dry ice, which is carbon dioxide in a solid state at −78°C, changes to a gas without first being a liquid. This is the process of sublimation, where matter goes directly from a solid to a gas, skipping the liquid phase.

SECTION 2

Combinations of Atoms
Hydrogen Bonds

Hydrogen bonds commonly occur between hydrogen and oxygen atoms. They also occur between hydrogen and nitrogen atoms and hydrogen and fluorine atoms. Although the attractions between atoms formed by hydrogen bonds are not strong enough to bond them into molecules (hydrogen bonds are only about five percent of the strength of covalent bonds), hydrogen bonds do contribute to the strength and stability of a molecule. They also influence the three-dimensional structure of some larger molecules in the human body, such as proteins and DNA. Hydrogen bonds help form the "rungs" of the ladder in the double helix model of a DNA molecule. The bonds are formed because hydrogen atoms of one base pair are attracted to the nitrogen or oxygen atoms of the nearby base.

Mixtures

A colloid or a colloidal dispersion differs from solutions and heterogeneous mixtures because of the size of the particles. A homogeneous mixture, or a solution, has the smallest particles, all of which are dissolved in the solution and do not settle out. A heterogeneous mixture has the largest particles. When a heterogeneous mixture is in a liquid form the particles will remain suspended as the mixture is stirred. When the mixture is left to stand, the particles will eventually settle out like sand in water. In a colloidal dispersion the particles are small enough to remain suspended; however, unlike a solution, a colloid will scatter light passing through the mixture. Colloids can exist in several forms. Some types of colloids consist of liquids that are dispersed into a gas. Fog, in which water droplets are suspended in air, and aerosol sprays are examples. Paint is an example of a colloidal dispersion where a solid has been dispersed into a liquid medium. In colloids such as marshmallows and polyurethane foam a gas is dispersed into a solid medium.

SECTION 3

Properties of Matter
Plasma

The electrons of an atom can be completely separated from the atom itself under conditions of extremely high energy, such as those produced at temperatures of about 10,000°C. When electrons are separated from an atom, plasma—a gaseous mixture of positive ions and electrons—is formed. Besides the Sun and other stars, other familiar examples of plasma include neon signs, fluorescent lamps, and auroras. Auroras occur at high latitudes near Earth's poles. Aurora borealis, "northern lights," occurs in the northern hemisphere and aurora australis, "southern lights," occurs in the southern hemisphere. Auroras are created when charged particles are carried past Earth's magnetic field by the solar wind. As these charged particles move past Earth's magnetic field, tremendous electrical currents are set up. These currents flow into Earth's atmosphere at both the north and south magnetic poles. The electrical currents ionize gas particles in Earth's atmosphere. As the ionized gas particles capture electrons and recombine, light is emitted causing the celestial light known as the aurora. The main colors of auroras are green and red.

Changes in Physical Properties

One of the unique properties of water is that the solid phase, ice, is less dense than the liquid phase. Fresh water has its highest density at 4°C. This property accounts for the fact that there is overturn in lakes in the fall and spring. As surface water cools to 4°C in the fall, it becomes more dense than the water below it and therefore sinks. This process brings oxygen to the bottom waters of lakes and returns nutrients to the surface. As the surface water continues to cool below 4°C, it becomes less dense than the water below it. It does not sink; it forms ice if the temperature drops to 0°C. The ice acts as an insulator for the deeper water, enabling aquatic life to survive the winter. In the spring as the surface water warms up to 4°C, it reaches its maximum density and sinks, thus beginning the spring overturn.

SCIENCE Online

For additional content background on this topic, go to the Glencoe Science Web site at science.glencoe.com.

Mike Macri/Masterfile

Chapter Vocabulary

What do you think?

Science Journal The photograph is of silicon atoms.

What is most striking about this picture—water or ice? What do these things have in common? How are they different? In this chapter, you will find the answers to these questions. You also will learn about the matter that makes up your surroundings and makes up your body.

What do you think?

Science Journal Look at the picture below with a classmate. Discuss what you think these might be. Here's a hint: *They could be part of the landscape of a far-off planet or something in your desk.* Write your answer in your Science Journal.

516

Theme Connection

Scale and Structure The theme of scale and structure is highlighted through the use of large-scale models that illustrate the internal structure of atoms and molecules. This theme is also developed through the discussion of the properties of matter, which are determined by the structure of atoms and molecules.

 **EXPLORE ACTIVITY**

On Earth water is unique because it is found as a solid, liquid, or gas. On a cool autumn morning, you might see gaseous water condensing into fog over a lake or a river whose surface soon will be solid ice. The following activity will help you visualize how matter can change states.

Change the state of water

Safety Precautions

1. Pour 500 mL of water into a 1,000-mL glass beaker.
2. Mark the level of water in the beaker with the bottom edge of a piece of tape.
3. Place the beaker on a hot plate.
4. With the help of an adult, heat the water until it boils for 5 min. Let the water cool.
5. With the help of an adult, compare the level of the water to the bottom edge of the tape.

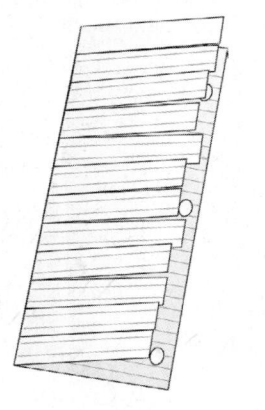

Observe

What came out of the beaker as the water boiled? Did the amount of water that you started with change? In your Science Journal, explain what happened to the water.

 **FOLDABLES**
Reading & Study Skills

Before You Read

Making a Vocabulary Study Fold
Knowing the definition of vocabulary words is a good way to ensure that you understand the content of the chapter.

1. Place a sheet of notebook paper in front of you so the short side is at the top and the holes are on the right side. Fold the paper in half from the left side to the right side.
2. Through the top thickness of paper, cut along every third line from the outside edge to the center fold, forming tabs.
3. Before you read, write vocabulary words from each section in this chapter on the front of the tabs. Under each tab, write what you think the word means.
4. As you read the chapter, add to and correct your definitions.

517

 **EXPLORE ACTIVITY**

Purpose Use the Explore Activity to introduce students to the different states of matter. Inform students that water is found in its solid, liquid, and gaseous states on Earth's surface. L1 **IS Visual-Spatial**

Preparation Several days before beginning this chapter, obtain a hot plate and a 1,000-mL glass beaker.

Materials hot plate, 1,000-mL glass beaker, water, tape

Teaching Strategies
• Have students compare their results with those of other students. Discuss differences and similarities.

Safety Precautions Provide adult supervision as students heat the water, making certain no one touches hot surfaces.

Observe

Steam moved out of the beaker as the water was heated to boiling. Some of the water was changed to the gaseous state when the water boiled. This water escaped from the beaker as steam. As a result, the amount of liquid water that remained was less than the original amount.

☑ Assessment

Oral Ask students to discuss their results in groups. Have one representative from each group explain to the class the group's conclusions. Use **Performance Assessment in the Science Classroom**, p. 89.

FOLDABLES
Reading & Study Skills

Before You Read

Dinah Zike Study Fold
Purpose Students will be exposed to the chapter's content and vocabulary before they read, and will be encouraged to search for terms and definitions as they read. The resulting Foldable can be used as an assessment tool and study guide before, during, and after reading.

📁 For additional help, see Foldables Worksheet, p. 13 in **Chapter Resources Booklet,** or go to the Glencoe Science Web site at **science.glencoe.com.** See After You Read in the Study Guide at the end of this chapter.

SECTION

Atoms

1 Motivate

Bellringer Transparency

Display the Section Focus Transparency for Section 1. Use the accompanying Transparency Activity Master. L2 ELL

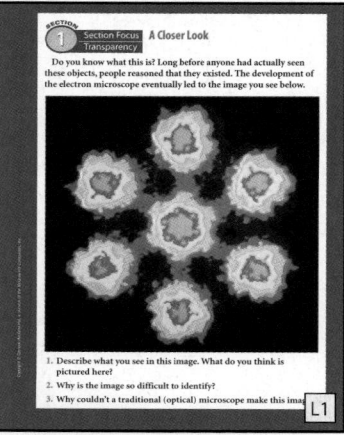

Tie to Prior Knowledge

Help students recall that most soft drink cans are made from the lightweight element aluminum. Ask them to list other objects made of aluminum. Possible answer: lawn chairs and chalkboard borders

---

As You Read

What You'll Learn

- **Identify** the states of matter.
- **Describe** the internal structure of an atom.
- **Compare** isotopes of an element.

Vocabulary

matter	electron
atom	atomic number
element	mass number
proton	isotope
neutron	

Why It's Important

Nearly everything around you—air, water, food, and clothes—is made of atoms.

The Building Blocks of Matter

What do the objects you see, the air you breathe, and the food you eat have in common? They are matter. **Matter** is anything that has mass and takes up space. Heat and light are not matter, because they have no mass and do not take up space. Glance around the room. If all the objects you see are matter, why do they look so different from one another?

Atoms Matter, in its various forms, surrounds you. You can't see all matter as clearly as you see water, which is a transparent liquid, or rocks, which are colorful solids. You can't see air, for example, because air is colorless gas. The forms or properties of one type of matter differ from the properties of another, because matter is made up of tiny particles called **atoms.** The structures of different types of atoms and how they join together determine all the properties of matter that you can observe. **Figure 1** illustrates how small objects, like atoms, can be put together in different ways.

Figure 1
Like atoms, the same few blocks can combine in many ways. *How could this model help explain the variety of matter?*

Section ✓Assessment Planner

PORTFOLIO
Science Journal, p. 519

PERFORMANCE ASSESSMENT
Try at Home MiniLAB, p. 519
Skill Builder Activities, p. 522
See page 542 for more options.

CONTENT ASSESSMENT
Section, p. 522
Challenge, p. 522
Chapter, pp. 542–543

The Structure of Matter Matter is joined together much like the blocks shown in **Figure 1.** The building blocks of matter are atoms. The types of atoms in matter and how they attach to each other give matter its properties.

Elements When atoms combine, they form many different types of matter. Your body contains several types of atoms combined in different ways. These atoms form the proteins, DNA, tissues, and other matter that make you the person you are. Most other objects that you see also are made of several different types of atoms. However, some substances are made of only one type of atom. **Elements** are substances that are made of only one type of atom and cannot be broken down into simpler substances by normal chemical or physical means.

Elements are useful for making a variety of items you depend on every day. They also combine to make up the minerals that compose Earth's crust. Some minerals, however, are made up of only one element. These minerals, which include copper and silver, are called native elements. **Table 1** shows some common elements and their uses. A table of the elements, called the periodic table of the elements, is included on the inside back cover of this book.

TRY AT HOME

Mini LAB

Searching for Elements

Procedure
1. Obtain a copy of the **periodic table of the elements** and familiarize yourself with the elements.
2. Search your house for items made of various elements.
3. Use a **highlighter** to highlight the elements you discovered on your copy of the periodic table.

Analysis
1. Were certain types of elements more common?
2. Infer why you did not find many of the elements.

Table 1 Some Common Uses of Elements

Element	Sulfur	Silver	Copper	Carbon
Native State of the Element	Sulfur	Silver	Copper	Graphite
Uses of the Element	Fertilizer	Tableware	Wire	Ski wax

The Building Blocks of Matter

Caption Answer
Figure 1 Both atoms and blocks can be combined in a variety of ways to form many different substances and structures.

Mini LAB

Purpose Students identify everyday materials that are made of only one element. L2
ELL LS **Visual-Spatial**
Materials Periodic Table of the Elements, highlighter

Teaching Strategies
- Obtain copies of the Periodic Table that students can highlight and write on.
- Help students begin by explaining that some gems, such as diamonds, are made of only one element.

Analysis
1. Possible answer: Metallic elements, such as iron, copper, and gold, were more common.
2. Most elements are found in compounds with other elements. For example salt is a compound of sodium and chlorine.

Assessment

Content To further assess students' understanding, have them work in groups of three to identify items in the classroom made of only one element. Possible answers: oxygen in the air, copper wire, aluminum containers Use **PASC**, p. 91.

Science Journal

Electrical Wire Have students research why electrical wire is often made of copper. Then have them write a report in their Science Journals identifying the traits of copper that make it suited for electrical wire. Copper is a good conductor of electricity. L1 P

Resource Manager

Chapter Resources Booklet
    Transparency Activity, p. 40
    Directed Reading for Content Mastery, pp. 15, 16
    Note-taking Worksheets, pp. 29–31
    MiniLAB, p. 3

Modeling the Atom

Activity

Display the elements noted in **Table 1** as well as other common elements. Ask students to identify the atomic mass and state of matter of each element. Have them relate the properties of each element to its position in the periodic table.

IDENTIFYING
Misconceptions

Students may think that all matter is visible. Address this misconception by finding the mass of a deflated balloon, inflating the balloon, and finding the mass of the filled balloon. Guide students in recognizing that the filled balloon has more mass than the empty balloon because of the presence of air. Since air has mass and takes up space, it is matter even though it is invisible.

Quick Demo

Use interlocking plastic blocks to demonstrate how atoms are the building blocks of matter.

Fun Fact

If an atom were the size of a football stadium, the nucleus of the atom would be the size of a marble located in the center of the stadium.

Figure 2
This model airplane is a small-scale version of a large object.

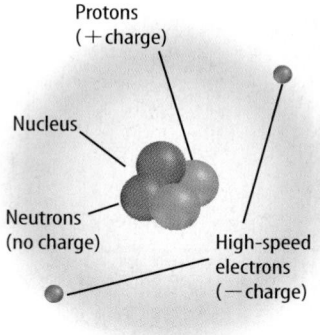

Figure 3
This model of a helium atom shows two protons and two neutrons in the nucleus, and two electrons in the electron cloud.

Modeling the Atom

How can you study things that are too small to be seen with the unaided eye? When something is too large or too small to observe directly, models can be used. The model airplane, shown in **Figure 2,** is a small version of a larger object. A model also can describe tiny objects, such as atoms, that otherwise are difficult or impossible to see.

The History of the Atomic Model The current model of the atom is based on the work of many scientists over hundreds of years. The idea that matter is composed of atoms dates back more than 2,300 years when the Greek philosopher Democritus (dih MAH krih tuhs) proposed that matter is composed of small particles. He called these particles atoms and said that different types of matter were composed of different types of atoms. More than 2,000 years later, John Dalton expanded on these ideas. He theorized that all atoms of an element contain the same type of atom.

Protons and Neutrons In the early 1900s, additional work led to the development of the current model of the atom, shown in **Figure 3.** Three basic particles make up an atom—protons, neutrons (NOO trahnz), and electrons. **Protons** are particles that have a positive electric charge. **Neutrons** have no electric charge. Both particles are located in the nucleus—the center of an atom. With no negative charge to balance the positive charge of the protons, the charge of the nucleus is positive.

Electrons Particles with a negative charge are called **electrons,** and they exist outside of the nucleus. In 1913, Niels Bohr, a Danish scientist, proposed that an atom's electrons travel in orbitlike paths around the nucleus. He also proposed that electrons in an atom have energy that depends on their distance from the nucleus. Electrons in paths that are closer to the nucleus have lower energy, and electrons further from the nucleus have higher energy.

The Current Atomic Model Over the next several decades, research showed that although electrons do have specific amounts of energy, they do not travel in orbitlike paths. Instead, electrons move in an electron cloud surrounding the nucleus. Electrons can be anywhere within the cloud, but evidence suggests that they are located near the nucleus most of the time. To understand how this might work, imagine a beehive. The hive represents the nucleus of an atom. The bees swarming around the hive are like electrons moving around the nucleus. As they swarm, you can't predict their exact location, but they usually stay close to the hive.

Curriculum Connection

Archaeology Have students research how archaeologists use isotopes to determine the age of artifacts such as clothing, wood, bones, and structures. Possible answer: Carbon-14 decays over time. Archaeologists can determine the ages of many objects containing carbon by determining its relative abundance.

Visual Learning

Figure 3 The model in this figure shows an atom of helium with two electrons, two protons, and two neutrons. Ask students to identify the electrical charge of a proton, neutron, and electron. A proton is positive, a neutron has no charge, and an electron is negative. Have students determine the overall charge of the atom's nucleus and of the atom as a whole. +2, no charge

Counting Atomic Particles

You now know where protons, neutrons, and electrons are located, but how many of each are in an atom? The number of protons in an atom depends on the element. All atoms of the same element have the same number of protons. For example, all iron atoms—whether in train tracks or breakfast cereal—contain 26 protons, and all atoms with 26 protons are iron atoms. The number of protons in an atom is equal to the **atomic number** of the element. This number can be found above the element symbol on the periodic table. Notice that as you go from left to right on the periodic table, the atomic number of the element increases by one.

✔ **Reading Check** *How many protons are in an atom of gold, which has an atomic number of 79?*

How many electrons? In a neutral atom, the number of protons is equal to the number of electrons. This makes the overall charge of the atom zero. Therefore, for a neutral atom:

Atomic number = number of protons = number of electrons

Atoms of an element can lose or gain electrons and still be the same element. When this happens, the atom is no longer neutral. Atoms with fewer electrons than protons have a positive charge, and atoms with more electrons than protons have a negative charge.

How many neutrons? Unlike protons, atoms of the same element can have different numbers of neutrons. The number of neutrons in an atom isn't found on the periodic table. Instead, you need to know the atom's mass number. The **mass number** of an atom is equal to the number of protons plus the number of neutrons. The number of neutrons is determined by subtracting the atomic number from the mass number. In **Figure 4,** the number of neutrons can be determined by counting the blue spheres and the number of protons by counting orange spheres. Atoms of the same element that have different numbers of neutrons are called **isotopes.** **Table 2** lists useful isotopes of some elements.

✔ **Reading Check** *How are isotopes of the same element different?*

SECTION 1 Atoms **521**

Some isotopes of elements are radioactive. Physicians can introduce these isotopes into a patient's circulatory system. The low-level radiation they emit allows the isotopes to be tracked as they move throughout the patient's body. Explain how this would be helpful in diagnosing a disease.

Figure 4
This carbon atom is common in organic material. *What is this atom's mass number?*

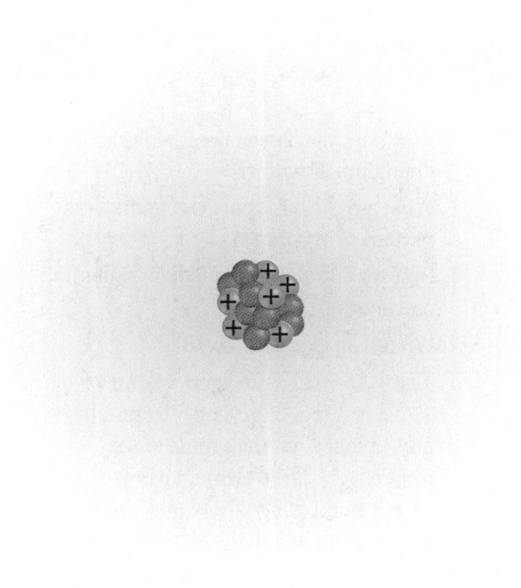

Counting Atomic Particles

The movement of tagged blood can be evaluated for abnormalities. Problems of the circulatory system can be detected in this way.

✔ **Reading Check**

Answer 79

Activity

Have groups of students brainstorm a list of elements that can be found in Earth's rocks. When lists are completed, ask a member of each group to share the results. Then tell students that oxygen is the most common element found in Earth's rocks. Ask students to explain how oxygen, a gas, is also a major part of Earth's solid rocks. Possible answer: Oxygen combines with other elements, forming compounds found in rocks. Guide students in recognizing that the properties of elements change when they become part of a compound.

Caption Answer
Figure 4 14

✔ **Reading Check**

Answer Isotopes of the same element contain different numbers of neutrons in their nuclei.

Teacher FYI

Protons and neutrons are made up of smaller particles called quarks. These unstable particles show up when atomic nuclei are hit by high-energy particles. There appear to be six different types of quarks. The types of quark that make up protons and neutrons determine the charge of each particle. Gluons hold the quarks together.

Resource Manager

Chapter Resources Booklet
    Enrichment, p. 26
    Reinforcement, p. 23
Cultural Diversity, p. 55

Have students use common materials to construct atomic models of the hydrogen-1, hydrogen-2, and carbon-12 isotopes. L2 IS **Kinesthetic**

Challenge

Have students select three different elements from the periodic table and list the information identified on the table for each element. Ask students to describe what each symbol or number represents. Have them share their information in a visual such as a chart or diagram. Possible answer: Fe, iron; atomic number, 26 = number of protons or electrons; atomic mass, 55.845 = average mass of atoms

Performance Have groups of students create and share unique representations of the structure of matter. Use **Performance Assessment in the Science Classroom,** p. 123.

Table 2 Some Useful Isotopes

Isotope	Number of Protons	Number of Neutrons	Number of Electrons	Atomic Number	Mass Number
Hydrogen-1	1	0	1	1	1
Hydrogen-2	1	1	1	1	2
Hydrogen-3	1	2	1	1	3
Carbon-12	6	6	6	6	12
Carbon-14	6	8	6	6	14
Uranium-234	92	142	92	92	234
Uranium-235	92	143	92	92	235
Uranium-238	92	146	92	92	238

Uses of Isotopes Scientists have found uses for isotopes that benefit humans. For example, medical doctors use radioactive isotopes to treat certain types of cancer, such as prostate cancer. Geologists use isotopes to determine the ages of some rocks and fossils.

As you continue to investigate matter in this chapter, you will explore how atoms of different elements combine to form the materials around you.

Section 1 Assessment

1. How does the air you breathe fit the definition of matter?
2. What are the basic particles found in the nucleus of an atom?
3. How do isotopes of an element differ from one another?
4. What is an element?
5. **Think Critically** Oxygen-16 and oxygen-17 are isotopes of oxygen. The numbers 16 and 17 represent their mass numbers, respectively. If the element oxygen has an atomic number of 8, how many protons and neutrons are in these two isotopes?

Skill Builder Activities

6. **Comparing and Contrasting** Review the material in Section 1. How do atoms and elements differ? How are they similar? **For more help, refer to the** Science Skill Handbook.
7. **Solving One-Step Equations** The mass number of a nitrogen atom is 14. Find its atomic number in the periodic table shown on the inside back cover. Then determine the number of neutrons in its nucleus by subtracting the atomic number from the mass number. **For more help, refer to the** Math Skill Handbook.

Answers to Section Assessment

1. Air has mass and takes up space.
2. protons and neutrons
3. Different isotopes of the same element contain different numbers of neutrons.
4. An element is a substance that is made of only one type of atom and cannot be broken down by normal chemical or physical means.
5. Oxygen-16 has eight protons and eight neutrons; oxygen-17 has eight protons and nine neutrons.
6. Atoms, the building blocks of all matter, are composed of three kinds of particles. Atoms are the basic units that compose all matter. An element is matter made of only one type of atom. Both atoms and elements are forms of matter.
7. 7; mass number (14) — atomic number (7) = 7 neutrons

Combinations of Atoms

Interactions of Atoms

When you take a shower, eat your lunch, or do your homework on the computer, you probably don't think about elements. But everything you touch, eat, or use is made from them. Elements are all around you and in you.

There are about 90 naturally occurring elements on Earth. When you think about the variety of matter in the universe, you might find it difficult to believe that most of it consists of combinations of these same elements. How could so few elements produce so many different things? This happens because elements can combine in countless ways. For example, the same oxygen atoms that you breathe also might be found in many other objects, as shown in **Figure 5.** As you can see, each combination of atoms is unique. How do these combinations form and what holds them together?

As You Read

What **You'll Learn**

■ **Describe** ways atoms combine to form compounds.
■ **List** differences between compounds and mixtures.

Vocabulary
compound
ion
mixture
heterogeneous mixture
homogeneous mixture
solution

Why **It's Important**
On Earth, most matter exists as compounds or mixtures.

B Oxygen also is present in the juices of these apples.

A Solid limestone has oxygen within its structure.

Figure 5
Oxygen is a common element found in many different solids, liquids, and gases. *How can the same element, made from the same type of atoms, be found in so many different materials?*

C This canister contains pure oxygen gas.

SECTION 2 Combinations of Atoms **523**

SECTION

2

Combinations of Atoms

1 Motivate

Bellringer Transparency

Display the Section Focus Transparency for Section 2. Use the accompanying Transparency Activity Master. L2
ELL

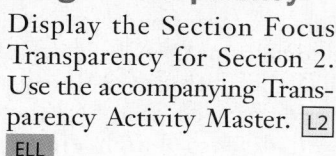

Tie to Prior Knowledge

Remind students that electrons are located outside the nucleus in the electron cloud. Ask students which electrons, those closer to the nucleus or those farther from the nucleus, would most likely react to form compounds. those farther from the nucleus

---

Section ✓ *Assessment* Planner

PORTFOLIO
Cultural Diversity, p. 525
PERFORMANCE ASSESSMENT
MiniLAB, p. 527
Skill Builder Activities, p. 528
See page 542 for more options.

CONTENT ASSESSMENT
Section, p. 528
Challenge, p. 528
Chapter, pp. 542–543

Resource Manager

Chapter Resources Booklet
Transparency Activity, p. 41
Directed Reading for Content Mastery, p. 16

Interactions of Atoms

Caption Answer

Discussion

Explain to students that table salt is a compound of sodium and chlorine (NaCl). Have them use the periodic table on the inside back cover to hypothesize and discuss which elements might replace sodium in this compound. Elements above or below sodium on the chart will replace it in compounds. HCl is hydrogen chloride, KCl is the mineral sylvite, which is also a salt.

✔ Reading Check

Answer three; two hydrogen atoms and one oxygen atom

Bonding

Quick Demo

Soak steel wool in vinegar to remove the soap or any other coating on the wool. Rinse the steel wool and place it in a shallow dish. Leave the uncovered dish on a windowsill. Have students observe any changes that occur. Have them explain the cause of the changes. The steel wool will become covered in a red-brown coating. Iron in the steel wool reacted with oxygen in the air in the presence of water to form iron oxide compounds (rust). **Visual-Spatial**

Figure 6
The water you drink is a compound consisting of hydrogen and oxygen atoms.

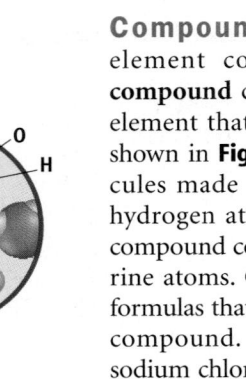

SCIENCE Online

Research Visit the Glencoe Science Web site at **science.glencoe.com** for more information about bonding and the periodic table. Communicate to your class what you learn.

524 CHAPTER 18 Matter

Compounds When atoms of more than one element combine, they form a compound. A **compound** contains atoms of more than one type of element that are chemically bonded together. Water, shown in **Figure 6,** is a compound consisting of molecules made up of one oxygen atom bonded to two hydrogen atoms. Table salt—sodium chloride—is a compound consisting of sodium atoms bonded to chlorine atoms. Compounds are represented by chemical formulas that show the ratios and types of atoms in the compound. For example, the chemical formula for sodium chloride is NaCl. The formula for water is H_2O.

✔ Reading Check *How many atoms does a water molecule have?*

The properties of compounds often are very different from the properties of the elements that combine to form them. Sodium is a soft, silvery metal, and chlorine is a greenish, poisonous gas, but the compound they form is the white, crystalline table salt you use to season food. Under normal conditions on Earth, the hydrogen and oxygen that form water are gases. Water can be solid ice, liquid water, or gaseous vapor. Which state do you think is most common for water at Earth's south pole?

Chemical Properties A property that describes a change that occurs when one substance reacts with another is called a chemical property. For example, one chemical property of water is that it changes to hydrogen and oxygen gas when an electric current passes through it. The chemical properties of a substance depend on what elements are in that substance and how they are arranged. Iron atoms in the mineral biotite will react with water and oxygen to form iron oxide, or rust, but iron mixed with chromium and nickel in stainless steel resists rusting.

Bonding

The forces that hold the atoms in compounds together are called chemical bonds. Some atoms are reactive and form bonds easily. Other atoms are much less reactive. For example, atoms that have eight electrons in the outermost portion of their electron cloud are not likely to combine with other atoms. If an atom has fewer than eight electrons in the outermost portion of its electron cloud, it is unstable and is more likely to combine with other atoms. One exception to this rule is the element helium, with only two electrons in its electron cloud. This atom is stable and does not react easily.

Resource Manager

Chapter Resources Booklet
  Enrichment, p.27
  Transparency Activity, pp. 43–44
Cultural Diversity, p. 65

SCIENCE Online
Internet Addresses _____
_____
_____
_____

Explore the Glencoe Science Web site at **science.glencoe.com** to find out more about topics in this section.

Covalent Bonds Atoms can combine to form compounds in two different ways. One way is by sharing the electrons in the outer portion of their electron clouds. The type of bond that forms by sharing outer electrons is a covalent bond. A group of atoms connected by covalent bonds is called a molecule. For example, two atoms of hydrogen can share outer electrons with one atom of oxygen to form a molecule of water, as shown in **Figure 7.** Each of the hydrogen atoms has one outer electron and the oxygen has six outer electrons. This arrangement causes hydrogen and oxygen atoms to bond together. Each of the hydrogen atoms becomes stable by sharing one electron with the oxygen atom, and the oxygen atom becomes stable by sharing two electrons with the two hydrogen atoms.

Ionic Bonds In addition to sharing electrons, atoms also combine if they become positively or negatively charged. This type of bond is called an ionic bond. Atoms can be neutral, or under certain conditions, atoms can lose or gain electrons. When an atom loses electrons, it has more protons than electrons, so the atom is positively charged. When an atom gains electrons, it has more electrons than protons, so the atom is negatively charged. Electrically charged atoms are called **ions.**

Ions are attracted to each other when they have opposite charges. This is similar to the way magnets behave. If the ends of a pair of magnets have the same type of pole, they repel each other. Conversely, if the ends have opposite poles, they attract one another. Ions form electrically neutral compounds when they join. The mineral halite, commonly used as table salt, forms in this way. A sodium (Na) atom loses an outer electron and becomes a positively charged ion. As shown in **Figure 8,** if the sodium ion comes close to a negatively charged chlorine (Cl) ion, they attract each other and form the salt you use on french fries or popcorn.

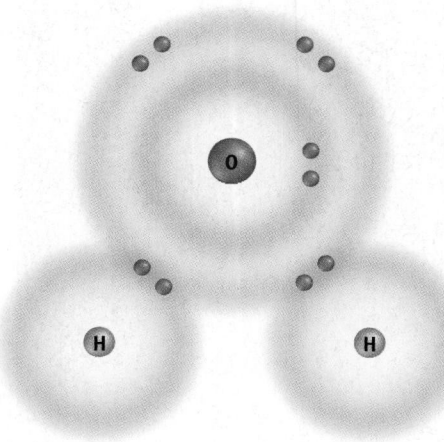

Figure 7
A molecule of water consists of two atoms of hydrogen that share outer electrons with one atom of oxygen.

Figure 8
Table salt forms when a sodium ion and a chlorine ion are attracted to one another. *What kind of bond holds ions together?*

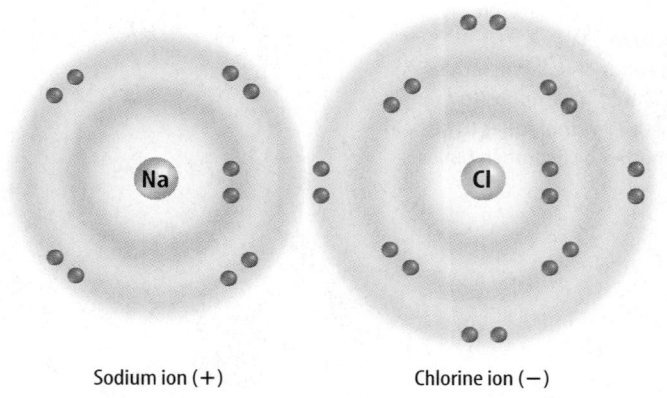

Sodium ion (+)   Chlorine ion (−)

Use Science Words
Word Meaning Explain to students that one type of chemical bond is called a covalent bond. Have them use knowledge of word parts to define the term *covalent*. Co- refers to sharing and -*valent* refers to the valence (outer) electrons. In a covalent bond, valence electrons are shared.

Use an Analogy
Place two small magnets on a desk in front of the class. Explain that the north pole of one magnet is facing the south pole of the other. Ask students to hypothesize what will happen when the two magnets come close to each other. Then, test the accuracy of their predictions by slowly moving the magnets toward each other. Use the reaction of magnets with opposite poles as an analogy for the combining of ions that have opposite electrical charges.

Teacher FYI

The number of electrons in the outer shell of an atom determines whether it will react with another atom. An atom tends to be stable when it has eight electrons in its outer shell. Sodium has one electron in its outer shell, while chlorine has seven. Sodium gives up its outer electron and chlorine picks it up. Now each atom has a stable electron configuration. As charged ions, the atoms combine to form salt.

Caption Answer
Figure 8 ionic

Cultural Diversity

Ocher Ocher is an iron oxide compound that is used in a variety of ways, such as treating wounds and tanning hides and as a pigment for art and body decoration. Ocher was used in the prehistoric production of rock paintings at Lascaux, France. It is still used today for coloration in artwork. One source of ocher, the iron ore hematite, which produces a bright red coloration, appears to have been mined in the African country of Swaziland as early as 44,000 years ago. Have students research cultures that use body coloration. Have them find the reasons for this practice and what materials are used to produce the coloration. Have them write a report on their findings. [L2] **Linguistic** [P]

Teacher FYI

If it weren't for hydrogen bonding, the boiling point of water would be much lower. Hydrogen bonding causes water to be a relatively nonvolatile liquid at room temperature.

Visual Learning

Figure 10 Water droplets form because of cohesion, which is a result of hydrogen bonds. Ask students to find out if hydrogen bonding is like other bonding. No, hydrogen bonds do not involve the transfer or sharing of electrons. They are bonds caused by attractions between opposite partial charges.

Figure 9
Electrons move freely between the copper atoms in this wire. *What type of bond holds copper atoms together?*

Metallic Bonds Metallic bonds are found in metals such as copper, gold, aluminum, and silver. In this type of bond, electrons are free to move from one positively charged ion to another. This free movement of electrons is responsible for key characteristics of metals. The movement of electrons, or conductivity, allows metals like copper, shown in **Figure 9,** to pass an electric current easily.

Hydrogen Bonds Some types of bonds, such as hydrogen bonds, can form without the interactions of electrons. The arrangement of hydrogen and oxygen atoms in water molecules causes them to be polar molecules. A polar molecule has a positive end and a negative end. This happens because the atoms do not share electrons equally. When hydrogen and oxygen atoms form a molecule with covalent bonds, the hydrogen atoms produce an area of partial positive charge and the oxygen atom produces an area of partial negative charge. The positive end of one molecule is attracted to the negative end of another molecule, as shown in **Figure 10,** and a weak hydrogen bond is formed. The different parts of the water molecule are slightly charged, but as a whole, the molecule has no charge. This type of bond is easily broken, indicating that the charges are weak.

Figure 10
The ends of polar molecules, such as water, have opposite charges. This allows molecules to be held together by hydrogen bonds.

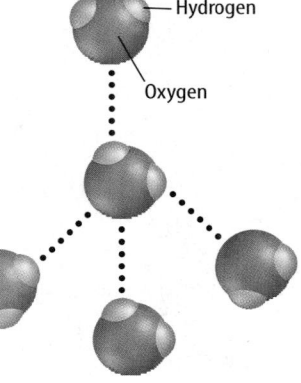

Hydrogen

Oxygen

Hydrogen bonds are responsible for several properties of water, some of which are unique. Cohesion is the attraction between water molecules that allows them to form raindrops and to form beads on flat surfaces. Hydrogen bonds cause water to exist as a liquid, rather than a gas, at room temperature. As water freezes, hydrogen bonds force water molecules apart, into a structure that is less dense than liquid water.

✔ Active Reading

Metacognition Journal In this strategy, each student analyzes his or her own thought processes. Have students divide a sheet of paper in half by folding it lengthwise. On the left have them record what they have learned about a topic. On the right, have them record the reason they learned it. Have students write a Metacognition Journal about chemical bonds.

Teacher FYI

Mixtures are classified according to how well the component substances are mixed together. If the components of a mixture are thoroughly dispersed, the mixture is called a solution. Solutions may be gases, liquids, or solids.

Figure 11
This rock contains a variety of minerals that together form a mixture.

Mixtures

Sometimes compounds and elements mix together but do not combine chemically. A **mixture** is composed of two or more substances that are not chemically combined. There are two different types of mixtures—heterogeneous and homogeneous. The components of a **heterogeneous mixture** are not mixed evenly and each component retains its own properties. Maybe you've seen a rock like the one in **Figure 11.** Several different minerals are mixed together, but if you were to examine the minerals separately, you would find that they have the same properties and appearance as they have in the rock.

The components of a **homogeneous mixture** are evenly mixed throughout. You can't see the individual components. Another name for a homogeneous mixture is a **solution**. The properties of the components of this type of mixture often are different from the properties of the mixture. Ocean water is an example of a liquid solution that consists of salts mixed with liquid water.

Reading Check *What is a solution?*

Separating Mixtures and Compounds

The components of a mixture can be separated by physical means. For example, you can sit at your desk and pick out the separate items in your backpack, or you can let the water evaporate from a saltwater mixture and the salt will remain.

Separating the components of a mixture is a relatively easy task compared to separating those of a compound. The substances in a compound must be separated by chemical means. This means that an existing compound can be changed to one or more new substances by chemically breaking down the original compound. For example, a drop of dilute hydrochloric acid (HCl) can be placed on calcium carbonate ($CaCO_3$) and carbon dioxide (CO_2) is released. To break down most compounds, several steps usually are required.

Resource Manager

Chapter Resources Booklet
    MiniLAB, p. 4
    Lab Activity, pp. 9–10
Science Inquiry Labs, p. 51

**Assessment**

Oral To further assess students' understanding of different forms of matter, have them classify various materials found in the classroom. Use **Performance Assessment in the Science Classroom,** p. 89.

Mini LAB

Classifying Forms of Matter

Procedure
1. Make a chart with columns titled Mixtures, Compounds, and Elements.
2. Classify each of these items into the proper column on your chart: **air, sand, hydrogen, muddy water, sugar, ice, sugar water, water, salt, oxygen, copper.**
3. Make a solution using two or more of the items listed above.

Analysis
1. How does a solution differ from other types of mixtures?
2. How does an element differ from a compound?

Mixtures

Mini LAB

Purpose Students will determine the differences between mixtures, compounds, and elements. L1 **KS** **Kinesthetic Teaching Strategy** Students can make a solution by mixing salt or sugar into a beaker of water. Students' charts should resemble the one below.

Mixtures	Compounds	Elements
air	water	oxygen
muddy water	ice	hydrogen
sugar	sugar	copper
water	salt	
sugar water		
sand		

Analysis
1. One substance is thoroughly and evenly mixed in another substance.
2. Compounds are chemical combinations of two or more elements that cannot be separated physically.

Reading Check

Answer a mixture in which the components are evenly mixed

Separating Mixtures and Compounds

Make a Model

Ask students to make molecular models of compounds using common classroom items. Have them place the completed models in a large box to represent a mixture. Ask students how they would separate the mixture and then the compounds. To separate the mixture just separate the molecules; to separate the compounds you must break the bonds holding them together.

Exploring Matter

Chemistry INTEGRATION

Since its chemical properties have not changed, salt can be tasted in the water. Physical properties have changed. As the salt dissolves, ions of sodium and chlorine dissociate from the crystal and form a solution with the water.

Figure 12
The ocean is a mixture of many different forms of matter. The ocean water itself is a solution.

Chemistry INTEGRATION

When one substance dissolves in another, some of the properties of the dissolving substance change. When salt dissolves in water, decide whether its chemical or physical properties change.

Exploring Matter

Air, sweetened tea, salt water, and the contents of your backpack are examples of mixtures. The combination of rocks, fish, and coral shown in **Figure 12** also is a mixture. In each case, the materials within the mixture are not chemically combined. The individual components are made of compounds, or elements. The atoms that make up these compounds lost their individual properties when they combined. Even though atoms are known as the building blocks of matter, they are composed of protons, neutrons, and electrons, which are even smaller. As you continue to explore matter, apply what you've learned about atoms, elements, compounds, mixtures, and solutions to your studies.

Section 2 Assessment

1. How do atoms or ions combine to form compounds?

2. Why is sweetened tea considered to be a solution rather than a compound?

3. Describe the chemical property of iron that results in rust.

4. Explain what makes a solution different from a heterogeneous mixture.

5. **Think Critically** How can you determine whether salt water is a solution or a compound?

Skill Builder Activities

6. **Comparing and Contrasting** How are solutions and compounds similar? How are they different? **For more help, refer to the** Science Skill Handbook.

7. **Communicating** Design an investigation that would show whether sugar water is a mixture or a compound. Discuss your design with your teacher. Perform the investigation and write the results in your Science Journal. **For more help, refer to the** Science Skill Handbook.

528   CHAPTER 18 Matter

Answers to Section Assessment

1. Atoms share electrons to form molecules of a compound. They can also lose or gain electrons to form ions. Ions attract each other and combine to form compounds.

2. The chemical properties of the sugar and the tea have not changed. They can be separated by evaporation.

3. Iron will combine with oxygen to form iron oxide.

4. One substance is thoroughly and evenly mixed in another substance in a solution. In a heterogeneous mixture they are unevenly mixed.

5. by determining whether the salt and water will separate by evaporation

6. In both, two or more substances are involved. The components of a solution retain their properties; the properties of components of a compound change.

7. Let sugar water evaporate. Sugar will be left behind. Sugar water is a mixture.

Scales of Measurement

BENCH TESTED

How would you describe some of the objects in your classroom? Perhaps your desktop is about one-half the size of a door. Measuring physical properties in a laboratory experiment will help you make better observations.

What You'll Investigate
How are physical properties of objects measured?

Materials
triple beam balance
100-mL graduated cylinder
metersticks (2)
non-mercury thermometers (3)
stick or dowel

rock sample
string
globe
water

Goals
■ **Measure** various physical properties in SI.
■ **Determine** sources of error.

Safety Precautions
Never "shake down" lab thermometers.

Procedure

1. Go to every station and determine the measurement requested. Record your observations in a data table and list sources of error.
   a. Use a balance to determine the mass, to the nearest 0.1 g, of the rock sample.
   b. Use a graduated cylinder to measure the water volume to the nearest 0.5 mL.
   c. Use three thermometers to determine the average temperature, to the nearest 0.5°C, at a selected location in the room.
   d. Use a meterstick to measure the length, to the nearest 0.1 cm, of the stick or dowel.
   e. Use a meterstick and string to measure the circumference of the globe. Be accurate to the nearest 0.1 cm.

Measurement and Error

Sample at Station	Value of Measurement	Causes of Error
a. rock	mass = _____ g	possible answers include:
b. water	volume = _____ mL	
c. (location)	average temp. = _____ °C	human error
d. stick or dowel	length = _____ cm	instrument error
e. globe	circumference = _____ cm	rounding error

Conclude and Apply

1. **Compare** your results with those of other students who measured the same objects. Review the values provided by your teacher. How do the values you obtained compare with those provided by your teacher and other students?

2. **Calculate** your percentage of error in each case. Use this formula.

$$\% \ error = \frac{your \ value \ - \ teacher's \ value}{teacher's \ value} \times 100$$

3. Decide what percentage of error will be acceptable. Generally, being within five percent to seven percent of the correct value is considered good. If your values exceed ten percent error, what could you do to improve your results and reduce error? What was the most common source of error?

Communicating Your Data

Compare your conclusions with those of other students in your class. **For more help, refer to the** Science Skill Handbook.

Purpose
Students will demonstrate safety, accuracy, and precision in using simple laboratory equipment to determine some of the physical properties of sample objects. L1

N Kinesthetic

Process Skills measuring in SI, communicating, using numbers, interpreting data, forming operational definitions

Time Required 40 minutes

Safety Precautions Caution students to handle equipment and materials with care.

Teaching Strategy Set up stations in advance for each of the five tasks.

Troubleshooting Each sample should be identified with a letter or number to avoid confusion.

Answers to Questions

1. Answers will vary depending on the samples used and students' results.
2. Answers will vary depending on the samples used and students' results.
3. Taking several measurements of the same property should decrease error. A common source of error is improper measuring methods.

✓ Assessment

Oral To further assess students' understanding of the physical properties of objects, have them measure various objects in the classroom. Use **PASC,** p. 91.

Resource Manager

Chapter Resources Booklet
Reinforcement, p. 24
Activity Worksheet, pp. 5–6

Physical Science Critical Thinking/Problem Solving, p. 10

Communicating Your Data

Have students discuss sources of error. For example, balance not preset at 0 g, sliding indicator not set in slot; incorrect reading of liquid level in graduated cylinder; inaccurate thermometers, misreading of temperature scale; not starting measurement at 0 cm on meterstick; and other improper methods. L2

SECTION

Matter

 Motivate

Bellringer Transparency

 Display the Section Focus Transparency for Section 3. Use the accompanying Transparency Activity Master. L2

ELL

SECTION
3 | Section Focus Transparency | **Water Doesn't Look Tense**

You've probably drunk, bathed, and swum in water without thinking about its very interesting properties. Surface tension, for example, is a property of liquids that describes their tendency to form a thin, film-like barrier at the surface.

1. How is the insect able to walk on the water's surface?
2. How is this different from floating?
3. What other properties of water can you name?

L2

Tie to Prior Knowledge

Ask a volunteer to name the physical properties of an item in the classroom. Have listeners use the information to name the item. Guide students in recognizing that the properties of an item are unique.

SECTION
3

Properties of Matter

As You Read

What **You'll Learn**
- **Distinguish** between chemical and physical properties.
- **List** the four states of matter.

Vocabulary
density

Why **It's Important**
You can recognize many substances by their physical properties.

Physical Properties of Matter

In addition to the chemical properties of matter that you have already investigated in this chapter, matter also has other properties that can be described. You might describe a pair of blue jeans as soft, blue, and about 80 cm long. A sandwich could have two slices of bread, lettuce, tomato, cheese, and turkey. These descriptions can be made without altering the sandwich or the blue jeans in any way. The properties that you can observe without changing a substance into a new substance are physical properties.

One physical property that you will use to describe matter is density. **Density** is a measure of the mass of an object divided by its volume. Generally, this measurement is given in grams per cubic centimeter (g/cm^3). For example, the average density of liquid water is about 1 g/cm^3. So 1 cm^3 of pure water has a mass of about 1 g.

An object that's more dense than water will sink in water. On the other hand, an object that's not as dense as water will float in water. When oil spills occur on the ocean, as shown in **Figure 13,** the oil floats on the surface of the water and washes up on beaches. Because the oil floats, even a small spill can spread out and cover large areas.

Figure 13
Oil spills on the ocean spread across the surface of the water.
How does the density of oil compare to the density of water?

530 CHAPTER 18 Matter

Section ✓*Assessment* Planner

PORTFOLIO
Extension, p. 533
PERFORMANCE ASSESSMENT
Math Skills Activity, p. 531
Skill Builder Activities, p. 535
See page 542 for more options.

CONTENT ASSESSMENT
Section, p. 535
Challenge, p. 535
Chapter, pp. 542–543

States of Matter

On Earth, matter occurs in four physical states. These four states are solid, liquid, gas, and plasma. You might have had solid toast and liquid milk or juice for breakfast this morning. You breathe air, which is a gas. A lightning bolt during a storm is an example of matter in its plasma state. What are the differences among these four states of matter?

Solids The reason some matter is solid is that its particles are in fixed positions relative to each other. The individual particles vibrate, but they don't switch positions with each other. Solids have a definite shape and take up a definite volume.

Suppose you have a puzzle that is completely assembled. The pieces are connected so one piece cannot switch positions with another piece. However, the pieces can move a little. For example, you can push on one end of the puzzle and move each individual puzzle piece, but the pieces of the puzzle stay attached to one another. The puzzle pieces in this model represent particles of a substance in a solid state. Such particles are strongly attracted to each other and resist being separated.

Math Skills Activity

Calculating Density

You want to find the density of a small cube of an unknown material. It measures 1 cm × 1 cm × 2 cm. It has a mass of 8 g.

Solution

1 *This is what you know:*　　mass: $m = 8$ g
　　　　　　　　　　　　　　　volume: $v = 1$ cm × 1 cm × 2 cm = 2 cm^3

2 *This is what you need to find:*　density: d

3 *This is the equation you need to use:*　$d = m/v$

4 *Substitute the known values:*　$d = 8$ g/2 cm^3
　　　　　　　　　　　　　　　　$d = 4$ g/cm^3

Check your answer by multiplying by the volume. Do you calculate the same mass that was given? Explain.

Practice Problem

You discover a gold bar while exploring an old shipwreck. It measures 10 cm × 5 cm × 2 cm. It has a mass of 1,930 g. Find the density of gold.

For more help refer to the Math Skill Handbook.

SECTION 3 Properties of Matter **531**

IDENTIFYING
Misconceptions

Students may not realize that matter can change from a solid to a gas without going through the liquid phase. This process is called sublimation.

Quick Demo

Obtain a piece of dry ice (carbon dioxide in a frozen, solid state). Place the dry ice on a plate in view of students. The dry ice will quickly change into carbon dioxide gas via sublimation. Students should note that it doesn't pass through a liquid state. **CAUTION:** *Do not touch the dry ice. Always use a thermal mitt and tongs to manipulate the ice. Perform the demonstration in a well-ventilated area.*

✓ Reading Check

Answer Air fresheners release molecules that spread out and fill the room.

SCIENCE
Online

Research Visit the Glencoe Science Web site at **science. glencoe.com** for information about the four states of matter. Communicate to your class what you learn.

Figure 14
The Sun is an example of a plasma.

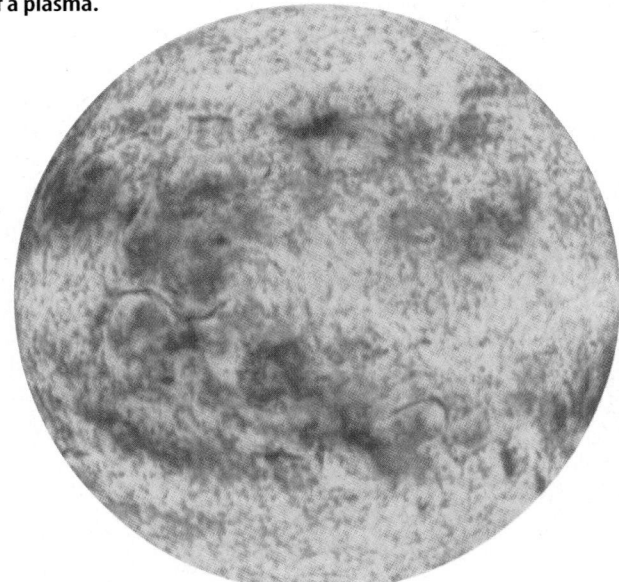

Liquids Particles in a liquid are attracted to each other, but are not in fixed positions as they are in the solid shown in **Figure 15A.** This is because liquid particles have more energy than solid particles. This energy allows them to move around and change positions with each other.

When you eat breakfast, you might have several liquids at the table such as syrup, juice, and milk. These are substances in the liquid state, even though one flows more freely than the others at room temperature. The particles in a liquid can change positions to fit the shape of the container they are held in. You can pour any liquid into any container, and it will flow until it matches the shape of its new container.

Gases The particles that make up gases have enough energy to overcome any attractions between them. This allows them to move freely and independently. Unlike liquids and solids, gases spread out and fill the container in which they are placed. Air fresheners work in a similar way. If an air freshener is placed in a corner, it isn't long before the particles from the air freshener have spread throughout the room. Look at the hot-air balloon shown in **Figure 15C.** The particles in the balloon are evenly spaced throughout the balloon. The balloon floats in the sky, because the hot air inside the balloon is less dense than the colder air around it.

✓ Reading Check   *Why do air fresheners work?*

Plasma The most common state of matter in the universe is plasma. This state is associated with high temperatures. Can you name something that is in the plasma state? Stars like the Sun, shown in **Figure 14,** are composed of matter in the plasma state. Plasma also exists in Jupiter's magnetic field. On Earth, plasma is found in lightning bolts, as shown in **Figure 15D.** Plasma is composed of ions and electrons. It forms when high temperatures cause some of the electrons normally found in an atom's electron cloud to escape and move outside of the electron cloud.

532   CHAPTER 18 Matter

LAB DEMONSTRATION

Purpose to see that molecular attraction affects how a liquid flows
Materials syrup, milk, two 250-mL beakers
Preparation Set out containers of syrup and milk so that both will be at room temperature for the demonstration.

Procedure Instruct students to observe as you pour syrup and milk into two separate containers. Ask students to contrast the rates at which the two liquids flow.
Expected Outcome Students will note that the two liquids flowed at different rates and that the syrup was thicker.

✓ *Assessment*

Why does the syrup move more slowly than the milk? The syrup flows more slowly because it is thicker. This is caused by a stronger attraction between molecules in the syrup than in the milk.

Figure 15

Matter on Earth exists naturally in four different states—solid, liquid, gas, and plasma—as shown here. The state of a sample of matter depends upon the amount of energy its atoms or molecules possess. The more energy that matter contains, the more freely its atoms or molecules move, because they are able to overcome the attractive forces that tend to hold them together.

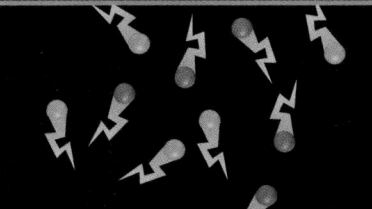

D PLASMA Electrically charged particles in lightning are free moving.

A SOLID In a solid such as galena, the tightly packed atoms or molecules lack the energy to move out of position.

B LIQUID The atoms or molecules in a liquid such as water have enough energy to overcome some attractive forces and move over and around one another.

C GAS In air and other gases, atoms or molecules have sufficient energy to separate from each other completely and move in all directions.

533

Visualizing States of Matter

Have students examine the pictures and read the captions. Then ask the following questions.

How are the properties of shape and volume used to distinguish among a solid, a liquid, and a gas? A solid has a definite shape and volume. A liquid has a definite volume, but takes the shape of its container. A gas takes up the total volume available and has no shape other than the container that encloses it.

Activity

Organize the class into several groups. Call out a letter of the alphabet. Give the groups 30 seconds to write as many examples as they can for each of the three states of matter that begins with that letter; for example, *A:* gas—air, liquid—alcohol, solid—aluminum. Then ask a group member to read the list. Repeat with other letters. Discuss which state of matter they found easiest to identify from the examples.

Extension

Have students investigate plasmas that occur in everyday objects such as fluorescent lamps, neon signs, and sodium vapor streetlights. Ask students to make a poster describing how one of these devices works. L2

IN **Visual-Spatial** P

Inclusion Strategies

Behaviorally Disordered Hide an open bottle of vinegar or clove oil in the classroom. Have students raise their hands when they detect the odor. Ask students to describe the direction of the flow of molecules of the gas from the bottle through the air.

Resource Manager

Chapter Resources Booklet
   Lab Activity, pp. 11–12
   Enrichment, p. 28
Science Inquiry Labs, p. 43

Changing the State of Matter

Activity

Put 100 mL of water and five ice cubes in a 600-mL beaker. Record the temperature of the water. Slowly heat the beaker, and record the water temperature at one-minute intervals. Note when the ice melts and when the water begins to boil. Measure and record the temperature as the water boils for five minutes. Have students graph the temperature of the water as a function of time. L3

- **What was the maximum temperature reached when ice was still in the water?** 0°C
- **What was the maximum temperature reached?** 100°C
- **What do the horizontal portions of your graph represent?** changes of state

Changes in Physical Properties

Visual Learning

Figure 17 Have students hypothesize why ice is less dense than liquid water. Molecules move farther apart as water freezes.

Reading Check

Answer Ice is less dense than water.

Figure 16
A solid metal can be changed to a liquid by adding thermal energy to its molecules. *What is happening to the molecules during this change?*

Figure 17
If ice were more dense than water, lakes would freeze solid from the bottom up. *What effect might this have on the fish?*

Changing the State of Matter

Matter is changed from a liquid to a solid at its freezing point and from a liquid to a gas at its boiling point. You may know the freezing and boiling points of water. Water changes from a liquid to a solid at its freezing point of 0°C. It boils at 100°C. Water is the only substance that occurs naturally on Earth as a solid, liquid, and gas. Other substances don't naturally occur in these three states on Earth because of the limited temperature range Earth experiences. For example, temperatures on Earth do not get cold enough for solid carbon dioxide to exist naturally. However, it can be produced by humans.

The attraction between particles of a substance and their rate of movement are factors that determine the state of matter. When thermal energy is added to ice, the rate of movement of its molecules increases. This allows the molecules to move more freely and causes the ice to melt. As **Figure 16** shows, even solid metal can be converted into liquid when enough thermal energy is added.

Changes in state also occur because of increases or decreases in pressure. You can demonstrate this with an ice cube. When subjected to pressure, the ice will change to liquid water when no thermal energy is added. This occurs because the melting temperature of the ice is lowered as more pressure is added. This might explain how the base of a glacier can move around some rock obstacles. It is thought that the pressure of the glacier on the rock melts the ice, creating a thin layer of water. The water then flows around the obstacle and refreezes on the other side.

Changes in Physical Properties

Chemical properties of matter don't change when the matter changes state, but some of its physical properties change. For example, the density of water changes as water changes state. Ice floats in liquid water, as seen in **Figure 17,** because it is less dense than liquid water. This is unique, because most materials are denser in their solid state than in their liquid state.

Reading Check *Why does ice float in water?*

Some physical properties of substances don't change when they change state. For example, water is colorless and transparent in each of its states.

Inclusion Strategies

Visually Impaired Help students recognize the different states of matter by having them use other senses to detect each state of matter. Have them touch a wood block and the liquid in a cup of water. Have them sense a gas by having them smell an open bottle of vanilla. As an alternative, place a cup of ice near the students so they can feel the change from the solid to the liquid state of water.

Changing Mars's Matter

Matter in one state often can be changed to another state by adding or removing thermal energy. Changes in thermal energy might explain why Mars appears to have had considerable water on its surface in the past but now has little or no water on its surface. Recent images of Mars reveal that there might still be some groundwater that occasionally reaches the surface, as shown in **Figure 18.** But what could explain the huge water-carved channels that formed long ago? Much of the liquid water on Mars might have changed state as the planet cooled to its current temperature. Scientists believe that some of Mars's liquid water soaked into the ground and froze, forming permafrost. Some of the water might have frozen to form the polar ice caps. Even more of the water might have evaporated into the atmosphere and escaped to space.

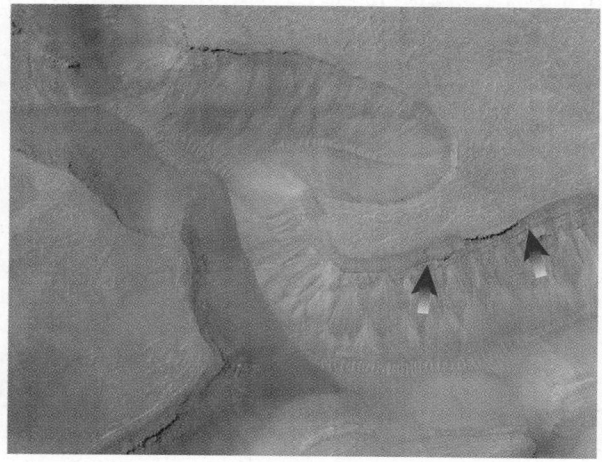

Figure 18
Groundwater might reach the surface of Mars along the edge of this large channel.

Section 3 Assessment

1. List the four states of matter in order from lowest to highest in terms of amount of particle movement.

2. Compare and contrast the movement of water molecules when water is in a solid, liquid, and gaseous state. How is the movement of water molecules dependent upon temperature?

3. As water freezes, what happens to the water molecules that causes ice to float? Why is this unique?

4. What type of properties of a substance can be observed without changing it into a new substance?

5. **Think Critically** Suppose you blow up a balloon and then place it in a freezer. Later, you find that the balloon has shrunk and has drops of frozen liquid in it. Explain what has happened.

Skill Builder Activities

6. **Classifying** Classify the following items into the four types of matter: *groundwater, lightning, lava, snow, textbook, ice cap, notebook, apple juice, eraser, glass, cotton, helium, iron oxide, lake, limestone,* and *water vapor.* Compare and contrast their characteristics. **For more help, refer to the** Science Skill Handbook.

7. **Using Graphics Software** Research the melting and boiling points in degrees Celsius of several compounds, including water. Use your computer to make a line graph showing the temperatures at which these several compounds change state from solid to liquid to gas. Rearrange your data in order of increasing melting and boiling points. **For more help, refer to the** Technology Skill Handbook.

Reteach

Demonstrate how water changes state. Place an ice cube in a pan on your desk. As the ice cube warms, it will change to liquid water. Then show students how ice will change to a liquid when pressure is applied by pressing down on the ice with wood block or other large object. **Visual-Spatial**

Challenge

Ask students to explain how changes in the state of solid water aid an ice skater. Pressure applied by the ice skate on the ice and an increase in temperature caused by friction with the ice causes some solid water to change state, producing a film of liquid water over which the skate can slide.

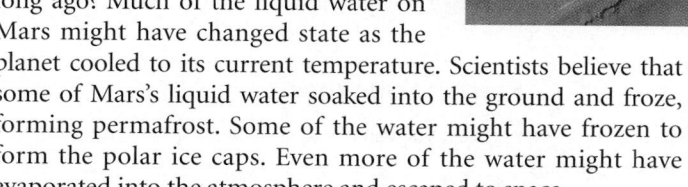

Performance Assess students' understanding of states of matter by having them make a table of the breakfast items they had that morning. Have them list all items in their breakfast as solid, liquid, or gas. Possible answer: cereal—solid, milk or juice—liquid, and water vapor (from hot tea)—gas Use **Performance Assessment in the Science Classroom,** p. 109.

Answers to Section Assessment

1. solid, liquid, gas, plasma
2. Movement of the molecules occurs in each state. Molecules vibrate in place in solid ice. In liquid water, molecules vibrate more rapidly and move past each other. In water vapor (gas), molecules move freely and rapidly. Increases in temperature will increase movement.
3. As water freezes, molecules move apart, making ice less dense than water. When other materials change from liquid to solid, molecules move together.
4. physical properties
5. As air temperature was lowered, air molecules moved closer together, shrinking the balloon. Molecules of water vapor condensed to form liquid water, which then froze.
6. solid: snow, textbook, ice cap, notebook, eraser, glass, cotton, iron oxide, limestone; liquid: groundwater, lava, apple juice, lake; gas: helium, water vapor; plasma: lightning; compare: they are all states of matter; contrast: the amount of movement of and the spacing between the molecules is different in each state
7. Check students' work.

Activity
Design Your Own Experiment

Determining Density

Which has a greater density—a rock or a sponge? Is cork more dense than clay? Density is the ratio of an object's mass to its volume.

Recognize the Problem

Purpose

Students will design and carry out an experiment to measure the volume and mass of various objects and to determine their densities. L1 IS **Interpersonal**

Process Skills

measuring in SI, using numbers, interpreting data, inferring, communicating, making and using tables, forming a hypothesis, designing an experiment, separating and controlling variables

Time Required

two class periods: one class period for students to devise a method of measuring the volume of objects and to complete the measurements; one class period for students to calculate the density of the objects and to discuss the procedure and outcome

Form a Hypothesis

Possible Hypotheses

- The volume of an object can be determined by submerging it in water and measuring the volume of water displaced.
- The volume of a cubic or prismatic object can be determined by multiplying its length, width, and height.
- The density of an object is determined by dividing its mass by its volume.

Recognize the Problem

How can you determine the densities of several objects in your classroom?

Form a Hypothesis

State a hypothesis about what process you can use to measure and compare the densities of several materials.

Possible Materials

pan
triple-beam balance
100-mL beaker
250-mL graduated cylinder
water
sponge
piece of quartz
piece of clay
small wooden block
small metal block
small cork
rock
ruler

Goals

- **List** some ways that the density of an object can be measured.
- **Design** an experiment that compares the densities of several materials.

Safety Precautions

WARNING: *Be wary of sharp edges on some of the materials and take care not to break the beaker or graduated cylinder. Wash hands thoroughly with soap and water when finished.*

536

Test Your Hypothesis

Possible Procedures

- Most students will realize that the volume and mass of each object must be determined in order to calculate the density. However, students may have difficulty devising a method for measuring volume.

- Measuring the volume of water displaced by an object will provide the volume of the object.

- The volume of objects with straight sides can be obtained by measuring their width, length, and height.

- The mass of an object can be obtained by using the pan balance.

Test Your Hypothesis

Plan

1. As a group, agree upon and write the hypothesis statement.

2. As a group, list the steps that you need to take to test your hypothesis. Be specific, describing exactly what you will do at each step. List your materials.

3. While working as a group, use this equation: density = mass/volume. Devise a method of determining the mass and volume of each material to be tested.

4. **Design** a data table in your Science Journal so that it is ready to use as your group collects data.

Check the Plan

1. Read over your entire experiment to make sure that all steps are in a logical order.

2. Should you run the process more than once for any of the materials?

3. **Identify** any constants, variables, and controls of the experiment.

4. Make sure your teacher approves your plan before you start.

Do

1. Carry out the experiment as planned.

2. While the experiment is going on, write any observations that you make and complete the data table in your Science Journal.

Analyze Your Data

1. Do you observe anything about the way objects with greater density feel compared with objects of lower density?

2. Which of the objects you tested would float in water? Which would sink?

Draw Conclusions

1. Based on your results, would you hypothesize that a cork is more dense, the same density, or less dense than water?

2. Without measuring the density of an object that floats, conclude how you know that it has a density of less than 1.0 g/cm³.

3. Would the density of the clay be affected if you were to break it into smaller pieces?

$\mathcal{C}$ommunicating
Your Data

Write an informational pamphlet on different methods for determining the density of objects. Include equations and a step-by-step procedure.

ACTIVITY   537

Teaching Strategies

Tie to Prior Knowledge Have students recall that density can be compared by attempting to float one material within another.

Troubleshooting Use oil-based clay that is not water-soluble. Since the wood block may absorb water, it should not be left in water for any extended length of time.

Expected Outcome

Students should be able to measure the volume and mass of each object and calculate densities within a 10 percent error.

Analyze Your Data

1. Denser objects feel heavier than less dense objects of the same size. Objects like these are said to have greater heft.

2. Cork, sponge, wooden block float in water. Other objects sink.

Error Analysis

Ask students why comparing the heft of two different-sized objects would not be as useful.

Draw Conclusions

1. The cork is less dense than water.

2. Water has a density of 1 g/cm³.

3. As long as the same sample is used, the density of the clay is not affected by the size of the piece.

$\checkmark$ *Assessment*

Performance To further assess students' understanding of density and measuring physical properties, have them repeat the above experiment using different samples of the materials they tested. Have them list possible causes of any differences observed. Use **Performance Assessment in the Science Classroom**, p. 89.

$\mathcal{C}$ommunicating
Your Data

Use a computer spreadsheet to make a data table for your results. Table column headings should be *object, length, width, height, volume, mass,* and *density*. Table row headings, under object, should be *sponge, quartz, clay, wood block, metal block, cork,* and *rock*.

Content Background

Aside from being the heaviest of the abundant natural elements, uranium was also the first element discovered to be radioactive. Today uranium is found naturally in many minerals and is used as fuel for nuclear reactors.

Discussion

Have students recall what the mass number of an atom represents. Possible answer: The mass number of an atom is equal to the number of protons plus the number of neutrons. **What are isotopes of atoms and how are they represented symbolically?** Possible answer: Isotopes are atoms of the same element that have a different number of neutrons and therefore a different mass number. In print, they are indicated by the name of the atom or its symbol followed by the mass number; for example, uranium-234.

Activity

Organize students into groups. Each group can research information on one of the groups on the periodic table. Have students include which elements are in the group, information on the properties of those elements, some common uses of those elements, and possibly some fun facts about the elements. Students can present their results in a show-and-tell format using visual aids they have made. Encourage students to be creative with the format of their presentations. For example, for the element sodium, students can bring in salt as an example of a common use.

Science Stats

Amazing Atoms

Did you know . . .

. . . The diameter of an atom is about 100,000 times as great as the diameter of its nucleus. Suppose that when you sit in a chair, you represent the nucleus of an atom. The nearest electron in your atom would be about 120 km away—nearly half the distance across the Florida peninsula.

. . . Uranium has the greatest mass of the abundant natural elements. One atom of uranium has a mass number that is more than 235 times greater than the mass number of one hydrogen atom, the element with the least mass. However, the diameter of a uranium atom is only about three times the size of a hydrogen atom, similar to the difference between a baseball and a volleyball.

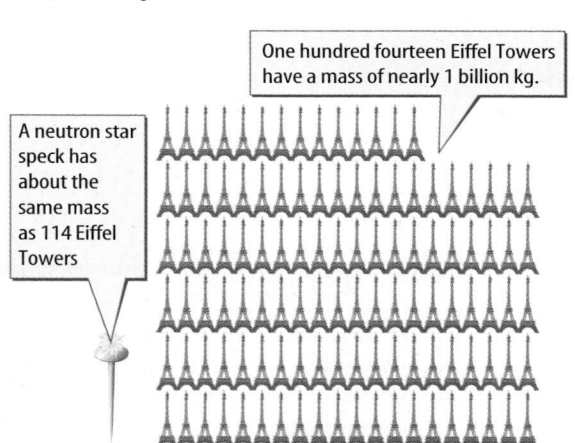

One hundred fourteen Eiffel Towers have a mass of nearly 1 billion kg.

A neutron star speck has about the same mass as 114 Eiffel Towers

. . . The densest material in the universe is found in a neutron star. The core of this type of star is made only of neutrons. Although neutron stars are small, measuring about 10 km to 20 km in diameter, they have a greater mass than the Sun. One tiny pinhead-sized speck of a neutron star would have the same mass as about 114 Eiffel Towers.

538 CHAPTER 18 Matter

Curriculum Connection

Math Have students make a circle graph that represents the percentage of the different elements that compose air. **How do the percentages in the graph compare with the elements found in Earth's crust?** Both graphs show that two elements—nitrogen and oxygen in air, and oxygen and silicon in Earth's crust—have the largest percentages. Air and Earth's crust contain small amounts of other elements. Earth's crust contains more oxygen than air does.

... The melting point of Cesium is 28.4°C. It would melt in your hand if you held it. You would not want to hold cesium, though, because it would react strongly with your skin. In fact, the metal might even catch fire.

... An atomic fountain clock is the world's most accurate timepiece. This timepiece is called an atomic fountain clock because it uses a fountainlike movement of atoms to record time. The atoms are cooled to an extremely low temperature and tossed into a vacuum chamber. The natural vibrations of the atoms are measured. Atomic fountain clocks gain or lose only 1 s in more than 20 million years.

... More than ninety elements occur naturally. However, about 98% of Earth's crust consists of only the eight elements shown here.

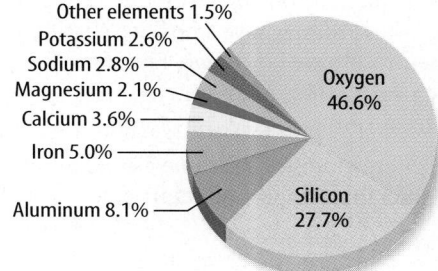

Other elements 1.5%
Potassium 2.6%
Sodium 2.8%
Magnesium 2.1%
Calcium 3.6%
Iron 5.0%
Aluminum 8.1%
Oxygen 46.6%
Silicon 27.7%

Do the Math

1. Looking at the circle graph, which is the third most abundant element in Earth's crust?
2. How much lower is the melting point of cesium than the average human body temperature of 37°C?
3. The diameter of the Sun is 1,392,000 km. How many neutron stars, each measuring 15 km in diameter, would fit along the Sun's diameter when placed side to side?

Go Further

Do research on the Glencoe Science Web site at **science.glencoe.com** to find out more about atoms and isotopes. What is a radioactive isotope of an element? How are isotopes used in science?

SCIENCE STATS **539**

Teaching Strategies
Have students review how to read a circle graph.

Answers
1. Aluminum at 8.1 percent
2. 8.6°C
3. 92,800 neutron stars

Go Further
Have students present their results in a simple chart with the headings: "Isotope" and "Scientific Use." Have students choose one example of radioactive decay, such as uranium-238, and illustrate the entire sequence on a poster. Information on the half-life of the isotopes can be included as well.

SCIENCE
Online
Internet Addresses
_____
_____
_____
Explore the Glencoe Science Web site at **science.glencoe.com** to find out more about topics in this feature.

Reviewing Main Ideas

Preview

Students can answer the questions in their Science Journals. Discuss the answers as you go through the chapter. **Linguistic**

Review

Students can write their answers, then compare them with those of other students. **Interpersonal**

Reteach

Students can look at the illustrations and describe details that support the main ideas of the chapter. **Visual-Spatial**

Answers to Chapter Review

SECTION 1

1. Atoms can combine in different ways to form different forms of matter, just as a few blocks can combine in many different ways.

SECTION 2

2. Each item in the book bag retains its own physical properties.

SECTION 3

2. Plasma is composed of ions and electrons where many of the electrons are outside of the ion's electron cloud.

4. Liquid water is more dense.

Reviewing Main Ideas

Section 1 Atoms

1. Matter is anything that has mass and takes up space. *How is matter similar to the snap-together blocks shown below?*

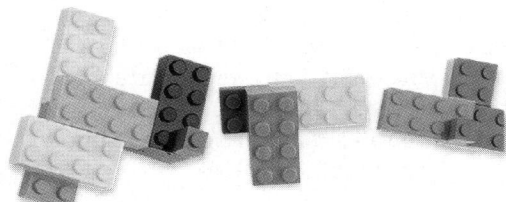

2. Protons and neutrons make up the nucleus of an atom. Protons have a positive charge, and neutrons have no charge. Electrons have a negative charge and surround the nucleus, forming an electron cloud.

3. Isotopes are atoms of the same element that have different numbers of neutrons.

Section 2 Combinations of Atoms

1. Atoms join to form compounds and molecules. A compound is a substance made of two or more elements. The properties of a compound differ from the chemical and physical properties of the elements of which it is composed.

2. A mixture is a substance in which the components are not chemically combined. *Why are the contents of the book bag, shown to the right, considered to be a mixture and not a compound?*

Section 3 Properties of Matter

1. Physical properties can be observed and measured without causing a chemical change in a substance. Chemical properties can be observed only when one substance reacts with another substance.

2. Atoms or molecules in a solid are in fixed positions relative to one another. In a liquid, the atoms or molecules are close together but are freer to change positions. Atoms or molecules in a gas move freely to fill any container. *What makes up plasma, such as the lightning bolts to the right?*

3. Water is the only substance on Earth that occurs naturally as a solid, liquid, and gas. Other substances do not exist in all three states on Earth because of Earth's narrow temperature range.

4. One physical property that is used to describe matter is density. Density is a ratio of the mass of an object to its volume. A material that is less dense will float in a material that is more dense. *Ice floats in liquid water, so which state of water is more dense?*

FOLDABLES
Reading & Study Skills

After You Read

Use each vocabulary word on your Vocabulary Study Fold in a sentence about matter and write it next to the definition of the word.

FOLDABLES
Reading & Study Skills

After You Read

After students have read the chapter and completed the Foldable described in Before You Read, have them do the activity on the student page.

Dinah Zike

Visualizing Main Ideas

Complete the following concept map on matter. Use the following terms: liquids, plasma, matter, *and* solids.

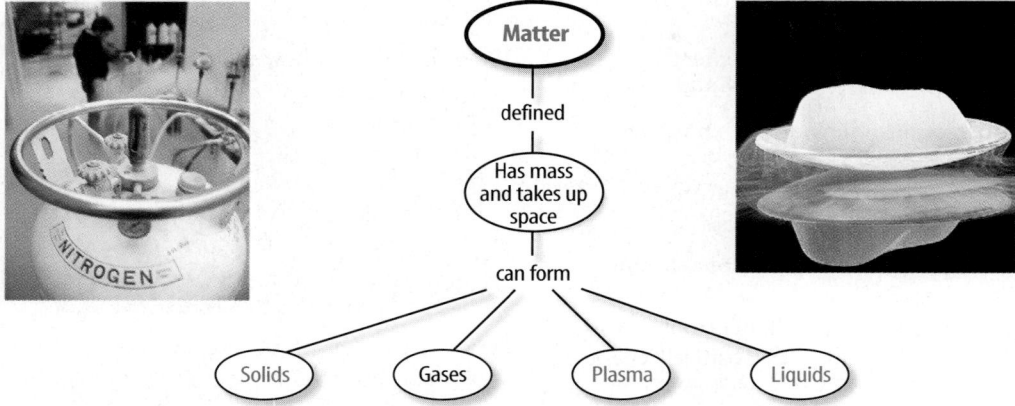

Matter

defined

Has mass and takes up space

can form

Solids • Gases • Plasma • Liquids

Vocabulary Review

Vocabulary Words

a. atom
b. atomic number
c. compound
d. density
e. electron
f. element
g. ion
h. isotope
i. heterogeneous mixture
j. homogeneous mixture
k. mass number
l. matter
m. mixture
n. neutron
o. proton
p. solution

THE PRINCETON REVIEW Study Tip

Take good notes, even during lab. Lab experiments reinforce key concepts, and looking back on these notes can help you better understand what happened and why.

Using Vocabulary

Explain the difference between the vocabulary words in each of the following sets.

1. atom, element
2. mass number, atomic number
3. solution, heterogeneous mixture
4. matter, compound, element
5. heterogeneous mixture, homogeneous mixture
6. proton, neutron, electron
7. isotope, atom
8. atom, ion
9. mixture, compound
10. neutron, mass number

CHAPTER STUDY GUIDE 541

Visualizing Main Ideas

See student page.

Vocabulary Review

Using Vocabulary

1. Atoms are composed of protons, neutrons, and electrons. Elements are substances that contain only one type of atom.
2. Atomic number is the number of protons in an atom's nucleus. Mass number is the number of protons and neutrons in an atom's nucleus.
3. A solution is a mixture in which one substance is thoroughly and evenly mixed in another substance. In a heterogeneous mixture, the substances are not mixed evenly.
4. Matter can be in the form of a compound (two or more elements) or an element (one type of atom).
5. In a homogeneous mixture, one substance is thoroughly and evenly mixed in another substance. In a heterogeneous mixture, the substances are not mixed evenly.
6. Protons and neutrons are in the nucleus of an atom; electrons are outside the nucleus. A proton has a positive charge. A neutron has no charge. An electron has a negative charge.
7. Atoms are the basic particles of matter. Isotopes are atoms of the same element that have different numbers of neutrons in their nuclei.
8. An atom has a neutral charge. An ion is an atom that has lost or gained electrons and therefore has a charge.
9. Compounds contain atoms of two or more elements that are chemically bonded. Mixtures are composed of two or more substances that are not chemically combined.
10. A neutron is an uncharged particle in the nucleus of an atom. The mass number of an atom is the total number of protons and neutrons found in its nucleus.

Chapter 18 Assessment

Checking Concepts

1. C
2. B
3. A
4. A
5. B
6. A
7. D
8. D
9. B
10. D

Thinking Critically

11. The number of protons in the nucleus of the atom is equal to the number of electrons in the electron cloud.
12. carbon-14 (8)
13. Yes; isotopes differ in the number of neutrons.
14. They will combine to form a compound. Lithium has only one electron in the outermost portion of its electron cloud. Chlorine has seven. Both atoms will "seek" to have a total of eight electrons in the outermost portion of their electron clouds; therefore, they will readily combine.
15. The oil and water is a mixture. It is not a solution because neither the water nor the oil is evenly spread throughout the other.

Checking Concepts

Choose the word or phrase that best answers the question.

1. Which of the following contains only one type of atom?
   - A) compound
   - B) mixture
   - C) element
   - D) solution

2. Which of the following has a positive electric charge?
   - A) electron
   - B) proton
   - C) neutron
   - D) atom

3. In an atom, what forms a cloud around the nucleus?
   - A) electrons
   - B) protons
   - C) neutrons
   - D) positively charged particles

4. A carbon atom has a mass number of 12. How many protons and how many neutrons does it have?
   - A) 6, 6
   - B) 12, 12
   - C) 6, 12
   - D) 12, 6

5. On Earth, oxygen usually exists as which of the following?
   - A) solid
   - B) gas
   - C) liquid
   - D) plasma

6. Which of the following isotopes has seven neutrons?
   - A) boron-12
   - B) nitrogen-12
   - C) carbon-14
   - D) hydrogen-2

7. Which type of bond occurs because of the polar molecules of water?
   - A) ionic
   - B) covalent
   - C) metallic
   - D) hydrogen

8. Which of the following are electrically charged?
   - A) molecule
   - B) solution
   - C) isotope
   - D) ion

9. What type of property is the color of your clothes?
   - A) chemical property
   - B) physical property
   - C) isotopic property
   - D) molecular property

10. Which of the following is not a physical property of water?
    - A) transparent
    - B) colorless
    - C) higher density than ice
    - D) changes to hydrogen and oxygen when electricity passes through it

Thinking Critically

11. If an atom has no electric charge, what can be said about the number of protons and electrons it contains?

12. Carbon has six protons and nitrogen has seven protons. Which has the greatest number of neutrons—carbon-13, carbon-14, or nitrogen-14?

13. Would isotopes of the same element have the same number of electrons? Explain.

14. A chlorine atom comes in contact with a lithium atom. Do they combine to form a compound? Why or why not?

15. You pour cooking oil into a glass of water. You briefly stir the materials in the glass. Does the glass contain a mixture? Does it contain a solution? Explain.

Chapter ✓Assessment Planner

Portfolio Encourage students to place in their portfolios one or two items of what they consider to be their best work. Examples include:
- Science Journal, p. 519
- Cultural Diversity, p. 525
- Extension, p. 533

Performance Additional performance assessments, Performance Task Assessment Lists, and rubrics for evaluating these activities can be found in Glencoe's **Performance Assessment in the Science Classroom.**

Chapter 18 Assessment

Developing Skills

16. Classifying Use the periodic table of the elements, located on the inside back cover, to classify the following substances as elements or compounds: iron, aluminum, carbon dioxide, gold, water, and sugar.

17. Making and Using Graphs Use the following data to make a line graph. For each isotope, plot the mass number along the y-axis and the atomic number along the x-axis. What is the relationship between mass number and atomic number?

Atomic Number versus Mass Number

Element	Atomic Number	Mass Number
Fluorine	9	19
Lithium	3	7
Carbon	6	12
Nitrogen	7	14
Beryllium	4	9
Boron	5	11
Oxygen	8	16
Neon	10	20

Performance Assessment

18. Song with Lyrics Create a song about how matter changes state by changing the words to a song you know. Include in your song as many states of matter as possible.

TECHNOLOGY

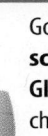 Go to the Glencoe Science Web site at **science.glencoe.com** or use the **Glencoe Science CD-ROM** for additional chapter assessment.

THE PRINCETON REVIEW — Test Practice

Marlena was instructed by her teacher to find examples of elements and their isotopes. The examples she found are presented in the table below.

Element	Number of Protons	Number of Neutrons
Hydrogen-1	1	0
Hydrogen-2	1	1
Hydrogen-3	1	2
Carbon-12	6	6
Carbon-14	6	8
Oxygen-16	8	8
Oxygen-18	8	10

Study the table and answer the following questions.

1. The hydrogen atom listed first is different from the hydrogen-2 and hydrogen-3 isotopes, because the first hydrogen isotope has _____ .
A) only one neutron
B) fewer neutrons
C) more electrons
D) more neutrons

2. The mass number of an atom is equal to the number of protons and neutrons in its nucleus. According to this definition, which of these has the highest mass number?
F) hydrogen-3
G) carbon-14
H) oxygen-18
J) oxygen-16

Chapter 18 Assessment

THE PRINCETON REVIEW — Test Practice

The Test-Taking Tip was written by The Princeton Review, the nation's leader in test preparation.
1. B
2. H

Developing Skills

16. iron—element, aluminum—element, carbon dioxide—compound, gold—element, water—compound, sugar—compound
17. The mass number increases as the atomic number increases at a ratio of approximately 2:1.

Performance Assessment

18. Songs may be simple as long as the lyrics describe changes in the state of matter. Use **Performance Assessment in the Science Classroom**, p. 151.

✓Assessment Resources

 Reproducible Masters

Chapter Resources Booklet
Chapter Review, pp. 33–34
Chapter Tests, pp. 35–38
Assessment Transparency Activity, p. 45

Glencoe Science Web site
Interactive Tutor
Chapter Quizzes

Glencoe Technology
- Assessment Transparency
- Interactive CD-ROM Chapter Quizzes
- ExamView Pro Test Bank
- Vocabulary PuzzleMaker Software
- MindJogger Videoquiz

Section/Objectives	Standards		Activities/Features
Chapter Opener	**National**	**State/Local**	**Explore Activity:** Compare properties, p. 545 **Before You Read,** p. 545
	See p. 6T for a Key to Standards.		
Section 1 Physical and Chemical Properties 🕐 3 sessions 📦 1.5 blocks 1. **Identify** physical and chemical properties of matter.	National Content Standards: UCP3, A1, B1		**MiniLAB:** Measuring Properties, p. 548 **Earth Science Integration,** p. 549 **Science Online,** p. 550 **Activity:** Finding the Difference, p. 551
Section 2 Physical and Chemical Changes 🕐 5 sessions 📦 2.5 blocks 1. **Compare** several physical and chemical changes. 2. **Identify** examples of physical and chemical changes.	National Content Standards: UCP3, A1, B1, F5, G2		**MiniLAB:** Comparing Changes, p. 555 **Science Online,** p. 555 **Astronomy Integration,** p. 557 **Math Skills Activity,** p. 558 **Visualizing Recycling,** p. 560 **Activity:** Battle of the Toothpastes, pp. 562–563 **Science Stats:** Strange Changes, pp. 564–565

Activity Materials	Reproducible Resources	Section Assessment	Technology
Explore Activity: samples of obsidian and pumice, clear container	**Chapter Resources Booklet** Foldables Worksheet, p. 17 Directed Reading Overview, p. 19 Note-taking Worksheets, pp. 31–32	GLENCOE'S ASSESSMENT ADVANTAGE	
MiniLAB: 10-mL graduated cylinder, balance **Activity:** meterstick, spring scale, block of wood, metal bar or ruler, plastic bin, drinking glass, water, rubber ball, paper, carpet, magnet, feather, rock, plant or flower, soil, sand, a vegetable, apple, slice of bread, dry cereal, egg	**Chapter Resources Booklet** Transparency Activity, p. 42 MiniLAB, p. 3 Enrichment, p. 29 Reinforcement, p. 27 Directed Reading, p. 20 Activity Worksheet, pp. 5–6 Lab Activity, pp. 9–12 **Reading and Writing Skill Activities,** p. 17	**Portfolio** Assessment, p. 550 **Performance** MiniLAB, p. 548 Skill Builder Activities, p. 550 **Content** Section Assessment, p. 550	Section Focus Transparency Interactive CD-ROM Guided Reading Audio Program
MiniLAB: a piece of fine steel wool, paper plate, tap water **Activity:** 2 or 3 different brands of toothpaste, drinking glasses or bowls, hard boiled eggs, concentrated lemon juice, apple juice water, artist's paint brush	**Chapter Resources Booklet** Transparency Activity, p. 43 MiniLAB, p. 4 Enrichment, p. 30 Reinforcement, p. 28 Directed Reading, pp. 21, 22 Transparency Activity, pp. 45–46 Activity Worksheet, pp. 7–8 Lab Activity, pp. 13–16 **Mathematics Skill Activities,** p. 9 **Science Inquiry Labs,** pp. 25, 51 **Home and Community Involvement,** p. 27 **Cultural Diversity,** p. 5 **Life Science Critical Thinking/ Problem Solving,** p. 8 **Lab Management and Safety,** p. 67	**Portfolio** Assessment, p. 555 **Performance** MiniLAB, p. 555 Skill Builder Activities, p. 561 **Content** Section Assessment, p. 561	Section Focus Transparency Teaching Transparency Interactive CD-ROM Guided Reading Audio Program

Need materials?
Contact Science Kit at 1-800-828-7777 or www.sciencekit.com on the Internet.

End of Chapter Assessment

GLENCOE'S ASSESSMENT ADVANTAGE

Blackline Masters	Technology	Professional Series
Chapter Resources Booklet Chapter Review, pp. 35–36 Chapter Tests, pp. 37–40 **Standardized Test Practice by The Princeton Review,** pp. 81–84	MindJogger Videoquiz Interactive CD-ROM Vocabulary PuzzleMakers ExamView Pro Test Bank Interactive Lesson Planner Interactive Teacher Edition	Performance Assessment in the Science Classroom (PASC)

Transparencies

Section Focus

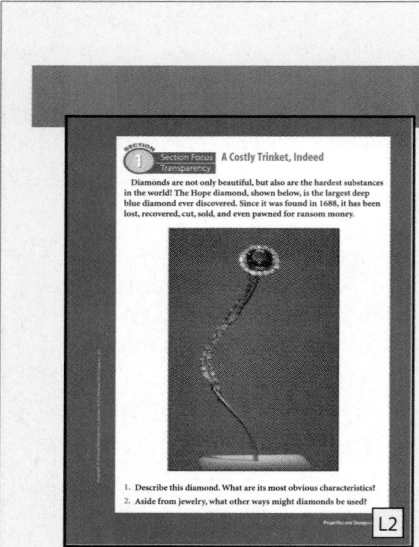

This is a representation of key blackline masters available in the Teacher Classroom Resources. See Resource Manager boxes within the chapter for additional information.

Assessment

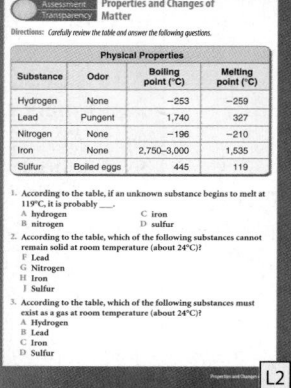

Teaching

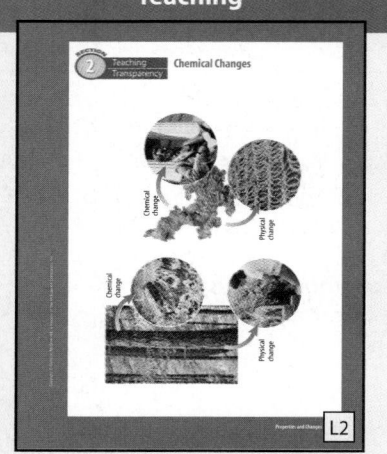

Key to Teaching Strategies

The following designations will help you decide which activities are appropriate for your students.

L1 Level 1 activities should be appropriate for students with learning difficulties.

L2 Level 2 activities should be within the ability range of all students.

L3 Level 3 activities are designed for above-average students.

ELL ELL activities should be within the ability range of English Language Learners.

COOP LEARN Cooperative Learning activities are designed for small group work.

LS Multiple Learning Styles logos, as described on page 22T, are used throughout to indicate strategies that address different learning styles.

P These strategies represent student products that can be placed into a best-work portfolio.

Hands-on Activities

Activity Worksheets

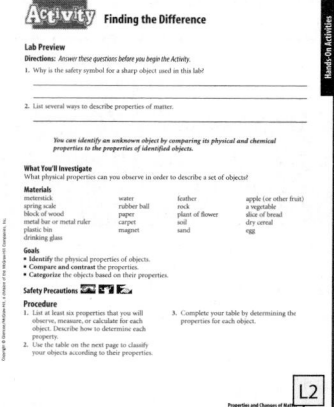

Laboratory Activities

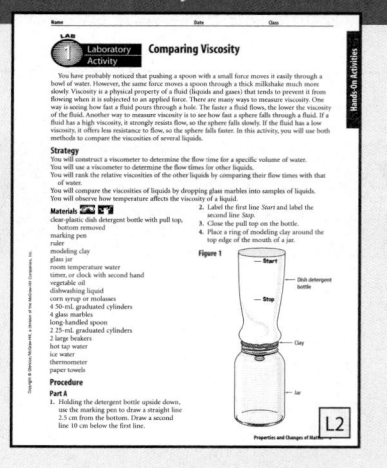

Meeting Different Ability Levels

Content Outline

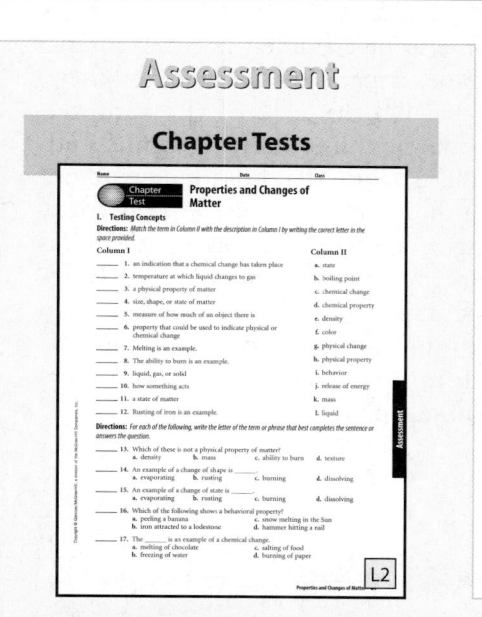

Note-taking Worksheet — **Properties and Changes of Matter**

Section 1 Physical and Chemical Properties

L2

Reinforcement

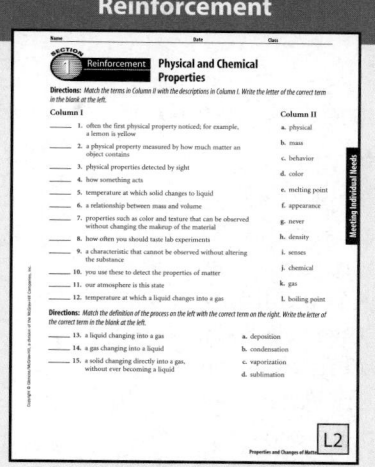

SECTION 1 Reinforcement — **Physical and Chemical Properties**

L2

Directed Reading

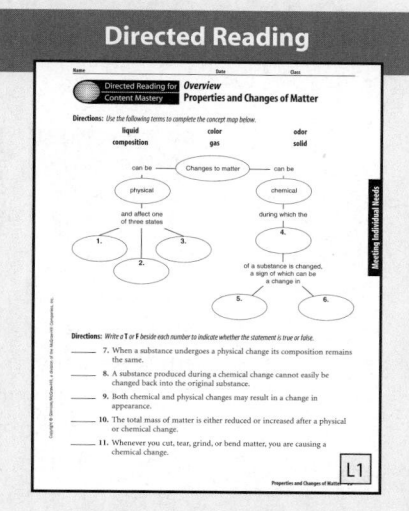

Directed Reading for Content Mastery — *Overview* **Properties and Changes of Matter**

L1

Enrichment

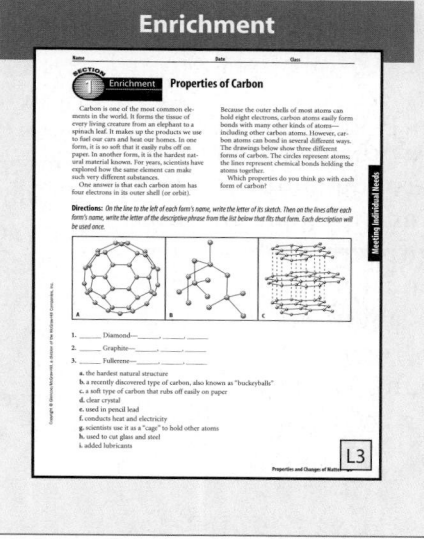

SECTION 1 Enrichment — **Properties of Carbon**

L3

Spanish Directed Reading

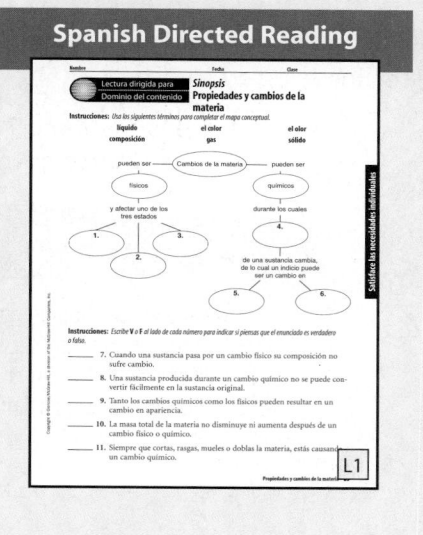

Lectura dirigida para Dominio del contenido — *Sinopsis* **Propiedades y cambios de la materia**

L1

Assessment

Chapter Tests

Chapter Test — **Properties and Changes of Matter**

I. Testing Concepts

L2

Test Practice Workbook

Standardized Test Practice — Teacher Edition

Glencoe **Science**

LEVEL GREEN

L1

Chapter Review

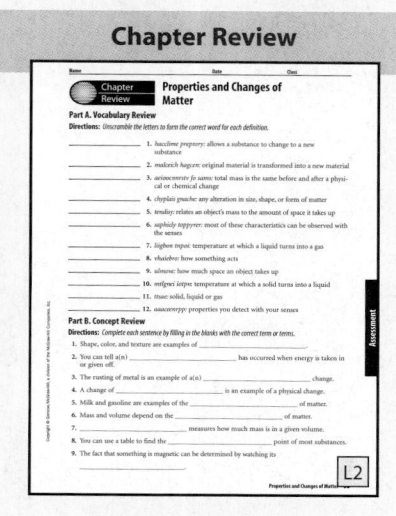

Chapter Review — **Properties and Changes of Matter**

Part A. Vocabulary Review

L2

Science Content Background

SECTION 1

Physical and Chemical Properties

Physical Properties

You must be careful in describing some physical properties, particularly properties such as solubility. Describing solubility can involve a reaction and, for that reason, may not be a true physical property. For example, if you say that sodium is soluble in water that would imply that the sodium simply dissolves in water. Instead, sodium reacts with water to form hydrogen gas and an aqueous sodium hydroxide solution.

Chemical Properties

A substance's chemical properties describe its ability to react with other substances or to decompose. For example, one chemical property of limestone, or calcium carbonate, is its ability to react with hydrochloric acid, producing carbon dioxide, water, and calcium chloride.

Fun Fact

In black and white photographic film, a chemical change occurs when silver bromide (AgBr) is exposed to light and turns dark.

Another chemical property of calcium carbonate is the ability to decompose, forming calcium oxide and carbon dioxide when heated.

The ability to corrode many metals is a chemical property of some acids. For example, when sulfuric acid corrodes aluminum, the aluminum atoms are oxidized (lose electrons) to form positively charged aluminum ions, while the hydrogen ions in the sulfuric acid are reduced (gain electrons) to form hydrogen atoms.

Intensive and Extensive Properties

Properties can also be classified as either intensive or extensive, depending on whether their value changes with the size of the sample. Intensive properties, like melting point and temperature, have values that do not depend on the amount of the sample. Extensive properties, like mass, length, and volume, have values that do depend on the sample size. Density is an intensive physical property that relates the mass of an object to its volume. Density is temperature dependent because most substances change in volume when heated or cooled.

Jeff Greenberg/PhotoEdit

SECTION 2 Physical and Chemical Changes

Physical Changes

Knowledge of physical changes and the circumstances under which they occur can be used to separate mixtures. Distillation is a change-of-state operation that is used to separate substances with different boiling points. Distillation is used to separate drinking water from seawater and hydrocarbons, such as gasoline and kerosene, from petroleum.

Chemical Changes

Chemical reaction is another term for chemical change. In a chemical change, atoms are rearranged. If a precipitate, gas, color change, or energy change occurs, a chemical change probably has taken place. Almost all chemical changes involve either taking in (endothermic) or giving off (exothermic) energy. However, not all changes that absorb or release energy are chemical. A cold pack is an example of physical change (dissolution) that absorbs heat.

Conservation of Mass

The French chemist, Antoine Lavoisier (1743–1794), found that when a chemical reaction was carried out in a closed system, the total mass of the system was not changed. Perhaps the most important chemical reaction Lavoisier performed was the decomposition of the red oxide of mercury to form metallic mercury and a gas he named oxygen. This reaction had been carried out by other scientists, but he was the first to weigh all the substances present before and after the reaction. He was also the first to interpret the reaction correctly. Lavoisier carried out many quantitative experiments, even those with animals. Lavoisier summarized all of his findings in the law of conservation of mass.

Fun Fact

Photochromic sunglasses darken when exposed to light because of the chemical change in the silver chloride (AgCl) embedded in the glass.

SCIENCE Online
For additional content background on this topic, go to the Glencoe Science Web site at science.glencoe.com.

Charles D. Winters/Photo Researchers, Inc.

Properties and Changes of Matter

Chapter Vocabulary

physical property, p. 546
chemical property, p. 550
physical change, p. 552
chemical change, p. 554
law of conservation of mass,
   p. 561

What do you think?

Science Journal The photo shows pumice, an igneous rock formed when lava cools on or near Earth's surface. Pumice is actually glass.

Properties and Changes of Matter

At very high temperatures deep within Earth, solid rock melts. When a volcano erupts, the liquid lava cools and turns back to rock. One of the properties of rock is its state—solid, liquid, or gas. Other properties include color, shape, texture, and weight. As lava changes from a liquid to a solid, what happens to its properties? In this chapter, you will learn about physical and chemical properties and changes of matter.

What do you think?

Science Journal Look at the picture below with a classmate. Discuss what you think this might be. Here's a hint: *It can keep your feet smooth.* Write your answer or best guess in your Science Journal.

544

Theme Connection

Stability and Change Matter can be described by its physical and chemical properties. These properties determine the physical and chemical changes that different types of matter can undergo.

EXPLORE ACTIVITY

W hen a volcano erupts, it spews lava and gases. Lava is hot, melted rock from deep within Earth. After it reaches Earth's surface, the lava cools and hardens into solid rock. The minerals and gases within the lava, as well as the rate at which it cools, determine the characteristics of the resulting rocks. In this activity, you will compare two types of volcanic rock.

Compare properties

1. Obtain samples of the rocks obsidian (uhb SIH dee un) and pumice (PUH mus) of about the same size from your teacher.
2. Compare the colors of the two rocks.
3. Decide which sample is heavier.
4. Look at the surfaces of the two rocks. How are the surfaces different?
5. Place each rock in water and observe.

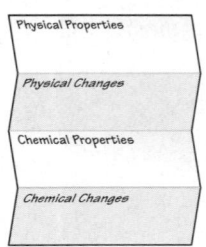

Observe

What things are different about these rocks? In your Science Journal, make a table that compares the observations you made about the rocks.

Before You Read

FOLDABLES
Reading & Study Skills

Making an Organizational Study Fold Make the following Foldable to help you organize your thoughts into clear categories about properties and changes.

1. Place a sheet of paper in front of you so the short side is at the top. Fold the paper in half from the top to the bottom two times. Unfold all the folds.

2. Trace over all the fold lines and label the folds *Physical Properties, Physical Changes, Chemical Properties,* and *Chemical Changes* as shown.

3. As you read the chapter, write information about matter's physical and chemical properties and changes on your Foldable.

Physical Properties

Physical Changes

Chemical Properties

Chemical Changes

545

EXPLORE ACTIVITY

Purpose Use the Explore Activity to help students understand that obsidian and pumice, two rocks formed from volcanic lava, have different properties. L1
ELL LS **Kinesthetic**

Preparation Obtain pumice and obsidian samples and a clear container.

Materials pumice and obsidian samples, a clear cup or container that will hold each sample, water

Teaching Strategy In Step 5, advise students to lower the obsidian and pumice samples into the cup slowly to avoid splashing.

Observe

Tables should show that pumice has a rough surface while obsidian is smooth. For a similar-sized sample, the obsidian is much heavier. Pumice floats in water (or at least is more buoyant) while obsidian sinks.

✓ Assessment

Process Have students use a balance to determine the mass of their rock samples and use water displacement in a graduated cylinder to determine the volume of each rock sample. Explain what density is, and show students how to calculate the densities of the pumice and obsidian. Use **Performance Assessment in the Science Classroom,** p. 89.

FOLDABLES
Reading & Study Skills

Before You Read

Dinah Zike Study Fold

Purpose Students make and use a Foldable table to collect information on the physical and chemical properties and changes of matter, and use the data to compare and contrast physical and chemical changes and physical and chemical properties.

📁 For additional help, see Foldables Worksheet, p. 17 in **Chapter Resources Booklet,** or go to the Glencoe Science Web site at **science.glencoe.com.** See After You Read in the Study Guide at the end of this chapter.

1 Motivate

Bellringer Transparency

Display the Section Focus Transparency for Section 1. Use the accompanying Transparency Activity Master. L2

ELL

Tie to Prior Knowledge

Have students recall occasions when they had to describe an object using their senses.

✔ Reading Check

Answer a characteristic that can be observed without changing the composition of a substance

Caption Answer

Figure 1 Answers will vary.

Physical and Chemical Properties

As You Read

What You'll Learn
■ Identify physical and chemical properties of matter.

Vocabulary
physical property
chemical property

Why It's Important
Understanding the different properties of matter will help you to better describe the world around you.

Figure 1
All matter can be described by physical properties that can be observed using the five senses. *What types of matter do you think you could see, hear, taste, touch, and smell at the fair?*

Physical Properties

It's a busy day at the state fair as you and your classmates navigate your way through the crowd. While you follow your teacher, you can't help but notice the many sights and sounds that surround you. Eventually, you fall behind the group as you spot the most amazing ride you have ever seen. You inspect it from one end to the other. How will you describe it to the group when you catch up to them? What features will you use in your description?

Perhaps you will mention that the ride is large, blue, and made of wood. These features are all physical properties, or characteristics, of the ride. A **physical property** is a characteristic you can observe without changing or trying to change the composition of the substance. How something looks, smells, sounds, or tastes are all examples of physical properties. Look at **Figure 1.** You can describe all types of matter and differentiate between them by observing their properties.

✔ Reading Check   *What is a physical property of matter?*

Section ✔ Assessment Planner

PORTFOLIO
Assessment, p. 550
PERFORMANCE ASSESSMENT
MiniLAB, p. 548
Skill Builder Activities, p. 550
See page 568 for more options.

CONTENT ASSESSMENT
Section, p. 550
Challenge, p. 550
Chapter, pp. 568–569

Using Your Senses Some physical properties describe the appearance of matter. You can detect many of these properties with your senses. For example, you can see the color and shape of the ride at the fair. You can also touch it to feel its texture. You can smell the odor or taste the flavor of some matter. (You should never taste anything in the laboratory.) Consider the physical properties of the items in **Figure 2**.

State To describe a sample of matter, you need to identify its state. Is the ride a solid, a liquid, or a gas? This property, known as the state of matter, is another physical property that you can observe. The ride, your chair, a book, and a pen are examples of matter in the solid state. Milk, gasoline, and vegetable oil are examples of matter in the liquid state. The helium in a balloon, air in a tire, and neon in a sign are examples of matter in the gas state. You can see examples of solids, liquids, and gases in **Figure 3**.

Perhaps you are most familiar with the three states of water. You can drink or swim in liquid water. You use the solid state of water, which is ice, when you put the solid cubes in a drink or skate on a frozen lake. Although you can't see it, water in the gas state is all around you in the air.

Figure 2
A Some matter has a characteristic color, such as this sulfur pile.
B You can use a characteristic smell or taste to identify these fruits. **C** Even if you didn't see it, you could probably identify this sponge by feeling its texture.

Figure 3
The state of a sample of matter is an important physical property.

C This colorful sign uses the element neon, which is generally found in the gas state.

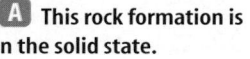 **A** This rock formation is in the solid state.

 **B** The oil flowing out of a bottle is in the liquid state.

② Teach

Physical Properties

Make a Model

Have each student make a model of a water molecule by using a large circle to represent oxygen and two small circles to represent hydrogen. Direct them to connect the small circles to the large circle with chenille stems and glue. As you discuss solids, liquids, and gases, collect students' molecules and arrange them on a large piece of construction paper. Glue some of them closely together in a hexagonal arrangement to represent the molecules in solid ice. Arrange the next set more randomly and with spaces between them to represent liquid water. Then lay out a few molecules with large spaces between them to represent gaseous water vapor. Keep these models on the wall to remind students that the molecule for water did not change; instead the arrangement of the molecules determined state. L1 ELL IS **Kinesthetic**

Visual Learning

Figure 3 Have students describe the physical properties shown in the pictures. rock formation: brown, orange, sharp, sandy, solid; oil: brown, thick, liquid; neon sign: bright, colorful, yellow

Physical Properties, continued

Purpose Students measure mass and volume of a water sample and determine its density.

Materials 10-mL graduated cylinder, balance

Teaching Strategies

• Review with students how to read the volume of a liquid in a graduated cylinder using the meniscus.

Analysis

1. The mass of the water could not be measured unless the water is in a container. The mass of the container is subtracted from the total mass.

2. It would be greater.

✓ Assessment

Performance Using their calculated density, have students calculate the mass of water that would have a volume of 7.5 mL and perform an experiment to confirm the answer. Use **PASC**, p. 27.

Activity

Give students classroom objects that are rectangular solids, such as a chalkboard eraser, and have them calculate the volume of each by finding the product of the width, height, and depth.

L2 ⁣LS Logical-Mathematical

Mini LAB

Measuring Properties

Procedure 🥽 👕

1. Measure the mass of a **10-mL graduated cylinder.**
2. Fill the graduated cylinder with **water** to the 10-mL mark and measure the mass of the graduated cylinder and water.
3. Determine the mass of the water by subtracting the mass of the graduated cylinder from the mass of the graduated cylinder and water.
4. Determine the density of water by dividing the mass of the water by the volume of the water.

Analysis

1. Why did you need to measure the mass of the empty graduated cylinder?
2. How would your calculated density be affected if you added more than 10-mL of water?

Figure 4
A spring scale is used to measure an object's weight.

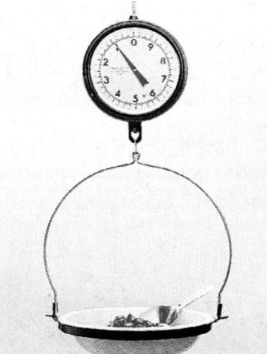

Size Dependent Properties Some physical properties depend on the size of the object. Suppose you need to move a box. The size of the box would be important in deciding if you need to use your backpack or a truck. You can begin by measuring the width, height, and depth of the box. If you multiply them together, you calculate the box's volume. The volume of an object is the amount of space it occupies.

Another physical property that depends on size is mass. Recall that the mass of an object is a measurement of how much matter it contains. A bowling ball has more mass than a basketball. Weight is a measurement of force. Weight depends on the mass of the object and on gravity. If you were to travel to other planets, your weight would change but your size and mass would not. Weight is measured using a spring scale like the one in **Figure 4.**

Size Independent Properties Another physical property, density, does not depend on the size of an object. Density measures the amount of mass in a given volume. To calculate the density of an object, divide its mass by its volume. The density of water is the same in a glass as it is in a tub. Another property, solubility, also does not depend on size. Solubility is the number of grams of one substance that will dissolve in 100 g of another substance at a given temperature. The amount of drink mix that can be dissolved in 100 g of water is the same in a pitcher as it is when it is poured into a glass. Size dependent and independent properties are shown in **Table 1.**

Melting and Boiling Point Melting and boiling point also do not depend upon an object's size. The temperature at which a solid changes into a liquid is called its melting point. The temperature at which a liquid changes into a gas is called its boiling point. The melting and boiling points of several substances, along with some of their other physical properties, are shown in **Table 2.**

Table 1 Properties of Matter	
Physical Properties	
Dependent on sample size	mass, weight, volume
Independent of sample size	density, melting/boiling point, solubility, ability to attract a magnet, state of matter, color.

🔬 LAB DEMONSTRATION

Purpose to measure the melting and boiling points of water

Materials large beaker, several ice cubes made from distilled water, thermometer, hot plate, hot pad

Procedure Place the ice in the container, then measure the temperature of the ice. Heat the ice. Measure the temperature of the water and ice mixture. Continue to heat the water until it boils, and then measure the temperature of the boiling water. Write all three temperatures on the board.

Expected Outcome Students observe the temperatures for the melting and boiling points of water.

✓ Assessment

What happened to the ice between the first and second temperature checks? Its molecules gained energy and broke apart to change the ice to a liquid. **What is the second temperature called?** melting point **What happened to water at its boiling point?** It turned to gas.

Table 2 Physical Properties of Several Substances (at atmospheric temperature and pressure)

Substance	Color	State	Density (g/cm³)	Melting Point (°C)	Boiling Point (°C)
Bromine	Red-brown	Liquid	3.12	−7	59
Chlorine	Yellowish	Gas	0.0032	−101	−34
Mercury	Silvery-white	Liquid	13.5	−39	357
Neon	Colorless	Gas	0.0009	−249	−246
Oxygen	Colorless	Gas	0.0014	−219	−183
Sodium chloride	White	Solid	2.17	801	1,413
Sulfur	Yellow	Solid	2.07	115	445
Water	Colorless	Liquid	1.00	0	100

Behavior Some matter can be described by the specific way in which it behaves. For example, some materials pull iron toward them. These materials are said to be magnetic. The lodestone in **Figure 5** is a rock that is naturally magnetic.

Other materials can be made into magnets. You might have magnets on your refrigerator or locker at school. The door of your refrigerator also has a magnet within it that holds the door shut tightly.

✔ Reading Check *What are some examples of physical properties of matter?*

Earth Science INTEGRATION

Scientists can learn about the history of the Moon by analyzing the properties of moon rocks. The properties of some moon rocks, for example, are similar to those of rocks produced by volcanoes on Earth. In this way, scientists learned that the Moon once had volcanic activity. Make a list of questions to ask about the properties of a moon rock.

Figure 5
This lodestone attracts certain metals to it. Lodestone is a natural magnet.

Chemical Properties

SCIENCE Online
Internet Addresses

_____
_____
_____
_____
_____
_____

Explore the Glencoe Science Web site at **science.glencoe.com** to find out more about topics in this section.

Figure 6
Notice the difference between the new matches and the matches that have been burned. The ability to burn is a chemical property of matter.

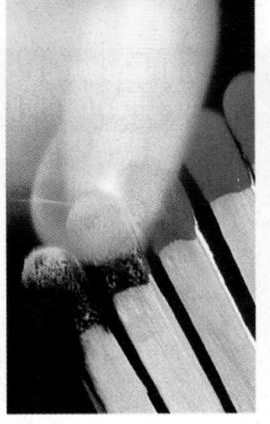
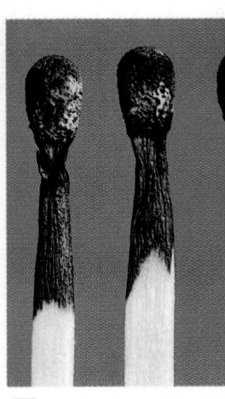

A   **B**   **C**

SCIENCE Online

Research Visit the Glencoe Science Web site at **science.glencoe.com** for more information about methods of measuring matter. Make a poster showing how to make measurements involving several different samples of matter.

Chemical Properties

Some properties of matter cannot be identified just by looking at a sample. For example, nothing happens if you look at the matches in **Figure 6A.** But if someone strikes the matches on a hard, rough surface they will burn, as shown in **Figure 6B.** The ability to burn is a chemical property. A **chemical property** is a characteristic that cannot be observed without altering the substance. As you can see in **Figure 6C,** the matches are permanently changed after they are burned. Therefore this property can be observed only by changing the composition of the match. Another way to define a chemical property, then, is the ability of a substance to undergo a change that alters its identity. You will learn more about changes in matter in the following section.

Section 1 Assessment

1. What physical properties could you use to describe a baseball?

2. How are your senses important to identifying physical properties of matter?

3. How is density related to mass and volume? Explain and write an equation.

4. Describe a chemical property in your own words. Give an example.

5. **Think Critically** Explain why density and solubility are size-independent physical properties of matter.

Skill Builder Activities

6. **Comparing and Contrasting** How is a chemical property different from a physical property? **For more help, refer to the** Science Skill Handbook.

7. **Solving One-Step Equations** You need to fill a bucket with water. The volume of the bucket is 5 L and you are using a cup with a volume of 50 mL. How many cupfulls will you need? There's a hint: *1 L = 1000 mL*. **For more help, refer to the** Math Skill Handbook.

550 CHAPTER 19 Properties and Changes of Matter

Answers to Section Assessment

1. Possible answers: state (solid), shape (spherical), texture, color, mass, volume, density
2. It is through the senses that you gather information about the world around you. For example, you use your senses to detect an object's shape, color, texture, taste, sound, temperature, smell, weight, state, and behavior, as well as to make measurements.
3. Density is calculated by dividing the mass of an object by its volume.
4. characteristic that determines a substance's ability to interact with other substances in a way that changes its identity
5. Density and solubility are size independent because they are a ratio of two size-dependent properties.

As one property increases, so does the other. The ratio doesn't change.
6. A physical property can be observed without changing the composition of the substance. A chemical property cannot be observed without altering the composition of the sample.
7. 100 cups

Activity

Finding the Difference

You can identify an unknown object by comparing its physical and chemical properties to the properties of identified objects.

What You'll Investigate
What physical properties can you observe in order to describe a set of objects?

Materials

meterstick	rock
spring scale	plant or flower
block of wood	soil
metal bar or metal ruler	sand
plastic bin	apple (or other fruit)
drinking glass	vegetable
water	slice of bread
rubber ball	dry cereal
paper	egg
carpet	feather
magnet	

Goals
- **Identify** the physical properties of objects.
- **Compare and Contrast** the properties.
- **Categorize** the objects based on their properties.

Safety Precautions 🕿 🧤 🔪 ⊘

Procedure
1. List at least six properties that you will observe, measure, or calculate for each object. Describe how to determine each property.
2. In your Science Journal, create a data table with a column for each property and rows for the objects.
3. Complete your table by determining the properties for each object.

Conclude and Apply
1. Which properties were you able to observe easily? Which required making measurements? Which required calculations?
2. **Compare and contrast** the objects based on the information in your table.
3. Choose a set of categories and group your objects into those categories. Some examples of categories are large/medium/small, heavy/moderate/light, bright/moderate/dull, solid/liquid/gas, etc. Were the categories you chose useful for grouping your objects? Why or why not?

𝒞ommunicating
Your Data

Compare your results with those of other students in your class. **Discuss** the properties of objects that different groups included on their tables. Make a large table including all of the objects that students in the class studied.

𝒞ommunicating
Your Data

Students may want to use a computer database to organize their class table.

Resource Manager

Chapter Resources Booklet
   Activity Worksheet, pp. 5–6
   Reinforcement, p. 27
Reading and Writing Skill Activities, p. 17

Activity

BENCH TESTED

Purpose Students will identify physical characteristics and classify objects based on these characteristics. [L2] [IS] **Kinesthetic**

Process Skills collecting data, observing, classifying, comparing and contrasting, making and using tables, drawing conclusions

Time Required 40 minutes

Safety Precautions Students should wear goggles and aprons during this lab.

Teaching Strategies Set up an area where students can get a few items at a time.

Answers to Questions
1. Easy to identify: possible answers: color, texture, physical state. Required measurements: possible answers: mass, length. Required calculations: possible answer: density.
2. Answers will vary.
3. Answers will vary.

✓𝒜ssessment

Oral Ask students the following questions. **What are some physical properties that depend on the amount of material present?** Possible answers: mass, length, volume **What are some physical properties that are independent of the amount of material present?** Possible answers: density, boiling point, melting point. Use **PASC,** p. 89.

SECTION

Physical and Chemical Changes

Physical and Chemical Changes

1 Motivate

Bellringer Transparency

Display the Section Focus Transparency for Section 2. Use the accompanying Transparency Activity Master. [L2]

[ELL]

Tie to Prior Knowledge

Review the concepts of physical properties and chemical properties. Ask students to give an example of each. Explain that in this section they will learn some ways to distinguish between physical and chemical changes.

As You Read

What **You'll Learn**

- **Compare** several physical and chemical changes.
- **Identify** examples of physical and chemical changes.

Vocabulary

physical change
chemical change
law of conservation of mass

Why **It's Important**

Physical and chemical changes affect your life every day.

Physical Changes

What happens when the artist turns the lump of clay shown in **Figure 7** into a work of art? The composition of the clay does not change. Its appearance, however, changes dramatically. The change from a lump of clay to a work of art is a physical change. A **physical change** is one in which the form or appearance of matter changes, but not its composition. The lake in **Figure 7** also experiences a physical change. Although the water changes state due to a change in temperature, it is still made of the elements hydrogen and oxygen.

Changing Shape Have you ever crumpled a sheet of paper into a ball? If so, you caused physical change. Whether it exists as one flat sheet or a crumpled ball, the matter is still paper. Similarly, if you cut fruit into pieces to make a fruit salad, you do not change the composition of the fruit. You change only its form. Generally, whenever you cut, tear, grind, or bend matter, you are causing a physical change.

Figure 7
Although each sample looks quite different after it experiences a change, the composition of the matter remains the same. These changes are examples of physical changes.

Section ✓*Assessment* Planner

PORTFOLIO
Assessment, p. 555

PERFORMANCE ASSESSMENT
Try at Home MiniLAB, p. 555
Math Skills Activity, p. 558
Skill Builder Activities, p. 561
See page 568 for more options.

CONTENT ASSESSMENT
Section, p. 561
Challenge, p. 561
Chapter, pp. 568–569

Dissolving What type of change occurs when you add sugar to iced tea, as shown in **Figure 8**? Although the sugar seems to disappear, it does not. Instead, the sugar dissolves. When this happens, the particles of sugar spread out in the liquid. The composition of the sugar stays the same, which is why the iced tea tastes sweet. Only the form of the sugar has changed.

Figure 8
Physical changes are occurring constantly. The sugar blending into the iced tea is an example of a physical change.

Changing State Another common physical change occurs when matter changes from one state to another. When an ice cube melts, for example, it becomes liquid water. The solid ice and the liquid water have the same composition. The only difference is the form.

Matter can change from any state to another. Freezing is the opposite of melting. During freezing, a liquid changes into a solid. A liquid also can change into a gas. This process is known as vaporization. During the reverse process, called condensation, a gas changes into a liquid. **Figure 9** summarizes these changes.

In some cases, matter changes between the solid and gas states without ever becoming a liquid. The process in which a solid changes directly into a gas is called sublimation. The opposite process, in which a gas changes into a solid, is called deposition.

Figure 9
Look at the photographs below to identify the different physical changes that bromine undergoes as it changes from one state to another.

Solid state

Gas state

Liquid state

More gas

Liquid state

SECTION 2 Physical and Chemical Changes **553**

Curriculum Connection

History Heat hardens clay into a form that can be used for pottery. Intense heating causes a chemical, as well as physical, change to the clay. Because pottery does not easily decompose, historians have used pottery remains to study ancient civilizations. Ask students to research one early civilization and give a short presentation about the pottery it produced. Civilizations include Maya, Toltec, Inca, Aztec, Cush, Olmec, Cretan, and those in Egypt, Mesopotamia, and the Indus Valley. L3

2 Teach

Physical Changes

Use Science Words
Word Usage Have students use the word *dissolve* in a sentence that describes its meaning and type of change. Possible answer: A substance dissolves when its particles spread out in a liquid; this is a physical change. L2 ELL IS **Linguistic**

Quick Demo
Weigh out a 20–30 g sample of dry ice. Place the sample in a zipper-closure plastic bag and allow students to observe it. Release gas from the bag periodically as students observe. Ask students to list the physical properties and physical changes they observe. physical properties: mass, white, solid; physical changes: sublimates into a gas L2 ELL IS **Visual-Spatial**

Make a Model
Give each student a small lump of clay and an index card. Have them divide the clay in half and create small sculptures with one-half of the clay. Tell them to leave the other half of the clay in a lump and to place both pieces on the index card with the label "Physical Change." L1 ELL IS **Kinesthetic**

Resource Manager

Chapter Resources Booklet
Transparency Activity, p. 43
Directed Reading for Content Mastery, pp. 21, 22
Cultural Diversity, p. 5

Chemical Changes

Visual Learning

Reading Check

Fun Fact

Quick Demo

Figure 10
These brilliant fireworks result from chemical changes. *What is a chemical change?*

Chemical Changes

It's the Fourth of July in New York City. Brilliant fireworks are exploding in the night sky. When you look at fireworks, such as these in **Figure 10,** you see dazzling sparkles of red and white trickle down in all directions. The explosion of fireworks is an example of a chemical change. During a **chemical change,** substances are changed into different substances. In other words, the composition of the substance changes.

You are familiar with another chemical change if you have ever left your bicycle out in the rain. After a while, a small chip in the paint leads to an area of a reddish, powdery substance. This substance is rust. When iron in steel is exposed to oxygen and water in air, iron and oxygen atoms combine to form the principle component in rust. In a similar way, coins tarnish when exposed to air. These chemical changes are shown in **Figure 11.**

✓ **Reading Check** *How is a chemical change different from a physical change?*

Figure 11
Each of these examples shows the results of a chemical change. In each case, the substances that are present after the change are different from those that were present before the change.

Cultural Diversity

Alchemists Greek, Arabic, and Chinese alchemists began studying chemical changes more than 2,000 years ago. Their work contributed greatly to the understanding of chemical substances and changes. Have students investigate different aspects of alchemy and present their findings to the class. Possible subjects include the processing of metals and the transmutation of metals into gold, the use of minerals and other chemicals for healing, chemical apparatuses developed by alchemists, elements identified by alchemists, and the making of cosmetics and perfumes. L3 IS **Linguistic**

Figure 12
The brilliant colors of autumn result from a chemical change.

Signs of Chemical Changes

Physical changes are relatively easy to identify. If only the form of a substance changes, you have observed a physical change. How can you tell whether a change is a chemical change? If you think you are unfamiliar with chemical changes, think again.

You have witnessed a spectacular change if you have seen the leaves of trees change colors in autumn, but you are not seeing a chemical change. Chemicals called pigments give tree leaves their color. In **Figure 12,** the pigment that is responsible for the green color you see during the summer is chlorophyll (KLOHR uh fihl). Two other pigments result in the colors you see in the red tree. Throughout the spring and summer, chlorophyll is present in much greater amounts than these other pigments, so you see leaves as green. In autumn, however, changes in temperature and rainfall amounts cause trees to stop producing chlorophyll. The chlorophyll that is already present undergoes a chemical change in which it loses its green color. Without chlorophyll, the red and yellow pigments, which are always present, can be seen.

Color Perhaps you have found that a half-eaten apple turns brown. The reason is that a chemical change occurs when food spoils. Maybe you have toasted a marshmallow or a slice of bread and watched them turn black. In each case, the color of the food changes as it is cooked because a chemical change occurs.

SCIENCE Online

Research Visit the Glencoe Science Web site at **science.glencoe.com** for more information about how to recognize chemical changes. Choose one example not mentioned in the chapter and present it to the class as a poster or in an oral report.

TRY AT HOME
Mini LAB

Comparing Changes
Procedure
1. Separate a piece of **fine steel wool** into two halves.
2. Dip one half in **tap water.**
3. Place each piece of steel wool on a separate **paper plate** and let them sit overnight.
4. Repeat step two with the same half of steel wool for five days.

Analysis
1. Did you observe any changes in the steel wool? If so, describe them.
2. If you observed changes, were they physical or chemical? How do you know?

Signs of Chemical Changes

Life Science INTEGRATION

The plant pigments that are responsible for the yellow and orange colors of leaves are carotenoids. The pigments responsible for red and purple colors are called anthocyanins. Anthocyanins change color depending on the acidity of the cell sap in the plant.

TRY AT HOME
Mini LAB

Purpose Students will observe a chemical change in a piece of steel wool. L1 ELL
IS **Kinesthetic**
Materials piece of fine steel wool, tap water, paper plate
Teaching Strategy Have students tear the steel wool or cut it with tin snips.
Analysis
1. The steel wool dipped in water turned orange.
2. chemical, because the color changed

Assessment

Portfolio Have each student prepare a series of drawings of the steel wool over a two-week period. Students should include descriptions of the chemical changes with the drawings. Use **PASC,** p. 127. P

SCIENCE Online

Internet Addresses
_____
_____
_____
_____
Explore the Glencoe Science Web site at **science.glencoe.com** to find out more about topics in this section.

Resource Manager

Chapter Resources Booklet
    MiniLAB, p. 4
Life Science Critical Thinking/Problem Solving, p. 8
Home and Community Involvement, p. 27

Visual Learning

Figure 14 Discuss with students the physical and chemical properties of each item. On the board, make a listing of the class's observations. L2 ELL
IS Visual-Spatial

Discussion

What evidence do you have that chemical changes occur as fruits and vegetables ripen?
Possible answers: apples and tomatoes turn red, pears and bananas become yellow, oranges turn from green to orange

Extension

Tell students that reactions that give off energy are called exothermic, while those that require energy are called endothermic. Limestone buildings and statues are chemically changed by acid rain. Have students find out what the chemical changes are and whether the reaction is exothermic or endothermic. Calcium carbonate reacts with sulfuric acid to produce water and calcium sulfate, which wash away, and carbon dioxide gas. The reaction is exothermic. L3
IS Logical-Mathematical

Figure 13
Cake batter undergoes a chemical change as it absorbs energy during cooking.

Figure 14
A Energy is released when a firefly glows, B when fuel is burned in a camping stove, and C when sodium and chlorine undergo a chemical change to form table salt.

Energy Another sign of a chemical change is the release or gain of energy by an object. Many substances must absorb energy in order to undergo a chemical change. For example, energy is absorbed during the chemical changes involved in cooking. When you bake a cake or make pancakes, energy is absorbed by the batter as it changes from a runny mix into what you see in **Figure 13.**

Another chemical change in which a substance absorbs energy occurs during the production of cement. This process begins with the heating of limestone. Ordinarily, limestone will remain unchanged for centuries. But when it absorbs energy during heating, it undergoes a chemical change in which it turns into lime and carbon dioxide.

Energy also can be released during a chemical change. The fireworks you read about earlier released energy in the form of light that you can see. As shown in **Figure 14A,** a chemical change within a firefly releases energy in the form of light. Fuel burned in the camping stove shown in **Figure 14B** releases energy you see as light and feel as heat. You also can see that energy is released when sodium and chlorine are combined and ignited in **Figure 14C.** During this chemical change, the original substances change into sodium chloride, which is ordinary table salt.

Science Journal

Energy in Physical and Chemical Changes
Ask students to list all the changes they can think of that involve the absorption or release of energy and classify each as a chemical or physical change. Changes might include cooking (chemical), boiling water (physical), burning fuel (chemical), cooling your hand by putting it in cold water (physical). L2
IS Logical-Mathematical

Teacher FYI

Adding energy does not necessarily produce a chemical change. Adding heat to substances can cause them to warm up or to change state, neither of which is a chemical change. In the same way, the release of energy does not necessarily indicate that a chemical change has occurred.

Odor It takes only one experience with a rotten egg to learn that they smell much different than fresh eggs. When eggs and other foods spoil, they undergo chemical change. The change in odor is a clue to the chemical change. This clue can be used to save lives. When you smell an odd odor in foods, such as chicken, pork, or mayonnaise, you know that the food has undergone a chemical change. You can use this clue to avoid eating spoiled food and protect yourself from becoming ill.

Gases or Solids Look at the antacid tablet in **Figure 15A.** You can produce similar bubbles if you pour vinegar on baking soda. The formation of a gas is a clue to a chemical change. What other products undergo chemical changes and produce bubbles?

Figure 15B shows another clue to a chemical change—the formation of a solid. A solid that separates out of a solution during a chemical change is called a precipitate. The precipitate in the photograph forms when a solution containing sodium iodide is mixed with a solution containing lead nitrate.

Astronomy
INTEGRATION

A meteoroid is a chunk of metal or stone in space. Every day, meteoroids enter Earth's atmosphere. When this happens, the meteoroid burns as a result of friction with gases in the atmosphere. A streak of light produced during this chemical change is known as a meteor or shooting star. In your Science Journal, infer why most meteoroids never reach Earth's surface.

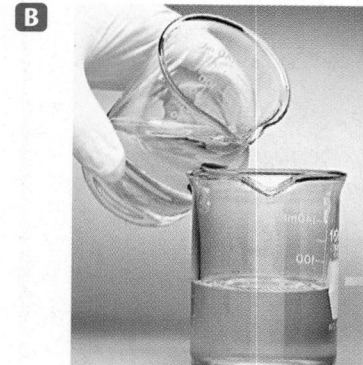

Figure 15
A The bubbles of gas formed when this antacid tablet is dropped into water indicate a chemical change. **B** The solid forming from two liquids is another sign that a chemical change has taken place.

SECTION 2 Physical and Chemical Changes **557**

Astronomy
INTEGRATION

When a meteoroid burns up in Earth's atmosphere, it is called a meteor; when it strikes Earth, it is called a meteorite. Most meteoroids are debris from asteroid collisions or broken-up comets. Answers will vary but should include that during the chemical change that occurs in the atmosphere, most meteors burn up.

Quick Demo

Pour 10 mL of vinegar into a large glass container. Measure and record the temperature of the vinegar. Add 5 mL of baking soda to the vinegar, and take the temperature again. The heat and gas produced are evidence that a chemical reaction has occurred. Explain that in this reaction, the baking soda reacted with the vinegar to form sodium acetate, water, and the gas, carbon dioxide. L2 ELL
LS Visual-Spatial

IDENTIFYING
Misconceptions

The production of bubbles of gas does not necessarily mean a chemical change has taken place. In carbonated soft drinks, carbon dioxide gas dissolved in the liquid forms bubbles when the bottle or can is opened. Bubbles also form when a liquid changes state to a gas by boiling.

Teacher FYI

The main ingredient in car air bags is sodium azide, NaN_3. Upon impact at speeds above 10–15 mph, a sensor transmits an electrical signal that ignites a detonator compound in the bag. Heat from the detonator causes the sodium azide to decompose into sodium and nitrogen gas, which, in 0.03 seconds, inflates the bag.

Resource Manager

Chapter Resources Booklet
  Lab Activity, pp. 13–16
Science Inquiry Labs, p. 25
Earth Science Critical Thinking/Problem Solving, p. 15

Caption Answer

Figure 16 No; the ashes are the result of a chemical change.

✔ Reading Check

Answer Possible answers: change in color, loss or gain of energy, odor, production of a gas or solid, the change is not easily reversible

---

Math Skills Activity

National Math Standards

Correlation to Mathematics Objectives
1, 2, 4, 6, 8, 9

Answer to Problem

This is what you know:
  temperature = 156° F
This is what you want to find:
  temperature in degrees Celsius
This is the equation you need to use:
  (℃ × 1.8) + 32 = °F
Rearrange the equation to solve for ℃.
  ℃ = (°F − 32)/1.8
Then substitute the known value for °F.
  ℃ = (156 − 32)/1.8 = 68.9℃

Figure 16
As wood burns, it turns into a pile of ashes and gases that rise into the air. *Can you turn ashes back into wood?*

Not Easily Reversed How do physical and chemical changes differ from one another? Think about ice for a moment. After solid ice melts into liquid water, it can refreeze into solid ice if the temperature drops enough. Freezing and melting are physical changes. The substances produced during a chemical change cannot be changed back into the original substances by physical means. For example, the wood in **Figure 16** changes into ashes and gases that are released into the air. After wood is burned, it cannot be restored to its original form as a log.

Think about a few of the chemical changes you just read about to see if this holds true. An antacid tablet cannot be restored to its original form after being dropped in water. Rotten eggs cannot be made fresh again, and pancakes cannot be turned back into batter. The substances that existed before the chemical change no longer exist.

✔ Reading Check *What signs indicate a chemical change?*

Math Skills Activity

Converting Temperatures

Fahrenheit is a non-SI temperature scale. Because it is used so often, it is useful to be able to convert from Fahrenheit to Celsius. The equation that relates Celsius degrees to Fahrenheit degrees is:

(℃ × 1.8) + 32 = °F

Using this information, what is 15°F on the Celsius scale?

Solution

1 *This is what you know:*   temperature = 15°F

2 *This is what you want to find:*   temperature in degrees Celsius

3 *This is the equation you need to use:*   (℃ × 1.8) + 32 = °F

4 *Rearrange the equation to solve for ℃.*   (℃ × 1.8) + 32 = °F
    ℃ = (°F − 32)/1.8

Then substitute the known value for °F.   ℃ = (15 − 32)/1.8 = −9.4° C

Check your answer by substituting the Celsius temperature into the original equation. Did you calculate the Fahrenheit temperature that was given in the question?

Practice Problem

Water is being heated on the stove at 156°F. What is this temperature on the Celsius scale?

For help refer to the Math Skill Handbook.

Inclusion Strategies

Gifted Have students investigate what must occur to change the ashes left after a piece of wood has burned into new wood and identify each as a chemical or physical change. The ashes must become part of soil (physical). A tree must grow in the soil (chemical). The tree must absorb the minerals in the ash (physical), and incorporate them in its wood (chemical). [L3]

Ⓛ Logical-Mathematical

✔ Active Reading

Reflective Journal In this strategy, students identify what they have learned about the nature of physical and chemical changes. Have students divide sheets of paper into several columns and record their thoughts under headings such as "What I learned," "What surprises did I experience," "What questions do I have," and "Overall response." Have students then write a Reflective Journal entry for an activity in this section.

Chemical Versus Physical Change

Now you have learned about many different physical and chemical changes. You have read about several characteristics that you can use to distinguish between physical and chemical changes. The most important point for you to remember is that in a physical change, the composition of a substance does not change and in a chemical change, the composition of a substance does change. When a substance undergoes a physical change, only its form changes. In a chemical change, both form and composition change.

When the wood and copper in **Figure 17** undergo physical changes, the original wood and copper still remain after the change. When a substance undergoes a chemical change, however, the original substance is no longer present after the change. Instead, different substances are produced during the chemical change. When the wood and copper in **Figure 17** undergo chemical changes, wood and copper have changed into new substances with new physical and chemical properties.

Physical and chemical changes are used to recycle or reuse certain materials. **Figure 18** discusses the importance of some of these changes in recycling.

Figure 17
When a substance undergoes a physical change, its composition stays the same. When a substance undergoes a chemical change, it is changed into different substances.

Chemical change

Physical change

Chemical change

Physical change

Inclusion Strategies

Visually Impaired Describe and discuss in detail with these students each of the photographs in **Figure 17.** Ask another student to describe the observable physical properties in each photo and tell how he or she knows which shows a physical change and which shows a chemical change. L2 LS **Visual-Spatial**

Resource Manager

Chapter Resources Booklet
 Enrichment, p. 30
Mathematics Skill Activities, p. 9
Physical Science Critical Thinking/Problem Solving, p. 10

Chemical versus Physical Changes

IDENTIFYING Misconceptions

There are situations in which each of the signs of a chemical change discussed in these pages occurs during a physical change. This can cause confusion. A chemical change has occurred only if new substances have been created. Make sure students understand that changes in color and odor, the production of gases or precipitates, the absorption or release of energy, and the fact that a change is difficult to reverse are indications that they should look further to see whether a new substance has been produced.

Use an Analogy

Tell students that chemical changes occur and new substances form when electrons interact to form bonds between different kinds of atoms. Discuss the following analogy. Think of the members of a basketball team as electrons associated with a basketball atom. They practice together and play games with other basketball teams. These are analogous to physical changes. The basketball players interact but no new substance is formed. Suppose some of the players decide to join with players from a soccer team to form a sports club. These players are like electrons that have formed bonds with a different kind of atom to form a new substance.

Visualizing Recycling

Have students examine the pictures and read the captions. Then ask the following questions.

- **What are some examples of physical changes described in this feature?** Possible answer: Pulverizing or crushing of glass; melting of plastics and re-forming them; the shredding of plastics; shredding of rubber; crushing, flattening, and chopping apart of car bodies; separating iron and steel from other materials with a magnet.

- **Why is it better to remove steel wires from rubber tires?** Possible answer: It would prevent pieces of wire from sticking out of pavement where it could damage vehicles tires or from playground surfaces where it could cause injuries. Also, the steel could then be recycled with the other metal car parts.

Activity

Have small groups of students research making new glass bottles from cullet. Have each group make a poster that illustrates the chemical and physical changes that are involved in the process. [L2] COOP LEARN

[IS] **Visual-Spatial and Interpersonal**

Extension

Students can write poems or songs about physical and chemical changes involved in recycling. Ask volunteers to read their poems or sing their songs for the class. [L3]

[IS] **Auditory-Musical**

Figure 18

Recycling is a way to separate wastes into their component parts and then reuse those components in new products. In order to be recycled, wastes need to be both physically—and sometimes chemically—changed. The average junked automobile contains about 62 percent iron and steel, 28 percent other materials such as aluminum, copper, and lead, and 10 percent rubber, plastics, and various materials.

Electro-magnet

Steel

◀ **Rubber tires** can be shredded and added to asphalt pavement and playground surfaces. New recycling processes make it possible to supercool tires to a temperature at which the rubber is shattered like glass. A magnet can then draw out steel from the tires and parts of the car.

▼ After being **crushed and flattened**, car bodies are chopped into small pieces. Metals are separated from other materials using physical processes. Some metals are separated using powerful magnets. Others are separated by hand.

◀ **Glass** can be pulverized and used in asphalt pavement, new glass, and even artwork. This sculpture, named *Groundswell*, was created by artist Maya Lin, using recycled windshield glass.

▲ Some **plastics** can be melted and formed into new products. Others are ground up or shredded and used as fillers or insulating materials.

Resource Manager

Chapter Resources Booklet
   Reinforcement, p. 28
   Transparency Activity, pp. 45–46

Performance Assessment in the Science Classroom, p. 44

Conservation of Mass

During a chemical change, the form or the composition of the matter changes. The particles within the matter rearrange to form new substances, but they are not destroyed and new particles are not created. The number and type of particles remains the same. As a result, the total mass of the matter is the same before and after a physical or chemical change. This is known as the **law of conservation of mass.**

This law can sometimes be difficult to believe, especially when the materials remaining after a chemical change might look different from those before it. In many chemical changes in which mass seems to be gained or lost, the difference is often due to a gas being given off or taken in. The difference, for example, before and after the candle in **Figure 19** is burned is in the gases released into the air. If the gases could be contained in a chamber around the candle, you would see that the mass does not change.

The scientist who first performed the careful experiments necessary to prove that mass is conserved was Antoine Lavoisier (AN twan • luh VWAH see ay) in the eighteenth century. It was Lavoisier who recognized that the mass of gases that are given off or taken from the air during chemical changes account for any differences in mass.

Figure 19
The candle looks as if it lost mass when it was burned. However, if you could trap and measure the gases given up during burning you would find that the mass of the candle and the gases is equal to the mass of the original candle.

Section Assessment

1. What happens during a physical change?

2. List five physical changes you can observe in your home. Explain how you decided that each change is physical.

3. What kind of change occurs on the surface of bread when it is toasted—physical or chemical? Explain.

4. What does it mean to say that mass is conserved during a chemical change?

5. **Think Critically** A log is reduced to a small pile of ash when it burns. The law of conservation of mass states that the total mass of matter is the same before and after a chemical change. Explain the difference in mass between the log and the ash.

Skill Builder Activities

6. **Classifying** Classify the following changes as physical or chemical: baking a cake, folding towels, burning gasoline, melting snow, grinding beef into a hamburger, pouring milk into a glass, making cookies, and cutting a sheet of paper into paper dolls. **For more help, refer to the** Science Skill Handbook.

7. **Solving One-Step Equations** Magnesium and oxygen undergo a chemical change to form magnesium oxide. How many grams of magnesium oxide will be produced when 0.486 g of oxygen completely react with 0.738 g of magnesium? **For more help, refer to the** Math Skill Handbook.

Answers to Section Assessment

1. Matter is changed in appearance but not in composition.

2. Examples include cutting paper, pouring milk on cereal, mowing the lawn, and melting ice. These are physical changes because the matter does not change composition.

3. Chemical; the bread changes in color and odor, absorbs heat energy,

becomes dark, and cannot be returned to its original form.

4. The particles within the matter are rearranged, but the total mass of the matter remains the same.

5. The difference in mass is a result of the mass of gas that was formed in the reaction and escaped.

6. physical: folding towels, melting snow, grinding beef, pouring milk, cutting paper; chemical: baking a cake, burning gasoline, making cookies

7. 1.22 g

Use Science Words

Word Origins Tell students that the word *conservation* comes from the Latin prefix *con-*, meaning "with or together," and the Latin verb *servare*, meaning "to keep or guard." Ask how these meanings relate to the law of conservation of mass. Mass is kept or guarded so that it is kept together, or the same.
L2 IS **Linguistic**

3 Assess

Reteach

Ask students to look at the illustrations on these pages and describe the physical properties, chemical properties, physical changes, and chemical changes they see. L2 ELL
IS **Visual-Spatial**

Challenge

Have students look at objects in the classroom and discuss the physical and chemical changes that took place as they were made. Wood for desks was physically changed from trees; rubber for erasers and plastic for chairs were produced by chemical changes, then physically shaped. L2
IS **Logical-Mathematical**

✓ Assessment

Content Have students list five indications that a chemical change may have taken place. changes in color, odor, and energy, the production of gases or solids, and the fact that a change is difficult to reverse
Use **Performance Assessment in the Science Classroom,** p. 89.

Activity

Recognize the Problem

Purpose

Students will infer the effectiveness of different brands of toothpaste in preventing tooth decay. L2 IS **Kinesthetic**

Process Skills

designing an experiment, forming a hypothesis, recording and analyzing data, comparing, inferring, predicting

Time Required

One 45-minute period and daily observations for a week

Alternate Materials

You might want to include a tube of toothpaste that does not contain sodium fluoride in its ingredients list.

Form a Hypothesis

Possible Hypothesis

Most student hypotheses will reflect that toothpastes containing sodium fluoride will prevent the eggshells from reacting with the acid.

Test Your Hypothesis

Possible Procedures

Brush a different brand of toothpaste over each eggshell. Leave two eggshells without toothpaste. Place half the treated eggs in lemon juice and the other half in apple juice. Place one untreated egg in each juice. Observe the eggs each day for one week for signs of a chemical reaction.

Teaching Strategies

It is not necessary that all groups use the same brands of toothpaste.

Troubleshooting

Students should be sure to coat all parts of the eggs with toothpaste. Any unprotected parts will react with the acid.

Activity — Design Your Own Experiment

Battle of the Toothpastes

Your teeth are made of a compound called hydroxyapatite (hi DRAHK see A puh tite). The sodium fluoride in toothpaste undergoes a chemical reaction with hydroxyapatite to form a new compound on the surface of your teeth. This compound resists food acids that cause tooth decay, another chemical change. In this activity, you will design an experiment to test the effectiveness of different toothpaste brands. The compound found in your teeth is similar to the mineral compound found in eggshells. Treating hard-boiled eggs with toothpaste is similar to brushing your teeth with toothpaste. Soaking the eggs in food acids such as vinegar for several days will produce similar conditions as eating foods, which contain acids that will produce a chemical change in your teeth, for several months.

Recognize the Problem

Which brands of toothpaste provide the greatest protection against tooth decay?

Form a Hypothesis

Form a hypothesis about the effectiveness of different brands of toothpaste.

Goals

- **Observe** how toothpaste helps prevent tooth decay.
- **Design** an experiment to test the effectiveness of various toothpaste brands.

Safety Precautions

Possible Materials

2 or 3 different brands of toothpaste
drinking glasses or bowls
hard boiled eggs
concentrated lemon juice
apple juice
water
artist's paint brush

Resource Manager

Chapter Resources Booklet
Activity Worksheet, pp. 7–8
Science Inquiry Labs, p. 51
Lab Management and Safety, p. 67

Egg	Day 1	Day 2	Day 3
Toothpaste 1			
Toothpaste 2			
No Toothpaste			

Test Your Hypothesis

Plan

1. **Describe** how you will use the materials to test the toothpaste.
2. **List** the steps you will follow to test your hypothesis.
3. **Decide** on the length of time that you will conduct your experiment.
4. **Identify** the control and variables you will use in your experiment.
5. **Create** a data table in your Science Journal to record your observations, measurements, and results.
6. **Describe** how you will measure the amount of protection each toothpaste brand provides.

Do

1. Make sure your teacher approves your plan before you start.
2. **Conduct** your experiment as planned. Be sure to follow all proper safety precautions.
3. **Record** your observations in your data table.

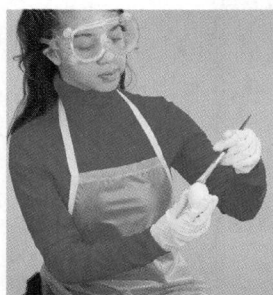

Analyze Your Data

1. **Compare** the untreated eggshells with the shells you treated with toothpaste.
2. **Compare** the condition of the eggshells you treated with different brands of toothpaste.
3. **Compare** the condition of the eggshells soaked in lemon juice and in apple juice.
4. **Identify** unintended variables you discovered in your experiment that might have influenced the results.

Draw Conclusions

1. Did the results support your hypothesis? **Identify** strengths and weaknesses of your hypothesis.
2. **Explain** why the eggs treated with toothpaste were better protected than the untreated eggshells.
3. **Identify** which brands of toothpaste, if any best protected the eggshells from decay.
4. **Evaluate** the scientific explanation for why adding fluoride to toothpaste and drinking water prevents tooth decay.
5. **Predict** what would happen to your protected eggs if you left them in the food acids for several weeks.
6. **Infer** why it is a good idea to brush with fluoride toothpaste.

Compare your results with the results of your classmates. **Create** a poster advertising the benefits of fluoride toothpaste.

ACTIVITY   **563**

Expected Outcome

Eggshells coated with a sodium fluoride toothpaste should show little or no reaction with the acid. The control eggshell should show evidence of being eaten away and softening after several days.

Analyze Your Data

1. The untreated eggshell shows evidence of a chemical reaction, while the treated eggshells do not.
2. Answers will depend on the brands of toothpaste tested.
3. The eggshell in lemon juice should show more evidence of a reaction.
4. Answers will vary.

Error Analysis

Have students compare their results and their hypotheses and explain why any differences occurred.

Draw Conclusion

1. Answers will be determined by student hypotheses.
2. The sodium fluoride in the toothpaste prevented the eggshells from chemically reacting with the food acid.
3. Answers will vary.
4. Evidence indicates that fluoride prevents a compound similar to that in teeth from reacting with food acids.
5. The protection would lose its effectiveness and the eggshells would react with the acids.
6. Regular brushing with fluoride toothpaste prevents chemicals in teeth from reacting with food acids.

Encourage students to use a computer graphics program to prepare their posters.

Science Stats

Content Background

One advantage of hydrogen peroxide over other bleaches is that, as it oxidizes, it breaks down into oxygen and water. Other bleaches might contain materials such as chlorine that can harm the environment if they are present in large quantities.

Discussion

Contact a local packing store for samples of packing peanuts made from corn and those made from traditional plastic. Show students how the corn-based packing decomposes when placed in water but the plastic packing material does not. **How would using such a biodegradable packing material benefit the environment?** The material would decompose into an environmentally safe material when it got wet in a landfill.

Activity

Have students keep track of how many soft drink cans they empty in a week. Have them research how much energy is saved when they recycle these cans. Recycling takes only 5% of the energy needed to refine aluminum from ore. Have groups of students prepare posters to place around the school promoting recycling. If possible, obtain permission from the school administration to establish a recycling program in the school.

Science Stats

Strange Changes

Did you know...

...A hair colorist is also a chemist!

Colorists use hydrogen peroxide and ammonia to swell and open the cuticle-like shafts on your hair. Once these are open, the chemicals in hair dye can get into your natural pigment molecules and chemically change your hair color. The first safe commercial hair color was created in 1909 in France.

...Americans consume about 175 million kg of sauerkraut each year.

During the production of sauerkraut, bacteria produce lactic acid. The acid chemically breaks down the material in the cabbage, making it translucent and tangy.

...More than 450,000 metric tons of plastic packaging are recycled each year in the U.S.

Discarded plastics undergo physical changes including melting and shredding. They are then converted into flakes or pellets, which are used to make new products. Recycled plastic is used to make clothes, furniture, carpets, and even lumber.

564   CHAPTER 19 Properties and Changes of Matter

SCIENCE Online

Internet Addresses

_____

_____

_____

_____

Explore the Glencoe Science Web site at **science.glencoe.com** to find out more about topics in this feature.

Connecting To Math

...The U.S. population consumes about 1.36 billion L of gasoline each day.

When ignited in an enclosed space, such as in an internal combustion engine, gasoline undergoes many chemical changes to deliver the energy needed for an automobile to move.

Projected Recycling Rates by Material, 2000

Material	1995 Recycling	Proj. Recycling
Paper/Paperboard	40.0%	43 to 46%
Glass	24.5%	27 to 36%
Ferrous Metal	36.5%	42 to 55%
Aluminum	34.6%	46 to 48%
Plastics	5.3%	7 to 10%
Yard Waste	30.3%	40 to 50%
Total Materials	27.0%	30 to 35%

...It is possible to change corn into plastic!
Normally plastics are made from petroleum, but chemists have discovered how to chemically convert corn and other plants into plastic. A factory in Nebraska is scheduled to produce about 140,000 metric tons of the corn-based plastic by 2002.

Do the Math

1. There are 275 million people in the United States. Calculate the average amount of sauerkraut consumed by each person in the United States in one year.
2. How many liters of gasoline does the U.S. population consume during a leap year?
3. If chemists can produce 136 kg of plastic from 27 kg of corn, how much corn is needed to make 816 kg of plastic?

Go Further

Every time you cook, you make physical and chemical changes to food. Go to the Glencoe Science Web site at **science.glencoe.com** or to your local or school library to find out what chemical or physical changes take place when cooking ingredients are heated or cooled.

Connecting To Math

Do the Math

Teaching Strategies
- Have interested students investigate the recycling symbols on many plastic items. These symbols consist of a number contained in a triangle made from three arrows.
- Have students research what each recycling symbol means and which types of plastics are recycled in their locale.
- Show students a diagram of how an internal combustion engine operates. Emphasize to them that the proper proportion of gasoline and oxygen is necessary for efficient use of fuel.

Answers
1. 0.636 kg/person
2. about 498 billion L
3. 162 kg of corn

Go Further

Physical changes include change in state, such as melting. Before investigating chemical changes, ask students, as a class, to brainstorm signs that indicate a chemical change has occurred. Such indications include: energy release or absorption and color or odor change.

Visual Learning

Projected Recycling Rates by Material, 2000 By what percent will the recycling rate increase from 1995 to 2000 for glass and paper? 2.5 to 11.5%; 3.0 to 6.0%, respectively Have students use a dictionary to find out what *ferrous* means. A ferrous metal is any metal that is primarily iron, such as steel. **If 259 kg of aluminum products were used by a family, what mass of that aluminum was likely to be recycled in 1995?** 89.6 kg **The recycling rate is over 60% for aluminum cans. Why doesn't this percent match those in the table?** Aluminum is used in many other products that are not as likely to be recycled. Such products include foil, bicycle parts, and window screen.

Chapter 19 Study Guide

Reviewing Main Ideas

Preview

Students can answer the questions in their Science Journals. Discuss the answers as you go through the chapter. **LS Linguistic**

Review

Students can write their answers, then compare them with those of other students. **LS Interpersonal**

Reteach

Students can look at the illustrations and describe details that support the main ideas of the chapter. **LS Visual-Spatial**

Answers to Chapter Review

SECTION 1
3. 1,500 cm³
5. ability to burn

SECTION 2
4. a change in color

Reviewing Main Ideas

Section 1 Physical and Chemical Properties

1. Matter can be described by its characteristics, or properties.

2. A physical property is a characteristic that can be observed without altering the composition of the sample.

3. Physical properties include color, shape, smell, taste, and texture, as well as measurable quantities such as mass, volume, density, melting point, and boiling point. *What is the volume of this box?*

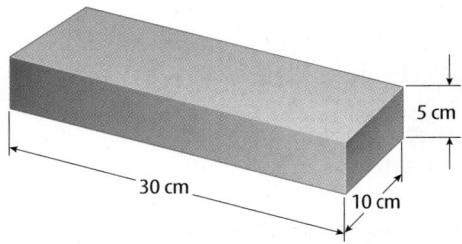

30 cm   10 cm   5 cm

4. Matter can exist in different states—solid, liquid, or gas. The state of matter is a physical property.

5. A chemical property is a characteristic that cannot be observed without changing what the sample is made of. *What chemical property is being shown here?*

Section 2 Physical and Chemical Changes

1. During a physical change, the composition of matter stays the same but the appearance changes in some way.

2. Physical changes occur when matter is ripped, cut, torn, or bent, or when matter changes from one state to another.

3. A chemical change occurs when the composition of matter changes.

4. Signs of chemical change include changes in energy, color, odor, or the production of gases or solids. *What evidence from this photo indicates a chemical change?*

5. According to the law of conservation of mass, mass cannot be created or destroyed. As a result, the mass of the substances that were present before a physical or chemical change is equal to the mass of the substances that are present after the change.

FOLDABLES Reading & Study Skills   **After You Read**

To help you review matter's physical and chemical properties and changes, use the information on your Foldable.

FOLDABLES Reading & Study Skills   **After You Read**

After students have read the chapter and completed the Foldable described in Before You Read, have them do the activity on the student page.

Dinah Zike

Visualizing Main Ideas

Complete the following concept map on matter.

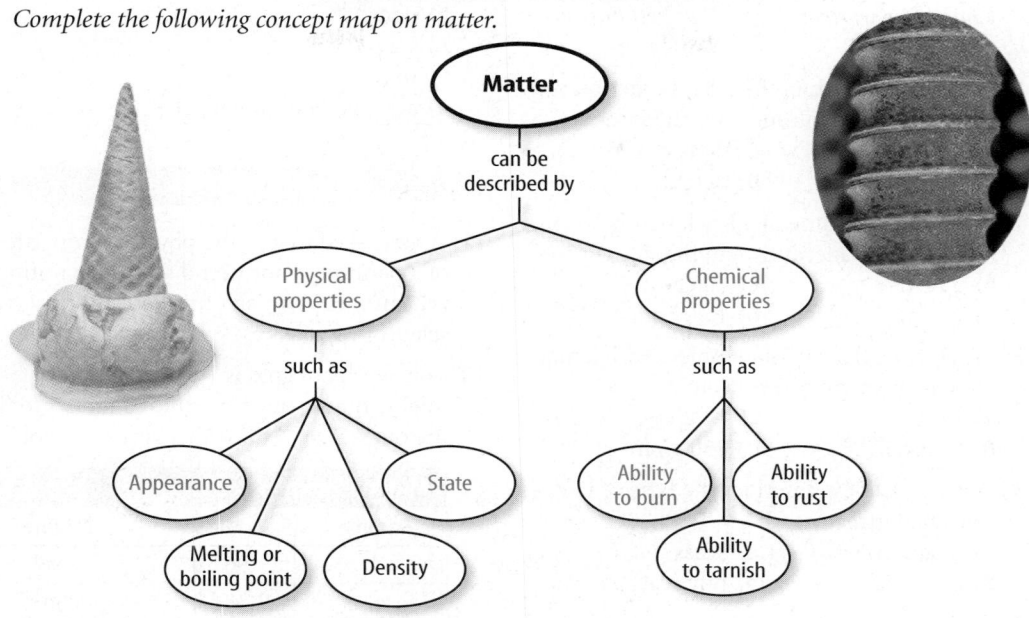

Visualizing Main Ideas

See student page.

Vocabulary Review

Using Vocabulary

1. Color can be observed without changing the object.
2. Melting point, boiling point, and density do not change with the amount of matter.
3. The appearance of matter changes but the composition does not change.
4. A change of state is a physical change.
5. During a chemical change, substances are changed into different substances.
6. Clues that a chemical change has occurred include change in color, loss or gain of energy, change of smell, and production of a gas or solid.
7. Accept all reasonable answers. One example of a chemical change is burning wood.
8. The law of conservation of mass states that the total mass of matter is the same before and after a physical or chemical change.

Vocabulary Review

Vocabulary Words

a. chemical change
b. chemical property
c. physical change
d. physical property
e. law of conservation of mass

Study Tip

Study the material you *don't* understand first. It's easy to review the material you know but it's harder to force yourself to learn the difficult concepts. Reread any topics that you find confusing. You should take notes as you read.

Using Vocabulary

Use what you know about the vocabulary words to answer the following questions. Use complete sentences.

1. Why is color a physical property?

2. What is a physical property that does not change with the amount of matter?

3. What happens during a physical change?

4. What type of change is a change of state?

5. What happens during a chemical change?

6. What are three clues that a chemical change has occurred?

7. What is an example of a chemical change?

8. What is the law of conservation of mass?

Checking Concepts

1. C
2. C
3. C
4. A
5. D
6. C
7. B
8. C
9. B
10. C

Thinking Critically

11. Beautiful is an opinion; it cannot be measured.
12. Divide the mass of each sample by its volume, and compare the densities. Sample A: 96.5 ÷ 5 = 19.3; Sample B: 38.6 ÷ 4 = 9.65; Sample A is more likely to be gold.
13. Bending is a physical change because it does not change the composition of the gold.
14. No; some physical changes, such as changing from a liquid to a solid, involve the release of energy, and some chemical changes, such as burning wood, involve the release of energy.
15. During a change of matter, either the form or composition of the matter changes. However, the particles within the matter are not destroyed nor are new particles created. As a result, the total mass of the matter is the same before and after a physical or chemical change.

Checking Concepts

Choose the word or phrase that best answers the question.

1. What changes when the mass of an object increases while volume stays the same?
   - A) color
   - B) length
   - C) density
   - D) height

2. What is the volume of a brick that is 20 cm long, 10 cm wide, and 3 cm high?
   - A) 33 cm^3
   - B) 90 cm^3
   - C) 600 cm^3
   - D) 1,200 cm^3

3. What is the density of an object with a mass of 50 g and a volume of 5 cm^3?
   - A) 45 g/cm^3
   - B) 55 g/cm^3
   - C) 10 g/cm^3
   - D) 250 g/cm^3

4. What word best describes the type of materials that attract iron?
   - A) magnetic
   - B) chemical
   - C) mass
   - D) physical

5. Which is an example of a chemical property?
   - A) color
   - B) mass
   - C) density
   - D) ability to burn

6. Which is an example of a physical change?
   - A) metal rusting
   - B) silver tarnishing
   - C) water boiling
   - D) paper burning

7. What characteristic best describes what happens during a physical change?
   - A) composition changes
   - B) composition stays the same
   - C) form stays the same
   - D) mass is lost

8. Which is an example of a chemical change?
   - A) water freezes
   - B) wood is carved
   - C) bread is baked
   - D) wire is bent

9. Which is NOT a clue that could indicate a chemical change?
   - A) change in color
   - B) change in shape
   - C) change in energy
   - D) change in odor

10. What property stays the same during physical and chemical changes?
    - A) density
    - B) shape
    - C) mass
    - D) arrangement of particles

Thinking Critically

11. When asked to give the physical properties of a painting, your friend says the painting is beautiful. Why isn't this description a true scientific property?

12. The density of gold is 19.3 g/cm^3. How might you use the properties of matter to figure out which of these two samples is gold?

Mineral Samples		
Sample	**Mass**	**Volume**
A	96.5 g	5 cm^3
B	38.6 g	4 cm^3

13. A jeweler bends gold into a beautiful ring. What type of change is this? Explain.

14. You are told that a sample of matter gives off energy as it changes. Can you conclude which type of change occurred? Why or why not?

15. What happens to mass during chemical and physical changes? Explain.

Developing Skills

16. **Classifying** Decide whether the following properties are physical or chemical.
    - a. Sugar can change into alcohol.
    - b. Iron can rust.
    - c. Alcohol can vaporize.
    - d. Paper can burn.
    - e. Sugar can dissolve.

Chapter ✓Assessment Planner

Portfolio Encourage students to place in their portfolios one or two items of what they consider to be their best work. Examples include:
- Assessment, p. 550
- Assessment, p. 555

Performance Additional performance assessments, Performance Task Assessment Lists, and rubrics for evaluating these activities can be found in Glencoe's **Performance Assessment in the Science Classroom.**

17. Classifying Decide whether the following changes are physical or chemical.
a. Milk spoils.
b. Dynamite explodes.
c. Eggs and milk are stirred together.
d. Ice cream freezes.

18. Comparing and Contrasting Relate such human characteristics as hair and eye color and height and weight to physical properties of matter. Relate human behavior to chemical properties. Think about how you observe these properties.

19. Interpreting Scientific Illustrations Describe the changes shown below and explain why they are different.

Performance Assessment

20. Write a Story Write a story describing an event that you have experienced. Then go back through the story and circle any physical or chemical properties you mentioned. Underline any physical or chemical changes you included.

TECHNOLOGY

Go to the Glencoe Science Web site at **science.glencoe.com** or use the **Glencoe Science CD-ROM** for additional chapter assessment.

Test Practice

Unknown matter can be identified by taking a sample of it and comparing its physical properties to those of already identified substances.

Physical Properties		
Substance	Flash Point (°C)	Density (g/cm³)
Gasoline	− 45.6	0.720
Palmitic Acid	206.0	0.852
Aluminum	645.0	2.702
Methane	− 187.7	0.466

Study the table and answer the following questions.

1. A scientist has a sample of a substance with a density greater than 1 g/cm³. According to the table, which substance might it be?
A) Gasoline **C)** Aluminum
B) Palmitic acid **D)** Methane

2. Some substances are very combustible and ignite by themselves if they are warm enough. The flashpoint of a substance is the lowest temperature at which it can catch fire spontaneously. If all the substances in the table have to be stored together, at which of the following temperatures should they be stored?
F) 100°C **H)** −100°C
G) 0°C **J)** −200°C

Test Practice

The Test-Taking Tip was written by The Princeton Review, the nation's leader in test preparation.
1. C
2. J

Developing Skills

16. a. chemical, b. chemical, c. physical, d. chemical, e. physical
17. a. chemical, b. chemical, c. physical, d. physical
18. Human characteristics can be observed without interacting with a person. For example, you can observe hair and eye color from a distance. Human behavior can be observed only by observing that person's interactions.
19. Cutting cake involved only a physical change since only the cake's appearance changed whereas burning a candle involved a definite chemical change.

Performance Assessment

20. Use **Performance Assessment in the Science Classroom**, p. 155.

✓Assessment Resources

Reproducible Masters
Chapter Resources Booklet
Chapter Review, pp. 35–36
Chapter Tests, pp. 37–40
Assessment Transparency Activity, p. 47

Glencoe Science Web site
Interactive Tutor
Chapter Quizzes

Glencoe Technology
Assessment Transparency
Interactive CD-ROM Chapter Quizzes
ExamView Pro Test Bank
Vocabulary PuzzleMaker Software
MindJogger Videoquiz

Standardized Test Practice

QUESTION 1: C

Students must recall chronology of events from the passage to identify which answer choice occurred first.

- **Choice A** No; this event occurred after Mendeleev made his predictions.
- **Choice B** No; this happened much later, in the 20th century.
- **Choice C** Yes; this event occurred first.
- **Choice D** No; this happened much later, in the 20th century.

Teaching Tip

Suggest students make a timeline to help them answer questions about sequence of events in a passage.

QUESTION 2: F

Students must use clues from the passage such as *made . . . in the laboratory* to identify that the best meaning of the underlined word *artificially* is choice F, *unnaturally*.

Read the passage. Then read each question that follows the passage. Decide which is the best answer to each question.

Grouping the Elements Using their Properties

By 1860, scientists had discovered a total of 63 chemical elements. Dmitri Mendeleev, a Russian chemist, thought that there had to be some order among the elements.

He made a card for each element. On the card, he listed the physical and chemical properties of the element, such as atomic mass, density, color, and melting point. He also wrote each element's combining power, or its ability to form compounds with other elements.

When he arranged the cards in order of increasing atomic mass, Mendeleev noticed that the elements followed a periodic, or repeating, pattern. After every seven cards, the properties repeated. He placed each group of seven cards in rows, one row under another. He noticed that the columns in his chart formed groups of elements that had similar chemical and physical properties.

In a few places, Mendeleev had to move a card one space to the left or right to maintain the similarities of his groups. This left a few empty spaces. He predicted that they would be filled with elements that were unknown. He even predicted their properties. Fifteen years later, three new elements were discovered and placed in the empty spaces of the periodic table. Their physical and chemical properties agreed with Mendeleev's predictions.

Today there are more than 100 known elements. An extra column has been added for the noble gases, a group of elements that were not yet discovered in Mendeleev's time.

Members of this group almost never combine with other elements. As new elements are discovered or are made <u>artificially</u>, scientists can place them in their proper place on the periodic table thanks to Mendeleev.

Test-Taking Tip   To answer questions about a sequence of events, make a time line of what happened in each paragraph of the passage.

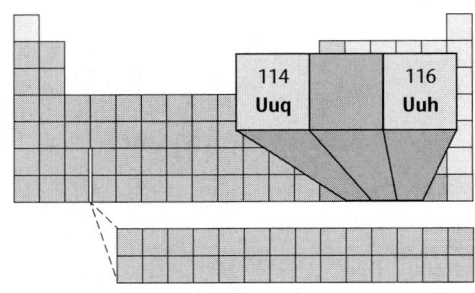

Even the modern periodic table has empty spaces for elements that have not been discovered yet.

1. Which of the following occurred FIRST in the passage?
   A) Three new elements were discovered 15 years after Mendeleev developed the periodic table.
   B) The noble gases were discovered and added to the periodic table.
   C) Mendeleev predicted properties of unknown elements.
   D) New elements were made in the laboratory and added to the periodic table.

2. The word <u>artificially</u> in this passage means _____.
   F) unnaturally
   G) artistically
   H) atomically
   J) radioactively

Reasoning and Skills

Read each question and choose the best answer.

Changes in States of Matter

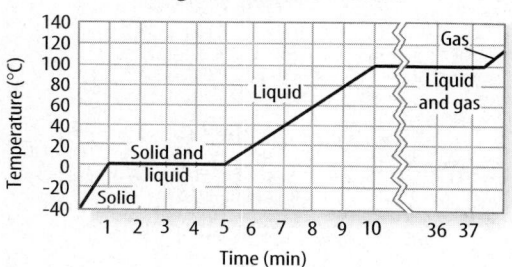

1. The graph shows the change in temperature that occurs as ice changes to water vapor. How much higher than the starting temperature is the boiling point?
   A) 40°C
   C) 140°C
   B) 100°C
   D) 180°C

Test-Taking Tip Boiling point is the flat section of the graph where liquid changes to gas.

2. What is being measured in the illustration?
   F) boiling point
   H) density
   G) melting point
   J) flammability

Test-Taking Tip Think about what you would measure with a thermometer in a liquid that you are heating.

Properties of Selected Pure Substances

Substance	Melting Point (°C)	Boiling Point (°C)	Color
Aluminum	660.4	2,519	silver metallic
Argon	−189.2	−185.7	colorless
Mercury	−38.8	356.6	silver metallic
Water	0	100	colorless

3. Room temperature is about 20°C. In the table, which substance is a solid at room temperature?
   A) aluminum
   B) argon
   C) mercury
   D) water

Test-Taking Tip Remember that negative temperatures are below zero.

Read this question carefully before writing your answer on a separate sheet of paper.

4. The density of pure water is 1.00 g/cm³. Ice floats on water, thus, the density of ice is *less* than that of water. Design an experiment to determine the density of an ice cube. List all the necessary steps.
   (Volume = Length × Width × Height; Density = Mass / Volume)

Test-Taking Tip Consider all the information provided in the question.

Reasoning and Skills

QUESTION 1: C

Students must interpret the graph to identify the correct answer. Because the starting temperature was −40°C and the boiling point is 100°C, the correct answer is choice C, *140°C*.

QUESTION 2: F

Students must carefully examine the diagram. Because the substance in the beaker is already a liquid and appears to be boiling, the correct answer is choice F, *boiling point*.

QUESTION 3: A

Students must retrieve information from the table to identify the correct answer. Because there is only one substance with a melting point greater than 20°C, the correct answer is choice A, *aluminum*.

Teaching Tip

Review with students how to analyze the chart to determine at what temperature each substance changes from a solid to a liquid.

QUESTION 4: Answers will vary.

Answers should include measuring the length, width, and height of the ice cube with a metric ruler in order to find volume. In addition, the mass of the ice cube should be determined using a triple-beam balance. After these measurements have been determined, students should describe how to calculate volume and density.

UNIT 7

UNIT 7 Waves, Sound, and Light

Unit Contents

✔ Pre-Reading Activity

Have students look at illustrations and photographs that depict different forms of energy.

How Are Radar & Popcorn Connected?

572

Teacher to Teacher

"While discussing wave crests, troughs, and wavelengths, place a clear, oblong, heat-resistant baking dish on an overhead projector. Add water. Generate waves with a pencil point, and use pieces of wood as barriers. To reinforce the concepts, have students make waves with a coiled-spring toy and locate the parts of a wave."

Tonya K. Hancock, Teacher
Davis Drive Middle School
Raleigh, NC

Radar systems—such as the one in this modern air traffic control room—use radio waves to detect objects. In the 1940s, the radio waves used for radar were generated by a device called a magnetron. One day, an engineer working on a radar project was standing near a magnetron when he noticed that the candy bar in his pocket had melted. Intrigued, the engineer got some unpopped popcorn and placed it next to the magnetron. Sure enough, the kernels began to pop. The engineer realized that the magnetron's short radio waves, called microwaves, caused the molecules in the food to move more quickly, increasing the food's temperature. Soon, magnetrons were being used in the first microwave ovens. Today, microwave ovens are used to pop popcorn—and heat many other kinds of food—in kitchens all over the world.

SCIENCE CONNECTION

ELECTROMAGNETIC RADIATION Microwaves and other kinds of radio waves are forms of electromagnetic radiation. So are X rays, gamma rays, infrared radiation, ultraviolet radiation, and visible light. These various forms of electromagnetic radiation differ in the length and frequency of their waves. Find out the wavelengths of the kinds of electromagnetic radiation named above. Then create a diagram that arranges these kinds of radiation in order from longest to shortest.

Introducing the Unit

How Are Radar & Popcorn Connected?

All radio waves, including microwaves are electromagnetic waves. Electromagnetic waves carry energy, just as sound waves and water waves do.

Electromagnetic waves consist of oscillating electric and magnetic fields. These fields can transfer energy to atoms and molecules by causing their electric charges to oscillate. Sometimes the fields cause the molecules to oscillate. For example, a water molecule is a polar molecule. One end has a positive charge and the other end has a negative charge. When microwaves encounter water molecules, they make the molecules flip back and forth.

Food materials, such as popcorn kernels, usually contain water molecules. These water molecules absorb microwaves and flip back and forth, colliding with other water molecules. These collisions increase the temperature of the water molecules. Inside the popcorn kernels, the moisture inside the kernel changes to steam, and the kernel explodes.

SCIENCE CONNECTION

Activity
Using index cards, make a deck of cards that show the wavelengths of the various forms of electromagnetic radiation. Have students take turns shuffling and arranging the cards in order of decreasing wavelength.

SCIENCE *Online*
Internet Addresses
_____
_____
_____
_____
Explore the Glencoe Science Web site at **science.glencoe.com** to find out more about topics in this unit.

Section/Objectives	Standards		Activities/Features
Chapter Opener	**National**	**State/Local**	**Explore Activity:** Observe wave behavior, p. 575
	See p. 6T for a Key to Standards.		**Before You Read,** p. 575
Section 1 What are waves? 🕐 1 session 📦 0.5 block 1. **Explain** the relationship among waves, energy, and matter. 2. **Describe** the difference between transverse waves and compressional waves.	National Content Standards: UCP5, A1, B1, B3		**MiniLAB:** Comparing Sounds, p. 579 **Physics Integration,** p. 580
Section 2 Wave Properties 🕐 2 sessions 📦 1 block 1. **Describe** the relationship between the frequency and wavelength of a wave. 2. **Explain** why waves travel at different speeds.	National Content Standards: UCP3, A1, B3		**Health Integration,** p. 584 **Science Online,** p. 585 **Activity:** Waves on a Spring, p. 586
Section 3 Wave Behavior 🕐 4 sessions 📦 2 blocks 1. **Explain** how waves can reflect from some surfaces. 2. **Explain** how waves change direction when they move from one material into another. 3. **Describe** how waves are able to bend around barriers.	National Content Standards: UCP2, A1, B1, B3		**MiniLAB:** Observing How Light Refracts, p. 588 **Science Online,** p. 591 **Problem-Solving Activity:** Can you create destructive interference?, p. 591 **Visualizing Interference,** p. 592 **Activity:** Wave Speed, pp. 594–595 **Science Stats:** Waves, Waves, and More Waves, pp. 596–597

Activity Materials	Reproducible Resources	Section Assessment	Technology
Explore Activity: clear-plastic plate, a cork or straw, dropper, water	**Chapter Resources Booklet** Foldables Worksheet, p. 15 Directed Reading Overview, p. 17 Note-taking Worksheets, pp. 31–32		
MiniLAB: wooden ruler	**Chapter Resources Booklet** Transparency Activity, p. 42 MiniLAB, p. 3 Enrichment, p. 28 Reinforcement, p. 25 Directed Reading, p. 18 Transparency Activity, pp. 45–46	**Portfolio** Activity, p. 578 **Performance** MiniLAB, p. 579 Skill Builder Activities, p. 580 **Content** Section Assessment, p. 580	Section Focus Transparency Teaching Transparency Interactive CD-ROM Guided Reading Audio Program
Activity: long, coiled spring toy, 5 cm colored yarn, meterstick, stopwatch *Need materials?* Contact Science Kit at 1-800-828-7777 or www.sciencekit.com on the Internet.	**Chapter Resources Booklet** Transparency Activity, p. 43 Enrichment, p. 29 Reinforcement, p. 26 Directed Reading, p. 19 Activity Worksheet, pp. 5–6 Lab Activity, pp. 9–11 **Reading and Writing Skill Activities,** p. 33 **Home and Community Involvement,** p. 42	**Portfolio** Extension, p. 583 Science Journal, p. 584 **Performance** Skill Builder Activities, p. 585 **Content** Section Assessment, p. 585	Section Focus Transparency Interactive CD-ROM Guided Reading Audio Program
MiniLAB: large, opaque drinking glass or cup of water, white soda straw **Activity:** coiled spring toy, stopwatch, meterstick, tape	**Chapter Resources Booklet** Transparency Activity, p. 44 Enrichment, p. 30 Reinforcement, p. 27 Directed Reading, pp. 19, 20 MiniLAB, p. 4 Lab Activity, pp. 13–14 Activity Worksheet, pp. 7–8 **Lab Management and Safety,** p. 65 **Mathematics Skill Activities,** p. 47	**Portfolio** Challenge, p. 593 **Performance** MiniLAB, p. 588 Problem-Solving Activity, p. 591 Skill Builder Activities, p. 593 **Content** Section Assessment, p. 593	Section Focus Transparency Interactive CD-ROM Guided Reading Audio Program

End of Chapter Assessment

Blackline Masters	Technology	Professional Series
Chapter Resources Booklet Chapter Review, pp. 35–36 Chapter Tests, pp. 37–40 **Standardized Test Practice by The Princeton Review,** pp. 85–88	MindJogger Videoquiz Interactive CD-ROM Vocabulary PuzzleMakers ExamView Pro Test Bank Interactive Lesson Planner Interactive Teacher Edition	Performance Assessment in the Science Classroom (PASC)

Transparencies

Section Focus

Section Focus Transparency 1 Ride the Wave!

Surfing may seem like a fairly new sport, but it's not. In fact, people think there were surfers in Hawaii in the 1400s. When Captain Cook landed in the Hawaiian Islands in 1778, he was greeted by an islander on a surfboard!

1. Name some different kinds of waves.
2. What do you think creates waves on the ocean?
3. Describe the path of light from the Sun to the camera that took this picture.

L2

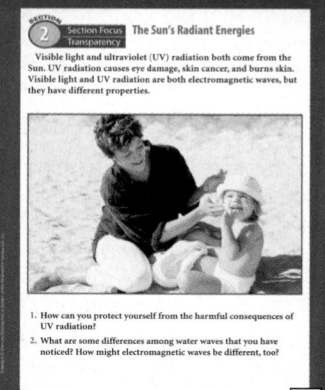

Section Focus Transparency 2 The Sun's Radiant Energies

Visible light and ultraviolet (UV) radiation both come from the Sun. UV radiation causes eye damage, skin cancer, and burns skin. Visible light and UV radiation are both electromagnetic waves, but they have different properties.

1. How can you protect yourself from the harmful consequences of UV radiation?
2. What are some differences among water waves that you have noticed? How might electromagnetic waves be different, too?

L2

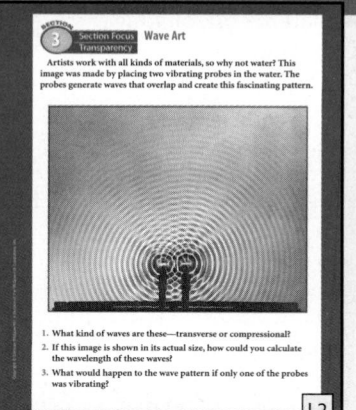

Section Focus Transparency 3 Wave Art

Artists work with all kinds of materials, so why not water? This image was made by placing two vibrating probes in the water. The probes generate waves that overlap and create this fascinating pattern.

1. What kind of waves are these—transverse or compressional?
2. If this image is shown in its actual size, how could you calculate the wavelength of these waves?
3. What would happen to the wave pattern if only one of the probes was vibrating?

L2

This is a representation of key blackline masters available in the Teacher Classroom Resources. See Resource Manager boxes within the chapter for additional information.

Assessment

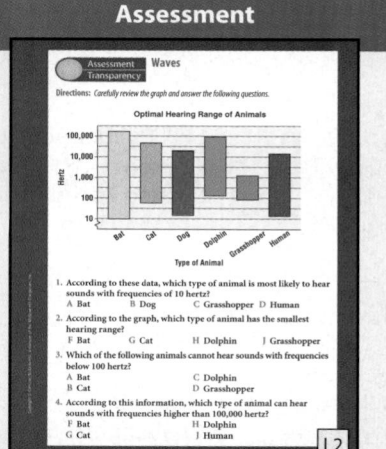

Assessment Transparency Waves

Directions: Carefully review the graph and answer the following questions.

Optimal Hearing Range of Animals

1. According to these data, which type of animal is most likely to hear sounds with frequencies of 10 hertz?
   A Bat   B Dog   C Grasshopper   D Human
2. According to the graph, which type of animal has the smallest hearing range?
   F Bat   G Cat   H Dolphin   J Grasshopper
3. Which of the following animals cannot hear sounds with frequencies below 100 hertz?
   A Bat   C Dolphin
   B Cat   D Grasshopper
4. According to this information, which type of animal can hear sounds with frequencies higher than 100,000 hertz?
   F Bat   H Dolphin
   G Cat   J Human

L2

Teaching

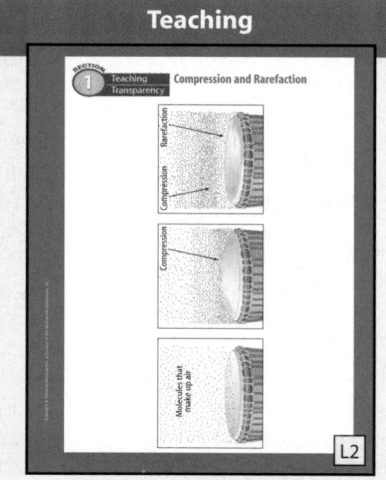

Teaching Transparency 1 Compression and Rarefaction

L2

Key to Teaching Strategies

The following designations will help you decide which activities are appropriate for your students.

L1 Level 1 activities should be appropriate for students with learning difficulties.

L2 Level 2 activities should be within the ability range of all students.

L3 Level 3 activities are designed for above-average students.

ELL ELL activities should be within the ability range of English Language Learners.

COOP LEARN Cooperative Learning activities are designed for small group work.

LS Multiple Learning Styles logos, as described on page 22T, are used throughout to indicate strategies that address different learning styles.

P These strategies represent student products that can be placed into a best-work portfolio.

Hands-on Activities

Activity Worksheets

Activity Waves on a Spring

Lab Preview
Directions: Answer these questions before you begin the Activity.
1. Why should you wear goggles when performing this activity?

2. How will you use yarn in this activity?

Waves are rhythmic disturbances that carry energy through matter or space. Studying waves can help you understand how the Sun's energy reaches Earth and sounds travel through the air.

What You'll Investigate
What are some of the properties of transverse and compressional waves on a coiled spring?

Materials
long, coiled spring toy
colored yarn (3 cm)
meterstick
stopwatch

Goals
• Create transverse and compressional waves on a coiled spring toy.
• Investigate wave properties such as speed and amplitude.

Safety Precautions
CAUTION: *Avoid overstretching or tangling the spring to prevent injury or damage.*

Procedure
1. Work in pairs or groups and clear a place on an uncarpeted floor about 6 m × 2 m.
2. Stretch the spring between two people to the length suggested by your teacher. Measure the length.
3. Create a wave with a quick, sideways snap of the wrist. Time several waves as they travel the length of the spring. Record the average time in the data table in the Data and Observations section.
4. Repeat step 3 using waves that have slightly larger amplitudes.
5. Squeeze together about 20 of the coils. Observe what happens to the unsqueezed coils. Release the coils and observe.
6. Quickly push the spring toward your partner, then pull it back.
7. Tie the yarn to a coil near the middle of the spring. Repeat step 6, observing the string.

L2

Laboratory Activities

Laboratory Activity 1 Examining Wave Motion

We are constantly being bombarded by waves—light waves, sound waves, and radio waves just to name three. Even though we often can't see the actual wave action, all waves have measurable aspects in common.

Strategy
You will determine the frequency of a wave.
You will determine the amplitude of a wave.

Materials
cone-shaped cup
ring stand with ring
salt, 100 g
string for cup handle, about 10 cm
string to suspend cup, about 30 cm
dark-colored paper
stopwatch
metric ruler
pencil

Procedure
Part A—Set Up
1. Poke a very small hole in the bottom of the cone-shaped cup. Punch two small holes near the top of the cup at opposite sides, and tie the 10-cm string to make a handle for the cup. Use the 30-cm string to hang the cup from the ring on the ring stand.
2. Cover the hole in the bottom of the cup with your finger, and fill the cup with salt. Place the dark-colored paper below the cup. A small amount of salt should trickle out of the cup onto the paper.
3. Pull the cup upward, keeping the string taut so that the angle that the string forms with the vertical is between 10 and 20 degrees. Gently release the cup, and allow it to swing back and forth over the paper. Observe that the salt streaming from the end of the cone forms a straight line on the paper. Stop the cup from swinging and pour the salt on the paper back into the cup.

Part B—Frequency
1. Determine the frequency of a wave, which in this case is how many times the cup passes a fixed point each second.

One student should use the stopwatch to measure the time while another student counts the complete cycles of the cup.
2. Pull the cup upward as described in step 3 of Part A. Release the cup and start the stopwatch simultaneously. Count ten complete cycles of the cup, and stop the watch just as the cup reaches its maximum height at the end of the fifth cycle. Record the time in Table 1 in the Data and Observations section.
3. Repeat step 2 three more times. Stop the cup from swinging and pour the salt on the paper back into the cup.
4. Divide the recorded time for five cycles for each trial by 5 to calculate the time in seconds needed to complete one cycle. Average the frequency for each trial to get the average frequency. Record the average in the Data and Observations section.

L2

Meeting Different Ability Levels

Content Outline

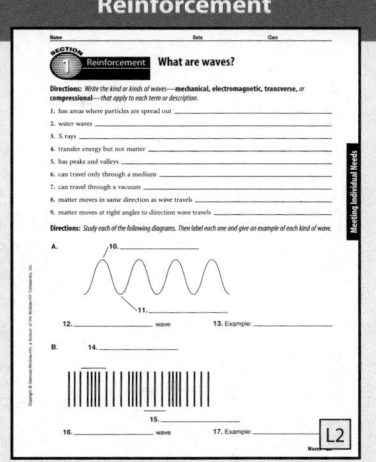

L2

Reinforcement

L2

Directed Reading

L1

Assessment

Chapter Tests

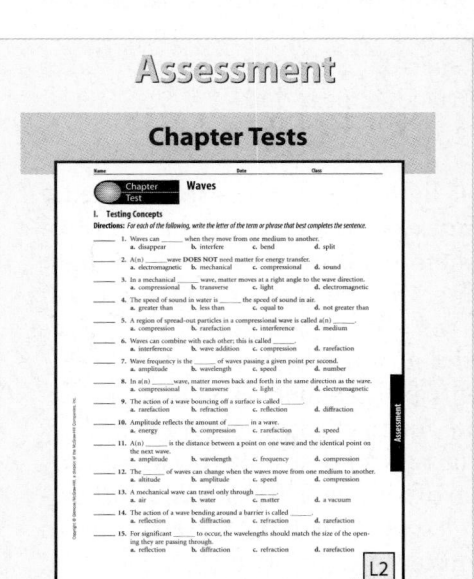

L2

Enrichment

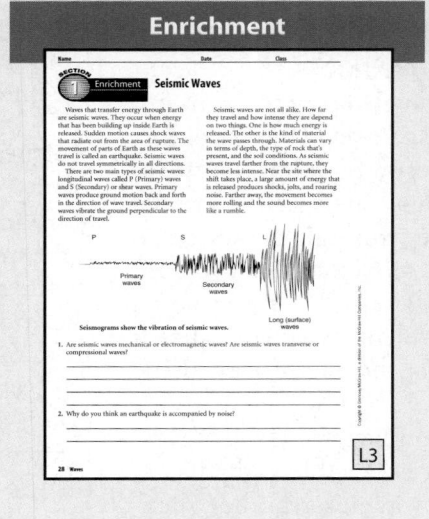

L3

Spanish Directed Reading

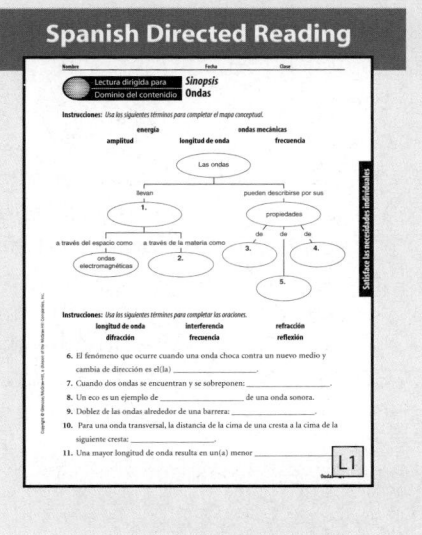

L1

Test Practice Workbook

L2

Chapter Review

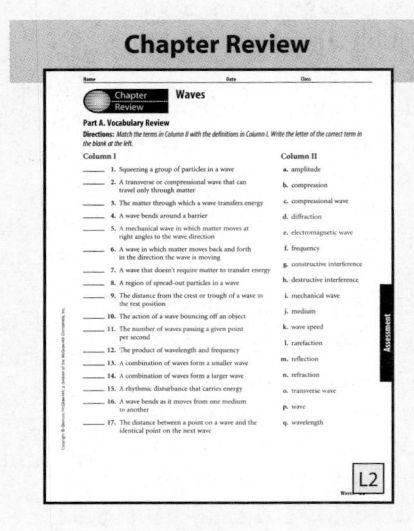

L2

Science Content Background

SECTION 1

What are waves?

What is a wave?

Electromagnetic waves have a dual nature. In describing their emission from matter or absorption by matter, they sometimes behave as particles, usually called photons. During their propagation, they usually behave as waves. In electromagnetic waves, which are always transverse, electric and magnetic fields oscillate perpendicular to the direction the waves travel.

SECTION 2

Wave Properties

Wave Movements

Waves travel outward from an energy source. If a rock is thrown into a pond, energy traveling outward from the center is seen as waves that decrease in amplitude as they move through the water. A wave will move through one complete cycle in one wavelength. The period (T) of a wave is the time it takes one wavelength to pass a fixed point. A wave's period is the reciprocal of its frequency.

Light waves are electromagnetic waves. Visible light has a range of wavelengths between about 400 nm and 700 nm. We know the elements present in stars by the wavelengths of light they emit, which are detected by spectroscopes.

The speed of light in a vacuum is constant at about 3×10^8 m/s. Michelson and Morley accurately measured the speed of light by reflecting light rays from a mountaintop to a rotating mirror.

The amplitude of a sound wave determines its sound intensity, or how loud it is. The more the sound wave carries energy, the louder the sound is. Two or more sounds produced at the same time can be unpleasant (dissonant) or pleasant (harmonious). The ratios of the frequencies of the tones determine whether or not they sound pleasing to the ear.

Fun Fact

Massive bodies have strong gravitational fields. If these bodies undergo some sort of regular motion, oscillations in their gravity fields can, according to theory, be detected. Scientists are currently trying to develop methods of detecting these gravity waves.

Wave Behavior

SECTION 3

Reflection

The angle of incidence (the incoming wave angle) equals the angle of reflection (the outgoing wave angle). This is known as the law of reflection. The angles of incidence and reflection are measured relative to a line drawn perpendicular to the reflecting surface. Diffuse reflection occurs as the light bounces at different angles from uneven surfaces. Diffuse reflection makes the uneven surfaces appear dull.

Refraction

In the case of light waves, a constant called a substance's index of refraction is the speed of light in a vacuum divided by the speed of light in the substance. Refraction of light occurs if the index of refraction changes as light goes from one medium to another.

Refraction can be beneficial. For example, eyeglasses and contact lenses correct vision by refracting light rays so that they focus properly on the retina of the eye. Binoculars, microscopes, and telescopes also utilize refraction to produce magnified images of small objects and objects at great distances.

Diffraction

The phenomenon called diffraction occurs as waves bend around barriers or spread through apertures. Diffraction of light can produce fringes (a series of bright and dark lines) as light waves bend around the edges of objects such as razor blades, diffraction gratings, or the teeth of a comb. The fringes, which can be seen on a screen, are a series of constructive and destructive interference patterns. As the light passes through the aperture, each point on the aperture can be considered a new point source of light, a concept known as Huygens's principle. The light reaching a particular point on the screen comes from different points on the aperture, and thus has traveled different distances to the screen. The interference patterns are produced, because at different points the phases of the waves add constructively or destructively.

Wave Interference

Sound waves can be made to interfere constructively or destructively as they reflect from a curved wall or a curved backdrop in a concert hall. Much planning and great expense go into designing the acoustics in a fine performance hall.

Seismic waves are produced by energy traveling through the material medium of Earth. Seismic waves are of three types—S, P, and surface waves. S waves (secondary waves) are transverse or shear and cannot travel through fluids. These seismic waves reflect off the fluid outer core of Earth. P waves, or primary waves, are compressional, or longitudinal, waves. They may pass through all of Earth's materials and are detected first. Surface waves are seismic waves that occur along Earth's surface. They cause up-down and rolling motions on the surface, which is why they are so destructive.

Fun Fact

The rainbow pattern seen on the back of compact disks is a diffraction pattern that results from the reflection of the different wavelengths of visible light.

SCIENCE Online

For additional content background on this topic, go to the Glencoe Science Web site at science.glencoe.com.

Barry L. Runk/Grant Heilman Photography, Inc.

Waves

Chapter Vocabulary

What do you think?

Science Journal The filters shown are polarizing filters. These filters allow only light waves that vibrate in a specific direction to pass through them. Waves in ordinary light vibrate in all directions.

On a breezy day in Maui, Hawaii, windsurfers ride the ocean waves. What forces are operating on the windsurfer and his sailboard? The wind catches the sails and helps propel the sailboard, but waves also are at work. Waves carry energy. You can see the ocean waves in this picture, but there are many kinds of waves you cannot see. Microwaves heat your food, radio waves transmit the music you listen to into your home, and sound waves carry that music from the radio to your ears. In this chapter, you will learn about different types of waves and how they behave.

What do you think?

Science Journal Look at the picture below with a classmate. Discuss what you think this might be. Hint: *Some sunglasses have this kind of lens.* Write your answer or best guess in your Science Journal.

Theme Connection

Energy Waves are periodic disturbances that carry energy. The larger the amplitude of the wave, the more energy is transferred.

I t's a beautiful autumn day. You are sitting by a pond in a park. Music blares from a school marching band practicing for a big game. The music is carried by waves. A fish jumps, making a splash. Waves spread past a leaf that fell from a tree, causing the leaf to move. In the following activity, you'll observe how waves carry energy that can cause objects to move.

Observe wave behavior

1. Fill a large, clear plastic plate with 1 cm of water.

2. Use a dropper to release a single drop of water onto the water's surface. Repeat.

3. Float a cork or straw on the water.

4. When the water is still, repeat step 2 from a height of 10 cm, then again from 20 cm.

Observe

In your Science Journal, record your observations. How did the motion of the cork depend on the height of the dropper?

Before You Read

FOLDABLES
Reading & Study
Skills

Making a Concept Map Study Fold Make the following Foldable to organize information by diagramming ideas about waves.

1. Place a sheet of paper in front of you so the long side is at the top. Fold the bottom of the paper to the top, stopping about four centimeters from the top.

2. Draw an oval above the fold. Write *Mechanical Waves* inside the oval.

3. Fold the paper in half from the left side to the right side and then unfold. Through the top thickness of the paper, cut along the fold line to form two tabs.

4. Draw an oval on each tab. Write *Transverse Waves* in one oval and *Compressional Waves* in the other, as shown. Draw arrows from the large oval to the smaller ovals.

5. As you read the chapter, write information about the two types of mechanical waves under the tabs.

> Mechanical Waves
>
> Transverse Waves   Compressional Waves

575

Purpose Use the Explore Activity to give students an opportunity to observe and describe wave behavior. L2 ELL COOP LEARN
LS **Logical-Mathematical**
Materials large, clear-plastic plate; small cork or piece of a soda straw; dropper; water

Teaching Strategies

• Suggest that students observe closely because the waves will move quickly.

• Tell students to be sure the water is still before adding drops of water. They also should be careful not to disturb the water when adding the cork.

Observe

Circular waves travel outward from the point where the drops hit the water's surface. Drops released from a height of 20 cm cause larger waves and transfer more energy than do drops released from a height of 10 cm. The cork bobs up and down as the waves pass but does not move horizontally.

✓Assessment

Process Provide students with diagrams of transverse waves with different amplitudes. Ask them to identify which diagram shows waves generated by dropping water from a greater height. Use **Performance Assessment in the Science Classroom,** p. 89.

FOLDABLES
Reading & Study
Skills

Before You Read

Dinah Zike Study Fold
Purpose Have students make and use a Foldable concept map to list examples of and record information on two types of mechanical waves—transverse waves and compressional waves. After reading, students can use the Foldable as a study guide.

📁 For additional help, see Foldables Worksheet p. 15 in **Chapter Resources Booklet,** or go to the Glencoe Science Web site at **science.glencoe.com.** See After You Read in the Study Guide at the end of this chapter.

SECTION

1

What are waves?

1 Motivate

Bellringer Transparency

Display the Section Focus Transparency for Section 1. Use the accompanying Transparency Activity Master. L2

ELL

Tie to Prior Knowledge

Ask students to describe any waves they know of. Discuss with them the form of energy transferred by each wave.

As You Read

***What* You'll Learn**

- **Explain** the relationship among waves, energy, and matter.
- **Describe** the difference between transverse waves and compressional waves.

Vocabulary

wave
mechanical wave
transverse wave
compressional wave
electromagnetic wave

***Why* It's Important**

You can hear music and other sounds because of waves.

Figure 1
The wave and the thrown ball carry energy in different ways.

What is a wave?

When you are relaxing on an air mattress in a pool and someone does a cannonball dive off the diving board, you suddenly find yourself bobbing up and down. You can make something move by giving it a push or pull, but the person jumping didn't touch your air mattress. How did the energy from the dive travel through the water and move your air mattress? The up-and-down motion was caused by the peaks and valleys of the ripples that moved from where the splash occurred. These peaks and valleys make up water waves.

Waves Carry Energy **Waves** are rhythmic disturbances that carry energy without carrying matter, as shown in **Figure 1A.** You can see the energy of the wave from a speedboat traveling outward, but the water only moves up and down. If you've ever felt a clap of thunder, you know that sound waves can carry large amounts of energy. You also transfer energy when you throw something to a friend, as in **Figure 1B.** However, there is a difference between a moving ball and a wave. A ball is made of matter, and when it is thrown, the matter moves from one place to another. So, unlike the wave, throwing a ball involves the transport of matter as well as energy.

A The waves created by a boat move mostly up and down, but the energy travels outward from the boat.

B When the ball is thrown, the ball carries energy as it moves forward.

Section ✓*Assessment* Planner

PORTFOLIO
Activity, p. 578
PERFORMANCE ASSESSMENT
MiniLAB, p. 579
Skill Builder Activities, p. 580
See page 600 for more options.

CONTENT ASSESSMENT
Section, p. 580
Challenge, p. 580
Chapter, pp. 600–601

A Model for Waves

How does a wave carry energy without transporting matter? Imagine a line of people, as shown in **Figure 2A.** The first person in line passes a ball to the second person, who passes the ball to the next person, and so on. Passing a ball down a line of people is a model for how waves can transport energy without transporting matter. Even though the ball has traveled, the people in line have not moved. In this model, you can think of the ball as representing energy. What do the people in line represent?

Think about the ripples on the surface of a pond. The energy carried by the ripples travels through the water. The water is made up of water molecules. It is the individual molecules of water that pass the wave energy, just as the people in **Figure 2A** pass the ball. The water molecules transport the energy in a water wave by colliding with the molecules around them, as shown in **Figure 2B.**

✔ **Reading Check** *What is carried by waves?*

Mechanical Waves

In the wave model, the ball could not be transferred if the line of people didn't exist. The energy of a water wave could not be transferred if no water molecules existed. These types of waves, which use matter to transfer energy, are called **mechanical waves.** The matter through which a mechanical wave travels is called a medium. For ripples on a pond, the medium is the water.

A mechanical wave travels as energy is transferred from particle to particle in the medium. For example, a sound wave is a mechanical wave that can travel through air, as well as solids, liquids, and other gases. The sound wave travels through air by transferring energy from gas molecule to gas molecule. Without a medium such as air, you would not hear sounds. In outer space sound waves can't travel because there is no air.

Figure 2
A As the students pass the ball, the students' positions do not change—only the position of the ball changes. **B** In a water wave, water molecules bump each other and pass energy from molecule to molecule.

Resource Manager

Chapter Resources Booklet

Note-taking Worksheets, pp. 31–32
Transparency Activity, p. 42
Directed Reading for Content Mastery, pp. 17, 18

Visual Learning

Figure 2B Tell students that the water molecules near the surface of a wave actually travel in small circles. Have students model this movement with a cork in water. L1 ELL **Kinesthetic**

2 Teach

What is a wave?

Discussion

Ask students to describe how being near a source of deep, loud sounds, such as heavy machinery or the subwoofer of a stereo, demonstrates that waves carry energy. You can feel the vibrations as well as hear the sound. L1
Auditory-Musical

A Model For Waves

Make a Model

Have students duplicate the model described in the text. As they do this, emphasize that they are like the molecules of water through which a wave flows. Point out that the ball is made of matter, but in the model it represents energy. L1
ELL COOP LEARN **Kinesthetic**

✔ **Reading Check**

Answer energy

Mechanical Waves

IDENTIFYING Misconceptions

Students might be surprised that some waves are described as mechanical. The word *mechanical* comes from the Greek word *mechane*, meaning "a device." Based on this, have students discuss why *mechanical* is an appropriate term to use for waves that need matter to move. One definition of *machine* is a device that transmits energy. In a mechanical wave, matter transmits energy. L3 **Linguistic**

Mechanical Waves, continued

Use an Analogy

Ask students to think of people "doing the wave" in a stadium. Point out that this wave is similar to a transverse mechanical wave because the people, like particles, move up and down at right angles to the direction the wave moves. L2 IS **Visual-Spatial**

Quick Demo

Put a clear plate with colored water on an overhead projector. Ask students to predict what will happen to a floating object as waves are generated in the water. Generate waves either by dropping small objects into the water or by moving a finger in the water. The floating object will bob up and down because the water waves are very much like transverse waves. L3 IS **Visual-Spatial**

☑ **Reading Check**

Answer crests

Activity

Ask students to list on chart paper examples of mechanical waves. Have them draw each type of wave, describe each wave as transverse or compressional, and label the different parts of each wave. L2 COOP LEARN IS **Visual-Spatial** P

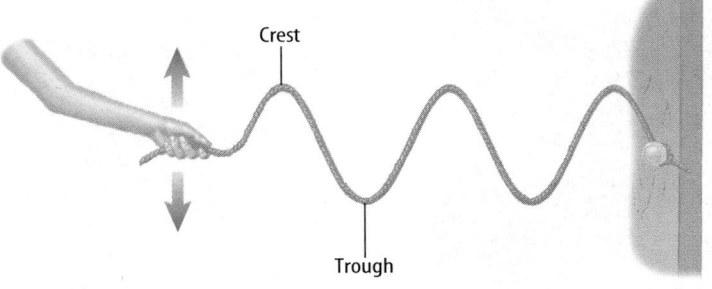

Figure 3
The high points on the wave are called crests and the low points are called troughs.

Figure 4
A compressional wave can travel through a coiled spring toy.

A As the wave motion begins, the coils near the string are close together and the other coils are far apart.

B The wave, seen in the squeezed and stretched coils, travels along the spring.

C The string and coils did not travel with the wave. Each coil moved forward and then back to its original position.

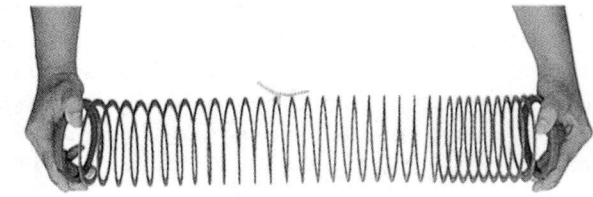

Transverse Waves In a mechanical **transverse wave,** the wave energy causes the matter in the medium to move up and down or back and forth at right angles to the direction the wave travels. You can make a model of a transverse wave. Stretch a long rope out on the ground. Hold one end in your hand. Now shake the end in your hand back and forth. By adjusting the way you shake the rope, you can create a wave that seems to slide along the rope.

When you first started shaking the rope, it might have appeared that the rope itself was moving away from you. But it was only the wave that was moving away from your hand. The wave energy moves through the rope, but the matter in the rope doesn't travel. You can see that the wave has peaks and valleys at regular intervals. As shown in **Figure 3,** the high points of transverse waves are called crests. The low points are called troughs.

☑ **Reading Check** *What are the highest points of transverse waves called?*

Teacher FYI

There are three main types of seismic waves. Primary (P) waves oscillate back and forth along the direction the wave travels. Secondary (S) waves oscillate perpendicular to the direction of wave motion. Surface waves cause horizontal and, sometimes, vertical ground surface movement.

☑ Active Reading

Bubble Map Using a bubble map helps students start ideas flowing about a given topic. Words are clustered to describe a concept. Students can use the bubble map for a prewrite, to generate ideas before writing in their Journals, or to review for a test. Have students design a Bubble Map for the different types of waves described in this section.

Compressional Waves Mechanical waves can be either transverse or compressional. In a **compressional wave,** matter in the medium moves forward and backward in the same direction that the wave travels. You can make a compressional wave by squeezing together and releasing several coils of a coiled spring toy, as shown in **Figure 4.**

You see that the coils move only as the wave passes. They then return to their original position. So, like transverse waves, compressional waves carry only energy forward along the spring. In this example, the spring is the medium the wave moves through, but the spring does not move along with the wave.

Sound Waves Sound waves are compressional waves. How do you make sound waves when you talk or sing? If you hold your fingers against your throat while you hum, you can feel vibrations. These vibrations are the movements of your vocal cords. If you touch a stereo speaker while it's playing, you can feel it vibrating, too. All waves are produced by something that is vibrating.

Making Sound Waves

How do vibrating objects make sound waves? Look at the drum shown in **Figure 5.** When you hit the drumhead it starts vibrating up and down. As the drumhead moves upward, the molecules next to it are pushed closer together. This group of molecules that are closer together is a compression. As the compression is formed, it moves away from the drumhead, just as the squeezed coils move along the coiled spring toy in **Figure 4.**

When the drumhead moves downward, the molecules near it have more room and can spread farther apart. This group of molecules that are farther apart is a rarefaction (rar uh FAK shun). The rarefaction also moves away from the drumhead. As the drumhead vibrates up and down, it forms a series of compressions and rarefactions that move away and spread out in all directions. This series of compressions and rarefactions is a sound wave.

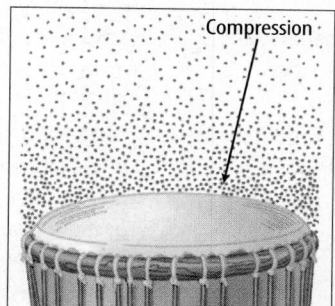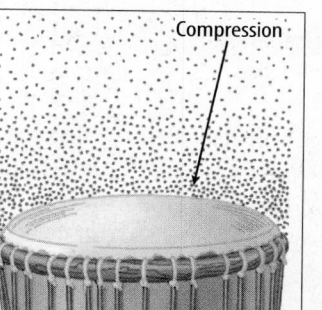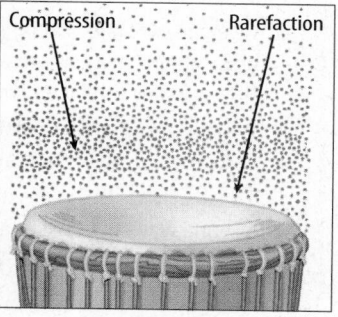

Molecules that make up air

Compression

Compression   Rarefaction

Comparing Sounds

Procedure 👓

1. Hold a **wooden ruler** firmly on the edge of your **desk** so that most of it extends off the edge of the desk.
2. Pluck the free end of the ruler so that it vibrates up and down. Use gentle motion at first, then pluck with more energy.
3. Repeat step 2, moving the ruler about 1 cm further onto the desk each time until only about 5 cm extend off the edge.

Analysis

1. Compare the loudness of the sounds that are made by plucking the ruler in different ways.
2. Describe the differences in the sound as the end of the ruler extended farther from the desk.

Figure 5

A vibrating drumhead makes compressions and rarefactions in the air. *How are compressions and rarefactions different?*

Teacher FYI

Compressional waves are often called longitudinal waves.

Making Sound Waves

Purpose Students compare and contrast various sounds made by a vibrating object. L2

ELL IS **Auditory-Musical**

Materials wooden ruler

Teaching Strategies Monitor students to ensure their results include information about the length of the ruler hanging over the table.

Troubleshooting Make sure students do not pluck hard enough to break the ruler.

Analysis

1. Using more energy produces louder sounds.
2. The greater the length of the vibrating object, the lower the pitch produced.

✓ *Assessment*

Performance Give students materials of different lengths and ask them to choose and make sounds with the ones that produce lower-pitched sounds. Use **PASC,** p. 97.

Caption Answer

Figure 5 Particles are squeezed together in compressions and move farther apart in rarefactions.

Resource Manager

Chapter Resources Booklet

Transparency Activity, pp. 45–46
Enrichment, p. 28
Reinforcement, p. 25
MiniLAB, p. 3

Inclusion Strategies

Hearing Impaired Some students may not be able to hear the sounds made by the ruler as they do the MiniLAB. Have these students pay attention to feeling the vibrations. They should be able to feel the vibrations with the hand holding the ruler on the desk. Suggest they pluck the ruler several times while paying attention to what they feel. When they are familiar with the feeling, they can finish the lab.

Electromagnetic Waves

There are 24 GPS satellites, and they orbit Earth at a height of about 20,000 km. Their electromagnetic radio waves can be received all over Earth, regardless of the weather. GPS was designed for and is operated by the U.S. Department of Defense and provides positioning information to military submarines, helicopters, ships, bombers, tanks, and missiles. However, since the signals can be received by an unlimited number of users, they are increasingly important in everyday civilian navigation.

③ Assess

Reteach

Demonstrate compressional and transverse waves using a spring toy. Have students identify each type of wave and the parts of the waves. L2
Visual-Spatial

Challenge

Ask students to investigate the behavior of surface waves near the seashore and make posters showing what they find. As the waves approach land, water molecules near the surface experience more elliptical movement, causing the waves to form high crests that eventually crash into land. L3 **Visual-Spatial**

✓Assessment

Process Have students draw diagrams of transverse and compressional waves, labeling the crests and troughs. Use **PASC**, p. 127.

Physics
INTEGRATION

Maybe you've used a global positioning system (GPS) receiver to determine your location while driving, boating, or hiking. Earth-orbiting satellites send electromagnetic radio waves that transmit their exact locations and times of transmission. The GPS receiver uses information from four of these satellites to determine your location to within about 16 m.

Electromagnetic Waves

When you listen to the radio, watch TV, or use a microwave oven to cook, you use a different kind of wave—one that doesn't need matter as a medium.

Waves that do not require matter to carry energy are called **electromagnetic waves.** Electromagnetic waves are transverse waves that are produced by the motion of electrically charged particles. Just like mechanical waves, electromagnetic waves also can travel through a medium such as a solid, liquid, or gas. Radio waves are electromagnetic waves that travel through the air from a radio station, and then through the solid walls of your house to reach your radio. However, unlike mechanical waves, electromagnetic waves can travel through outer space or through a vacuum where no matter exists.

Useful Waves In space, which has no air or any other medium, orbiting satellites beam radio waves to TVs, radios, and cellular phones on Earth's surface. However, radio waves are not the only electromagnetic waves traveling in space. Infrared, visible, and ultraviolet waves travel from the Sun through space before they reach Earth's atmosphere. Infrared waves feel warm when they strike your skin. Without visible light you wouldn't see color or be able to read this page. You use sunscreen to protect yourself from ultraviolet rays. Other useful electromagnetic waves include X rays. X rays are useful not only in medical applications, but also for security checks in airports as luggage is scanned.

Section ① Assessment

1. Describe the movement of a floating object on a pond when struck by a wave.

2. Why can't a sound wave travel from a satellite to Earth?

3. Give one example of a transverse wave and one example of a compressional wave. How are they similar and different?

4. What is the difference between a mechanical wave and an electromagnetic wave?

5. **Think Critically** How is it possible for a sound wave to transmit energy but not matter?

Skill Builder Activities

6. **Concept Mapping** Create a concept map that shows the relationships among the following: *waves, mechanical waves, electromagnetic waves, compressional waves,* and *transverse waves.* **For more help, refer to the** Science Skill Handbook.

7. **Using a Word Processor** Use word-processing software to write short descriptions of the waves you encounter during a typical day. **For more help, refer to the** Technology Skill Handbook.

Answers to Section Assessment

1. It bobs up and down.
2. It requires a medium through which to travel, and there is no medium in space.
3. Possible answer: Water waves are transverse waves. Sound waves are compressional waves. Compressional waves cause vibration in the direction of wave movement. Transverse waves cause vibration at right angles to the wave's direction. Both involve periodic motion and carry energy.
4. Mechanical waves use matter to transmit energy. Electromagnetic waves do not require matter to carry energy.
5. The wave causes molecules of matter to vibrate and bump neighbor molecules.
6. Answers should show mechanical waves as compressional or transverse; electromagnetic waves are transverse.
7. Answers might include radio waves, sound waves, or waves in a bathtub.

Wave Properties

Amplitude

Can you describe a wave? For a water wave, one way might be to tell how high the wave rises above, or falls below, the normal level. This distance is called the wave's amplitude. The **amplitude** of a transverse wave is one-half the distance between a crest and a trough, as shown in **Figure 6A.** In a compressional wave, the amplitude is greater when the particles of the medium are squeezed closer together in each compression and spread farther apart in each rarefaction.

Amplitude and Energy A wave's amplitude is related to the energy that the wave carries. For example, the electromagnetic waves that make up bright light have greater amplitudes than the waves that make up dim light. Waves of bright light carry more energy than the waves that make up dim light. In a similar way, loud sound waves have greater amplitudes than soft sound waves. Loud sounds carry more energy than soft sounds. If a sound is loud enough, it can carry enough energy to damage your hearing.

As you can see in **Figure 6B,** when a hurricane strikes a coastal area, the resulting water waves can damage almost anything that stands in their path. The large waves caused by a hurricane carry more energy than the small waves or ripples on a pond.

As You Read

***What* You'll Learn**
- **Describe** the relationship between the frequency and wavelength of a wave.
- **Explain** why waves travel at different speeds.

Vocabulary
amplitude
wavelength
frequency

***Why* It's Important**
The energy carried by a wave depends on its amplitude.

Figure 6

A transverse wave has an amplitude.

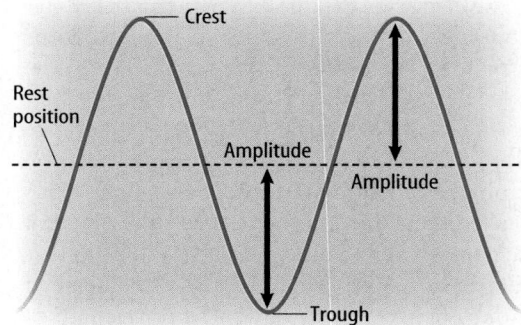

A The amplitude is a measure of how high the crests are or how deep the troughs are.

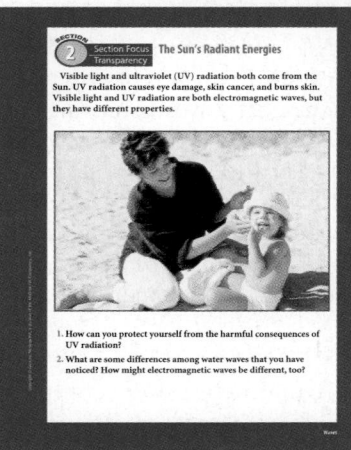

B A water wave of large amplitude carried the energy that caused this damage.

SECTION 2 Wave Properties **581**

1 Motivate

Bellringer Transparency

Display the Section Focus Transparency for Section 2. Use the accompanying Transparency Activity Master. L2
ELL

1. How can you protect yourself from the harmful consequences of UV radiation?
2. What are some differences among water waves that you have noticed? How might electromagnetic waves be different, too?

Tie to Prior Knowledge

Ask students whether it takes more or less energy to twirl a jump rope high enough to clear a short person or a tall person. tall Explain that in this section, they will learn how to describe the energy different waves carry.

Resource Manager

Chapter Resources Booklet
Transparency Activity, p. 43
Directed Reading for Content Mastery, p. 19

Section ✔*Assessment* Planner

PORTFOLIO
Extension, p. 582
Science Journal, p. 584
PERFORMANCE ASSESSMENT
Skill Builder Activities, p. 585
See page 600 for more options.

CONTENT ASSESSMENT
Section, p. 585
Challenge, p. 585
Chapter, pp. 600–601

Amplitude

Activity

Ask students to bring in magazine and newspaper articles about tidal waves (tsunamis) and earthquakes around the world. Display the articles and discuss with students the relationship between energy, wave amplitude, and the amount of destruction caused. L2 IS **Interpersonal**

Extension

Explain that both compressional and transverse waves are commonly graphed as sine waves with amplitude on the vertical axis and wavelength on the horizontal axis. Have students prepare this type of graph for both waves shown in **Figure 8**. The graph of the transverse wave should closely resemble the wave on the oscilloscope in **Figure 8A**. On the graph of the compressional wave, the height of the graphed wave should reflect the intensity of the compression, while the wavelength should represent the distance between compressions and rarefactions. L3 IS **Visual-Spatial** P

A For transverse waves, measure from crest to crest or trough to trough.

B For compressional waves, measure from compression to compression or rarefaction to rarefaction.

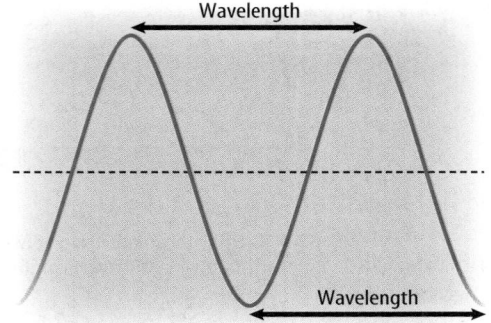

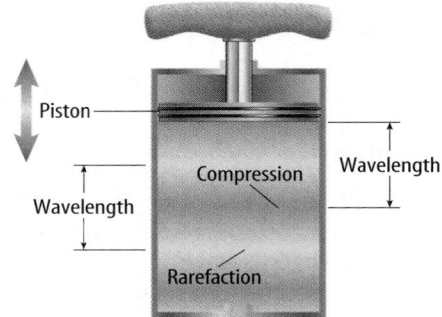

Figure 7
Wavelength is measured differently for transverse and compressional waves.

Figure 8
The wavelengths and frequencies of electromagnetic waves vary.

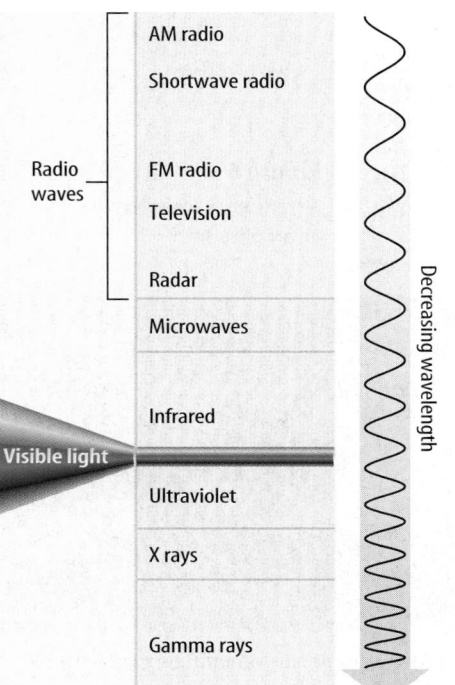

Earth Science INTEGRATION

The devastating effect that a wave with large amplitude can have is seen in the aftermath of tsunamis. Tsunamis are huge sea waves that are caused by underwater earthquakes along faults on the seafloor. The movement of the seafloor along the fault produces the wave. As the wave moves toward shallow water and slows down, the amplitude of the wave grows. The tremendous amounts of energy tsunamis carry cause great damage when they move ashore.

Wavelength

Another way to describe a wave is by its wavelength. For a transverse wave, **wavelength** is the distance from the top of one crest to the top of the next crest, or from the bottom of one trough to the bottom of the next trough, as shown in **Figure 7A.** For a compressional wave, the wavelength is the distance between the center of one compression and the center of the next compression, or from the center of one rarefaction to the center of the next rarefaction, as shown in **Figure 7B.**

Electromagnetic waves have wavelengths that range from kilometers, for radio waves, to less than the diameter of an atom, for X rays and gamma rays. This range is called the electromagnetic spectrum. **Figure 8** shows the names given to different parts of the electromagnetic spectrum. Visible light is only a small part of the electromagnetic spectrum. It is the wavelength of visible light waves that determines their color. For example, the wavelength of red light waves is longer than the wavelength of green light waves.

Visual Learning

Figure 8 Electromagnetic waves sometimes behave as if they are made of particles called photons. Waves with a longer wavelength have lower energy per photon than waves with a shorter wavelength. The amplitude of the waves depends on the energy per unit area (i.e., the number of photons per unit area), not the energy per photon.

Teacher FYI

The threshold of human hearing for sound intensity (loudness) is 0 dB (10^{-12} watts/m^2). Hearing damage commences at sustained levels of about 85 dB. Normal conversation has an intensity of about 60 dB. A jet engine can generate noise levels of about 120 dB to 140 dB.

Frequency

The **frequency** of a wave is the number of wavelengths that pass a given point in 1 s. The unit of frequency is the number of wavelengths per second, or hertz (Hz). Recall that waves are produced by something that vibrates. The faster the vibration is, the higher the frequency is of the wave that is produced.

☑ **Reading Check** *How is the frequency of a wave measured?*

A Sidewalk Model For waves that travel with the same speed, frequency and wavelength are related. To model this relationship, imagine people on two parallel moving sidewalks in an airport, as shown in **Figure 9.** One sidewalk has four travelers spaced 4 m apart. The other sidewalk has 16 travelers spaced 1 m apart.

Now imagine that both sidewalks are moving at the same speed and approaching a pillar between them. On which sidewalk will more people go past the pillar? On the sidewalk with the shorter distance between people, four people will pass the pillar for each one person on the other sidewalk. When four people pass the pillar on the first sidewalk, 16 people pass the pillar on the second sidewalk.

Figure 9
When people are farther apart on a moving sidewalk, fewer people pass the pillar every minute.

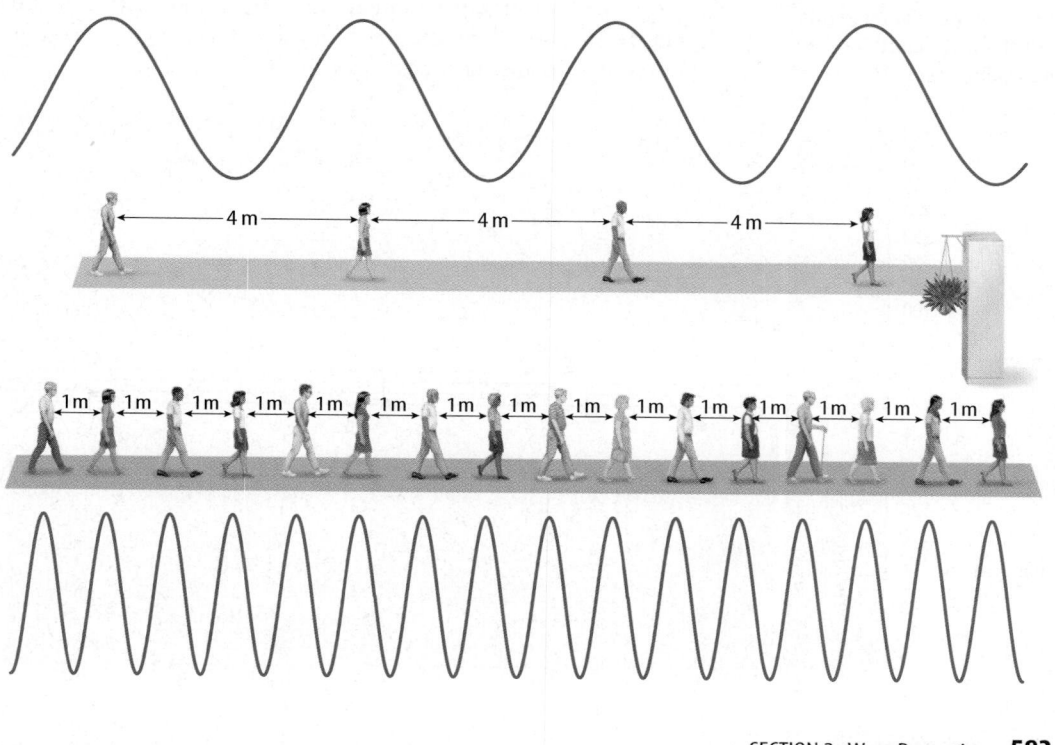

Frequency

Use Science Words

Word Origin Have students investigate the origin of the word *hertz* and why it is used to describe frequency. The unit hertz was named after Heinrich Hertz, a German physicist who studied electromagnetic waves. ⌷L2⌷ **IN Linguistic**

☑ **Reading Check**

Answer in wavelengths per second

Extension

Many animals communicate using sounds that are inaudible to humans. Have students research animals that do this and prepare reports about the frequencies at which the animals make sounds. Possible animals to study include whales and dolphins, which use ultrasonic frequencies, and elephants and hippos, which use infrasonic frequencies. ⌷L3⌷ **IN Linguistic**

Discussion

How does pressing a string on a guitar affect the frequency of the sound produced? It shortens the string, which increases the frequency of the sound the string produces when it is plucked. **How does this relate to the sounds produced by a harp?** On a harp, the short strings produce high frequency sounds and the long strings produce low frequency sounds. ⌷L2⌷ **IN Auditory-Musical**

Resource Manager

Chapter Resources Booklet
  Enrichment, p. 29
Home and Community Involvement, p. 42
Reading and Writing Skill Activities, p. 33

Curriculum Connection

Music Have students find out what quarter tones are and play recordings of music with quarter tones for the class. The difference in frequency between two adjacent pitches in some types of music, including Hindu music, is about half that between adjacent pitches in western music. These pitches are called quarter tones. ⌷L3⌷ **ELL IN Auditory-Musical**

Frequency, continued

Activity

Have each student fill a bowl with water and dip a pencil into and out of the water to form waves. They should notice that dipping the pencil with low frequency produces waves with longer wavelengths (greater distance between crests) than dipping the pencil with high frequency. Have students use a stopwatch to help calibrate the frequencies of their waves. L1

ELL LS **Kinesthetic**

Quick Demo

Have students who play instruments demonstrate compressional waves of high and low frequency by producing notes of varying pitch. If an oscilloscope is available, connect it to a transducer (microphone) to show students the wavelengths and amplitudes of the notes. L2

ELL LS **Auditory-Musical**

Health

INTEGRATION

The wavelengths are much shorter that those of the soundwaves we hear.

Health

INTEGRATION

Sound waves with ultra-high frequencies cannot be heard by the human ear, but are used by medical professionals in several ways. They perform echocardiograms of the heart, produce ultrasound images of internal organs, break up blockages in arteries and kill bacteria and sterilize surgical instruments. *How do the wavelengths of these sound waves compare to sound waves you can hear?*

Figure 10
The frequency of the notes on a musical scale increases as the notes get higher in pitch, but the wavelength of the notes decreases.

Frequency and Wavelength Suppose that each person in **Figure 9** represents the crest of a wave. Then the movement of people on the first sidewalk is like a wave with a wavelength of 4 m. For the second sidewalk, the wavelength would be 1 m. On the first sidewalk, where the wavelength is longer, the people pass the pillar *less* frequently. Longer wavelengths result in smaller frequencies. On the second sidewalk, where the wavelength is shorter, the people pass the pillar *more* frequently. Higher frequencies result in shorter wavelengths. This is true for all waves that travel at the same speed. As the frequency of a wave increases, its wavelength decreases.

Color and Pitch Because frequency and wavelength are related, either the wavelength or frequency of a light wave determines the color of the light. For example, blue light has a larger frequency and shorter wavelength than red light.

In a sound wave, either the wavelength or frequency determines the pitch. Pitch is the highness or lowness of a sound. A flute makes musical notes with a high pitch and produces sounds of high frequency. A tuba produces notes with a low pitch and a low frequency. When you sing a musical scale, the pitch and frequency increase from note to note. Wavelength and frequency are also related for sound waves traveling in air. As the frequency of sound waves increases, their wavelength decreases. **Figure 10** shows how the frequency and wavelength change for notes on the musical scale.

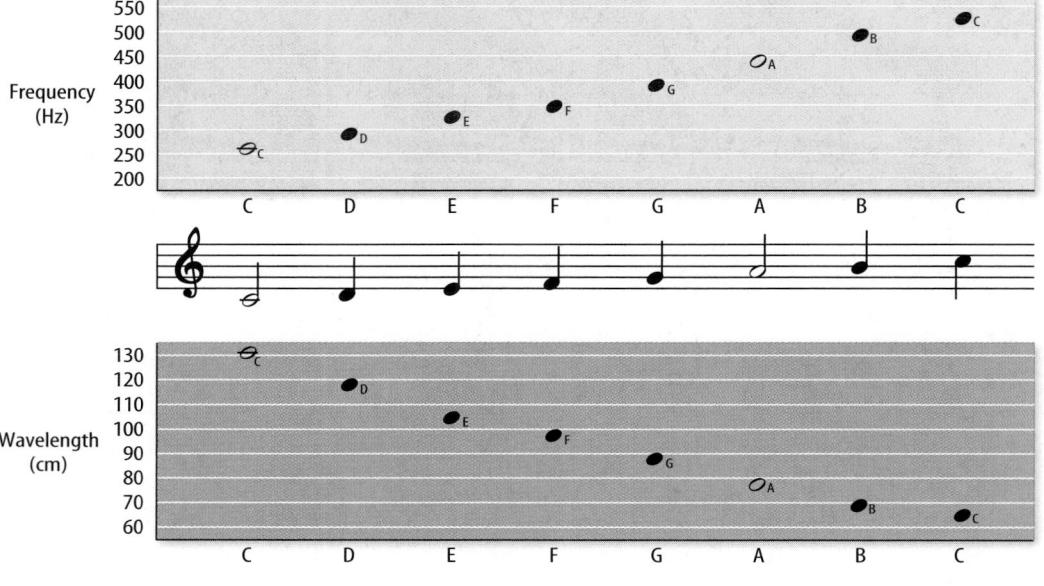

584 CHAPTER 20 Waves

Science Journal

Musical Instruments Ask students to investigate various musical instruments and write in their Science Journals what vibrates on each instrument to make sound and how this produces certain pitches. Students might mention the reed of a clarinet or the lips of a trumpet player. Air inside the instrument also vibrates. The shape and material of the instrument affect pitch. L3 LS **Linguistic** P

Resource Manager

Chapter Resources Booklet
    Reinforcement, p. 26
Cultural Diversity, p. 61

Wave Speed

You've probably watched a distant thunderstorm approach on a hot summer day. You see a bolt of lightning flash between a dark cloud and the ground. Do the sound waves, or thunder, produced by the lightning bolt reach your ears at the same instant you see the lightning? If the thunderstorm is many kilometers away, several seconds will pass between when you see the lightning and when you hear the thunder. This happens because light travels much faster in air than sound does. Light is an electromagnetic wave that travels through air at about 300 million m/s. On the other hand, sound is a mechanical wave that travels through air at about 340 m/s.

Mechanical waves such as sound usually travel faster in a medium in which the atoms that make up the medium are closer together. Sound travels faster in solids than in liquids and faster in liquids than in gases. This is because atoms are closer to each other in a solid than in a liquid, and closer together in a liquid than in a gas.

Electromagnetic waves such as light behave differently than mechanical waves. Unlike mechanical waves, they travel faster in gases than in solids or liquids. You know that you can get to your next class faster if the hallways are nearly empty than if they are filled with other students. Electromagnetic waves behave the same way. If many atoms are in the medium, electromagnetic waves are slowed down. For example, the speed of light is one and a half times faster in air than it is in glass.

SCIENCE *Online*

Research Visit the Glencoe Science Web site at **science.glencoe.com** for information about wave speed in different materials. Make a graph to show the differences.

Section 2 Assessment

1. How does the frequency of a wave change as its wavelength changes?

2. Why is a sound wave with a large amplitude more likely to damage your hearing than one with a small amplitude?

3. What accounts for the time difference in seeing and hearing a fireworks display?

4. Why is the statement "The speed of light is 300 million m/s" not always correct?

5. **Think Critically** Explain the differences between the waves that make up bright, green light and dim, red light.

Skill Builder Activities

6. **Predicting** A biologist studying bison puts her ear next to the ground. By doing this she knows that the herd is coming toward her. Explain. **For more help, refer to the** Science Skill Handbook.

7. **Solving One-Step Equations** The product of the wavelength and the frequency of a wave is the speed of the wave. If a sound wave traveling through water has a speed of 1,470 m/s and a frequency of 2,340 Hz, what is its wavelength? **For more help, refer to the** Math Skill Handbook.

Answers to Section Assessment

1. The frequency increases as the wavelength decreases.
2. Waves having large amplitudes carry more energy than waves with small amplitudes.
3. Light travels much faster than sound.
4. The speed of light varies, depending on the medium through which it

travels. The speed of light is 300 million m/s in air.
5. The waves that make up bright green light have shorter wavelengths, higher frequencies, and larger amplitudes.
6. The biologist can hear the vibrations in the ground caused by the moving herd.

7. wavelength = wave speed ÷ wave frequency = 1,470 m/s ÷ 2,340 Hz = 0.628 m

Wave Speed

SCIENCE *Online*
Internet Addresses
_____
_____
_____

Explore the Glencoe Science Web site at **science.glencoe.com** to find out more about topics in this section.

3 Assess

Reteach

Have students use a spiral drawing toy to demonstrate the amplitude, wavelength, and frequency of a wave. L1
N Kinesthetic

Challenge

Compare the sound of a siren moving toward you with the sound of a siren moving away from you. When the siren is moving toward you, the wavelengths of the compressional waves decrease, resulting in higher pitches. As the siren moves away from you, the wavelengths increase and the pitches get lower. This is known as the Doppler effect. L3
N Logical-Mathematical

✓ Assessment

Process Fill test tubes with different amounts of water and tap on them gently with a glass stirring rod. Have students explain the differences between the pitches produced. The more water in a tube, the shorter the wavelength of air that fits in the tube, so the higher the pitch produced when the glass is tapped. Use **PASC**, p. 89.

Activity

Purpose Students make waves with a coiled-spring toy and observe the waves. L2 ELL COOP LEARN LS **Kinesthetic**

Process Skills observing and inferring, comparing and contrasting, interpreting data, classifying, making and using tables

Time Required 45 minutes

Safety Precautions Space student groups far enough apart that the coiled springs do not interfere with each other.

Teaching Strategies
- Help students compare the two types of waves they generate.
- Help students recognize the parts of a wave.

Troubleshooting Watch students to ensure that they do not tangle or overstretch the coiled springs.

Answers to Questions
1. In steps 4 and 5, transverse waves were produced. In steps 6 to 8, compressional waves were produced.
2. Check students' work.
3. rarefaction
4. The yarn moved back and forth from a fixed position, while the wave moved along the spring from one end to the other.

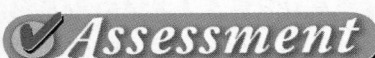
Assessment

Process Have students draw and label the parts of each type of wave they generated in the activity. Use **PASC,** p. 127.

Activity

Waves on a Spring

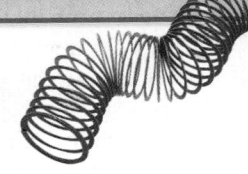

Waves are rhythmic disturbances that carry energy through matter or space. Studying waves can help you understand how the Sun's energy reaches Earth and sounds travel through the air.

What You'll Investigate
What are some of the properties of transverse and compressional waves on a coiled spring?

Materials
long, coiled spring toy
colored yarn (5 cm)
meterstick
stopwatch

Goals
- **Create** transverse and compressional waves on a coiled spring toy.
- **Investigate** wave properties such as speed and amplitude.

Safety Precautions
WARNING: *Avoid overstretching or tangling the spring to prevent injury or damage.*

Procedure
1. **Prepare** a data table such as the one shown.

Wave Data	
Length of stretched spring toy	4.20 m
Average time for a wave to travel from end to end—step 4	1.35 s
Average time for a wave to travel from end to end—step 5	1.25 s

2. Work in pairs or groups and clear a place on an uncarpeted floor about 6 m × 2 m.

3. Stretch the springs between two people to the length suggested by your teacher. Measure the length.
4. Create a wave with a quick, sideways snap of the wrist. Time several waves as they travel the length of the spring. Record the average time in your data table.
5. Repeat step 4 using waves that have slightly larger amplitudes.
6. Squeeze together about 20 of the coils. Observe what happens to the unsqueezed coils. Release the coils and observe.
7. Quickly push the spring toward your partner, then pull it back.
8. Tie the yarn to a coil near the middle of the spring. Repeat step 7, observing the string.

Conclude and Apply
1. **Classify** the wave pulses you created in each step as compressional or transverse.
2. **Calculate** and compare the speeds of the waves in steps 4 and 5.
3. **Classify** the unsqueezed coils in step 6 as a compression or a rarefaction.
4. **Compare and contrast** the motion of the yarn in step 8 with the motion of the wave.

Communicating Your Data
Write a summary paragraph of how this activity demonstrated any of the vocabulary words from the first two sections of the chapter. **For more help,** refer to the **Science Skill Handbook.**

Communicating Your Data
Have students use a computer graphics program to create a display explaining the results of the activity.

Resource Manager
Chapter Resources Booklet
Lab Activity, pp. 9–11
Activity Worksheet, pp. 5–6

Wave Behavior

Reflection

What causes the echo when you yell across an empty gymnasium or down a long, empty hallway? Why can you see your face when you look in a mirror? The echo of your voice and the face you see in the mirror are caused by wave reflection.

Reflection occurs when a wave strikes an object or surface and bounces off. An echo is reflected sound. Sound reflects from all surfaces. Your echo bounces off the walls, floor, ceiling, furniture, and people. You see your face in a mirror or a still pond, as shown in **Figure 11A,** because of reflection. Light waves produced by a source of light such as the Sun or a lightbulb bounce off your face, strike the mirror, and reflect back to your eyes.

When a surface is smooth and even, the reflected image is clear and sharp. However, when light reflects from an uneven or rough surface, you can't see a sharp image because the reflected light scatters in many different directions, as shown in **Figure 11B.**

✔ **Reading Check** *What causes reflection?*

As You Read

***What* You'll Learn**
- **Explain** how waves can reflect from some surfaces.
- **Explain** how waves change direction when they move from one material into another.
- **Describe** how waves are able to bend around barriers.

Vocabulary
reflection
refraction
diffraction
interference

***Why* It's Important**
The reflection of waves enables you to see objects around you.

A The smooth surface of a still pond enables you to see a sharp, clear image of yourself.

B If the surface of the pond is rough and uneven, your reflected image is no longer clear and sharp.

Figure 11
The image formed by reflection depends on the smoothness of the surface.

Wave Behavior

1 Motivate

Bellringer Transparency

Display the Section Focus Transparency for Section 3. Use the accompanying Transparency Activity Master. L2 ELL

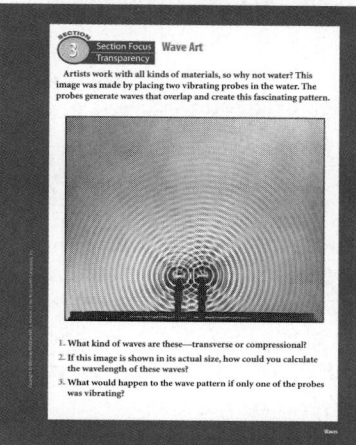

Tie to Prior Knowledge

Remind students that visible light rays are electromagnetic waves. Discuss whether they can see themselves in a mirror without light rays. Explain that in this section, they will learn how waves reflect and refract.

Section ✓ *Assessment* Planner

PORTFOLIO
Challenge, p. 593
PERFORMANCE ASSESSMENT
Try at Home MiniLAB, p. 588
Problem-Solving Activity, p. 591
Skill Builder Activities, p. 593
See page 600 for more options.

CONTENT ASSESSMENT
Section, p. 593
Challenge, p. 593
Chapter, pp. 600–601

Reflection

☑ **Reading Check**

Answer the bouncing of a wave off an object

Refraction

Quick Demo

Demonstrate that different colors of white light refract at different angles by shining an intense beam of white light through a prism in a darkened room. L2 ELL LS **Visual-Spatial**

TRY AT HOME
Mini LAB

Purpose Students observe how light refracts. L1 ELL

LS **Visual-Spatial**

Materials white soda straw, opaque drinking glass or cup; water

Teaching Strategy The larger the diameter of the glass or cup, the easier it will be to see the refraction. Also, tell students to fill the glass or cup almost to the top.

Analysis

1. The straw appears to be straight.
2. The straw appears to bend at the water's surface. Light reflects from the straw and refracts as it passes from the water into the air. The speed of the light waves is also reduced in water.

☑ **Assessment**

Performance Have students draw ray diagrams in their Science Journals that show how the light waves refract. Use **PASC**, p. 127.

TRY AT HOME
Mini LAB

Observing How Light Refracts

Procedure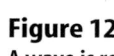
1. Fill a **large, opaque drinking glass or cup** with **water.**
2. Place a **white soda straw** in the water at an angle.
3. Looking directly down into the cup from above, observe the straw where it meets the water.
4. Placing yourself so that the straw angles to your left or right, slowly back away about 1 m. Observe the straw as it appears above, at, and below the surface of the water.

Analysis
1. Describe the straw's appearance from above.
2. Compare the straw's appearance above and below the water's surface in step 4.

Refraction

A wave changes direction when it reflects from a surface. Waves also can change direction in another way. Perhaps you have tried to grab a sinking object when you are in a swimming pool, only to come up empty-handed. Yet you were sure you grabbed right where you saw the object. You missed grabbing the object because the light rays from the object changed direction as they passed from the water into the air. The bending of a wave as it moves from one medium into another is called **refraction.**

Refraction and Wave Speed Remember that the speed of a wave can be different in different materials. For example, light waves travel faster in air than in water. Refraction occurs when the speed of a wave changes as it passes from one substance to another, as shown in **Figure 12.** A line that is perpendicular to the water's surface is called the normal. When a light ray passes from air into water, it slows down and bends toward the normal. When the ray passes from water into air, it speeds up and bends away from the normal. The larger the change in speed of the light wave is, the larger the change in direction is.

You notice refraction when you look down into a fishbowl. Refraction makes the fish appear to be closer to the surface but farther away from you than it is, as shown in **Figure 13.** Light rays reflected from the fish are bent away from the normal as they pass from water to air. Your brain interprets the light that enters your eyes by assuming that light rays always travel in straight lines. As a result, the light rays seem to be coming from a fish that is in a different location.

Figure 12
A wave is refracted when it changes speed. **A** As the light ray passes from air to water, it refracts toward the normal. **B** As the light ray passes from water to air, it refracts away from the normal.

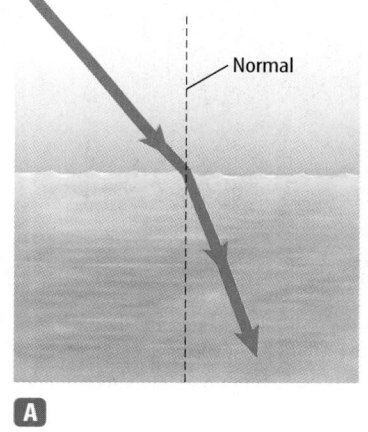
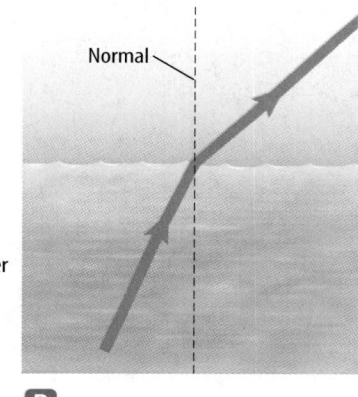

Cultural Diversity

An Advanced Warning System The Chinese used pottery jars to detect the sounds of an advancing enemy. Leather membranes were stretched over the mouths of empty 80-L pottery jars. The jars were lowered into deep shafts that were dug a few paces apart around the city, and men with good hearing were stationed nearby. Not only could they hear the sounds of an approaching army, but by listening to different sounds from the shafts, the watchers also could judge from which direction the enemy was coming and how far away the enemy was. **Why do you think the jars were put in shafts deep underground?** The thudding footsteps of the approaching army produced low-frequency, long-wavelength vibrations in the ground. The shafts had to be deep enough to receive those sound vibrations and amplify them. L3 LS **Logical-Mathematical**

Color from Refraction Refraction causes prisms to separate sunlight into many colors and produces rainbows too. **Figure 14** illustrates how refraction and reflection produce a rainbow when light waves from the Sun pass into and out of water droplets in the air.

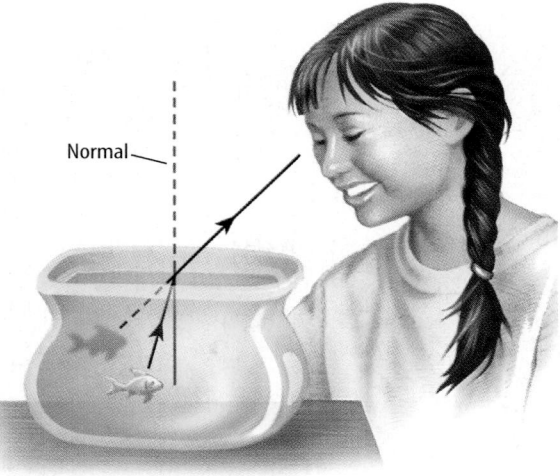

Normal

✔ **Reading Check** *What produces a rainbow?*

Diffraction

Why can you hear music from the band room when you are down the hall? You can hear the music because the sound waves bend as they pass through an open doorway. This bending isn't caused by refraction. Remember that refraction occurs when waves change speed, but sound waves have the same speed in the band room and in the hallway. Instead, the bending is caused by diffraction. **Diffraction** is the bending of waves around a barrier.

Diffraction of Light Waves Can light waves diffract, too? You can hear your friends in the band room but you can't see them until you reach the open door. Therefore, you know that light waves do not diffract as much as sound waves do.

Are light waves able to diffract at all? Light waves do bend around the edges of an open door. However, for an opening as wide as a door, the amount the light bends is extremely small. As a result, the diffraction of light is far too small to allow you to see around a corner.

Figure 13
When you look at the goldfish in the water, the fish is in a different position than it appears.

Figure 14
Light rays refract as they enter and leave each water drop. Each color refracts at different angles because of their different wavelengths, so they separate into the colors of the visible spectrum.

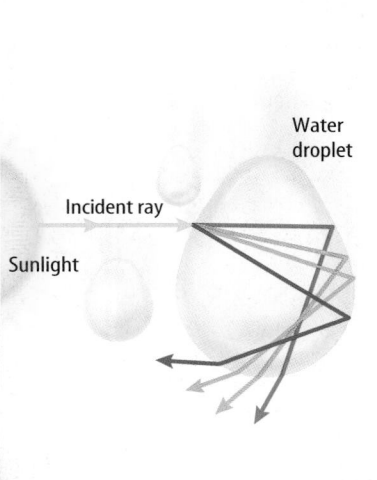

Water droplet

Incident ray

Sunlight

SECTION 3 Wave Behavior **589**

✔ **Reading Check**

Answer Sunlight refracts as it enters raindrops, reflects from the far inside surfaces of the drops, and refracts as it leaves the drops.

Visual Learning

Figure 14 When you look at the rainbow produced by the waterfall, you see an arc of colors. The refraction of light from water drops actually produces a circle of light, but we can only see the top of the circle because the ground blocks out the lower part. Red is at the top because, as you see in the sketch of the raindrop, red is bent less. Blue is at the bottom because it is bent more. L1 ELL IS **Visual-Spatial**

Diffraction

Quick Demo

Tell each student to straighten the first two fingers of one hand, spreading the fingers slightly to make a small slit between them. Then have students view a bright light through the slit. They will see fringes, or black lines, between their fingers as a result of diffraction. L1 ELL IS **Kinesthetic**

Resource Manager

Chapter Resources Booklet
Transparency Activity, p. 44
Enrichment, p. 30
MiniLAB, p. 4

Teacher FYI

The speed of light in a material depends on the characteristics of the material and the frequency of the incident light. High-frequency, short-wavelength light, such as violet light, usually travels more slowly in a material than lower-frequency, longer-wavelength light, such as red light. This means the violet light bends more than the red light as it moves from a vacuum (or air) to a denser medium.

What happens when waves meet?

Activity

Help students understand how to graph the addition of waves by demonstrating it on an overhead projector. Overlap transparencies of drawings of waves as you add them together.
L2 LS **Visual-Spatial**

Discussion

Have students consider what happens when three waves overlap. **If three waves interfere at a given point and have amplitudes of +3 units, +2 units, and −5 units, what is the amplitude of the resultant wave at that point?** 0 units L3
LS **Logical-Mathematical**

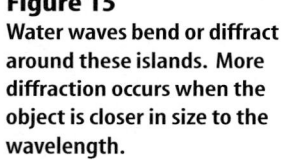

IDENTIFYING Misconceptions

Students may think that as waves move from one medium to another and are refracted, the wavelength and frequency of the waves change. However, the frequency doesn't change. Because the wave speed changes and the frequency stays the same, the wavelength changes.

Diffraction and Wavelength The reason that light waves don't diffract much when they pass through an open door is that the wavelengths of visible light are much smaller than the width of the door. Light waves have wavelengths between about 400 and 700 billionths of a meter, while the width of doorway is about one meter. Sound waves that you can hear have wavelengths between a few millimeters and about 10 m. They bend more easily around the corners of an open door. A wave is diffracted more when its wavelength is similar in size to the barrier or opening.

Diffraction of Water Waves Perhaps you have noticed water waves bending around barriers. For example, when water waves strike obstacles such as the islands shown in **Figure 15,** they don't stop moving. Here the size and spacing of the islands is not too different from the wavelength of the water waves. So the water waves bend around the islands, and keep on moving. They also spread out after they pass through openings between the islands. If the islands were much larger than the water wavelength, less diffraction would occur.

What happens when waves meet?

Suppose you throw two pebbles into a still pond. Ripples spread from the impact of each pebble and travel toward each other. What happens when two of these ripples meet? Do they collide like billiard balls and change direction? Waves behave differently from billiard balls when they meet. Waves pass right through each other and continue moving as though the other waves never existed.

Figure 15
Water waves bend or diffract around these islands. More diffraction occurs when the object is closer in size to the wavelength.

LAB DEMONSTRATION

Purpose to observe wave behavior
Materials 2 pencils; paper; large, rectangular glass baking dish; water
Preparation Fill the dish with water to a depth of 2 cm. Use several books on each side to suspend the pan over a sheet of white paper. Place a strong light about 40 cm above the pan. Dim all other lights.

Procedure To form waves, vibrate a vertical pencil up and down on one side of the pan. Show interference by vibrating two vertical pencils, about 10 cm apart, up and down at one end of the pan. Place an object in the path of the waves to show diffraction.

Expected Outcome Students observe reflection, diffraction, and interference.

✓ Assessment

What would the waves have looked like if you had held the pencil horizontally instead of vertically when vibrating it? They would have formed a line of waves instead of circles.

Wave Interference While two waves overlap a new wave is formed by adding the two waves together. The ability of two waves to combine and form a new wave when they overlap is called **interference.** After they overlap, the individual waves continue to travel on in their original form.

The different ways waves can interfere are shown in **Figure 16** on the next page. Sometimes when the waves meet, the crest of one wave overlaps the crest of another wave. This is called constructive interference. The amplitudes of these combining waves add together to make a larger wave while they overlap. Destructive interference occurs when the crest of one wave overlaps the trough of another wave. Then the amplitudes of the two waves combine to make a wave with a smaller amplitude. If the two waves have equal amplitudes and meet crest to trough, they cancel each other while the waves overlap.

Waves and Particles Like waves of water, when light travels through a small opening, such as a narrow slit, the light spreads out in all directions on the other side of the slit. If small particles, instead of waves, were sent through the slit, they would continue in a straight line without spreading. The spreading, or diffraction, is only a property of waves. Interference also doesn't occur with particles. If waves meet, they reinforce or cancel each other, then travel on. If particles approach each other, they either collide and scatter or miss each other completely. Interference, like diffraction, is a property of waves, not particles.

SCIENCE Online

Research Visit the Glencoe Science Web site at **science.glencoe.com** for more information about wave interference.

Problem-Solving Activity

Can you create destructive interference?

Your brother is vacuuming and you can't hear the television. Is it possible to diminish the sound of the vacuum so you can hear the TV? Can you eliminate unpleasant sounds and keep the sounds you do want to hear?

Identifying the Problem

It is possible to create a frequency that will destructively interfere with the sound of the vacuum and not the television. The graph shows the waves created by the vacuum and the television.

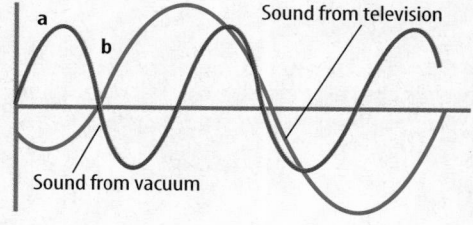

a
b
Sound from television
Sound from vacuum

Solving the Problem

1. Can you create the graph of a wave that will eliminate the noise from the vacuum but not the television?
2. Can you create the graph of a wave that would amplify the sound of the television?

SECTION 3 Wave Behavior **591**

SCIENCE Online

Internet Addresses

_____

_____

_____

Explore the Glencoe Science Web site at **science.glencoe.com** to find out more about topics in this section.

Extension

Explain to students that when an incident wave (one moving toward an object) and a reflected wave (one bounced off an object) meet, they sometimes form a standing, or stationary, wave. Because of the interference pattern, the standing wave doesn't appear to be traveling. You can demonstrate a standing wave using a rope. Tie one end of the rope firmly to a doorknob or a laboratory table. Shake the other end to produce various standing wave patterns. L3

 Visual-Spatial

Discussion

How does interference affect the way music sounds in different concert halls? Constructive and destructive interference patterns in a concert hall determine whether sound waves produced by individual voices or instruments combine to form waves that are pleasant or displeasing to listeners' ears. L3

 Logical-Mathematical

Math Skills Activity

National Math Standards

Correlation to Mathematics Objectives
2, 5, 6, 8–10

Answers

1. The wave must be out of phase with the vacuum wave. That is, it must have a trough when the vacuum wave has a crest, and vice versa.

2. Any wave that crests and troughs in the same place will amplify the wave.

Visualizing Interference

Have students examine the pictures and read the captions. Then ask the following questions.

Two waves both with an amplitude of 2 m pass through each other. The maximum amplitude reached is 4 m. **Is this constructive or destructive interference?** constructive

Two waves both with an amplitude of 2 m approach each other and the peak of the crest of one wave passes through the bottom of the trough of the other wave. **What is the amplitude of the resulting wave at that instant?** zero L2

LS Visual-Spatial

Activity

Have two students hold the ends of a long rope. Ask students to practice making waves with the rope by moving their hands vertically or horizontally in quick strokes. The students should then work together to set up constructive and destructive interference with the waves in their ropes. L3 **LS Kinesthetic**

Extension

Challenge students to find out how radio waves are used in radar and how stealth airplanes are built to evade detection by radar. Have students work in pairs to make posters showing the airplane profiles used and the materials used to enable these planes to avoid detection.

Figure 16

Whether they are ripples on a pond or huge ocean swells, when water waves meet they can combine to form new waves in a process called interference. As shown below, wave interference can be constructive or destructive.

Constructive Interference

In constructive interference, a wave with greater amplitude is formed.

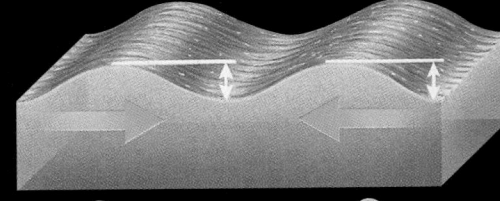

A   **B**

The crests of two waves—A and B—approach each other.

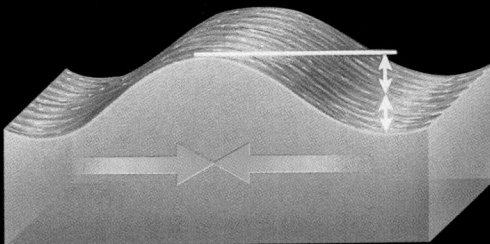

The two waves form a wave with a greater amplitude while the crests of both waves overlap.

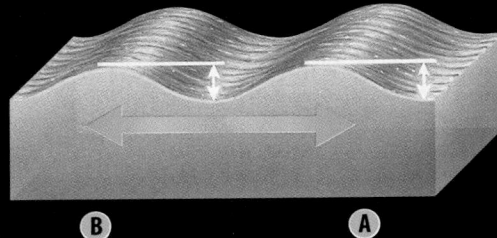

B   **A**

The original waves pass through each other and go on as they started.

Destructive Interference

In destructive interference, a wave with a smaller amplitude is formed.

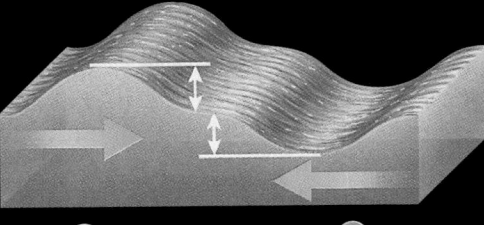

A   **B**

The crest of one wave approaches the trough of another.

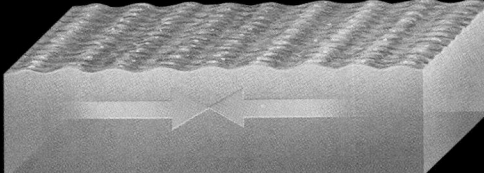

If the two waves have equal amplitude, they momentarily cancel when they meet.

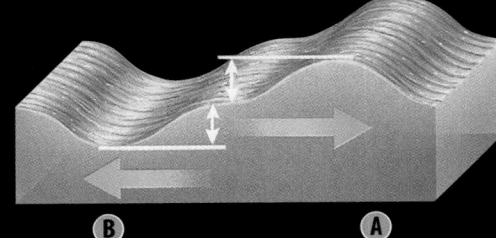

B   **A**

The original waves pass through each other and go on as they started.

Resource Manager

Chapter Resources Booklet
Lab Activity, pp. 13–14
Reinforcement, p. 27

Reducing Noise You might have seen someone use a power lawn mower or a chain saw. In the past, many people who performed these tasks damaged their hearing because of the loud noises produced by these machines. Today, specially designed ear protectors absorb the sound from lawn mowers and chain saws. The ear protectors absorb energy and lower the amplitudes of the harmful waves. The waves that reach the ears have smaller amplitudes and won't damage eardrums.

Using Interference Pilots and passengers of small planes have a more complicated problem. They can't use ordinary ear protectors to shut out all the noise of the plane's motor. If they did, the pilots wouldn't be able to hear instructions from air-traffic controllers, and the passengers wouldn't be able to hear each other talk. To solve this problem, engineers invented ear protectors, as shown in **Figure 17,** that have electronic circuits. These circuits detect noise from the aircraft and produce sound frequencies that destructively interfere with the noise. However, the sound frequencies produced do not interfere with human voices, so people can hear and understand normal conversation. In these examples, destructive interference can be a benefit.

Figure 17
Some airplane pilots use special ear protectors that cancel out engine noise but don't block human voices.

Section 3 Assessment

1. Why don't you see your reflection in a building made of rough, white stone?

2. If you're standing on one side of a building, how are you able to hear the siren of an ambulance on the other side?

3. What behavior of light enables magnifying glasses and contact lenses to bend light rays and help people see more clearly?

4. What is diffraction? How does the amount of diffraction depend on wavelength?

5. **Think Critically** Why don't light rays that stream through an open window into a darkened room spread evenly through the entire room?

Skill Builder Activities

6. **Comparing and Contrasting** When light rays pass from water into a certain type of glass, the rays refract toward the normal. Compare and contrast the speed of light in water and in the glass. **For more help, refer to the** Science Skill Handbook.

7. **Communicating** Watch carefully as you travel home from school or walk down your street. What examples of wave reflection and refraction do you notice? Describe each of these in your Science Journal and explain your reasons. **For more help, refer to the** Science Skill Handbook.

3 Assess

Reteach
Divide the class in half and conduct a baseball game review with words from this chapter. Players match words with meanings and are out when they miss a word. Each team has three outs before the turn shifts to the other team. L2 COOP LEARN
IS Interpersonal

Challenge
Have pairs of students prepare posters showing the types of waves produced by a combination of (1) two transverse waves in which crests overlap, (2) two transverse waves in which crests and troughs overlap, (3) two compressional waves in which crests overlap, and (4) two compressional waves in which crests and troughs overlap. L3
COOP LEARN **IS Visual-Spatial** P

✓ Assessment

Content Have students draw diagrams illustrating the refraction, reflection, diffraction, and interference of waves. Use **Performance Assessment in the Science Classroom,** p. 127.

Answers to Section Assessment

1. The rough surface scatters light in all directions.
2. Sound diffracts easily around objects such as buildings.
3. refraction
4. bending of waves around a barrier; A wave is diffracted more when its wavelength is similar in size to the barrier or opening.

5. Waves of light travel in straight lines. The waves of light that come through the window travel in straight lines until they reach objects that absorb or reflect them. Also, the light waves have very small wavelengths, so very little diffraction occurs as they move through a wide opening such as a window.

6. Because the light rays refract toward the normal, their speed must be lower in the glass than in water.
7. Answers might include reflection of light off a puddle or window or refraction of light through a prism. Others may mention the reflection of sirens, horns, or traffic noise.

Activity

Recognize the problem

Purpose

Students will model the behavior of seismic waves by creating transverse standing waves on a demonstration spring or coiled toy spring. Factors such as length, type of spring, and frequency will be varied and controlled to determine how the speed of a wave within a coil depends upon such factors. By comparing their results with those of others, students can make generalizations about waves within a spring, and by analogy, seismic waves within the earth.

Process Skills

observing, measuring, calculating, separating and controlling variables, predicting

Time Required

45 minute class

Materials

Demonstration springs sold by science educational supply companies create the best waves. Toy springs can also be used to create waves, and if springs are not available, a length of rope or hose will serve as a substitute wave maker. A metric tape measure can replace a meterstick.

Safety Precautions

Caution students not to use or swing the spring anywhere but on the floor.

Form a Hypothesis

Possible Hypothesis

The hypothesis of most students will reflect that the speed of a wave is determined by dividing the distance the wave travels by the time it takes for the wave to travel one wavelength.

Activity *Design Your Own Experiment*

Wave Speed

When an earthquake occurs, it produces waves that are recorded at points all over the world by instruments called seismographs. By comparing the data that they collected from these seismographs, scientists discovered that the interior of Earth must be made of layers of different materials. These data showed that the waves traveled at different speeds as they passed through different parts of Earth's interior.

Recognize the Problem

How can the speed of a wave be measured?

Form a Hypothesis

In some materials, waves travel too fast for their speeds to be measured directly. Think about what you know about the relationship among the frequency, wavelength, and speed of a wave in a medium. Make a hypothesis about how you can use this relationship to measure the speed of a wave within a medium.

Goals
- **Measure** the speed of a wave within a coiled spring toy.
- **Predict** whether the speed you measured will be different in other types of coiled spring toys.

Materials
coiled spring toy   meterstick
stopwatch   tape
*clock with a second hand
*Alternate materials

Safety Precautions

Resource Manager

Chapter Resources Booklet
   Activity Worksheet, pp. 7–8
Lab Management and Safety, p. 65

SCIENCE *Online*

Internet Addresses

_____

_____

_____

Explore the Glencoe Science Web site at **science.glencoe.com** to find out more about topics in this activity.

Test Your Hypothesis

Plan

1. Make a data table in your Science Journal like the one shown.
2. In your Science Journal, write a detailed description of the coiled spring toy you are going to use. Be sure to include its mass and diameter, the width of a coil, and what it is made of.
3. **Decide** as a group how you will measure the frequency and length of waves in the spring toy. What are your variables? Which variables must be controlled? What variable do you want to measure?
4. Repeat your experiment three times.

Wave Data	Trial 1	Trial 2	Trial 3
Length spring was stretched (m)	3.30	3.30	3.91
Number of crests	2	3	4
Wavelength (m)	3.30	2.20	1.96
# of vibrations timed	10	10	10
# of seconds vibrations were timed	5.49	3.60	6.01
Wave speed (m/s)	6.01	6.12	6.29

Do

1. Make sure your teacher approves your plan before you start.
2. Carry out the experiment.
3. While you are doing the experiment, record your observations and measurements in your data table.

Analyze Your Data

1. **Calculate** the frequency of the waves by dividing the number of vibrations you timed by the number of seconds you timed them. Record your results in your data table.
2. Use the following formula to calculate the speed of a wave in each trial.

$$\text{wavelength} \times \frac{\text{wave frequency}}{} = \frac{\text{wave speed}}{}$$

3. Average the wave speeds from your trials to determine the average speed of a wave in your coiled spring toy.

Draw Conclusions

1. Which variables affected the wave speed in spring toys the most? Which variables affected the speed the least? Was your hypothesis supported?
2. What factors caused the wave speed measured in each trial to be different?

Communicating Your Data

Post a description of your coiled spring toy and the results of your experiment on a bulletin board in your classroom. **Compare and contrast** your results with other students in your class.

ACTIVITY 595

Assessment

Oral Ask students how they might determine the speed of water waves that are crashing ashore at a beach. Time the waves coming ashore to determine the frequency. Estimate the distance between wave crests to determine wavelength. The product of these two numbers is the speed of the wave. Use **PASC,** p. 89

Communicating Your Data

Encourage students to record their data in electronically designed spreadsheets.

Test Your Hypothesis

Possible Procedures

Help your student groups create standing waves. While a student holds one end of the coiled-spring toy stationary, have another student move the other end from side to side with a rhythm that produces a standing wave.

Tie to Prior Knowledge

Most students will have observed waves moving through a medium such as ocean waves or ripples on a pond.

Expected Outcome

Students will create standing transverse waves and measure their frequency, wavelengths, and speeds. From this data, they will predict the speed of waves in other types of coiled springs.

Analyze Your Data

1. Based on the sample data in the table, frequencies were as follows: Trial 1, 1.82 Hz; Trial 2, 2.78 Hz; Trial 3, 3.21 Hz.
2. Based on the sample data in the table, speeds were as follows: Trial 1, 6.00 m/s; Trial 2, 6.12 m/s; Trial 3, 6.29 m/s.
3. Average wave speed is 6.14 m/s.

Error Analysis

Ask student groups to compare data with other groups and explain any significant discrepancies.

Draw Conclusions

1. Answers will vary.
2. Possible answer: how fast the spring toy was shaken.

Science Stats

Content Background

Electromagnetic, ocean, and sound are different types of waves. Each of these waves propagate in a different manner. Electromagnetic waves do not require a medium for travel and can carry energy through the vacuum of space. The following names of these waves are familiar to us: radio, microwave, infrared, visible light, ultraviolet, X rays, and gamma rays. Surface ocean waves are a mixture of longitudinal and transverse waves that carry energy through the water. Sound waves are longitudinal waves that can carry energy through solids, liquids, and gases. The velocity of waves can be determined by the equation velocity = wavelength × frequency.

Discussion

Waves are described by their frequency (pulses per second), wavelength (distance from two corresponding points on two successive waves), amplitude (distance from trough or crest to baseline), and speed. **What do the numbers represent in each of the examples?** 34 meters, amplitude; 966 km/h, speed; 800 pulses per second, frequency; 8 km/s and 4.8 km/s, speed

Extension

Have students research the speeds of light and sound. The speed of light is 3.00×10^8 m/s. The speed of sound varies with the type of medium and other conditions such as density, temperature, and pressure.

Science Stats

Waves, Waves, and More Waves

Did you know...

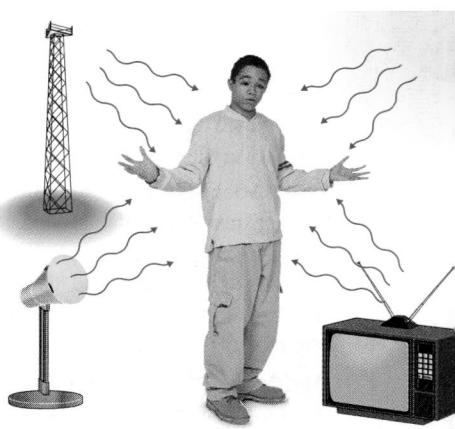

... You are constantly surrounded by a sea of waves even when you're on dry land! Electromagnetic waves around us are used to cook our food and transmit signals to our radios and televisions. Light itself is an electromagnetic wave.

... The highest recorded ocean wave was 34 meters high, which is comparable to the height of a ten-story building. This super wave was seen in the North Pacific Ocean and recorded by the crew of the naval ship *USS Ramapo* in 1933.

... Tsunamis—huge ocean waves—can travel at speeds over 900 km/h.

... Waves let dolphins see with their ears! A dolphin sends out ultrasonic pulses, or clicks, at rates of 800 pulses per second. These sound waves are reflected back to the dolphin after they hit another object. This process—echolocation—allows dolphins to recognize obstacles and meals.

596   CHAPTER 20 Waves

SCIENCE Online
Internet Addresses

_____
_____
_____

Explore the Glencoe Science Web site at **science.glencoe.com** to find out more about topics in this feature.

. . . Earthquakes produce a variety of seismic waves—

waves that ripple through Earth after subsurface rock breaks suddenly. The fastest are P and S waves. P waves are compressional waves that travel at about 8 km/s. S waves, which move like ocean waves, travel at about 4.8 km/s.

Electromagnetic Wavelengths

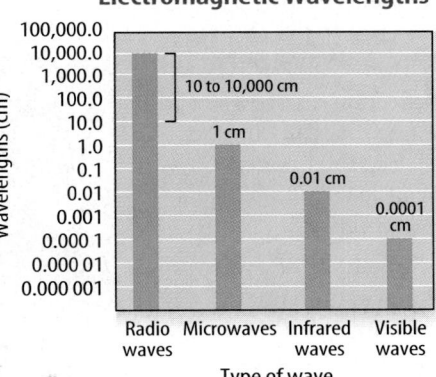

. . . Radio waves from space were discovered in 1932 by Karl G. Jansky, an American engineer. His amazing discovery led to creation of radio astronomy, a field that explores parts of the universe that are hidden by interstellar dust or can't be seen with telescopes.

Do the Math

1. A museum with a dolphin exhibit plays dolphin clicks for its visitors 250 times slower than the rate at which the dolphins emit them. How many clicks do the visitors hear in 10 s?
2. Tsunamis form in the ocean when an earthquake occurs on the ocean floor. How long will it take a tsunami to travel 4,500 km?
3. Make a bar graph to show the speeds of P waves, S waves and tsunamis. Use km/h as your unit of speed.

Go Further

Go to **science.glencoe.com** to learn about discoveries by radio astronomers. Graph the distances of these discoveries from Earth.

Do the Math

Teaching Strategies

Remind students that distance = velocity × time, and that there are 3,600 seconds in an hour.

Answers

1. 32 pulses
2. 5.7 h at 900 km/h
3. Students should make a bar graph with tsunamis traveling 900 km/h, P waves at 28,800 km/h, and S waves at 17,280 km/h.

Go Further

Have students find the frequency of radio waves. **Are these waves low frequency or high frequency waves in the electromagnetic spectrum?** low

---

Visual Learning

Electromagnetic Wavelengths How many times greater is the wavelength of infrared waves than that of visible waves? 100 times **How many times greater is the wavelength for microwaves compared to infrared waves?** 100 times **How many times greater is the wavelength for microwaves compared to visible waves?** 10,000 times

Chapter 20 Study Guide

Reviewing Main Ideas

Preview

Students can answer the questions in their Science Journals. Discuss the answers as you go through the chapter. **Linguistic**

Review

Students can write their answers, then compare them with those of other students. **Interpersonal**

Reteach

Students can look at the illustrations and describe details that support the main ideas of the chapter. **Visual-Spatial**

Answers to Chapter Review

SECTION 1
4. The boat moves perpendicular to the direction of motion of the waves.

SECTION 2
4. amplitude

SECTION 3
1. The surface is rough, so the light waves bounce off in many directions.

Reviewing Main Ideas

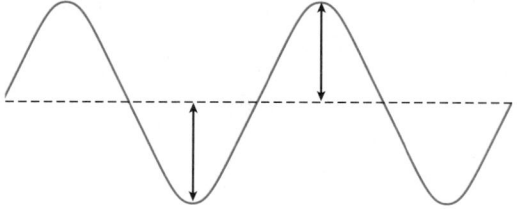

Section 1 What are waves?

1. Waves are rhythmic disturbances that carry energy but not matter.

2. Mechanical waves can travel only through matter. Electromagnetic waves can travel through matter and space.

3. In a mechanical transverse wave, matter in the medium moves back and forth at right angles to the direction the wave travels.

4. In a compressional wave, matter in the medium moves forward and backward in the same direction as the wave. *How does the boat in the picture move as the water wave goes by?*

Section 2 Wave Properties

1. The amplitude of a transverse wave is the distance between the rest position and a crest or a trough.

2. The energy carried by a wave increases as the amplitude increases.

3. Wavelength is the distance between neighboring crests or neighboring troughs.

4. The frequency of a wave is the number of wavelengths that pass a given point in 1 s. *What property of a wave is shown by the figure at the top of the next column?*

5. Waves travel through different materials at different speeds.

Section 3 Wave Behavior

1. Reflection occurs when a wave strikes an object or surface and bounces off. *Why doesn't the foil show a clear image?*

2. The bending of a wave as it moves from one medium into another is called refraction. A wave changes direction, or refracts, when the speed of the wave changes.

3. The bending of waves around a barrier is called diffraction.

4. Interference occurs when two or more waves combine and form a new wave while they overlap.

FOLDABLES
Reading & Study Skills
After You Read
Use your Concept Map Study Fold to compare and contrast transverse and compressional mechanical waves.

FOLDABLES
Reading & Study Skills
After You Read
After students have read the chapter and completed the Foldable described in Before You Read, have them do the activity on the student page.

Dinah Zike

Visualizing Main Ideas

Complete the following spider map about waves.

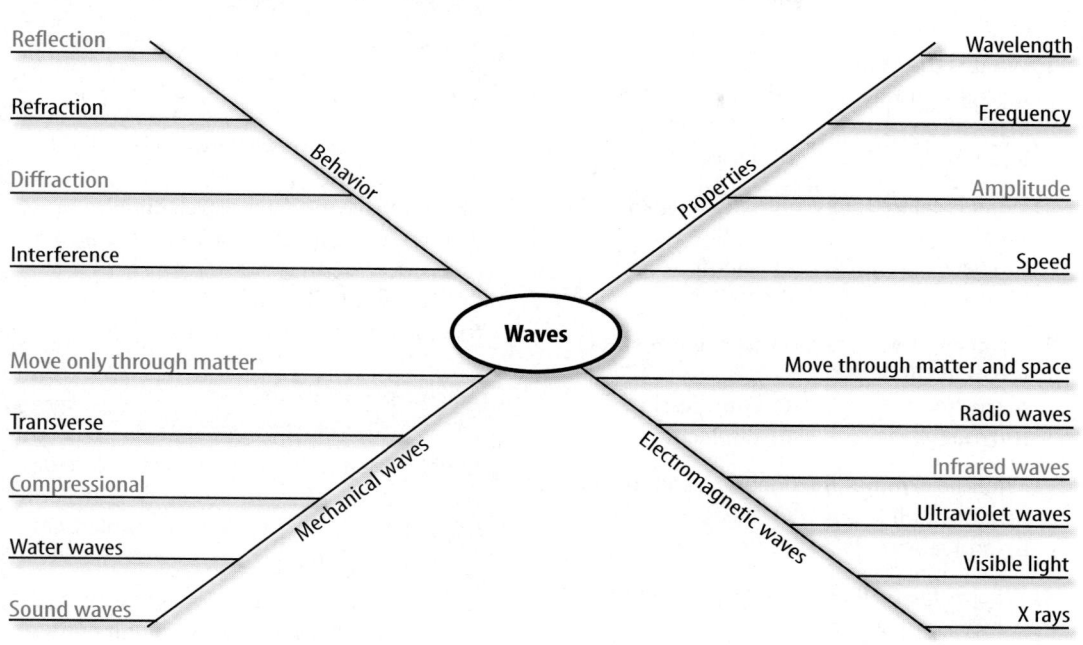

Reflection

Refraction

Diffraction

Interference

Behavior

Move only through matter

Transverse

Compressional

Water waves

Sound waves

Mechanical waves

Waves

Wavelength

Frequency

Amplitude

Speed

Properties

Move through matter and space

Radio waves

Infrared waves

Ultraviolet waves

Visible light

X rays

Electromagnetic waves

Visualizing Main Ideas

See student page.

Vocabulary Review

Using Vocabulary

1. Refraction
2. compressional wave
3. wavelength
4. amplitude
5. electromagnetic wave

Vocabulary Review

Vocabulary Words

a. amplitude
b. compressional wave
c. diffraction
d. electromagnetic wave
e. frequency
f. interference
g. mechanical wave
h. reflection
i. refraction
j. transverse wave
k. wave
l. wavelength

Study Tip

After you've read a chapter, go back to the beginning and speed-read through what you've just read. This will help your memory.

Using Vocabulary

Using the list, replace the underlined words with the correct vocabulary words.

1. <u>Diffraction</u> is the change in direction of a wave going from one medium to another.

2. The type of wave that has rarefactions is a <u>transverse wave</u>.

3. The distance between two adjacent crests of a transverse wave is the <u>frequency</u>.

4. The more energy a wave carries, the greater its <u>wavelength</u> is.

5. A <u>mechanical wave</u> can travel through space without a medium.

Checking Concepts

1. D
2. C
3. B
4. B
5. A
6. D
7. A
8. C
9. D
10. A

Thinking Critically

11. Compressional; each car is pushed into the next. The cars then rebound. This is like a compressional wave.
12. Yes; yes; electromagnetic waves can travel through space and matter.
13. The frequency decreases because fewer wavelengths pass a given point in 1 s.
14. because the rough surface reflects the light rays in many different directions
15. Light travels much faster than sound, so the flash of the cannon will reach you before the sound will.

Chapter 20 Assessment

Checking Concepts

Choose the word or phrase that best answers the question.

1. What is the material through which mechanical waves travel?
   A) charged particles C) a vacuum
   B) space D) a medium

2. What is carried from particle to particle in a water wave?
   A) speed C) energy
   B) amplitude D) matter

3. What are the lowest points on a transverse wave called?
   A) crests C) compressions
   B) troughs D) rarefactions

4. What determines the pitch of a sound wave?
   A) amplitude C) speed
   B) frequency D) refraction

5. What is the distance between adjacent wave compressions?
   A) one wavelength C) 1 m/s
   B) 1 km D) 1 Hz

6. What occurs when a wave strikes an object or surface and bounces off?
   A) diffraction
   B) refraction
   C) a transverse wave
   D) reflection

7. What is the name for a change in the direction of a wave when it passes from one medium into another?
   A) refraction C) reflection
   B) interference D) diffraction

8. What type of wave is a sound wave?
   A) transverse C) compressional
   B) electromagnetic D) refracted

9. When two waves overlap and interfere destructively, what does the resulting wave have?
   A) a greater amplitude
   B) more energy
   C) a change in frequency
   D) a lower amplitude

10. What is the difference between blue light and green light?
    A) They have different wavelengths.
    B) One is a transverse wave and the other is not.
    C) They have different pitch.
    D) One is mechanical and the other is not.

Thinking Critically

11. Explain what kind of wave—transverse or compressional—is produced when an engine bumps into a string of coupled railroad cars on a track.

12. Is it possible for an electromagnetic wave to travel through a vacuum? Through matter? Explain your answers.

13. Why does the frequency of a wave decrease as the wavelength increases?

14. Why don't you see your reflected image when you look at a white, rough surface?

15. If a cannon fires at a great distance from you, why do you see the flash before you hear the sound?

Developing Skills

16. **Solving One-Step Equations** An electromagnetic wave travels at the speed of light and has a wavelength of 0.022 m. If the wave speed is equal to the wavelength times the frequency, what is the frequency of the wave?

Chapter ✓Assessment Planner

Portfolio Encourage students to place in their portfolios one or two items of what they consider to be their best work. Examples include:
- Activity, p. 578
- Extension, p. 583
- Science Journal, p. 584
- Challenge, p. 593

Performance Additional performance assessments, Performance Task Assessment Lists, and rubrics for evaluating these activities can be found in Glencoe's **Performance Assessment in the Science Classroom.**

17. Forming Hypotheses Form a hypothesis that can explain this observation. Waves A and B travel away from Earth through Earth's atmosphere. Wave A continues on into space, but wave B does not.

18. Recognizing Cause and Effect Explain how the object shown below causes compressions and rarefactions as it vibrates in air.

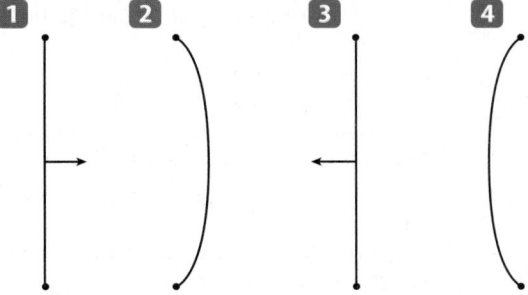

19. Comparing and Contrasting AM radio waves have wavelengths between about 200 m and 600 m, and FM radio waves have wavelengths of about 3 m. Why can AM radio signals often be heard behind buildings and mountains but FM radio signals cannot?

Performance Assessment

20. Making Flashcards Work with a partner to make flashcards for the bold-faced terms in the chapter. Illustrate each term on the front of the cards. Write the term and its definition on the back of the card. Use the cards to review the terms with another team.

TECHNOLOGY

 Go to the Glencoe Science Web site at **science.glencoe.com** or use the **Glencoe Science CD-ROM** for additional chapter assessment.

THE PRINCETON REVIEW — Test Practice

Kamisha's science teacher told her that her remote control sent signals to the TV and VCR by using infrared waves. She decided to do some research about waves. The information she gathered is shown in the diagram below.

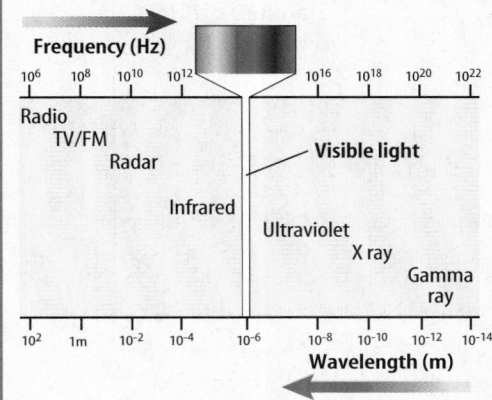

1. According to the diagram, which type of wave has a wavelength greater than 1 m?
   A) radio
   B) infrared
   C) ultraviolet
   D) X ray

2. According to the diagram, which type of wave has the HIGHEST frequency?
   F) radio
   G) ultraviolet
   H) X ray
   J) gamma ray

THE PRINCETON REVIEW — Test Practice

The Test-Taking Tip was written by The Princeton Review, the nation's leader in test preparation.
1. A
2. J

Developing Skills

16. about 13.6 billion Hz
17. Wave A is an electromagnetic wave and wave B is a mechanical wave.
18. The vibrating object moves back and forth, colliding with the molecules in the air around it. As the object moves forward, it pushes molecules together to form a compression. As the object moves back toward its original position and beyond, it creates a rarefaction—a region in which molecules are spread farther apart.
19. Because their longer wavelengths are closer to the size of buildings and mountains, AM radio waves diffract around them more than FM radio waves do.

Performance Assessment

20. Use **Performance Assessment in the Science Classroom**, p. 127.

✓Assessment Resources

📁 **Reproducible Masters**

Chapter Resources Booklet
   Chapter Review, pp. 35–36
   Chapter Tests, pp. 37–40
   Assessment Transparency Activity, p. 47

Glencoe Science Web site
   Interactive Tutor
   Chapter Quizzes

Glencoe Technology
   🎙 Assessment Transparency
   💿 Interactive CD-ROM Chapter Quizzes
   💿 ExamView Pro Test Bank
   💿 Vocabulary PuzzleMaker Software
   📼 MindJogger Videoquiz

Section/Objectives	Standards		Activities/Features
Chapter Opener	**National**	**State/Local**	**Explore Activity:** Observe throat vibrations, p. 603 **Before You Read,** p. 603
	See p. 7T for a Key to Standards		
Section 1 What is sound? ● 3 sessions ⬚ 1.5 blocks 1. **Identify** the characteristics of sound waves. 2. **Explain** how sound travels. 3. **Describe** the Doppler effect.	National Content Standards: UCP2, A1, B3, D3, F5		**MiniLAB:** Comparing and Contrasting Sounds, p. 606 **Science Online,** p. 609 **Astronomy Integration,** p. 610 **Problem-Solving Activity:** How does Doppler radar work?, p. 610 **Visualizing the Doppler Effect,** p. 611 **Activity:** Observe and Measure Reflection of Sound, p. 614
Section 2 Music ● 5 sessions ⬚ 2.5 blocks 1. **Explain** the difference between music and noise. 2. **Describe** how different instruments produce music. 3. **Explain** how you hear.	National Content Standards: UCP2, A1, B3, C1, F1, F5		**Environmental Science Integration,** p. 616 **MiniLAB:** Modeling a Stringed Instrument, p. 618 **Science Online,** p. 621 **Activity:** Music, p. 624 **Science and Society:** It's a Wrap, p. 626

Activity Materials	Reproducible Resources	Section Assessment	Technology
Explore Activity: no materials needed	**Chapter Resources Booklet** Foldables Worksheet, p. 15 Guided Reading Overview, p. 17 Note-taking Worksheets, pp. 29–30	GLENCOE'S ASSESSMENT ADVANTAGE	
MiniLAB: set of keys; tub or wide, deep bowl; metal spoon, cotton string **Activity:** 2 cardboard tubes (20- to 30-cm long), watch with a second hand that ticks audibly, protractor	**Chapter Resources Booklet** Transparency Activity, p. 40 MiniLAB, p. 3 Enrichment, p. 27 Reinforcement, p. 25 Guided Reading, p. 18 Activity Worksheet, pp. 5–6 Lab Activity, pp. 9–10 **Mathematics Skill Activities,** p. 9 **Reading and Writing Skill Activities,** p. 7 **Science Inquiry Labs,** p. 27	**Portfolio** Assessment, p. 606 Extension, p. 612 **Performance** MiniLAB, p. 606 Problem-Solving Activity, p. 610 Skill Builder Activities, p. 613 **Content** Section Assessment, p. 613	♪ Section Focus Transparency ◉ Interactive CD-ROM 🎧 Guided Reading Audio Program
MiniLAB: rubber band, shoe box **Activity:** musical instruments, measuring tape, tuning forks *Need materials?* Contact Science Kit at 1-800-828-7777 or www.sciencekit.com on the Internet.	**Chapter Resources Booklet** Transparency Activity, p. 41 MiniLAB, p. 4 Enrichment, p. 28 Reinforcement, p. 26 Guided Reading, pp. 19, 20 Activity Worksheet, pp. 7–8 Transparency Activity, pp. 43–44 Lab Activity, pp. 11–14 **Cultural Diversity,** p. 61 **Lab Management and Safety,** p. 64	**Portfolio** Assessment, p. 623 Communicating Your Data, p. 625 **Performance** MiniLAB, p. 618 Skill Builder Activities, p. 623 **Content** Section Assessment, p. 623	♪ Section Focus Transparency ♪ Teaching Transparency ◉ Interactive CD-ROM 🎧 Guided Reading Audio Program

End of Chapter Assessment

Blackline Masters	Technology	Professional Series
Chapter Resources Booklet Chapter Review, pp. 33–34 Chapter Tests, pp. 35–38 **Standardized Test Practice by The Princeton Review,** pp. 89–92	▭ MindJogger Videoquiz ◉ Interactive CD-ROM ◉ Vocabulary PuzzleMakers ◉ ExamView Pro Test Bank ◉ Interactive Lesson Planner ◉ Interactive Teacher Edition	Performance Assessment in the Science Classroom (PASC)

Transparencies

Section Focus

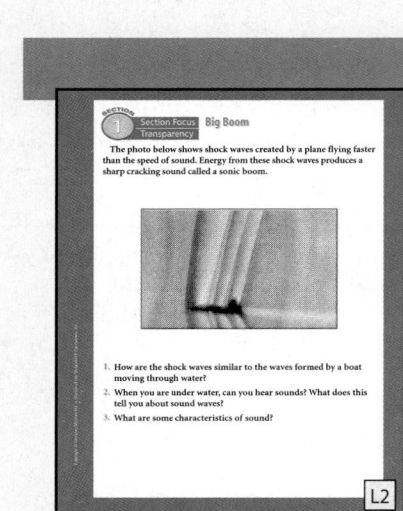

Section Focus Transparency — Big Boom

The photo below shows shock waves created by a plane flying faster than the speed of sound. Energy from these shock waves produces a sharp cracking sound called a sonic boom.

1. How are the shock waves similar to the waves formed by a boat moving through water?
2. When you are under water, can you hear sounds? What does this tell you about sound waves?
3. What are some characteristics of sound?

L2

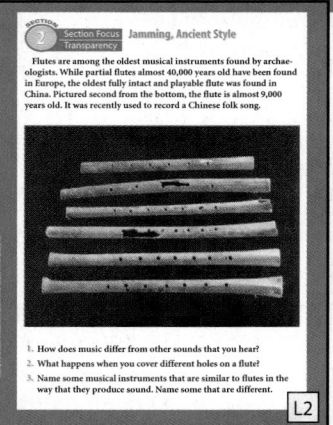

Section Focus Transparency — Jamming, Ancient Style

Flutes are among the oldest musical instruments found by archaeologists. While partial flutes almost 40,000 years old have been found in Europe, the oldest fully intact and playable flute was found in China. Pictured second from the bottom, the flute is almost 9,000 years old. It was recently used to record a Chinese folk song.

1. How does music differ from other sounds that you hear?
2. What happens when you cover different holes on a flute?
3. Name some musical instruments that are similar to flutes in the way that they produce sound. Name some that are different.

L2

This is a representation of key blackline masters available in the Teacher Classroom Resources. See Resource Manager boxes within the chapter for additional information.

Key to Teaching Strategies

The following designations will help you decide which activities are appropriate for your students.

L1 Level 1 activities should be appropriate for students with learning difficulties.

L2 Level 2 activities should be within the ability range of all students.

L3 Level 3 activities are designed for above-average students.

ELL ELL activities should be within the ability range of English Language Learners.

COOP LEARN Cooperative Learning activities are designed for small group work.

LS Multiple Learning Styles logos, as described on page 22T, are used throughout to indicate strategies that address different learning styles.

P These strategies represent student products that can be placed into a best-work portfolio.

Assessment

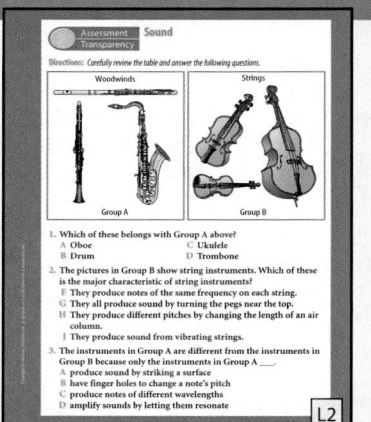

Assessment Transparency — Sound

Directions: Carefully review the table and answer the following questions.

Woodwinds — Group A
Strings — Group B

1. Which of these belongs with Group A above?
   A Oboe   C Ukulele
   B Drum   D Trombone
2. The pictures in Group B show string instruments. Which of these is the major characteristic of string instruments?
   F They produce notes of the same frequency on each string.
   G They all produce sound by turning the pegs near the top.
   H They produce different pitches by changing the length of an air column.
   J They produce sound from vibrating strings.
3. The instruments in Group A are different from the instruments in Group B because only the instruments in Group A ___.
   A produce sound by striking a surface
   B have finger holes to change a note's pitch
   C produce notes of different wavelengths
   D amplify sounds by letting them resonate

L2

Teaching

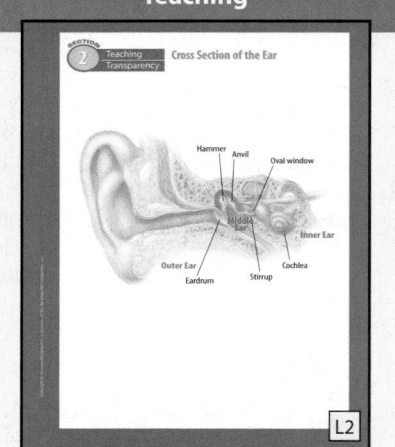

Teaching Transparency — Cross Section of the Ear

Hammer, Anvil, Oval window, Middle Ear, Inner Ear, Outer Ear, Eardrum, Stirrup, Cochlea

L2

Hands-on Activities

Activity Worksheets

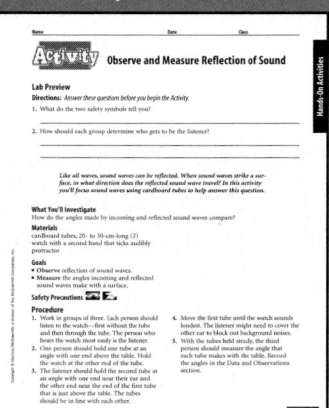

Activity — Observe and Measure Reflection of Sound

Lab Preview
Directions: *Answer these questions before you begin the Activity.*
1. What do the two safety symbols tell you?
2. How should each group determine who gets to be the listener?

Like all waves, sound waves can be reflected. When sound waves strike a surface, in what direction does the reflected sound wave travel? In this activity you'll focus sound waves using cardboard tubes to help answer this question.

What You'll Investigate
How do the angles made by incoming and reflected sound waves compare?
Materials
cardboard tubes, 26- to 30-cm-long (2)
watch with a second hand that ticks audibly
protractor
Goals
• Observe reflection of sound waves.
• Measure the angles incoming and reflected sound waves make with a surface.
Safety Precautions
Procedure
1. Work in groups of three. Each person should listen to the watch—first without the tube and then through the tube. The person who hears the watch most easily is the listener.
2. One person should hold one tube at an angle with one end above the table. Hold the watch at the other end of the tube.
3. The listener should hold the second tube at an angle with one end near their ear and the other end near the end of the first tube that is just above the table. The tubes should be in line with each other.
4. Move the first tube until the watch sounds loudest. The listener might need to cover the other ear to block out background noises.
5. With the tubes held steady, the third person should measure the angle that each tube makes with the table. Record the angles in the Data and Observations section.

L2

Laboratory Activities

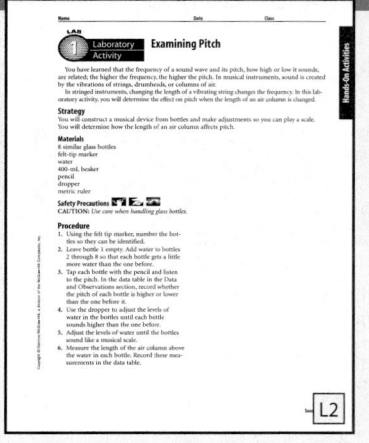

Laboratory Activity — Examining Pitch

You have learned that the frequency of a sound wave and its pitch, how high or low it sounds, are related; the higher the frequency, the higher the pitch. In musical instruments, sound is created by the vibrations of strings, drumheads, or columns of air.
In stringed instruments, changing the length of a vibrating string changes the frequency. In this laboratory activity, you will determine the effect on pitch when the length of an air column is changed.

Strategy
You will construct a musical device from bottles and make adjustments so you can play a scale.
You will determine how the length of an air column affects pitch.
Materials
8 similar glass bottles
felt-tip marker
water
400-mL beaker
dropper
metric ruler
Safety Precautions
CAUTION: *Use care when handling glass bottles.*
Procedure
1. Using the felt-tip marker, number the bottles so they can be identified.
2. Leave bottle 1 empty. Add water to bottles 2 through 8 so that each bottle gets a little more water than the one before.
3. Tap each bottle with the pencil and listen to the pitch. In the data table in the Data and Observations section, record whether the pitch of each bottle is higher or lower than the one before it.
4. Use the dropper to adjust the levels of water in the bottles until each bottle sounds higher than the one before.
5. Adjust the levels of water until the bottles sound like a musical scale.
6. Measure the length of the air column above the water in each bottle. Record these measurements in the data table.

L2

Meeting Different Ability Levels

Content Outline

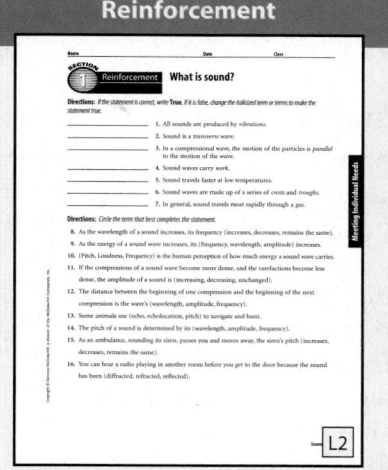

L2

Reinforcement

L2

Directed Reading

L1

Assessment

Chapter Tests

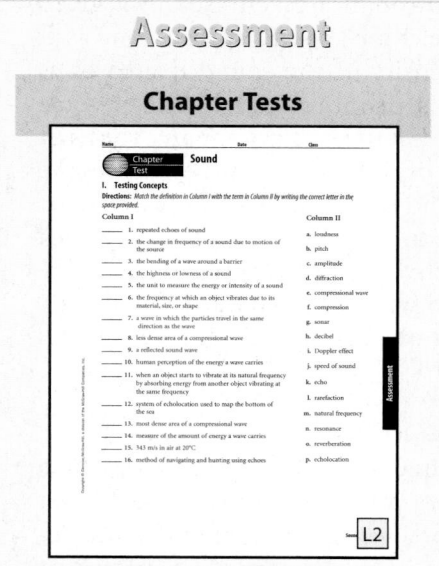

L2

Enrichment

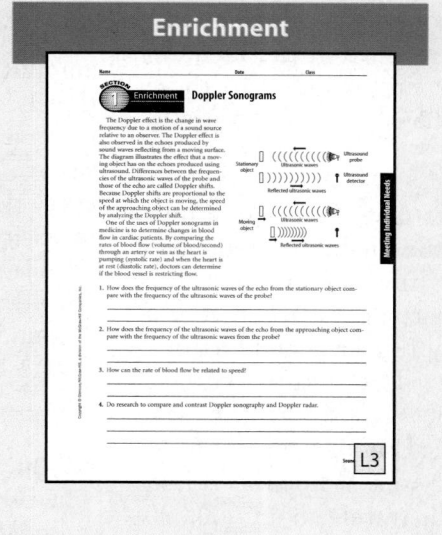

L3

Spanish Directed Reading

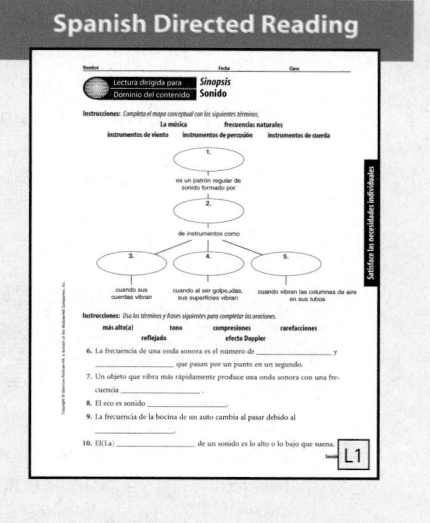

L1

Test Practice Workbook

L1

Chapter Review

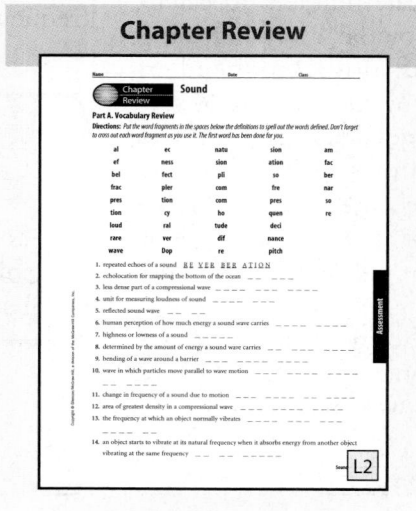

L2

Science Content Background

SECTION 1

What is sound?

Sound Waves

Sound waves are mechanical waves, which means they need a medium to travel through and they can't travel through a vacuum. It is the sound energy that travels through a medium, not the particles of the medium. The particles of the medium move back and forth as the sound wave passes but then return to their original positions.

Sound waves are called *compressional* or *longitudinal* waves. The compressions and rarefractions produced by sound waves cause temporary changes in the pressure of the medium it travels through. Our ears respond to these pressure changes and interpret them as sound.

The Speed of Sound

The speed of sound is how fast the sound energy travels through the medium. Frequency is the rate at which the particles of the medium vibrate back and forth.

The approximate speed of sound through air at room temperature is 343 m/s. While this is fast, light travels about 900,000 times faster. This explains why we see lightning before we hear thunder. To calculate how far away lightning is, multiply the speed of sound by the number of seconds between seeing the lightning and hearing the thunder. If this is three seconds, then the lightning is 3 s × 343 m/s = 1,029 m away. For an approximate distance in miles divide the time by five.

The more massive the molecules of a gas are, the more slowly sound travels through it. This is because particles with more mass have more inertia. For example, sound travels about three times faster in helium than it does in air. The squeaky voice produced when talking through helium from a balloon occurs because the sound travels faster from the speaker's vocal chords than it would through normal air. The pitch is not increased, but the different resonance produced results in a different timbre to the voice. (Warning: Breathing helium can be dangerous and it is NOT recommended.)

Amplitude and Loudness

Sound intensity can be thought of as how much energy passes through a given area in a given amount of time. Since sound spreads out as it travels, the intensity of the sound decreases as it travels and is proportional to the inverse square of the distance. This means that for every doubling of distance from the source, the intensity of sound is reduced to one-quarter.

Humans can detect very low levels of sound. This threshold is defined as 0 dB. A sound of 0 dB will move our eardrum as little as one-billionth of a centimeter, but we can still hear it.

Frequency and Pitch

The unit of frequency is the Hertz (Hz), which is equal to one cycle per second. The higher the frequency of a wave, the smaller is its wavelength. The velocity of a wave is equal to its frequency multiplied by its wavelength.

Fun Fact

We can use echolocation to estimate the distance of large objects such as the wall of a canyon. Yell and time how long it takes to hear the echo. Since the sound makes a round trip journey, take one half the time and multiply it by the speed of sound. For example, if it takes 2 seconds to hear the echo from the wall, the approximate distance of the canyon wall is 1 s × 343 m/s = 343 m from you.

SCIENCE Online

For additional content background on this topic, go to the Glencoe Science Web site at science.glencoe.com.

Crandall/The Image Works

Music

What is music?

The sounds produced by different frequencies are referred to as *pitch*. People with well-trained ears can detect frequency differences of as little as 3 Hz.

Resonance plays an important role in the production of music. Resonance occurs when an object absorbs energy from something vibrating at a certain frequency, and then begins to vibrate at that frequency. Many objects can absorb energy from sound waves vibrating at a number of frequencies. These frequencies are the object's natural frequencies of vibration.

When musical instruments are made to vibrate, they produce sound waves corresponding to their natural frequencies. The sound you hear is the combination of the natural frequencies. This combination is different for each type of instrument and gives an instrument its distinctive sound.

The Ear

The ear amplifies sound vibrations. Resonance in the ear canal can amplify sounds with frequencies between about 2,000 Hz and 5,500 Hz by up to ten times. In the middle ear, some frequencies can be amplified by 20 to 30 times by the lever system formed by bones of the middle ear, and by the difference in area between the ear drum and the oval window. As a result, some sounds can be amplified by several hundred times.

Fun Fact

Middle C on a piano has a frequency of 261.6 Hz and a wavelength of 131 cm.

Sound

Chapter Vocabulary

What do you think?

Science Journal The photo shows a guitar string vibrating. The vibration of the string produces the sound.

Sound

H ave you ever experienced complete silence? Unless you have stood in a room like this one, you probably have not. This room is lined with materials that absorb sound waves and eliminate sound reflections. The sounds that you hear are created by vibrations. How do vibrations make sounds with different pitches? What makes a sound loud or soft? In this chapter, you will learn the answers to these questions. You will also learn how musical instruments create sound and how the ear enables you to hear sound.

What do you think?

Science Journal Look at the picture below with a classmate. Discuss what might be happening. Here's a hint: *Sound is caused by vibrations.* Write your answer or best guess in your Science Journal.

602

Theme Connection

Stability and Change Sound waves are produced by periodic changes in the motion, or vibration, of an object. Changes in sound waves bring about changes in sounds.

EXPLORE ACTIVITY

When you speak or sing, you push air from your lungs past your vocal cords, which are two flaps of tissue inside your throat. When you tighten your vocal cords, you can make the sound have a higher pitch. Do this activity to explore how you change the shape of your throat to vary the pitch of sound.

Observe throat vibrations

1. Hold your fingers against the front of your throat and say *Aaaah.* Notice the vibration against your fingers.

2. Now vary the pitch of this sound from low to high and back again. How do the vibrations in your throat change? Record your observations.

3. Change the sound to an *Ooooh.* What do you notice as you listen? Record your observations.

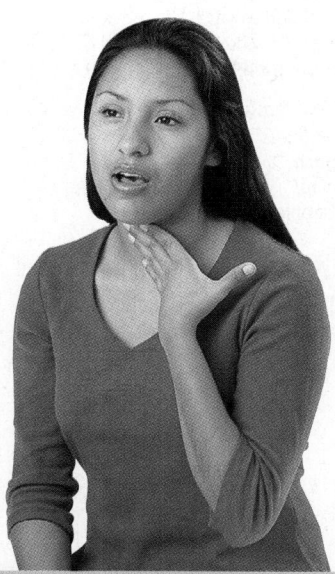

Observe

In your Science Journal, describe how the shape of your throat changed the pitch.

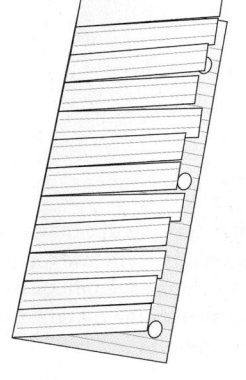

FOLDABLES
Reading & Study Skills

Before You Read

Making a Question Study Fold Asking yourself questions helps you stay focused so you will better understand sound when you are reading the chapter.

1. Place a sheet of notebook paper in front of you so the short side is at the top and the holes are on the right side. Fold the paper in half from the left side to the right side.

2. Through the top thickness of paper, cut along every third line from the outside edge to the fold, forming tabs.

3. Before you read the chapter, write a question you have about sound on the front of each tab. As you read the chapter, answer your questions and add more information.

603

EXPLORE ACTIVITY

Purpose Use the Explore Activity to demonstrate how the throat changes as the voice changes in pitch. `L2` `ELL`

`IS` **Auditory-Musical**

Teaching Strategies

- After they observe the tone (pitch) difference in a single sound, suggest students try holding their hands to their throats while speaking. Pitch varies with the emphasis given to different words. The last word of a question, for example, is usually at a higher pitch.

- If you have students who speak languages other than English, have them determine how the pitches vary when the same sentence is said in a different language. Some languages use different rules for pitch to indicate a question, statement, or exclamation. Others use changing pitch to alter the meanings of words.

✓Assessment

Process Ask students to sing or speak for about 10 seconds while other students sketch a graph of how pitch varies, using dashes at different heights above a line. *If students ask a question, the pitch would start on a mid-tone and end on a higher pitch.* Use **PASC,** p. 111.

FOLDABLES
Reading & Study Skills

Before You Read

Dinah Zike Study Fold

Purpose In this activity, students start thinking about sound before they read the chapter by asking questions to guide their reading. Students record the answers to their questions in a Foldable, which then becomes a study guide.

📁 For additional help, see Foldables Worksheet, p. 13 in **Chapter Resources Booklet,** or go to the Glencoe Science Web site at **science.glencoe.com.** See After You Read in the Study Guide at the end of this chapter.

1 Motivate

Bellringer Transparency

Display the Section Focus Transparency for Section 1. Use the accompanying Transparency Activity Master. L2

ELL

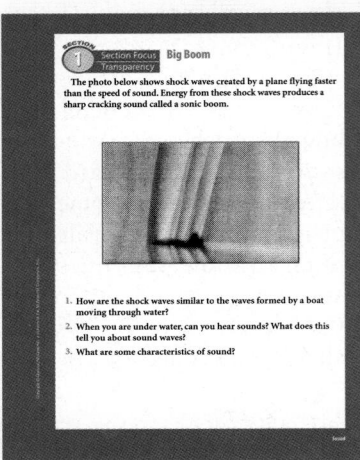

Section Focus Transparency — Big Boom

The photo below shows shock waves created by a plane flying faster than the speed of sound. Energy from these shock waves produces a sharp cracking sound called a sonic boom.

1. How are the shock waves similar to the waves formed by a boat moving through water?
2. When you are under water, can you hear sounds? What does this tell you about sound waves?
3. What are some characteristics of sound?

Tie to Prior Knowledge

Ask students what happens when a rock is tossed into a body of water such as a pond or lake. Waves of energy move outward along the water's surface in all directions from the point where the object strikes the water. Explain that sound is a form of energy that also travels in waves. Sound waves, however, are compressional waves, while the waves in the water are transverse waves.

Resource Manager

Chapter Resources Booklet

Transparency Activity, p. 40
Guided Reading for Content Mastery, p. 17, 18

What **You'll Learn**

- **Identify** the characteristics of sound waves.
- **Explain** how sound travels.
- **Describe** the Doppler effect.

Vocabulary
loudness
pitch
echo
Doppler effect

Why **It's Important**
Sound gives important information about the world around you.

Sound and Vibration

Think of all the sounds you've heard since you awoke this morning. Did you hear your alarm clock blaring, car horns honking, or locker doors slamming? Every sound has something in common with every other sound. Each is produced by something that vibrates.

Sound Waves

How does an object that is vibrating produce sound? When you speak, the vocal cords in your throat vibrate. These vibrations cause other people to hear your voice. The vibrations produce sound waves that travel to their ears. The other person's ears interpret these sound waves.

A wave carries energy from one place to another without transferring matter. An object that is vibrating in air, such as your vocal cords, produces a sound wave. The vibrating object causes air molecules to move back and forth. As these air molecules collide with those nearby, they cause other air molecules to move back and forth. In this way, energy is transferred from one place to another. A sound wave is a compressional wave, like the wave moving through the coiled spring toy in **Figure 1.** In a compressional wave, particles in the material move back and forth along the direction the wave is moving. In a sound wave, air molecules move back and forth along the direction the sound wave is moving.

Figure 1
When the coils of a coiled spring toy are squeezed together, a compressional wave moves along the spring. The coils move back and forth as the compressional wave moves past them.

Section ✓*Assessment* Planner

PORTFOLIO
Assessment, p. 606
Extension, p. 612
PERFORMANCE ASSESSMENT
Try at Home MiniLAB, p. 606
Problem-Solving Activity, p. 610

Skill Builder Activities, p. 613
See page 630 for more options.
CONTENT ASSESSMENT
Section, p. 613
Challenge, p. 613
Chapter, pp. 630–631

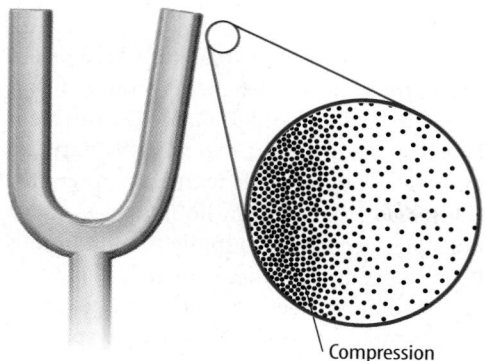

A When the tuning fork vibrates outward, it forces the air molecules next to it together, creating a region of compression.

Compression

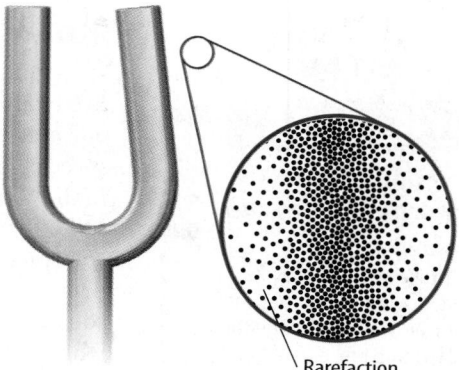

B When the tuning fork moves back, the air molecules next to it spread apart, creating a region of rarefaction.

Rarefaction

Making Sound Waves When an object vibrates, it exerts a force on the surrounding air. For example, as the end of the tuning fork moves outward into the air, it pushes the air molecules together, as shown in **Figure 2A.** As a result, a region where the air molecules are closer together, or more dense, is created. This region of higher density is called a compression. When the end of the tuning fork moves back, it creates a region of lower density called a rarefaction, as shown in **Figure 2B.** As the tuning fork continues to vibrate, a series of compressions and rarefactions is formed. The compressions and rarefactions move away from the tuning fork as molecules in these regions collide with other nearby molecules.

Like other waves, a sound wave can be described by its wavelength and frequency. The wavelength of a sound wave is shown in **Figure 3.** The frequency of a sound wave is the number of compressions or rarefactions that pass by a given point in one second. An object that vibrates faster forms a sound wave with a higher frequency.

Figure 2
A tuning fork makes a sound wave as the ends of the fork vibrate in the air. *Can a sound wave travel in a vacuum?*

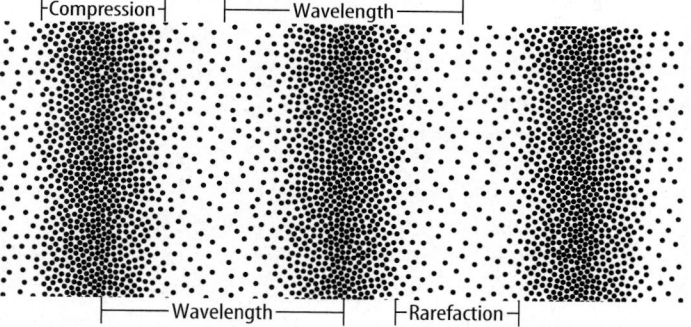

Compression — Wavelength — Wavelength — Rarefaction

Figure 3
Wavelength is the distance from one compression to another or one rarefaction to another.

Sound and Vibration

Discussion

Explain to students that people sometimes experience sound by feeling the vibrations. Ask students to suggest examples of situations in which people might be able to feel the vibrations caused by sound. Possible answers: when a loud stereo vibrates the floor of a room or thunder shakes windows. L2

 **Logical-Mathematical**

Sound Waves

Caption Answer

Figure 2 no

IDENTIFYING Misconceptions

Students may think that sound travels in space. While loud explosions make space battles simulated in movies more exciting, it is not realistic. Remind students that particles of matter are spaced very widely in space. The matter particles are too spread out to vibrate against one another and transmit sound.

☑ Active Reading

Jigsaw In this collaborative learning technique, individuals become experts on a portion of a text and share their expertise with a small group, called their home group. Everyone shares responsibility for learning the assigned reading. Assign each person in each home group an expert number (1 through 5, for example) and a section of text to read and master. Have students gather into the expert groups that correspond to the numbers they were assigned. Have them read, discuss, and master chapter concepts and determine how best to teach them to their home groups and share the content they learned in their expert groups. Have students use the Jigsaw strategy with the concepts about sound introduced in this section.

The Speed of Sound

TRY AT HOME

Mini LAB

Purpose to observe that sound can travel through materials other than air L2

IS Auditory-Musical

Materials ring of keys, tub or wide bowl filled with water, towel, metal spoon, about 2 m of cotton string

Teaching Strategy Ask students about other times they have heard sounds underwater.

Analysis

1. Both transmitted sounds. The keys sounded as they had before; the spoon had a deep, bell-like tone.
2. In water, the keys sound much as they do in air. Through string, the spoon has a louder, deeper, more complex tone than it does in air.

Assessment

Process Ask students to make an illustration of each part of the experiment, with labels showing how the sound of the metal striking something was transmitted to their ears. Use **PASC,** p. 127. P

TRY AT HOME

Mini LAB

Comparing and Contrasting Sounds

Procedure

1. Shake a set of **keys** and listen to the sound they make in air. Then submerge the keys and one ear in **water.** (A **tub** or a wide, deep **bowl** will work.) Again, shake the keys and listen to the sound. Use a **towel** to dry the keys.
2. Tie a **metal spoon** in the middle of a length of **cotton string.** Strike the spoon on something to hear it ring. Now press the ends of the string against your ears and repeat the experiment. What do you hear?

Analysis

1. Did you hear sounds transmitted through water and through string? Describe the sounds.
2. Compare and contrast the sounds in water and in air.

The Speed of Sound

Sound waves can travel through other materials besides air. Even though sound waves travel in the same way through different materials as they do in air, they might travel at different speeds. As a sound wave travels through a material, the particles in the material it is moving through collide with each other. In a solid, molecules are closer together than in liquids or gases, so collisions between molecules occur more rapidly than in liquids or gases. As a result, the speed of sound is usually fastest in solids, where molecules are closest together, and slowest in gases, where molecules are farthest apart. **Table 1** shows the speed of sound through different materials.

The Speed of Sound and Temperature The temperature of the material that sound waves are traveling through also affects the speed of sound. As a substance heats up, its molecules move faster, so they collide more frequently. The more frequent the collisions are, the faster the speed of sound is in the material. For example, the speed of sound in air at 0°C is 331 m/s; at 20°C, it is 343 m/s.

Amplitude and Loudness

What's the difference between loud sounds and quiet sounds? When you play a song at high volume and low volume, you hear the same instruments and voices, but something is different. The difference is that loud sound waves generally carry more energy than soft sound waves do.

Loudness is the human perception of how much energy a sound wave carries. Not all sound waves with the same energy are as loud. Sounds with frequencies between 3,000 Hz and 4,000 Hz sound louder than other sound waves that have the same energy.

Table 1 Speed of Sound Through Different Materials	
Material	**Speed (m/s)**
Air	343
Water	1,483
Steel	5,940
Glass	5,640

LAB DEMONSTRATION

Purpose to observe the transfer of energy in sound waves

Materials cardboard tube, balloon, rubber bands, candle, matches or lighter, scissors

Procedure Cut pieces from the balloon and stretch them over the two open ends of the cardboard tube. Secure them with the rubber bands, making a drum. Poke a small hole in one end of the drum. Hold this end about 10 cm from a lighted candle, and tap the other end.

Expected Outcome The vibrations made at one end travel through the tube, forcing air through the hole at the other end. This blows out the candle.

Assessment

Does the strength of the tap on the drum affect the distance from which a candle could be blown out? Explain. Yes; the stronger the tap, the greater the energy in the sound wave. With more energy, the wave can travel farther.

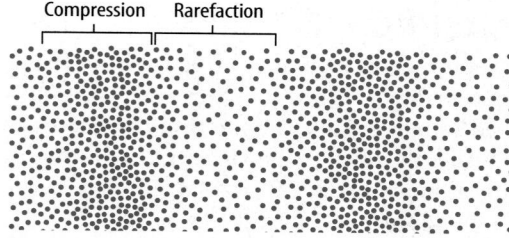

A This sound wave has a lower amplitude.

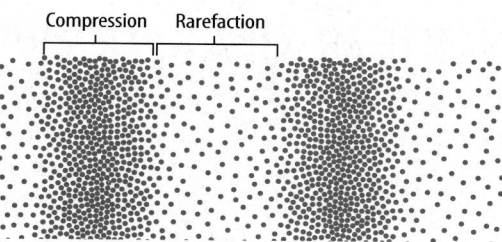

B This sound wave has a higher amplitude. Particles in the material are more compressed in the compressions and more spread out in the rarefactions.

Amplitude and Energy The amount of energy a wave carries depends on its amplitude. For a compressional wave such as a sound wave, the amplitude is related to how spread out the molecules or particles are in the compressions and rarefactions, as **Figure 4** shows. The higher the amplitude of the wave is, the more compressed the particles in the compression are and the more spread out they are in the rarefactions. More energy had to be transferred by the vibrating object that created the wave to force the particles closer together or spread them farther apart. Sound waves with greater amplitude carry more energy and sound louder. Sound waves with smaller amplitude carry less energy and sound quieter.

> **✓ Reading Check** *What determines the loudness of different sounds?*

The Decibel Scale Perhaps an adult has said to you, "Turn down your music, it's too loud! You're going to lose your hearing!" Although the perception of loudness varies from person to person, the energy carried by sound waves can be described by a scale called the decibel (dB) scale. **Figure 5** shows the decibel scale. An increase of 10 dB means that the energy carried by the sound has increased ten times, but an increase of 20 dB means that the sound carries 100 times more energy.

Hearing damage begins to occur at sound levels of about 85 dB. The amount of damage depends on the frequencies of the sound and the length of time a person is exposed to the sound. Some music concerts produce sound levels as high as 120 dB. The energy carried by these sound waves is about 30 billion times greater than the energy carried by sound waves that are made by whispering.

Figure 4
The amplitude of a sound wave depends on how spread out the particles are in the compressions and rarefactions of the wave.

Figure 5
The loudness of sound is measured on the decibel scale.

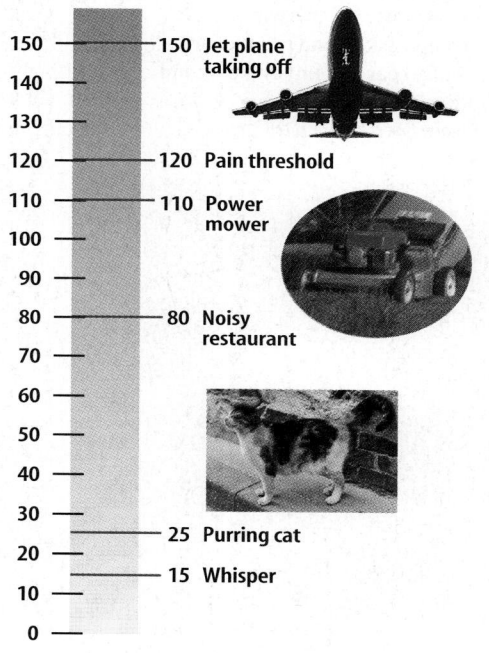

150	150 Jet plane taking off
140	
130	
120	120 Pain threshold
110	110 Power mower
100	
90	
80	80 Noisy restaurant
70	
60	
50	
40	
30	
20	25 Purring cat
10	15 Whisper
0	

Teacher FYI

The loudness of sound decreases as it travels away from a source because the waves lose energy as particles of the medium collide with each other and because they radiate out from the source. Sound intensity decreases at $1/r^2$, where r is the distance from the source. For example, the intensity of a sound 100 m from its source is about one-fourth the intensity of the same sound 50 m from its source.

✓ Reading Check

Answer the energy of the sound waves

Activity

Have students bring in various whistles. Go outside and have them blow the whistles separately and rank them from loudest to softest. Afterward, have students examine the whistles to find out what produced the vibration and look for features that caused one whistle to be louder than another. L2 ELL
IS Auditory-Musical

Visual Learning

Figure 5 Point out the pain threshold, at about 120 dB. **What types of sounds exceed this threshold?** Possible answers: loud music at a concert or a jet taking off
L2 **IS** Logical-Mathematical

Resource Manager

Chapter Resources Booklet
 Note-taking Worksheets, pp. 29–30
 MiniLAB, p. 3
Home amd Community Involvement, p. 29

Science Journal

Decibels Ask students to find out what the word *decibel* means and how it was coined. Have them write their responses in their Science Journals. A decibel is one-tenth of a bel, named in honor of Alexander Graham Bell. L2 **IS** Linguistic

Frequency and Pitch

The **pitch** of a sound is how high or low it sounds. For example, a piccolo produces a high-pitched sound or tone, and a tuba makes a low-pitched sound. Pitch corresponds to the frequency of the sound. The higher the pitch is, the higher the frequency is. A sound wave with a frequency of 440 Hz, for example, has a higher pitch than a sound wave with a frequency of 220 Hz.

The human ear can detect sound waves with frequencies between about 20 Hz and 20,000 Hz. However, some animals can detect even higher and lower frequencies. For example, dogs can hear frequencies up to almost 50,000 Hz. Dolphins and bats can hear frequencies as high as 150,000 Hz, and whales can hear frequencies higher than those heard by humans.

Recall that frequency and wavelength are related. If two sound waves are traveling at the same speed, the wave with the shorter wavelength has a higher frequency. If the wavelength is shorter, then more compressions and rarefactions will go past a given point every second than for a wave with a longer wavelength, as shown in **Figure 6.** Sound waves with a higher pitch have shorter wavelengths than those with a lower pitch.

The Human Voice When you make a sound, you exhale past your vocal cords, causing them to vibrate. The length and thickness of your vocal cords help determine the pitch of your voice. Shorter, thinner vocal cords vibrate at higher frequencies than longer or thicker ones. This explains why children, whose vocal cords are still growing, have higher voices than adults. Muscles in the throat can stretch the vocal cords tighter, letting people vary their pitch within a limited range.

Figure 6
The upper sound wave has a shorter wavelength than the lower wave. If these two sound waves are traveling at the same speed, the upper sound wave has a higher frequency than the lower one. For this wave, more compressions and rarefactions will go past a point every second than for the lower wave. *Which wave has a higher pitch?*

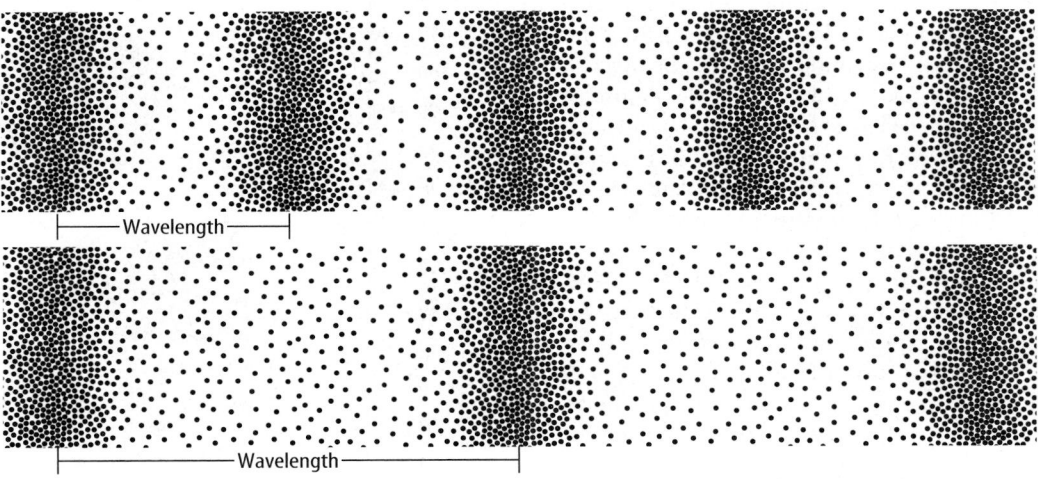

Wavelength

Wavelength

608   CHAPTER 21 Sound

Cultural Diversity

Measuring Bells More than 2,000 years ago, the Chinese used tuned bells as the basis of their entire system of measurement. They divided the scale into twelve pitches, and had official sets of twelve bells. A stringed tuner about 2.1 m long called a chün was used to standardize the pitches of bells throughout China. The length of a chün would be varied until the pitch of the chün matched the pitch of a standard bell. The chün could then be used to determine the pitch of a bell in a distant city. Pitch pipes later replaced the bells.

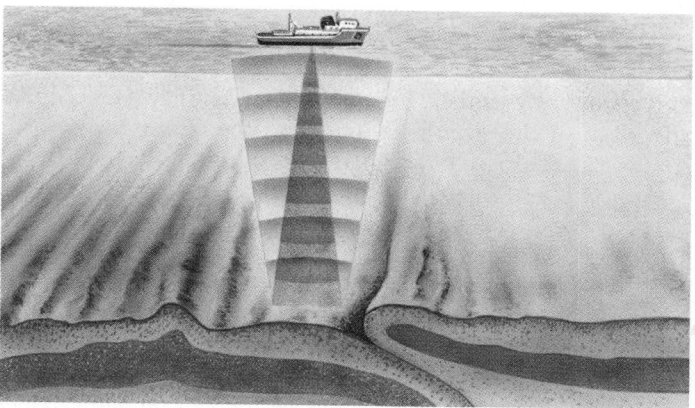

Echoes

Sound reflects off of hard surfaces, just like a water wave bounces off the side of a bath tub. A reflected sound wave is called an **echo.** If the distance between you and a reflecting surface is great enough, you might hear the echo of your voice. This is because it might take a few seconds for the sound to travel to the reflecting surface and back to your ears.

Sonar systems use sound waves to map objects underwater, as shown in **Figure 7.** The amount of time it takes an echo to return depends on how far away the reflecting surface is. By measuring the length of time between emitting a pulse of sound and hearing its echo off the ocean floor, the distance to the ocean floor can be measured. Using this method, sonar can map the ocean floor and other undersea features. Sonar also can be used to detect submarines, schools of fish, and other objects.

Echolocation Some animals use a method called echolocation to navigate and hunt. Bats, for example, emit high-pitched squeaks and listen for the echoes. The type of echo it hears helps the bat determine exactly where an insect is, as shown in **Figure 8.** Dolphins also use a form of echolocation. Their high-pitched clicks bounce off of objects in the ocean, allowing them to navigate in the same way.

People with visual impairments also have been able to use echolocation. Using their ears, they can interpret echoes to estimate the size and shape of a room, for example.

Research Visit the Glencoe Science Web site at **science.glencoe.com** for more information on how sonar is used to detect objects underwater. Communicate to your class what you learn.

Figure 8
Bats use echolocation to hunt. *Why is this technique good for hunting at night?*

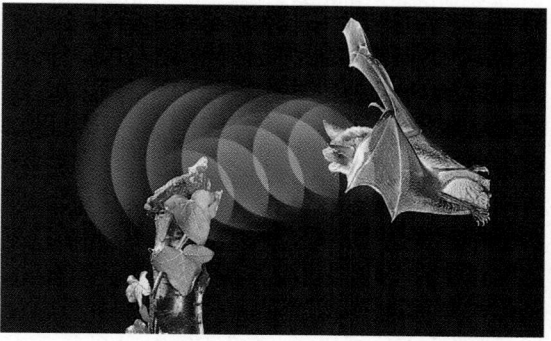

The Doppler Effect

Astronomy
INTEGRATION

When stars or galaxies are moving away from us, their light is shifted to lower frequencies, toward the red end of the spectrum. Astronomers call this a red shift. When stars or galaxies are moving toward us, their light is shifted to higher frequencies, toward the blue end of the spectrum. This is called a blue shift. Evidence from the Doppler shifts of galaxies suggests that almost all of them are moving away from Earth.

Astronomy
INTEGRATION

The frequency of light waves is also changed by the Doppler shift. If a light source is moving away from an observer, the frequencies of the emitted light waves decrease. Research how the Doppler shift is used by astronomers to determine how other objects in the universe are moving relative to Earth.

The Doppler Effect

Perhaps you've heard an ambulance siren as the ambulance speeds toward you, then goes past. You might have noticed that the pitch of the siren gets higher as the ambulance moves toward you. Then as the ambulance moves away, the pitch of the siren gets lower. The change in frequency that occurs when a source of sound is moving relative to a listener is called the **Doppler effect. Figure 9** shows why the Doppler effect occurs.

The Doppler effect occurs whether the sound source or the listener is moving. If you drive past a factory as its whistle blows, the whistle will sound higher pitched as you approach. As you move closer you encounter each sound wave a little earlier than you would if you were sitting still, so the whistle has a higher pitch. When you move away from the whistle, each sound wave takes a little longer to reach you. You hear fewer wavelengths per second, which makes the sound lower in pitch.

Radar guns that are used to measure the speed of cars and baseball pitches also use the Doppler effect. Instead of a sound wave, the radar gun sends out a radio wave. When the radio wave is reflected, its frequency changes depending on the speed of the object and whether it is moving toward the gun or away from it. The radar gun uses the change in frequency of the reflected wave to determine the object's speed.

Problem-Solving Activity

How does Doppler radar work?

Doppler radar is used by the National Weather Service to detect areas of precipitation and to measure the speed at which a storm moves. Because the wind moves the rain, Doppler radar can "see" into a strong storm and expose the winds. Tornadoes that might be forming in the storm then can be identified.

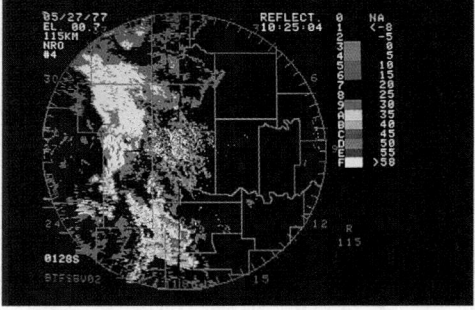

Identify the Problem

An antenna sends out pulses of radio waves as it rotates. The waves bounce off raindrops and return to the antenna at a different frequency, depending on whether the rain is moving toward the antenna or away from it. The change in frequency is due to the Doppler shift.

Solving the Problem

1. If the frequency of the reflected radio waves increases, how is the rain moving relative to the radar station?
2. In a tornado, winds are rotating. How would the radio waves reflected by rotating winds be Doppler-shifted?

Problem-Solving Activity

National Math Standards

Correlation to Mathematics Objectives
6, 8, 9, 10

Answers
1. The rain is moving toward the radar station.
2. The frequency would shift alternately up and down.

Science Journal

Doppler Effect Filmmakers need to put realistic sounds in animated films. Have students write descriptions in their Science Journals of ways to simulate the sounds of cars whizzing by characters standing by the side of the road in an animated film. Possible response: Make sounds that increase in pitch as the cars approach and decrease in pitch as the cars move away. [L2] [IS] **Logical-Mathematical**

Figure 9

Y ou've probably heard the siren of an ambulance as it races through the streets. The sound of the siren seems to be higher in pitch as the ambulance approaches and lower in pitch as it moves away. This is the Doppler effect, which occurs when a listener and a source of sound waves are moving relative to each other.

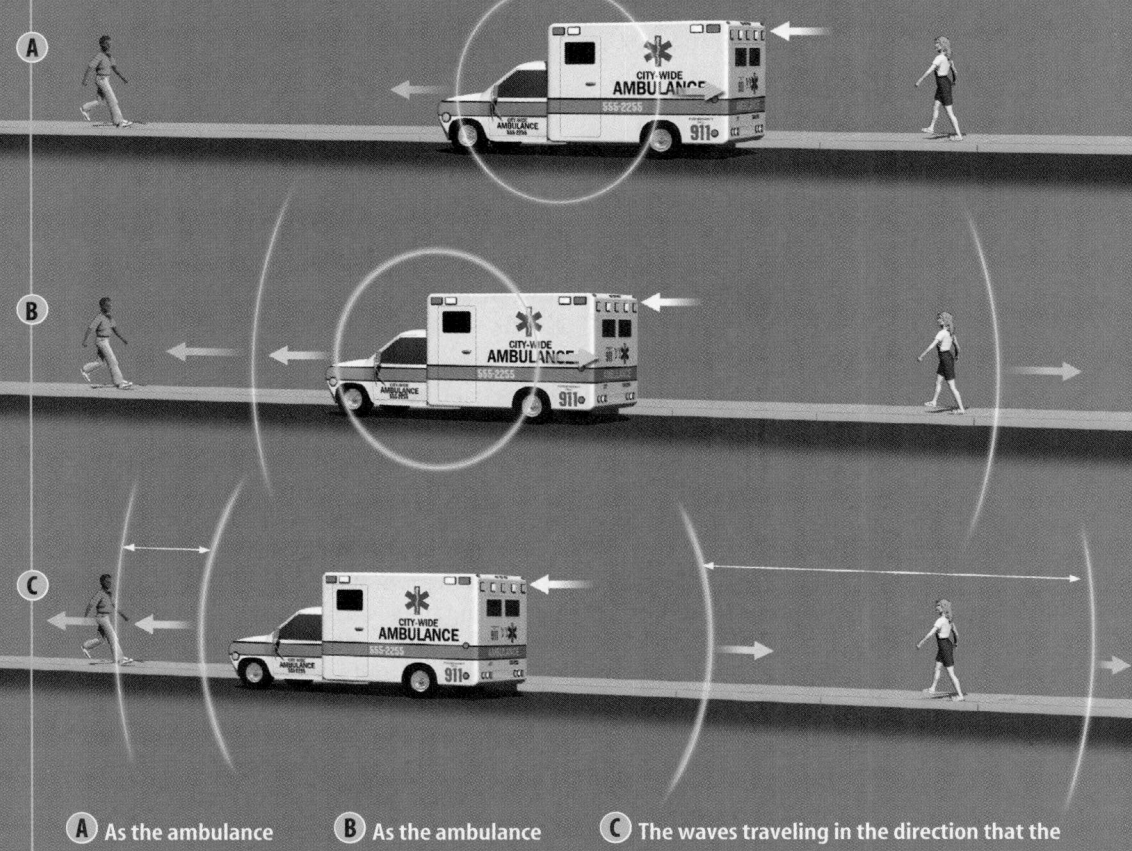

A As the ambulance speeds down the street, its siren emits sound waves. Suppose the siren emits the compression part of a sound wave as it goes past the girl.

B As the ambulance continues moving, it emits another compression. Meanwhile, the first compression spreads out from the point from which it was emitted.

C The waves traveling in the direction that the ambulance is moving have compressions closer together. As a result, the wavelength is shorter and the boy hears a higher frequency sound as the ambulance moves toward him. The waves traveling in the opposite direction have compressions that are farther apart. The wavelength is longer and the girl hears a lower frequency sound as the ambulance moves away from her.

Resource Manager

Chapter Resources Booklet
Enrichment, p. 27
Reinforcement, p. 25
Mathematics Skill Activities, p. 9

Visualizing the Doppler Effect

Have students examine the pictures and read the captions. Then ask the following questions.

- **If the source of sound begins to move faster, what will happen to the frequency?** The frequency will be shifted even higher in front of the source, and even lower behind the source.

- **What would happen if the source moved as fast as the sound wave it creates?** The waves would bunch up in front of the source. This would intensify the sound, creating a sonic boom like that created by a supersonic airplane.

Activity

Have students work in pairs to demonstrate the Doppler effect in water waves. Have one student in each pair use a finger to make waves in a shallow glass baking dish. Once the waves are moving steadily, have the student move his or her finger toward one side of the dish, while maintaining a steady movement up and down to generate waves. Have the other student observe what happens to the waves. Tell students to switch roles so each will have an opportunity to observe the waves. L2 LS **Kinesthetic**

Extension

Have students research how the Doppler effect is used in medicine. Specifically, they can investigate how doctors use Doppler shifts to analyze blood flow through arteries. L3 LS **Linguistic**

Diffraction of Sound Waves

Discussion

Hearing sound from around a corner is so common you don't think about it. But what would happen if light, which is also a wave, diffracted around the corner of a doorway? You would be able to see what was going on in a room without being in the direct line of sight. The people in the room would also be able to see you. L3

LS Logical-Mathematical

Extension

Point out to students that like light waves, sound waves also refract, or change direction, when they pass from one medium to another. Have students research and report on the ways in which sound waves are refracted as they pass through different mediums. When sound waves move to a medium in which they travel more quickly, they bend toward the boundary between the two regions. When sound waves move to a region in which they travel more slowly, they are refracted away from the boundary. Sound can be refracted at boundaries between warm and cold air. L3 **LS Linguistic** P

Using Sound Waves

Use Science Words

Word Meaning Have students find the meaning of the prefix *ultra-* and relate this meaning to the meaning of ultrasound. *Ultra-* means "beyond what is ordinary," or "super." Ultrasound is sound that is at high frequencies that are beyond ordinary frequencies. L2 **LS Linguistic**

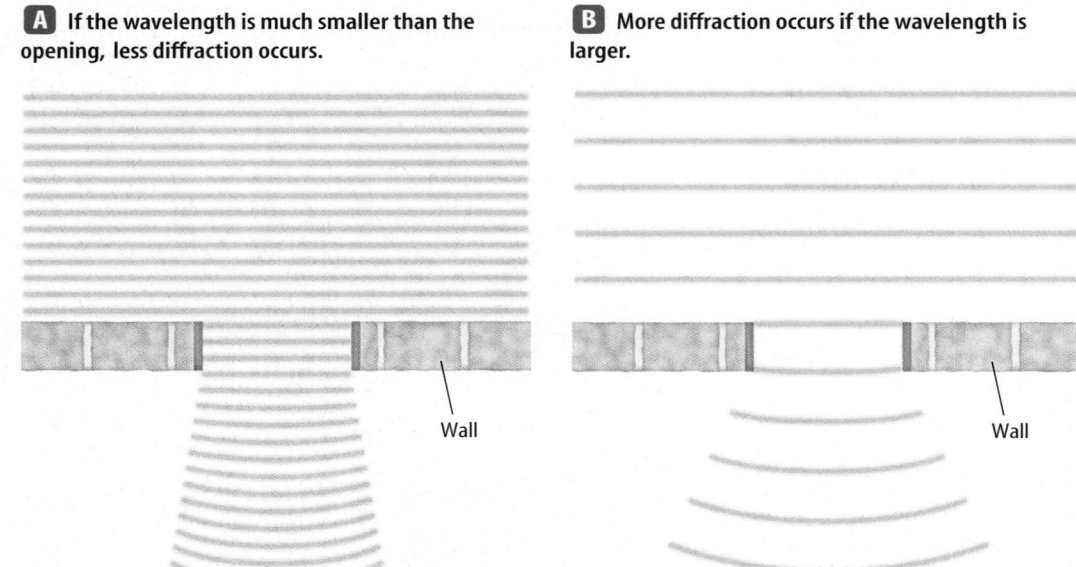

A If the wavelength is much smaller than the opening, less diffraction occurs.

B More diffraction occurs if the wavelength is larger.

Wall

Wall

Figure 10
The spreading of a wave by diffraction depends on the wavelength and the size of the opening.

Diffraction of Sound Waves

Like other waves, sound waves diffract. This means they can bend around obstacles or spread out after passing through narrow openings. The amount of diffraction depends on the wavelength of the sound wave compared to the size of the obstacle or opening. If the wavelength is much smaller than the obstacle, almost no diffraction occurs. As the wavelength becomes closer to the size of the obstacle, the amount of diffraction increases.

You can observe diffraction of sound waves by visiting the school band room during practice. If you stand in the doorway, you will hear the band normally. However, if you stand to one side outside the door or around a corner, you will hear the lower-pitched instruments better. **Figure 10** shows why this happens. The sound waves that are produced by the lower-pitched instruments have lower frequencies and longer wavelengths. These wavelengths are closer to the size of the door opening than the higher-pitched sound waves are. As a result, the longer wavelengths diffract more, and you can hear them even when you're not standing in the doorway.

The diffraction of lower frequencies in the human voice allows you to hear someone talking even when the person is around the corner. This is different from an echo. Echoes occur when sound waves bounce off a reflecting surface. Diffraction occurs when a wave spreads out after passing through an opening, or when a wave bends around an obstacle.

Teacher FYI

Some stereo speakers or stereo systems account for differences in the diffraction of sound waves of different frequencies by usually having only one woofer for the low notes, but several tweeters, pointed in different directions, for the high notes.

Resource Manager

Chapter Resources Booklet
  Activity Worksheet, pp. 5–6
  Lab Activity, pp. 9–10
Reading and Writing Skill Activities, p. 7

Using Sound Waves

Sound waves can be used to treat certain medical problems. A process called ultrasound uses high-frequency sound waves as an alternative to some surgeries. For example, some people develop small, hard deposits in their kidneys or gallbladders. A doctor can focus ultrasound waves at the kidney or gallbladder. The ultrasound waves cause the deposits to vibrate rapidly until they break apart into small pieces. Then, the body can get rid of them.

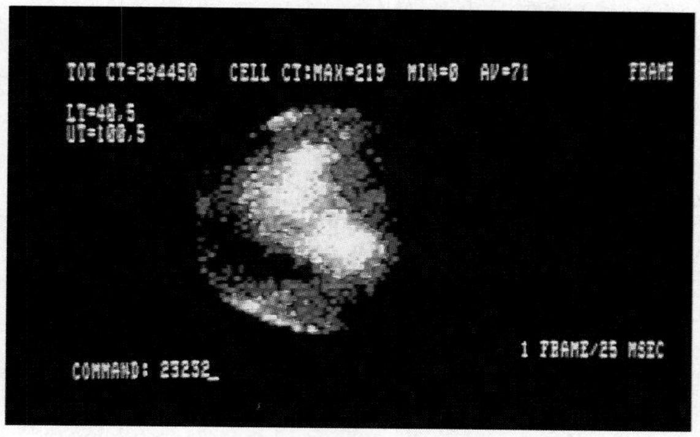

Ultrasound can be used to make images of the inside of the body, just as sonar is used to map the seafloor. One common use of ultrasound is to examine a developing fetus. Also, ultrasound along with the Doppler effect can be used to examine the functioning of the heart. An ultrasound image of the heart is shown in **Figure 11.** This technique can help determine if the heart valves and heart muscle are functioning properly, and how blood is flowing through the heart.

The Doppler effect can be also used with sonar to determine the speed and direction of a detected object, such as a submarine or a school of fish.

Figure 11
Ultrasound is used to make this image of the heart. *How else is ultrasound used in medicine?*

Caption Answer
Figure 11 Possible answer: to examine a developing fetus

③ Assess

Reteach

Draw a sample sound wave on the board. Ask volunteers to draw waves corresponding to the following: Same pitch, louder: Wave has same frequency, greater amplitude. Same pitch, softer: Wave has same frequency, smaller amplitude. Higher pitch, same volume: Wave has shorter wavelength, same amplitude. Lower pitch, same volume: Wave has longer wavelength, same amplitude. L2
Visual-Spatial

Challenge

As a train comes toward you, the Doppler effect causes the sound you hear to be higher in pitch. Suppose instead of standing still you were rushing toward the oncoming train. **Would you expect the Doppler shift in the frequency of the train's sound to increase, stay the same, or disappear? Explain.** Increase; because you and the train are coming together more quickly than if you were standing still, the Doppler shift is even greater. L3
Logical-Mathematical

✓ Assessment

Process Ask students to demonstrate that sound is a vibration. Possible answers: Students may show that an object such as a rubber band makes no sound when it is not vibrating, but does make sound when it vibrates. Use **PASC,** p. 143.

Section ① Assessment

1. When the amplitude of a sound wave is increased, what happens to the loudness of the sound? The pitch?

2. How does the wavelength of a sound affect the way it moves around corners?

3. How does the temperature of a material affect the speed of sound passing through it? Explain why in terms of the particles within the material.

4. What causes the Doppler effect, and in what ways is it used?

5. **Think Critically** Chemists sometimes use ultrasound machines to clean glassware. How could sound be used to remove particles from glass?

Skill Builder Activities

6. **Using an Electronic Spreadsheet** Think about ten different sounds you've heard today. Make a computer spreadsheet that lists each sound, the vibrating object that made the sound, and how the object was vibrating. **For more help, refer to the Technology Skill Handbook.**

7. **Solving One-Step Equations** If sound travels through water at 1,483 m/s, how far will it travel in 5 s? The speed of sound through air at 20° C is about 343 m/s. How far will sound travel through air in the same amount of time? **For more help, refer to the Math Skill Handbook.**

SECTION 1 What is sound? **613**

Answers to Section Assessment

1. Loudness increases and pitch stays the same.
2. Sounds whose waves are about the same length as the opening are diffracted the most around the corner. Low-pitched sound waves are about the same wavelength as doorways, so they travel more easily around the corners of the doorway.
3. As temperature increases, the speed of sound increases. At higher temperatures the particles move faster and collide more often.
4. The Doppler effect occurs when the source of a wave is moving relative to an observer. It is used in many ways, including by police to measure the speed of cars and trucks on the highway.
5. by vibrating the particles off the glass
6. Check students' work.
7. water: 5 s × 1,483 m/s = 7,415 m; air: 5 s × 343 m/s = 1,709 m.

Activity

Purpose Students observe that sound waves can be reflected and focused. `L2` `ELL` `COOP LEARN` `IS` **Auditory-Musical**

Process Skills observing and inferring, measuring, drawing conclusions

Time Required 30 minutes

Teaching Strategies

- Announce the lab at least the day before, so enough ticking watches can be located. Check that students can hear the watches ticking.
- Smooth surfaces reflect sound; don't try the experiment on carpeting.
- Students should work quietly so that the ticking of the watch can be heard.

Troubleshooting The two tubes need to be in the same plane. You should be able to hold a piece of poster board up so that the sides of both tubes rest along the poster board. If the tubes are not in the same plane, students will not hear the watch.

Answers to Questions

1. The angles are approximately equal. Sound is reflected so that the angle of incidence equals the angle of reflection.
2. It would be difficult, if not impossible, to hear the ticking of the watch reflected off a soft surface.

Activity

Observe and Measure Reflection of Sound

Like all waves, sound waves can be reflected. When sound waves strike a surface, in what direction does the reflected sound wave travel? In this activity, you'll focus sound waves using cardboard tubes to help answer this question.

What You'll Investigate
How do the angles made by incoming and reflected sound waves compare?

Materials
cardboard tubes, 20- to 30-cm-long (2)
watch with a second hand that ticks audibly
protractor

Goals
- **Observe** reflection of sound waves.
- **Measure** the angles incoming and reflected sound waves make with a surface.

Safety Precautions

Procedure

1. Work in groups of three. Each person should listen to the watch—first without a tube and then through a tube. The person who hears the watch most easily is the listener.
2. One person should hold one tube at an angle with one end above a table. Hold the watch at the other end of the tube.
3. The listener should hold the second tube at an angle, with one end near his or her ear and the other end near the end of the first tube that is just above the table. The tubes should be in the same vertical plane.

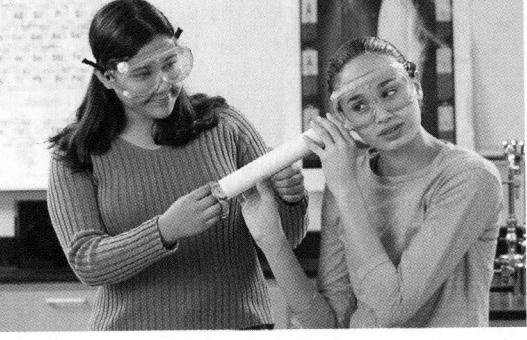

4. Move the first tube until the watch sounds loudest. The listener might need to cover the other ear to block out background noises.
5. With the tubes held steady, the third person should measure the angle that each tube makes with the table.

Conclude and Apply

1. Are the two angles approximately equal or quite different? How does the angle of reflection compare with the angle made by the incoming wave?
2. Predict how your results would change if the waves reflected from a soft surface instead of a hard surface.

Communicating Your Data

Make a scientific illustration to show how the experiment was done. Describe your results using the illustration. **For more help, refer to the** Science Skill Handbook.

✔ Assessment

Process Compare and contrast the reflection of sound with the reflection of light in a mirror. Have two students stand to either side of a mirror. **Can they see themselves in the mirror?** no **Can they see each other?** Yes; both are examples of reflection: the angle between observer and reflecting surface must be the same as the angle between the initial sound or image and that surface. Use **PASC,** p. 89.

Communicating Your Data

Students can view each other's illustrations. As they review the illustrations, they should ask themselves, "If I hadn't done the experiment myself, would I be able to do it based on the illustration?"

Music

What is music?

What do you like to listen to—rock 'n' roll, country, blues, jazz, rap, or classical? Music and noise are groups of sounds. Why do humans hear some sounds as music and other sounds as noise?

The answer involves sound patterns. Music is a group of sounds that have been deliberately produced to make a regular pattern. Look at **Figure 12.** The sounds that make up music usually have a regular pattern of pitches, or notes. Some natural sounds, such as the patter of rain on a roof, the sound of ocean waves splashing, or the songs of birds can sound musical. On the other hand, noise is usually a group of sounds with no regular pattern. Sounds you hear as noise are irregular and disorganized, such as the sounds of traffic on a city street or the roar of jet aircraft.

However, the difference between music and noise can vary from person to person. What one person considers to be music, another person might consider noise.

Natural Frequencies Music is created by vibrations. When you sing, your vocal cords vibrate. When you beat a drum, the drumhead vibrates. When you play a guitar, the strings vibrate.

If you tap on a bell with a hard object, the bell produces a sound. When you tap on a bell that is larger or smaller or has a different shape you hear a different sound. The bells sound different because each bell vibrates at different frequencies. A bell vibrates at frequencies that depend on its shape and the material it is made from. Every object will vibrate at certain frequencies called its **natural frequencies.**

As You Read

What You'll Learn
- **Explain** the difference between music and noise.
- **Describe** how different instruments produce music.
- **Explain** how you hear.

Vocabulary
natural frequency
resonance
fundamental frequency

overtone
reverberation
eardrum

Why It's Important
By better understanding how music is produced, you can improve the quality of the sounds you make.

Figure 12
Music and noise have different types of sound patterns.

A Noise has no specific or regular sound wave pattern.

B Music is organized sound. Music has regular sound wave patterns and structures.

SECTION 2 Music **615**

Section ✓*Assessment* Planner

PORTFOLIO
Assessment, p. 623
PERFORMANCE ASSESSMENT
MiniLAB, p. 618
Skill Builder Activities, p. 623
See page 630 for more options.

CONTENT ASSESSMENT
Section, p. 623
Challenge, p. 623
Chapter, pp. 630–631

SECTION

Music

1 Motivate

Bellringer Transparency
Display the Section Focus Transparency for Section 1. Use the accompanying Transparency Activity Master. L2 ELL

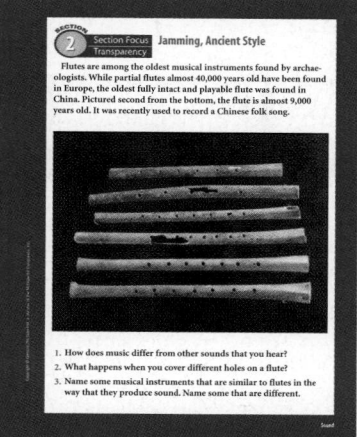

Tie to Prior Knowledge
Ask students to name any musical instruments they may play. Tell them that this section explains the science of music.

Resource Manager

Chapter Resources Booklet
Transparency Activity, p. 41
Guided Reading for Content Mastery, pp. 19, 20

What is music?

Discussion

Discuss with students how music differs from noise. **What natural sounds seem and do not seem musical?** Possible answer: Sounds are musical when they make distinguishable pitches and have a regular pattern. L2

 **Auditory-Musical**

✔ Reading Check

Answer size, shape, and material of the vibrating object

Environmental Science
INTEGRATION

Have students find out about the effect of resonance on the first Tacoma Narrows Bridge, also known as Galloping Gertie. On November 7, 1940, wind started the suspension bridge moving and it collapsed. Some scientists believe the cause of the collapse was resonance, and that the wind caused the bridge to vibrate at its natural frequency. L2  **Linguistic**

Quick Demo

Find a container with a plastic lid to use as a drum. Tap the lid while it is off the container. Then fit the lid over the empty container and tap it again. The second sound is louder, because the can and air inside also vibrate. This is an example of resonance. L2
Auditory-Musical

Environmental Science
INTEGRATION

Resonance is important in fields outside of music. Earthquake-proof buildings, for example, are designed to resonate at frequencies that are different from those encountered in earthquakes.

Musical Instruments and Natural Frequencies Many objects vibrate at one or more natural frequencies when they are struck or disturbed. Like a bell, the natural frequency of any object depends on the size and shape of the object and the material it is made from. Musical instruments use the natural frequencies of strings, drumheads, or columns of air contained in pipes to produce various musical notes.

✔ Reading Check

What determines the natural frequencies?

Resonance You may have seen the comedy routine in which a loud soprano sings high enough to shatter glass. Sometimes sound waves cause an object to vibrate. When a tuning fork is struck, it vibrates at its natural frequency and produces a sound wave with the same frequency. Suppose you have two tuning forks with the same natural frequency. You strike one tuning fork, and the sound waves it produces strike the other tuning fork. These sound waves would cause the tuning fork that wasn't struck to absorb energy and vibrate. This is an example of resonance. **Resonance** occurs when an object is made to vibrate at its natural frequencies by absorbing energy from a sound wave or another object vibrating at these frequencies.

Musical instruments use resonance to amplify their sounds. Look at **Figure 13.** The vibrating tuning fork has caused the table to vibrate at the same frequency, or resonate. The combined vibrations of the table and the tuning fork increase the loudness of the sound waves produced.

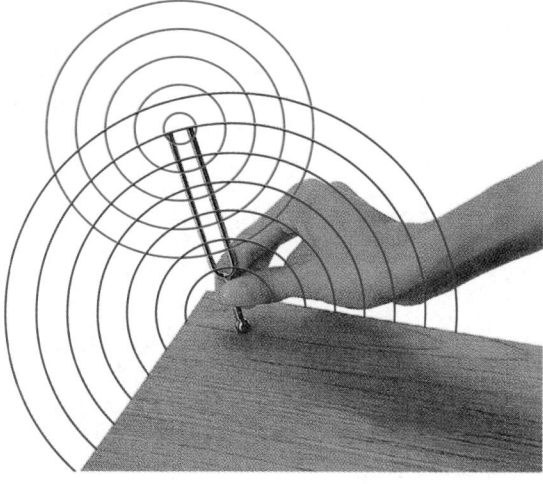

Figure 13
When a vibrating tuning fork is placed against a table, resonance might cause the table to vibrate.

Inclusion Strategies

Hearing Impaired Help these students sense the vibrations of sound waves. Have a student hold a balloon while you make a sound. The sound waves will vibrate the balloon, and the vibration will be passed to the student's fingers. Have students use balloons to help them sense sounds during all the sound-producing activities performed in this section.

Visual Learning

Figure 13 Discuss with students the effect touching the vibrating tuning fork to the table has on the sound made by the tuning fork. Vibrations from the tuning fork cause the table to resonate, which makes the sound louder. L2 **Visual-Spatial**

Overtones

Before a concert, all orchestra musicians tune their instruments by playing the same note. Even though the note has the same pitch, it sounds different for each instrument. It also sounds different from a tuning fork that vibrates at the same frequency as the note.

A tuning fork produces a single frequency, called a pure tone. However, the notes produced by musical instruments are not pure tones. Most objects have more than one natural frequency at which they can vibrate. As a result, they produce sound waves of more than one frequency.

If you play a single note on a guitar, the pitch that you hear is the lowest frequency produced by the vibrating string. The lowest frequency produced by a vibrating object is the **fundamental frequency.** The vibrating string also produces higher frequencies. These higher frequencies are **overtones.** Overtones have frequencies that are multiples of the fundamental frequency, as in **Figure 14.** The number and intensity of the overtones produced by each instrument are different and give instruments their distinctive sound quality.

Musical Scales

A musical instrument is a device that produces musical sounds. These sounds are usually part of a musical scale that is a sequence of notes with certain frequencies. For example, **Figure 15** shows the sequence of notes that belong to the musical scale of C. Notice that the frequency produced by the instrument doubles after eight successive notes of the scale are played. Other musical scales consist of a different sequence of frequencies.

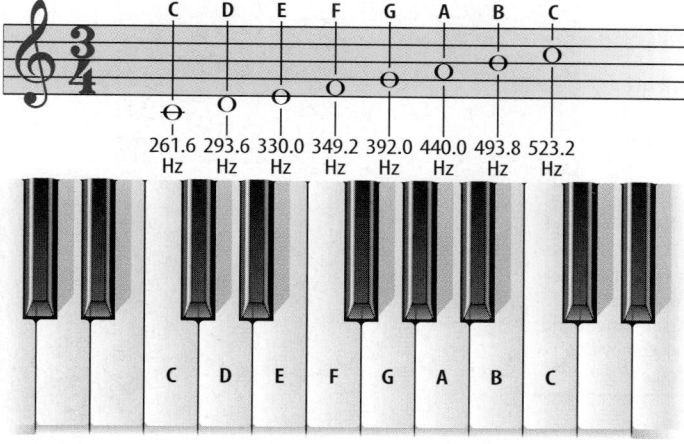

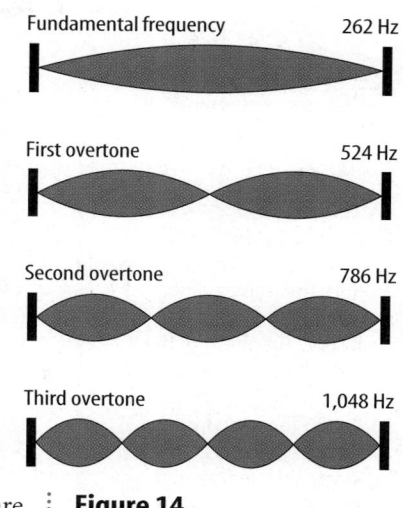

Fundamental frequency 262 Hz

First overtone 524 Hz

Second overtone 786 Hz

Third overtone 1,048 Hz

Figure 14
A string vibrates at a fundamental frequency, as well as at overtones. The overtones are multiples of that frequency.

How many musical instruments can you name? To find out more about musical instruments, see the **Musical Instruments Field Guide** at the back of the book.

Figure 15
A piano produces a sequence of notes that are a part of a musical scale. *How are the frequencies of the two C notes on this scale related?*

Cultural Diversity

Have interested students research instruments from other countries that are not common in the United States. Have students share their findings in oral reports. Possible instruments include Australia's didgeridoo, Scotland's bagpipes, various instruments that resemble xylophones in Korea, and traditional guitar in parts of Africa and Asia. L3
IS Linguistic

Overtones

Activity

Collect cardboard tubes of different lengths, and turn on music. Have students cover one ear and listen to the sound through different tubes. Ask students what they observe when listening through different tubes. Because the tubes are of different sizes, they resonate at different frequencies, amplifying sounds at those frequencies only. The sound you hear changes depending on the length of the tube you listen through. L2 **IS Auditory-Musical**

Quick Demo

Strike a tuning fork, and then play the same note on a musical instrument. Ask students to compare the sounds. The sounds are different because the number and intensity of the overtones produced by each are different. L2
IS Auditory-Musical

Visual Learning

Figure 14 A musician can use a knowledge of overtones to control the sound his or her instrument produces. For example, suppose a guitarist presses down at the center of an already vibrating string. The fundamental and the second overtone will both be suppressed, but the first and third overtones will continue to sound. L3
IS Visual-Spatial

Musical Instruments

Caption Answer

Figure 15 The frequency of the higher C is double that of the lower C.

Mini LAB

Purpose Students observe how changes in a vibrating string change the sound it produces.

L2 IS **Auditory- Musical**

Materials rubber band, box

Teaching Strategy Have students use rubber bands of varying lengths and thicknesses.

Analysis

1. Stretching the rubber band increased the tension and increased the pitch. This matches the predictions for stringed instruments given in the text.

2. The sound became louder when the box was included. This agrees with the text's prediction about using a resonator with a string.

✓ Assessment

Process Have each student make a small model harp using several rubber bands and a resonator box. Bands may be identical, with different amounts of tension, or they may vary in size. Students should be able to explain and demonstrate how the different conditions for each band affect the sound produced, and the role of the resonator. Use **Performance Assessment in the Science Classroom,** p. 123.

Mini LAB

Modeling a Stringed Instrument

Procedure

1. Stretch a **rubber band** between your fingers.
2. Pluck the rubber band. Listen to the sound and observe the shape of the vibrating band. Record what you hear and see.
3. Stretch the band farther and repeat step 2.
4. Shorten the length of the band that can vibrate by holding your finger on one point. Repeat step 2.
5. Stretch the rubber band over an open box, such as a **shoe box.** Repeat step 2.

Analysis

1. How did the sound change when you stretched the rubber band? Was this what you expected? Explain.
2. How did the sound change when you stretched the band over the box? Did you expect this? Explain.

Stringed Instruments

Stringed instruments, like the cello shown in **Figure 16,** produce music by making strings vibrate. Different methods are used to make the strings vibrate—guitar strings are plucked, piano strings are struck, and a bow is slid across cello strings. The strings often are made of wire. The pitch of the note depends on the length, diameter, and tension of the string—if the string is shorter, narrower, or tighter, the pitch increases. For example, pressing down on a vibrating guitar string shortens its length and produces a note with a higher pitch. Similarly, the thinner guitar strings produce a higher pitch than the thicker strings.

Amplifying Vibrations The sound produced by a vibrating string is soft. To amplify the sound, stringed instruments usually have a hollow chamber, or box, called a resonator, which contains air. The resonator absorbs energy from the vibrating string and vibrates at its natural frequencies. For example, the body of a guitar is a resonator that amplifies the sound that is produced by the vibrating strings. The vibrating strings cause the guitar's body and the air inside it to resonate. As a result, the vibrating guitar strings sound louder, just as the tuning fork that was placed against the table sounded louder.

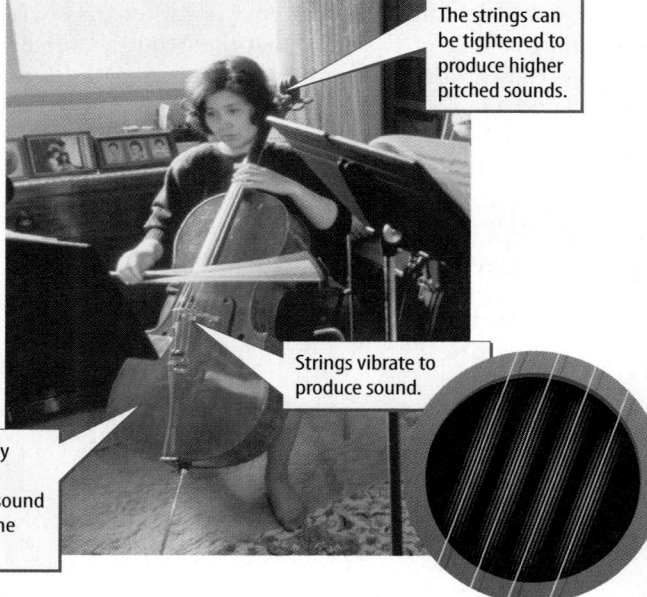

The strings can be tightened to produce higher pitched sounds.

Strings vibrate to produce sound.

The cello's body resonates and amplifies the sound produced by the strings.

Figure 16
A cello is a stringed instrument. When strings vibrate, the natural frequencies of the instrument's body amplify the sound.

Visual Learning

Figure 16 Point out the pegs at the end of the strings, which are used to adjust tension. Individual strings also have different thicknesses, which gives them different natural frequencies and pitches. Note the bridge, supporting the strings. Ask what function the bridge performs. The bridge transfers the vibrations of the strings to the soundboard in the body of the instrument. L2

IS **Visual-Spatial**

Resource Manager

Chapter Resources Booklet
MiniLAB, p. 4
Cultural Diversity, p. 61

Percussion

Percussion instruments, such as the drum shown in **Figure 17A,** are struck to make a sound. Striking the top surface of the drum causes it to vibrate. The vibrating drumhead is attached to a chamber that resonates and amplifies the sound.

Drums and Pitch Some drums have a fixed pitch, but some can be tuned to play different notes. For example, if the drumhead on a kettledrum is tightened, the natural frequency of the drumhead is increased. As a result, the pitches of the sounds that are produced by the kettledrum get higher. A steel drum, shown in **Figure 17B,** plays different notes in the scale when different areas in the drum are struck. In a xylophone, wood or metal bars of different lengths are struck. The longer the bar is, the lower the note that it produces is.

Brass and Woodwinds

Just as the bars of a xylophone have different natural frequencies, so do the air columns in pipes of different lengths. Brass and woodwind instruments, such as those in **Figure 18,** are essentially pipes or tubes of different lengths that sometimes are twisted around to make them easier to hold and carry. To make music from these instruments, the air in the pipes is made to vibrate at various frequencies.

Different methods are used to make the air column vibrate. A musician playing a brass instrument, such as a trumpet, makes the air column vibrate by vibrating the lips and blowing into the mouthpiece. Woodwinds such as clarinets, saxophones, and oboes contain one or two reeds in the mouthpiece that vibrate the air column when the musician blows into the mouthpiece. Flutes also are woodwinds, but a flute player blows across a narrow opening to make the air column vibrate.

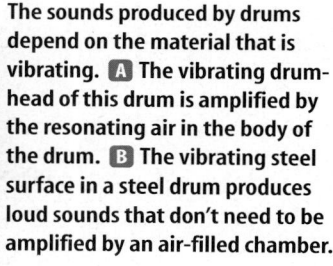
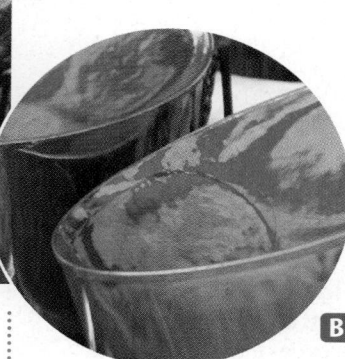

Figure 17
The sounds produced by drums depend on the material that is vibrating. **A** The vibrating drumhead of this drum is amplified by the resonating air in the body of the drum. **B** The vibrating steel surface in a steel drum produces loud sounds that don't need to be amplified by an air-filled chamber.

Figure 18
Brass and woodwind instruments produce sounds in a vibrating column of air. *What other instruments make sound this way?*

SECTION 2 Music **619**

Brass and Woodwinds, continued

Quick Demo

A slide whistle makes a smoothly varying tone rather than a series of notes. To make a slide whistle, you need a metal pipe and a dowel that just fits into the pipe. Attach the end of a party whistle as a mouthpiece. Blow over the top of the pipe or into the mouthpiece while sliding the dowel up and down from the bottom. Or, show students a toy slide whistle. Have students explain what happens as you move the slide. As you vary the length of the vibrating column of air, you vary the pitch. A shorter air column has a higher pitch. L2 IS **Visual-Spatial**

Activity

Have students who play wind or brass instruments demonstrate how the instruments work to the class. As part of their presentations, have students explain how they change the pitch of their instruments. L2 IS **Visual-Spatial**

Beats

Quick Demo

Bring to class a digital tuner, and ask students to bring their musical instruments. Ask pairs of students with the same type of instrument to use the digital tuner to help them tune the 440A on their instruments so that one instrument produces a pitch with a frequency of 440 Hz and the other produces a pitch with a frequency of 435 Hz. Have the students play their A's simultaneously, while the remaining students in the class count the beats produced. They should hear 5 beats per second. L2 IS **Auditory-Musical**

Figure 19
A flute changes pitch as holes are opened and closed.

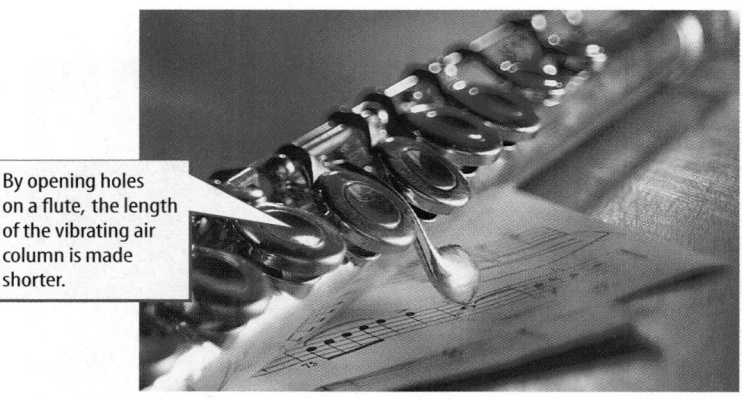

By opening holes on a flute, the length of the vibrating air column is made shorter.

Changing Pitch in Woodwinds To change the note that is being played in a woodwind instrument, a musician changes the length of the resonating column of air. By making the length of the vibrating air column shorter, the pitch of the sound produced is made higher. In a woodwind such as a flute, saxophone, or clarinet, this is done by closing and opening finger holes along the length of the instrument, as shown in **Figure 19.**

Changing Pitch in Brass In brass instruments, musicians vary the pitch in other ways. One is by blowing harder to make the air resonate at a higher natural frequency. Another way is by pressing valves that change the length of the tube.

Beats

When two notes are close in frequency, they interfere in a distinctive way. The two waves combine to form a wave that varies slowly in loudness. This slow variation creates beats. **Figure 20** shows the beats that are produced by the interference of two waves with frequencies of 9 Hz and 12 Hz. The frequency of the beat is the difference in the frequencies—in this case 3 Hz. Listening to two tones at the same time with a frequency difference of 3 Hz, you would hear the sound get louder and softer—a beat—three times each second.

Figure 20
Beats are formed when two frequencies that are nearly the same are played together. The sound wave in **A** has a frequency of 12 Hz and the sound wave in **B** has a frequency of 9 Hz. When these two sounds are played together, they interfere and form the wave in **C** that has a frequency of 3 Hz. You would hear 3 beats each second.

A

B

C

Curriculum Connection

History The earliest complete, playable instrument known is a flute from China, dating to about 9,000 years ago. This flute is made from a bird bone and has seven main holes. A tiny extra hole, drilled next to the final hole, appears to adjust a slight defect in the pitch, giving some idea of the practical musical knowledge of the flute's maker. Parts of bone flutes as much as 30,000 years old have been found in parts of Europe. **Why might people have used bones for flutes? What other items would also work?** Bird bones are hollow, and other bones can be hollowed. Hollow plants, such as reeds, can be used, but they would not survive as well in the archaeological record. L2 IS **Logical-Mathematical**

Beats Help Tune Instruments Beats are used to help tune instruments. For example, a piano tuner might hit a tuning fork and then the corresponding key on the piano. Beats are heard when the difference in pitch is small. The piano string is tuned properly when the beats disappear. You might have heard beats while listening to an orchestra tune before a performance. You also can hear beats produced by two engines vibrating at slightly different frequencies.

Reverberation

Sound is reflected by hard surfaces. In an empty gymnasium, the sound of your voice can be reflected back and forth several times by the floor, walls, and ceiling. Repeated echoes of sound are called **reverberation.** In a gym, reverberation makes the sound of your voice linger before it dies out. Some reverberation can make voices or music sound bright and lively. However, reverberation can produce a confusing mess of noise if too many sounds linger for too long. Too little reverberation makes the sound flat and lifeless. Concert halls and theaters, such as the one in **Figure 21,** are designed to produce the appropriate level of reverberation. Acoustical engineers use soft materials to reduce echoes. Special panels that are attached to the walls or suspended from the ceiling are designed to reflect sound toward the audience.

SCIENCE Online

Research Visit the Glencoe Science Web site at **science.glencoe.com** for more information about how concert halls are designed to produce the proper amount of reverberation. Communicate to your class what you learn.

Figure 21
The shape of a concert hall and the materials it contains are designed to control the reflection of sound waves.

SECTION 2 Music **621**

Reverberation

SCIENCE Online

Internet Addresses

_____
_____
_____
_____

Explore the Glencoe Science Web site at **science.glencoe.com** to find out more about topics in this section.

Use Science Words

Word Meaning Acoustical engineers design buildings and other structures to enhance or reduce sound. Have students find the two meanings of the word *acoustics.* the scientific study of sound; the total effect of sound in a place, especially an enclosed space. L2
LS Linguistic

Inclusion Strategies

Gifted Have students write reports describing what happens when two sound waves meet. When crests overlap, waves interfere constructively, and the amplitude of the wave increases. If the initial waves are identical, the amplitude of the wave doubles. If the crests in one meet the troughs in the other, the waves interfere destructively. If identical waves interfere exactly destructively, they cancel each other. L3

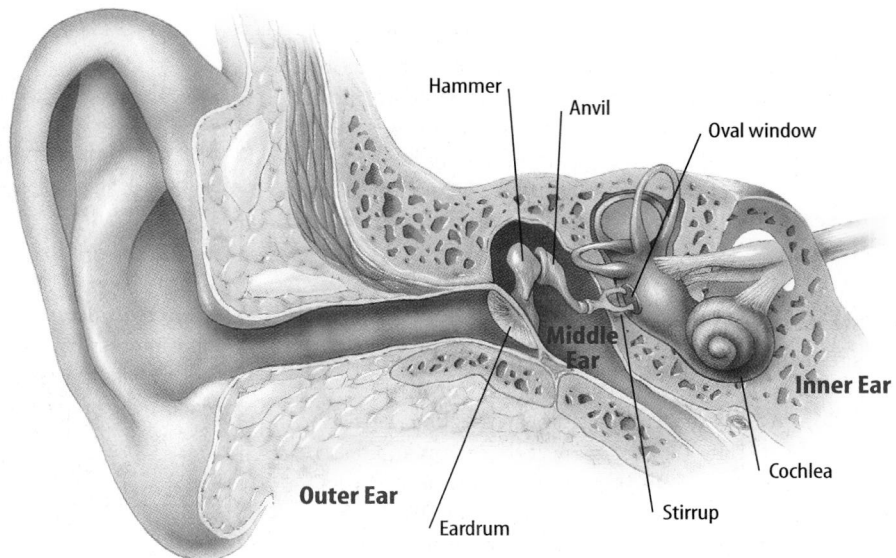

Hammer · Anvil · Oval window · Middle Ear · Inner Ear · Cochlea · Outer Ear · Eardrum · Stirrup

Figure 22
The human ear has three different parts—the outer ear, the middle ear, and the inner ear.

Figure 23
Animals, such as rabbits and owls, have ears that are adapted to their different needs.

The Ear

Sound is all around you. Sounds are as different as the loud buzz of an alarm clock and the quiet hum of a bee. You hear sounds with your ears. The ear is a complex organ that is able to detect a wide range of sounds. The human ear is illustrated in **Figure 22.** It has three parts—the outer ear, the middle ear, and the inner ear.

The Outer Ear—Sound Collector Your outer ear collects sound waves and directs them into the ear canal. Notice that your outer ear is shaped roughly like a funnel. This shape helps collect sound waves.

Animals that rely on hearing to locate predators or prey often have larger, more adjustable ears than humans, as shown in **Figure 23.** A barn owl, which relies on its excellent hearing for hunting at night, does not have outer ears made of flesh. Instead, the arrangement of its facial feathers helps direct sound to its ears. Some sea mammals, on the other hand, have only small holes for outer ears, even though their hearing is good.

The Middle Ear—Sound Amplifier When sound waves reach the middle ear, they vibrate the **eardrum,** which is a membrane that stretches across the ear canal like a drumhead. When the eardrum vibrates, it transmits vibrations to three small connected bones—the hammer, anvil, and stirrup. The bones amplify the vibrations, just as a lever can change a small movement at one end into a larger movement at the other.

622   CHAPTER 21 Sound

The Inner Ear—Sound Interpreter The stirrup vibrates a second membrane called the oval window. This marks the start of the inner ear, which is filled with fluid. Vibrations in the fluid are transmitted to hair-tipped cells lining the cochlea, as shown in **Figure 24.** Different sounds vibrate the cells in different ways. The cells generate signals containing information about the frequency, intensity, and duration of the sound. The nerve impulses travel along the auditory nerve and are transmitted to the part of the brain that is responsible for hearing.

 *Where are waves detected and interpreted in the ear?*

Hearing Loss

The ear can be damaged by disease, age, and exposure to loud sounds. For example, constant exposure to loud noise can damage hair cells in the cochlea. If damaged mammalian hair cells die, some loss of hearing results because mammals cannot make new hair cells. Also, some hair cells and nerve fibers in the inner ear degenerate and are lost as people age. It is estimated that about 30 percent of people over 65 have some hearing loss due to aging.

The higher frequencies are usually the first to be lost. The loss of the higher frequencies also distorts sound. The soft consonant sounds, such as those made by the letters *s, f, h, sh,* and *ch,* are hard to hear. People with high-frequency hearing loss have trouble distinguishing these sounds in ordinary conversation.

Figure 24
The inner ear contains tiny hair cells that convert vibrations into nerve impulses that travel to the brain.

✔ **Reading Check**

Answer Sound is detected by the eardrum and interpreted in the cochlea.

③ Assess

Reteach

Ask students to suppose they are stranded on a deserted island. Have them describe some ways they might go about making a drum, a stringed instrument, or a wind instrument. Possible answers: A stringed instrument might be made by stretching a plant fiber between two sticks. A drum might be made by stretching an animal skin over a hollowed out log. L2
IS Linguistic

Challenge

Western musical harmony is based on triad chords consisting of the notes *do, mi,* and *sol.* The overtones produced by a piano are called the overtone series and form the basis of western harmony. Have students find out how this works. The first six overtones produced by a note on the piano include *do, do* an octave higher, *sol* an octave and a fifth above *do, do* two octaves higher, and *mi* two octaves and a third above *do.* L2
IS Logical-Mathematical

✔ Assessment

Portfolio Have students write descriptions of how closing holes on a woodwind instrument changes the pitch made by the instrument. Closing holes increases the length of the column of air in the instrument, causing the pitch to go down. Use **PASC,** p. 159. P

Section ② Assessment

1. How are music and noise different?

2. Two bars on a xylophone are 10 cm and 14 cm long. Which bar will produce a lower pitch when struck? Explain.

3. Why would the sound of a guitar string sound louder when attached to the body of the guitar than when plucked alone?

4. What are the parts of the human ear, and how do they enable you to hear sound?

5. **Think Critically** As the size of stringed instruments increases from violin to viola, cello, and bass, the sound of the instruments becomes lower pitched. Explain.

Skill Builder Activities

6. **Making Models** Illustrate the fundamental and first overtone for a string. **For more help, refer to the** Science Skill Handbook.

7. **Communicating** Imagine that human hearing is much more sensitive than it currently is. Write a story describing a day in the life of your main character. Be sure to describe your setting in detail. For example, does your story take place in a crowded city or a scenic national park? How would life be different? Describe your story in your Science Journal. **For more help, refer to the** Science Skill Handbook.

Answers to Section Assessment

1. Musical sounds have been deliberately produced to make a regular pattern.
2. The 14-cm bar; the larger the vibrating object, usually the deeper the sound it produces.
3. The body of the guitar acts as a resonator, magnifying the sound.
4. The parts of the ear include the outer ear, the middle ear, and the inner ear.

The outer ear collects sound, the middle ear amplifies sound, and the inner ear interprets sound.
5. The larger instruments have longer strings and larger resonators, which produce lower pitches.
6. Drawings should be similar to **Figure 14**.

7. Possible scenarios: The modern world would be too loud; we would be aware of different parts of nature, such as the sound of an insect or small animal moving; music would change to accommodate our more sensitive hearing; we might be overwhelmed by the sounds of traffic.

Activity

BENCH TESTED

Recognize the Problem

Purpose

Students compare and contrast different instruments and observe how changes in the different instruments correspond to changes in the pitches produced. [L2] [ELL] [COOP LEARN] IS **Auditory-Musical**

Process Skills

observing, inferring, comparing and contrasting, measuring, recognizing cause and effect, controlling variables, formulating hypotheses, making and using tables, interpreting data

Time Required

one class period to make measurements, one class period to analyze and check results

Materials

Make sure students are prepared in advance to bring in instruments that they know how to play.

Safety Precautions

Warn students not to stand in the way of the musicians.

Form a Hypothesis

Possible Hypothesis

To play a higher note, the vibrating part of the instrument (string, bar, column of air) must be shortened. To play G, for example, the vibrating part must be shortened to two-thirds the length it has when the C below it is played.

Activity *Design Your Own Experiment*

Music

The pitch of a note that is played on an instrument sometimes depends on the length of the string, the air column, or some other vibrating part. Exactly how does sound correspond to the size or length of the vibrating part? Is this true for different instruments?

Recognize the Problem

What causes different instruments to produce different notes?

Form a Hypothesis

Based on your reading and observations, make a hypothesis about what changes in an instrument to produce different notes.

Goals
- **Design** an experiment to compare the changes that are needed in different instruments to produce a variety of different notes.
- **Observe** which changes are made when playing different notes.
- **Measure and record** these changes whenever possible.

Possible Materials

musical instruments
measuring tape
tuning forks

Safety Precautions

Properly clean the mouthpiece of any instrument before it is used by another student.

Test Your Hypothesis

Possible Procedure

Choose two notes, such as C and G. Measure the length of the vibrating part of each instrument when the two notes are played. Record your results in a table.

Instrument	What vibrates?	Length of vibrating part	Any other differences?

Test Your Hypothesis

Plan

1. You should do this activity as a class, using as many instruments as possible. You might want to go to the music room or invite friends and relatives who play an instrument to visit the class.

2. As a group, decide how you will measure changes in instruments. For wind instruments, can you measure the length of the vibrating air column? For stringed instruments, can you measure the length and thickness of the vibrating string?

3. Refer to the table of wavelengths and frequencies for notes in the scale. Note that no measurements are given—if you measure C to correspond to a string length of 30 cm, for example, the note G will correspond to two thirds of that length.

4. Decide which musical notes you will compare. Prepare a table to collect your data. List the notes you have selected.

Do

1. Make sure your teacher approves your plan before you start.

2. Carry out the experiment as planned.

3. While doing the experiment, record your observations and complete the data table.

Ratios of Wavelengths and Frequencies of Musical Notes		
Note	Wavelength	Frequency
C	1	1
D	8/9	9/8
E	4/5	5/4
F	3/4	4/3
G	2/3	3/2
A	3/5	5/3
B	8/15	15/8
C	1/2	2

Analyze Your Data

1. **Compare** the change in each instrument when the two notes are produced.

2. **Compare and contrast** the changes between instruments.

3. What were the controls in this experiment?

4. What were the variables in this experiment?

5. How did you eliminate bias?

Draw Conclusions

1. How does changing the length of the vibrating column of air in a wind instrument affect the note that is played?

2. **Describe** how you would modify an instrument to increase the pitch of a note that is played.

Communicating
Your Data

Demonstrate to another teacher or to family members how the change in the instrument produces a change in sound.

ACTIVITY   625

Assessment

Oral Ask students how they would analyze an instrument they'd never seen before. How could they tell what kind of instrument it was? How could they determine how it varied its pitch? Use **Performance Assessment in the Science Classroom**, p. 97.

Communicating
Your Data

Have students make illustrated tables of their data that include pictures of the different instruments. Tables should include descriptions of how the instrument changes when the pitch is changed.

Content Background

Explain that sound waves are longitudinal waves that originate when there is a disturbance in the air. Vibrating objects or sudden movement in the air can cause a disturbance. In the case of candy wrappers, the sudden repositioning of the plastic wrapper causes sudden movement in the air molecules near the plastic wrap. This small shock wave causes the air molecules to vibrate at the same frequency as the original movement. As a result, areas where molecules are bunched together (compression) or spread apart (rarefaction) are formed. These longitudinal waves are transmitted through the air as sound waves.

A sound wave traveling through air causes very small rapid changes in the air pressure. These changes in pressure, once detected by the ear, are funnelled into the ear canal. At the end of the canal, the energy of the wave is transferred to the eardrum. The eardrum vibrates at the same frequency as the original wave and transfers the energy to the middle ear. The middle ear, which is composed of the hammer, anvil, and stirrup, acts as a safety buffer before transferring the energy of the wave to the inner ear. Once in the inner ear, the energy is sorted and converted to nerve impulses, which are passed on to the brain.

The brain analyzes the sound, and, as a result, you hear the sound inside your head.

TIME SCIENCE AND Society

SCIENCE ISSUES THAT AFFECT YOU!

It's a Wrap!

snap! pop! crackle! snap! crackle! snap! pop!

No matter how quickly or slowly you open a candy wrapper, it always will make a noise

You're at the movies, and it's the most exciting part of the film. The audience is silent with their eyes riveted to the screen. At that moment, you decide to unwrap the candy you got at the concession stand—"CRACKLE!" The loud noise isn't from the movie. It's from the candy wrapper. Your friends shush you. So you try to open the wrapper more carefully—"POP!" Now you try opening it more slowly—"SNAP!" No matter how you open the candy wrapper—fast or slow—it makes a lot of annoying noise.

626

Resources for Teachers and Students

Sound: More Than What You Hear, Christopher F. Lampton, Enslow Publishers Inc., New Jersey, 1992.

Sound Fundamentals Funtastic Science Activities for Kids, Robert W. Wood, McGraw-Hill Companies, Inc, 1997.

The Handy Physics Answer, P. Erik Gundersen, Visible Ink Press, 1999.

Just about everyone has been in that situation at a movie or a concert. And just about everyone has wondered why you can't unwrap candy without making a racket—no matter how hard you try. But now, finally, thanks to the work of a few curious physicists, we know the answer.

To test the plastic problem, researchers took some crinkly wrappers and put them in a silent room. Then the researchers stretched out the wrappers and recorded the sound they made. Next, the crinkling sound was run through a computer. After analyzing the sound, the research team discovered something very interesting—the wrapper didn't make a nonstop, continuous sound. Instead, it made many little separate popping noises. Each of these sound bursts took only a thousandth of a second.

Pop Goes the Wrapper

The researchers found that the loudness of the pops had nothing to do with how fast the plastic was unwrapped. The pops randomly took place. The reason? Little creases in the plastic suddenly snapped into a new position as the wrapper was stretched.

So, if you unwrap candy more slowly, the time between pops will be longer, but the amount of noise made by the pops will be the same. And whether you open the wrapper fast or slow, you'll always hear pops. "And there's nothing you can do about it," said a member of the research team.

Is there another payoff to the candy wrapper research? One scientist said that by understanding what makes a plastic wrapper "snap" when it changes shape, the information can actually help doctors understand molecules in the human body. These molecules, like plastic, can change shape.

But, in the meantime, what are you supposed to do when you absolutely have to open candy in a silent theater? Be considerate of others in the audience. Open the candy as fast as you can, and just get it over with. You can even wait until a noisy part of the movie to hide the crinkle, or open the candy before the film begins.

The pop chart

SOUND LEVEL OVER TIME

The sound that a candy wrapper makes is emitted as a series of pulses or clicks. So, opening a wrapper slowly only increases the length of time in between clicks, but the amount of noise remains the same. (TALLER SPIKES SIGNIFY LOUDER CLICKS)

Clicks

LOUDNESS

0 seconds   0.5   1

Source: Eric Kramer, Simon's Rock College, 2000

CONNECTIONS Recall and Retell Have you ever opened a candy wrapper in a quiet place? Did it bother other people? If so, did you try to open it more slowly? What happened?

SCIENCE
Online
For more information, visit
science.glencoe.com

CONNECTIONS Have students work in small groups to make lists of different kinds of candies. Next, have students arrange their lists from the noisiest to open to the least noisy. Ask students to describe the outer wrappers of the noisiest and least noisy. Their descriptions should include the type of material used and how easy it is to open. Have students share their conclusions with the class. **LS Interpersonal**

SCIENCE
Online

Internet Addresses

_____

_____

_____

Explore the Glencoe Science Web site at **science.glencoe.com** to find out more about topics in this feature.

Discussion

Suggest students debate this question: **If a tree falls in the forest and no one is there to hear it, is sound formed?** The answer depends on how sound is defined. If sound is characterized as what the human ear perceives, then the answer is no. But if sound is defined as a wave of energy traveling through a medium, then the answer is yes. **LS Interpersonal**

Activity

Divide the class into small groups, and then distribute one piece of wrapped hard candy to each student. Have students take turns trying to unwrap the candy as quietly as possible. Ask students to record the methods used to open the candy and the effectiveness of each. If time permits, have the quietest students from each group compete for quietest in the class. **LS Auditory-Musical**

Investigate the Issue

Ask students to share stories of situations when they may have surprised others with a loud noise or were distracted by a loud noise from someone else. Possible answers should include: a quiet setting like a classroom, and a sudden loud noise such as dropping something, coughing, sneezing, or their stomach growling. Encourage discussion among students about why sudden sounds can be so distracting, using quiet study areas, such as the library, as a basis for the discussion.

Chapter **21** Study Guide

Reviewing Main Ideas

Preview

Students can answer the questions in their Science Journals. Discuss the answers as you go through the chapter. **IS Linguistic**

Review

Students can write their answers, then compare them with those of other students. **IS Interpersonal**

Reteach

Students can look at the illustrations and describe details that support the main ideas of the chapter. **IS Visual-Spatial**

Answers to Chapter Review

SECTION 1

2. through the tracks
5. it goes up

SECTION 2

4. Resonance causes the body of the violin and the air inside the violin to vibrate.

Reviewing Main Ideas

Section 1 What is sound?

1. Sound is a compressional wave that travels through matter, such as air. Sound is produced by something that vibrates.

2. The speed of sound is different in different materials. In general, sound travels faster in solids than in liquids, and faster in liquids than in gases. *Will the sound of a train travel faster through the air or through these tracks?*

3. The larger the amplitude of a sound wave, the more energy it carries. The loudness of a sound wave increases as its amplitude increases.

4. The pitch of a sound wave corresponds to its frequency. Sound waves can reflect, or bounce, from objects and diffract, or bend around objects.

5. The Doppler effect occurs when the source of sound and the listener are in motion relative to each other. Sound is shifted up or down in pitch. *What happens to the pitch of the train's horn as it approaches the person?*

Section 2 Music

1. Music is made of sounds that are used in a regular pattern. Noise is made of sounds that are irregular and disorganized.

2. Objects vibrate at their natural frequencies. These depend on the shape of the object and the material it's made of.

3. Resonance occurs when an object is made to vibrate by absorbing energy at one of its natural frequencies.

4. Musical instruments produce notes by vibrating at their natural frequencies. Resonance is used to amplify the sound. *How does resonance make this violin sound louder?*

5. Beats occur when two sounds of nearly the same frequency interfere. The beat frequency is the difference in frequency of the sounds.

6. The ear collects sound waves, amplifies the vibrations, and converts the vibrations to nerve impulses.

FOLDABLES Reading & Study Skills **After You Read**

Use the library to find answers to any questions remaining on your Question Study Foldable.

FOLDABLES Reading & Study Skills **After You Read**

After students have read the chapter and completed the Foldable described in Before You Read, have them do the activity on the student page.

Dinah Zike

Visualizing Main Ideas

Complete the following concept map on sound.

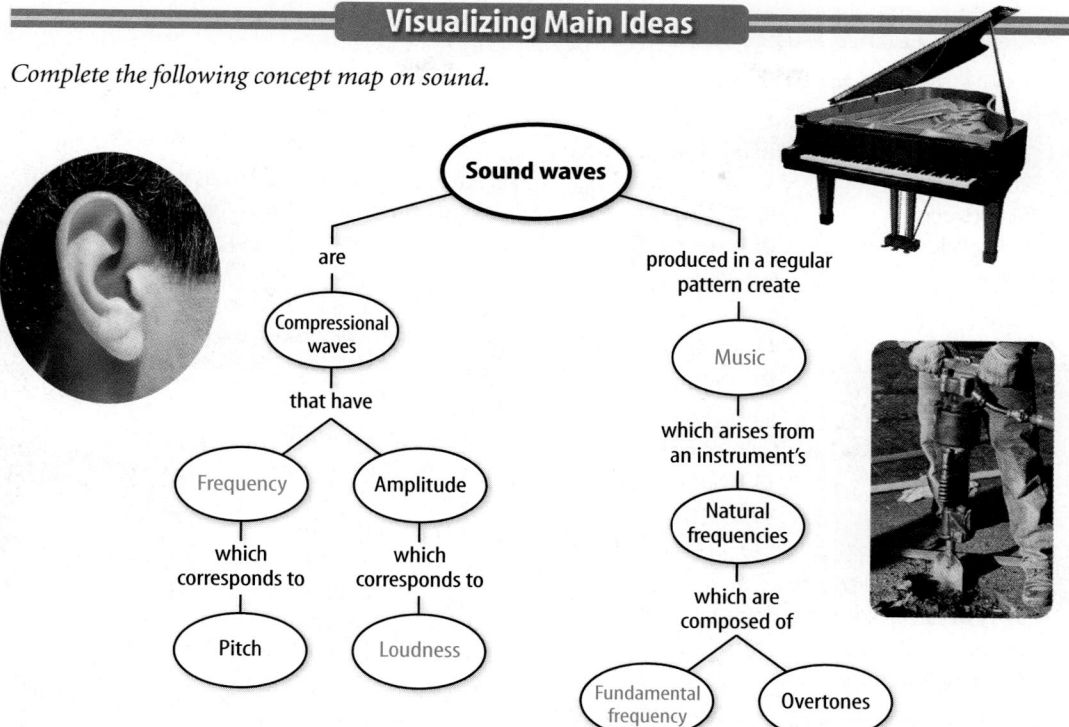

Sound waves

are → Compressional waves

that have → Frequency, Amplitude

Frequency — **which corresponds to** → Pitch

Amplitude — **which corresponds to** → Loudness

produced in a regular pattern create → Music

which arises from an instrument's → Natural frequencies

which are composed of → Fundamental frequency, Overtones

Vocabulary Review

Vocabulary Words

a. Doppler effect
b. eardrum
c. echo
d. fundamental frequency
e. loudness
f. natural frequency
g. overtone
h. pitch
i. resonance
j. reverberation

THE PRINCETON REVIEW **Study Tip**

Recopy your notes from class. As you do, explain each concept in more detail to make sure that you understand it completely.

Using Vocabulary

Distinguish between the terms in each of the following pairs.

1. overtones, fundamental frequency
2. pitch, sound wave
3. pitch, Doppler effect
4. loudness, resonance
5. fundamental, natural frequency
6. loudness, amplitude
7. natural frequency, overtone
8. reverberation, resonance

CHAPTER STUDY GUIDE 629

Visualizing Main Ideas

See student page.

Vocabulary Review

Using Vocabulary

1. The lowest frequency produced by a vibrating object is the fundamental frequency. The higher frequencies at which it vibrates are overtones.
2. Pitch corresponds to the frequency of a sound wave.
3. The pitch of a sound wave gets higher if the source of the sound and the listener are approaching each other and gets lower if they are moving farther apart. This phenomenon is called the Doppler effect.
4. Loudness corresponds to the energy, or amplitude, of a sound wave. Resonance refers to the tendency of an object to vibrate at its natural frequencies.
5. The fundamental frequency is the lowest natural frequency of an object.
6. The loudness of a sound is related to the amplitude of the sound wave.
7. Natural frequencies produced by vibrating objects include the fundamental frequency, which is the lowest natural frequency the object produces, and the overtones, which are multiples of the fundamental frequency.
8. Resonance occurs when an object is made to vibrate at its natural frequency by absorbing energy from a sound wave produced by another vibrating object. Reverberation occurs when sound is reflected many times to produce repeated echoes.

Checking Concepts

1. A
2. B
3. D
4. C
5. A
6. A
7. A
8. C
9. D
10. C

Thinking Critically

11. The pipes act as resonators, each pipe resonating at the pitch produced by the bar above it and amplifying it.
12. The shift in frequency is not large enough to be detected by your ear.
13. Sound vibration would not be amplified as it is in a normal ear. Ability to hear quiet sounds would be affected.
14. Possible frequencies would be 522 Hz and 526 Hz.
15. When you hold the triangle, you keep it from vibrating freely. It cannot vibrate at its natural frequencies, so little sound is produced.

Chapter 21 Assessment

Checking Concepts

Choose the word or phrase that best answers the question.

1. A tone that is lower in pitch is lower in what characteristic?
   A) frequency
   B) wavelength
   C) loudness
   D) resonance

2. If frequency increases, what decreases if speed stays the same?
   A) pitch
   B) wavelength
   C) loudness
   D) resonance

3. What part of the ear is damaged most easily by continued exposure to loud noise?
   A) eardrum
   B) stirrup
   C) oval window
   D) hair cells

4. What is an echo?
   A) diffracted sound
   B) resonating sound
   C) reflected sound
   D) Doppler-shifted sound

5. A trumpeter depresses keys to make the column of air resonating in the trumpet shorter. What happens to the note that is being played?
   A) The pitch is higher.
   B) The pitch is lower.
   C) It is quieter.
   D) It is louder.

6. When tuning a violin, a string is tightened. What happens to the note that is being played on that string?
   A) The pitch is higher.
   B) The pitch is lower.
   C) It is quieter.
   D) It is louder.

7. If air becomes warmer, what happens to the speed of sound in air?
   A) It increases.
   B) It decreases.
   C) It doesn't change.
   D) It oscillates.

8. Sound is what type of wave?
   A) slow
   B) transverse
   C) compressional
   D) fast

9. What does the middle ear do?
   A) focuses sound
   B) interprets sound
   C) collects sound
   D) transmits and amplifies sound

10. An ambulance siren speeds away from you. What happens to the pitch you hear?
    A) It increases.
    B) It becomes louder.
    C) It decreases.
    D) Nothing happens.

Thinking Critically

11. Some xylophones have open pipes of different lengths hung under each bar. The longer the bar is, the longer the corresponding pipe is. Explain how these pipes amplify the sound of the xylophone.

12. Why don't you notice the Doppler effect for a slow-moving train?

13. Suppose the movement of the bones in the middle ear were reduced. Which would be more affected—the ability to hear quiet sounds or the ability to hear certain frequencies? Explain your answer.

14. Two flutes are playing at the same time. One flute plays a note with frequency 524 Hz. If two beats are heard per second, what are the possible frequencies the other flute is playing?

15. The triangle is a percussion instrument consisting of an open metal triangle hanging from a string. The triangle is struck by a metal rod, and a chiming sound is heard. If the metal triangle is held in the hand rather than by the string, a quiet, dull sound is made when it is struck. Explain why holding the triangle makes it sound quieter.

Chapter ✓Assessment Planner

Portfolio Encourage students to place in their portfolios one or two items of what they consider to be their best work. Examples include:
- Assessment, p. 606
- Extension, p. 612
- Assessment, p. 623
- Communicating Your Data, p. 625

Performance Additional performance assessments, Performance Task Assessment Lists, and rubrics for evaluating these activities can be found in Glencoe's **Performance Assessment in the Science Classroom.**

Developing Skills

16. Predicting If the holes of a flute are all covered while playing, then all uncovered, what happens to the length of the vibrating air column? What happens to the pitch of the note?

17. Identifying and Manipulating Variables and Controls Describe an experiment to demonstrate that sound is diffracted.

18. Making and Using Tables Make a table to show the first three overtones for a note of G, which has a frequency of 392 Hz.

19. Interpreting Scientific Illustrations The picture shows pan pipes. How are different notes produced by blowing on pan pipes?

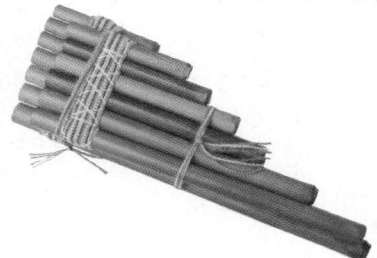

Performance Assessment

20. Recital Perform a short musical piece on an instrument. Explain how your actions changed the notes that were produced.

21. Pamphlet Create a pamphlet describing how a hearing aid works.

TECHNOLOGY

Go to the Glencoe Science Web site at **science.glencoe.com** or use the **Glencoe Science CD-ROM** for additional chapter assessment.

THE PRINCETON REVIEW — Test Practice

Sound travels in waves that change as the pitch and loudness of the sound vary. These pictures illustrate four recorded sounds.

Q.

R.

S.

T.
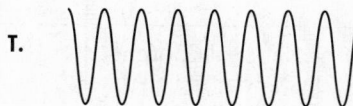

Study the pictures and answer the following questions.

1. Which of the four sounds was getting louder while it was recorded?
- **A)** Q
- **B)** R
- **C)** S
- **D)** T

2. Which sound had the highest pitch while it was recorded?
- **F)** Q
- **G)** R
- **H)** S
- **J)** T

THE PRINCETON REVIEW — Test Practice

The Test-Taking Tip was written by The Princeton Review, the nation's leader in test preparation.
1. C
2. J

Developing Skills

16. When all holes are covered, the column is longer and the note is lower. When all holes are uncovered, the column is shorter, and the note is higher.

17. Possible answer: set up a radio playing in a room. Leave the room, and stand to one side of the door. If you can hear the music, it must be diffracted around the edge of the door to reach your ears.

18.

Fundamental	384 Hz
First overtone	768 Hz
Second overtone	1,152 Hz
Third overtone	1,536 Hz

19. Air is blown across the top of each individual pipe, resonating the column of air. Each pipe has its own pitch. The longer the pipe, the deeper the note.

Performance Assessment

20. Check students' explanations. Use PASC, p. 129.

21. Explanations should include information about how the device collects, transmits, and amplifies sound. Use PASC, p. 143.

Assessment Resources

Reproducible Masters

Chapter Resources Booklet
Chapter Review, pp. 33–34
Chapter Tests, pp. 35–38
Assessment Transparency Activity, p. 45

Glencoe Science Web site
Interactive Tutor
Chapter Quizzes

Glencoe Technology
- Assessment Transparency
- Interactive CD-ROM Chapter Quizzes
- ExamView Pro Test Bank
- Vocabulary PuzzleMaker Software
- MindJogger Videoquiz

Section/Objectives	Standards		Activities/Features
Chapter Opener	National	State/Local	**Explore Activity:** Detecting invisible light, p. 633 **Before You Read,** p. 633
	See p. 7T for a Key to Standards.		
Section 1 The Nature of Electromagnetic Waves 🕐 2 sessions 📦 1 block 1. **Explain** how electromagnetic waves are produced. 2. **Describe** the properties of electromagnetic waves.	National Content Standards: UCP2, A1, B3		**Science Online,** p. 635 **MiniLAB:** Observing Electric Fields, p. 637
Section 2 The Electromagnetic Spectrum 🕐 2 sessions 📦 1 block 1. **Explain** differences among kinds of electromagnetic waves. 2. **Identify** uses for different kinds of electromagnetic waves.	National Content Standards: UCP2, A1, B3, D3, F5		**MiniLAB:** Observing the Focusing of Infrared Rays, p. 641 **Life Science Integration:** p. 644 **Visualizing the Universe,** p. 646 **Activity:** Prisms of Light, p. 648
Section 3 Using Electromagnetic Waves 🕐 3 sessions 📦 1.5 blocks 1. **Explain** different methods of electronic communication. 2. **Compare and contrast** AM and FM signals.	National Content Standards: UCP2, A1, B3, F5, G3		**Astronomy Integration,** p. 650 **Math Skills Activity:** Calculating the Wavelength of Radio Frequencies, p. 651 **Science Online:** p. 652 **Activity:** Spectrum Inspection, p. 654 **Science and History:** Hopping the Frequencies, p. 656

Activity Materials	Reproducible Resources	Section Assessment	Technology
Explore Activity: large sheet of black paper, tape, scissors, metric ruler, glass prism, 2 thermometers, watch or clock	**Chapter Resources Booklet** Foldables Worksheet, p. 15 Directed Reading Overview, p. 17 Note-taking Worksheets, pp. 31–33	GLENCOE'S **ASSESSMENT** ADVANTAGE	
MiniLAB: hard plastic comb, wool sweater or flannel shirt, water faucet	**Chapter Resources Booklet** Transparency Activity, p. 42 MiniLAB, p. 3 Enrichment, p. 28 Reinforcement, p. 25 Directed Reading, p. 18 **Cultural Diversity,** p. 61 **Science Inquiry Labs,** p. 21	**Portfolio** Science Journal, p. 635 **Performance** MiniLAB, p. 637 Skill Builder Activities, p. 638 **Content** Section Assessment, p. 638	Section Focus Transparency Interactive CD-ROM Guided Reading Audio Program
MiniLAB: concave mirror, meterstick, electric heater **Activity:** 3 microscope slides, transparent tape, clay, flashlight, water	**Chapter Resources Booklet** Transparency Activity, p. 43 MiniLAB, p. 4 Enrichment, p. 29 Reinforcement, p. 26 Directed Reading, p. 18 Lab Activity, pp. 9–11 Activity Worksheet, pp. 5–6 **Reading and Writing Skill Activities,** p. 25	**Portfolio** Extension, p. 643 **Performance** MiniLAB, p. 641 Skill Builder Activities, p. 647 **Content** Section Assessment, p. 647	Section Focus Transparency Interactive CD-ROM Guided Reading Audio Program
Activity: diffraction grating, clear tubular incandescent light with dimmer switch; red, yellow, blue colored pencils *Need materials?* Contact Science Kit at 1-800-828-7777 or www.sciencekit.com on the Internet.	**Chapter Resources Booklet** Transparency Activity, p. 44 Enrichment, p. 30 Reinforcement, p. 27 Directed Reading, pp. 19, 20 Lab Activity, pp. 13–14 Transparency Activity, pp. 45–46 Activity Worksheet, pp. 7–8 **Mathematics Skill Activities,** p. 9 **Lab Management and Safety,** p. 73	**Portfolio** Curriculum Connection, p. 651 **Performance** Math Skills Activity, p. 651 Skill Builder Activities, p. 653 **Content** Section Assessment, p. 653	Section Focus Transparency Teaching Transparency Interactive CD-ROM Guided Reading Audio Program

GLENCOE'S ASSESSMENT ADVANTAGE	End of Chapter Assessment		
Blackline Masters	**Technology**		**Professional Series**
Chapter Resources Booklet Chapter Review, pp. 35–36 Chapter Tests, pp. 37–40 **Standardized Test Practice by The Princeton Review,** pp. 93–96	MindJogger Videoquiz Interactive CD-ROM Vocabulary PuzzleMakers ExamView Pro Test Bank Interactive Lesson Planner Interactive Teacher Edition		Performance Assessment in the Science Classroom (PASC)

Transparencies

Section Focus

Section Focus Transparency 1 — Most Enlightening

This picture captured an image of lightning at the very moment that it struck the Eiffel Tower. As you look at this dramatic picture, try to imagine what this area of Paris looked like in the moments before and after the lightning strike.

1. How does lightning during a nighttime storm give you information about your surroundings?
2. When a storm is in the distance, why do you see a bolt of lightning before you hear the clap of thunder?
3. What other sources of light can you name?

L2

Section Focus Transparency 2 — Crystal Clear

Many people like to hang crystals in windows where sunlight can shine on them. As light passes through the different faces of the crystal, beautiful light patterns can appear on the wall.

1. What colors do you see in the crystal?
2. What is the source of the light rays striking the crystal?
3. How might the pattern of light made by the crystal change throughout the day?

L2

Section Focus Transparency 3 — Taller Than Ever(est)

In 1954, the height of Mount Everest was determined to be 8,848 m (29,028 feet). In 1999, a team of researchers used the Global Positioning System (GPS) to check this 1954 figure. They found the height of Everest to be two meters taller! Another use of the GPS is being demonstrated below. This man is using GPS to determine his location and display it on a map.

1. What are some communication devices that use electromagnetic waves to transmit signals?
2. Which mountain height do you think is more accurate, the 1954 figure or the 1999 figure? Explain.

L2

This is a representation of key blackline masters available in the Teacher Classroom Resources. See Resource Manager boxes within the chapter for additional information.

Key to Teaching Strategies

The following designations will help you decide which activities are appropriate for your students.

L1 Level 1 activities should be appropriate for students with learning difficulties.

L2 Level 2 activities should be within the ability range of all students.

L3 Level 3 activities are designed for above-average students.

ELL ELL activities should be within the ability range of English Language Learners.

COOP LEARN Cooperative Learning activities are designed for small group work.

LS Multiple Learning Styles logos, as described on page 22T, are used throughout to indicate strategies that address different learning styles.

P These strategies represent student products that can be placed into a best-work portfolio.

Assessment

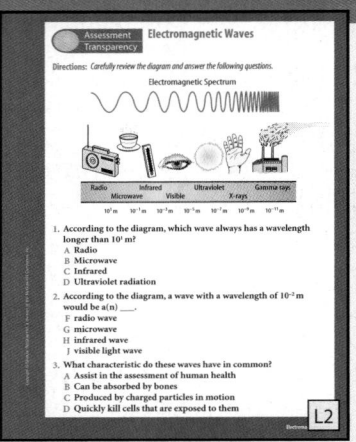

Assessment Transparency — Electromagnetic Waves

Directions: *Carefully review the diagram and answer the following questions.*

1. According to the diagram, which wave always has a wavelength longer than 10^1 m?
   A Radio
   B Microwave
   C Infrared
   D Ultraviolet radiation
2. According to the diagram, a wave with a wavelength of 10^{-2} m would be a(n) ___.
   F radio wave
   G microwave
   H infrared wave
   J visible light wave
3. What characteristic do these waves have in common?
   A Assist in the assessment of human health
   B Can be absorbed by bones
   C Produced by charged particles in motion
   D Quickly kill cells that are exposed to them

L2

Teaching

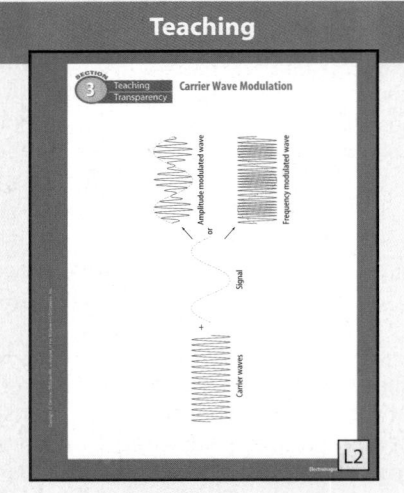

Teaching Transparency 3 — Carrier Wave Modulation

L2

Hands-on Activities

Activity Worksheets

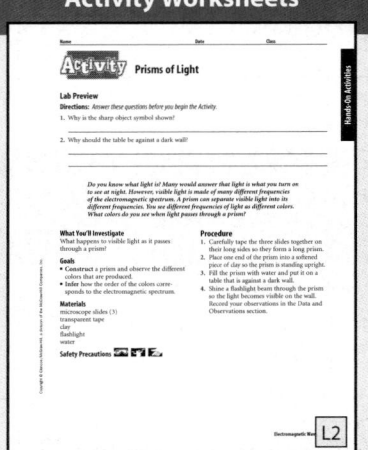

Activity — Prisms of Light

Lab Preview
Directions: *Answer these questions before you begin the Activity.*

1. Why is the sharp object symbol shown?

2. Why should the table be against a dark wall?

Do you know what light is? Many would answer that light is what you turn on to see at night. However, visible light is made of many different frequencies of the electromagnetic spectrum. A prism can separate visible light into its different frequencies. You see different frequencies of light as different colors. What colors do you see when light passes through a prism?

What You'll Investigate
What happens to visible light as it passes through a prism?

Goals
• **Construct** a prism and observe the different colors that are produced.
• **Infer** how the order of the colors corresponds to the electromagnetic spectrum.

Materials
microscope slides (3)
transparent tape
clay
flashlight
water

Safety Precautions

Procedure
1. Carefully tape the three slides together on their long sides so they form a long prism.
2. Place one end of the prism into a softened piece of clay so the prism is standing upright.
3. Fill the prism with water and put it on a table that is against a dark wall.
4. Shine a flashlight beam through the prism so the light becomes visible on the wall. Record your observations in the Data and Observations section.

L2

Laboratory Activities

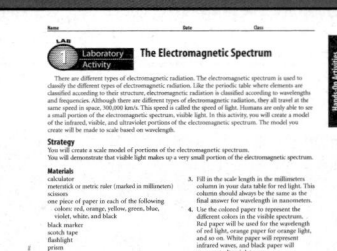

Laboratory Activity 1 — The Electromagnetic Spectrum

There are different types of electromagnetic radiation. The electromagnetic spectrum is used to classify the different types of electromagnetic radiation. Like the periodic table where elements are classified according to their structure, electromagnetic radiation is classified according to wavelengths and frequencies. Although there are different types of electromagnetic radiation, they all travel at the same speed in space, 300,000 km/s. This speed is called the speed of light. Humans are only able to see a small portion of the electromagnetic spectrum, visible light. In this activity, you will create a model of the infrared, visible, and ultraviolet portions of the electromagnetic spectrum. The model you create will be made to scale based on wavelength.

Strategy
You will create a scale model of portions of the electromagnetic spectrum.
You will demonstrate that visible light makes up a very small portion of the electromagnetic spectrum.

Materials
calculator
metric stick or metric ruler (marked in millimeters)
scissors
one piece of paper in each of the following colors: red, orange, yellow, green, blue, violet, white, and black
black marker
scotch tape
flashlight
prism

Procedure
1. The wavelengths for the visible, infrared, and ultraviolet portions of the spectrum are represented in meters in the table in the Data and Observations section. Complete a metric conversion calculation to find the length of the waves in nanometers. One nanometer is 10^{-9} of a meter so that 10^{-9} m equals 10 nanometers, 10^{-8} m equals 100 nanometers, and 10^{-7} m equals 1,000 nanometers. The scale that will be used to build the model of the spectrum is 1 nanometer equals 1 millimeter. Record your calculations in the table in the Data and Observations section.
2. Work together as a class on the metric conversion calculation for red light. It is good to begin with red light rather than infrared, which is listed first in the data table, because the length of the scale model for infrared light is significantly longer than the scale models of any of the visible light colors.

3. Fill in the scale length in the millimeters column in your data table for red light. This column should always be the same as the final answer for wavelength in nanometers.
4. Use the colored paper to represent the different colors in the visible spectrum. Red paper will be used for the wavelength of red light, orange paper for orange light, and so on. White paper will represent infrared waves, and black paper will represent ultraviolet waves.
5. Cut a strip of red paper that is 2.5 cm wide and the same length in the number you have written in your column for scale length in millimeters.
6. Once you have a strip of red paper that is 750 mm (75 cm) long, mark the actual wave length of red light, 7.5 × 10⁻⁷ m, on the strip.
7. Complete a metric conversion calculation and cut strips for each of the electromagnetic waves represented in the data table. When you have finished, you should have eight strips of paper of different lengths and colors in your model.
8. Align your strips horizontally, directly underneath each other, with the longest strip (which should be infrared) on top and the shortest strip (which should be ultraviolet) on the bottom. Tape all the strips together to make one large sheet.
9. Shine the flashlight through the prism in order to see the visible spectrum.

L2

Meeting Different Ability Levels

Content Outline

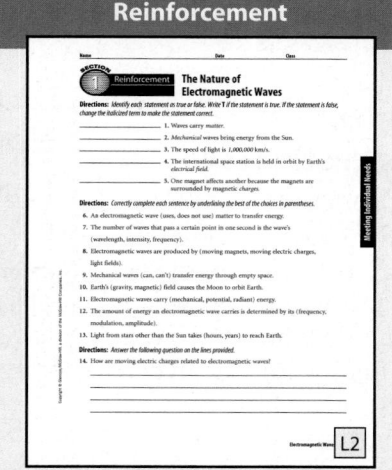

Reinforcement

Directed Reading

Assessment

Chapter Tests

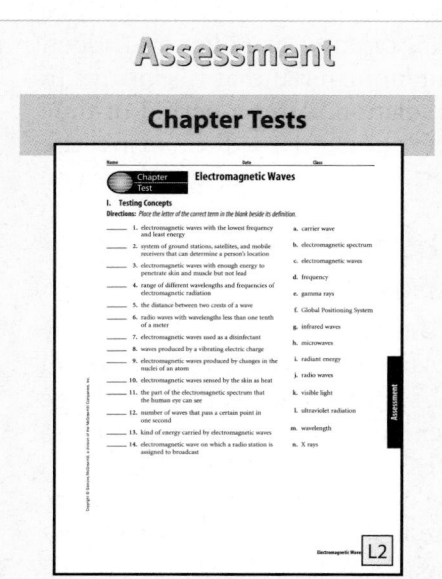

Enrichment

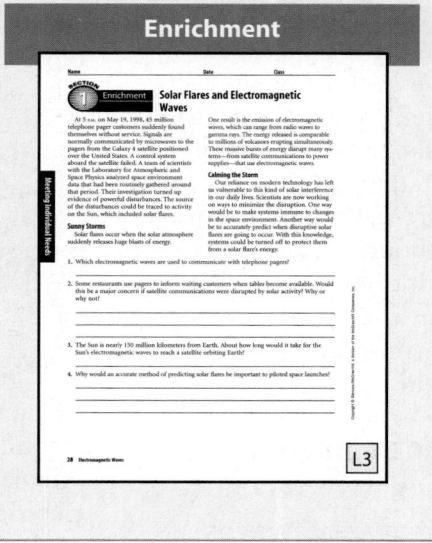

Spanish Directed Reading

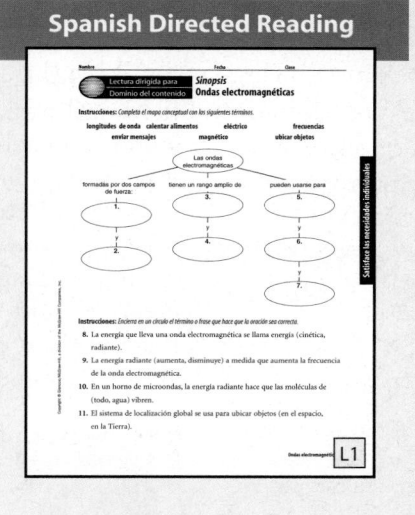

Test Practice Workbook

Chapter Review

Science Content Background

 **SECTION 1**

The Nature of Electromagnetic Waves

Waves in Space

For many years scientists thought that electromagnetic waves were mechanical waves like sound waves and water waves, and needed a medium in which to travel. Space was thought to be filled with this hypothetical medium, called the *ether*. However, all attempts to detect the ether proved unsuccessful, and near the end of the nineteenth century, it was realized that the ether did not exist.

Properties of Electromagnetic Waves

An electromagnetic wave consists of an electric field and a magnetic field oscillating at right angles to each other and to the direction the wave is traveling. The frequency at which these fields oscillate is the frequency of the wave. The wave can travel without a medium because of electromagnetic induction: an oscillating electric field creates an oscillating magnetic field; and an oscillating magnetic field creates an oscillating electric field.

 **SECTION 2**

The Electromagnetic Spectrum

Electromagnetic Waves

The electromagnetic spectrum is divided into a number of bands, such as radio waves, infrared waves, and visible light. Each band extends over a range of frequencies or wavelengths that is somewhat arbitrary. In some cases bands may overlap.

Infrared Waves

All objects emit electromagnetic waves. The higher the temperature of the object, the higher the frequencies of the emitted electromagnetic waves. Much of the electromagnetic radiation emitted by objects near room temperature is infrared radiation. The surface of the Sun is a temperature of about 6,000 K and much of the electromagnetic radiation it emits is visible light.

Student Misconception

Light is very different from other electromagnetic waves such as X rays.

Refer to the facing page for teaching strategies to address this misconception. Refer to pages 639–647 for content related to this topic.

X Rays and Gamma Rays

Radiation detectors detect X rays and gamma rays by the tendency of these rays to ionize atoms. Workers who may be exposed to these types of radiation often wear radiation badges. The badges contain material that is sensitive to these types of radiation. After a period of time the badges are checked to determine the amount of radiation the workers have received.

SECTION 3

Using Electromagnetic Waves

Using Radio Waves

Although Guglielmo Marconi was given credit for inventing radio, a large amount of the credit should have been given to Nikola Tesla. Tesla invented the means to turn electrical energy into radio waves. Electrons are made to oscillate in an antenna in order to produce radio waves.

On some nights you can pick up an AM station a few hundred miles from where it was broadcast. This is because the AM radio waves reflect off of the ionosphere. FM radio waves need to travel in a straight line to reach you, and this limits their range.

SCIENCE *Online*

For additional content background on this topic, go to the Glencoe Science Web site at science.glencoe.com.

IDENTIFYING ▷ **Misconceptions**

Find Out What Students Think

Students may think that . . .

• **Light is very different from other electromagnetic waves such as X rays.**

Students can see light, but they cannot see other electromagnetic waves. Thus they may think of them as different entities. Additionally, some electromagnetic waves, such as X rays and ultraviolet rays, often are perceived as hazardous, while light is perceived as harmless.

Activity

Write the following on the board for the class to see. **Which of the following pairs of waves are most similar, "light and sound" or "light and X rays"? Explain your answer.** Ask students to write their answers in their Science Journals. Then have selected students read their answers. Have students try to convince others about their point of view.

Promote Understanding

Demonstration and Activity

Explain that sound waves and water waves need a medium to travel through, while electromagnetic waves can travel through a vacuum. Show students some other similarities among electromagnetic waves.

• Show light reflected by using a mirror and a flashlight.

• Show infrared reflection by using a mirror and a remote control to turn on a television or VCR.

• Show shadow formation by using the flashlight and a board eraser to cast a shadow on the wall.

• Shine an ultraviolet light on a fluorescent rock and then put the eraser in front of it to produce a shadow effect. You can also show developed X-ray film and explain how it shows the shadows of bones.

Explain that visible light, ultraviolet, infrared, and X-ray radiation are all types of electromagnetic radiation.

• Assign student groups one of the following types of waves: radio, microwaves, infrared, visible light, ultraviolet, X rays, and gamma rays. For their type of wave they should use the Internet or library to find the wavelength range, how to detect it, how it is used by people, and if it is harmful to people. If it is harmful to people, they should describe the dangers.

• Have students share their results with other groups until all students have received information about these seven types of electromagnetic waves.

Assess

After completing the chapter, see *Identifying Misconceptions* in the Study Guide.

Electromagnetic Waves

Chapter Vocabulary

What do you think?

Science Journal This photograph shows the radio telescope near Arecibo, Puerto Rico. Scientists use telescopes such as these to study electromagnetic waves from space.

Electromagnetic Waves

Wherever you go, you are being bombarded by electromagnetic waves. Some, such as visible light, can be seen. Infrared rays can't be seen but feel warm on your skin. The paint on the tricycle in this picture is being heat cured in an infrared oven. In this chapter, you will learn how electromagnetic waves are formed. You also will learn ways in which electromagnetic waves are used, from cooking to satellite communications.

What do you think?

Science Journal Look at the photograph below with a classmate. Discuss what you think this might be. Here is a hint: *Scientists built this to get a clearer picture.* Write your answer or best guess in your Science Journal.

632

Theme Connection

Energy Visible light is only one of the many types of electromagnetic waves. This chapter identifies other types of electromagnetic waves and discusses the ways they are used.

L ight is a type of wave called an electromagnetic wave. You see light every day, but visible light is only one type of electromagnetic wave. Other electromagnetic waves are all around you, but you cannot see them. How can you detect electromagnetic waves that can't be seen with your eyes?

Detecting invisible light

1. Cut a slit 2 cm long and 0.25 cm wide in the center of a sheet of black paper.
2. Cover a window that is in direct sunlight with the paper.
3. Position a glass prism in front of the light coming through the slit so it makes a visible spectrum on the floor or table.
4. Place one thermometer in the spectrum and a second thermometer just beyond the red light.
5. Measure the temperature in each region after 5 min.

Observe

Write a paragraph in your Science Journal comparing the temperatures of the two regions and offer an explanation for the observed temperatures.

Before You Read

FOLDABLES
Reading & Study
Skills

Making a Main Ideas Study Fold Make the following Foldable to help you identify the major topics about electromagnetic waves.

1. Stack four sheets of paper in front of you so the short sides are at the top.
2. Slide the top sheet up so about 2 cm of the next sheet shows. Slide each sheet up so about 2 cm of the next sheet shows.
3. Fold the sheets top to bottom to form eight tabs. Staple along the top fold.
4. Label the tabs *Electromagnetic Spectrum, Radio Waves, Microwaves, Infrared Rays, Visible Light, Ultraviolet Light, X Rays,* and *Gamma Rays.*
5. As you read the chapter, list the things you learn about these electromagnetic waves under the tabs.

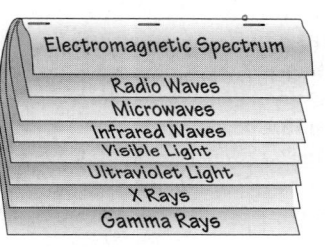

633

FOLDABLES
Reading & Study
Skills

Before You Read

Dinah Zike Study Fold

Purpose Students make a Foldable to help them determine what they know about electromagnetic waves before they read the chapter. They then use the Foldable to record and organize their notes as they read.

For additional help, see Foldables Worksheet, p. 15 in **Chapter Resources Booklet,** or go to the Glencoe Science Web site at **science.glencoe.com.** See After You Read in the Study Guide at the end of this chapter.

EXPLORE ACTIVITY

Purpose Use the Explore Activity to introduce students to the concept that electromagnetic radiation includes other waves besides light. L2 ELL IS **Kinesthetic**

Preparation Locate a window that gets direct sunlight at the time of day that you wish students to do this activity. Check the weather to make sure the day will be sunny.

Paint the bulbs of the thermometers black to increase the temperature rise for the thermometer placed below the red portion of the spectrum. A computer temperature probe may also be used.

Because some window glass absorbs infrared waves, this activity could also be performed outdoors. Place a piece of white paper in the bottom of a box. Tape the prism to the top edge of a box so the spectrum appears on the paper.

Materials black construction paper, tape, metric ruler, scissors, glass prism, two thermometers, watch

Teaching Strategy Explain to students that the visible light from the sun contains many different wavelengths of radiation, and that the prism spreads the wavelengths apart so they can be seen separately.

Observe

The electromagnetic waves from the Sun slightly raise the temperature of the thermometers in the visible spectrum and just below the red light. The thermometer in the infrared region is slightly warmer than the one in the visible region because it absorbs more energy.

Assessment

Oral Ask students what they think the temperature would be of a thermometer placed just beyond the violet end of the spectrum. the same as for visible light Use **Performance Assessment in the Science Classroom,** p. 89.

The Nature of Electromagnetic Waves

SECTION

1 Motivate

Bellringer Transparency

Display the Section Focus Transparency for Section 1. Use the accompanying Transparency Activity Master. L2

ELL

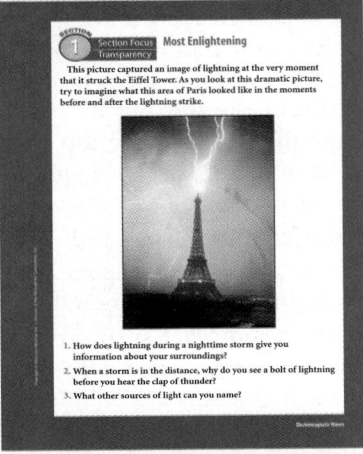

Section Focus Transparency

Most Enlightening

This picture captured an image of lightning at the very moment that it struck the Eiffel Tower. As you look at this dramatic picture, try to imagine what this area of Paris looked like in the moments before and after the lightning strike.

1. How does lightning during a nighttime storm give you information about your surroundings?

2. When a storm is in the distance, why do you see a bolt of lightning before you hear the clap of thunder?

3. What other sources of light can you name?

Tie to Prior Knowledge

Ask students to name types of waves or rays that they know exist but that they cannot see. Explain that these waves, which share many of the features of visible light but are also different in some ways, are the subject of this chapter.

The Nature of Electromagnetic Waves

As You Read

What You'll Learn

■ **Explain** how electromagnetic waves are produced.
■ **Describe** the properties of electromagnetic waves.

Vocabulary
electromagnetic wave
radiant energy

Why It's Important
The energy Earth receives from the Sun is carried by electromagnetic waves.

Waves in Space

On a clear day you feel the warmth in the Sun's rays, and you see the brightness of its light. Energy is being transferred from the Sun to your skin and eyes. Who would guess that the way in which this energy is transferred has anything to do with radios, televisions, microwave ovens, or the X-ray pictures that are taken by a doctor or dentist? Yet the Sun and the objects shown in **Figure 1** use the same type of wave to move energy from place to place.

Transferring Energy A wave transfers energy from one place to another without transferring matter. How do waves transfer energy? Waves, such as water waves and sound waves, transfer energy by making particles of matter move. The energy is passed along from particle to particle as they collide with their neighbors. Mechanical waves are the types of waves that use matter to transfer energy.

How can a wave transfer energy from the Sun to Earth? Mechanical waves, for example, can't travel in the space between Earth and the Sun where no matter exists. Instead, this energy is carried by a different type of wave called an electromagnetic wave. An **electromagnetic wave** is a wave that can travel through empty space and is produced by charged particles that are in motion.

Figure 1
Getting an X ray at the dentist's office and talking on a cell phone are possible because energy is carried through space by electromagnetic waves.

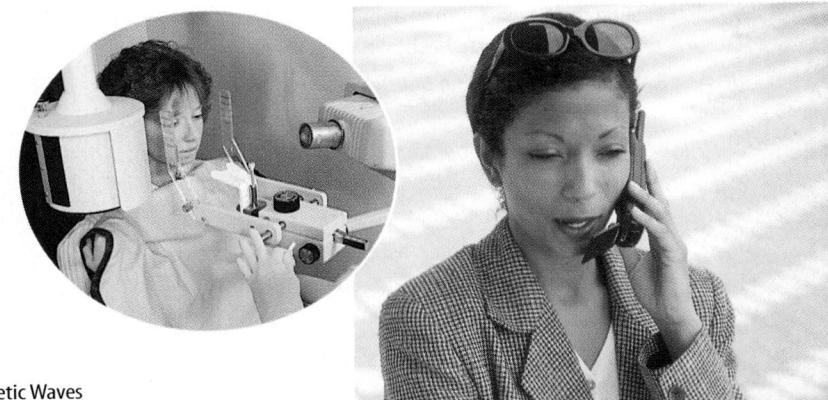

Section ✓Assessment Planner

PORTFOLIO
Science Journal, p. 635
PERFORMANCE ASSESSMENT
Try At Home MiniLAB, p. 637
Skill Builder Activities, p. 638
See page 660 for more options.

CONTENT ASSESSMENT
Section, p. 638
Challenge, p. 638
Chapter, pp. 660–661

Force due to gravity

Forces and Fields

An electromagnetic wave is made of two parts—an electric field and a magnetic field. These fields are force fields. A force field enables an object to exert forces on other objects, even though they are not touching. Earth produces a force field called the gravitational field. This field exerts the force of gravity on all objects that have mass.

☑ **Reading Check** *What force field surrounds Earth?*

How does Earth's force field work? If you throw a ball in the air as high as you can, it always falls back to Earth. At every point along the ball's path, the force of gravity pulls down on the ball, as shown in **Figure 2A**. In fact, at every point in space above or at Earth's surface, a ball is acted on by a downward force exerted by Earth's gravitational field. The force exerted by this field on a ball could be represented by a downward arrow at any point in space. **Figure 2B** shows this force field that surrounds Earth and extends out into space. In fact, it is Earth's gravitational field that causes the Moon to orbit Earth.

Magnetic Fields You know that magnets repel and attract each other even when they aren't touching. Two magnets exert a force on each other when they are some distance apart because each magnet is surrounded by a force field called a magnetic field. Just as a gravitational field exerts a force on a mass, a magnetic field exerts a force on another magnet and on magnetic materials. Magnetic fields cause other magnets to line up along the direction of the magnetic field.

Figure 2
A gravitational field surrounds all objects, such as Earth.

A When a ball is thrown, Earth's gravitational field exerts a downward force on the ball at every point along the ball's path.

B Earth's gravitational field extends out through space, exerting a force on all masses.

Research In addition to a gravitational field, Earth also is surrounded by a magnetic field. Visit the Glencoe Science Web site at **science.glencoe.com** for more information about Earth's gravitational and magnetic force fields. Place the information you gather on a poster to share with your class.

Making Electromagnetic Waves

Make a Model

To help students visualize electromagnetic waves, have them make a model of one. Each student should draw or trace a sine wave on a piece of cardboard, and then draw or trace an identical sine wave on a second piece of cardboard. Have students cut the cardboard, following the outlines of the sine waves. Students should then cut one of the waves in half lengthwise and glue or tape the two halves to either side of the other wave at right angles to it. Make sure students position the waves so that the crest of a vertical wave corresponds to the crest of a horizontal wave. L2

IS **Kinesthetic**

Figure 3
Force fields surround all magnets and electric charges.

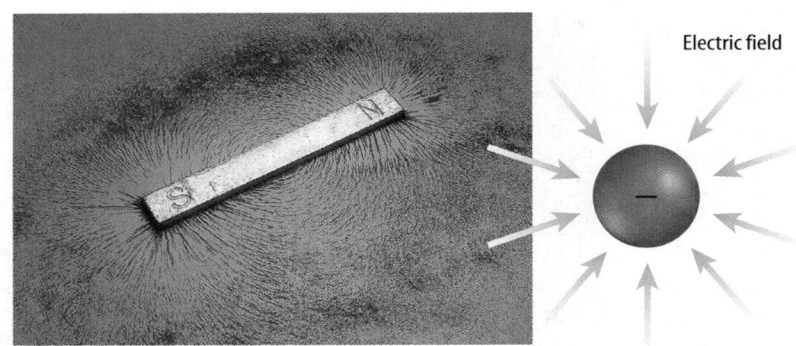

Electric field

A A magnetic field surrounds all magnets. The magnetic field exerts a force on iron filings, causing them to line up with the field.

B The electric field around an electric charge extends out through space, exerting forces on other charged particles.

Figure 4
Electrons moving in a wire produce a magnetic field in the surrounding space.

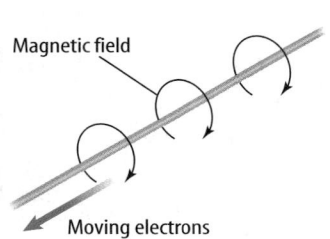

Magnetic field

Moving electrons

Electric Fields Recall that atoms contain protons, neutrons, and electrons. Protons and electrons have a property called electric charge. The two types of electric charge are positive and negative. Protons have positive charge and electrons have negative charge.

Just as a magnet is surrounded by a magnetic field, a particle that has electric charge, such as a proton or an electron, is surrounded by an electric field, as shown in **Figure 3.** The electric field is a force field that exerts a force on all other charged particles that are in the field.

Making Electromagnetic Waves

An electromagnetic wave is made of electric and magnetic fields. How is such a wave produced? Think about a wave on a rope. You can make a wave on a rope by shaking one end of the rope up and down. Electromagnetic waves are produced by making charged particles, such as electrons, move back and forth, or vibrate.

A charged particle always is surrounded by an electric field. But a charged particle that is moving also is surrounded by a magnetic field. For example, when an electric current flows in a wire, electrons are moving in the wire. As a result, the wire is surrounded by a magnetic field, as shown in **Figure 4.** So a moving charged particle is surrounded by an electric field and a magnetic field.

LAB DEMONSTRATION

Purpose to help students visualize the concept of a field

Materials magnet, glass or clear plastic plate, iron filings

Procedure Sprinkle iron filings on the plate. Hold the magnet beneath the plate. Gently shake the plate and have students observe what happens.

Expected Outcome The iron filings align themselves with the magnetic field to produce a map of the field.

Assessment

Why do some of the filings point straight upward? The field is pointing directly upward, or out of the plane of the plate.

Producing Waves

When you shake a rope up and down, you produce a wave that moves away from your hand. As a charged particle vibrates by moving up and down or back and forth, it produces changing electric and magnetic fields that move away from the vibrating charge in all directions. These changing fields traveling in all directions form an electromagnetic wave. **Figure 5A** shows these changing fields along one direction.

Properties of Electromagnetic Waves

Like all waves, an electromagnetic wave has a frequency and a wavelength. When you create a wave on a rope, you move your hand up and down while holding the rope. Look at **Figure 5B.** Frequency is how many times you move the rope through one complete up and down cycle in 1 s. Wavelength is the distance from one crest to the next or from one trough to the next.

Wavelength and Frequency An electromagnetic wave is produced by a vibrating charged particle. When the charge makes one complete vibration, one wavelength is created, as shown in **Figure 5A.** Like a wave on a rope, the frequency of an electromagnetic wave is the number of wavelengths that pass by a point in 1 s. This is the same as the number of times in 1 s that the charged particle makes one complete vibration.

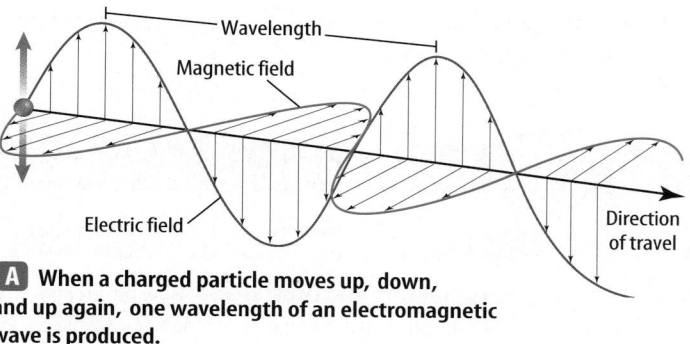

A When a charged particle moves up, down, and up again, one wavelength of an electromagnetic wave is produced.

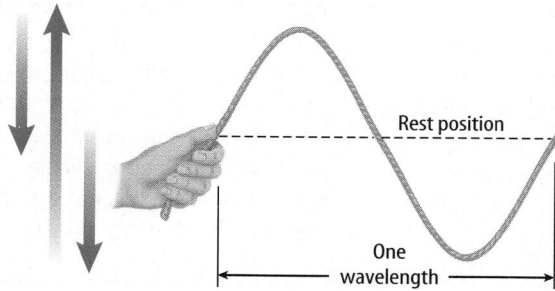

B By shaking the end of a rope down, up, and down again, you make one wavelength.

Figure 5
The vibrating motion of an electric charge produces an electromagnetic wave. One complete cycle of vibration produces one wavelength of a wave.

Mini LAB
TRY AT HOME

Observing Electric Fields

Procedure
1. Rub a **hard, plastic comb** vigorously with a **wool sweater or wool flannel shirt.**
2. Turn on a **water faucet** to create the smallest possible continuous stream of water.
3. Hold the comb near the stream of water and observe.

Analysis
1. What happened to the stream of water when you held the comb near it?
2. Explain why the stream of water behaved this way.

Properties of Electromagnetic Waves

Mini LAB
TRY AT HOME

Purpose Students observe the effects of an electric field. L2
IS Kinesthetic
Materials hard plastic comb, wool sweater or wool flannel shirt, water faucet

Teaching Strategies
• Instruct students not to touch the stream of water with their combs.
• Instruct them to hold the comb near the water stream immediately after rubbing it with the wool.

Analysis
1. The stream of water bent toward the comb.
2. Rubbing the comb with the clothing gave it a charge and produced an electric field. The electric field of the comb attracted the water molecules, which also have a slight charge.

✓Assessment

Oral Ask students to explain the difference between the electric field they created and the electric field of an electromagnetic wave. The electric field of an electromagnetic wave is changing and moving, but the electric field they generated was stationary. Use **PASC,** p. 89.

Inclusion Strategies

Learning Disabled Help students visualize wave properties by asking them to use chenille stems to make models of waves. Ask them to make a high-frequency wave and a low-frequency wave. **What is the difference between the two waves?** The crests and troughs of high-frequency waves are closer to each other than those of low-frequency waves.
L1 **IS** Kinesthetic

Resource Manager

Visual Learning

Figure 5 Review with students the locations of crests and troughs of a wave. Clarify that one wavelength is a complete vibration of one wave and can be measured from crest to crest, from trough to trough, or between any two corresponding points on a wave.

Properties of Electromagnetic Waves, continued

✓ **Reading Check**

Answer the energy carried by an electromagnetic wave

IDENTIFYING Misconceptions

Stress that the term *speed of light* refers to the speed at which all electromagnetic waves travel. At this speed, light given off by the Sun reaches Earth in about eight minutes. An X ray traveling from the Sun to Earth also would take about eight minutes.

3 Assess

Reteach

Ask volunteers to draw waves having large and small frequencies. Use the diagrams to review the parts of a wave, wavelength, and frequency. [L1]
IS **Visual-Spatial**

Challenge

Light from the Sun takes about eight minutes to reach Earth. Use the speed of light to estimate the distance between Earth and the Sun. $d = v \times T = (300,000 \text{ km/s}) \times (480 \text{ s}) = 144,000,000 \text{ km}$ [L3]
IS **Logical-Mathematical**

✓ Assessment

Content Ask students to write paragraphs describing what a force field is. Ask them to give an example of a force field they have experienced. Possible answer: a magnetic field such as that observed in the Lab Demonstration Use **PASC**, p. 159.

Alpha Centauri

Figure 6
The light that reaches Earth today from Alpha Centauri left the star more than four years ago.

Radiant Energy The energy carried by an electromagnetic wave is called **radiant energy.** What happens if an electromagnetic wave strikes another charged particle? The electric field part of the wave exerts a force on this particle and causes it to move. Some of the radiant energy carried by the wave is transferred into the energy of motion of the particle.

✓ **Reading Check**   *What is radiant energy?*

The amount of energy that an electromagnetic wave carries is determined by the wave's frequency. The higher the frequency of the electromagnetic wave, the more energy it has.

The Speed of Light All electromagnetic waves, such as light, microwaves, and X rays, travel through space at the same speed. This speed has been measured as about 300,000 km/s in space. Because light is an electromagnetic wave, this speed sometimes is called the speed of light. If something could travel at the speed of light, it could travel around the world more than seven times in 1 s. Even though light travels incredibly fast, stars other than the Sun are so far away that it takes years for the light they emit to reach Earth. **Figure 6** shows one of the closest stars to the solar system, Alpha Centauri. This star is more than 40 trillion km from Earth.

Section 1 Assessment

1. What is an electromagnetic wave?
2. How are electromagnetic waves produced?
3. What two fields surround a moving charged particle?
4. How does the amount of energy carried by a low-frequency wave compare to the amount carried by a high-frequency wave?
5. **Think Critically** Unlike sound waves, electromagnetic waves can travel through a vacuum. What observations can you make to support this statement?

Skill Builder Activities

6. **Comparing and Contrasting** How are electromagnetic waves similar to mechanical waves? How are they different? **For more help, refer to the** Science Skill Handbook.
7. **Calculating Ratios** To go from Earth to Mars, light takes 4 min and a spacecraft takes four months. To go to the nearest star, light takes four years. How long would the same spacecraft take to travel to the nearest star? **For more help, refer to the** Math Skill Handbook.

Answers to Section Assessment

1. a wave that can travel through empty space and that is produced by charged particles in motion
2. by charged particles in motion
3. electric field and magnetic field
4. A high-frequency wave carries more energy than a low-frequency wave does.

5. Possible answers include that light reaches Earth from the Sun.
6. Both mechanical waves and electromagnetic waves carry energy. Mechanical waves require matter through which to travel, but electromagnetic waves don't.
7. The spaceship travels in one month

as far as light travels in one minute. There are approximately 43,200 minutes in one month, so it takes the spaceship 43,200 times as long to travel a given distance as it takes light. It would take the ship 172,800 years to reach the star.

The Electromagnetic Spectrum

Electromagnetic Waves

The room you are sitting in is bathed in a sea of electromagnetic waves. These electromagnetic waves have a wide range of wavelengths and frequencies. For example, TV and radio stations broadcast electromagnetic waves that pass through walls and windows. These waves have wavelengths from about 1 m to over 500 m. Light waves that you see are electromagnetic waves that have wavelengths more than a million times shorter than the waves broadcast by radio stations.

Classifying Electromagnetic Waves The wide range of electromagnetic waves with different frequencies and wavelengths is called the **electromagnetic spectrum. Figure 7** shows the electromagnetic spectrum. Though many different types of electromagnetic waves exist, they all are produced by electric charges that are moving or vibrating. The faster the charge moves or vibrates, the higher the energy of the resulting electromagnetic waves is. Electromagnetic waves carry radiant energy that increases as the frequency increases. For waves that travel with the same speed, the wavelength increases as frequency decreases. So the energy carried by an electromagnetic wave decreases as the wavelength increases.

As You Read

What You'll Learn
- **Explain** differences among kinds of electromagnetic waves.
- **Identify** uses for different kinds of electromagnetic waves.

Vocabulary

electromagnetic spectrum	ultraviolet radiation
radio wave	X ray
infrared wave	gamma ray
visible light	

Why It's Important
Electromagnetic waves are used to cook food, to send and receive information, and to diagnose medical problems.

Figure 7
Electromagnetic waves have a spectrum of different frequencies and wavelengths.

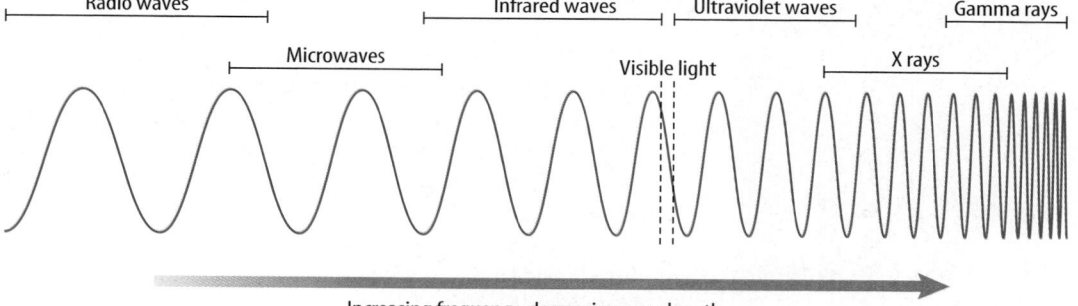

Radio waves — Microwaves — Infrared waves — Visible light — Ultraviolet waves — X rays — Gamma rays

Increasing frequency, decreasing wavelength

Section ✔Assessment Planner

PORTFOLIO
Extension, p. 643

PERFORMANCE ASSESSMENT
MiniLAB, p. 641
Skill Builder Activities, p. 647
See page 660 for more options.

CONTENT ASSESSMENT
Section, p. 647
Challenge, p. 647
Chapter, pp. 660–661

1 Motivate

Bellringer Transparency
Display the Section Focus Transparency for Section 2. Use the accompanying Transparency Activity Master. [L2] ELL

Tie to Prior Knowledge
Ask students whether they have microwave ovens in their homes. Discuss what a microwave is. Then challenge students to explain what the prefix *micro-* refers to. It refers to the fact that the wavelengths of microwaves are shorter than those of radio or TV waves.

Resource Manager

Chapter Resources Booklet
Transparency Activity, p. 43
Directed Reading for Content Mastery, p.18

Electromagnetic Waves

Visual Learning

Figure 7 Point out the wide range of the electromagnetic spectrum. Explain that although humans are able to see only the small sliver of the spectrum known as visible light, many instruments are able to observe the other areas. Ask a volunteer to read the names of the parts of the electromagnetic spectrum, from lowest frequency to highest. L1

IS Visual-Spatial

Radio Waves

Extension

Ask students whether they ever have lost the signal of a radio station while traveling in a car. Have them find out whether AM or FM signals travel farther and why. FM waves are shorter than AM waves, so they are easily blocked by objects. AM waves can be reflected off the ionosphere and bounce back to Earth and thus travel a longer distance. L2

IS Linguistic

Use Science Words

Word Origins The word *radio* is short for *radiotelegraphy.* Ask students to break *radiotelegraphy* into its parts, find the meaning of each part, and explain what the parts combine to mean. The prefix *radi-* means "radiant energy "or" radiation," and comes from the Latin word *radius,* meaning "ray." *Tele-* is from the Greek word *tele,* meaning "far away." The suffix *-graph* is from the Greek *graphein,* meaning "to write." A radiotelegraph is a device that transmits or receives communication over a distance by means of radiation. L3 **IS Linguistic**

Figure 8
Antennas are useful in generating and detecting radio waves.

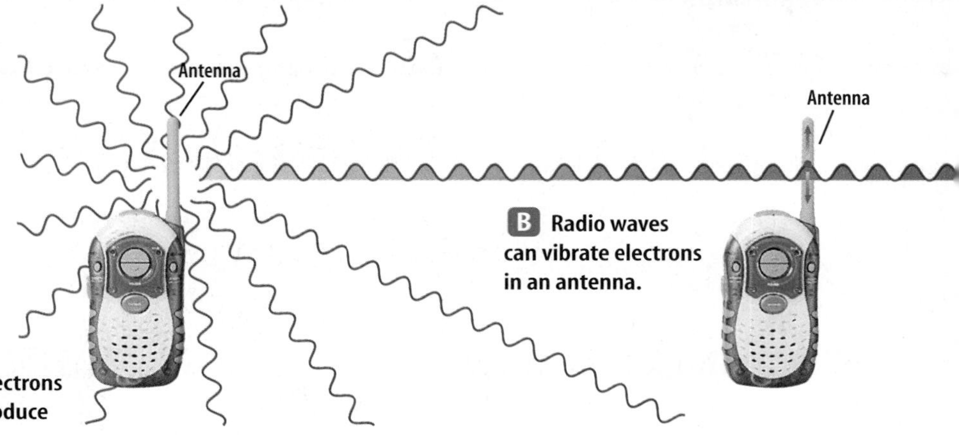

A Vibrating electrons in an antenna produce radio waves.

B Radio waves can vibrate electrons in an antenna.

Figure 9
Towers such as the one shown here are used to send and receive microwaves.

Radio Waves

Electromagnetic waves with wavelengths longer than about 0.3 m are called radio waves. **Radio waves** have the lowest frequencies of all the electromagnetic waves and carry the least energy. Television signals, as well as AM and FM radio signals, are types of radio waves. Like all electromagnetic waves, radio waves are produced by moving charged particles. One way to make radio waves is to make electrons vibrate in a piece of metal, as shown in **Figure 8A.** This piece of metal is called an antenna. By changing the rate at which the electrons vibrate, radio waves of different frequencies can be produced that travel outward from the antenna.

Detecting Radio Waves These radio waves can cause electrons in another piece of metal, such as another antenna, to vibrate, as shown in **Figure 8B.** As the electrons in the receiving antenna vibrate, they form an alternating current. This alternating current can be used to produce a picture on a TV screen and sound from a loudspeaker. Varying the frequency of the radio waves broadcast by the transmitting antenna changes the alternating current in the receiving antenna. This produces the different pictures you see and sounds you hear on your TV.

Microwaves Radio waves with wavelengths between about 0.3 m and 0.001 m are called microwaves. They have a higher frequency and a shorter wavelength than the waves that are used in your home radio. Microwaves are used to transmit some phone calls, especially from cellular and portable phones. **Figure 9** shows a microwave tower.

Microwave ovens use microwaves to heat food. Microwaves produced inside a microwave oven cause water molecules in your food to vibrate faster, which makes the food warmer.

640 CHAPTER 22 Electromagnetic Waves

Resource Manager

Chapter Resources Booklet
MiniLAB, p. 4
Lab Activity, pp. 9–11

Earth Science Critical Thinking/Problem Solving, pp. 8, 13

Science Journal

Radio Frequencies Have students examine radios they have at home and record the range of frequencies spanned by AM and FM bands. Ask students to determine if AM and FM overlap anywhere, and have them record their findings in their Science Journals. AM stations broadcast in kilohertz (kHz) and FM stations broadcast in megahertz (MHz). The bands do not overlap. L2 **IS Intrapersonal**

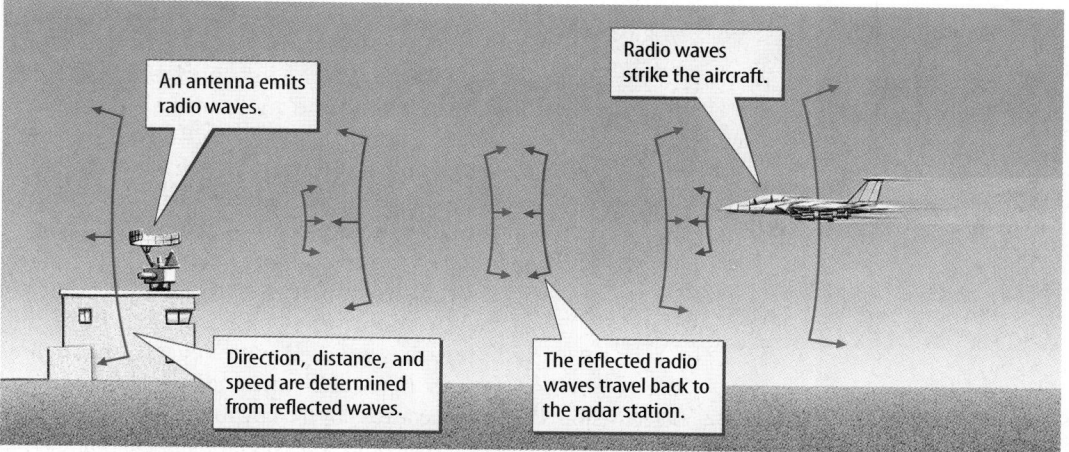

An antenna emits radio waves.

Radio waves strike the aircraft.

Direction, distance, and speed are determined from reflected waves.

The reflected radio waves travel back to the radar station.

Radar You might be familiar with echolocation, in which sound waves are reflected off an object to determine its size and location. Some bats and dolphins use echolocation to navigate and hunt. Radar, an acronym for RAdio Detecting And Ranging, uses electromagnetic waves to detect objects in the same way. Radar was first used during World War II to detect and warn of incoming enemy aircraft.

 **Reading Check** *What does radar do?*

A radar station sends out radio waves that bounce off an object such as an airplane. Electronic equipment measures the time it takes for the radio waves to travel to the plane, be reflected, and return. Because the speed of the radio waves is known, the distance to the airplane can be calculated from the following formula.

$$\text{distance} = \text{speed} \times \text{time}$$

An example of radar being used is shown in **Figure 10.** Because electromagnetic waves travel so quickly, the entire process takes only a fraction of a second.

Infrared Waves

You might know from experience that when you stand near the glowing coals of a barbecue or the red embers of a campfire, your skin senses the heat and becomes warm. Your skin may also feel warm near a hot object that is not glowing. The heat you are sensing with your skin is from electromagnetic waves. These electromagnetic waves are called **infrared waves** and have wavelengths between about one thousandth and 0.7 millionths of a meter.

Figure 10
Radar stations determine direction, distance, and speed of aircraft.

Mini LAB

Observing the Focusing of Infrared Rays

Procedure
1. Place a **concave mirror** 2 m to 3 m away from an **electric heater.** Turn on the heater.
2. Place the palm of your hand in front of the mirror and move it back until you feel heat on your palm. Note the location of the warm area.
3. Move the heater to a new location. How does the warm area move?

Analysis
1. Did you observe the warm area? Where?
2. Compare the location of the warm area to the location of the mirror.

SECTION 2 The Electromagnetic Spectrum **641**

Visible Light

Figure 11
A pit viper hunting in the dark can detect the infrared waves that the warm body of its prey emits.

Figure 12
When objects are heated, their electrons vibrate faster. When the temperature is high enough, the vibrating electrons will emit visible light.

642

Detecting Infrared Waves Infrared rays are emitted by almost every object. In any material the atoms and molecules are in constant motion. Electrons in the atoms and molecules also move and vibrate. As a result, they give off electromagnetic waves. Most of the electromagnetic waves given off by an object at room temperature are infrared waves and have a wavelength of about 0.000 01 m, or one hundred thousandth of a meter.

Infrared detectors can detect objects that are warmer or cooler than their surroundings. For example, areas covered with vegetation, such as forests, tend to be cooler than their surroundings. Using infrared detectors on satellites, the areas covered by forests and other vegetation, as well as water, rock, and soil, can be mapped. Some types of night vision devices use infrared detectors that enable objects to be seen in nearly total darkness.

Animals and Infrared Waves Some animals also can detect infrared waves. Snakes called pit vipers, such as the one shown in **Figure 11,** have a pit located between the nostril and the eye that detects infrared waves. Rattlesnakes, copperheads, and water moccasins are pit vipers. These pits help pit vipers hunt at night by detecting the infrared waves their prey emits.

Visible Light

As the temperature of an object increases, the atoms and molecules in the object move faster. The electrons also vibrate faster, and produce electromagnetic waves of higher frequency and shorter wavelength. If the temperature is high enough, the object might glow, as in **Figure 12.** Some of the electromagnetic waves that the hot object is emitting are now detectable with your eyes. Electromagnetic waves you can detect with your eyes are called **visible light.** Visible light has wavelengths between about 0.7 and 0.4 millionths of a meter. What you see as different colors are electromagnetic waves of different wavelengths. Red light has the longest wavelength (lowest frequency), and blue light has the shortest wavelength (highest frequency).

Most objects that you see do not give off visible light. They simply reflect the visible light that is emitted by a source of light, such as the Sun or a lightbulb.

Electromagnetic Waves From the Sun

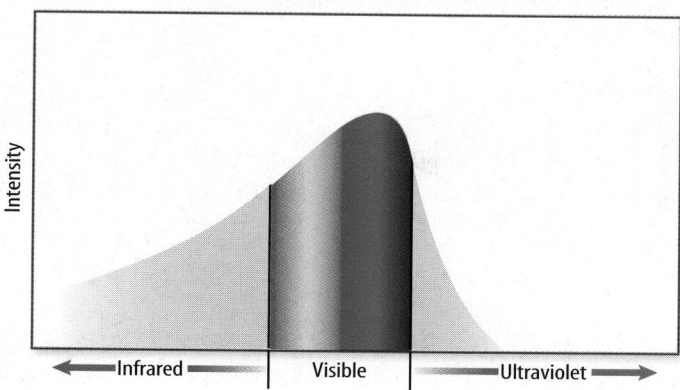

Infrared ◄—— Visible ——► Ultraviolet

Ultraviolet Radiation

Ultraviolet radiation is higher in frequency than visible light and has even shorter wavelengths—between 0.4 millionths of a meter and about ten billionths of a meter. Ultraviolet radiation has higher frequencies than visible light and carries more energy. The radiant energy carried by an ultraviolet wave can be enough to damage the large, fragile molecules that make up living cells. Too much ultraviolet radiation can damage or kill healthy cells.

Figure 13 shows the electromagnetic waves emitted by the Sun, some of which are in the ultraviolet region. Too much exposure to those ultraviolet waves can cause sunburn. Exposure to these waves over a long period of time can lead to early aging of the skin and possibly skin cancer. You can protect yourself from receiving too much ultraviolet radiation by wearing sunglasses and sunscreen, and staying out of the Sun when it is most intense.

Beneficial Uses of UV Radiation A few minutes of exposure each day to ultraviolet radiation from the Sun enables your body to produce the vitamin D it needs. Most people receive that amount during normal activity. The body's natural defense against too much ultraviolet radiation is to tan. However, a tan can be a sign that overexposure to ultraviolet radiation has occurred.

Ultraviolet radiation's cell-killing effect has led to its use as a disinfectant for surgical equipment in hospitals. In some high school chemistry labs, ultraviolet rays are used to sterilize goggles, as shown in **Figure 14.**

Figure 14
Sterilizing devices, such as this goggle sterilizer, use ultraviolet waves to kill organisms on the equipment.

Ultraviolet Radiation

Caption Answer
Figure 13 visible

Extension

Ultraviolet radiation that reaches Earth is made up of two types, UVA and UVB. Both types can contribute to skin cancer and sunburn. Ask students to find out what UVA and UVB are and what each type of UV radiation does. Have them make miniposters illustrating their findings. UVA is UV radiation with wavelengths of 320–400 nanometers. UVA penetrates the skin more deeply than UVB does and is mostly responsible for wrinkling and leathering of the skin. UVA also may directly cause some skin cancers. UVB is UV radiation with wavelengths of 290–320 nanometers. UVB produces sunburn and is considered the main cause of skin cancer. L2 ⟦S⟧ **Visual-Spatial** P

Teacher FYI

Sunscreens chemically absorb UV rays, and sunblocks physically deflect them. Sunscreen blocks higher frequency UVB radiation effectively but provides less UVA protection. The Skin Cancer Foundation recommends that people use sunscreen with an SPF of at least 15, which blocks 93 percent of UVB.

Use Science Words

Word Meaning Ask students to look in a dictionary to find the meanings of the prefixes *infra-* and *ultra-*. Have them then explain why these prefixes are used in the terms infrared and ultraviolet. The prefix *infra-* means "below," and the prefix *ultra-* means "situated beyond." Infrared means "below red," and ultraviolet means "situated beyond violet." L2 ⟦S⟧ **Linguistic**

Science Journal

SPF Have students investigate different types of sunscreens and report on what SPF numbers mean. Ask students to determine which sunscreen is best for their individual skin types and write their findings in their Science Journals. SPF means sun protection factor. It is an indication of how much longer you can stay in the sun without burning than you could without a sunscreen with that SPF. L2 ⟦S⟧ **Intrapersonal**

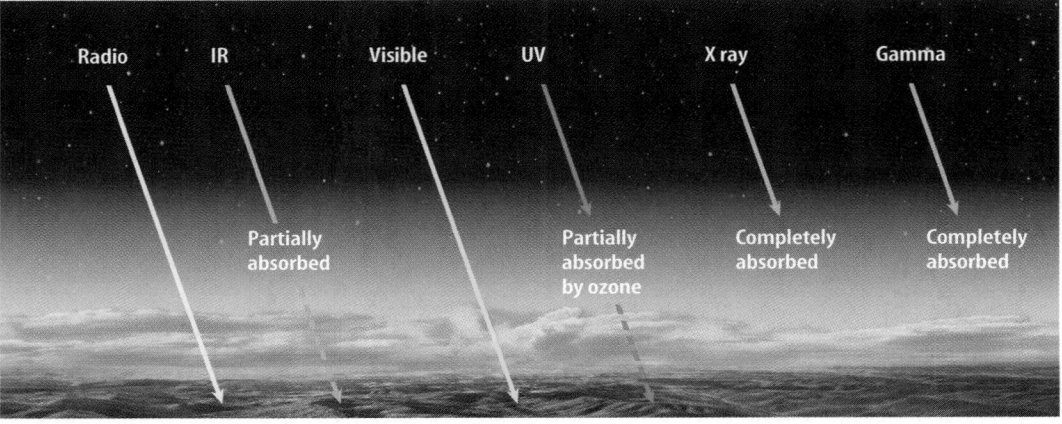

Partially absorbed

Partially absorbed by ozone

Completely absorbed

Completely absorbed

Since warm-blooded animals generate their own body heat, they don't have to rely on their environment to maintain their temperature and can inhabit a wide range of climates. However, warm-blooded animals spend a large amount of energy maintaining their body temperatures, so they need to eat a large amount of food. Cold-blooded animals don't expend as much energy to heat their bodies, so they need to eat less food. Pit vipers would have an easier time detecting warm-blooded animals.

X Rays and Gamma Rays

Use an Analogy

Compare the role of sunscreen to that of the ozone layer. Point out that just as sunscreen blocks some ultraviolet radiation from the skin and prevents burning, the ozone layer blocks some ultraviolet radiation from reaching Earth's surface, where it could be harmful to the cells of living things. Without the ozone shield, there probably would be very little life on Earth.

Figure 15
Earth's atmosphere serves as a shield to block certain types of electromagnetic waves from reaching the surface.

Warm-blooded animals, such as mammals, produce their own body heat. Cold-blooded animals, such as reptiles, absorb heat from the environment. Brainstorm the possible advantages of being either warm-blooded or cold-blooded. Which animals would be easier for a pit viper to detect?

The Ozone Layer Much of the ultraviolet radiation arriving at Earth is absorbed in the upper atmosphere by ozone, as shown in **Figure 15.** Ozone is a molecule that has three oxygen atoms and is formed high in Earth's atmosphere.

However, chemical compounds called CFCs, which are used in air conditioners and refrigerators, can react chemically with ozone. This reaction causes ozone to break down and increases the amount of ultraviolet radiation that penetrates the atmosphere. To prevent this, the use of CFCs is being phased out.

Ultraviolet radiation is not the only type of electromagnetic wave absorbed by Earth's atmosphere. Higher energy waves of X rays and gamma rays also are absorbed. The atmosphere is transparent to radio waves and visible light and partially transparent to infrared waves.

X Rays and Gamma Rays

Ultraviolet rays can penetrate the top layer of your skin. **X rays,** with an even higher frequency than ultraviolet rays, have enough energy to go right through skin and muscle. A shield made from a dense metal, such as lead, is required to stop X rays.

Gamma rays have the highest frequency and, therefore, carry the most energy. Gamma rays are the hardest to stop. They are produced by changes in the nuclei of atoms. When protons and neutrons bond together in nuclear fusion or break apart from each other in nuclear fission, enormous quantities of energy are released. Some of this energy is released as gamma rays.

Just as too much ultraviolet radiation can hurt or kill cells, too much X ray or gamma radiation can have the same effect. Because the energy of the waves is so much higher, the exposure that is needed to cause damage is much less.

Curriculum Connection

Math X rays were discovered accidentally by Wilhelm Roentgen in 1895. Because they were a mystery and x is the usual symbol for an unknown in mathematics, they were named X rays. Have students find out what the unit named for Roentgen measures and what other units are used to make similar measurements. *A roentgen is a unit for absorbed energy or dose from nuclear radiation. Other units for absorbed dose are the gray and the rad.*

Using High-Energy Electromagnetic Radiation The fact that X rays can pass through the human body makes them useful for medical diagnosis, as shown in **Figure 16.** X rays pass through the less dense tissues in skin and other organs. These X rays strike a film, creating a shadow image of the denser tissues. X-ray images help doctors detect injuries and diseases, such as broken bones and cancer. A CT scanner uses X rays to produce images of the human body as if it had been sliced like a loaf of bread.

Although the radiation received from getting one medical or dental X ray is not harmful, the cumulative effect of numerous X rays can be dangerous. The operator of the X-ray machine usually stands behind a shield to avoid being exposed to X rays. Lead shields or aprons are used to protect the parts of the patient's body that are not receiving the X rays.

Using Gamma Rays Although gamma rays are dangerous, they also have beneficial uses, just as X rays do. A beam of gamma rays focused on a cancerous tumor can kill the tumor. Gamma radiation also can cleanse food of disease-causing bacteria. More than 1,000 Americans die each year from *Salmonella* bacteria in poultry and *E. coli* bacteria in meat. Although gamma radiation has been used since 1963 to kill bacteria in food, this method is not widely used in the food industry.

Astronomy Across the Spectrum

Some astronomical objects produce no visible light and can be detected only through the infrared and radio waves they emit. Some galaxies emit X rays from regions that do not emit visible light. Studying stars and galaxies like these using only visible light would be like looking at only one color in a picture. **Figure 17** shows how different electromagnetic waves can be used to study the universe.

Figure 16
Dense tissues such as bone absorb more X rays than softer tissues do. Consequently, dense tissues leave a shadow on film that can be use to diagnose medical and dental conditions.

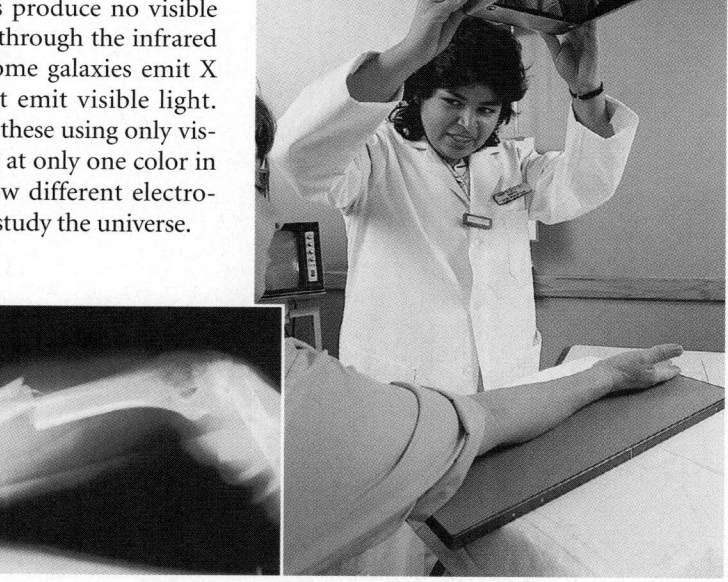

IDENTIFYING Misconceptions

Students often will associate any use of the word *radiation* incorrectly with nuclear connotations. Point out that gamma rays and X rays can result from nuclear changes. However, none of the other types of electromagnetic radiation studied in this chapter are associated with nuclear decay.

Visual Learning

Figure 16 After students have examined the images and read the caption, have them identify which of the following tissues would show up most clearly on an X-ray photograph—the teeth or the tongue. Why? The teeth would show up more clearly because they are more dense than the tongue.
L2 [IS] **Logical-Mathematical**

Astronomy Across the Spectrum

Extension

Have students find out what spectroscopy is and some of its uses. Ask them to make multimedia presentations of their findings to the class. Spectroscopy is the study of how electromagnetic radiation interacts with matter. Spectroscopic studies can be used to identify the substances that make up objects, including stars and other bodies in space. L3 [IS] **Linguistic**

✓ Active Reading

Jigsaw In this collaborative learning technique, individuals become experts on a portion of a text and share their expertise with a small group, called their home group. Everyone shares the responsibility for learning the assigned reading. Assign each person in each group an expert number (1 through 5, for example). Have students gather into the expert groups that correspond to the number they were assigned. Have them read, discuss, and master chapter concepts and determine how best to teach these concepts to their home groups. Have students return to their home groups and share the content they learned in their expert groups. Have students use the Jigsaw strategy as they learn about different types of electromagnetic waves.

Visualizing the Universe

Have students examine the pictures and read the captions. Then ask the following questions.

Why have astronomers only recently studied wavelengths other than visible light? Possible answer: Detecting these different types of waves requires advanced technologies that were not always available.

Why might the sun or other celestial objects look different when various types of waves are being detected? Possible answer: While an object may be a strong emitter of one type of wave, it may not emit another type. Dust, atmosphere, or other objects may block out certain wavelengths too.

Activity

Have students look at photographs of various celestial objects from a variety of different types of telescopes. Have students locate the type of wavelength used for each photograph on the electromagnetic spectrum. [L2] [IS] **Visual-Spatial**

Extension

Have students search for astronomical pictures that are made from wavelengths other than visible light. Students should prepare a presentation for their class using their photographs. [L2] [IS] **Visual-Spatial**

Figure 17

For centuries, astronomers studied the universe using only the visible light coming from planets, moons, and stars. But many objects in space also emit X rays, ultraviolet and infrared radiation, and radio waves. Scientists now use telescopes that can "see" these different types of electromagnetic waves. As these images of the Sun reveal, the new tools are providing remarkable views of objects in the universe.

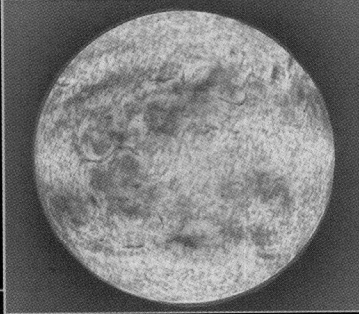

▲ **INFRARED RADIATION** An infrared telescope reveals that the Sun's surface temperature is not uniform. Some areas are hotter than others.

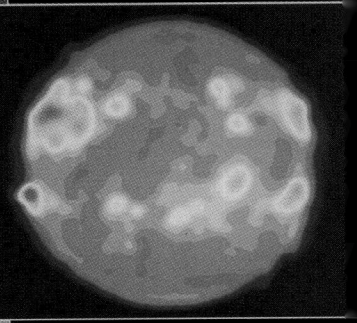

▲ **RADIO WAVES** Radio telescopes detect radio waves given off by the Sun, which have much longer wavelengths than visible light.

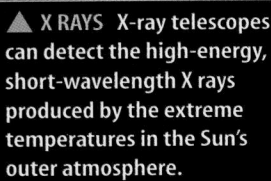

▲ **X RAYS** X-ray telescopes can detect the high-energy, short-wavelength X rays produced by the extreme temperatures in the Sun's outer atmosphere.

▶ **ULTRAVIOLET RADIATION** Telescopes sensitive to ultraviolet radiation—electromagnetic waves with shorter wavelengths than visible light—can "see" the Sun's outer atmosphere.

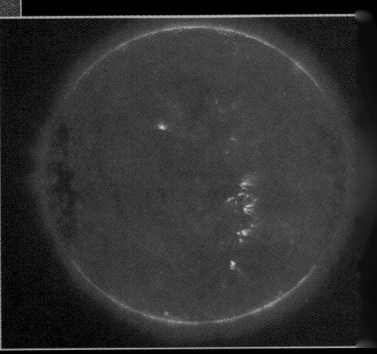

646 CHAPTER 22 Electromagnetic Waves

Resource Manager

Chapter Resources Booklet
  Enrichment, p. 29

Figure 18
Launching satellite observatories above Earth's atmosphere is the only way to see the universe at electromagnetic wavelengths that are absorbed by Earth's atmosphere.

Astronomy
INTEGRATION

Satellite Observations Recall from **Figure 15** that Earth's atmosphere blocks some parts of the electromagnetic spectrum. For example, X rays, gamma rays, most ultraviolet rays, and some infrared rays cannot pass through. However, telescopes in orbit above Earth's atmosphere can obtain more information than can be obtained at Earth's surface about stars, galaxies, and other objects in the universe. **Figure 18** shows three such satellites—the Extreme Ultraviolet Explorer, the Chandra X-Ray Observatory, and the Infrared Space Observatory.

✔ **Reading Check** *Why are telescopes sent into space on artificial satellites?*

Section 2 Assessment

1. List three types of electromagnetic waves produced by the Sun.
2. Why is ultraviolet light more damaging to cells than infrared light is?
3. Give an application of infrared waves.
4. Describe the difference between X rays and gamma rays.
5. **Think Critically** Why does Earth emit mainly infrared waves and the Sun emit visible light and ultraviolet waves?

Skill Builder Activities

6. **Recognizing Cause and Effect** If visible light is the effect, what is the cause? Do the different colors of light have different causes? **For more help, refer to the** Science Skill Handbook.
7. **Using a Database** What do images of the same object look like if different wavelengths are detected? Use a database to research this topic and present a report to your class. **For more help, refer to the** Technology Skill Handbook.

Answers to Section Assessment

1. Possible answer: ultraviolet radiation, visible light, radio waves, infrared waves
2. It has a higher frequency and more energy, so it can penetrate the skin.
3. Possible answer: Pit vipers use infrared to sense their prey in the dark.
4. Gamma rays have a higher frequency and more energy than X rays do.
5. The frequencies of the electromagnetic waves emitted by an object increase as the temperature increases. The Sun is much hotter than Earth, and so it emits more higher-frequency electromagnetic radiation than Earth emits.
6. Charges moving and radiating energy cause light. Yes; each color is caused by charges moving at a different frequency.
7. Students should find that objects have different characteristics when viewed in different wavelengths.

Purpose Students observe that light is composed of various colors or frequencies. L2

IS Visual-Spatial

Process Skills observing, inferring, recognizing cause and effect, formulating models

Time Required 40 minutes

Safety Precautions Caution students to be careful not to break the glass slides.

Teaching Strategy The prism may need to be moved around to produce a spectrum.

Answers to Questions

1. red, orange, yellow, green, blue, violet
2. Raising the flashlight so it is above the prism causes the colors to shift downward. Lowering the flashlight shifts the colors upward.
3. The order of the colors doesn't change.
4. Red light waves have been bent the least and violet light waves have been bent the most.
5. The amount of bending increases as the wavelength decreases and the frequency increases.

✓ Assessment

Process Have students hypothesize about the role of the water in the prism. Then have them test their hypotheses by removing the water and seeing the effect this has on the spectrum. The water makes the different colors separate more. Without the water, the spectrum is harder to see. Use **Performance Assessment in the Science Classroom,** p. 97.

Activity

Prisms of Light

Do you know what light is? Many would answer that light is what you turn on to see at night. However, white light is made of many different frequencies of the electromagnetic spectrum. A prism can separate white light into its different frequencies. You see different frequencies of light as different colors. What colors do you see when light passes through a prism?

What You'll Investigate
What happens to visible light as it passes through a prism?

Goals
- **Construct** a prism and observe the different colors that are produced.
- **Infer** how the bending of light waves depends on their wavelength.

Materials
microscope slides (3)   flashlight
transparent tape   water
clay

Safety Precautions

Procedure

1. Carefully tape the three slides together on their long sides so they form a long prism.
2. Place one end of the prism into a softened piece of clay so the prism is standing upright.
3. Fill the prism with water and put it on a table that is against a dark wall.
4. Shine a flashlight beam through the prism so the light becomes visible on the wall.

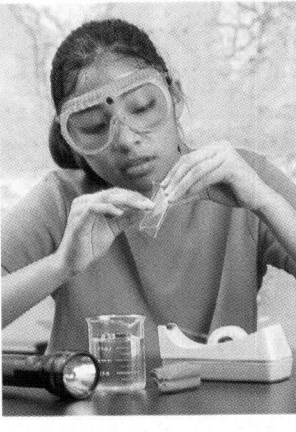

Conclude and Apply

1. What was the order of the colors you saw on the wall?
2. How does the position of the colors on the wall change as you change the direction of the flashlight beam?
3. How does the order of colors on the wall change as you change the direction of the flashlight beam?
4. After passing through the water prism, which color light waves have changed direction, or have been bent, the most? Which color has been bent the least?
5. How does the amount of bending of a light wave depend on its wavelength? How does it depend on the frequency?

Communicating Your Data

Compare your conclusions with those of other students in your class. **For more help, refer to the** Science Skill Handbook.

Communicating Your Data

Have each student make a labeled diagram that illustrates the procedure and results of the experiment.

Resource Manager

Chapter Resources Booklet
Activity Worksheet, pp. 5–6

3 Using Electromagnetic Waves

Telecommunications

In the past week, have you spoken on the phone, watched television, done research on the Internet, or listened to the radio? Today you can talk to someone far away or transmit and receive information over long distances almost instantly. Thanks to telecommunications, the world is becoming increasingly connected through the use of electromagnetic waves.

Using Radio Waves

Radio waves usually are used to send and receive information over long distances. Using radio waves to communicate has several advantages. For example, radio waves pass through walls and windows easily. Radio waves do not interact with humans, so they are not harmful to people like ultraviolet rays or X rays are. So most telecommunication devices, such as TVs, radios, and telephones, use radio waves to transmit information such as images and sounds. **Figure 19** shows how radio waves can be used to transmit information—in this case transmitting information that enables sounds to be reproduced at a location far away.

As You Read

What You'll Learn
- **Explain** different methods of electronic communication.
- **Compare and contrast** AM and FM signals.

Vocabulary
Carrier wave
Global Positioning System

Why It's Important
Telecommunication enables people to contact others and collect information worldwide.

Figure 19
Transmitting sounds by radio waves uses conversions among sound, electrical, and radiant energies.

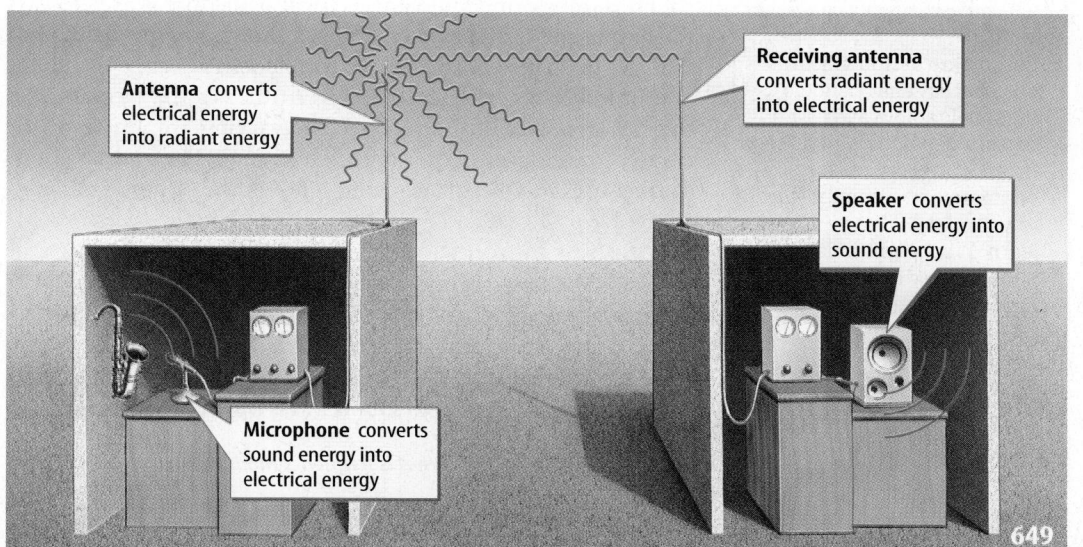

Antenna converts electrical energy into radiant energy

Receiving antenna converts radiant energy into electrical energy

Speaker converts electrical energy into sound energy

Microphone converts sound energy into electrical energy

649

SECTION

3 Using Electromagnetic Waves

1 Motivate

Bellringer Transparency
Display the Section Focus Transparency for Section 3. Use the accompanying Transparency Activity Master. L2 ELL

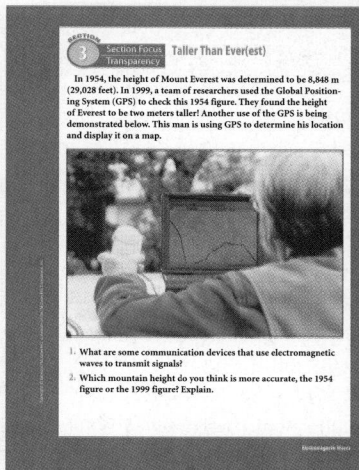

Section Focus Transparency — Taller Than Ever(est)

In 1954, the height of Mount Everest was determined to be 8,848 m (29,028 feet). In 1999, a team of researchers used the Global Positioning System (GPS) to check this 1954 figure. They found the height of Everest to be two meters taller! Another use of the GPS is being demonstrated below. This man is using GPS to determine his location and display it on a map.

1. What are some communication devices that use electromagnetic waves to transmit signals?
2. Which mountain height do you think is more accurate, the 1954 figure or the 1999 figure? Explain.

Tie to Prior Knowledge
Ask students whether they have ever used a cordless, cellular, or digital phone. Point out that all of these communication devices work using electromagnetic waves.

Section ✓Assessment Planner

PORTFOLIO
Curriculum Connection, p. 651
PERFORMANCE ASSESSMENT
Math Skills Activity, p. 651
Skill Builder Activities, p. 653
See page 660 for more options.

CONTENT ASSESSMENT
Section, p. 653
Challenge, p. 653
Chapter, pp. 660–661

Using Radio Waves

Visual Learning

Figure 19 Review with students the generation of an electromagnetic wave in an antenna shown in this figure. **What determines the frequency of the wave?** how fast the charge moves up and down in the antenna **What determines the wavelength of the wave?** The wavelength is determined by the frequency and the speed of the waves.
L2 IS **Visual-Spatial**

Astronomy INTEGRATION

Pulsars are small, heavy, collapsed stars called neutron stars that rotate about once per second. They have enormous magnetic fields. They emit beams of radio waves once per rotation. If Earth happens to be on the path of the beam, we detect a regular periodic radio signal. Because it is so regular, it is easy to understand how it may have been interpreted as a signal from an alien civilization.

Fun Fact

Because they were originally believed to be communications from an alien civilization, pulsars were almost named LGMs, which stood for "Little Green Men."

✔ Reading Check

Answer in radio transmission, the variation of the frequency of a carrier wave to carry information

---

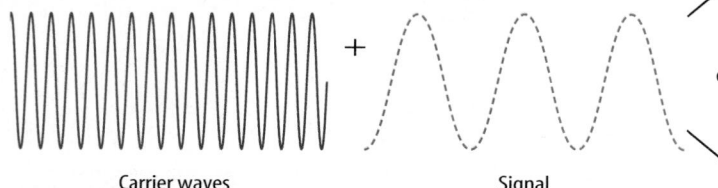

Figure 20
A signal can be carried by a carrier wave in two ways— amplitude modulation or frequency modulation.

Carrier waves   +   Signal   or   Amplitude modulated wave

Frequency modulated wave

Astronomy INTEGRATION

Pulsars are astronomical objects that emit periodic bursts of radio waves. The pattern of pulses is regular. Investigate how pulsars originate and communicate to your class what you learn. Why might pulsars have seemed to be signals from intelligent life?

Radio Transmission How is information, such as images or sounds, broadcast by radio waves? Each radio and television station is assigned a particular frequency at which it broadcasts radio waves. The radio waves broadcast by a station at its assigned frequency are the **carrier waves** for that station. To listen to a station you tune your radio or television to the frequency of the station's carrier waves. To carry information on the carrier wave, either the amplitude or the frequency of the carrier wave is changed, or modulated.

Amplitude Modulation The letters *AM* in AM radio stand for amplitude modulation, which means that the amplitude of the carrier wave is changed to transmit information. The original sound is transformed into an electrical signal that is used to vary the amplitude of the carrier wave, as shown in **Figure 20.** Note that the frequency of the carrier wave doesn't change—only the amplitude changes. An AM receiver tunes to the frequency of the carrier wave. In the receiver, the varying amplitude of the carrier waves produces an electric signal. The radio's loudspeaker uses this electric signal to produce the original sound.

Frequency Modulation FM radio works in much the same way as AM radio, but the frequency instead of the amplitude is modulated, as shown in **Figure 20.** An FM receiver contains electronic components that use the varying frequency of the carrier wave to produce an electric signal. As in an AM radio, this electric signal is converted into sound waves by a loudspeaker.

✔ Reading Check   *What is frequency modulation?*

Science Journal

Early Communication Have students write about how they think information was spread before any type of electronic communication existed. Challenge them to describe the speed and accuracy of such communication and compare it with ways they communicate today.
L1 IS **Linguistic**

Cultural Diversity

Early Observations in Astronomy In 1054, Chinese astronomers observed a massive supernova explosion where the Crab Nebula now exists. A pulsar now can be detected at the heart of this nebula. Have students calculate how many years ago the supernova exploded and how many times their age this is. The formula (this year − 1054) ÷ student's age will give the answer. L2
IS **Logical-Mathematical**

Telephones

A telephone contains a microphone in the mouthpiece that converts a sound wave into an electric signal. The electric signal is carried through a wire to the telephone switching system. There, the signal might be sent through other wires or be converted into a radio or microwave signal for transmission through the air. The electric signal also can be converted into a light wave for transmission through fiber-optic cables.

At the receiving end, the signal is converted back to an electric signal. A speaker in the earpiece of the phone changes the electric signal into a sound wave.

✔ Reading Check *What device converts sound into an electric signal?*

Math Skills Activity

Calculating the Wavelength of Radio Frequencies

Example Problem

You are listening to an FM station with a frequency of 94.9 MHz or 94,900,000 Hz. How long are the wavelengths that strike the antenna? For any wave, the wavelength equals the wave speed divided by the frequency. The speed of radio waves is 300,000,000 m/s. The SI unit of frequency, Hz, is equal to l/s.

Solution

1 *This is what you know:*
frequency = 94,900,000 Hz
wave speed = 300,000,000 m/s

2 *This is what you need to find:*
wavelength

3 *This is the equation you need to use:*
wavelength = wave speed/frequency

4 *Substitute the known values:*
wavelength = (300,000,000 m/s)/(94,900,000 Hz)
= 3.16 m

Check your answer by multiplying the units. Do you calculate a unit of distance for your answer?

Practice Problems

1. Your friend prefers an AM radio station at 1,520 kHz (1,520 thousand vibrations each second). What is the wavelength of this frequency? Which has a longer wavelength, AM or FM radio waves?

2. An AM radio station operates at 580 kHz (580 thousand vibrations each second). What is the wavelength of this frequency? What is the relationship between frequency and wavelength?

For more help, refer to the Math Skill Handbook.

SECTION 3 Using Electromagnetic Waves **651**

Use Science Words

Word Meaning Ask students to find the origin of the term *cell phone*. The term *cell phone* refers to the cell, or the area that one tower can serve. A cell tower can cover up to a 15 km radius. Tower cells overlap so that coverage isn't lost. L2 IS **Linguistic**

Discussion

Why is there a limit to the number of people who can talk on cell phones in a particular cell at the same time? Each phone uses a different frequency. If all of the assigned frequencies are being used, no other phones can be used at that time. L3 IS **Logical-Mathematical**

Communications Satellites

Make a Model

Have students find the locations of two or three geosynchronous communications satellites above Earth and make models showing their positions. Geosynchronous satellites orbit Earth directly above the equator once every 24 hours, so that each is always above the same point on the equator. They maintain an altitude of about 35,800 km. L2

IS **Visual-Spatial**

The Global Positioning System

✔ **Reading Check**

Answer Possible answers: vehicle navigation, surveying, hiking navigation, navigating at sea

Figure 21
Electromagnetic waves make using telephones easier.

A Cordless phones use radio waves to allow users to talk from anywhere in the house.

B Radio waves enable cell phone users to send or receive calls without using wires.

Research Visit the Glencoe Science Web site at **science.glencoe.com** for more information about how satellites are used in around-the-world communications. Summarize what you learn in an informational handout.

Remote Phones A telephone does not have to transmit its signal through wires. In a cordless phone, the electrical signal produced by the microphone is transmitted through an antenna in the handset to the base. **Figure 21A** shows how incoming signals are transmitted from the base to the handset. A cellular phone uses an antenna to broadcast and receive information between the phone and a base station, as shown in **Figure 21B.** The base station uses radio waves to communicate with other stations in a network.

Pagers The base station also is used in a pager system. When you dial a pager, the signal is sent to a base station. From there, an electromagnetic signal is sent to the pager. The pager beeps or vibrates to indicate that someone has called. With a touch-tone phone, you can transmit numeric information, such as your phone number, which the pager will receive and display.

Communications Satellites

How do you send information to the other side of the world? Radio waves can't be sent directly through Earth. Instead, radio signals are sent to satellites. The satellites can communicate with other satellites or with ground stations. Some communications satellites are in geosynchronous orbit, meaning each satellite remains above the same point on the ground.

Resource Manager

Chapter Resources Booklet
Lab Activity, pp. 13–14
Transparency Activity, pp. 45–46
Activity Worksheet, pp. 7–8
Lab Management and Safety, p. 73

Internet Addresses
_____
_____
_____
_____

Explore the Glencoe Science Web site at **science.glencoe.com** to find out more about topics in this section.

The Global Positioning System

Satellites also are used as part of the **Global Positioning System,** or GPS. GPS is used to locate objects on Earth. The system consists of satellites, ground-based stations, and portable units with receivers, as illustrated in **Figure 22.**

A GPS receiver measures the time it takes for radio waves to travel from several satellites to the receiver. This determines the distance to each satellite. The receiver then uses this information to calculate its latitude, longitude, and elevation. The accuracy of GPS receivers ranges from a few hundred meters for hand-held units, to several centimeters for units that are used to measure the movements of Earth's crust.

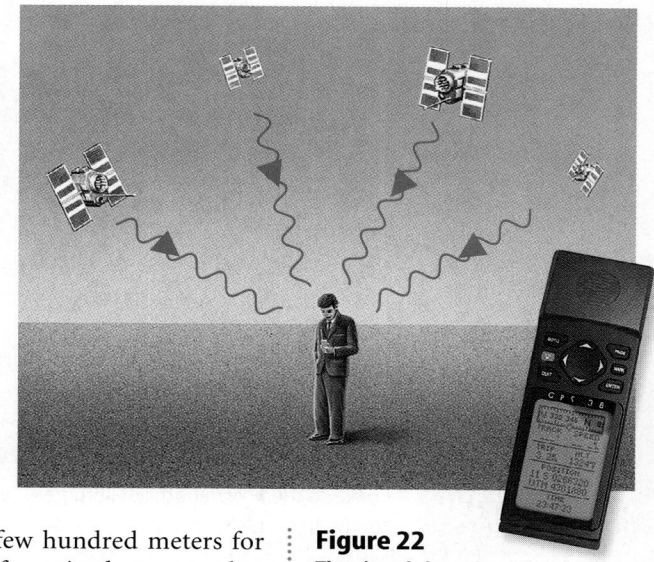

Figure 22
The signals broadcast from GPS satellites enable portable, hand-held receivers to determine the position of an object or person.

Reading Check *What is GPS used for?*

Many of these forms of communication have been developed over the past few decades. For example, an Internet connection transfers images and sound using the telephone network, just as a television signal transfers images and sound using radio waves. What forms of telecommunications do you think you'll be using a few decades from now?

Section 3 Assessment

1. What is a modulated radio signal?
2. What does a microphone do? What does a speaker do?
3. What types of information does a GPS receiver provide for its user?
4. What is a communications satellite?
5. **Think Critically** Make a diagram showing how a communication satellite could be used to relay information from a broadcasting station in New York to a receiving station in London.

Skill Builder Activities

6. **Researching Information** Find out more about a form of telecommunications, such as email or shortwave radio. **For more help,** refer to the Science Skill Handbook.

7. **Communicating** Think of a story you have enjoyed about a time before telecommunications or one in which telecommunication was not possible. How would telecommunications have changed the story? **For more help,** refer to the Science Skill Handbook.

Visual Learning

Figure 22 Point out the variety of components used in the Global Positioning System. Explain that 24 satellites are used to get complete coverage of the planet. The distance to three or four satellites must be measured to determine the position of an object.

3 Assess

Reteach

Explain the energy transformations that occur as sound is transported via a normal telephone. Help students make diagrams to outline the steps. L2
Visual-Spatial

Challenge

Ask students to find the difference between a digital signal and analog signal. A digital signal is composed of combinations of 1's and 0's that carry information. An analog signal transmits information as a continually varying waveform. L3 **Linguistic**

Assessment

Process Have students write short explanations of how a normal telephone, a cordless phone, and a cell phone send information. A normal telephone sends information as electrical signals that travel through telephone wire. A cordless phone sends information as radio waves from the phone to the receiver, then through phone lines as electrical signals. A cell phone sends signals only as radio waves to a base station. Use **PASC,** p. 159.

Recognize the Problem

Purpose
Students identify the color spectrum of a light source and relate the wavelength of the colors to the temperature of the light source. L2
IS **Logical-Mathematical**

Process Skills
observing, interpreting data, inferring, communicating, comparing and contrasting, recognizing cause and effect, forming operational definitions, forming a hypothesis, designing an experiment

Time Required
40 minutes

Materials
Dimmer switches can be obtained at local hardware stores.

Alternate Materials
Use clear 4-, 15-, 25-, 60-, and 100-watt lightbulbs if a dimmer is not available.

Safety Precautions
Caution students that current from a 120-V AC wall socket can be lethal. Remind students that lightbulbs can become hot.

Spectrum Inspection

You've heard the term "red-hot" used to describe something that is unusually hot. When a piece of metal is heated it may give off a red glow or even a yellow glow. All objects emit electromagnetic waves. How do the wavelengths of these waves depend on the temperature of the object?

Recognize the Problem

How do the wavelengths of light produced by a lightbulb depend on the temperature of the lightbulb?

Form a Hypothesis

The brightness of a lightbulb increases as its temperature increases. Form a hypothesis describing how the wavelengths emitted by a lightbulb will change as the brightness of a lightbulb changes.

Goals
- **Design** an experiment that determines the relationship between brightness and the wavelengths emitted by a lightbulb.
- **Observe** the wavelengths of light emitted by a lightbulb as its brightness changes.

Safety Precautions

WARNING: Be sure all electrical cords and connections are intact and that you have a dry working area. Do not touch the bulbs as they may be hot.

Possible Materials
diffraction grating
power supply with variable resistor switch
clear, tubular lightbulb and socket
red, yellow, and blue colored pencils

Inclusion Strategies

Learning Disabled Before beginning the activity, have students discuss the relationship between color, frequency, and energy. Ask questions that help students realize that colors near the red end of the spectrum have lower frequencies, longer wavelengths, and lower energy. They should also realize that hotter objects emit more blue light.

Curriculum Connection

Astronomy The color of a star is an indication of its temperature. The coolest stars are reddish, and the hottest stars are slightly blue. Encourage students to look outside at night and attempt to identify different colors of stars. L2
IS **Naturalist**

Test Your Hypothesis

Plan

1. **Decide** how you will determine the effect of lightbulb brightness on the colors of light that are emitted.

2. As shown in the photo at the right, you will look toward the light through the diffraction grating to detect the colors of light emitted by the bulb. The color spectrum will appear to the right and to the left of the bulb.

3. **List** the specific steps you will need to take to test your hypothesis. Describe precisely what you will do in each step. Will you first test the bulb at a bright or dim setting? How many settings will you test? (Try at least three.) How will you record your observations in an organized way?

4. **List** the materials you will need for your experiment. Describe exactly how and in which order you will use these materials.

5. **Identify** any constants and variables in your experiment.

Do

1. Make sure your teacher approves your plan before you start.

2. **Perform** your experiment as planned.

3. While doing your experiment, write down any observations you make in your Science Journal.

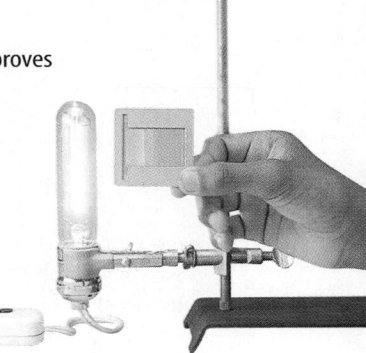

Analyze Your Data

1. Use the colored pencils to draw the color spectrum emitted by the bulb at each brightness.

2. Which colors appeared as the bulb became brighter? Did any colors disappear?

3. How did the wavelengths emitted by the bulb change as the bulb became brighter?

4. Infer how the frequencies emitted by the lightbulb changed as it became hotter.

Draw Conclusions

1. If an object becomes hotter, what happens to the wavelengths it emits?

2. How do the wavelengths that the bulb emits change if it is turned off?

3. From your results, infer whether red stars or yellow stars are hotter.

Communicating
Your Data

Compare your results with others in your class. How many different colors were seen?

Assessment

Process Predict how the spectrum you see in the diffraction grating would differ if you looked at different types of bulbs, such as a colored lightbulb, neon light, or fluorescent bulb. Test your predictions. The spectrum will vary with the nature of the light source and its temperature. Use **PASC**, p. 97.

Communicating
Your Data

Have students compare the drawings they made of the spectrum for the different settings of the dimmer switch.

Possible Hypothesis

Students may hypothesize that the spectra remain the same regardless of the brightness of the light source.

Test Your Hypothesis

Possible Procedures

Align the grating with the filament and observe the spectrum. Vary power to the lamp and observe the spectrum again.

Teaching Strategy

Students should hold the diffraction grating near their eyes for best observations.

Expected Outcome

Students should observe all colors from bright light but decreased blue from dimmer light.

Analyze Your Data

1. Drawings should show all colors present from bright lights, but less blue as the brightness decreases.

2. All colors are visible when the bulb is bright. Bluish colors fade in dimmer light.

3. Short wavelengths are visible from brighter light.

4. Short wavelengths are visible from a hotter bulb.

Error Analysis

What would you see if the diffraction grating were not aligned with the axis of the filament?

Draw Conclusions

1. It emits shorter wavelengths.

2. The bulb cools off, so the wavelengths increase beyond the red end of the spectrum.

3. yellow stars

Content Background

Today there are three main types of wireless networking technology.

Radio operates in the public portion of the radio spectrum. It uses spread-spectrum technology. Spread-spectrum technology has two major methods of operation: direct sequence and frequency hopping, the type Ms. Lamarr was instrumental in developing.

Microwave technology is typically used in long-range setups and satellite communications.

Finally, there is infrared laser communication, which uses coherent beams of infrared light to transmit data.

Frequency-hopping spread-spectrum technology (FHSS) was developed by the military for secure communications. Every few milliseconds, a FHSS signal bounces between different specific points in a designated area of the electromagnetic spectrum, reducing interference from other signals and making it very difficult to listen in on the transmission. The drawback is that FHSS is relatively slow, and in congested cities with a lot of radio traffic, range can be reduced. Under those circumstances, FHSS is roughly the equivalent of being a lane hopper in rush-hour traffic.

Hedy Lamarr, actor and inventor

Hopping the

Ringgggg. There it is—that familiar beep! Out come the cellular phones—from purses, pockets, book bags, belt clips, and briefcases. At any given moment, a million wireless signals are flying through the air—and not just cell phone signals. With radio and television signals, Internet data, and even Global Positioning System information coming at us, the air seems like a pretty crowded place. How do all of these signals get to the right place? How does a cellular phone pick out its own signal from among the clutter? The answer lies in a concept developed in 1940 by Hedy Lamarr.

Lamarr was born in Vienna, Austria. In 1937, she left Austria to escape Hitler's invading Nazi army. Lamarr left for another reason, as well. She was determined to pursue a career as an actor. And she became a famous movie star.

In 1940, Lamarr came up with an idea to keep radio signals that guided torpedoes from being jammed. Her idea, called frequency hopping, involved breaking the radio signal that was guiding the torpedo into tiny parts and rapidly changing their frequency. The enemy would not be able to keep up with the frequency changes and thus would not be able to divert the torpedo from its target. Lamarr worked with a partner who helped her figure out how to make the idea work. They were awarded a patent for their idea in 1942.

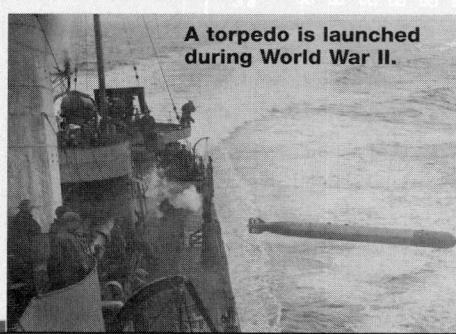

A torpedo is launched during World War II.

656

Resources for Teachers and Students

Practical Spread Spectrum: Frequency Hopping, Book II, by Charles O. Phillips, Aegean Park Press, 1996.

Wireless Radio: A Brief History, by Lewis Coe, McFarland and Company, 1996.

Spread Spectrum

Lamarr's idea was ahead of its time. The digital technology that allowed efficient operation of her system wasn't invented until decades later. However, after 1962, frequency hopping was adopted and used in U.S. military communications. It was the development of cellular phones, however, that benefited the most from Lamarr's concept.

Cellular phones and other wireless technologies operate by breaking their signals into smaller parts, called packets. The packets are encoded in a certain way for particular receivers and are spread across bands of the electromagnetic spectrum. In this way, millions of users can use the same frequencies at the same time.

Frequencies

CONNECTIONS Brainstorm **How are you using wireless technology in your life right now? List ways it makes your life easier. Are there drawbacks to some of the uses for wireless technology? What are they?**

SCIENCE *Online*

For more information, visit science.glencoe.com

CONNECTIONS Discuss with students how the Internet has made life easier and if it has caused any problems. If students have access to cell phones, ask what the good and bad points of this technology have been. Even students who do not have access to this technology should be able to deduce such information.

SCIENCE *Online*

Internet Addresses

_____

_____

_____

Explore the Glencoe Science Web site at **science.glencoe.com** to find out more about topics in this feature.

Discussion

Why was Ms. Lamarr's idea ahead of its time? When she introduced the idea, the technology wasn't available to make it work well. L2
IS **Logical-Mathematical**

Historical Significance

To make students better aware of the history of radio, have them learn about the history of radio through a research project. As a class, make a timeline to illustrate the history of radio. Break the class into groups and give each group a ten or twenty year span of history to study, starting with the turn of the twentieth century. Have each group find the discoveries and inventions that occurred during its assigned period of time that significantly advanced the wireless communication industry and present their findings to the class.

Reviewing Main Ideas

Preview

Students can answer the questions in their Science Journals. Discuss the answers as you go through the chapter. **LS** **Linguistic**

Review

Students can write their answers, then compare them with those of other students. **LS** **Interpersonal**

Reteach

Students can look at the illustrations and describe details that support the main ideas of the chapter. **LS** **Visual-Spatial**

Answers to Chapter Review

SECTION 1

2. Both waves have a frequency and wavelength. Both carry energy.

SECTION 2

2. The infrared camera detects the infrared radiation given off by the person's body.

SECTION 3

3. Possible answer: After your voice is transformed into an electrical signal, that signal may be sent by radio or microwaves to another location.

Reviewing Main Ideas

Section 1 The Nature of Electromagnetic Waves

1. Vibrating charges generate vibrating electric and magnetic fields. These vibrating fields travel through space and are called electromagnetic waves.

2. Electromagnetic waves, like all waves, have wavelength, frequency, amplitude, and carry energy. *How are ocean waves similar to electromagnetic waves?*

Section 2 The Electromagnetic Spectrum

1. Radio waves have the longest wavelength and lowest energy. Radar uses radio waves to locate objects.

2. All objects emit infrared waves. Most objects you see reflect the visible light emitted by a source of light. *How could a person be seen in total darkness?*

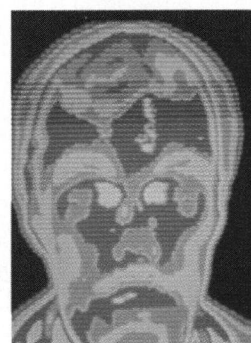

3. Ultraviolet waves have a higher frequency and carry more energy than visible light.

4. X rays and gamma rays are highly penetrating and can be dangerous to living organisms.

Section 3 Using Electromagnetic Waves

1. Communications systems use visible light, radio waves, or electrical signals to transmit information.

2. Radio and TV stations use modulated carrier waves to transmit information.

3. Electromagnetic waves are used in telephone technologies to make communication easier and faster. *What is one way an electromagnetic wave is used in telephone communication?*

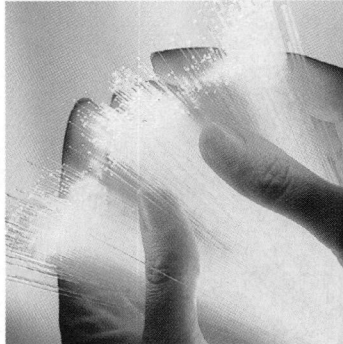

4. Communications satellites relay information from different points on Earth so a transmission can go around the globe. The Global Positioning System uses satellites to determine the position of an object on Earth.

FOLDABLES
Reading & Study Skills

After You Read

Using the information on your Foldable, compare and contrast visible and invisible waves that form the electromagnetic spectrum.

FOLDABLES
Reading & Study Skills

After You Read

After students have read the chapter and completed the Foldable described in Before You Read, have them do the activity on the student page.

Dinah Zike

Visualizing Main Ideas

Complete the following spider map about electromagnetic waves.

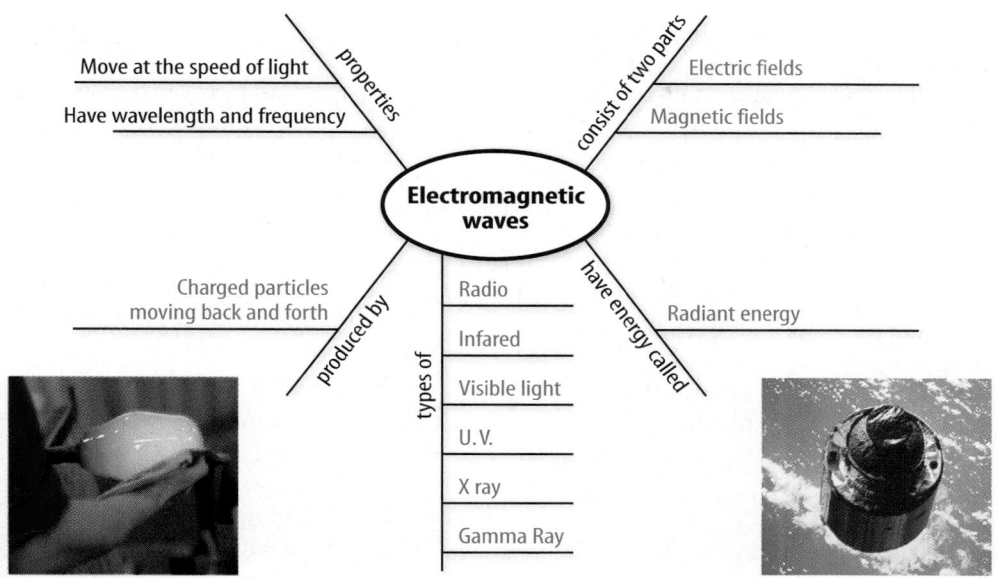

properties
- Move at the speed of light
- Have wavelength and frequency

consist of two parts
- Electric fields
- Magnetic fields

Electromagnetic waves

produced by
- Charged particles moving back and forth

types of
- Radio
- Infared
- Visible light
- U.V.
- X ray
- Gamma Ray

have energy called
- Radiant energy

Visualizing Main Ideas

See student page.

Vocabulary Review

Using Vocabulary

1. Infrared waves have higher frequencies and more energy than radio waves do.
2. In radio communication, a carrier wave is a radio wave of a particular frequency and amplitude that is modulated in either amplitude or frequency to carry information.
3. A communications satellite is a geosynchronous satellite used to transfer communication signals. GPS is a system of satellites and receivers used to determine locations on Earth.
4. Visible light is the section of the electromagnetic spectrum that we see with our eyes. Ultraviolet radiation is electromagnetic radiation at a slightly higher frequency than visible light.
5. Gamma rays have a higher frequency and more energy than X rays do and can cause more harm to living things.
6. An electromagnetic wave consists of oscillating electric and magnetic fields. The energy carried by an electromagnetic wave is called radiant energy.
7. Radio stations broadcast information using carrier waves. An AM radio signal carries information by changing or modulating the amplitude of the carrier wave.
8. An infrared wave has a slightly lower frequency than red light, and an ultraviolet wave has a slightly higher frequency than violet light.

Vocabulary Review

Vocabulary Words

a. carrier wave
b. electromagnetic spectrum
c. electromagnetic wave
d. gamma ray
e. Global Positioning System
f. infrared wave
g. radiant energy
h. radio wave
i. ultraviolet radiation
j. visible light
k. X ray

Using Vocabulary

Explain the difference between the terms in each of the following pairs.

1. infrared wave, radio wave
2. radio wave, carrier wave
3. communications satellite, Global Positioning System
4. visible light, ultraviolet radiation
5. X ray, gamma ray
6. electromagnetic wave, radiant energy
7. carrier wave, AM radio signal
8. infrared wave, ultraviolet wave

THE PRINCETON REVIEW

Study Tip

After you read a chapter, write ten questions that it answers. Wait one day and then try to recall the answers. Look up what you can't remember.

IDENTIFYING Misconceptions

Assess

Use the assessment as follow-up to page 632F after students have completed the chapter.

Procedure Provide this list of electromagnetic waves: radio, microwaves, infrared, visible light, ultraviolet, X rays, and gamma rays. Have students compare and contrast visible light with any two other types of electromagnetic waves by completing charts giving the wavelength range, means of detection, uses, and dangers of the three types of electromagnetic waves.

Expected Outcome Students should realize that light is similar to electromagnetic radiation of other wavelengths.

Checking Concepts

1. D
2. D
3. C
4. A
5. B
6. B
7. D
8. D
9. D
10. A

Thinking Critically

11. Even though infrared waves carry less energy than visible light waves, many materials absorb infrared waves more effectively than visible light. Thermometers often are made from these materials, and become warmer when placed in the infrared region of the spectrum than when placed in the visible region.

12. They also can receive electromagnetic radiation that the atmosphere absorbs.

13. The fact that the light it gives off has higher frequencies than red light indicates that it is hotter than the object glowing red.

14. If the tissue in the tumor is dense enough, X rays will not pass through it and it will show up as a dark shadow on X-ray film.

15. Possible answer: Unlike higher-frequency electromagnetic waves, radio waves can pass through many materials. As a result, radio waves can be transmitted and received from inside buildings and cars.

Checking Concepts

Choose the word or phrase that best answers the question.

1. Which type of force field surrounds a moving electron?
   A) electric and magnetic   C) magnetic
   B) electric   D) none of these

2. What does a microphone transform?
   A) light waves to sound waves
   B) radio waves to an electrical signal
   C) sound waves to electromagnetic waves
   D) sound waves to an electrical signal

3. Which of the following electromagnetic waves have the lowest frequency?
   A) visible light   C) radio waves
   B) infrared waves   D) X rays

4. What happens to the energy of an electromagnetic wave as its frequency increases?
   A) It increases.
   B) It decreases.
   C) It stays the same.
   D) It oscillates up and down.

5. What type of wave can hot objects emit?
   A) radio   C) visible
   B) infrared   D) ultraviolet

6. What can detect radio waves?
   A) film   C) eyes
   B) antenna   D) skin

7. Which wave can pass through people?
   A) infrared   C) ultraviolet
   B) visible   D) gamma

8. Which color has the lowest frequency?
   A) green   C) yellow
   B) violet   D) red

9. What is the key device that allows cordless phones to function?
   A) X ray   C) GPS
   B) satellite   D) antenna

10. What does *A* in AM stand for?
    A) amplitude   C) astronomical
    B) antenna   D) Alpha centauri

Thinking Critically

11. Infrared light was discovered when a scientist placed a thermometer in each band of the light spectrum produced by a prism. Would the area just beyond red have been warmer or cooler than the room? Explain.

12. Astronomers have built telescopes on Earth that have flexible mirrors that can eliminate the distortions due to the atmosphere. What advantages would a space-based telescope have over these?

13. Heated objects often give off visible light of a particular color. Explain why an object that glows bluish-white is hotter than one that glows red.

14. How can an X ray be used to determine the location of a cancerous tumor?

15. Why are many communications systems based on radio waves?

Developing Skills

16. **Calculating Ratios** How far does light travel in 1 min? How does this compare with the distance to the Moon?

17. **Recognizing Cause and Effect** As you ride in the car, the radio alternates between two different stations. How can the antenna pick up two stations at once?

18. **Classifying** List the colors of the visible spectrum in order of increasing frequency.

Chapter ✓Assessment Planner

Portfolio Encourage students to place in their portfolios one or two items of what they consider to be their best work. Examples include:
- Science Journal, p. 635
- Extension, p. 643
- Curriculum Connection, p. 651

Performance Additional performance assessments, Performance Task Assessment Lists, and rubrics for evaluating these activities can be found in Glencoe's **Performance Assessment in the Science Classroom.**

19. Comparing and Contrasting Compare and contrast ultraviolet and infrared light.

20. Concept Mapping Electromagnetic waves are grouped according to their frequencies. In the following concept map, write each frequency group and one way humans make use of the electromagnetic waves in that group. For example, in the second set of ovals, you might write "X rays" and "to see inside the body."

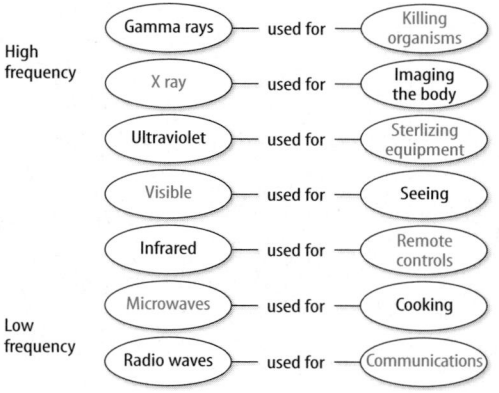

High frequency

Gamma rays	used for	Killing organisms
X ray	used for	Imaging the body
Ultraviolet	used for	Sterlizing equipment
Visible	used for	Seeing
Infrared	used for	Remote controls
Microwaves	used for	Cooking
Radio waves	used for	Communications

Low frequency

Performance Assessment

21. Oral Presentation Explain to the class how a radio signal is generated, transmitted, and received.

22. Poster Make a poster showing the parts of the electromagnetic spectrum. Show how frequency, wavelength, and energy change throughout the spectrum. How is each wave generated? What are some uses of each?

TECHNOLOGY

Go to the Glencoe Science Web site at **science.glencoe.com** or use the **Glencoe Science CD-ROM** for additional chapter assessment.

THE PRINCETON REVIEW — Test Practice

Mr. Rubama's class was studying how radio waves are transmitted. An experimental setup involving radio waves and glass is shown below.

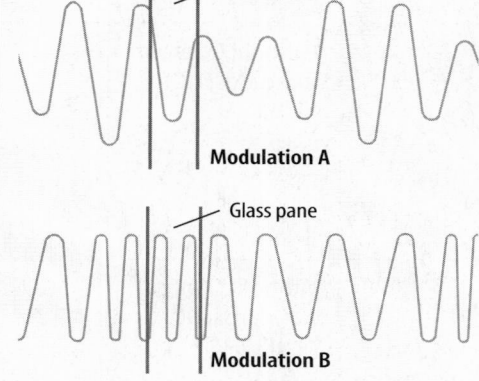

Glass pane

Modulation A

Glass pane

Modulation B

Study the illustrations and answer the following questions.

1. Which of these questions would most likely be answered by this experiment?
- **A)** How fast do radio waves travel through the air?
- **B)** Why do some waves travel more quickly than other waves?
- **C)** Where do radio waves come from?
- **D)** Can radio waves travel through glass?

2. Which of the following describes how the wave in Modulation A is different from the wave in Modulation B?
- **F)** It is a radio wave.
- **G)** It is frequency modulated
- **H)** It is amplitude modulated
- **J)** It is a carrier wave.

THE PRINCETON REVIEW — Test Practice

The Test-Taking Tip was written by The Princeton Review, the nation's leader in test preparation.
1. D
2. H

Developing Skills

16. $d = vt = 60$ sec/min $\times$ 300,000 km/sec = 18,000,000 km/min; This is about 63 times the distance to the Moon, which is about 384,000 km.

17. You are at the point where the areas covered by the two radio stations overlap.

18. red, orange, yellow, green, blue, violet

19. Infrared has a lower frequency, lower energy, and longer wavelength than ultraviolet light.

20. See student page.

Performance Assessment

21. Students should show or explain sound being converted into electrical signals and these signals being transmitted as electromagnetic waves, received, and reconverted into sound waves. Use **PASC**, p. 143.

22. The spectrum should cover electromagnetic waves from radio to gamma rays. Many uses are listed in this chapter. Use **PASC**, p. 145.

✓Assessment Resources

 Reproducible Masters

Chapter Resources Booklet
Chapter Review, pp. 35–36
Chapter Tests, pp. 37–40
Assessment Transparency Activity, p. 47

Glencoe Science Web site
Interactive Tutor
Chapter Quizzes

Glencoe Technology
- Assessment Transparency
- Interactive CD-ROM Chapter Quizzes
- ExamView Pro Test Bank
- Vocabulary PuzzleMaker Software
- MindJogger Videoquiz

Section/Objectives	Standards		Activities/Features
	National	**State/Local**	
Chapter Opener	See p. 7T for a Key to Standards.		**Explore Activity:** Observe the bending of light, p. 663 **Before You Read,** p. 663
Section 1 Properties of Light ⏱ 2 sessions 📦 1 block 1. **Describe** the wave nature of light. 2. **Explain** how light interacts with materials. 3. **Determine** why objects appear to have color	National Content Standards: UCP2, A1, B3		**MiniLAB:** Observing Colors in the Dark, p. 665
Section 2 Reflection and Mirrors ⏱ 2 sessions 📦 1 block 1. **Explain** how light is reflected from rough and smooth surfaces. 2. **Determine** how mirrors form an image. 3. **Describe** how concave and convex mirrors form an image	National Content Standards: UCP2, A1, B3, E1		**Physics Integration,** p. 671 **Visualizing Reflections in Concave Mirrors,** p. 673 **Activity:** Reflection from a Plane Mirror, p. 675
Section 3 Refraction and Lenses ⏱ 3 sessions 📦 1.5 blocks 1. **Determine** why light rays refract. 2. **Explain** how convex and concave lenses form images.	National Content Standards: UCP2, B3, E1, F1		**Science Online,** p. 678
Section 4 Using Mirrors and Lenses ⏱ 4 sessions 📦 2 blocks 1. **Explain** how microscopes magnify objects. 2. **Explain** how telescopes make distant objects visible. 3. **Describe** how a camera works.	National Content Standards: UCP2, A1, B3, E1, E2, F1, G1, G3		**MiniLAB:** Forming an Image with a Lens, p. 682 **Science Online,** p. 684 **Problem-Solving Activity:** Which film speed do you use?, p. 684 **Activity:** Image Formation by a Convex Lens, p. 686 **Oops! Accidents in Science:** Eyeglasses: Inventor Unknown, p. 688

NATIONAL GEOGRAPHIC

Teacher's Corner

PRODUCTS AVAILABLE FROM NATIONAL GEOGRAPHIC SOCIETY
To order call 1-800-368-2728:
Books
Waves: The Electromagnetic Universe
Videos
Color: Light Fantastic

Light
INDEX TO NATIONAL GEOGRAPHIC SOCIETY
The following articles may be used for research relating to this chapter:
"Life Without Light," by Charles Fisher, October 1996.

"Eyes of Science," by Rick Gore, March 1978.
"The Incredible Universe," by Kenneth F. Weaver, May 1974.

Activity Materials	Reproducible Resources	Section Assessment	Technology
Explore Activity: 2 paper cups, 2 pennies, water	**Chapter Resources Booklet** Foldables Worksheet, p. 17 Directed Reading Overview, p.19 Note-taking Worksheets, pp. 35–38	GLENCOE'S ASSESSMENT ADVANTAGE	
MiniLAB: 6 pieces of paper of different colors (10 cm x 10 cm each), pencil, darkened room	**Chapter Resources Booklet** Transparency Activity, p. 48 MiniLAB, p. 3 Lab Activities, pp. 9–12, 13–16 Enrichment, p. 31 Reinforcement, p. 27 Directed Reading, p. 20	**Portfolio** Make a Model, p. 666 **Performance** MiniLAB, p. 665 Skill Builder Activities, p. 668 **Content** Section Assessment, p. 668	Section Focus Transparency Interactive CD-ROM Guided Reading Audio Program
Activity: flashlight, protractor, metric ruler, scissors, tape, small plane mirror (at least 10 cm per side), black construction paper, modeling clay, white unlined paper	**Chapter Resources Booklet** Transparency Activity, p. 49 Enrichment, p. 32 Reinforcement, p. 28 Directed Reading, p. 20 Activity Worksheet, pp. 5–6 **Mathematics Skill Activities**, p. 47	**Portfolio** Visual Learning, p. 670 **Performance** Skill Builder Activities, p. 674 **Content** Section Assessment, p. 674	Section Focus Transparency Interactive CD-ROM Guided Reading Audio Program
Need materials? **Contact Science Kit at 1-800-828-7777 or www.sciencekit.com on the Internet.**	**Chapter Resources Booklet** Transparency Activity, p. 20 Enrichment, p. 33 Reinforcement, p. 29 Directed Reading, p. 21 Transparency Activity, pp. 53–54	**Portfolio** Science Journal, p. 679 **Performance** Skill Builder Activities, p. 680 **Content** Section Assessment, p. 680	Section Focus Transparency Teaching Transparency Interactive CD-ROM Guided Reading Audio Program
MiniLAB: glass test tube filled with water and sealed with stopper, card (10 cm x 10 cm, pencil **Activity:** convex lens, modeling clay, meterstick, flashlight, masking tape, cardboard with a white surface (20 cm square)	**Chapter Resources Booklet** Transparency Activity, p. 51 MiniLAB, p. 4 Enrichment, p. 34 Reinforcement, p. 30 Directed Reading, pp. 21, 22 Activity Worksheet, pp. 7–8 **Lab Management and Safety**, p. 64	**Portfolio** Assessment, p. 685 **Performance** MiniLAB, p. 682 Problem-Solving Activity, p. 684 Skill Builder Activities, p. 685 **Content** Section Assessment, p. 685	Section Focus Transparency Interactive CD-ROM Guided Reading Audio Program

End of Chapter Assessment

GLENCOE'S ASSESSMENT ADVANTAGE

Blackline Masters	Technology	Professional Series
Chapter Resources Booklet Chapter Review, pp. 41–42 Chapter Tests, pp. 43–46 **Standardized Test Practice by The Princeton Review,** pp. 97–100	MindJogger Videoquiz Interactive CD-ROM Vocabulary PuzzleMakers ExamView Pro Test Bank Interactive Lesson Planner Interactive Teacher Edition	Performance Assessment in the Science Classroom (PASC)

Transparencies

Section Focus

Section Focus Transparency — Wavelength

These are water lilies floating in a pond on a sunny day. How would these lilies appear at night or on an overcast day? The French painter Claude Monet was very fascinated by light, and he often painted water lilies like these.

1. Describe the colors you see in this picture. How might they differ if the picture were taken at night?
2. What happens to light that strikes the water? What happens when it strikes the lilies?
3. Give some examples of the effects of the Sun's energy on Earth.

L2

Section Focus Transparency — Just Popped up for a Shave

This large mirror is going to be used in a reflecting telescope. Astronomers use reflecting telescopes to view faint stars and galaxies. According to the company that helped make this mirror, it is "so smooth that if it were expanded to the size of the U.S., there would be no bumps higher than a speed bump."

1. Why is it important that the mirror is very smooth?
2. The technician is applying a thin coat of aluminum. Why?
3. How can a mirror make something appear larger or smaller?

L2

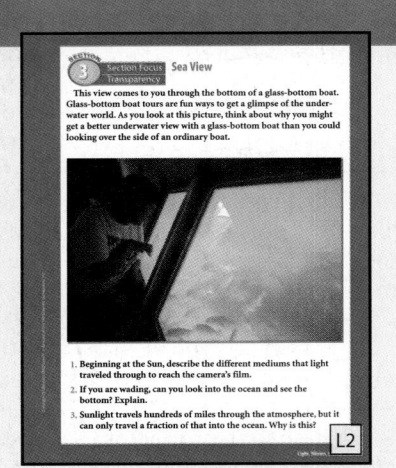

Section Focus Transparency — Sea View

This view comes to you through the bottom of a glass-bottom boat. Glass-bottom boat tours are fun ways to get a glimpse of the underwater world. As you look at this picture, think about why you might get a better underwater view with a glass-bottom boat than you could looking over the side of an ordinary boat.

1. Beginning at the Sun, describe the different mediums that light traveled through to reach the camera's film.
2. If you are wading, can you look into the ocean and see the bottom? Explain.
3. Sunlight travels hundreds of miles through the atmosphere, but it can only travel a fraction of that into the ocean. Why is this?

L2

This is a representation of key blackline masters available in the Teacher Classroom Resources. See Resource Manager boxes within the chapter for additional information.

Assessment

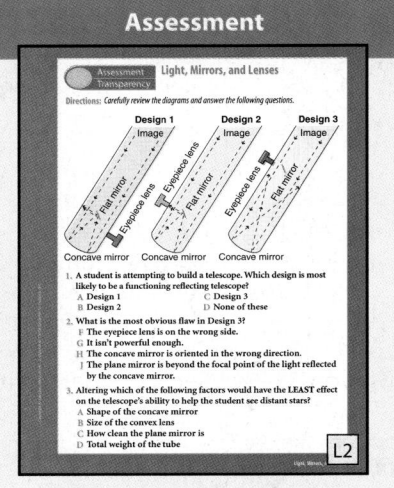

Assessment Transparency — Light, Mirrors, and Lenses

Directions: *Carefully review the diagrams and answer the following questions.*

1. A student is attempting to build a telescope. Which design is most likely to be a functioning reflecting telescope?
   A Design 1   C Design 3
   B Design 2   D None of these
2. What is the most obvious flaw in Design 3?
   F The eyepiece lens is on the wrong side.
   G It isn't powerful enough.
   H The concave mirror is oriented in the wrong direction.
   J The plane mirror is beyond the focal point of the light reflected by the concave mirror.
3. Altering which of the following factors would have the LEAST effect on the telescope's ability to help the student see distant stars?
   A Shape of the concave mirror
   B Size of the convex lens
   C How clean the plane mirror is
   D Total weight of the tube

L2

Teaching

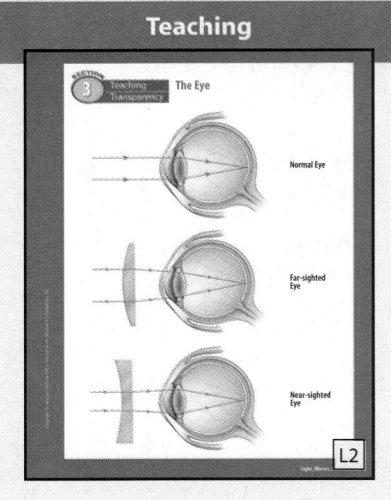

Teaching Transparency — The Eye

Normal Eye

Far-sighted Eye

Near-sighted Eye

L2

Key to Teaching Strategies

The following designations will help you decide which activities are appropriate for your students.

L1   Level 1 activities should be appropriate for students with learning difficulties.

L2   Level 2 activities should be within the ability range of all students.

L3   Level 3 activities are designed for above-average students.

ELL   ELL activities should be within the ability range of English Language Learners.

COOP LEARN   Cooperative Learning activities are designed for small group work.

LS   Multiple Learning Styles logos, as described on page 22T, are used throughout to indicate strategies that address different learning styles.

P   These strategies represent student products that can be placed into a best-work portfolio.

Hands-on Activities

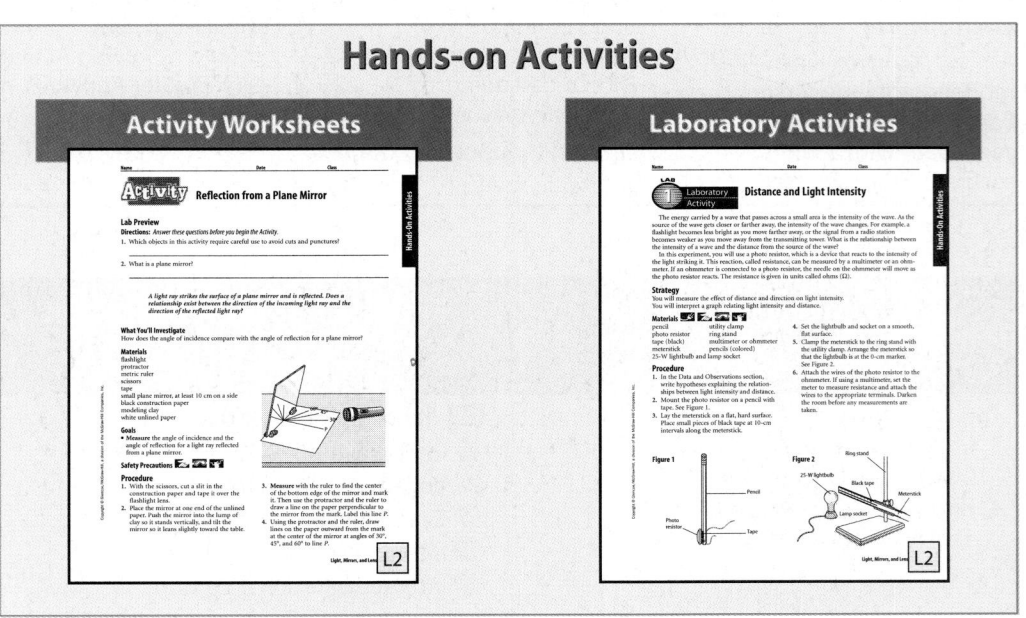

Activity Worksheets

Activity — Reflection from a Plane Mirror

Lab Preview
Directions: *Answer these questions before you begin the Activity.*
1. Which objects in this activity require careful use to avoid cuts and punctures?
2. What is a plane mirror?

A light ray strikes the surface of a plane mirror and is reflected. Does a relationship exist between the direction of the incoming light ray and the direction of the reflected light ray?

What You'll Investigate
How does the angle of incidence compare with the angle of reflection for a plane mirror?

Materials
flashlight
protractor
metric ruler
scissors
tape
small plane mirror, at least 10 cm on a side
black construction paper
modeling clay
white unlined paper

Goals
• **Measure** the angle of incidence and the angle of reflection for a light ray reflected from a plane mirror.

Safety Precautions

Procedure
1. With the scissors, cut a slit in the construction paper and tape it over the flashlight lens.
2. Place the mirror at one end of the unlined paper. Push the mirror into the lump of clay so it stands vertically, and tilt the mirror so it leans slightly toward the table.
3. Measure with the ruler to find the center of the bottom edge of the mirror and mark it. Then use the protractor and the ruler to draw a line on the paper perpendicular to the mirror from the mark. Label this line *P*.
4. Using the protractor and the ruler, draw lines on the paper outward from the mark at the center of the mirror at angles of 30°, 45°, and 60° to line *P*.

L2

Laboratory Activities

Laboratory Activity — Distance and Light Intensity

The energy carried by a wave that passes across a small area is the intensity of the wave. As the source of the wave gets closer or farther away, the intensity of the wave changes. For example, a flashlight becomes less bright as you move farther away, or the signal from a radio station becomes weaker as you move away from the transmitting tower. What is the relationship between the intensity of a wave and the distance from the source of the wave?

In this experiment, you will use a photo resistor, which is a device that reacts to the intensity of the light striking it. This reaction, called resistance, can be measured by a multimeter or an ohmmeter. If an ohmmeter is connected to a photo resistor, the needle on the ohmmeter will move as the photo resistor reacts. The resistance is given in units called ohms (Ω).

Strategy
You will measure the effect of distance and direction on light intensity.
You will interpret a graph relating light intensity and distance.

Materials
pencil
photo resistor
tape (black)
meterstick
25-W lightbulb and lamp socket
utility clamp
ring stand
multimeter or ohmmeter
pencils (colored)

Procedure
1. In the Data and Observations section, write hypotheses explaining the relationships between light intensity and distance.
2. Mount the photo resistor on a pencil with tape. See Figure 1.
3. Lay the meterstick on a flat, hard surface. Place small pieces of black tape at 10-cm intervals along the meterstick.
4. Set the lightbulb and socket on a smooth, flat surface.
5. Clamp the meterstick to the ring stand with the utility clamp. Arrange the meterstick so that the lightbulb is at the 0-cm marker. See Figure 2.
6. Attach the wires of the photo resistor to the ohmmeter. If using a multimeter, set the meter to measure resistance and attach the wires to the appropriate terminals. Darken the room before any measurements are taken.

Figure 1

Figure 2

L2

Meeting Different Ability Levels

Content Outline

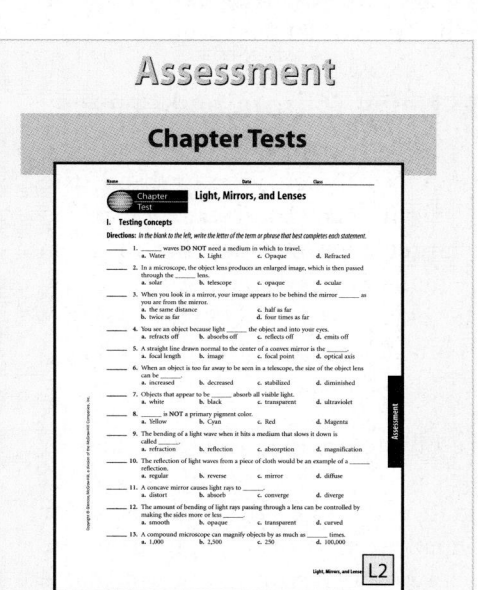

L2

Reinforcement

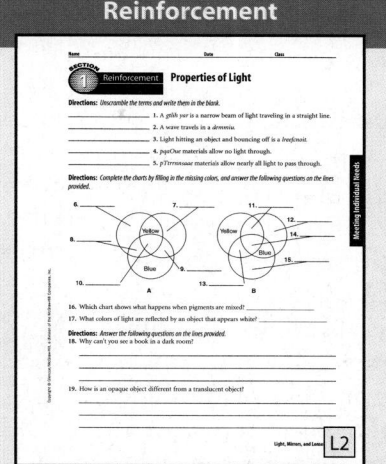

L2

Directed Reading

L1

Assessment

Chapter Tests

L2

Enrichment

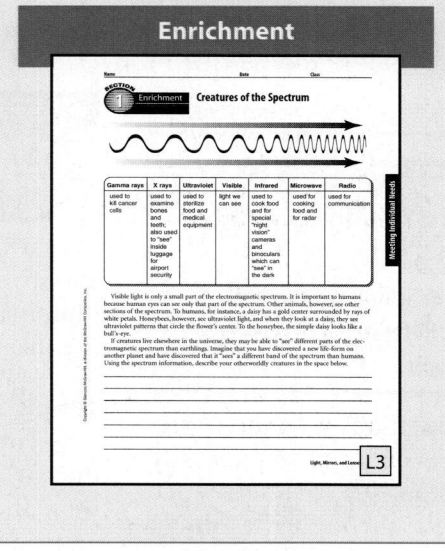

L3

Spanish Directed Reading

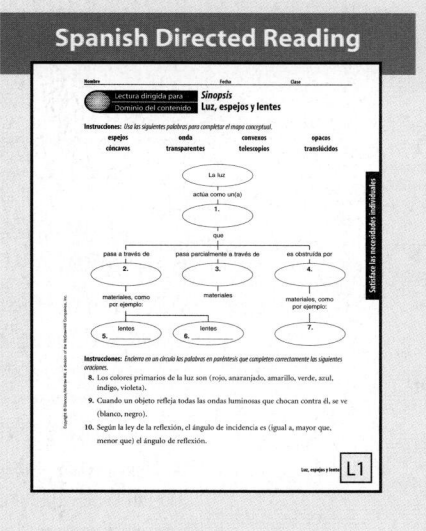

L1

Test Practice Workbook

L2

Chapter Review

L2

Science Content Background

SECTION 1

Properties of Light

Light and Matter

Light is an electromagnetic wave made of oscillating magnetic and electric fields. When a light wave strikes an object, some of the energy carried by the light wave is absorbed, and some is re-emitted. The re-emitted wave results when the oscillating electric field of the light wave causes electrons in the object to oscillate. These oscillating electrons then emit electromagnetic waves. The frequencies of the re-emitted waves depend on the types of atoms in the object and the bonding between atoms in the material.

Student Misconception

Light produces an effect but does not travel through matter or space.

Refer to the facing page for teaching strategies to address this misconception. Refer to pages 664–665 for content related to this topic.

As the light wave penetrates into the object it becomes less intense as energy is continually absorbed. If an object is opaque, the light wave cannot travel completely through the object before all of its energy is absorbed. If an object is transparent, very little energy is absorbed. Some objects that are opaque become translucent or transparent if they are made thin enough.

SECTION 2

Reflection and Mirrors

Reflection and Surfaces

Mirrors form two types of images. The image formed by a plane mirror, a convex mirror, or a concave mirror with the object inside the focal point is called a virtual image. A virtual image forms because no light waves emanate from where the image seems to be. A concave mirror forms a real image when the object is outside the focal point. In this case, light waves from the object are brought to focus at the location of the image, and the image can be projected onto a surface placed at this location.

SECTION 3

Refraction and Lenses

Concave and Convex Lenses

Lenses also from real and virtual images. Images formed when a lens or mirror causes light waves to diverge are virtual images. Images formed by converging light waves are real images.

SECTION 4

Using Mirrors and Lenses

Microscopes

As an image is magnified, the light from the image is spread over a much larger area, causing the image to appear dim. A high-powered microscope usually illuminates the object with bright light so that the magnified image is as bright as possible.

Telescopes

The large size of a telescope's objective lens or mirror enables it to gather much more light than the human eye alone. If an object is far away, only a small portion of the light from the object strikes an observer's eye. A bright, more detailed image can be formed if more of the light from the object is collected, and the image is further magnified.

SCIENCE *Online*

For additional content background on this topic, go to the Glencoe Science Web site at science.glencoe.com.

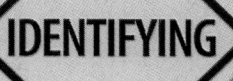 **IDENTIFYING** **Misconceptions**

Find Out What Students Think

Students may think that . . .

- **light comes from a source and produces an effect, but light does not travel through matter or vacuums as rays having a finite speed.**

Language and perception play a large role in people's conceptions about the world. People often use the term light to refer to illuminating electrical devices. Phrases such as "turn on the light" and "the light is broken" confirm these uses. The effects of light are constantly and directly observed. For example some things are lit up and others are in shadows. Further, when a light bulb has been turned on it seems to light up the room immediately thus masking the fact that the light took time to travel. Thinking of light as a source or an effect may interfere with an important foundation for optics—learning the concept of light as a traveling entity that moves at finite speeds.

Demonstration

Set up a flashlight on a stack of books. Have the flashlight point to a screen. Turn off the room lights and turn on the flashlight. Have students write down where there is light. They may initially only say there is light (a) at the bulb and (b) at the screen and not realize that light exists between the bulb and the screen as it travels.

Telegraph Colour Library/FPG International

Promote Understanding

Activity

Divide the class into groups.

- Give each group of students a flashlight and a paper screen.

- Have students in each group set their flashlight on books so it shines directly on the paper screen.

- Turn off the classroom lights.

- Ask students to observe the light from the flashlight.

- Ask students if there is light between the flashlight bulb and the paper screen. Have students in each group discuss the question and agree on an answer.

- Turn on the lights and have groups share their thoughts.

- Turn off the lights and then clap chalk erasers above each group's light beam so students can see the dust particles illuminated in the beam.

- Have students discuss again where there is light. Make sure they understand that light exists everywhere along the path from the bulb to the screen.

Assess

After completing the chapter, see *Identifying Misconceptions* in the Study Guide.

Light, Mirrors, and Lenses

Chapter Vocabulary

light ray, p. 664
medium, p. 665
reflection, p. 665
law of reflection, p. 669
focal point, p. 672
focal length, p. 672
refraction, p. 677
lens, p. 677
convex lens, p. 678
concave lens, p. 679
refracting telescope, p. 682
reflecting telescope, p. 683

What do you think?

Science Journal The picture shows optical fibers. The fibers have the property that light can enter or leave only through the ends. As a result, optical fibers can transmit light even if they are bent.

CHAPTER 23

Light, Mirrors, and Lenses

Y ou walk through a door of the fun house and are bombarded by images of yourself. In one mirror, your face seems smashed. You turn around and face another mirror—your chin and neck are gigantic. How do mirrors in a fun house make you look so strange? In this chapter, you'll learn how mirrors and lenses create images. You'll also learn why objects have the colors they have.

What do you think?

Science Journal Look at the picture below with a classmate. Discuss what you think this might be or what is happening. Here's a hint: *It helps you keep in touch.* Write down your answer or your best guess in your Science Journal.

662

Theme Connection

Energy Light waves carry energy. This energy can pass through materials, be absorbed by materials, and be reflected by materials.

Everything you see results from light waves entering your eyes. These light waves are either given off by objects, such as the Sun and lightbulbs, or reflected by objects, such as trees, books, and people. Lenses and mirrors can cause light to change direction and make objects seem larger or smaller. What happens to light as it passes from one material to another?

Observe the bending of light

1. Place two paper cups next to each other and put a penny in the bottom of each cup.

2. Fill one of the cups with water and observe how the penny looks.

3. Looking straight down at the cups, slide the cup with no water away from you just until you can no longer see the penny.

4. Pour water into this cup and observe what seems to happen to the penny.

Observe

In your Science Journal, record your observations. Did adding water make the cup look deeper or shallower?

FOLDABLES
Reading & Study Skills

Before You Read

Making a Question Study Fold Asking yourself questions helps you stay focused so you will better understand light, mirrors, and lenses when you are reading the chapter.

1. Stack two sheets of paper in front of you so the short side of both sheets is at the top.

2. Slide the top sheet up so about 4 cm of the bottom sheet shows.

3. Fold both sheets top to bottom to form four tabs and staple along the fold as shown.

4. Title the Foldable *Light, Mirrors, and Lenses* as shown. Write these questions on the flaps: *What are the properties of light? What is reflection? What is refraction?*

5. Before you read the chapter, try to answer the questions with what you already know. As you read the chapter, add to or correct your answers under the flaps.

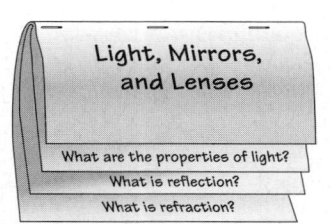

Light, Mirrors, and Lenses

What are the properties of light?
What is reflection?
What is refraction?

663

EXPLORE ACTIVITY

Purpose Use the Explore Activity to introduce students to the idea that light changes direction when it passes from one material to another. [L2] [ELL]
[LS] **Visual-Spatial**

Materials two paper cups, two pennies, water

Alternate Materials Any small opaque cups may be used provided they are not too tall.

Troubleshooting In step 4, the penny needs to remain in place so students can observe how the water affects what they see. Suggest that students place the penny near one side of the cup and pour the water near the other side.

Observe

Possible answer: Adding water made the cup seem shallower. When the cup was pushed away so that the penny was not visible, adding water made it possible to see the penny.

✔Assessment

Process Ask students to infer why adding water enabled them to see the penny that had been out of their sight. The water bent the light rays. Use **Performance Assessment in the Science Classroom**, p. 89.

FOLDABLES
Reading & Study Skills

Before You Read

Dinah Zike Study Fold

Purpose Use this activity to determine what students know about light, reflection, and refraction before they read the chapter. The activity results in a Foldable with three focus questions in which students can record notes and information as they read.

For additional help, see Foldables Worksheet, p. 17 in **Chapter Resources Booklet,** or go to the Glencoe Science Web site at **science.glencoe.com.** See After You Read in the Study Guide at the end of this chapter.

SECTION

Properties of Light

1 Motivate

Bellringer Transparency

Display the Section Focus Transparency for Section 1. Use the accompanying Transparency Activity Master. [L2] [ELL]

Tie to Prior Knowledge

Have students list types of waves with which they are familiar, such as ocean waves or sound waves. Discuss how these waves are similar to one another and how they are different. Explain that in this section they will learn about light waves.

Properties of Light

As You Read

What You'll Learn
- **Describe** the wave nature of light.
- **Explain** how light interacts with materials.
- **Determine** why objects appear to have color.

Vocabulary
light ray
medium
reflection

Why It's Important
Much of what you know about your surroundings comes from information carried by light waves.

Figure 1
Waves carry energy as they travel.

What is light?

Drop a rock on the smooth surface of a pond and you'll see ripples spread outward from the spot where the rock struck. The rock produced a wave much like the one in **Figure 1A.** A wave is a disturbance that carries energy through matter or space. The matter in this case is the water, and the energy originally comes from the impact of the rock. As the ripples spread out, they carry some of that energy.

Light is a type of wave that carries energy. A source of light such as the Sun or a lightbulb gives off light waves into space, just as the rock hitting the pond causes waves to form in the water. But while the water waves spread out only on the surface of the pond, light waves spread out in all directions from the light source. **Figure 1B** shows how light waves travel.

Sometimes, however, it is easier to think of light in a different way. A **light ray** is a narrow beam of light that travels in a straight line. You can think of a source of light as giving off, or emitting, a countless number of light rays that are traveling away from the source in all directions.

A Ripples on the surface of a pond are produced by an object hitting the water. As the ripples spread out from the point of impact, they carry energy.

B A source of light, such as a lightbulb, gives off light rays that travel away from the light source in all directions.

664 CHAPTER 23 Light, Mirrors, and Lenses

Section ✓*Assessment* Planner

PORTFOLIO
Make a Model, p. 666
PERFORMANCE ASSESSMENT
Try At Home MiniLAB, p. 665
Skill Builder Activities, p. 668
See page 692 for more options.

CONTENT ASSESSMENT
Section, 668
Challenge, p. 668
Chapter, pp. 692–693

Light Travels Through Space There is, however, one important difference between light waves and the water wave ripples on a pond. If the pond dried up and had no water, ripples could not form. Waves on a pond need a material—water—in which to travel. The material through which a wave travels is called a **medium.** Light is an electromagnetic wave and doesn't need a medium in which to travel. Electromagnetic waves can travel in a vacuum, as well as through materials such as air, water, and glass.

Light and Matter

What can you see when you are in a closed room with no windows and the lights are out? You can see nothing until you turn on a light or open a door to let in light from outside the room. Most objects around you do not give off light on their own. They can be seen only if light waves from another source bounce off them and into your eyes, as shown in **Figure 2.** The process of light striking an object and bouncing off is called **reflection.** Right now, you can see these words because light emitted by a source of light is reflecting from the page and into your eyes. Not all the light rays reflected from the page strike your eyes. Light rays striking the page are reflected in many directions, and only some of these rays enter your eyes.

✓ Reading Check *What must happen for you to see most objects?*

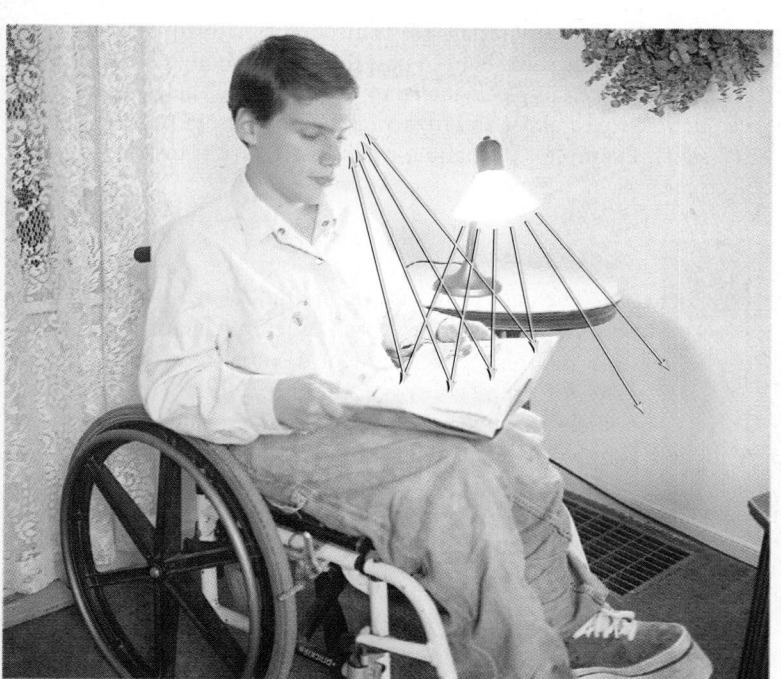

Figure 2
Light waves are given off by the lightbulb. Some of these light waves hit the page and are reflected. The student sees the page when some of these reflected waves enter the student's eyes.

Observing Colors in the Dark

Procedure
1. Get six pieces of **paper** that are different colors and about 10 cm × 10 cm.
2. Darken a room and wait 10 min for your eyes to adjust to the darkness.
3. Write on each paper what color you think the paper is.
4. Turn on the lights and see if your night vision detected the colors.

Analysis
1. If the room were perfectly dark, what would you see? Explain.
2. Your eyes contain structures called rods and cones. Rods don't detect color, but need only a little light. Cones detect color, but need more light. Which structure was working in the dark room? Explain.

Resource Manager

Chapter Resources Booklet
Transparency Activity, p. 48
MiniLAB, p. 3
Lab Activity, pp. 9–12, 13–16

Teacher FYI

Visible light is part of the electromagnetic spectrum—waves generated by oscillating electric and magnetic fields. The electromagnetic spectrum also includes radio waves, microwaves, X rays, infrared waves, gamma rays, and ultraviolet waves. The frequency and wavelength of an electromagnetic wave determines which type of wave it is.

---

② Teach

What is light?

IDENTIFYING
Misconceptions

Students may think that light produces an effect but does not travel through matter or space. See page 662F for teaching strategies related to this misconception.

Light and Matter

Purpose Students will investigate how their eyes respond to dim light. L2 ELL

IS Visual-Spatial

Materials six pieces of construction paper

Teaching Strategy Suggest students try the experiment in rooms with different levels of darkness.

Analysis
1. Nothing; seeing depends on light bouncing off an object.
2. Since some color could be seen, both rods and cones were working.

✔ Assessment

Process Have students work in small groups to design an experiment to test which colors are easiest to distinguish in dim light. Use **PASC,** p. 95.

✔ Reading Check

Answer Light must reflect off the objects and go into your eyes.

Light and Matter,
continued

Caption Answer

Figure 3 transparent materials

Make a Model

Glass is transparent to visible light, but is opaque to infrared waves. Objects in a greenhouse absorb the visible light and emit infrared waves, which can't escape. This causes the temperature in the greenhouse to increase. Have students build a small model of a greenhouse and set the model in the Sun. Have them measure and record the temperature of the air outside and inside this model. Have students compare temperatures and explain the reasons for any differences. L2 ELL COOP LEARN
Kinesthetic P

Color

Use Science Words

Word Meaning Have students define *wavelength* from the meanings of the parts of the word. Wavelength is the distance between two corresponding points on a wave. L2 **Linguistic**

Caption Answer

Figure 4 red, orange, yellow, green, blue, indigo, and violet

Extension

Tell students that fluorescent lights and incandescent lights don't produce white light. They produce slightly different colors, depending on the type of bulb used. Have students find out what colors these lights produce. Incandescent bulbs produce light that has more red than white light has, while fluorescent bulbs can vary considerably. L3 **Logical-Mathematical**

A An opaque object allows no light to pass through it.

B A translucent object allows some light to pass through it.

C A transparent object allows almost all light to pass through it.

Figure 3
Materials are opaque, translucent, or transparent depending on how much light passes through them. *Which type of material reflects the least amount of light?*

Figure 4
A beam of white light passing through a prism is separated into many colors. *What colors can you see emerging from the prism?*

Opaque, Translucent, and Transparent When light waves strike an object, some of the waves are absorbed by the object, some of the waves are reflected by it, and some of the light waves might pass through it. What happens to light when it strikes the object depends on the material that the object is made of.

All objects reflect and absorb some light waves. Materials that let no light pass through them are opaque (oh PAYK). You cannot see other objects through opaque materials. On the other hand, you clearly can see other objects through materials such as glass and clear plastic that allow nearly all the light that strikes them to pass through. These materials are transparent. A third type of material allows only some light to pass through. Although objects behind these materials are visible, they are not clear. These materials, such as waxed paper and frosted glass, are translucent (trans LEW sent). Examples of opaque, translucent, and transparent objects are shown in **Figure 3.**

Color

The light from the Sun might look white, but it is a mixture of colors. Each different color of light is a different wavelength. You sometimes can see the different colors of the Sun's light when it passes through raindrops to make a rainbow. As shown in **Figure 4,** white light is separated into different colors when it passes through a prism. The colors in white light range from red to violet. When light waves from all these colors enter the eye at the same time, the brain interprets the mixture as being white.

666   CHAPTER 23 Light, Mirrors, and Lenses

Curriculum Connection

Math The intensity of light striking a surface decreases as the surface gets farther from the source. This decrease is given by the formula $I = P/d^2$, where I is the light intensity, d is the distance to the source, and P is related to the power emitted by the light source. **If P remains constant, what will be the difference in the** **intensity of light striking a card 1 m from a lightbulb and light striking a card 4 m from the bulb?** The light striking the card 4 m from the lightbulb will have 1/16 less intensity than will the light striking the card 1 m from the lightbulb. L3

Logical-Mathematical

A

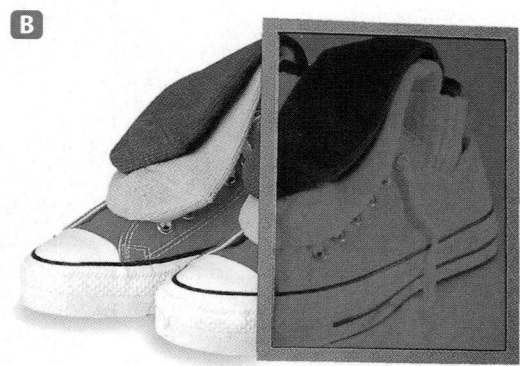

B

Figure 5A The socks reflect only blue light.

Figure 5B The red filter allows only red light through. None of the blue light reflected by the socks passes through, so they look black.

Why do Objects Have Color? Why does grass look green or a rose look red? When a mixture of light waves strikes an object that is not transparent, the object absorbs some of the light waves. Some of the light waves that are not absorbed are reflected. If an object reflects red waves and absorbs all the other waves, it looks red. Similarly, if an object looks blue, it reflects only blue light waves and absorbs all the others. An object that reflects all the light waves that strike it looks white, while one that reflects none of the light waves that strike it looks black. **Figure 5** shows gym shoes and socks as seen under white light and as seen when viewed through a red filter that allows only red light to pass through it.

Primary Light Colors How many colors exist? People often say white light is made up of red, orange, yellow, green, blue, and violet light. This isn't completely true, though. Many more colors than this exist. In reality, most humans can distinguish thousands of colors, including some such as brown, pink, and purple, that are not found among the colors of the rainbow.

Light of almost any color can be made by mixing different amounts of red, green, and blue light. Red, green, and blue are known as the primary colors. Look at **Figure 6.** White light is produced where beams of red, green, and blue light overlap. Yellow light is produced where red and green light overlap. You see the color yellow because of the way your brain interprets the combination of the red and green light striking your eye. This combination of light waves looks the same as yellow light produced by a prism, even though these light waves have only a single wavelength.

Figure 5
The color of an object depends on the light waves it reflects.
A Examine the pair of gym shoes and socks as they are seen under white light. *Why do the socks look blue under white light?*
B The same shoes and socks were photographed through a red filter. *Why do the blue socks look black when viewed under red light?*

Figure 6
By mixing light from the three primary colors—red, blue, and green—almost all of the visible colors can be made.

SECTION 1 Properties of Light **667**

Extension

Ask students how they know that light has been absorbed or reflected. Have them list the evidence for each, and compare their lists with those made by other students in the class. The darker an object, the more light it absorbs. Absorbing light also raises the temperature of an object. Therefore, objects that reflect light usually are cooler and lighter in color than those that absorb light. **IS Interpersonal**

Visual Learning

Figure 6 Explain that each of the three primary colors is a range of wavelengths. Red is a range of long wavelengths peaking in the red region. Green is a range of medium-length wavelengths peaking in the green region. Blue is a range of short wavelengths peaking in the blue region. Ask students to use this description to explain the yellow overlap region in the figure. Mixing the longer wavelengths that form red and the medium-length wavelengths that form green produces a range of wavelengths that peaks in the middle of these in the yellow region. L3 **IS Visual-Spatial**

✔ Active Reading

Think-Pair-Share This strategy encourages students to think first before discussing their ideas or thoughts about a topic. Students are asked to respond to a question by writing a response. After thinking for a few minutes, partners share responses to the question. Finally, the teacher asks the students to share responses with the class. Have students become involved in a Think-Pair-Share about color.

Color, continued

✔ **Reading Check**

Answer yellow, magenta, cyan

3 Assess

Reteach

Quiz students on combining colors. **What are the primary colors of light?** red, green, and blue **What are the primary pigment colors?** yellow, cyan, and magenta **What color is formed when red light and blue light combine?** magenta **What color is formed when yellow pigment and cyan pigment combine?** green L2 **IS** **Visual-Spatial**

Challenge

How is the rainbow produced when light passes through a prism similar to the rainbow seen on a puddle of water with oil on it? Possible answer: The thin layer of oil separates light into colors just as the glass prism does. L3 **IS** **Logical-Mathematical**

✔Assessment

Content Ask students to draw diagrams illustrating the difference between light waves and a light ray. A light ray is one of the countless rays emitted by a light source that move away from the source in all directions as light waves. Use **Performance Assessment in the Science Classroom,** p. 127.

Figure 7
The three primary color pigments—yellow, magenta, and cyan—can form almost all the visible colors when mixed together in various amounts.

Primary Pigment Colors If you like to paint, you might mix two or more different colors to make a new color. Materials like paint that are used to change the color of other objects, such as the walls of a room or an artist's canvas, are called pigments. Mixing pigments together forms colors in a different way than mixing colored lights does.

Like all materials that appear to be colored, pigments absorb some light waves and reflect others. The color of the pigment you see is the color of the light waves that are reflected from it. However, the primary pigment colors are not red, blue, and green—they are yellow, magenta, and cyan. You can make almost any color by mixing different amounts of these primary pigment colors, as shown in **Figure 7.**

✔ **Reading Check** *What are the primary pigment colors?*

Although primary pigment colors are not the same as the primary light colors, they are related. Each primary pigment color results when a pigment absorbs a primary light color. For example, a yellow pigment absorbs blue light and it reflects red and green light, which you see as yellow. A magenta pigment, on the other hand, absorbs green light and reflects red and blue light, which you see as magenta. Each of the primary pigment colors is the same color as white light with one primary color removed.

Section 1 Assessment

1. At night in your room, you are reading a magazine. Describe the path light takes that enables you to see the page.
2. Do the light rays traveling outward from a light source carry energy? Explain.
3. What colors are reflected by an object that appears black? Explain.
4. What is the difference between primary light colors and primary pigment colors?
5. **Think Critically** When you're in direct sunlight, why do you feel cooler if you're wearing light-colored clothes than if you're wearing darker-colored clothes?

Skill Builder Activities

6. **Drawing Conclusions** A white plastic bowl and a black plastic bowl have been sitting in the sunlight. You observe that the black bowl feels warmer than the white bowl. From this information, conclude which of the bowls absorbs and which reflects more sunlight. **For more help, refer to the** Science Skill Handbook.
7. **Communicating** Read an article about the greenhouse effect and draw a diagram in your Science Journal explaining how the greenhouse effect involves absorption. **For more help, refer to the** Science Skill Handbook.

668 **CHAPTER 23** Light, Mirrors, and Lenses

Answers to Section Assessment

1. Light from a lamp reflects off the magazine to your eyes.
2. An opaque object does not let light pass through, and a transparent object does.
3. No colors are reflected by an object that appears black.
4. Primary light colors can be mixed to produce any other color of light.

Primary pigment colors result when a pigment absorbs a primary light color.
5. The light-colored clothes reflect light, while the dark-colored clothes absorb light, which raises their temperature.
6. The black bowl absorbs more sunlight, and the white bowl reflects more sunlight.

7. Light passes through the atmosphere and is absorbed by Earth. It is reemitted as infrared radiation that can't escape easily through the atmosphere, so it warms the Earth.

Reflection and Mirrors

The Law of Reflection

You've probably noticed your image on the surface of a pool or lake. If the surface of the water was smooth, you could see your face clearly. If the surface of the water was wavy, however, your face might have seemed distorted. The image you saw was the result of light reflecting from the surface and traveling to your eyes. How the light was reflected determined the sharpness of the image you saw.

When a light ray strikes a surface and is reflected as in **Figure 8,** the reflected ray obeys the law of reflection. Imagine a line that is drawn perpendicular to the surface where the light ray strikes. This line is called the normal to the surface. The incoming ray and the normal form an angle called the angle of incidence. The reflected light ray forms an angle with the normal called the angle of reflection. According to the **law of reflection,** the angle of incidence is equal to the angle of reflection. This is true for any surface, no matter what material it is made of.

Reflection from Surfaces

Why can you see your reflection in some surfaces and not others? Why does a piece of shiny metal make a good mirror, but a piece of paper does not? The answers have to do with the smoothness of each surface.

As You Read

What You'll Learn
- **Explain** how light is reflected from rough and smooth surfaces.
- **Determine** how mirrors form an image.
- **Describe** how concave and convex mirrors form an image.

Vocabulary
law of reflection
focal point
focal length

Why It's Important
Mirrors can change the direction of light waves and enable you to see images, such as your own face, that normally would not be in view.

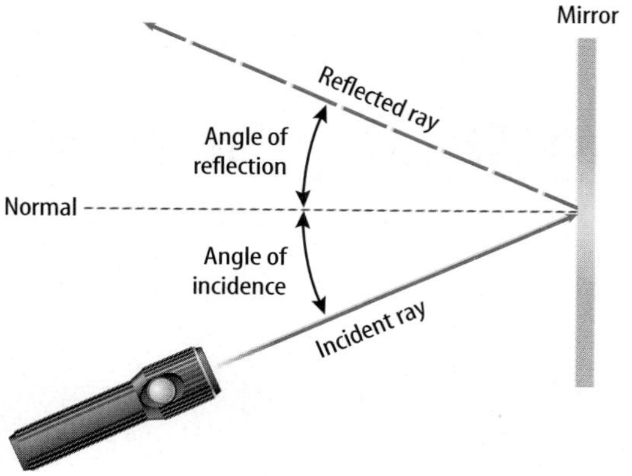

Figure 8
A light ray strikes a surface and is reflected. The angle of incidence is always equal to the angle of reflection. This is the law of reflection.

Mirror
Reflected ray
Angle of reflection
Normal
Angle of incidence
Incident ray

Section ✓Assessment Planner

PORTFOLIO
Visual Learning, p. 670
PERFORMANCE ASSESSMENT
Skill Builder Activities, p. 674
See page 692 for more options.

CONTENT ASSESSMENT
Section, p. 674
Challenge, p. 674
Chapter, pp. 692–693

Reflection and Mirrors

1 Motivate

Bellringer Transparency
Display the Section Focus Transparency for Section 2. Use the accompanying Transparency Activity Master. L2 ELL

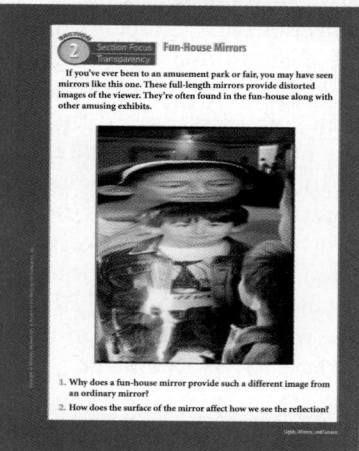

Tie to Prior Knowledge

Ask students to describe how a ball bounces off a flat surface. Compare the angles the ball makes with the surface before and after the bounce. The angles are the same. Tell students that when light is reflected off flat surfaces, the angle it makes with the surface before it reflects is the same as the angle it makes after it reflects.

The Law of Reflection

Quick Demo

Draw on the board a diagram showing a surface, a line normal to that surface, and a light ray striking the surface and being reflected. Point out to students the angle of incidence and the angle of reflection. Make sure these two angles are the same. L2 IS **Visual-Spatial**

Make a Model

Have students work in small groups to model the law of reflection. First, students should use chalk to draw a line normal to a wall. One student should then roll a ball toward the wall at a pre-determined angle to the normal. Another student will determine the angle of reflection that the ball makes as it bounces off the wall. Students should be able to relate this to the way light reflects off a flat surface. L2 IS **Kinesthetic**

Reflection from Surfaces

Teacher FYI

In order to give a mirror the ability to reflect, the hills and valleys on the surface must be smaller than the wavelengths of visible light, or smaller than about 400 billionths of a meter.

✓ Reading Check

Answer The rough surface causes light to be reflected in many different directions.

Figure 9
A highly magnified view of the surface of a paper towel shows that the surface is made of many cellulose wood fibers that make it rough and uneven.

Magnification: 35×

Figure 10
The roughness of a surface determines whether it looks like a mirror. **A** A rough surface causes parallel light rays to be reflected in many different directions. **B** A smooth surface causes parallel light rays to be reflected in a single direction. This type of surface looks like a mirror.

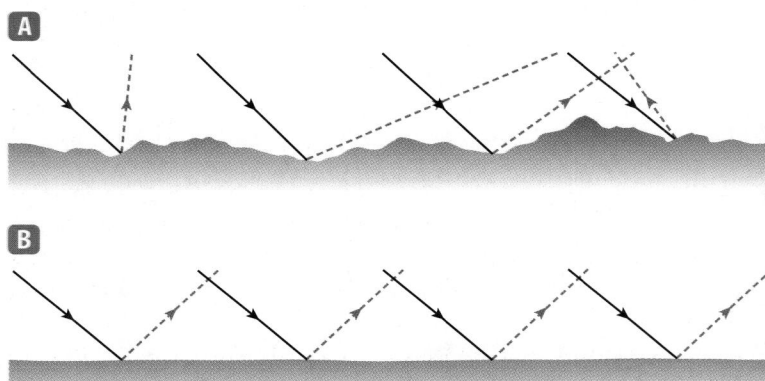

Regular and Diffuse Reflection Even though the surface of the paper might seem smooth, it's not as smooth as the surface of a mirror. **Figure 9** shows how rough the surface of a piece of paper looks when it is viewed under a microscope. The rough surface causes light rays to be reflected from it in many directions, as shown in **Figure 10A**. This uneven reflection of light waves from a rough surface is diffuse reflection. The smoother surfaces of mirrors, as shown in **Figure 10B,** reflect light waves in a much more regular way. For example, parallel rays remain parallel after they are reflected from a mirror. Reflection from mirrors is known as regular reflection. Light waves that are regularly reflected from a surface form the image you see in a mirror or any other smooth surface. Whether a surface is smooth or rough, every light ray that strikes it obeys the law of reflection.

✓ **Reading Check** *Why does a rough surface cause a diffuse reflection?*

Scattering of Light When diffuse reflection occurs, light waves that were traveling in a single direction are reflected, and then travel in many different directions. Scattering occurs when light waves traveling in one direction are made to travel in many different directions. Scattering also can occur when light waves strike small particles, such as dust. You may have seen dust particles floating in a beam of sunlight. When the light waves in the sunbeam strike a dust particle, they are scattered in all directions. You see the dust particle as bright specks of light when some of these scattered light waves enter your eye.

Visual Learning

Figure 10 Review with students the reflection of light from a rough surface shown in **Figure 10A** and the reflection of light from a smooth surface shown in **Figure 10B**. Ask students to draw diagrams showing how light is reflected from a piece of crumpled aluminum foil. The surface of the crumpled foil is rougher than a mirror but less rough than the surface shown in **Figure 10A**. Therefore the light would be reflected to form many different little images as from many little mirrors. L2 IS **Visual-Spatial** P

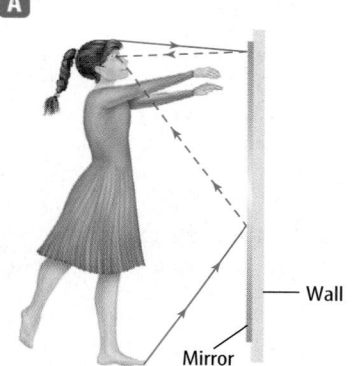

A

Wall

Mirror

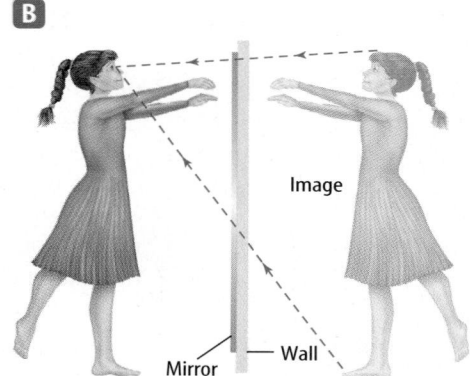

B

Image

Mirror — Wall

Reflection by Plane Mirrors Did you glance in the mirror before leaving for school this morning? If you did, you probably looked at your reflection in a plane mirror. A plane mirror is a mirror with a flat reflecting surface. In a plane mirror, your image looks much the same as it would in a photograph. However, you and your image are facing in opposite directions. This causes your left side and your right side to switch places on your mirror image. Also, your image seems to be coming from behind the mirror. How does a plane mirror form an image?

✔ **Reading Check**   *What is a plane mirror?*

Figure 11 shows a person looking into a plane mirror. Light waves from the Sun or another source of light strike each part of the person. These light rays bounce off of the person according to the law of reflection, and some of them strike the mirror. The rays that strike the mirror also are reflected according to the law of reflection. **Figure 11A** shows the path traveled by a few of the rays that have been reflected off the person and reflected back to the person's eye by the mirror.

The Image in a Plane Mirror Why does the image you see in a plane mirror seem to be behind the mirror? This is a result of how your brain processes the light rays that enter your eyes. Although the light rays bounced off the mirror's surface, your brain interprets them as having followed the path shown by the dashed lines in **Figure 11B.** In other words, your brain always assumes that light rays travel in straight lines without changing direction. This makes the reflected light rays look as if they are coming from behind the mirror, even though no source of light is there. The image also seems to be the same distance behind the mirror as the person is in front of the mirror.

Figure 11
A plane mirror forms an image by changing the direction of light rays. **A** Light rays that bounce off of a person strike the mirror. Some of these light rays are reflected into the person's eye. **B** The light rays that are shown entering the person's eye seem to be coming from a person behind the mirror.

Physics
INTEGRATION

When a particle like a marble or a basketball bounces off a surface, it obeys the law of reflection. Because light also obeys the law of reflection, people once thought that light must be a stream of particles. Today, experiments have shown that light can behave as though it were both a wave and a stream of energy bundles called photons. Read an article about photons and write a description in your Science Journal.

SECTION 2   Reflection and Mirrors   **671**

Inclusion Strategies

Visually Impaired For these students, make ray diagrams using yarn wrapped around pushpins pushed into cardboard, polystyrene, or plastic foam board. Pushpins should mark the locations of the mirror and the reflection. For convex and concave mirrors, include pushpins that mark the focal point and focal length of the mirrors. L2 🅻🆂 **Kinesthetic**

Activity
   Provide students with pieces of new aluminum foil. Have them first look at their reflections in the smooth foil, then crumple the foil and observe their reflections again. L2
🅻🆂 **Visual-Spatial**

✔ **Reading Check**

Answer a mirror with a flat reflecting surface

Physics
INTEGRATION

Many properties of light, such as diffraction and interference, are explained most easily by thinking of light as a wave. However, other properties, such as the ability of light to produce a current by ejecting electrons from a metal (the photoelectric effect), seem to indicate that light has a particulate nature. The packets of light energy that behave as particles are called photons. A photon is the particle that transfers electromagnetic force between particles.

Quick Demo
   Pass a hand mirror around the classroom. Ask students to look at their textbooks in the mirror. They will see that left and right are reversed in the mirror. L2
ELL 🅻🆂 **Visual-Spatial**

Activity
   Students will be better able to interpret light ray diagrams if they actually draw them. On the board, draw a simple sketch of an object such as a house. Next, draw rays of light bouncing off the top, middle, and bottom part of the object and striking a plane mirror. Let student volunteers draw in the reflected rays. This will show them how the left to right reversal occurs. Have students then draw similar diagrams of their own. L2 ELL
🅻🆂 **Visual-Spatial**

Concave and Convex Mirrors

Answer A concave mirror is curved inward; a convex mirror is curved outward.

Quick Demo

Have students bring in mirrors of all shapes and curvatures, such as metal bowls and spoons. Show how light reflects differently from each of these mirrors by dimming the lights and reflecting the light from a flashlight off each surface. If you have a concave mirror, you can demonstrate the focal point by slowly walking up to students, one at a time, with the mirror facing them. Students can watch their images disappear and then turn right side up in the mirror when they are between the mirror and its focal point. [L2]

IS **Visual-Spatial**

Extension

For mirrors and lenses, the focal length f, the image distance i, and the object distance o are related by the equation $1/f = 1/o + 1/i$. Have students find i of a concave mirror if $f = 3$ cm and $o = 5$ cm. i = 7.5 cm **What is the image distance if f remains 3 cm and $o = 2$ cm?** −6 cm Explain that the negative image distance means that the image is formed behind the mirror. This type of image is not a real image, since the light rays do not actually go through the mirror to form an image. This type of image is called a virtual image. [L3] IS **Logical-Mathematical**

Concave and Convex Mirrors

Some mirrors are not flat. A concave mirror has a surface that is curved inward, like the inside of a spoon. Unlike plane mirrors, concave mirrors cause light rays to come together, or converge. A convex mirror, on the other hand, has a surface that curves outward, like the outside of a spoon. Convex mirrors cause light waves to spread out, or diverge. These two types of mirrors form images that are different from the images that are formed by plane mirrors. Examples of a concave and a convex mirror are shown in **Figure 12.**

✔ **Reading Check**   *What's the difference between a concave and convex mirror?*

Concave Mirrors   The way in which a concave mirror forms an image is shown in **Figure 13.** A straight line drawn perpendicular to the center of a concave or convex mirror is called the optical axis. Light rays that travel parallel to the optical axis and strike the mirror are reflected so that they pass through a single point on the optical axis called the **focal point.** The distance along the optical axis from the center of the mirror to the focal point is called the **focal length.**

The image formed by a concave mirror depends on the position of the object relative to its focal point. If the object is farther from the mirror than the focal point, the image appears to be upside down, or inverted. The size of the image decreases as the object is moved farther away from the mirror. If the object is closer to the mirror than one focal length, the image is upright and gets smaller as the object moves closer to the mirror.

A concave mirror can produce a focused beam of light if a source of light is placed at the mirror's focal point, as shown in **Figure 13.** Flashlights and automobile headlights use concave mirrors to produce directed beams of light.

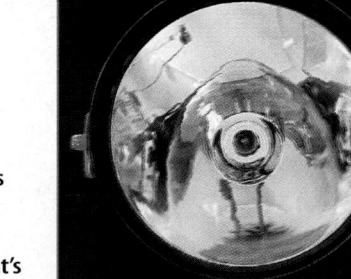

Figure 12
Not all mirrors are flat. **A** A concave mirror has a surface that's curved inward. **B** A convex mirror has a surface that's curved outward.

Curriculum Connection

Art The artist M.C. Escher is well known for his ability to use shadows and lighting to make the impossible look real. In his painting *Convex and Concave*, he uses curved surfaces to create an optical illusion. Show students a copy of this painting and have them discuss Escher's use of lighting on the convex and concave surfaces.

Inclusion Strategies

Learning Disabled If students have trouble remembering which type of curved surface is concave and which is convex, tell them to remember that a concave surface is curved inward like a cave. To practice using this mnemonic, have them name some curved surfaces and identify them as concave or convex.

Figure 13

Glance into a flat plane mirror and you'll see an upright image of yourself. But look into a concave mirror, and you might see yourself larger than life, right side up, or upside down—or not at all! This is because the way a concave mirror forms an image depends on the position of an object in front of the mirror, as shown here.

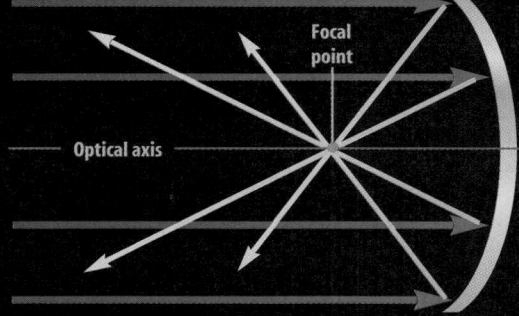

A concave mirror reflects all light rays traveling parallel to the optical axis so that they pass through the focal point.

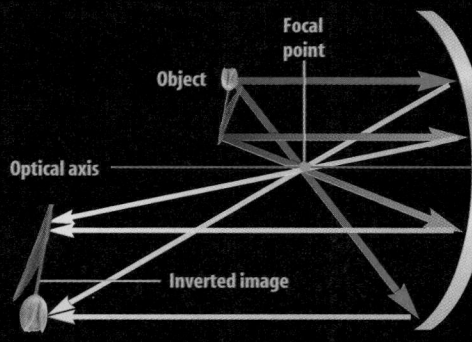

When an object, such as this flower, is placed beyond the focal point, the mirror forms an image that is inverted.

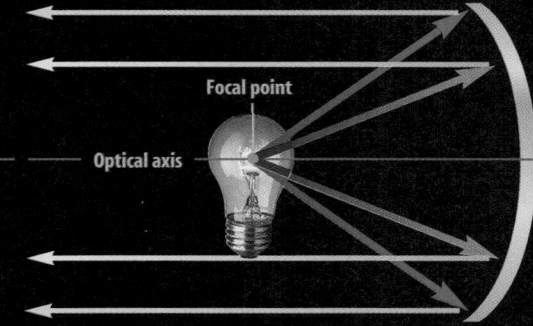

When a source of light is placed at the focal point, a beam of parallel light rays is formed. The concave mirror in a flashlight, for example, creates a beam of parallel light rays.

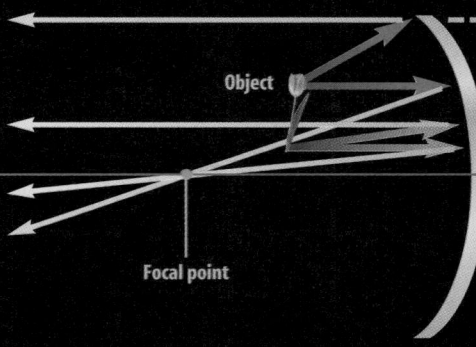

If the flower is between the focal point and the mirror, the mirror forms an upright, enlarged image.

SECTION 2 Reflection and Mirrors **673**

Visualizing Reflections in Concave Mirrors

Have students examine the pictures and read the captions. Then ask the following questions.

- **How could the focal point of a concave mirror be used?** Possible answer: since it concentrates all the light that comes in parallel to the optical axis, it could be used to heat something, start a fire, or cook food.

- **Where might you find a concave mirror?** Possible answers: flash light, car headlight, spotlight, telescope

Activity

Pass out shiny metal spoons to students. Have students look into the concave side of the spoons. Point out how the image is inverted as shown in the diagrams. Since the curvature of the spoon puts the focal point very near the spoon, it is usually impossible to put your eye inside the focal length and get an enlarged upright image. L2 IS **Visual-Spatial**

Extension

Have students investigate the difference between a spherical concave mirror and a parabolic mirror. Ask them to draw diagrams or make posters illustrating the difference between these two types of mirrors. Make sure students realize that a spherical mirror does not focus rays to a single point, but a parabolic mirror does.

Concave and Convex Mirrors, continued

Discussion

If the light rays reflected from a convex mirror spread apart, why is the image formed smaller than the reflected object? The image is formed as if the light rays met behind the mirror. Because the mirror is convex, if the light rays went through it, they would be bent toward the mirror's optical axis, making the image smaller. L3

IS **Logical-Mathematical**

③ Assess

Reteach

The directions of light rays given by the law of reflection are reversible. Students may think that if they can see someone in a mirror, that person cannot see them. Use a large plane mirror to show students that this is not true. L2 IS **Visual-Spatial**

Challenge

Ask students whether a satellite dish is a spherical reflector or a parabolic reflector. Why? Satellite dishes are parabolic reflectors so they can focus the incoming signals to a single point. L2 IS **Visual-Spatial**

✔Assessment

Performance Have students examine their images in both sides of shiny spoons while they move the spoons closer and then farther away. Ask them to form hypotheses about which side of the spoon would serve best as a rearview mirror. the back side Use **PASC**, p. 93.

Figure 14
A convex mirror always forms an image that is smaller than the object.

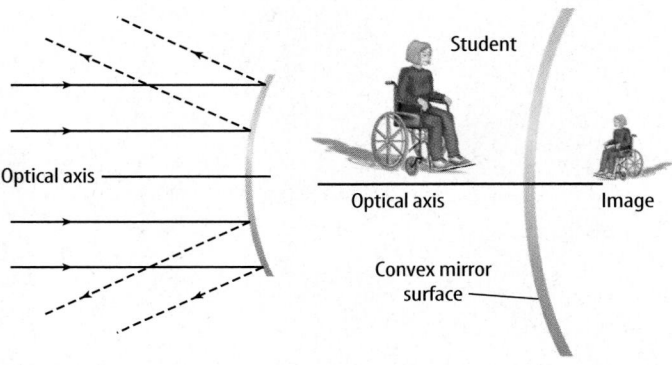

Optical axis

Student

Optical axis

Image

 Convex mirror surface

A A convex mirror causes incoming light rays that are traveling parallel to the optical axis to spread apart after they are reflected.

B No matter how far the object is from a convex mirror, the image is always upright and smaller than the object.

Convex Mirrors A convex mirror has a reflecting surface that curves outward. Because the reflecting surface curves outward, a convex mirror causes light rays to spread apart, or diverge, as shown in **Figure 14A.** Like the image formed by a plane mirror, the image formed by a convex mirror seems to be behind the mirror, as shown in **Figure 14B.** Also like a plane mirror, the image formed by a convex mirror is always upright. Unlike a plane mirror or a concave mirror, however, the image formed by a convex mirror is always smaller than the object.

Convex mirrors are used as security mirrors mounted above the aisles in stores and as outside rearview mirrors on cars, trucks and other vehicles. When used in this way, objects in the mirror seem smaller and farther away than they actually are. As a result, you can see a larger area reflected in a convex mirror. A convex mirror is said to have a larger angle of view than a plane mirror.

Section ② Assessment

1. Describe how light reflects from rough and smooth surfaces.

2. Why are concave mirrors used in flashlights and automobile headlights?

3. What happens to the image in a concave mirror when an object is closer to the mirror than one focal length?

4. Why do side mirrors on cars carry the warning that objects are closer than they appear to be?

5. **Think Critically** The surface of a car is covered with dust and looks dull. After the car is washed and waxed, you can see your image reflected in the car's surface. Explain.

Skill Builder Activities

6. **Forming Hypotheses** When you look at a window at night, you sometimes can see two images of yourself reflected from the window. Make a hypothesis to explain why two images are seen. **For more help, refer to the** Science Skill Handbook.

7. **Using an Electronic Spreadsheet** Design a table using spreadsheet software to compare the images formed by plane, concave, and convex mirrors. Include in your table how the images depend on the distance of the object from the mirror. **For more help, refer to the** Technology Skill Handbook.

Answers to Section Assessment

1. Light is reflected from a rough surface to form a diffuse image. Light is reflected from a smooth surface to form a clear image.
2. They focus the light into a narrow beam.
3. The image is upright and is magnified.

4. The mirrors are convex and make objects appear smaller than they are. The brain interprets this to mean that objects are farther away than they are.
5. With the dust removed and the wax filling in irregularities in the surface, the surface is smoother. This causes regular reflection to occur.

6. One image is caused by reflection from the inside surface of the glass, and one is caused by reflection from the outside surface of the glass.
7. Check students' work.

Activity

Reflection from a Plane Mirror

A light ray strikes the surface of a plane mirror and is reflected. Does a relationship exist between the direction of the incoming light ray and the direction of the reflected light ray?

What You'll Investigate

How does the angle of incidence compare with the angle of reflection for a plane mirror?

Materials

flashlight	small plane mirror,
protractor	at least 10 cm on a side
metric ruler	black construction paper
scissors	modeling clay
tape	white unlined paper

Goals

■ **Measure** the angle of incidence and the angle of reflection for a light ray reflected from a plane mirror.

Safety Precautions 🔬 🥽 👐

Procedure

1. With the scissors, cut a slit in the construction paper and tape it over the flashlight lens.

2. Place the mirror at one end of the unlined paper. Push the mirror into the lump of clay so it stands vertically, and tilt the mirror so it leans slightly toward the table.

3. **Measure** with the ruler to find the center of the bottom edge of the mirror and mark it. Then use the protractor and the ruler to draw a line on the paper perpendicular to the mirror from the mark. Label this line *P.*

4. Using the protractor and the ruler, draw lines on the paper outward from the mark at the center of the mirror at angles of 30°, 45°, and 60° to line *P.*

5. Turn on the flashlight and place it so the beam is along the 60° line. This is the angle of incidence. Locate the reflected beam on the paper, and measure the angle that the reflected beam makes with line *P.* Record this angle in your data table. This is the angle of reflection. If you cannot see the reflected beam, slightly increase the tilt of the mirror.

6. Repeat step 5 for the 30°, 45°, and *P* lines.

Conclude and Apply

1. What happened to the beam of light when it was shined along line *P?*

2. What can you infer about the relationship between the angle of incidence and the angle of reflection?

𝒞ommunicating
Your Data

Make a poster that shows your measured angles of reflection for angles of incidence of 30°, 45°, and 60°. Write the relationship between the angles of incidence and reflection at the bottom.

ACTIVITY 675

Refraction and Lenses

Refraction and Lenses

1 Motivate

Bellringer Transparency

Display the Section Focus Transparency for Section 3. Use the accompanying Transparency Activity Master. L2

ELL

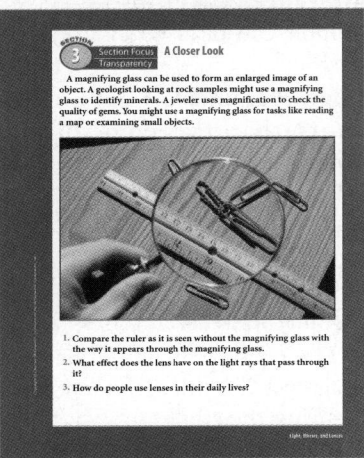

Tie to Prior Knowledge

Students may have noticed that a friend standing in a swimming pool seems shorter than he or she actually is. This illusion occurs because light bends as it passes from water to air.

As You Read

What You'll Learn
- **Determine** why light rays refract.
- **Explain** how convex and concave lenses form images.

Vocabulary
refraction
lens
convex lens
concave lens

Why It's Important
Many of the images you see every day in photographs, on TV, and in movies are made using lenses.

Figure 15
Light travels at different speeds in different materials.

Refraction

Objects that are in water can sometimes look strange. A pencil in a glass of water sometimes looks as if it's bent, or as if the part of the pencil in air is shifted compared to the part in water. A penny that can't be seen at the bottom of a cup suddenly appears as you add water to the cup. Illusions such as these are due to the bending of light rays as they pass from one material to another. What causes light rays to change direction?

The Speeds of Light

The speed of light in empty space is about 300 million m/s. Light passing through a material such as air, water, or glass, however, travels more slowly than this. This is because the atoms that make up the material interact with the light waves and slow them down. **Figure 15** compares the speed of light in some different materials.

Air

A The speed of light through air is about 300 million m/s.

Water

B The speed of light through water is about 227 million m/s.

Glass

C The speed of light through glass is about 197 million m/s.

Diamond

D The speed of light through diamond is about 125 million m/s.

Section ✓ *Assessment* Planner

PORTFOLIO
Science Journal, p. 679
PERFORMANCE ASSESSMENT
Skill Builder Activities, p. 680
See page 692 for more options.

CONTENT ASSESSMENT
Section, p. 680
Challenge, p. 680
Chapter, pp. 692–693

The Refraction of Light Waves

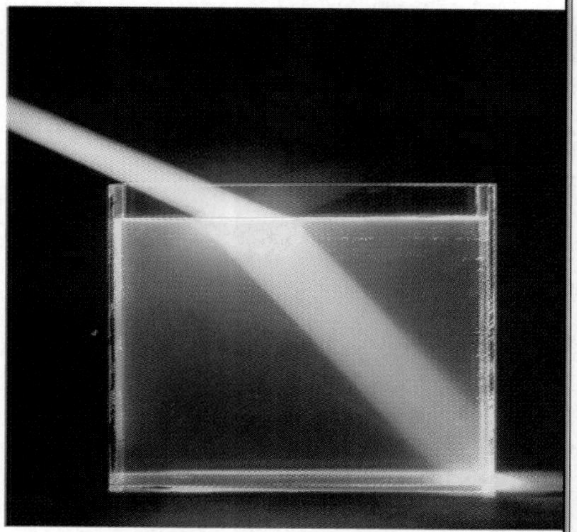

Light rays from the part of a pencil that is under-water travel through water, glass, and then air before they reach your eye. The speed of light is different in each of these mediums. What happens when a light wave travels from one medium into another in which its speed is different? If the wave is traveling at an angle to the boundary between the two media, it changes direction, or bends. This bending is due to the change in speed the wave undergoes as it moves from one medium into the other. The bending of light waves due to a change in speed is called **refraction**. **Figure 16** shows an example of refraction. The greater the change in speed is, the more the light wave bends, or refracts.

> ✔ **Reading Check** *What causes light to bend?*

Why does a change in speed cause the light wave to bend? Think about what happens to the wheels of a car as they move from pavement to mud at an angle, as in **Figure 17**. The wheels slip a little in the mud and don't move forward as fast as they do on the pavement. The wheel that enters the mud first gets slowed down a little, but the other wheel on that axle continues at the original speed. The difference in speed between the two wheels then causes the wheel axle to turn, so the car turns a little. Light waves behave in the same way.

Imagine again a light wave traveling at an angle from air into water. The first part of the wave to enter the water is slowed, just as the car wheel that first hit the mud was slowed. The rest of the wave keeps slowing down as it moves from the air into the water. As long as one part of the light wave is moving faster than the rest of the wave, the wave continues to bend.

Convex and Concave Lenses

Do you like photographing your friends and family? Have you ever watched a bird through binoculars or peered at something tiny through a magnifying glass? All of these activities involve the use of lenses. A **lens** is a transparent object with at least one curved side that causes light to bend. The amount of bending can be controlled by making the sides of the lenses more or less curved. The more curved the sides of a lens are, the more light will be bent after it enters the lens.

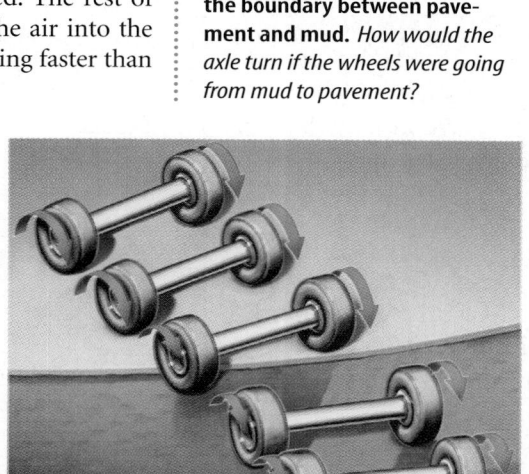

Figure 16
A light ray is bent as it travels from air into water. *In which medium does light travel more slowly?*

Figure 17
An axle turns as the wheels cross the boundary between pavement and mud. *How would the axle turn if the wheels were going from mud to pavement?*

SECTION 3 Refraction and Lenses **677**

Cultural Diversity

Ibn al-Haytham The Arab scientist Ibn al-Haytham (born A.D. 965) was the first to recognize that refraction occurs because light travels at different speeds through different substances. Have students present reports on other things al-Haytham learned about light. He was possibly the first to use the term ray of light, and he developed the idea that vision occurs in response to light hitting the eye. L2

Linguistic

Convex and Concave Lenses

Use Science Words

Word Origins Have students find the origin of the word *lens*. It comes from the Latin word *lens* meaning "lentil." Draw a lentil on the board. **What type of lens does a lentil resemble?** A lens with two convex sides.

✓ Reading Check

Answer Hold the lens more than two focal lengths from the object.

SCIENCE *Online*
Internet Addresses

_____

_____

Explore the Glencoe Science Web site at **science.glencoe.com** to find out more about topics in this section.

Figure 18
A convex lens forms an image that depends on the distance from the object to the lens.

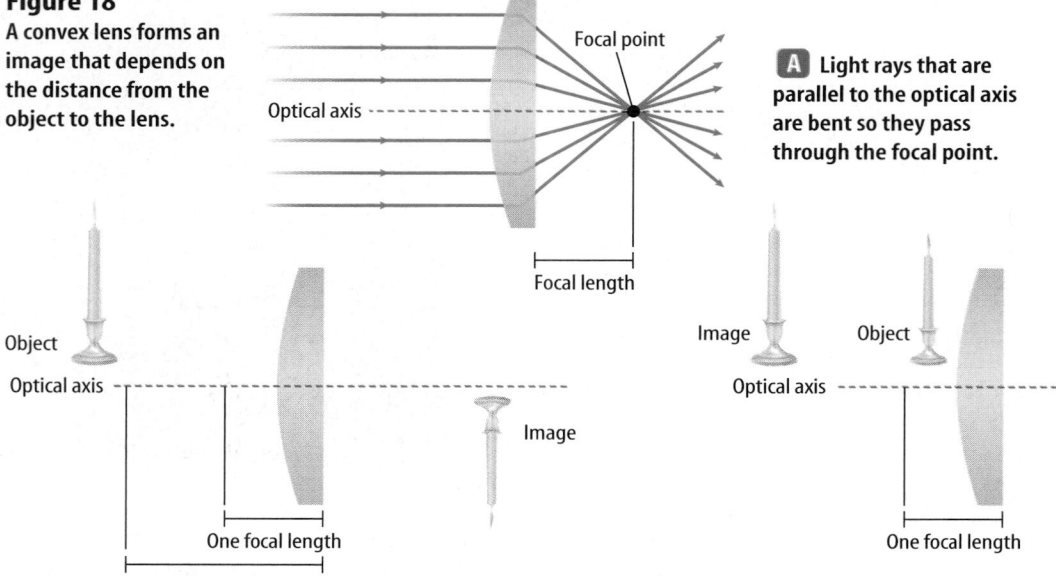

A Light rays that are parallel to the optical axis are bent so they pass through the focal point.

B If the object is more than two focal lengths from the lens, the image formed is smaller than the object and inverted.

C If the object is closer to the lens than one focal length, the image formed is enlarged and upright.

SCIENCE *Online*

Research Visit the Glencoe Science web site at **science.glencoe.com** for information about the optical devices that use convex lenses. Prepare a poster or other presentation for your class describing some of these devices.

Convex Lenses A lens that is thicker in the center than at the edges is a **convex lens.** In a convex lens, light rays traveling parallel to the optical axis are bent so they meet at the focal point, as shown in **Figure 18A.** The more curved the lens is, the closer the focal point is to the lens, and so the shorter the focal length of the lens is. Because convex lenses cause light waves to meet, they also are called converging lenses.

The image formed by a convex lens is similar to the image formed by a concave mirror. For both, the type of image depends on how far the object is from the mirror or lens. Look at **Figure 18B.** If the object is farther than two focal lengths from the lens, the image seen through the lens is inverted and smaller than the object.

✓ Reading Check
How can a convex lens be used to make objects appear upside down?

If the object is closer to the lens than one focal length, then the image formed is right-side up and larger than the object, as shown in **Figure 18C.** A magnifying glass forms an image in this way. As long as the magnifying glass is less than one focal length from the object, you can make the image larger by moving the magnifying glass away from the object.

 LAB DEMONSTRATION

Purpose to show how different materials refract light

Materials dropper, bottle, microscope immersion oil

Preparation The demonstration will not work with Pyrex glass.

Procedure Fill the bottle almost to the top with immersion oil. Put the dropper into the oil. Show the bottle to the students. Squeeze the dropper top and release. Show the bottle again.

Expected Outcome When the dropper filled with air is first put into the bottle, it is visible. When it is filled with immersion oil, it becomes invisible.

✓ *Assessment*

Why did the dropper disappear after the oil was added? The glass of the dropper bends light in nearly the same way as the immersion oil does.

Concave Lenses

A lens that is thicker at the edges than in the middle is a **concave lens.** A concave lens also is called a diverging lens. **Figure 19** shows how light rays traveling parallel to the optical axis are bent after passing through a concave lens.

A concave lens causes light rays to diverge, so light rays are not brought to a focus. The type of image that is formed by a concave lens is similar to one that is formed by a convex mirror. The image is upright and smaller than the object.

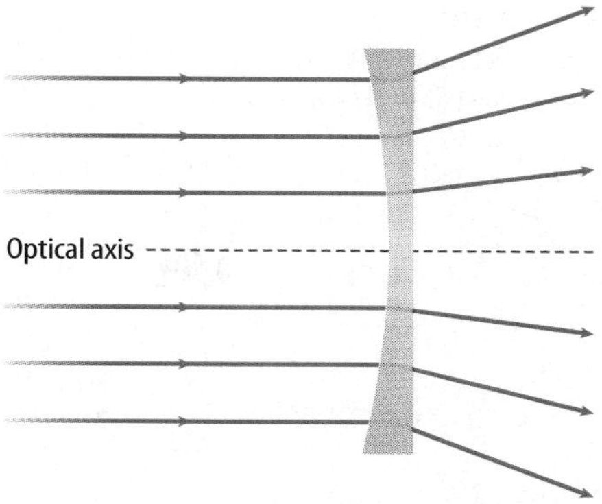

Total Internal Reflection

When you look at a glass window, you sometimes can see your reflection in the window. You see a reflection because some of the light waves reflected from you are reflected back to your eyes when they strike the window. This is an example of a partial reflection—only some of the light waves striking the window are reflected. However, sometimes all the light waves that strike the boundary between two transparent materials can be reflected. This process is called total internal reflection.

The Critical Angle To see how total internal reflection occurs, look at **Figure 20.** Light travels faster in air than in water, and the refracted beam is bent away from the normal. As the angle between the incident beam and the normal increases, the refracted beam bends closer to the air-water boundary. At the same time, more of the light energy striking the boundary is reflected and less light energy passes into the air.

If a light beam in water strikes the boundary so that the angle with the normal is greater than an angle called the critical angle, total internal reflection occurs. Then all the light waves are reflected at the air-water boundary, just as if a mirror were there. The size of the critical angle depends on the two materials involved. For light passing from water to air the critical angle is about 48 degrees.

Optical axis ---------------------------------

Figure 19
A concave lens causes light rays traveling parallel to the optical axis to diverge.

Figure 20
When a light beam passes from one medium to another, some of its energy is reflected (red) and some is refracted (blue). As the incident beam makes a larger angle with the normal, less light energy is refracted, and more is reflected. At the critical angle, all the light is reflected.

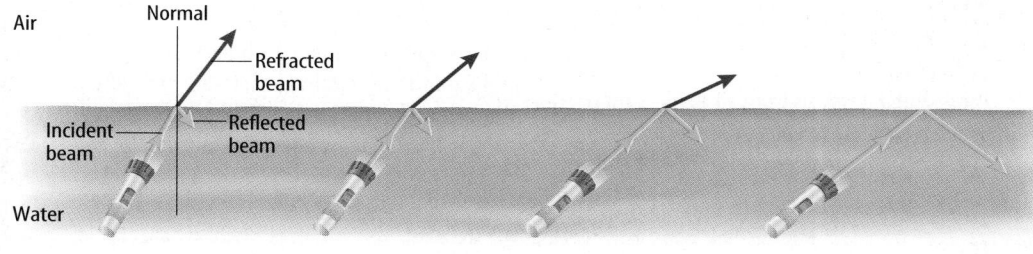

Air
Normal
Refracted beam
Incident beam
Reflected beam
Water

3 Assess

Reteach

Have students make ray diagrams of convex and concave lenses in which the object is two focal lengths from the lens. Tell them to choose objects that don't have vertical or horizontal symmetry so that the orientation after the light passes through the lens is clear. **Which type of lens always produces an upright image?** concave **Which type of lens is used to correct farsightedness?** convex L2

Visual-Spatial

Challenge

Have students describe what happens to light as it passes through air masses or air pockets of different temperatures. As light passes from a pocket of air at one temperature to a pocket of air at another temperature, it changes speed and is refracted. This refraction leads to the formation of mirages. L3

Logical-Mathematical

Assessment

Performance Draw on the board a ray diagram of light from an object moving to a lens. Have students predict the location, orientation, and size of the image produced. Use **PASC**, p. 89.

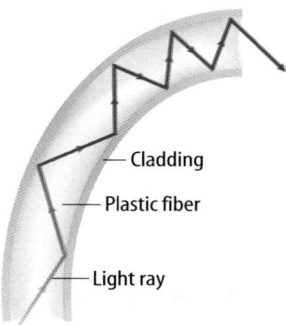

Figure 21
An optical fiber is made of materials that cause total internal reflection to occur. As a result, a light beam can travel for many kilometers through an optical fiber and lose almost no energy.

Optical Fibers

A device called an optical fiber can make a light beam travel in a path that is curved or even twisted. Optical fibers are thin, flexible, transparent fibers. An optical fiber is like a light pipe. Even if the fiber is bent, light that enters one end of the fiber comes out the other end.

Total internal reflection makes light transmission in optical fibers possible. A thin fiber of glass or plastic is covered with another material called cladding in which light travels faster. When light strikes the boundary between the fiber and the cladding, total internal reflection can occur. In this way, the beam bounces along inside the fiber as shown in **Figure 21**.

Using Optical Fibers Optical fibers are used most commonly in communications. For example, television programs and computer information can be coded in light signals. These signals then can be sent from one place to another using optical fibers. Because of total internal reflection, signals can't leak from one fiber to another and interfere with others. As a result, the signal is transmitted clearly. Phone conversations also can be changed into light and sent along optical fibers. One optical fiber the thickness of a human hair can carry thousands of phone conversations.

Section 3 Assessment

1. How is the image that is formed by a concave lens similar to the image that is formed by a convex mirror?

2. To magnify an object, would you use a convex lens or a concave lens?

3. Describe two ways, using convex and concave lenses, to form an image that is smaller than the object.

4. What are some uses for convex and concave lenses?

5. **Think Critically** A light wave is bent more when it travels from air to glass than when it travels from air to water. Is the speed of light greater in water or glass? Explain.

Skill Builder Activities

6. **Predicting** Air that is cool is more dense than air that is warm. Look at **Figure 15** and predict whether the speed of light is faster in warm air or cool air. **For more help, refer to the** Science Skill Handbook.

7. **Solving One-Step Equations** Earth is about 150 million km from the Sun. Use the formula

Distance = speed × time

to calculate how many seconds it takes a beam of light to travel from Earth to the Sun. About how many minutes does it take? About how many hours does it take? **For more help, refer to the** Math Skill Handbook.

680 CHAPTER 23 Light, Mirrors, and Lenses

Answers to Section Assessment

1. They are both upright and smaller than the object.
2. convex lens
3. A person could use a concave lens or a person could hold a convex lens more than two focal lengths from the object.
4. Convex lenses are used in microscopes, telescopes, hand lenses,

and cameras to magnify and focus objects. Concave lenses are used to correct nearsightedness.

5. The speed of light is greater in water. The greater the change in speed, the more the wave is bent. Since the wave is bent less as it travels from air to water, light must slow down less as it moves from air to water.

6. Light travels faster in warm air.
7. time = distance ÷ speed = 150,000,000 km ÷ 300,000 km/s = 500 s = 8.3 min = 0.14 hr

4 Using Mirrors and Lenses

Microscopes

For almost 500 years, lenses have been used to observe objects that are too small to be seen with the unaided eye. The first microscopes were simple and magnified less than 100 times. Today a compound microscope like the one in **Figure 22A** uses a combination of lenses to magnify objects by as much as 2,500 times.

Figure 22B shows how a microscope forms an image. An object, such as an insect or a drop of water from a pond, is placed close to a convex lens called the objective lens. This lens produces an enlarged image inside the microscope tube. The light rays from that image then pass through a second convex lens called the eyepiece lens. This lens further magnifies the image formed by the objective lens. By using two lenses, a much larger image is formed than a single lens can produce.

Figure 22
A compound microscope uses lenses to magnify objects.

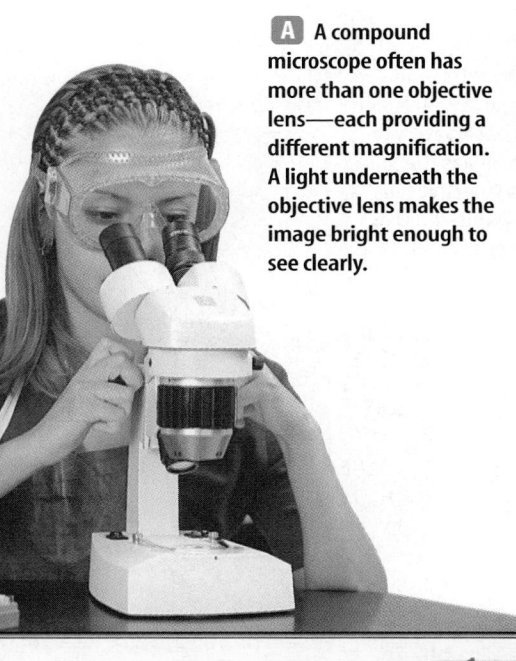

A A compound microscope often has more than one objective lens—each providing a different magnification. A light underneath the objective lens makes the image bright enough to see clearly.

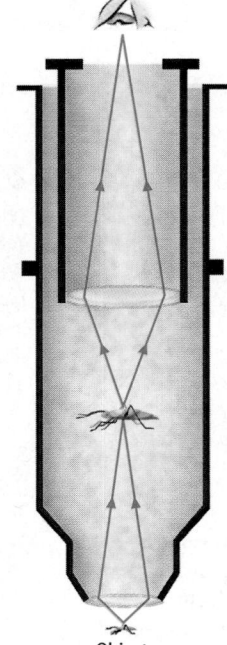

Eyepiece lens

Image formed by objective lens

Objective lens

Object

B The objective lens in a compound microscope forms an enlarged image, which is then magnified by the eyepiece lens.

As You Read

What You'll Learn
- **Explain** how microscopes magnify objects.
- **Explain** how telescopes make distant objects visible.
- **Describe** how a camera works.

Vocabulary
refracting telescope
reflecting telescope

Why It's Important
Microscopes and telescopes are used to view parts of the universe that can't be seen with the unaided eye.

Using Mirrors and Lenses

1 Motivate

Bellringer Transparency
Display the Section Focus Transparency for Section 4. Use the accompanying Transparency Activity Master. L2 ELL

Tie to Prior Knowledge

Discuss with students situations in which they may have seen objects reduced or enlarged by lenses. Ask them how they think the image on a movie screen becomes so large. The image on the film is enlarged using convex lenses.

Resource Manager

Chapter Resources Booklet
Transparency Activity, p. 51
Directed Reading for Content Mastery, pp. 21, 22

Section ✓Assessment Planner

PORTFOLIO
Assessment, p. 685
PERFORMANCE ASSESSMENT
MiniLAB, p. 682
Problem-Solving Activity, p. 684
Skill Builder Activities, p. 685
See page 692 for more options.

CONTENT ASSESSMENT
Section, p. 685
Challenge, p. 685
Chapter, pp. 692–693

Microscopes

Visual Learning

Figure 22 Point out the eyepiece lens and the objective lens on the microscope. Explain that any microscope with at least two lenses is called a compound microscope. A simple microscope is a magnifier such as a hand lens that has only one lens. L2 IN **Visual-Spatial**

Telescopes

Use an Analogy

Ask students how they might collect as much rainwater as possible. One way would be to use large containers that collect many raindrops. Explain that using a large container to collect raindrops is similar to using a large objective lens in a telescope to collect light.

✔ Reading Check

Answer It gathers light from objects to form images that are enlarged by the eyepiece.

Mini LAB

Purpose Students will investigate how a water lens affects images.

Materials test tube with stopper, index card, water

Troubleshooting If an air bubble enters the test tube as students fill it, have them hold the tube slightly slanted so the bubble stays at one end.

Analysis

1. double-convex along one axis.
2. Close to the card: the image was magnified; far from the card: the image was reduced and inverted.

Mini LAB

Forming an Image with a Lens

Procedure

1. Fill a **glass test tube** with **water** and seal it with a **stopper.**
2. Write your name on a **10-cm × 10-cm card.** Lay the test tube on the card and observe the appearance of your name.
3. Hold the test tube about 1 cm above the card and observe the appearance of your name. Record your observations.
4. Observe what happens to your name as you slowly move the test tube away from the card. Record your observations.

Analysis

1. Is the water-filled test tube a concave lens or a convex lens?
2. Compare the image that formed when the test tube was close to the card with the image that formed when the test tube was far from the card.

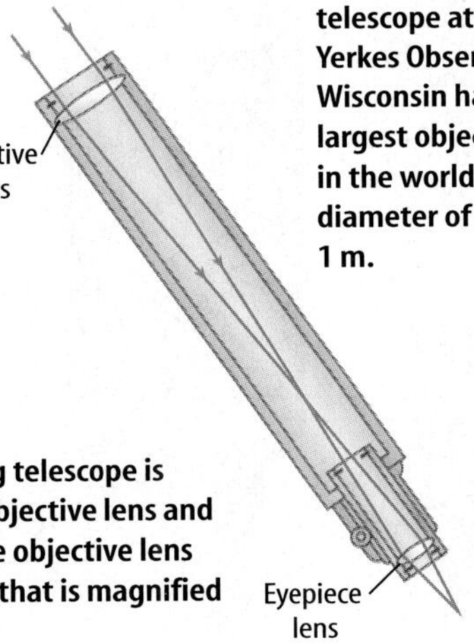

Figure 23
Refracting telescopes use a large objective lens to gather light from distant objects.

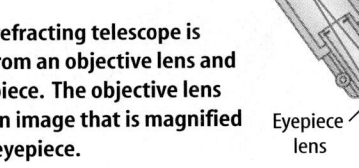

Objective lens

Eyepiece lens

A A refracting telescope is made from an objective lens and an eyepiece. The objective lens forms an image that is magnified by the eyepiece.

682 CHAPTER 23 Light, Mirrors, and Lenses

Telescopes

Just as microscopes are used to magnify very small objects, telescopes are used to examine objects that are very far away. The first telescopes were made at about the same time as the first microscopes. Much of what is known about the Moon, the solar system, and the distant universe has come from images and other information gathered by telescopes.

Refracting Telescopes The simplest **refracting telescopes** use two convex lenses to form an image of a distant object. Just as in a compound microscope, light passes through an objective lens that forms an image. That image is then magnified by an eyepiece, as shown in **Figure 23A.**

An important difference between a telescope and a microscope is the size of the objective lens. The main purpose of a telescope is not to magnify an image. A telescope's main purpose is to gather as much light as possible from distant objects. The larger an objective lens is, the more light that can enter it. This makes images of faraway objects look brighter and more detailed when they are magnified by the eyepiece. With a large enough objective lens, it's possible to see stars and galaxies that are many trillions of kilometers away. **Figure 23B** shows the largest refracting telescope ever made.

✔ Reading Check

How does a telescope's objective lens enable distant objects to be seen?

B The refracting telescope at the Yerkes Observatory in Wisconsin has the largest objective lens in the world. It has a diameter of about 1 m.

✔ Assessment

Process Ask students to predict how the image would be affected if the test tube was held so that its axis was perpendicular to the line along which the name is written. Have them test their predictions. Use **PASC**, p. 103.

Resource Manager

Chapter Resources Booklet
MiniLAB, p. 4

Physical Science Critical Thinking/Problem Solving, p. 22

Figure 24
Reflecting telescopes gather light by using a concave mirror.

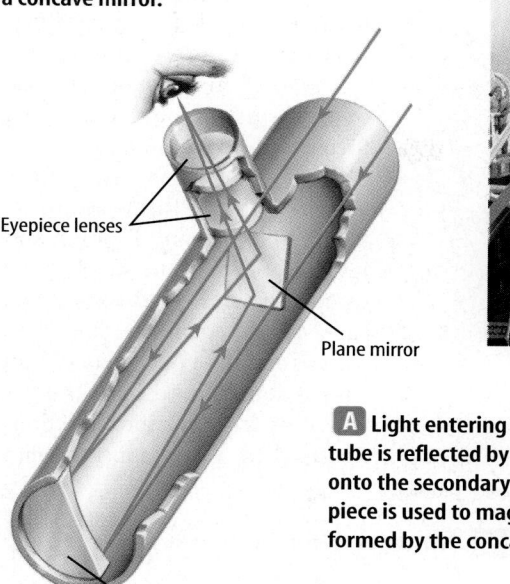

Eyepiece lenses

Plane mirror

Concave mirror

A Light entering the telescope tube is reflected by a concave mirror onto the secondary mirror. An eyepiece is used to magnify the image formed by the concave mirror.

B The Keck telescope in Mauna Kea, Hawaii, is the largest reflecting telescope in the world.

Reflecting Telescopes Refracting telescopes have size limitations. One problem is that the objective lens can be supported only around its edges. If the lens is extremely large, it cannot be supported enough to keep the glass from sagging slightly under its own weight. This causes the image that the lens forms to become distorted.

Reflecting telescopes can be made much larger than refracting telescopes. **Reflecting telescopes** have a concave mirror instead of a concave objective lens to gather the light from distant objects. As shown in **Figure 24A,** the large concave mirror focuses light onto a secondary mirror that directs it to the eyepiece, which magnifies the image.

Because only the one reflecting surface on the mirror needs to be made carefully and kept clean, telescope mirrors are less expensive to make and maintain than lenses of a similar size. Also, mirrors can be supported not only at their edges but also on their back sides. They can be made much larger without sagging under their own weight. The Keck telescope in Hawaii, shown in **Figure 24B,** is the largest reflecting telescope in the world. Its large concave mirror is 10 m in diameter, and is made of 36 six-sided segments. Each segment is 1.8 m in size and the segments are pieced together to form the mirror.

Cameras

✓ Reading Check

Answer a convex lens

Extension

Ask students if they have ever seen a photograph in which the eyes of everyone in the picture are red. Have students research to find out what causes this problem and how it can be avoided. The red eyes occur when light from the camera's flash reflects off blood vessels in the back of a person's eyes. It can be avoided in various ways, such as by turning on enough lights to cause the person's pupils to contract. L2
IS Linguistic

Make a Model

A pinhole camera produces an inverted image without a lens. The simplest form of a pinhole camera is just a box with a tiny hole at one end covered by a simple shutter. Light entering the hole is focused onto film in the box to produce an image. Have students work in pairs to research and make their own pinhole cameras. Ask students to explain why a small hole is necessary. A small hole allows in only a narrow beam of light in which the liquid rays are nearly parallel, so the image is sharp. L2 **IS Kinesthetic**

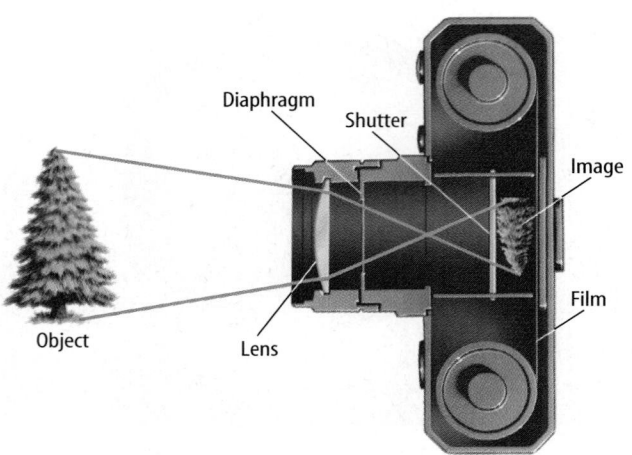

Figure 25
A camera uses a convex lens to form an image on a piece of light-sensitive film. The image formed by a camera lens is smaller than the object and is inverted.

Cameras

You probably see photographs taken by cameras almost every day. A typical camera uses a convex lens to form an image on a section of film, just as your eye's lens focuses an image on your retina. The convex lens has a short focal length so that it forms an image that is smaller than the object and inverted on the film. Look at the camera shown in **Figure 25.** When the shutter is open, the convex lens focuses an image on a piece of film that is sensitive to light. Light-sensitive film contains chemicals that undergo chemical reactions when light hits it. The brighter parts of the image affect the film more than the darker parts do.

✓ Reading Check *What type of lens does a camera use?*

If too much light strikes the film, the image formed on the film is overexposed and looks washed out. On the other hand, if too little light reaches the film, the photograph might be too dark. To control how much light reaches the film, many cameras have a device called a diaphragm. The diaphragm is opened to let more light onto the film and closed to reduce the amount of light that strikes the film.

Lasers

Perhaps you've seen the narrow, intense beams of laser light used in a laser light show. Intense laser beams are also used for different kinds of surgery. Why can laser beams be so intense? One reason is that a laser beam doesn't spread out as much as ordinary light as it travels.

Spreading Light Beams Suppose you shine a flashlight on a wall in a darkened room. The size of the spot of light on the wall depends on the distance between the flashlight and the wall. As the flashlight moves farther from the wall, the spot of light gets larger. This is because the beam of light produced by the flashlight spreads out as it travels. As a result, the energy carried by the light beam is spread over an increasingly larger area as the distance from the flashlight gets larger. As the energy is spread over a larger area, the energy becomes less concentrated and the intensity of the beam decreases.

684   CHAPTER 23 Light, Mirrors, and Lenses

Resource Manager

Chapter Resources Booklet
    Enrichment, p. 34
    Reinforcement, p. 30
Cultural Diversity, pp. 51, 57

SCIENCE *Online*
Internet Addresses
_____
_____
_____
_____
Explore the Glencoe Science Web site at **science.glencoe.com** to find out more about topics in this section.

Figure 26
Laser light is different from the light produced by a lightbulb.

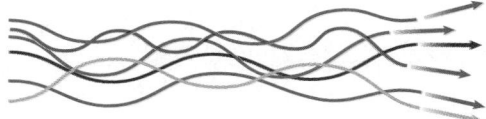

A The light from a bulb contains waves with many different wavelengths that are out of phase and traveling in different directions.

B The light from a laser contains waves with only one wavelength that are in phase and traveling in the same direction.

Using Laser Light Laser light is different from the light produced by the flashlight in several ways, as shown in **Figure 26.** One difference is that in a beam of laser light, the crests and troughs of the light waves overlap, so the waves are in phase.

Because a laser beam doesn't spread out as much as ordinary light, a large amount of energy can be applied to a very small area. This property enables lasers to be used for cutting and welding materials and as a replacement for scalpels in surgery. Less intense laser light is used for such applications as reading and writing to CDs or in grocery store bar-code readers. Surveyors and builders use lasers to measure distances, angles, and heights. Laser beams also are used to transmit information through space or through optical fibers.

Section Assessment

1. How is a compound microscope different from a magnifying lens?
2. Compare and contrast reflecting and refracting telescopes. Why aren't refracting telescopes bigger than reflecting telescopes?
3. Why is the objective lens of a refracting telescope bigger than the objective lens of a microscope?
4. Describe how laser light is different from the light produced by a light bulb.
5. **Think Critically** Could a camera with a concave lens instead of a convex lens still take pictures? Explain.

Skill Builder Activities

6. **Communicating** Using words, pictures, or other media, think of a way to explain to a friend how convex and concave lenses work. **For more help, refer to the** Science Skill Handbook.

7. **Solving One-Step Equations** The size of an image is related to the magnification of an optical instrument by the following formula:

   Image size = magnification × object size

   A blood cell has a diameter of about 0.001 cm. How large is the image formed by a microscope with a magnification of 1,000? **For more help, refer to the** Math Skill Handbook.

SECTION 4 Using Mirrors and Lenses **685**

Answers to Section Assessment

1. A magnifying lens has one lens. Compound microscopes use two or more lenses.
2. The objective lens of a refracting telescope can be supported only around its edges, and the lens's weight can cause it to bend slightly if it is too large. In place of this lens, a reflecting telescope uses a mirror that can be supported in back and be made larger.
3. The lens is large so it can collect a large amount of light.
4. A camera uses a convex lens with the film at its focal point. A wide-angle lens has a short focal length. A telephoto lens has a long focal length.
5. Accept all reasonable answers.

Students should justify their choices. Possible answer: A zoom lens because it can be used as a telephoto lens or a wide-angle lens.
6. Possible answers: Demonstrate the use of lenses, or show how lenses work using pictures or diagrams.
7. image size = 0.001 cm × 1,000 = 1 cm

Activity

What You'll Investigate

Purpose

Students investigate the images formed by a convex lens and observe how the image is affected when the distance between the lens and the light source is altered. L2

Kinesthetic

Process Skills

observing and inferring, recognizing cause and effect, measuring in SI, predicting, communicating, making and using tables

Time Required

1 hour

Materials

The flashlight should have a narrow, intense beam to produce a clear image. If possible, you should be able to adjust the collimation of the beam. To help students clearly see how the image size has changed, you may wish to have them mark off a centimeter or millimeter scale on the cardboard ahead of time. You could also print these out on cardstock using a computer.

Alternate Materials

Inexpensive lens supports are available from science supply companies. These can be attached to a meter stick to provide a clean, secure support. Similar supports are available for holding the cards.

Resource Manager

Chapter Resources Booklet
Activity Worksheet, pp. 7–8

Lab Management and Safety, p. 64

Activity

Image Formation by a Convex Lens

The type of image formed by a convex lens, also called a converging lens, is related to the distance of the object from the lens. This distance is called the object distance. The location of the image also is related to the distance of the object from the lens. The distance from the lens to the image is called the image distance. What happens to the position of the image as the object gets nearer or farther from the lens?

What You'll Investigate

How are the image distance and object distance related for a convex lens?

Materials

convex lens
modeling clay
meterstick
flashlight
masking tape
20-cm square piece of cardboard with a white surface

Goals

■ **Measure** the image distance as the object distance changes.
■ **Observe** the type of image formed as the object distance changes.

Safety Precautions

Inclusion Strategies

Learning Disabled Before beginning the activity, have student volunteers draw diagrams on the board showing a beam of light as it passes through a convex lens. Different diagrams should be drawn showing the object distance shorter than and longer than the focal length of the lens.

Curriculum Connection

Art Artists must have a basic understanding of optics when painting a picture that shows light reflected by surfaces or transmitted through objects. Have students use what they have learned about light shining through convex lenses to make paintings or drawings showing sunlight shining through a glass of water.

Using Scientific Methods

Procedure

1. **Design** a data table to record your data. Make three columns in your table—one column for the object distance, another for the image distance, and the third for the type of image.
2. Use the modeling clay to make the lens stand upright on the lab table.
3. Form the letter *F* on the glass surface of the flashlight with masking tape.
4. Turn on the flashlight and place it 1 m from the lens. Position the flashlight so the flashlight beam is shining through the lens.
5. **Record** the distance from the flashlight to the lens in the object distance column in your data table.
6. Hold the cardboard vertically upright on the other side of the lens, and move it back and forth until a sharp image of the letter *F* is obtained.

Convex Lens Data		
Object Distance (m)	Image Distance (m)	Image Type
1.00	0.43	inverted, small
0.50	0.75	inverted, larger
0.25	1.50	upright, larger

7. **Measure** the distance of the card from the lens using the meterstick, and record this distance in the Image Distance column in your data table.
8. **Record** in the third column of your data table whether the image is upright or inverted, and smaller or larger.
9. Repeat steps 4 through 8 for object distances of 0.50 m and 0.25 m and record your data in your data table.

Conclude and Apply

1. How did the image distance change as the object distance decreased?
2. How did the image change as the object distance decreased?
3. What would happen to the size of the image if the flashlight were much farther away than 1 m?

Communicating Your Data

Demonstrate this activity to a third-grade class and explain how it works. **For more help, refer to the** Science Skill Handbook.

ACTIVITY 687

Procedure

Teaching Strategies
- Slightly darkening the room will make the images easier to observe.
- The data obtained by students will depend on the type of lens and the focal length of the lens.

Tie to Prior Knowledge
Students may have noticed that looking through a clear glass of water produces a magnified image of an object.

Expected Outcome
Decreasing the object distance increases the image distance and increases the size of the image. If the object distance is less than the focal length of the lens, the image is virtual and can't be projected on the cardboard.

Conclude and Apply
1. It increased.
2. It became larger. When the object distance was less than the focal length of the lens, the image could no longer be seen on the cardboard.
3. It would be too small to see.

Error Analysis
Discuss with students how the image is affected if the flashlight beam is too spread out.

Assessment

Oral How would the data obtained for the image distance and the image type differ if a double convex lens were used instead of a plano-convex lens? The lens would bend the light more so the image distance and the image would be smaller. Use **PASC**, p. 89.

Communicating Your Data

When demonstrating the activity to the third-grade class, have students make simple drawings that show how the curve of the lens redirects the light to cause the image inversion and the increase or decrease in size.

ACTIVITY 687

Content Background

Most bending of light rays as they enter the eye occurs as light rays pass from air into the cornea. However the eye contains a flexible lens whose curvature gets adjusted to enable the eye to focus on objects at different distances. The focusing is done by a ring of muscles, called the ciliary muscles, located around the edge of the lens. As a person ages, the lens becomes thicker and less flexible. As a result, the ciliary muscles are unable to make the lens curve enough to focus on nearby objects. The farsightedness that occurs as a result of this is called *presbyopia*, from two Latin words meaning "old eye".

Discussion

Eyeglasses developed when methods people had been using to help themselves see more clearly were combined with technology that allowed lenses to be worn. **Describe some other inventions that resulted when people put together old methods with new technology.** Possible answer: An electrical toaster combines using heat to toast bread with the use of electrical resistance to produce heat. [L2]

IS Logical-Mathematical

Oops! Accidents in SCIENCE

SOMETIMES GREAT DISCOVERIES HAPPEN BY ACCIDENT!

Eyeglasses

"It is not yet twenty years since the art of making spectacles, one of the most useful arts on Earth, was discovered. I myself have seen and conversed with the man who made them first."

This quote from an Italian monk dates back to 1306 and is one of the first historical records to refer to eyeglasses. Unfortunately, the monk, Giordano, never actually named the man he met. Thus, the inventor of eyeglasses—one of the most widely used forms of technology today—remains unknown.

The mystery exists, in part, because different cultures in different places used some type of magnifying tool to improve their vision. These tools eventually merged into what today is recognized as a pair of glasses. For example, a rock-crystal lens made by early Assyrians who lived 3,500 years ago in what is now Iraq, may have been used to improve vision. About 2,000 years ago, the Roman writer Seneca looked through a glass globe of water to make the letters appear bigger in the books he read. By the 10th century, glasses were invented in China, but they were used to keep away bad luck, not to improve vision. Trade between China and Europe, however, likely led some unknown inventor to come up with an idea.

The inventor fused two metal-ringed magnifying lenses together so they could perch on the nose.

In 1456, the printing press was invented. Suddenly, there was more to read, which, in turn, made the ability to see clearly more important. In Europe, eyeglasses began to appear in paintings of scholars, clergy, and the upper classes—the only people who knew how to read at the time. Although the ability to read spread fairly quickly, eyeglasses were so expensive that only the rich could afford them. In the early 1700s, for example, glasses cost roughly $200, which is comparable to thousands of dollars today. By the mid-1800s, improvements in manufacturing techniques made eyeglasses much less expensive to make, and thus this important invention became widely available to people of all walks of life.

688

Resources for Teachers and Students

Samuele Mazza, *Spectacles*, San Francisco, Chronical Books, 1996.

Margery Nichelason, "What's Old and New in Eyewear," in *Cricket*, May 1995, pp. 42–44.

Anne Harding, "A Closer Look at Eye Surgery," in *Harvard Health Letter*, June 1996, Vol. 21 Issue 8, p. 4

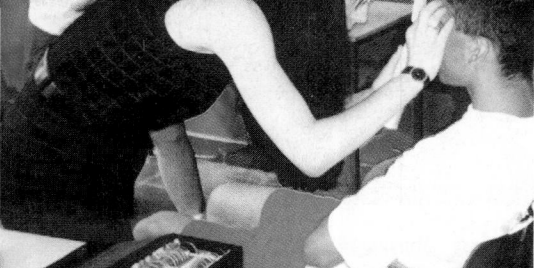

Inventor Unknown

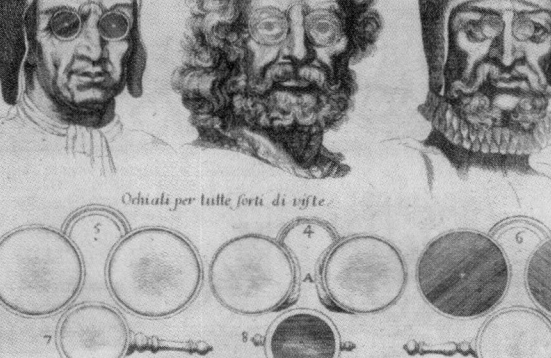

Ochiali per tutte forti di vifte.

Corn. Meyer Inv.

This Italian engraving from the 1600s shows glasses of all strengths.

How Eyeglasses Work

Eyeglasses are used to correct farsightedness and nearsightedness, as well as other vision problems. Farsighted people have difficulty seeing things close up because light rays from nearby objects do not converge enough to form an image on the retina. This problem can be corrected by using convex lenses that cause light rays to converge before they enter the eye. Nearsighted people have problems seeing distant objects because light rays from far-away objects are focused in front of the retina. Concave lenses that cause light rays to diverge are used to correct this vision problem.

CONNECTIONS Research In many parts of the world, people have no vision care, and eye diseases and poor vision go untreated. Research the work of groups that bring eye care to people. Start with eye doctor Cheryl Landry, who works with the Bosnian Children's Fund.

SCIENCE *Online*
For more information, visit science.glencoe.com

Activity

Eyeglasses are made up of lenses and the frames that keep them in place. In order for eyeglasses to be widely available, cheap ways to make effective frames had to be developed. Divide the class into groups and have each group design a cheap and effective way to keep lenses on a person's face. The lenses must stay positioned so the person can see through them, and the designs must not use metal. Have students make models of their designs to display for the class. L2 IS **Kinesthetic**

Analyze the Event

Have students consider the daily activities of most people during the time before eyeglasses came into common use. **Does this provide any clues about why glasses were slow to come into common use?** Many people probably didn't need to see clearly in order to do the tasks they had to do. Eyeglasses became more widespread after the printing press was developed and books became more plentiful. As a result more people learned to read. L2 IS **Logical-Mathematical**

CONNECTIONS Optometrist
Cheryl Landry has made several trips to Bosnia to provide eyecare to refugees. She began her crusade at her own expense. Crucial to her mission is collecting used eyeglasses that she can fit to the people there. Encourage students to collect eyeware that is no longer used so that the class can contribute to Dr. Landry's crusade.

SCIENCE *Online*

Internet Addresses

_____

_____

_____

Explore the Glencoe Science Web site at **science.glencoe.com** to find out more about topics in this feature.

Chapter 23 Study Guide

Reviewing Main Ideas

Preview

Students can answer the questions in their Science Journals. Discuss the answers as you go through the chapter. **IS Linguistic**

Review

Students can write their answers, then compare them with those of other students. **IS Interpersonal**

Reteach

Students can look at the illustrations and describe details that support the main ideas of the chapter. **IS Visual-Spatial**

Answers to Chapter Review

SECTION 1

3. It reflects wavelengths of light that correspond to red on the visible spectrum.

SECTION 2

2. The reflecting surface is curved.

SECTION 3

2. It would become smaller.

Reviewing Main Ideas

Section 1 Properties of Light

1. Light is a wave that can travel through different materials, including a vacuum.

2. When a light wave strikes an object, some of the light wave's energy is reflected, some is absorbed, and some might be transmitted through the object.

3. The color of a light wave depends on its wavelength. The color of an object depends on which wavelengths of light are reflected by the object. *Why does this flower look red?*

4. Almost any color can be made by mixing the primary light colors or the primary pigment colors.

Section 2 Reflection and Mirrors

1. Light reflected from the surface of an object obeys the law of reflection: the angle of incidence equals the angle of reflection.

2. Diffuse reflection occurs when a surface is rough. Regular reflection occurs from very smooth surfaces and produces a clear, mirrorlike image. *Is the image in the photo a diffuse reflection?*

3. Concave mirrors cause light waves to converge, or meet. Convex mirrors cause light waves to diverge, or spread apart.

Section 3 Refraction and Lenses

1. Light waves can change speed when they travel from one medium to another. The waves bend, or refract, at the boundary between the two media.

2. A convex lens causes light waves to converge, and a concave lens causes light waves to diverge. *What would happen to the image of the insect if the magnifying glass in the photo were moved farther away?*

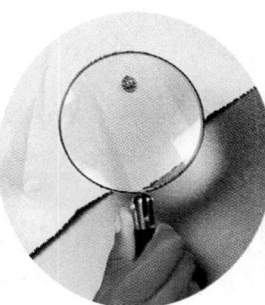

Section 4 Using Mirrors and Lenses

1. A compound microscope is used to enlarge small objects. A convex objective lens forms an enlarged image that is further enlarged by an eyepiece.

2. Most telescopes today are reflecting telescopes, which use a concave mirror to form a real image that is enlarged by an eyepiece.

3. Cameras use a convex lens to form an image on light-sensitive film.

FOLDABLES Reading & Study Skills

After You Read

On the back of the top flap of your Making a Question Study Fold, explain why most telescopes are reflecting telescopes.

FOLDABLES Reading & Study Skills

After You Read

After students have read the chapter and completed the Foldable described in Before You Read, have them do the activity on the student page.

Dinah Zike

Visualizing Main Ideas

Complete the following concept map.

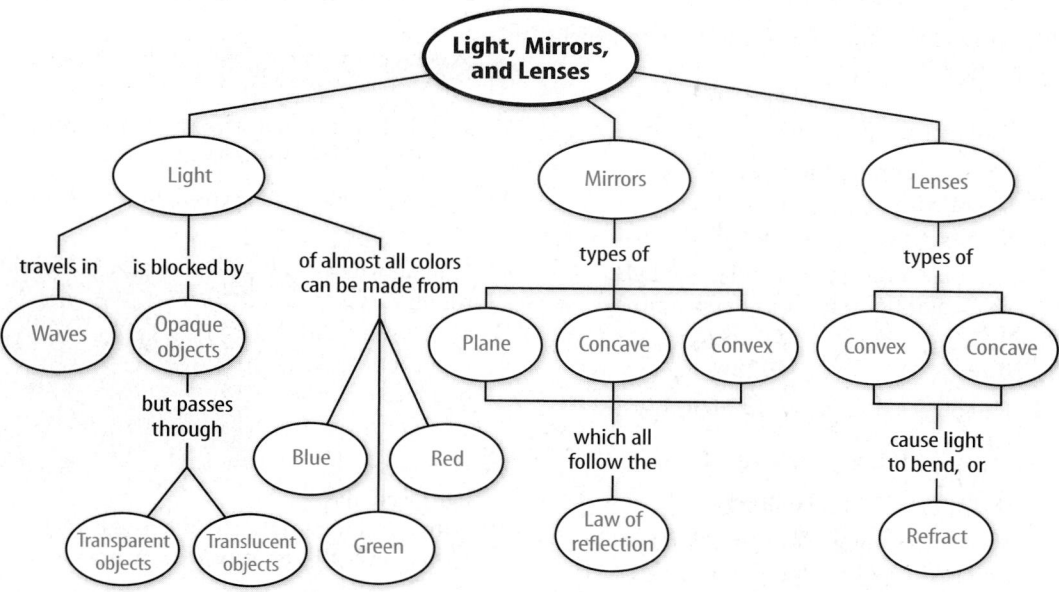

Visualizing Main Ideas

See student page.

Vocabulary Review

Using Vocabulary

1. Reflection occurs when light bounces off objects. Refraction occurs when light bends as it changes speed while moving from one medium to another.

2. A concave lens is thicker at the edges than in the middle and it diverges light rays. A convex lens is thicker in the middle than at the edges and it converges rays.

3. A medium is a substance through which a light ray travels.

4. The focal length is the distance from a lens or mirror to its focal point.

5. A medium is any material through which a wave travels. A lens is a material with at least one curved side through which a light wave may travel.

6. The law of reflection describes the relationship between incident and reflected light. Refraction is the bending of light rays when they change speed.

7. A refracting telescope uses lenses to collect light. A reflecting telescope uses a mirror to collect light.

8. A light ray is a beam of light traveling from a light source or from a material that has reflected it. The focal point is the point at which parallel light rays converge after traveling through a lens or being reflected by a mirror.

9. A lens is a transparent, curved material that causes light to bend. Focal length is the distance between a lens or a mirror and its focal point.

Vocabulary Review

Vocabulary Words

a. concave lens
b. convex lens
c. focal length
d. focal point
e. law of reflection
f. lens
g. light ray
h. medium
i. reflecting telescope
j. reflection
k. refracting telescope
l. refraction

 Study Tip

If you're not sure of the relationships between terms in a question, make a concept map of the terms to see how they fit together. Ask your teacher if the relationships you drew are correct.

Using Vocabulary

Explain the differences between the terms in the following sets.

1. reflection, refraction
2. concave lens, convex lens
3. light ray, medium
4. focal length, focal point
5. lens, medium
6. law of reflection, refraction
7. reflecting telescope, refracting telescope
8. focal point, light ray
9. lens, focal length

IDENTIFYING Misconceptions

Assess

Use the assessment as follow-up to page 662F after students have completed the chapter.

Procedure Ask students to imagine that at exactly 1:15 PM our Sun was magically turned off. Given that Earth is about 150,000,000 km from the Sun, at what time would Earth go dark? Pluto is about 40 times farther from the Sun than Earth is. At what time would someone on Pluto see the Sun go dark? Have students write their answers to these questions individually, then discuss them as a class.

Expected Outcome Light from the Sun takes approximately 8 minutes to reach Earth, so darkness would fall at 1:23 PM. A person on Pluto would see the Sun go dark at 6:35 PM.

Chapter 23 Assessment

Checking Concepts

1. B
2. C
3. A
4. C
5. A
6. C
7. B
8. C
9. D
10. C

Thinking Critically

11. no, only the rays that are traveling parallel to the optical axis
12. No; light rays that are parallel when they strike the surface of a plane mirror remain parallel after they are reflected and do not converge.
13. The water fills in irregularities in the surface, making it smooth.
14. No; refraction must occur for a lens to magnify an object. If the speed of light were the same in all materials, refraction would not occur.
15. Red or green spotlights would make the outfit appear black. These spotlights do not contain any blue light that the outfit could reflect. The outfit would absorb the red and green light from the spotlights and appear black.

Checking Concepts

Choose the word or phrase that completes the sentence or answers the question.

1. Light waves travel the fastest through which of the following?
   A) air
   C) water
   B) diamond
   D) a vacuum

2. What determines the color of light?
   A) a prism
   C) its wavelength
   B) its refraction
   D) its incidence

3. If an object reflects red and green light, what color does the object appear to be?
   A) yellow
   C) green
   B) red
   D) purple

4. If an object absorbs all the light that hits it, what color is it?
   A) white
   C) black
   B) blue
   D) green

5. What type of image is formed by a plane mirror?
   A) upright
   C) magnified
   B) inverted
   D) all of the above

6. How is the angle of incidence related to the angle of reflection?
   A) It's greater.
   C) It's the same.
   B) It's smaller.
   D) It's not focused.

7. Which of the following can be used to magnify objects?
   A) a concave lens
   C) a convex mirror
   B) a convex lens
   D) all of the above

8. Which of the following describes the light waves that make up laser light?
   A) same wavelength
   C) in phase
   B) same direction
   D) all of the above

9. What is an object that reflects some light and transmits some light called?
   A) colored
   C) opaque
   B) diffuse
   D) translucent

10. What is the main purpose of the objective lens or concave mirror in a telescope?
    A) invert images
    C) gather light
    B) reduce images
    D) magnify images

Thinking Critically

11. Do all light rays that strike a convex lens pass through the focal point?

12. Does a plane mirror focus light rays? Why or why not?

13. Explain why a rough surface, such as the road in this photo, is a better reflector when it is wet.

14. If the speed of light were the same in all materials, could lenses be used to magnify objects? Why or why not?

15. A singer is wearing a blue outfit. What color spotlights would make the outfit appear to be black? Explain.

Developing Skills

16. **Comparing and Contrasting** Compare and contrast plane and convex mirrors.

17. **Predicting** You see a person's eyes in a mirror. Explain whether he or she can see you.

18. **Testing a Hypothesis** A convex lens supposedly has a focal length of 0.50 m. Design an experiment that would determine whether the focal length of the lens is 0.50 m.

19. **Researching Information** Research the ways laser light is used to correct medical and vision problems. Write a page summarizing your results.

Chapter ✔Assessment Planner

Portfolio Encourage students to place in their portfolios one or two items of what they consider to be their best work. Examples include:
- Make a Model, p. 666
- Visual Learning, p. 670
- Science Journal, p. 679
- Assessment, p. 685

Performance Additional performance assessments, Performance Task Assessment Lists, and rubrics for evaluating these activities can be found in Glencoe's **Performance Assessment in the Science Classroom.**

20. Making and Using Graphs The graph below shows how the distance of an image from a convex lens is related to the distance of the object from the lens.

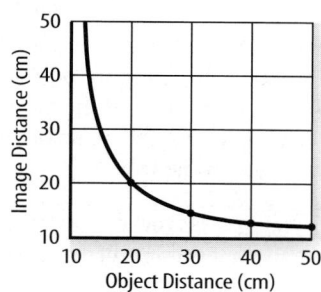

A) How does the image move as the object gets closer to the lens?

B) You can find the magnification of the image with the equation

$$\text{Magnification} = \frac{\text{image distance}}{\text{object distance}}$$

At which object distance is the magnification equal to 2?

Performance Assessment

21. Poster Make a poster describing the difference between the primary colors of light and the primary colors of pigment.

22. Reverse Writing In a plane mirror, images are reversed. With this in mind, write a "backwards" note to a friend and have him or her read it in a mirror.

TECHNOLOGY

Go to the Glencoe Science Web site at **science.glencoe.com** or use the **Glencoe Science CD-ROM** for additional chapter assessment.

Test Practice

Nelson learned that the speed of light is 300,000 km/s. Since he knew that the fastest passenger jet, the SST, flies faster than the speed of sound, he did some research to compare the speeds of sound and light.

The Speed of Sound and Light in Different Media

Medium	Speed of Sound (m/s)	Speed of Light (10^8 m/s)
Glass	5,971	2.0
Water	1,486	2.3
Air	335	3.0
Vacuum	0	3.0

Study the table above and answer the following questions.

1. According to the table, in which medium is the speed of sound the fastest and the speed of light the slowest?

A) glass
B) water
C) air
D) vacuum

2. According to the table, which medium is able to transmit only light?

F) glass
G) water
H) air
J) vacuum

Test Practice

The Test-Taking Tip was written by The Princeton Review, the nation's leader in test preparation.

1. A
2. J

Developing Skills

16. Images formed by both are always upright and appear to originate from behind the mirror. Images from a plane mirror are the same size as the object; images from a convex mirror are smaller than the object.

17. Yes. Light rays bouncing off your eyes will be reflected by the mirror into the other person's eyes.

18. Possible answers: You might use a telephoto lens to take a close-up of a flower because it would increase the image size. You might use a wide-angle lens to take a picture of the Grand Canyon because it would allow a wide view of the scenery.

19. The glass is transparent, the wall is opaque, and the frosted windows are translucent.

20. A) As the object gets closer to the lens, the image gets farther from the lens. **B)** The magnification increases as the object gets closer to the lens.

Performance Assessment

21. Posters should show that primary light colors can be mixed to produce any other color of light. Primary pigment colors result when a pigment absorbs a primary light color. Use **PASC**, p. 145.

22. When writing the notes, students should understand that the image reflected by a plane mirror is upright with left and right sides reversed. Use **PASC**, p.139.

✓Assessment Resources

📁 Reproducible Masters

Chapter Resources Booklet
Chapter Review, pp. 41–42
Chapter Tests, pp. 43–46
Assessment Transparency Activity, p. 55

Glencoe Science Web site
Interactive Tutor
Chapter Quizzes

Glencoe Technology

🔊 Assessment Transparency
💿 Interactive CD-ROM Chapter Quizzes
💿 ExamView Pro Test Bank
💿 Vocabulary PuzzleMaker Software
📼 MindJogger Videoquiz

THE PRINCETON REVIEW

Standardized Test Practice

QUESTION 1: C

Students must identify the answer choice that is the correct cause in the cause-and-effect relationship.

- **Choice A** No; the spyglass was not originally used to view the Moon. Galileo adapted the spyglass for that purpose.
- **Choice B** No; Roger Bacon developed basic ideas about the telescope.
- **Choice C** Yes; the spyglass was originally used to watch other people, such as enemy armies.
- **Choice D** No; although the spyglass was a Dutch invention, that is not the reason for its name.

QUESTION 2: F

Students must use information from the passage to identify the answer choice that is the best supported conclusion.

QUESTION 3: C

Students must use the key word *Americans* to locate important information in the passage and identify the correct answer choice.

Reading Comprehension

Read the passage. Then read each question that follows the passage. Decide which is the best answer to each question.

The History of the Telescope: An International Story

Roger Bacon, an English scientist, first wrote about the basic ideas behind the operation of a telescope in the 1200s. It was not until the early 1600s, however, that Hans Lippershey, a Dutchman who made spectacles for people with poor vision, made the first telescope. Lippershey noticed that objects appeared closer if he viewed them through a combination of a concave and a convex lens. He placed the lenses in a tube to hold them more easily. This was the world's first refracting telescope.

A few years later, an Italian scientist, Galileo, was the first to point a telescope toward the stars. Galileo learned of the Dutch invention in 1609. At the time, it was mainly used to see objects on Earth, such as distant ships and enemy armies. This is why the telescope was first called a "spyglass." Galileo made his own telescope and began using it to view the sky. Before this, Galileo had not been particularly interested in astronomy. That quickly changed as he recorded observations of the Moon's surface, spots on the Sun, and four moons circling Jupiter.

Another advance in telescope technology occurred in 1663 when James Gregory, a Scottish scientist, designed the first reflecting telescope. Isaac Newton built the first reflecting telescope 25 years later. The earliest, most valuable contribution to astronomy made by Americans was the construction of the Hooker telescope, a reflecting telescope on Mount Wilson. Completed in 1917, its 254 cm reflecting concave mirror allowed astronomers to see other galaxies clearly for the first time.

Since then, scientists have continued to design and build larger and more powerful telescopes. The development of the modern telescope is the result of many years of work by many scientists across the world.

> **Test-Taking Tip** As you read the passage, make a time line of the history of the telescope.

1. The telescope was first called a "spyglass" because it _____.
   - **A)** was helpful in observing the Moon and stars
   - **B)** was designed by Roger Bacon
   - **C)** could be used to watch other people
   - **D)** was first made by a Dutchman

2. According to the passage, scientists often _____.
   - **F)** build upon one another's work
   - **G)** are slow workers
   - **H)** aren't interested in many things
   - **J)** never read the work of other scientists

3. The earliest, most valuable contribution to astronomy made by Americans was _____.
   - **A)** the first refracting telescope built in the 1600s
   - **B)** Roger Bacon's basic ideas about the operation of a telescope in the 1200s
   - **C)** the construction of the Hooker telescope on Mount Wilson, which allowed astronomers to see other galaxies clearly for the first time
   - **D)** using a telescope to view the Moon's surface, spots on the Sun, and four moons circling Jupiter

Reasoning and Skills

Power of a Lens

Lens	Diopter	Focal length (m)
1	1/4	4
2	1/5	5
3	1/6	6
4	1/7	7
5	1/9	?

1. Diopters are one way to measure the strength of a lens. What is the focal length of lens 5?
- **A)** 5
- **B)** 8
- **C)** 9
- **D)** 10

Test-Taking Tip Study the values for the first four lenses and consider how the diopter value is related to the focal length.

Wavelengths of Electromagnetic Waves

Type of Wave	Wavelength
Radio wave	Greater than 0.3 m
Microwave	0.3 m – 0.001 m
Infrared wave	0.001 m – 0.0000007 m
Visible light	0.0000007 m – 0.0000004 m

2. A wave with a wavelength of 0.03 m would be what type of wave?
- **F)** radio wave
- **G)** microwave
- **H)** infrared wave
- **J)** visible light wave

Test-Taking Tip Read the table's column headings carefully and then reread the question.

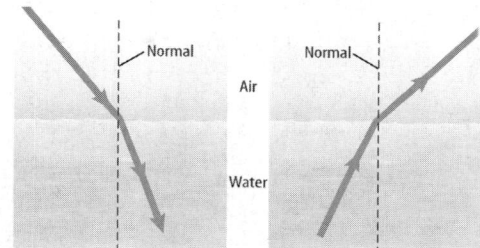

3. What is happening to the wave in this figure?
- **A)** it is being diffracted
- **B)** it is being refracted
- **C)** it is experiencing constructive interference
- **D)** it is experiencing destructive interference

Test-Taking Tip Review the difference between diffraction, refraction, constructive interference, and destructive interference.

4. Explain the relationship between the amplitude of a sound wave and the loudness of a sound. How is the amplitude of the sound wave related to the amount of energy it carries?

Test-Taking Tip Recall the definition of the terms *amplitude* and *loudness*.

Standardized Test Practice

Reasoning and Skills

QUESTION 1: C

Students must study the chart carefully in order to recognize a pattern in the data.

QUESTION 2: G

Students must study the chart carefully in order to decide where 0.03 fits in with the data.

- **Choice F** No; radio waves are greater than 0.3 meters and are much larger than 0.03 m.
- **Choice G** Yes; microwaves range from 0.3 m to 0.001 m. This range includes 0.03 m.
- **Choice H** No; infrared waves are smaller than 0.001 meters and are much smaller than 0.03 m.
- **Choice J** No; visible light waves are smaller than 0.0000007 meters and are much smaller than 0.03 m.

QUESTION 3: B

Students must understand that the bending of waves is called refraction.

QUESTION 4: Answers will vary.

Students should mention that amplitude is wave height, and is a measure of the energy the wave carries. The higher the amplitude, the louder the sound.

Student Resources

CONTENTS

Field GUIDE

About the Field Guide

- This field guide contains representative descriptions and photos of the cones of twelve types of conifers that enable the user to classify some cones.

- In using a field guide, students will apply steps of a scientific method as they observe, investigate, and draw conclusions.

- This field guide applies nationally; local and regional field guides are usually available. Remind students that plants vary and cones may not match exactly.

- Encourage students to use the field guide outside the classroom.

Tie to Prior Knowledge

Students may have seen cones on different needled trees and referred to all of them as pinecones. After using this field guide, they will be aware of the different needled plants and the uniqueness of their cones.

Field Activity

Student responses to this activity will vary. If students use cones from craft items, they may need help in identifying the species from which they came. Be sure they research each cone's plant in order to include a description of it. Student sketches of cones should reflect one of the shapes shown in the field guide.

Field GUIDE

When you hear the word *cone*, you might think of a tasty, edible holder for your favorite ice cream. Maybe you think of the orange cones used on highways and in public places to direct vehicular or pedestrian traffic. However, there's another type of cone in the environment that plays an important role for some plants. These cones are the reproductive organs of a large plant group called the conifers, or cone bearers. The seeds of pines, firs, spruces, redwoods, and other conifers are formed in cones.

Types of Cones

Conifers have two types of cones, male and female. The male cones produce pollen grains and break apart soon after they release pollen. Depending on the species of conifer, the female cones can stay on plants for up to three years. Female cones can be woody or berrylike. Woody cones consist of scales growing from a central stalk and vary in shape and size. Berrylike cones are round and either hard or soft. Each genus of conifers has a different type of female cone. They are so different from one another that you can use them to identify a conifer's genus.

Cones

Cone Characteristics

Cylindrical
This cone is shaped like a cylinder and is nearly uniform in size from the base to the tip.

Ovoid
Although this cone is shaped like a cylinder, it is smaller at the ends than in the middle.

Globose
This cone is rounded like a globe.

Conic
Shaped like a cone, it decreases in diameter from the base to the tip.

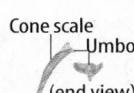
Cone scale
Umbo
(end view)

Umbo
A raised, triangular area at the tip of a cone scale varies in size and thickness.

Field Activity

Find three different cones in your neighborhood, a park, around your school, or as part of a craft item. Using this guide, identify the genus of each cone. Go to the Glencoe Science Web site at **science. glencoe.com** if you don't have cones in your neighborhood. Here you can link to different sites about cones. In your Science Journal, sketch each cone and write a description of the plant it came from.

Resources for Teachers and Students

Trees: An Explore your World Handbook, by Jon Arno, Discovery Books, 2000.

Conifers: The Illustrated Encyclopedia, by D.M. van Gelderen, Timber Press, 1996.

Field GUIDE

Cone Identification

This field guide contains some of the conifers. Plant features might differ in appearance because of environmental conditions.

Douglas Fir—*Psuedotsuga*

These ovoid cones on short stalks have a three-pointed, papery structure that extends from below each cone scale. The cones range from 5 cm to 10 cm in length.

Douglas fir cone

Juniper—*Juniperus*

These cones are hard, berrylike structures that stay on the tree or shrub for two to three years. They measure about 1.3 cm in diameter. They are bluish, pale green, reddish, or brown and covered with a white, waxy coating called a bloom.

Juniper berries

Spruce—*Picea*

These cones are cylindrical and brown with thin cone scales and tips that usually are pointed. They can be 6 cm to 15 cm long. They stay on the plant for two years and hang from branches on the upper third of the tree. As they mature, they become brittle.

Spruce cones

Redwood—*Sequoia*

Ovoid and reddish brown, these cones hang from the tips of needled twigs. They develop in one year and are small in comparison to the size of the tree—only 1.2 cm to 3 cm. The cone scales are flattened on their ends.

Redwood cones

FIELD GUIDE   699

Discussion

What are some of the characteristics of cones that scientists could use to classify a newly discovered species of tree? Possible answers: size, shape, color, and texture of the cone; its location on the tree; the length of time it stays on the tree

Quick Demo

Bring in branches from several different pines. Show students that pines have their needles in groups of two or three to five. Use enlarged pictures if pines are not available in your area. **LS Visual-Spatial**

Visual Learning

Junipers The female cones of the juniper plant are often referred to as "juniper berries." These cones have fleshy scales that are fused together, giving a berrylike appearance. The "berries" of some species of juniper are used to flavor food and beverages.

Fun Fact

The Giant Sequoias are the largest of the conifers. The largest Giant Sequoia tree is about 80 meters high and weighs about 2,500 metric tons.

Curriculum Connection

Geography Have students choose a type of conifer and research where it grows. Have students plot on a large world map the locations of the conifers they have researched. Discuss these locations, and have students draw conclusions based on their knowledge of climates in various locations around the world.
L2 LS Logical-Mathematical

SCIENCE Online
Internet Addresses
_____
_____
_____

Explore the Glencoe Science Web site at **al.science.glencoe.com** to find out more about topics in this field guide.

Content Background

In 1994 a park ranger in an Australian National Park discovered a species of coniferous tree thought to have been extinct for thousands of years. The trees were growing in a deep cavern about 150 km outside Sidney, Australia. Fossil evidence shows that this ancient form of conifer was plentiful during the Jurassic and Cretaceous periods. There currently are fewer than 100 trees of this species known to exist. Botanists and conservationists are working to ensure the species' survival.

Fun Fact

The seeds of nearly all pines are edible. They contain mostly oils, but the protein content ranges from 15 percent to 30 percent.

Activity

Have each student bring in an item or a picture of an item made from the wood of a conifer. Make a list of all of the uses of conifer wood represented by the items.

Extension

Have interested students research amber, the fossilized resin of pines. Amber sometimes contains fossilized insects and provides valuable information to paleontologists and other scientists. Have students report their findings to the class. **LS** **Linguistic**

Field GUIDE

Hemlock cones

Hemlock—*Tsuga*

These cones hang from twigs and are small, ovoid to cylindrical, and 2 cm to 7 cm long. The few cone scales have rounded tips. Although they develop in one year, they usually stay on the tree for more than one year.

Pine—*Pinus*

Each cone has a thick, woody scale tipped with an umbo. The umbo can have a small spine, or prickle. Most pine cones are cylindrical or conic and grow on a small stalk. They vary in length from about 4 cm (scrub pine) to 45 cm (sugar pine) and remain on the tree or shrub for two to three years.

Pine cone

Arborvitae—*Thuja*

These egg-shaped cones are 1.2 cm to 1.5 cm long. They have paired cone scales, usually from six to 12, that are straplike and end in a sharp point. The cones remain attached to the shrub after opening and releasing their seeds.

Arborvitae cones

Cypress—*Cupressus*

These globose cones, which are usually 2 cm to 2.5 cm in diameter, have only six to eight scales. The cone scales have a raised point in the center. They develop in about 18 months and stay closed and attached to the tree.

Cypress cones

Inclusion Strategies

Visually Impaired Help visually impaired students develop a key for several cones using sensory characteristics such as texture, size, and smell. **LS** **Kinesthetic**

False Cypress—*Chamaecyparis*

These small globose cones are only 0.5 cm to 4 cm in diameter with four to ten cone scales. Unlike the cones of the *Cupressus* trees, they open after they are fully developed.

False cypress cones

Swamp or Bald Cypress—*Taxodium*

Swamp cypress cones

This globose cone is about 2.5 cm across and develops in one year. The tips of the cone scales are four sided, forming an irregular pattern on the surface of the cone. Trees in this genus are recognized by the projections, called knees, that grow upward from around the base of the tree trunk.

Fir—*Abies*

Fir cones grow upright on branches and range from 5 cm to 20 cm in length. They are seldom used for identification because the scales drop off when they are developed, leaving only the bare central stalk.

Fir cones

Cedar—*Cedrus*

Cedar cones

These barrel-shaped cones with flattened tips grow upright on branches. They are 5 cm to 10 cm in length and nearly half as wide. After two years, the scales drop off. Cedar trees do not produce these cones until they are 40 to 50 years old.

FIELD GUIDE   701

Discussion

How might your life be different if all species of conifer trees were extinct? Possible answers: Some students may mention that if there were no conifers, they would have to use something different for a Christmas tree. Other students may mention that much of their furniture would not exist without conifers. Students may also point out the value of conifers as a beautiful part of nature that couldn't be enjoyed if they were extinct.

Make a Model

Have students use available materials to make a model of one of the types of cones discussed in this field guide. Students should label their model to indicate the shape and characteristics of the cone, as well as the type of tree on which it is found. Students should share their model with the class. L1 LS **Kinesthetic**

Visual Learning

Bald Cypress Show students additional pictures of bald cypress trees. Point out the knees that form around the base of the trunk. Some scientists think the knees provide stability in loose soil.

Science Journal

More on Cones Provide students with pictures of cones of genera not described in this guide. Have them use other field guides to identify the cones. Encourage students to write descriptions of these cones and their genera in their Science Journals. They should also explain the steps they used to identify the cones. LS **Logical-Mathematical**

Field GUIDE

About the Field Guide

- A field guide enables the user to classify or identify a feature or concept.
- In using a field guide, students will apply steps of a scientific method as they observe, investigate, and draw conclusions.
- This Faults and Folds field guide applies nationally; local and regional field guides are available for more specific local use. Two sources of regional information are listed at the bottom of this page.
- Encourage students to use this field guide outside.

Tie to Prior Knowledge

Students have seen many of the Earth structures discussed here as backdrops to movies and SUV commercials set in the West. Tell them they will appreciate these settings more after studying this field guide.

Field Activity

Have students work in small groups to compare their notes and classify the formations they documented. They should be able to distinguish between folds and faults and to further determine the types. Ask students if they can identify the forces at work to form the structures they saw. For example, compression from plate collisions could form an anticline.

Field GUIDE

Earth's crust is squeezed and pulled as tectonic plates move. Energy builds up in rocks and when it is released, it can dramatically and visibly change the structure of the land surface. Faults are fractures in Earth produced when sections of Earth's crust move past each other and release energy, sometimes during earthquakes. Small faults can be nearly invisible on the surface. Large faults, caused by intense, long-time crustal movement, can be huge cracks in the ground that extend for hundreds of miles. Types of faults include normal; reverse, or thrust; and strike-slip.

When tectonic plates collide, great mountain chains can be uplifted out of Earth. When rocks are subjected to stress, they do not always break and form faults—under some conditions, rocks will bend and fold. These folded rocks can reach Earth's surface. Upward-arching folds are known as anticlines. Downward-sagging folds are known as synclines. Folds can be large enough to form mountains or small enough to hold in your hand.

Earth's tectonic plates have been moving for hundreds of millions of years. Although they move very slowly—about 10 cm per year—they have moved across great distances over time.

702 STUDENT RESOURCES

Faults and Folds

Normal Fault: The Rio Grande Rift

Extending across a distance of more than 1,200 km, the Rio Grande Rift stretches from Colorado to Northern Mexico and separates the Colorado Plateau from the Great Plains. The Rio Grande Rift is an example of how normal faults can affect Earth's surface. It is the result of fractures in Earth's crust that are formed as the crust is pulled apart. The Rio Grande Rift is active and the faults in the rift release their built-up energy in the form of frequent, small tremors rather than as large earthquakes. The region also contains many volcanoes.

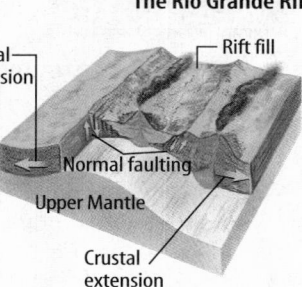

The Rio Grande Rift

Formation of rift

Field Activity

Go to **science.glencoe.com** to take an online geology field trip. Click on the links provided to view different rock formations throughout the United States. In your Science Journal, write or draw the overall structure and attitude, or positioning, of the rock formations.

Resources for Teachers and Students

The Roadside Geology series, Mountain Press Publishing Company, Missoula, Montana

The Geological Highway Map series, The American Association of Petroleum Geologists, Tulsa, Oklahoma

Thrust Fault: The Appalachian Mountains

The Appalachian Mountains were uplifted more than 300 million years ago during a plate collision. As the African and North American Plates collided, huge slices of Earth's crust were moved great distances along thrust faults. These slices of crust make up Earth's surface in some parts of the Appalachian Mountains today.

Fault Surface

Thrust fault

Hayward Fault

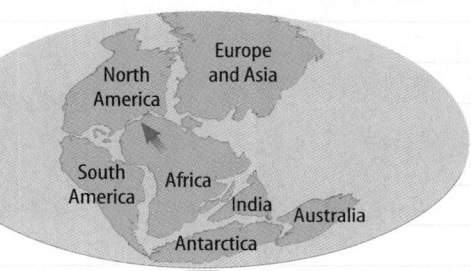

North America
Europe and Asia
South America
Africa
India
Australia
Antarctica

Tectonic Plate collision

NEVADA

Hayward Fault
San Francisco

San Andreas Fault

CALIFORNIA

Los Angeles

PACIFIC OCEAN

MEXICO

Location of Hayward Fault

Strike-Slip Fault: The Hayward Fault

This strike-slip fault—part of the 900-km San Andreas Fault system—extends about 120 km and is considered to be the state's second-strongest fault. It is a fracture in Earth's crust: the Pacific Plate to the west is moving northwest in relation to the North American Plate. Energy from this movement continues to build until it is released in the form of an earthquake. In 1868, an earthquake occurred along the Hayward Fault, damaging San Francisco.

FIELD GUIDE 703

Make a Model

Have student groups use different-colored modeling clay to make three identical stacks of horizontal rock layers. Then, have students use a spatula to cut a normal fault in one clay stack, a thrust fault in another, and a strike-slip fault in the third, moving the blocks appropriately. Ask the students to use their spatulas to model the effects of erosion on their faulted terrains and then to observe the surface morphology and the arrangement of different rock layer for each terrain.

Activity

Obtain interesting geologic maps from a university library or from your state geologic survey. Have students work in groups around each map, locating and identifying by symbol any normal, thrust, and strike-slip faults on the maps. Have them also examine other features on the maps.

Fun Fact

Estes Park, Colorado, and Park City, Utah, probably offer plenty of recreation, but that's beside the point. Their names refer instead to their geology—a *park* is a down-dropped piece of crust, as in a rift.

Visual Learning

Have students look at the picture of the Appalachians and ask them to explain how a plate collision could result in uplift. Then demonstrate by holding a meter stick at both ends and compressing until it bows upward.

Quick Demo

Lay a tablecloth over a smooth classroom desk. Have two students stand on opposite sides of the desk and push the tablecloth toward the center. This should create upward and downward folds similar to anticlines and synclines in folded rock. Ask students which folds resemble anticlines and which resemble synclines. **What force did the students who applied force represent?** Students pushing cloth toward the center acted as compressional forces do on plates.

Teacher FYI

Folding and faulting are different versions of crust deformation caused by crustal movement. Geologists believe the ultimate force behind such crustal movement is convection occurring in the asthenosphere portion of the upper mantle. Diverging convection currents produce tension; converging currents produce compression.

Extension

Challenge students to research the parts of anticlines and synclines, and the different types classified by geologists. The sides are called limbs; the angle of dip is called the axis. Folds can be classified as asymmetrical, overturned, recumbent, and plunging. Have students create informational posters displaying what they learned.

Field GUIDE

Fold: Anticline at Hartland Quay

Layers of sedimentary rock are folded in this spectacular anticline at Hartland Quay in Devon, England. The anticline has been eroded in the foreground exposing the ends of the tilted rock layers.

Anticline at Hartland Quay

Anticlines and synclines in sequence

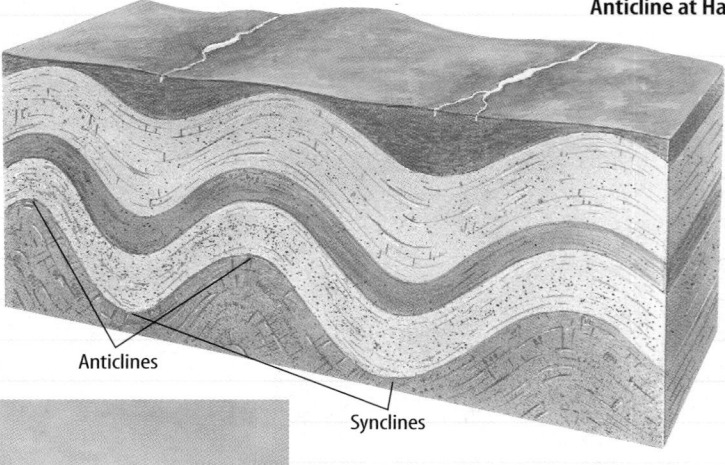

Anticlines

Synclines

Fold: Syncline on Mount Kidd

This syncline is part of Mount Kidd in Alberta, Canada, in the Kananaskis Valley of the Canadian Rockies. Unlike the American Rockies, which were originally large chunks of granite, the Canadian Rockies began as piles of sediment that were compressed when plates collided.

The syncline on Mount Kidd

Visual Learning

Direct students to inspect the pictures of anticlines and synclines. Ask them to identify the locations of the youngest and the oldest rock in each structure. The oldest rock rises up from the center in an anticline; it dips downward in a syncline. Should either structure be eroded, these locations become important. At the surface in an eroded anticline, older rock will be surrounded by younger rock. An eroded syncline features the youngest rock at its center. Make a diagram on the board to illustrate this idea.

Fold: The Alps

Location of the Alps

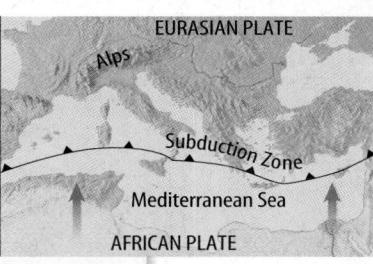

EURASIAN PLATE

Alps

Subduction Zone

Mediterranean Sea

AFRICAN PLATE

The Alps, which are a beautiful example of folded mountains, were formed as the African Plate began to move closer to the Eurasian Plate. The pressure exerted by this movement caused the land to fold, creating these peaks more than 15 million years ago.

The folded Alps

Erosion of the Blue Ridge Mountains

Ridge   Valley   Ridge

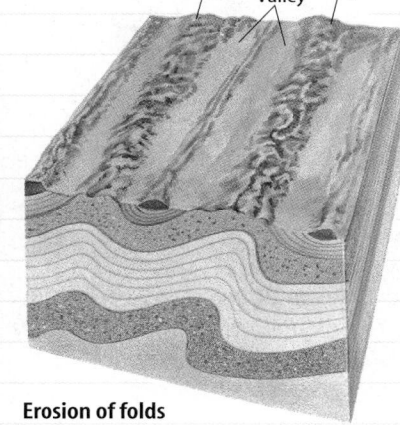

Erosion of folds

Fold: The Blue Ridge Mountains

Folded mountains derive their name from the abundance of folds in the rocks. The Blue Ridge Mountains in the Valley and Ridge region of the Appalachians are an excellent example of mountains formed by rocks that folded, then began to erode. The harder rocks formed ridges, and the softer rocks eroded to form valleys.

Use Science Words

Word Meaning Have students investigate the meaning of the word *anticline* and the word *syncline*. After they have finished investigating these two words, ask them to speculate about the meaning of the word *monocline*. The word *anticline* means, "opposite inclined" and reflects the fact that the limbs of an anticline dip in opposite directions. The word *syncline* means, "together inclined" and reflects the fact that the limbs of a syncline dip toward each other. A *monocline* is a fold with only one limb.

Discussion

Folding occurs when plates are subject to compression, usually because they are colliding with other plates. What might happen if the situation changed, and plates that had been compressed began to be pulled apart? Students might answer that the plate would "unfold." In fact, the likely result would be normal faulting.

Curriculum Connection

Geography The Valley and Ridge Province of the Appalachian Mountains consists of sedimentary rock layers deformed into a series of plunging anticlines and synclines. The ridges and valleys are sculpted by erosion. Resistant sandstone layers in the limbs of folds stand up to form ridges, and soft-shale layers are eroded into valleys. Explain to students how the Valley and Ridge Province formed, and have each student draw a plausible cross section of such a province in their Science Journal.

Field GUIDE

Field Guides

About the Field Guide

- This field guide contains descriptions that enable the user to identify and classify musical instruments.

- In using a field guide, students will apply steps of a scientific method as they observe, investigate, infer, and draw conclusions.

- This field guide describes some musical instruments commonly used in the United States. Information about musical instruments used in other countries and cultures can be found in musical dictionaries and encyclopedias.

- Encourage students to use the field guide outside the classroom.

Tie to Prior Knowledge

Ask students to name their favorite musical instruments. Have them describe how the instruments sound. For example, they might say a saxophone has a mellow sound or a piccolo has a shrill sound. Encourage students to compare the sounds made by various instruments.

Field Activity

If students have had little experience with musical instruments, show them pictures of assorted instruments before having them do the Field Activity. Encourage students to bring in any band or orchestra instruments they play and demonstrate them for the class.

Field GUIDE

Some people have defined music as "patterns of tones." A tone is a sound with a specific pitch. In music, a tone might also be called a note. Pitch describes how high or low the tone is. Like all sounds, musical tones are produced when an object vibrates. Higher pitches are produced by more vibrations per second, and therefore have a higher frequency.

Most musical instruments use resonance to amplify sounds. To amplify a sound means to increase its volume. Resonance occurs when one object causes another object to vibrate at the same frequency—or pitch.

How Resonance Works

A vibrating object produces sound waves. These waves can affect other objects and cause them to vibrate. As more matter vibrates, a louder sound is produced. For example, resonance is at work in a guitar. When a guitar's strings are plucked or strummed, the strings vibrate. The strings' vibrations make the thin soundboard—in this case, the front of the guitar—vibrate. The soundboard's vibrations make the air inside the guitar's hollow body vibrate. The vibrating air amplifies the sounds that were first produced by the strings.

Musical Instruments

Mandolin

Stringed Instruments

Tones are produced in stringed instruments by making stretched strings vibrate. Each string is tuned to a different pitch. When playing stringed instruments such as the harp, each string produces only one pitch. The player creates different pitches by plucking different strings.

When playing stringed instruments such as the guitar and violin, the player can change the pitch of each string by pressing down on one end and making it shorter. Stringed instruments may be strummed, plucked, or played with a bow.

Harp

Field Activity

Watch an orchestra or band perform in a live concert or on television. In your Science Journal, name all of the different instruments you recognize. Then use this field guide to identify the category in which each instrument is classified.

Resources for Teachers and Students

The New Grove Dictionary of Musical Instruments, Vol. 1, 2, 3, ed. Stanley Sadie, Macmillan Press, 1984.

Music (Eyewitness Books), by Neil Ardley, Alfred A. Knopf, Inc., 1989.

The Physics of Musical Instruments, by Neville H. Fletcher and Thomas D. Rossing, Springer-Verlag Telos, 1998.

Musical Instruments, Traditions Around the World, by Louise Tythacott, Thomson Learning, 1995.

Rattles, Bells, and Chiming Bars, by Karen Foster, Merlion Publishing, 1992.

Wind Instruments—Woodwinds

Woodwind instruments include the clarinet, the saxophone, and the recorder. These instruments are played by blowing into a mouthpiece or across a hole. Some woodwinds, such as clarinets, have a thin flexible reed in the mouthpiece that vibrates. The reed causes the air in the tube to vibrate. As the air vibrates inside the woodwind's hollow tube, tones are produced. Musicians change this instrument's pitch by covering holes with their fingers or by pressing keys that cover holes. Covering a hole changes the length of the column of air inside the tube.

Saxophone

Clarinet

Wind Instruments—Brass

Brass instruments include the trumpet, the trombone, and the tuba. Their mouthpieces are larger than woodwinds' mouthpieces. Brass instruments are played by pressing the lips against a mouthpiece and blowing so the lips vibrate. Musicians change brass instruments' pitches by tensing or relaxing their lips. With most brass instruments, the pitch also can be changed by pressing valves, which changes the length of the vibrating column of air inside the instrument.

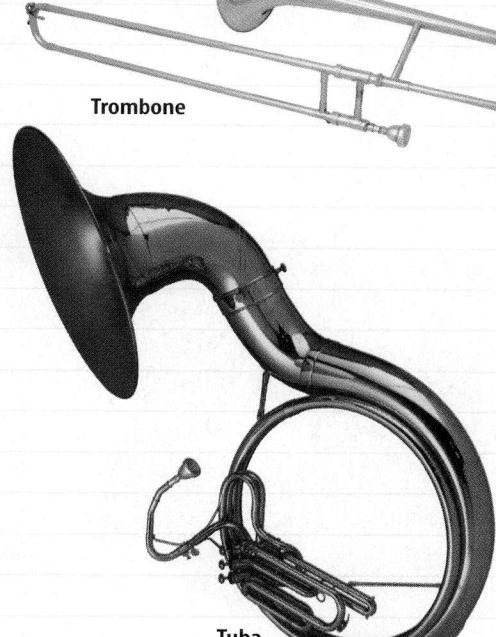

Trombone

Tuba

Quick Demo

Blow across the top of a soda bottle partially filled with water to demonstrate how the height of a resonating column affects sound. First, have a small amount of water in the bottle when you blow across it. Continue adding small amounts of water and blowing across the bottle so students can hear the change in pitch. **Why does the pitch become higher as more water is added to the bottle?** As the column of air becomes shorter, only short wavelengths can resonate in the bottle. The shorter wavelengths correspond to higher pitches.

Discussion

Does closing all the holes in the clarinet or saxophone produce a higher or lower pitch? Closing the holes produces a lower pitch because it lengthens the air column.

Curriculum Connection

Health Vocal cords produce sounds in much the same way as wind instruments do. These elastic folds of mucous membrane vibrate to form sounds as air blows over them; resonance increases the volume. **Why do men usually have lower voices than women?** Men's vocal cords are usually longer and thicker so the air passage is wider.
ᴸˢ **Logical-Mathematical**

Science Journal

Making Music Ask students to choose two different instruments. Have them write paragraphs in their Science Journals comparing and contrasting how each makes music. For example, students might compare a flute and a trumpet. ᴸˢ **Linguistic**

Science Words

Word Origin The word *idiophone* comes from the Greek words *idios*, meaning "pertaining to one's self," and *phonema*, meaning "sound." Ask students to explain how these word origins apply to the idiophone. *An idiophone produces sound by vibrating itself.*

Have students find another word that uses the root word "idio" and give its meaning. *Possible answer: idiosyncrasy, meaning "something peculiar about a person"*

Discussion

How would the sound produced by a xylophone differ if you held your hand against the wooden bars as you hit them with the mallet? *The vibrations would be dampened, so the sound would be a dull thud.*

Activity

Ask students to bring in any musical instruments that they play. Have volunteers demonstrate how their instruments sound and how they are played. Ask all volunteers to play the same simple tune, such as "Hot Cross Buns," so that the class can compare the differences in sound. For each of the instruments, have the class discuss how sound is produced. For stringed and wind instruments, students can discuss how changing the finger position or some other technique is used to alter the pitch. **IS** **Auditory-Musical**

Percussion Instruments—Idiophones

Idiophones vibrate to produce tones. Musicians play them by hitting, shaking, scraping, or plucking them. Idiophones such as cymbals, bells, gongs, music boxes, and xylophone keys play only one pitch. Triangles, clappers, rattles, and cymbals have indefinite pitches—their pitches depend on how they are played and how they are constructed.

Xylophone

Percussion Instruments—Membranophones

Membranophones produce sound when their membranes—the stretched tops of drums or the tiny membranes within kazoos—vibrate. Drums are usually struck with hands, with beaters such as drumsticks, or with knotted cords to produce tones.

Bongo

Electric Instruments

Electric instruments such as the electric guitar and electric violin are played like regular instruments. However, rather than using resonance to amplify their sound, their vibrations are converted to electrical signals that are amplified electronically. The amplified electric signal is then converted to sound by a loudspeaker.

Guitar and Amplifier

Teacher FYI

When a mallet strikes a xylophone bar, the bar vibrates with its middle first up and then down, while the ends are down and then up (opposite to the position of the middle of the bar). The xylophone must be constructed so that the bars are supported about a quarter of the way from the ends at the bar's vibrational nodes.

Inclusion Strategies

Learning Disabled To help students visualize how vibrations create the sound of a drum, place a handful of rice on the top of a drumhead. Direct students to observe how the rice vibrates as you hit the drumhead with a stick. Explain that just as the vibrating drumhead causes the rice to vibrate, it also causes air to vibrate, creating sound waves. L1 **IS** **Visual-Spatial and Auditory-Musical**

Piano

Keyboard Instruments—Piano

Each piano key is attached to a small hammer. When the player presses a key, the hammer hits a string and makes it vibrate. The strings are different lengths and each string produces a different pitch. The piano's body amplifies the tones.

Keyboards—Pipe Organ

Pressing a pipe organ's key opens a pipe to let air vibrate inside it. The pipes are different lengths, and each produces a different pitch.

Pipe Organ

Electronic Instruments

Unlike all other types of musical instruments, electronic instruments do not rely on vibrations to produce sounds. Instead, these instruments produce electrical signals that a computer then converts to sounds. Even though a synthesizer has a keyboard, it is classified as an electronic instrument because it produces sounds electronically. Today, it is the most widely used electronic instrument.

Synthesizer

FIELD GUIDE 709

Make a Model

Ask students to work in small groups to make models of musical instruments. For example, they could blow across soda bottles filled with different amounts of water to model a pipe organ. They might make a model of a xylophone by constructing a base with wooden slabs on it. Allow groups to be creative in designing their models. When they present their models to the class, each member of the group should be able to explain how sound is produced in the instrument. L2 COOP LEARN **Kinesthetic**

Visual Learning

Keyboard Instruments—Piano
Have students notice the shape of the grand piano. Explain that the wider area contains long strings for playing lower-pitched sounds and the narrower area contains shorter strings for playing higher-pitched sounds. Point out that the top of grand pianos are propped open to increase the volume of the sound. **Visual-Spatial**

Curriculum Connection

History One of the earliest forms of the piano was invented by Bartolomeo Cristofori in 1709. Since that time the piano has gone through numerous revisions, including the fortepiano, the square piano, the pianoforte, and the upright. Have students prepare reports about how the piano developed into its present-day form. L2 **Logical-Mathematical**

SCIENCE Online
Internet Addresses

_____
_____
_____

Explore the Glencoe Science Web site at **science.glencoe.com** to find out more about topics in this field guide.

Organizing Information

As you study science, you will make many observations and conduct investigations and experiments. You will also research information that is available from many sources. These activities will involve organizing and recording data. The quality of the data you collect and the way you organize it will determine how well others can understand and use it. In **Figure 1,** the student is obtaining and recording information using a microscope.

Putting your observations in writing is an important way of communicating to others the information you have found and the results of your investigations and experiments.

Researching Information

Scientists work to build on and add to human knowledge of the world. Before moving in a new direction, it is important to gather the information that already is known about a subject. You will look for such information in various reference sources. Follow these steps to research information on a scientific subject:

Step 1 Determine exactly what you need to know about the subject. For instance, you might want to find out what happened to local plant life when Mount St. Helens erupted in 1980.

Step 2 Make a list of questions, such as: When did the eruption begin? How long did it last? How large was the area in which plant life was affected?

Step 3 Use multiple sources such as textbooks, encyclopedias, government documents, professional journals, science magazines, and the Internet.

Step 4 List where you found the sources. Make sure the sources you use are reliable and the most current available.

Figure 1
Making an observation is one way to gather information directly.

Evaluating Print and Nonprint Sources

Not all sources of information are reliable. Evaluate the sources you use for information, and use only those you know to be dependable. For example, suppose you want information about the digestion of fats and proteins. You might find two Websites on digestion. One Web site contains "Fat Zapping Tips" written by a company that sells expensive, high-protein supplements to help your body eliminate excess fat. The other is a Web page on "Digestion and Metabolism" written by a well-respected medical school. You would choose the second Web site as the more reliable source of information.

In science, information can change rapidly. Always consult the most current sources. A 1985 source about the human genome would not reflect the most recent research and findings.

Interpreting Scientific Illustrations

As you research a science topic, you will see drawings, diagrams, and photographs. Illustrations help you understand what you read. Some illustrations are included to help you understand an idea that you can't see easily by yourself. For instance, you can't see the bones of a blue whale, but you can look at a diagram of a whale skeleton as labeled in **Figure 2** that helps you understand them. Visualizing a drawing helps many people remember details more easily. Illustrations also provide examples that clarify difficult concepts or give additional information about the topic you are studying.

Most illustrations have a label or a caption. A label or caption identifies the illustration or provides additional information to better explain it. Can you find the caption or labels in **Figure 2?**

Figure 2
A labeled diagram of the skeletal structure of a blue whale.

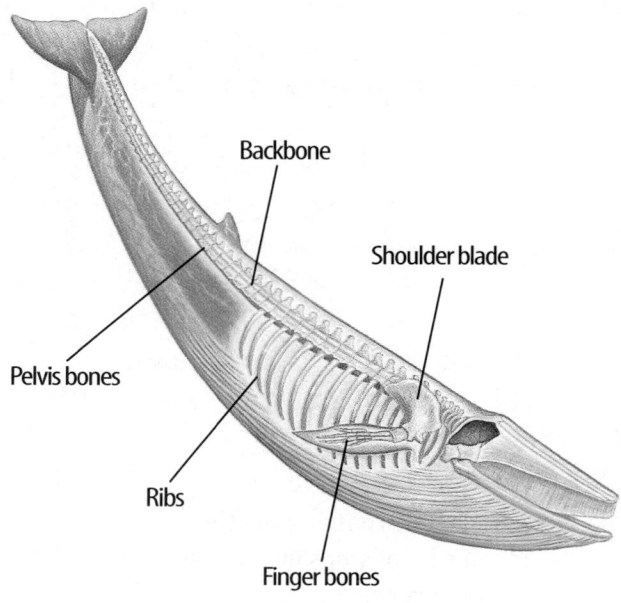

Backbone

Shoulder blade

Pelvis bones

Ribs

Finger bones

Venn Diagram

Although it is not a concept map, a Venn diagram illustrates how two subjects compare and contrast. In other words, you can see the characteristics that the subjects have in common and those that they do not.

The Venn diagram in **Figure 3** shows the relationship between two categories of organisms, plants and animals. Both share some basic characteristics as living organisms. However, there are differences in the ways they carry out various life processes, such as obtaining nourishment, that distinguish one from the other.

Concept Mapping

If you were taking a car trip, you might take some sort of road map. By using a map, you begin to learn where you are in relation to other places on the map.

A concept map is similar to a road map, but a concept map shows relationships among ideas (or concepts) rather than places. It is a diagram that visually shows how concepts are related. Because a concept map shows relationships among ideas, it can make the meanings of ideas and terms clear and help you understand what you are studying.

Overall, concept maps are useful for breaking large concepts down into smaller parts, making learning easier.

Figure 3
A Venn diagram shows how objects or concepts are alike and how they are different.

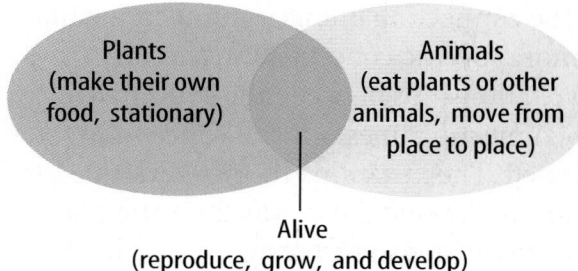

Plants
(make their own
food, stationary)

Animals
(eat plants or other
animals, move from
place to place)

Alive
(reproduce, grow, and develop)

Science Skill Handbook

Skill Handbooks

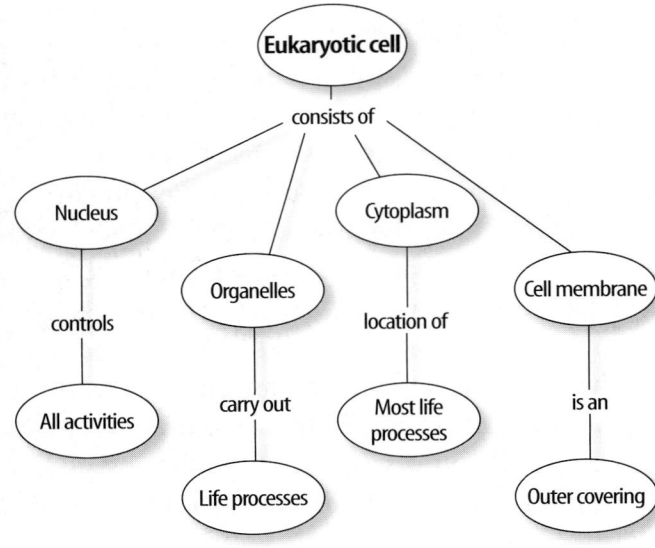

Figure 4
A network tree shows how concepts or objects are related.

Network Tree Look at the network tree in **Figure 4,** that shows details about a eukaryotic cell. A network tree is a type of concept map. Notice how some words are in ovals while others are written across connecting lines. The words inside the ovals are science terms or concepts. The words written on the connecting lines describe the relationships between the concepts.

When constructing a network tree, write the topic on a note card or piece of paper. Write the major concepts related to that topic on separate note cards or pieces of paper. Then arrange them in order from general to specific. Branch the related concepts from the major concept and describe the relationships on the connecting lines. Continue branching to more specific concepts. If necessary, write the relationships between the concepts on the connecting lines until all concepts are mapped. Then examine the network tree for relationships that cross branches, and add them to the network tree.

Events Chain An events chain is another type of concept map. It models the order, or sequence, of items. In science, an events chain can be used to describe a sequence of events, the steps in a procedure, or the stages of a process.

When making an events chain, first find the one event that starts the chain. This event is called the initiating event. Then, find the next event in the chain and continue until you reach an outcome. Suppose you are asked to describe the main stages in the growth of a plant from a seed. You might draw an events chain such as the one in **Figure 5.** Notice that connecting words are not necessary in an events chain.

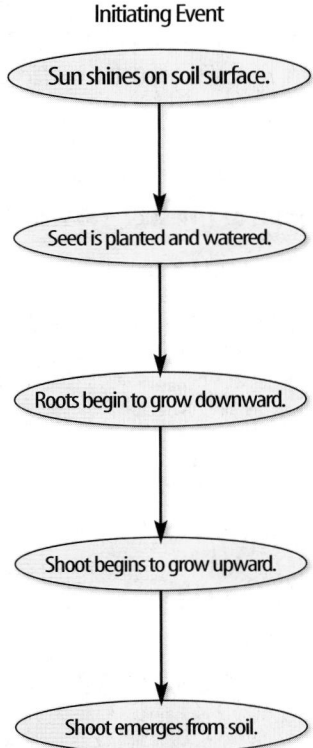

Figure 5
Events chains show the order of steps in a process or event.

Cycle Map A cycle concept map is a specific type of events chain map. In a cycle concept map, the series of events does not produce a final outcome. Instead, the last event in the chain relates back to the beginning event.

You first decide what event will be used as the beginning event. Once that is decided, you list events in order that occur after it. Words are written between events that describe what happens from one event to the next. The last event in a cycle concept map relates back to the beginning event. The number of events in a cycle concept varies but is usually three or more. Look at the cycle map in **Figure 6.**

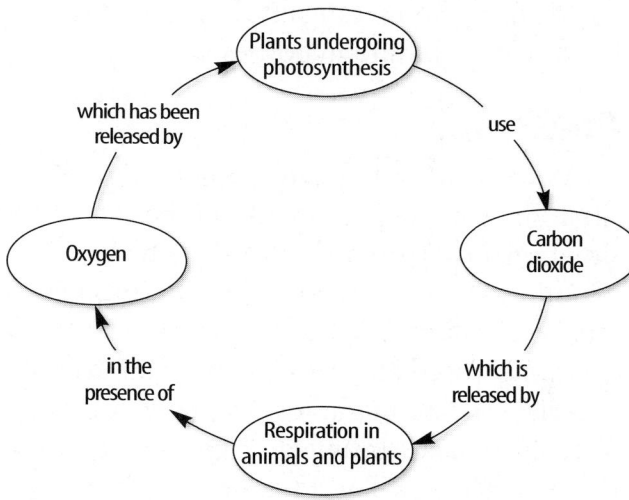

Figure 6
A cycle map shows events that occur in a cycle.

Spider Map A type of concept map that you can use for brainstorming is the spider map. When you have a central idea, you might find you have a jumble of ideas that relate to it but might not clearly relate to each other. The circulatory system spider map in **Figure 7** shows that if you write these ideas outside the main concept, then you can begin to separate and group unrelated terms so they become more useful.

Figure 7
A spider map allows you to list ideas that relate to a central topic but not necessarily to one another.

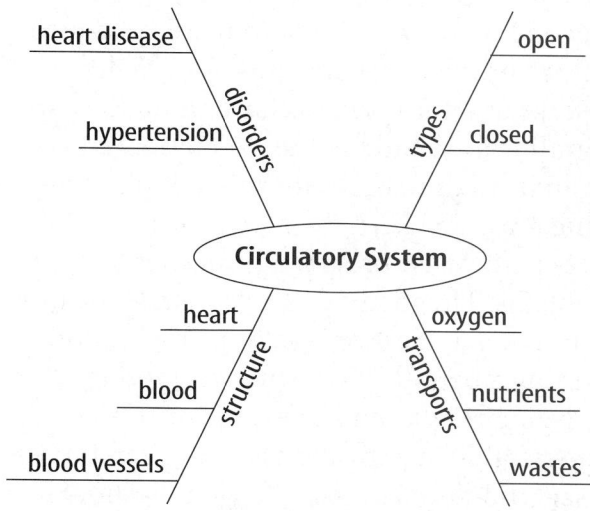

Writing a Paper

You will write papers often when researching science topics or reporting the results of investigations or experiments. Scientists frequently write papers to share their data and conclusions with other scientists and the public. When writing a paper, use these steps.

Step 1 Assemble your data by using graphs, tables, or a concept map. Create an outline.

Step 2 Start with an introduction that contains a clear statement of purpose and what you intend to discuss or prove.

Step 3 Organize the body into paragraphs. Each paragraph should start with a topic sentence, and the remaining sentences in that paragraph should support your point.

Step 4 Position data to help support your points.

Step 5 Summarize the main points and finish with a conclusion statement.

Step 6 Use tables, graphs, charts, and illustrations whenever possible.

You might say the work of a scientist is to solve problems. When you decide to find out why one corner of your yard is always soggy, you are problem solving, too. You might observe that the corner is lower than the surrounding area and has less vegetation growing in it. You might decide to see if planting some grass will keep the corner drier.

Scientists use orderly approaches to solve problems. The methods scientists use include identifying a question, making observations, forming a hypothesis, testing a hypothesis, analyzing results, and drawing conclusions.

Scientific investigations involve careful observation under controlled conditions. Such observation of an object or a process can suggest new and interesting questions about it. These questions sometimes lead to the formation of a hypothesis. Scientific investigations are designed to test a hypothesis.

Identifying a Question

The first step in a scientific investigation or experiment is to identify a question to be answered or a problem to be solved. You might be interested in knowing why an animal like the one in **Figure 8** looks the way it does.

Figure 8
When you see a bird, you might ask yourself, "How does the shape of this bird's beak help it feed?"

Forming Hypotheses

Hypotheses are based on observations that have been made. A hypothesis is a possible explanation based on previous knowledge and observations.

Perhaps a scientist has observed that bean plants grow larger if they are fertilized than if they are not. Based on these observations, the scientist can make a statement that he or she can test. The statement is a hypothesis. The hypothesis could be: *Fertilizer makes bean plants grow larger.* A hypothesis has to be something you can test by using an investigation. A testable hypothesis is a valid hypothesis.

Predicting

When you apply a hypothesis to a specific situation, you predict something about that situation. First, you must identify which hypothesis fits the situation you are considering. People use predictions to make everyday decisions. Based on previous observations and experiences, you might form a prediction that if fertilizer makes bean plants grow larger, then fertilized plants will yield more beans than plants not fertilized. Someone could use this prediction to plan to grow fewer plants.

Testing a Hypothesis

To test a hypothesis, you need a procedure. A procedure is the plan you follow in your experiment. A procedure tells you what materials to use, as well as how and in what order to use them. When you follow a procedure, data are generated that support or do not support the original hypothesis statement.

For example, suppose you notice that your guppies don't seem as active as usual when your aquarium heater is not working. You wonder how water temperature affects guppy activity level. You decide to test the hypothesis, "If water temperature increases, then guppy activity should increase." Then you write the procedure shown in **Figure 9** for your experiment and generate the data presented in the table below.

Procedure

1. Fill five identical glass containers with equal amounts of aquarium water.
2. Measure and record the temperature of the water in the first container.
3. Heat and cool the other containers so that two have higher and two have lower water temperatures.
4. Place a guppy in each container; count and record the number of movements each guppy makes in 5 minutes.

Figure 9
A procedure tells you what to do step by step.

Number of Guppy Movements

Container	Temperature (°C)	Movements
1	38	56
2	40	61
3	42	70
4	36	46
5	34	42

Are all investigations alike? Keep in mind as you perform investigations in science that a hypothesis can be tested in many ways. Not every investigation makes use of all the ways that are described on these pages, and not all hypotheses are tested by investigations. Scientists encounter many variations in the methods that are used when they perform experiments. The skills in this handbook are here for you to use and practice.

Identifying and Manipulating Variables and Controls

In any experiment, it is important to keep everything the same except for the item you are testing. The one factor you change is called the independent variable. The factor that changes as a result of the independent variable is called the dependent variable. Always make sure you have only one independent variable. If you allow more than one, you will not know what causes the changes you observe in the dependent variable. Many experiments also have controls—individual instances or experimental subjects for which the independent variable is not changed. You can then compare the test results to the control results.

For example, in the guppy experiment, you made everything the same except the temperature of the water. The glass containers were identical. The volume of aquarium water in each container and beginning water temperature were the same. Each guppy was like the others, as much as possible. In this way, you could be sure that any difference in the number of guppy movements was caused by the temperature change—the independent variable. The activity level of the guppy was measured as the number of guppy movements—the dependent variable. The guppy in the container in which the water temperature was not changed was the control.

Skill Handbooks

Collecting Data

Whether you are carrying out an investigation or a short observational experiment, you will collect data, or information. Scientists collect data accurately as numbers and descriptions and organize it in specific ways.

Observing Scientists observe items and events, then record what they see. When they use only words to describe an observation, it is called qualitative data. For example, a scientist might describe the color of a bird or the shape of a bird's beak as seen through binoculars. Scientists' observations also can describe how much there is of something. These observations use numbers, as well as words, in the description and are called quantitative data. For example, if a particular dog is described as being "furry, yellow, and short-haired," the data are clearly qualitative. Quantitative data for this dog might include "a mass of 14 kg, a height of 46 cm, and an age of 150 days." Quantitative data often are organized into tables. Then, from information in the table, a graph can be drawn. Graphs can reveal relationships that exist in experimental data.

When you make observations in science, you should examine the entire object or situation first, then look carefully for details. If you're looking at a plant, for instance, check general characteristics such as size and overall structure before using a hand lens to examine the leaves and other smaller structures such as flowers or fruits. Remember to record accurately everything you see.

Scientists try to make careful and accurate observations. When possible, they use instruments such as microscopes, metric rulers, graduated cylinders, thermometers, and balances. Measurements provide numerical data that can be repeated and checked.

Sampling When working with large numbers of objects or a large population, scientists usually cannot observe or study every one of them. Instead, they use a sample or a portion of the total number. To *sample* is to take a small, representative portion of the objects or organisms of a population for research. By making careful observations or manipulating variables within a portion of a group, information is discovered and conclusions are drawn that might apply to the whole population.

Estimating Scientific work also involves estimating. To *estimate* is to make a judgment about the size or the number of something without measuring or counting every object or member of a population. Scientists first count the number of objects in a small sample. Looking through a microscope lens, for example, a scientist can count the number of bacterial colonies in the 1-cm^2 frame shown in **Figure 10.** Then the scientist can multiply that number by the number of cm^2 in the petri dish to get an estimate of the total number of bacterial colonies present.

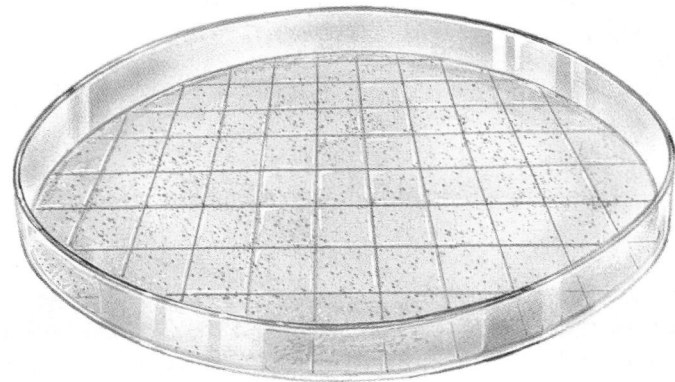

Figure 10
To estimate the total number of bacterial colonies that are present on a petri dish, count the number of bacterial colonies within a 1-cm^2 frame and multiply that number by the number of frames on the dish.

Measuring in SI

The metric system of measurement was developed in 1795. A modern form of the metric system, called the International System, or SI, was adopted in 1960. SI provides standard measurements that all scientists around the world can understand.

The metric system is convenient because unit sizes vary by multiples of 10. When changing from smaller units to larger units, divide by a multiple of 10. When changing from larger units to smaller, multiply by a multiple of 10. To convert millimeters to centimeters, divide the millimeters by 10. To convert 30 mm to centimeters, divide 30 by 10 (30 mm equal 3 cm).

Prefixes are used to name units. Look at the table below for some common metric prefixes and their meanings. Do you see how the prefix *kilo-* attached to the unit *gram* is *kilogram*, or 1,000 g?

Metric Prefixes			
Prefix	**Symbol**	**Meaning**	
kilo-	k	1,000	thousand
hecto-	h	100	hundred
deka-	da	10	ten
deci-	d	0.1	tenth
centi-	c	0.01	hundredth
milli-	m	0.001	thousandth

Now look at the metric ruler shown in **Figure 11.** The centimeter lines are the long, numbered lines, and the shorter lines are millimeter lines.

When using a metric ruler, line up the 0-cm mark with the end of the object being measured, and read the number of the unit where the object ends. In this instance it would be 4.50 cm.

Figure 11
This metric ruler shows centimeter and millimeter divisions.

Liquid Volume In some science activities, you will measure liquids. The unit that is used to measure liquids is the liter. A liter has the volume of 1,000 cm³. The prefix *milli-* means "thousandth (0.001)." A milliliter is one thousandth of 1 L and 1 L has the volume of 1,000 mL. One milliliter of liquid completely fills a cube measuring 1 cm on each side. Therefore, 1 mL equals 1 cm³.

You will use beakers and graduated cylinders to measure liquid volume. A graduated cylinder, as illustrated in **Figure 12,** is marked from bottom to top in milliliters. This graduated cylinder contains 79 mL of a liquid.

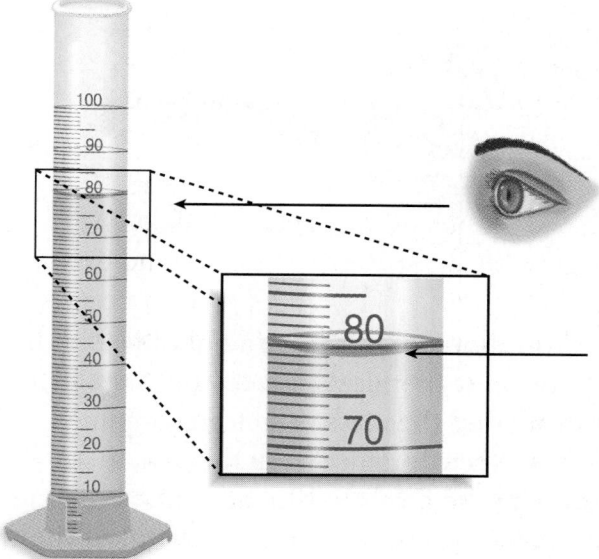

Figure 12
Graduated cylinders measure liquid volume.

Mass Scientists measure mass in grams. You might use a beam balance similar to the one shown in **Figure 13.** The balance has a pan on one side and a set of beams on the other side. Each beam has a rider that slides on the beam.

Before you find the mass of an object, slide all the riders back to the zero point. Check the pointer on the right to make sure it swings an equal distance above and below the zero point. If the swing is unequal, find and turn the adjusting screw until you have an equal swing.

Place an object on the pan. Slide the largest rider along its beam until the pointer drops below zero. Then move it back one notch. Repeat the process on each beam until the pointer swings an equal distance above and below the zero point. Sum the masses on each beam to find the mass of the object. Move all riders back to zero when finished.

Figure 13
A triple beam balance is used to determine the mass of an object.

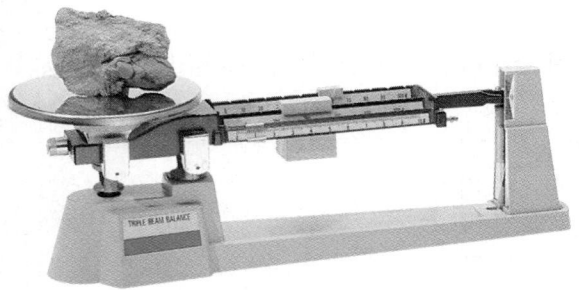

You should never place a hot object on the pan or pour chemicals directly onto the pan. Instead, find the mass of a clean container. Remove the container from the pan, then place the chemicals in the container. Find the mass of the container with the chemicals in it. To find the mass of the chemicals, subtract the mass of the empty container from the mass of the filled container.

Making and Using Tables

Browse through your textbook and you will see tables in the text and in the activities. In a table, data, or information, are arranged so that they are easier to understand. Activity tables help organize the data you collect during an activity so results can be interpreted.

Making Tables To make a table, list the items to be compared in the first column and the characteristics to be compared in the first row. The title should clearly indicate the content of the table, and the column or row heads should tell the reader what information is found in there. The table below lists materials collected for recycling on three weekly pick-up days. The inclusion of kilograms in parentheses also identifies for the reader that the figures are mass units.

Recyclable Materials Collected During Week			
Day of Week	**Paper (kg)**	**Aluminum (kg)**	**Glass (kg)**
Monday	5.0	4.0	12.0
Wednesday	4.0	1.0	10.0
Friday	2.5	2.0	10.0

Using Tables How much paper, in kilograms, is being recycled on Wednesday? Locate the column labeled "Paper (kg)" and the row "Wednesday." The information in the box where the column and row intersect is the answer. Did you answer "4.0"? How much aluminum, in kilograms, is being recycled on Friday? If you answered "2.0," you understand how to read the table. How much glass is collected for recycling each week? Locate the column labeled "Glass (kg)" and add the figures for all three rows. If you answered "32.0," then you know how to locate and use the data provided in the table.

Recording Data

To be useful, the data you collect must be recorded carefully. Accuracy is key. A well-thought-out experiment includes a way to record procedures, observations, and results accurately. Data tables are one way to organize and record results. Set up the tables you will need ahead of time so you can record the data right away.

Record information properly and neatly. Never put unidentified data on scraps of paper. Instead, data should be written in a notebook like the one in **Figure 14.** Write in pencil so information isn't lost if your data get wet. At each point in the experiment, record your information and label it. That way, your data will be accurate and you will not have to determine what the figures mean when you look at your notes later.

Figure 14
Record data neatly and clearly so they are easy to understand.

Recording Observations

It is important to record observations accurately and completely. That is why you always should record observations in your notes immediately as you make them. It is easy to miss details or make mistakes when recording results from memory. Do not include your personal thoughts when you record your data. Record only what you observe to eliminate bias. For example, when you record that a plant grew 12 cm in one day, you would note that this was the largest daily growth for the week. However, you would not refer to the data as "the best growth spurt of the week."

Making Models

You can organize the observations and other data you collect and record in many ways. Making models is one way to help you better understand the parts of a structure you have been observing or the way a process for which you have been taking various measurements works.

Models often show things that are very large or small or otherwise would be difficult to see and understand. You can study blood vessels and know that they are hollow tubes. The size and proportional differences among arteries, veins, and capillaries can be explained in words. However, you can better visualize the relative sizes and proportions of blood vessels by making models of them. Gluing different kinds of pasta to thick paper so the openings can be seen can help you see how the differences in size, wall thickness, and shape among types of blood vessels affect their functions.

Other models can be devised on a computer. Some models, such as disease control models used by doctors to predict the spread of the flu, are mathematical and are represented by equations.

Making and Using Graphs

After scientists organize data in tables, they might display the data in a graph that shows the relationship of one variable to another. A graph makes interpretation and analysis of data easier. Three types of graphs are the line graph, the bar graph, and the circle graph.

Line Graphs A line graph like in **Figure 15** is used to show the relationship between two variables. The variables being compared go on two axes of the graph. For data from an experiment, the independent variable always goes on the horizontal axis, called the *x*-axis. The dependent variable always goes on the vertical axis, called the *y*-axis. After drawing your axes, label each with a scale. Next, plot the data points.

A data point is the intersection of the recorded value of the dependent variable for each tested value of the independent variable. After all the points are plotted, connect them.

Bar Graphs Bar graphs compare data that do not change continuously. Vertical bars show the relationships among data.

To make a bar graph, set up the *y*-axis as you did for the line graph. Draw vertical bars of equal size from the *x*-axis up to the point on the *y*-axis that represents the value of *x*.

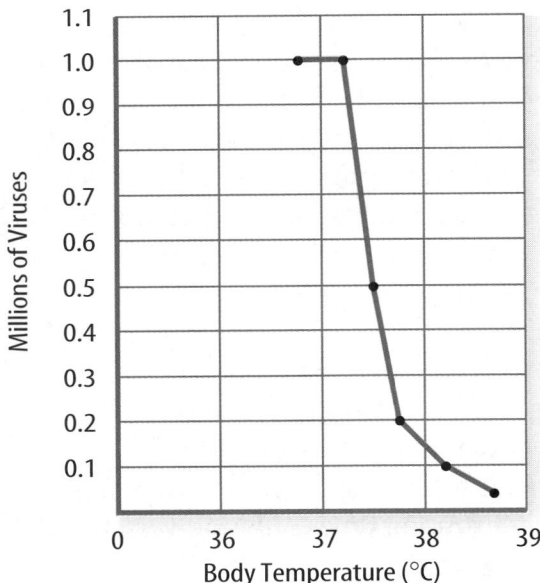

Effect of Temperature on Virus Production

Figure 15
This line graph shows the relationship between body temperature and the millions of infecting viruses present in a human body.

Figure 16
The number of wing vibrations per second for different insects can be shown as a bar graph or circle graph.

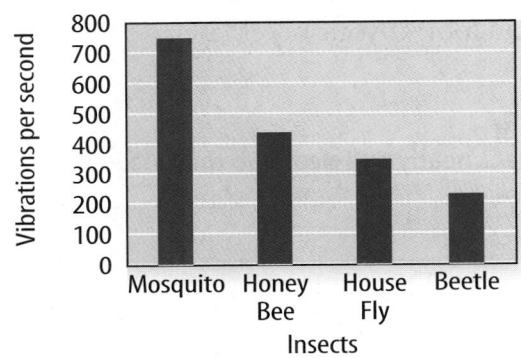

Wing Vibration Rates

Circle Graphs A circle graph uses a circle divided into sections to display data as parts (fractions or percentages) of a whole. The size of each section corresponds to the fraction or percentage of the data that the section represents. So, the entire circle represents 100 percent, one-half represents 50 percent, one-fifth represents 20 percent, and so on.

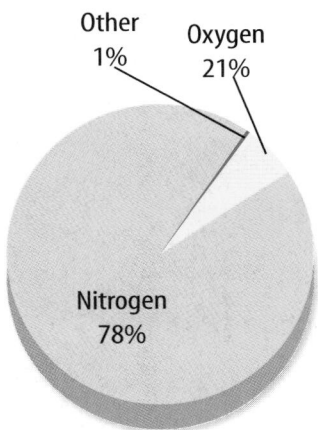

Analyzing Results

To determine the meaning of your observations and investigation results, you will need to look for patterns in the data. You can organize your information in several of the ways that are discussed in this handbook. Then you must think critically to determine what the data mean. Scientists use several approaches when they analyze the data they have collected and recorded. Each approach is useful for identifying specific patterns in the data.

Forming Operational Definitions

An operational definition defines an object by showing how it functions, works, or behaves. Such definitions are written in terms of how an object works or how it can be used; that is, they describe its job or purpose.

For example, a ruler can be defined as a tool that measures the length of an object (how it can be used). A ruler also can be defined as something that contains a series of marks that can be used as a standard when measuring (how it works).

Classifying

Classifying is the process of sorting objects or events into groups based on common features. When classifying, first observe the objects or events to be classified. Then select one feature that is shared by some members in the group but not by all. Place those members that share that feature into a subgroup. You can classify members into smaller and smaller subgroups based on characteristics.

How might you classify a group of animals? You might first classify them by putting all of the dogs, cats, lizards, snakes, and birds into separate groups. Within each group,

you could then look for another common feature by which to further classify members of the group, such as size or color.

Remember that when you classify, you are grouping objects or events for a purpose. For example, classifying animals can be the first step in identifying them. You might know that a cardinal is a red bird. To find it in a large group of animals, you might start with the classification scheme mentioned here. You'll locate a cardinal within the red grouping of the birds that you separate from the rest of the animals. A male ruby-throated hummingbird could be located within the birds by its tiny size and the bright red color of its throat. Keep your purpose in mind as you select the features to form groups and subgroups.

Figure 17
Color is one of many characteristics that are used to classify animals.

Comparing and Contrasting

Observations can be analyzed by noting the similarities and differences between two or more objects or events that you observe. When you look at objects or events to see how they are similar, you are comparing them. Contrasting is looking for differences in objects or events. The table below compares and contrasts the nutritional value of two cereals.

Nutritional Values		
	Cereal A	**Cereal B**
Calories	220	160
Fat	10 g	10 g
Protein	2.5 g	2.6 g
Carbohydrate	30 g	15 g

Recognizing Cause and Effect

Have you ever gotten a cold and then suggested that you probably caught it from a classmate who had one recently? If so, you have observed an effect and inferred a cause. The event is the effect, and the reason for the event is the cause.

When scientists are unsure of the cause of a certain event, they design controlled experiments to determine what caused it.

Interpreting Data

The word *interpret* means "to explain the meaning of something." Look at the problem originally being explored in an experiment and figure out what the data show. Identify the control group and the test group so you can see whether or not changes in the independent variable have had an effect. Look for differences in the dependent variable between the control and test groups.

These differences you observe can be qualitative or quantitative. You would be able to describe a qualitative difference using only words, whereas you would measure a quantitative difference and describe it using numbers. If there are qualitative or quantitative differences, the independent variable that is being tested could have had an effect. If no qualitative or quantitative differences are found between the control and test groups, the variable that is being tested apparently had no effect.

For example, suppose that three pepper plants are placed in a garden and two of the plants are fertilized, but the third is left to grow without fertilizer. Suppose you are then asked to describe any differences in the plants after two weeks. A qualitative difference might be the appearance of brighter green leaves on fertilized plants but not on the unfertilized plant. A quantitative difference might be a difference in the height of the plants or the number of flowers on them.

Inferring Scientists often make inferences based on their observations. An inference is an attempt to explain, or interpret, observations or to indicate what caused what you observed. An inference is a type of conclusion.

When making an inference, be certain to use accurate data and accurately described observations. Analyze all of the data that you've collected. Then, based on everything you know, explain or interpret what you've observed.

Drawing Conclusions

When scientists have analyzed the data they collected, they proceed to draw conclusions about what the data mean. These conclusions are sometimes stated using words similar to those found in the hypothesis formed earlier in the process.

Conclusions To analyze your data, you must review all of the observations and measurements that you made and recorded. Recheck all data for accuracy. After your data are rechecked and organized, you are almost ready to draw a conclusion such as "Plants need sunlight in order to grow."

Before you can draw a conclusion, however, you must determine whether the data allow you to come to a conclusion that supports a hypothesis. Sometimes that will be the case; other times it will not.

If your data do not support a hypothesis, it does not mean that the hypothesis is wrong. It means only that the results of the investigation did not support the hypothesis. Maybe the experiment needs to be redesigned, but very likely, some of the initial observations on which the hypothesis was based were incomplete or biased. Perhaps more observation or research is needed to refine the hypothesis.

Avoiding Bias Sometimes drawing a conclusion involves making judgments. When you make a judgment, you form an opinion about what your data mean. It is important to be honest and to avoid reaching a conclusion if no supporting evidence for it exists or if it was based on a small sample. It also is important not to allow any expectations of results to bias your judgments. If possible, it is a good idea to collect additional data. Scientists do this all the time.

For example, animal behaviorist Katharine Payne made an important observation about elephant communication. While visiting a zoo, Payne felt the air vibrating around her. At the same time, she also noticed that the skin on an elephant's forehead was fluttering. She suspected that the elephants were generating the vibrations and that they might be using the low-frequency sounds to communicate.

Payne conducted an experiment to record these sounds and simultaneously observe the behavior of the elephants in the zoo. She later conducted a similar experiment in Namibia in southwest Africa, where elephant herds roam. The additional data she collected supported the judgment Payne had made, which was that these low-frequency sounds were a form of communication between elephants.

Evaluating Others' Data and Conclusions

Sometimes scientists have to use data that they did not collect themselves, or they have to rely on observations and conclusions drawn by other researchers. In cases such as these, the data must be evaluated carefully.

How were the data obtained? How was the investigation done? Has it been duplicated by other researchers? Did they come up with the same results? Look at the conclusion, as well. Would you reach the same conclusion from these results? Only when you have confidence in the data of others can you believe it is true and feel comfortable using it.

Communicating

The communication of ideas is an important part of the work of scientists. A discovery that is not reported will not advance the scientific community's understanding or knowledge. Communication among scientists also is important as a way of improving their investigations.

Scientists communicate in many ways, from writing articles in journals and magazines that explain their investigations and experiments, to announcing important discoveries on television and radio, to sharing ideas with colleagues on the Internet or presenting them as lectures.

People who study science rely on computers to record and store data and to analyze results from investigations. Whether you work in a laboratory or just need to write a lab report with tables, good computer skills are a necessity.

Using a Word Processor

Suppose your teacher has assigned a written report. After you've completed your research and decided how you want to write the information, you need to put all that information on paper. The easiest way to do this is with a word processing application on a computer.

A computer application that allows you to type your information, change it as many times as you need to, and then print it out so that it looks neat and clean is called a word processing application. You also can use this type of application to create tables and columns, add bullets or cartoon art to your page, include page numbers, and even check your spelling.

Helpful Hints

- If you aren't sure how to do something using your word processing program, look in the help menu. You will find a list of topics there to click on for help. After you locate the help topic you need, just follow the step-by-step instructions you see on your screen.
- Just because you've spell checked your report doesn't mean that the spelling is perfect. The spell check feature can't catch misspelled words that look like other words. If you've accidentally typed *wind* instead of *wing*, the spell checker won't know the difference. Always reread your report to make sure you didn't miss any mistakes.

Figure 18
You can use computer programs to make graphs and tables.

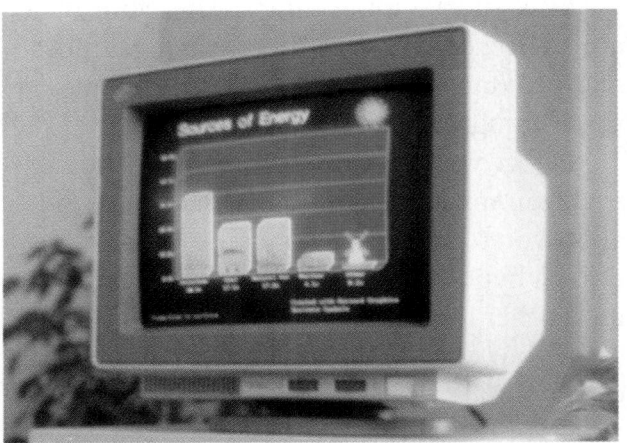

Using a Database

Imagine you're in the middle of a research project busily gathering facts and information. You soon realize that it's becoming more difficult to organize and keep track of all the information. The tool to use to solve information overload is a database. Just as a file cabinet organizes paper records, a database organizes computer records. However, a database is more powerful than a simple file cabinet because at the click of a mouse, the contents can be reshuffled and reorganized. At computer-quick speeds, databases can sort information by any characteristics and filter data into multiple categories.

Helpful Hints

- Before setting up a database, take some time to learn the features of your database software by practicing with established database software.
- Periodically save your database as you enter data. That way, if something happens such as your computer malfunctions or the power goes off, you won't lose all of your work.

Doing a Database Search

When searching for information in a database, use the following search strategies to get the best results. These are the same search methods used for searching Internet databases.

- Place the word *and* between two words in your search if you want the database to look for any entries that have both words. For example, "fox *and* mink" would give you information that mentions both fox and mink.
- Place the word *or* between two words if you want the database to show entries that have at least one of the words. For example "fox *or* mink" would show you information that mentions either fox or mink.
- Place the word *not* between two words if you want the database to look for entries that have the first word but do not have the second word. For example, "canine *not* fox" would show you information that mentions the term *canine* but does not mention the fox.

In summary, databases can be used to store large amounts of information about a particular subject. Databases allow biologists, Earth scientists, and physical scientists to search for information quickly and accurately.

Using an Electronic Spreadsheet

Your science fair experiment has produced lots of numbers. How do you keep track of all the data, and how can you easily work out all the calculations needed? You can use a computer program called a spreadsheet to record data that involve numbers. A spreadsheet is an electronic mathematical worksheet.

Type in your data in rows and columns, just as in a data table on a sheet of paper. A spreadsheet uses simple math to do data calculations. For example, you could add, subtract, divide, or multiply any of the values in the spreadsheet by another number. You also could set up a series of math steps you want to apply to the data. If you want to add 12 to all the numbers and then multiply all the numbers by 10, the computer does all the calculations for you in the spreadsheet. Below is an example of a spreadsheet that records data from an experiment with mice in a maze.

Helpful Hints

- Before you set up the spreadsheet, identify how you want to organize the data. Include any formulas you will need to use.
- Make sure you have entered the correct data into the correct rows and columns.
- You also can display your results in a graph. Pick the style of graph that best represents the data with which you are working.

Figure 19
A spreadsheet allows you to display large amounts of data and do calculations automatically.

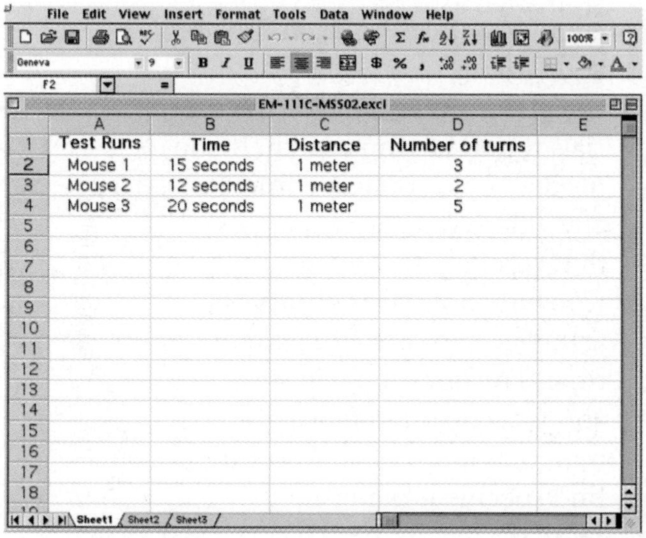

Using a Computerized Card Catalog

When you have a report or paper to research, you probably go to the library. To find the information you need in the library, you might have to use a computerized card catalog. This type of card catalog allows you to search for information by subject, by title, or by author. The computer then will display all the holdings the library has on the subject, title, or author requested.

A library's holdings can include books, magazines, databases, videos, and audio materials. When you have chosen something from this list, the computer will show whether an item is available and where in the library to find it.

Helpful Hints

- Remember that you can use the computer to search by subject, author, or title. If you know a book's author but not the title, you can search for all the books the library has by that author.

- When searching by subject, it's often most helpful to narrow your search by using specific search terms, such as *and, or,* and *not.* If you don't find enough sources, you can broaden your search.

- Pay attention to the type of materials found in your search. If you need a book, you can eliminate any videos or other resources that come up in your search.

- Knowing how your library is arranged can save you a lot of time. The librarian will show you where certain types of materials are kept and how to find specific holdings.

Using Graphics Software

Are you having trouble finding that exact piece of art you're looking for? Do you have a picture in your mind of what you want but can't seem to find the right graphic to represent your ideas? To solve these problems, you can use graphics software. Graphics software allows you to create and change images and diagrams in almost unlimited ways. Typical uses for graphics software include arranging clip art, changing scanned images, and constructing pictures from scratch. Most graphics software applications work in similar ways. They use the same basic tools and functions. Once you master one graphics application, you can use any other graphics application relatively easily.

Figure 20
Graphics software can use your data to draw bar graphs.

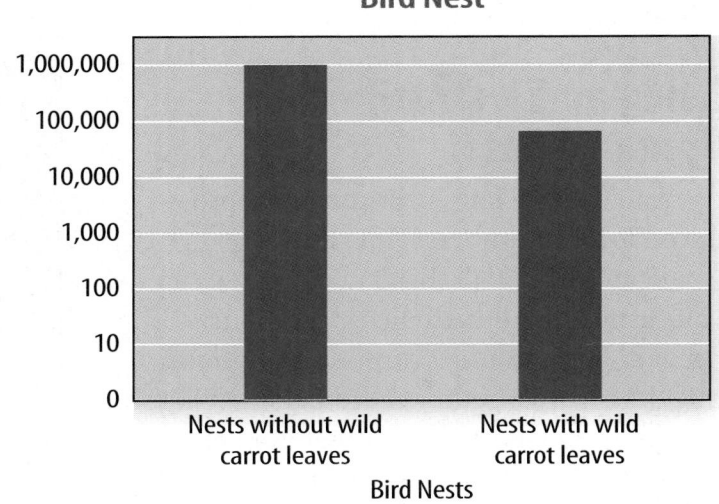

Number of Mites per Bird Nest

Figure 21
Graphics software can use your data to draw circle graphs.

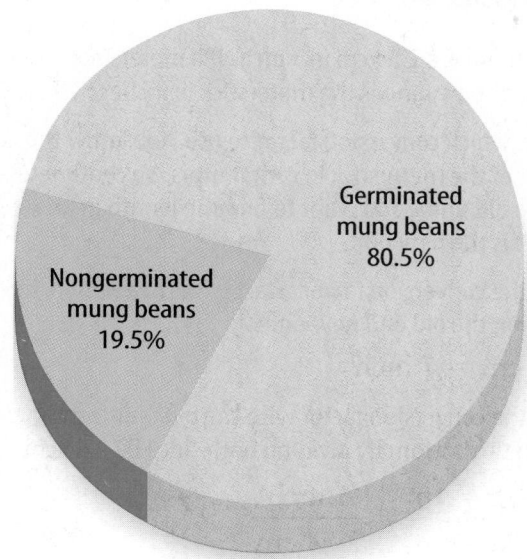

Germinated
mung beans
80.5%

Nongerminated
mung beans
19.5%

First, determine what important points you want to make in your presentation. Then, write an outline of what materials and types of media would best illustrate those points. Maybe you could start with an outline on an overhead projector, then show a video, followed by something from the Internet or a slide show accompanied by music or recorded voices. You might choose to use a presentation builder computer application that can combine all these elements into one presentation. Make sure the presentation is well constructed to make the most impact on the audience.

Figure 22
Multimedia presentations use many types of print and electronic materials.

Helpful Hints

- As with any method of drawing, the more you practice using the graphics software, the better your results will be.
- Start by using the software to manipulate existing drawings. Once you master this, making your own illustrations will be easier.
- Clip art is available on CD-ROMs and the Internet. With these resources, finding a piece of clip art to suit your purposes is simple.
- As you work on a drawing, save it often.

Developing Multimedia Presentations

It's your turn—you have to present your science report to the entire class. How do you do it? You can use many different sources of information to get the class excited about your presentation. Posters, videos, photographs, sound, computers, and the Internet can help show your ideas.

Helpful Hints

- Carefully consider what media will best communicate the point you are trying to make.
- Make sure you know how to use any equipment you will be using in your presentation.
- Practice the presentation several times.
- If possible, set up all of the equipment ahead of time. Make sure everything is working correctly.

Use this Math Skill Handbook to help solve problems you are given in this text. You might find it useful to review topics in this Math Skill Handbook first.

Converting Units

In science, quantities such as length, mass, and time sometimes are measured using different units. Suppose you want to know how many miles are in 12.7 km.

Conversion factors are used to change from one unit of measure to another. A conversion factor is a ratio that is equal to one. For example, there are 1,000 mL in 1 L, so 1,000 mL equals 1 L, or:

$$1,000 \text{ mL} = 1 \text{ L}$$

If both sides are divided by 1 L, this equation becomes:

$$\frac{1,000 \text{ mL}}{1 \text{ L}} = 1$$

The **ratio** on the left side of this equation is equal to 1 and is a conversion factor. You can make another conversion factor by dividing both sides of the top equation by 1,000 mL:

$$1 = \frac{1 \text{ L}}{1,000 \text{ mL}}$$

To **convert units,** you multiply by the appropriate conversion factor. For example, how many milliliters are in 1.255 L? To convert 1.255 L to milliliters, multiply 1.255 L by a conversion factor.

Use the **conversion factor** with new units (mL) in the numerator and the old units (L) in the denominator.

$$1.255 \text{ L} \times \frac{1,000 \text{ mL}}{1 \text{ L}} = 1,255 \text{ mL}$$

The unit L divides in this equation, just as if it were a number.

Example 1 There are 2.54 cm in 1 inch. If a meterstick has a length of 100 cm, how long is the meterstick in inches?

Step 1 Decide which conversion factor to use. You know the length of the meterstick in centimeters, so centimeters are the old units. You want to find the length in inches, so inch is the new unit.

Step 2 Form the conversion factor. Start with the relationship between the old and new units.

$$2.54 \text{ cm} = 1 \text{ inch}$$

Step 3 Form the conversion factor with the old unit (centimeter) on the bottom by dividing both sides by 2.54 cm.

$$1 = \frac{2.54 \text{ cm}}{2.54 \text{ cm}} = \frac{1 \text{ inch}}{2.54 \text{ cm}}$$

Step 4 Multiply the old measurement by the conversion factor.

$$100 \text{ cm} \times \frac{1 \text{ inch}}{2.54 \text{ cm}} = 39.37 \text{ inches}$$

The meterstick is 39.37 inches long.

Example 2 There are 365 days in one year. If a person is 14 years old, what is his or her age in days? (Ignore leap years)

Step 1 Decide which conversion factor to use. You want to convert years to days.

Step 2 Form the conversion factor. Start with the relation between the old and new units.

$$1 \text{ year} = 365 \text{ days}$$

Step 3 Form the conversion factor with the old unit (year) on the bottom by dividing both sides by 1 year.

$$1 = \frac{1 \text{ year}}{1 \text{ year}} = \frac{365 \text{ days}}{1 \text{ year}}$$

Step 4 Multiply the old measurement by the conversion factor:

$$14 \text{ years} \times \frac{365 \text{ days}}{1 \text{ year}} = 5,110 \text{ days}$$

The person's age is 5,110 days.

Practice Problem A cat has a mass of 2.31 kg. If there are 1,000 g in 1 kg, what is the mass of the cat in grams? 2310 g

Using Fractions

A **fraction** is a number that compares a part to the whole. For example, in the fraction $\frac{2}{3}$, the 2 represents the part and the 3 represents the whole. In the fraction $\frac{2}{3}$, the top number, 2, is called the numerator. The bottom number, 3, is called the denominator.

Sometimes fractions are not written in their simplest form. To determine a fraction's **simplest form,** you must find the greatest common factor (GCF) of the numerator and denominator. The greatest common factor is the largest common factor of all the factors the two numbers have in common.

For example, because the number 3 divides into 12 and 30 evenly, it is a common factor of 12 and 30. However, because the number 6 is the largest number that evenly divides into 12 and 30, it is the **greatest common factor.**

After you find the greatest common factor, you can write a fraction in its simplest form. Divide both the numerator and the denominator by the greatest common factor. The number that results is the fraction in its **simplest form.**

Example Twelve of the 20 corn plants in a field are more than 1.5 m tall. What fraction of the corn plants in the field is 1.5 m tall?

Step 1 Write the fraction.

$$\frac{\text{part}}{\text{whole}} = \frac{12}{20}$$

Step 2 To find the GCF of the numerator and denominator, list all of the factors of each number.

Factors of 12: 1, 2, 3, 4, 6, 12 (the numbers that divide evenly into 12)

Factors of 20: 1, 2, 4, 5, 10, 20 (the numbers that divide evenly into 20)

Step 3 List the common factors.

1, 2, 4.

Step 4 Choose the greatest factor in the list of common factors.

The GCF of 12 and 20 is 4.

Step 5 Divide the numerator and denominator by the GCF.

$$\frac{12 \div 4}{20 \div 4} = \frac{3}{5}$$

In the field, $\frac{3}{5}$ of the corn plants are more than 1.5 m tall.

Practice Problem There are 90 duck eggs in a population. Of those eggs, 66 hatch over a one-week period. What fraction of the eggs hatch over a one-week period? Write the fraction in simplest form. $\frac{11}{15}$

Math Skill Handbook

Calculating Ratios

A **ratio** is a comparison of two numbers by division.

Ratios can be written 3 to 5 or 3:5. Ratios also can be written as fractions, such as $\frac{3}{5}$. Ratios, like fractions, can be written in simplest form. Recall that a fraction is in **simplest form** when the greatest common factor (GCF) of the numerator and denominator is 1.

Example From a package of sunflower seeds, 40 seeds germinated and 64 did not. What is the ratio of germinated to not germinated seeds as a fraction in simplest form?

Step 1 Write the ratio as a fraction.

$$\frac{\text{germinated}}{\text{not germinated}} = \frac{40}{64}$$

Step 2 Express the fraction in simplest form. The GCF of 40 and 64 is 8.

$$\frac{40}{64} = \frac{40 \div 8}{64 \div 8} = \frac{5}{8}$$

The ratio of germinated to not germinated seeds is $\frac{5}{8}$.

Practice Problem Two children measure 100 cm and 144 cm in height. What is the ratio of their heights in simplest fraction form? $\frac{25}{36}$

Using Decimals

A **decimal** is a fraction with a denominator of 10, 100, 1,000, or another power of 10. For example, 0.854 is the same as the fraction $\frac{854}{1,000}$.

In a decimal, the decimal point separates the ones place and the tenths place. For example, 0.27 means twenty-seven hundredths, or $\frac{27}{100}$, where 27 is the **number of units** out of 100 units. Any fraction can be written as a decimal using division.

Example Write $\frac{5}{8}$ as a decimal.

Step 1 Write a division problem with the numerator, 5, as the dividend and the denominator, 8, as the divisor. Write 5 as 5.000.

Step 2 Solve the problem.

$$
\begin{array}{r}
0.625 \\
8\overline{)5.000} \\
\underline{4\,8} \\
20 \\
\underline{16} \\
40 \\
\underline{40} \\
0
\end{array}
$$

Therefore, $\frac{5}{8} = 0.625$.

Practice Problem Write $\frac{19}{25}$ as a decimal. 0.76

Using Percentages

The word *percent* means "out of one hundred." A **percent** is a ratio that compares a number to 100. Suppose you read that 77 percent of all fish on Earth live in the Pacific Ocean. That is the same as reading that the Earth's fish that live in the Pacific Ocean is $\frac{77}{100}$. To express a fraction as a percent, first find an equivalent decimal for the fraction. Then, multiply the decimal by 100 and add the percent symbol. For example, $\frac{1}{2} = 1 \div 2 = 0.5$. Then $0.5 \cdot 100 = 50 = 50\%$.

Example Express $\frac{13}{20}$ as a percent.

Step 1 Find the equivalent decimal for the fraction.

$$\begin{array}{r} 0.65 \\ 20\overline{)13.00} \\ \underline{12\,0} \\ 100 \\ \underline{100} \\ 0 \end{array}$$

Step 2 Rewrite the fraction $\frac{13}{20}$ as 0.65.

Step 3 Multiply 0.65 by 100 and add the % sign.

$0.65 \cdot 100 = 65 = 65\%$

So, $\frac{13}{20} = 65\%$.

Practice Problem In an experimental population of 365 sheep, 73 were brown. What percent of the sheep were brown?   20%

Skill Handbooks

Using Precision and Significant Digits

When you make a **measurement,** the value you record depends on the precision of the measuring instrument. When adding or subtracting numbers with different precision, the answer is rounded to the smallest number of decimal places of any number in the sum or difference. When multiplying or dividing, the answer is rounded to the smallest number of significant figures of any number being multiplied or divided. When counting the number of **significant figures,** all digits are counted except zeros at the end of a number with no decimal such as 2,500, and zeros at the beginning of a decimal such as 0.03020.

Example The lengths 5.28 and 5.2 are measured in meters. Find the sum of these lengths and report the sum using the least precise measurement.

Step 1 Find the sum.

$$\begin{array}{ll} 5.28 \text{ m} & \text{2 digits after the decimal} \\ \underline{+\ 5.2\ \ \text{ m}} & \text{1 digit after the decimal} \\ 10.48 \text{ m} & \end{array}$$

Step 2 Round to one digit after the decimal because the least number of digits after the decimal of the numbers being added is 1.

The sum is 10.5 m.

Practice Problem Multiply the numbers in the example using the rule for multiplying and dividing. Report the answer with the correct number of significant figures. $27\,\text{m}^2$

Math Skill Handbook

An **equation** is a statement that two things are equal. For example, $A = B$ is an equation that states that A is equal to B.

Sometimes one side of the equation will contain a **variable** whose value is not known. In the equation $3x = 12$, the variable is x.

The equation is solved when the variable is replaced with a value that makes both sides of the equation equal to each other. For example, the solution of the equation $3x = 12$ is $x = 4$. If the x is replaced with 4, then the equation becomes $3 \cdot 4 = 12$, or $12 = 12$.

To solve an equation such as $8x = 40$, divide both sides of the equation by the number that multiplies the variable.

$$8x = 40$$
$$\frac{8x}{8} = \frac{40}{8}$$
$$x = 5$$

You can check your answer by replacing the variable with your solution and seeing if both sides of the equation are the same.

$$8x = 8 \cdot 5 = 40$$

The left and right sides of the equation are the same, so $x = 5$ is the solution.

Sometimes an equation is written in this way: $a = bc$. This also is called a **formula.** The letters can be replaced by numbers, but the numbers must still make both sides of the equation the same.

Example 1 Solve the equation $10x = 35$.

Step 1 Find the solution by dividing each side of the equation by 10.

$$10x = 35 \qquad \frac{10x}{10} = \frac{35}{10} \qquad x = 3.5$$

Step 2 Check the solution.

$$10x = 35 \qquad 10 \times 3.5 = 35 \qquad 35 = 35$$

Both sides of the equation are equal, so $x = 3.5$ is the solution to the equation.

Example 2 In the formula $a = bc$, find the value of c if $a = 20$ and $b = 2$.

Step 1 Rearrange the formula so the unknown value is by itself on one side of the equation by dividing both sides by b.

$$a = bc$$
$$\frac{a}{b} = \frac{bc}{b}$$
$$\frac{a}{b} = c$$

Step 2 Replace the variables a and b with the values that are given.

$$\frac{a}{b} = c$$
$$\frac{20}{2} = c$$
$$10 = c$$

Step 3 Check the solution.

$$a = bc$$
$$20 = 2 \times 10$$
$$20 = 20$$

Both sides of the equation are equal, so $c = 10$ is the solution when $a = 20$ and $b = 2$.

Practice Problem In the formula $h = gd$, find the value of d if $g = 12.3$ and $h = 17.4$. $d = 1.41$

A **proportion** is an equation that shows that two ratios are equivalent. The ratios $\frac{2}{4}$ and $\frac{5}{10}$ are equivalent, so they can be written as $\frac{2}{4} = \frac{5}{10}$. This equation is an example of a proportion.

When two ratios form a proportion, the **cross products** are equal. To find the cross products in the proportion $\frac{2}{4} = \frac{5}{10}$, multiply the 2 and the 10, and the 4 and the 5. Therefore $2 \cdot 10 = 4 \cdot 5$, or $20 = 20$.

Because you know that both proportions are equal, you can use cross products to find a missing term in a proportion. This is known as **solving the proportion.** Solving a proportion is similar to solving an equation.

Example The heights of a tree and a pole are proportional to the lengths of their shadows. The tree casts a shadow of 24 m at the same time that a 6-m pole casts a shadow of 4 m. What is the height of the tree?

Step 1 Write a proportion.

$$\frac{\text{height of tree}}{\text{height of pole}} = \frac{\text{length of tree's shadow}}{\text{length of pole's shadow}}$$

Step 2 Substitute the known values into the proportion. Let h represent the unknown value, the height of the tree.

$$\frac{h}{6} = \frac{24}{4}$$

Step 3 Find the cross products.

$$h \cdot 4 = 6 \cdot 24$$

Step 4 Simplify the equation.

$$4h = 144$$

Step 5 Divide each side by 4.

$$\frac{4h}{4} = \frac{144}{4}$$

$$h = 36$$

The height of the tree is 36 m.

Practice Problem The proportions of bluefish are stable by the time they reach a length of 30 cm. The distance from the tip of the mouth to the back edge of the gill cover in a 35-cm bluefish is 15 cm. What is the distance from the tip of the mouth to the back edge of the gill cover in a 59-cm bluefish? 25.3 cm

• • • • • • • • • • • • **Using Statistics** • • • • • • • • • • • •

Statistics is the branch of mathematics that deals with collecting, analyzing, and presenting data. In statistics, there are three common ways to summarize the data with a single number—the mean, the median, and the mode.

The **mean** of a set of data is the arithmetic average. It is found by adding the numbers in the data set and dividing by the number of items in the set.

The **median** is the middle number in a set of data when the data are arranged in numerical order. If there were an even number of data points, the median would be the mean of the two middle numbers.

The **mode** of a set of data is the number or item that appears most often.

Another number that often is used to describe a set of data is the range. The **range** is the difference between the largest number and the smallest number in a set of data.

A **frequency table** shows how many times each piece of data occurs, usually in a survey. The frequency table below shows the results of a student survey on favorite color.

Color	Tally	Frequency
red	||||	4
blue	⊬⊬	5
black	||	2
green	|||	3
purple	⊬⊬ ||	7
yellow	⊬⊬ |	6

Based on the frequency table data, which color is the favorite?

Example The high temperatures (in °C) on five consecutive days in a desert habitat under study are 39°, 37°, 44°, 36°, and 44°. Find the mean, median, mode, and range of this set.

To find the mean:
Step 1 Find the sum of the numbers.

$$39 + 37 + 44 + 36 + 44 = 200$$

Step 2 Divide the sum by the number of items, which is 5.

$$200 \div 5 = 40$$

The mean high temperature is 40°C.

To find the median:
Step 1 Arrange the temperatures from least to greatest.

$$36, \ 37, \ \underline{39}, \ 44, \ 44$$

Step 2 Determine the middle temperature.

The median high temperature is 39°C.

To find the mode:
Step 1 Group the numbers that are the same together.

$$44, 44, 36, 37, 39$$

Step 2 Determine the number that occurs most in the set.

$$\underline{44, 44}, 36, 37, 39$$

The mode measure is 44°C.

To find the range:
Step 1 Arrange the temperatures from largest to smallest.

$$44, 44, 39, 37, 36$$

Step 2 Determine the largest and smallest temperature in the set.

$$\underline{44}, 44, 39, 37, \underline{36}$$

Step 3 Find the difference between the largest and smallest temperatures.

$$44 - 36 = 8$$

The range is 8°C.

Practice Problem Find the mean, median, mode, and range for the data set 8, 4, 12, 8, 11, 14, 16.
mean, 10; median, 11; mode, 8; range, 12

Safety in the Science Classroom

1. Always obtain your teacher's permission to begin an investigation.

2. Study the procedure. If you have questions, ask your teacher. Be sure you understand any safety symbols shown on the page.

3. Use the safety equipment provided for you. Goggles and a safety apron should be worn during most investigations.

4. Always slant test tubes away from yourself and others when heating them or adding substances to them.

5. Never eat or drink in the lab, and never use lab glassware as food or drink containers. Never inhale chemicals. Do not taste any substances or draw any material into a tube with your mouth.

6. Report any spill, accident, or injury, no matter how small, immediately to your teacher, then follow his or her instructions.

7. Know the location and proper use of the fire extinguisher, safety shower, fire blanket, first aid kit, and fire alarm.

8. Keep all materials away from open flames. Tie back long hair and tie down loose clothing.

9. If your clothing should catch fire, smother it with the fire blanket, or get under a safety shower. NEVER RUN.

10. If a fire should occur, turn off the gas then leave the room according to established procedures.

Follow these procedures as you clean up your work area

1. Turn off the water and gas. Disconnect electrical devices.

2. Clean all pieces of equipment and return all materials to their proper places.

3. Dispose of chemicals and other materials as directed by your teacher. Place broken glass and solid substances in the proper containers. Make sure never to discard materials in the sink.

4. Clean your work area. Wash your hands thoroughly after working in the laboratory.

First Aid	
Injury	**Safe Response ALWAYS NOTIFY YOUR TEACHER IMMEDIATELY**
Burns	Apply cold water.
Cuts and Bruises	Stop any bleeding by applying direct pressure. Cover cuts with a clean dressing. Apply ice packs or cold compresses to bruises.
Fainting	Leave the person lying down. Loosen any tight clothing and keep crowds away.
Foreign Matter in Eye	Flush with plenty of water. Use eyewash bottle or fountain.
Poisoning	Note the suspected poisoning agent.
Any Spills on Skin	Flush with large amounts of water or use safety shower.

Reference Handbook

SI—Metric/English, English/Metric Conversions

	When you want to convert:	To:	Multiply by:
Length	inches	centimeters	2.54
	centimeters	inches	0.39
	yards	meters	0.91
	meters	yards	1.09
	miles	kilometers	1.61
	kilometers	miles	0.62
Mass and Weight*	ounces	grams	28.35
	grams	ounces	0.04
	pounds	kilograms	0.45
	kilograms	pounds	2.2
	tons (short)	tonnes (metric tons)	0.91
	tonnes (metric tons)	tons (short)	1.10
	pounds	newtons	4.45
	newtons	pounds	0.22
Volume	cubic inches	cubic centimeters	16.39
	cubic centimeters	cubic inches	0.06
	liters	quarts	1.06
	quarts	liters	0.95
	gallons	liters	3.78
Area	square inches	square centimeters	6.45
	square centimeters	square inches	0.16
	square yards	square meters	0.83
	square meters	square yards	1.19
	square miles	square kilometers	2.59
	square kilometers	square miles	0.39
	hectares	acres	2.47
	acres	hectares	0.40
Temperature	To convert °Celsius to °Fahrenheit		°C × 9/5 + 32
	To convert °Fahrenheit to °Celsius		5/9 (°F − 32)

*Weight is measured in standard Earth gravity.

Care and Use of a Microscope

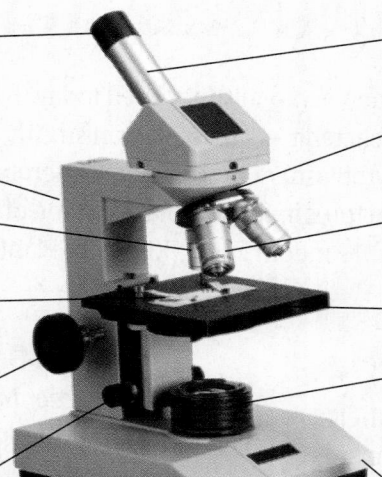

Eyepiece Contains magnifying lenses you look through.

Arm Supports the body tube.

Low-power objective Contains the lens with the lowest power magnification.

Stage clips Hold the microscope slide in place.

Coarse adjustment Focuses the image under low power.

Fine adjustment Sharpens the image under high magnification.

Body tube Connects the eyepiece to the revolving nosepiece.

Revolving nosepiece Holds and turns the objectives into viewing position.

High-power objective Contains the lens with the highest magnification.

Stage Supports the microscope slide.

Light source Provides light that passes upward through the diaphragm, the specimen, and the lenses.

Base Provides support for the microscope.

Caring for a Microscope

1. Always carry the microscope holding the arm with one hand and supporting the base with the other hand.

2. Don't touch the lenses with your fingers.

3. The coarse adjustment knob is used only when looking through the lowest-power objective lens. The fine adjustment knob is used when the high-power objective is in place.

4. Cover the microscope when you store it.

Using a Microscope

1. Place the microscope on a flat surface that is clear of objects. The arm should be toward you.

2. Look through the eyepiece. Adjust the diaphragm so light comes through the opening in the stage.

3. Place a slide on the stage so the specimen is in the field of view. Hold it firmly in place by using the stage clips.

4. Always focus with the coarse adjustment and the low-power objective lens first. After the object is in focus on low power, turn the nosepiece until the high-power objective is in place. Use ONLY the fine adjustment to focus with the high-power objective lens.

Making a Wet-Mount Slide

1. Carefully place the item you want to look at in the center of a clean, glass slide. Make sure the sample is thin enough for light to pass through.

2. Use a dropper to place one or two drops of water on the sample.

3. Hold a clean coverslip by the edges and place it at one edge of the water. Slowly lower the coverslip onto the water until it lies flat.

4. If you have too much water or a lot of air bubbles, touch the edge of a paper towel to the edge of the coverslip to draw off extra water and draw out unwanted air.

Diversity of Life: Classification of Living Organisms

A six-kingdom system of classification of organisms is used today. Two kingdoms—Kingdom Archaebacteria and Kingdom Eubacteria—contain organisms that do not have a nucleus and that lack membrane-bound structures in the cytoplasm of their cells. The members of the other four kingdoms have a cell or cells that contain a nucleus and structures in the cytoplasm, some of which are surrounded by membranes. These kingdoms are Kingdom Protista, Kingdom Fungi, Kingdom Plantae, and Kingdom Animalia.

Kingdom Archaebacteria

one-celled; some absorb food from their surroundings; some are photosynthetic; some are chemosynthetic; many are found in extremely harsh environments including salt ponds, hot springs, swamps, and deep-sea hydrothermal vents

Kingdom Eubacteria

one-celled; most absorb food from their surroundings; some are photosynthetic; some are chemosynthetic; many are parasites; many are round, spiral, or rod-shaped; some form colonies

Kingdom Protista

Phylum Euglenophyta one-celled; photosynthetic or take in food; most have one flagellum; euglenoids

Phylum Bacillariophyta one-celled; photosynthetic; have unique double shells made of silica; diatoms

Phylum Dinoflagellata one-celled; photosynthetic; contain red pigments; have two flagella; dinoflagellates

Phylum Chlorophyta one-celled, many-celled, or colonies; photosynthetic; contain chlorophyll; live on land, in freshwater, or salt water; green algae

Phylum Rhodophyta most are many-celled; photosynthetic; contain red pigments; most live in deep, saltwater environments; red algae

Phylum Phaeophyta most are many-celled; photosynthetic; contain brown pigments; most live in saltwater environments; brown algae

Phylum Rhizopoda one-celled; take in food; are free-living or parasitic; move by means of pseudopods; amoebas

Kingdom Eubacteria
Bacillus anthracis

Phylum Chlorophyta
Desmids

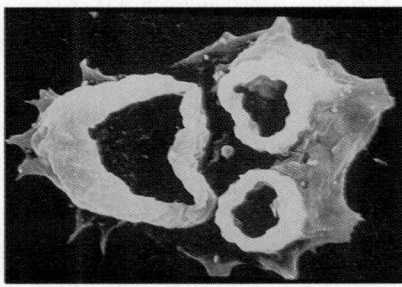

Amoeba

Phylum Zoomastigina one-celled; take in food; free-living or parasitic; have one or more flagella; zoomastigotes

Phylum Ciliophora one-celled; take in food; have large numbers of cilia; ciliates

Phylum Sporozoa one-celled; take in food; have no means of movement; are parasites in animals; sporozoans

Phylum Myxomycota
Slime mold

Phyla Myxomycota and Acrasiomycota one- or many-celled; absorb food; change form during life cycle; cellular and plasmodial slime molds

Phylum Oomycota many-celled; are either parasites or decomposers; live in freshwater or salt water; water molds, rusts and downy mildews

Kingdom Fungi

Phylum Zygomycota many-celled; absorb food; spores are produced in sporangia; zygote fungi; bread mold

Phylum Ascomycota one- and many-celled; absorb food; spores produced in asci; sac fungi; yeast

Phylum Basidiomycota many-celled; absorb food; spores produced in basidia; club fungi; mushrooms

Phylum Deuteromycota members with unknown reproductive structures; imperfect fungi; *Penicillium*

Mycophycota organisms formed by symbiotic relationship between an ascomycote or a basidiomycote and green alga or cyanobacterium; lichens

Phylum Oomycota
Phytophthora infestans

Lichens

Kingdom Plantae

Divisions Bryophyta (mosses), **Anthocerophyta** (hornworts), **Hepatophytal** (liverworts), **Psilophytal** (whisk ferns) many-celled nonvascular plants; reproduce by spores produced in capsules; green; grow in moist, land environments

Division Lycophyta many-celled vascular plants; spores are produced in conelike structures; live on land; are photosynthetic; club mosses

Division Sphenophyta vascular plants; ribbed and jointed stems; scalelike leaves; spores produced in conelike structures; horsetails

Division Pterophyta vascular plants; leaves called fronds; spores produced in clusters of sporangia called sori; live on land or in water; ferns

Division Ginkgophyta deciduous trees; only one living species; have fan-shaped leaves with branching veins and fleshy cones with seeds; ginkgoes

Division Cycadophyta palmlike plants; have large, featherlike leaves; produces seeds in cones; cycads

Division Coniferophyta deciduous or evergreen; trees or shrubs; have needlelike or scalelike leaves; seeds produced in cones; conifers

Division Anthophyta
Tomato plant

Division Gnetophyta shrubs or woody vines; seeds are produced in cones; division contains only three genera; gnetum

Division Anthophyta dominant group of plants; flowering plants; have fruits with seeds

Kingdom Animalia

Phylum Porifera aquatic organisms that lack true tissues and organs; are asymmetrical and sessile; sponges

Phylum Cnidaria radially symmetrical organisms; have a digestive cavity with one opening; most have tentacles armed with stinging cells; live in aquatic environments singly or in colonies; includes jellyfish, corals, hydra, and sea anemones

Phylum Platyhelminthes bilaterally symmetrical worms; have flattened bodies; digestive system has one opening; parasitic and free-living species; flatworms

Division Bryophyta
Liverwort

Phylum Platyhelminthes
Flatworm

Phylum Chordata

Phylum Nematoda round, bilaterally symmetrical body; have digestive system with two openings; free-living forms and parasitic forms; roundworms

Phylum Mollusca soft-bodied animals, many with a hard shell and soft foot or footlike appendage; a mantle covers the soft body; aquatic and terrestrial species; includes clams, snails, squid, and octopuses

Phylum Annelida bilaterally symmetrical worms; have round, segmented bodies; terrestrial and aquatic species; includes earthworms, leeches, and marine polychaetes

Phylum Arthropoda largest animal group; have hard exoskeletons, segmented bodies, and pairs of jointed appendages; land and aquatic species; includes insects, crustaceans, and spiders

Phylum Echinodermata marine organisms; have spiny or leathery skin and a water-vascular system with tube feet; are radially symmetrical; includes sea stars, sand dollars, and sea urchins

Phylum Chordata organisms with internal skeletons and specialized body systems; most have paired appendages; all at some time have a notochord, nerve cord, gill slits, and a postanal tail; include fish, amphibians, reptiles, birds, and mammals

Topographic Map Symbols

━━━━━	Primary highway, hard surface	∿	Index contour
━◆━◆━	Secondary highway, hard surface	··········	Supplementary contour
═════	Light-duty road, hard or improved surface	∿	Intermediate contour
=========	Unimproved road	⬭	Depression contours
+━+━+	Railroad: single track		
╫━╫━╫	Railroad: multiple track	━ ━ ━	Boundaries: national
+++++	Railroads in juxtaposition	━ ━ ━	State
		━ ━ ··	County, parish, municipal
▪▫▦	Buildings	━ ━ ━	Civil township, precinct, town, barrio
♦♦ ⊞ cem	Schools, church, and cemetery	━ ·━ ·━	Incorporated city, village, town, hamlet
▫▭▨	Buildings (barn, warehouse, etc)	·━ ·━ ··	Reservation, national or state
○ ○	Wells other than water (labeled as to type)	----------	Small park, cemetery, airport, etc.
●●● ⊘	Tanks: oil, water, etc. (labeled only if water)	━ ·· ━ ··	Land grant
⊙ ⚥	Located or landmark object; windmill	━━━━	Township or range line, U.S. land survey
⚒ ×	Open pit, mine, or quarry; prospect	━ ━ ━	Township or range line, approximate location
⌇⌇	Marsh (swamp)		
⌇⌇	Wooded marsh	∿	Perennial streams
☐	Woods or brushwood	→ ←	Elevated aqueduct
⫶⫶	Vineyard	○ ∿	Water well and spring
⫶⫶	Land subject to controlled inundation	∿×	Small rapids
⫶⫶	Submerged marsh	∿	Large rapids
▨	Mangrove	∿	Intermittent lake
⫶⫶	Orchard	∿	Intermittent stream
⫶⫶	Scrub	→=====←	Aqueduct tunnel
☐	Urban area	∿	Glacier
		∿×∿	Small falls
x7369	Spot elevation	∿	Large falls
670	Water elevation	⬭	Dry lake bed

Rocks

Rock Type	Rock Name	Characteristics
Igneous (intrusive)	Granite	Large mineral grains of quartz, feldspar, hornblende, and mica. Usually light in color.
	Diorite	Large mineral grains of feldspar, hornblende, and mica. Less quartz than granite. Intermediate in color.
	Gabbro	Large mineral grains of feldspar, augite, and olivine. No quartz. Dark in color.
Igneous (extrusive)	Rhyolite	Small mineral grains of quartz, feldspar, hornblende, and mica, or no visible grains. Light in color.
	Andesite	Small mineral grains of feldspar, hornblende, and mica or no visible grains. Intermediate in color.
	Basalt	Small mineral grains of feldspar, augite, and olivine or no visible grains. No quartz. Dark in color.
	Obsidian	Glassy texture. No visible grains. Volcanic glass. Fracture looks like broken glass.
	Pumice	Frothy texture. Floats in water. Usually light in color.
Sedimentary (detrital)	Conglomerate	Coarse grained. Gravel or pebble size grains.
	Sandstone	Sand-sized grains 1/16 to 2 mm.
	Siltstone	Grains are smaller than sand but larger than clay.
	Shale	Smallest grains. Often dark in color. Usually platy.
Sedimentary (chemical or organic)	Limestone	Major mineral is calcite. Usually forms in oceans, lakes, and caves. Often contains fossils.
	Coal	Occurs in swampy areas. Compacted layers of organic material, mainly plant remains.
Sedimentary (chemical)	Rock Salt	Commonly forms by the evaporation of seawater.
Metamorphic (foliated)	Gneiss	Banding due to alternate layers of different minerals, of different colors. Parent rock often is granite.
	Schist	Parallel arrangement of sheetlike minerals, mainly micas. Forms from different parent rocks.
	Phyllite	Shiny or silky appearance. May look wrinkled. Common parent rocks are shale and slate.
	Slate	Harder, denser, and shinier than shale. Common parent rock is shale.
Metamorphic (non-foliated)	Marble	Calcite or dolomite. Common parent rock is limestone.
	Soapstone	Mainly of talc. Soft with greasy feel.
	Quartzite	Hard with interlocking quartz crystals. Common parent rock is sandstone.

Minerals

Mineral (formula)	Color	Streak	Hardness	Breakage Pattern	Uses and Other Properties
Graphite (C)	black to gray	black to gray	1–1.5	basal cleavage (scales)	pencil lead, lubricants for locks, rods to control some small nuclear reactions, battery poles
Galena (PbS)	gray	gray to black	2.5	cubic cleavage perfect	source of lead, used for pipes, shields for X rays, fishing equipment sinkers
Hematite (Fe_2O_3)	black or reddish-brown	reddish-brown	5.5–6.5	irregular fracture	source of iron; converted to pig iron, made into steel
Magnetite (Fe_3O_4)	black	black	6	conchoidal fracture	source of iron, attracts a magnet
Pyrite (FeS_2)	light, brassy, yellow	greenish-black	6–6.5	uneven fracture	fool's gold
Talc ($Mg_3 Si_4O_{10} (OH)_2$)	white, greenish	white	1	cleavage in one direction	used for talcum powder, sculptures, paper, and tabletops
Gypsum ($CaSO_4 \cdot 2H_2O$)	colorless, gray, white, brown	white	2	basal cleavage	used in plaster of paris and dry wall for building construction
Sphalerite (ZnS)	brown, reddish-brown, greenish	light to dark brown	3.5–4	cleavage in six directions	main ore of zinc; used in paints, dyes, and medicine
Muscovite ($KAl_3Si_3 O_{10}(OH)_2$)	white, light gray, yellow, rose, green	colorless	2–2.5	basal cleavage	occurs in large, flexible plates; used as an insulator in electrical equipment, lubricant
Biotite ($K(Mg,Fe)_3 (AlSi_3O_{10}) (OH)_2$)	black to dark brown	colorless	2.5–3	basal cleavage	occurs in large, flexible plates
Halite (NaCl)	colorless, red, white, blue	colorless	2.5	cubic cleavage	salt; soluble in water; a preservative

Minerals

Mineral (formula)	Color	Streak	Hardness	Breakage Pattern	Uses and Other Properties
Calcite ($CaCO_3$)	colorless, white, pale blue	colorless, white	3	cleavage in three directions	fizzes when HCl is added; used in cements and other building materials
Dolomite ($CaMg(CO_3)_2$)	colorless, white, pink, green, gray, black	white	3.5–4	cleavage in three directions	concrete and cement; used as an ornamental building stone
Fluorite (CaF_2)	colorless, white, blue, green, red, yellow, purple	colorless	4	cleavage in four directions	used in the manufacture of optical equipment; glows under ultraviolet light
Hornblende ($(CaNa)_{2-3}$ $(Mg,Al,$ $Fe)_5-(Al,Si)_2$ Si_6O_{22} $(OH)_2$)	green to black	gray to white	5–6	cleavage in two directions	will transmit light on thin edges; 6-sided cross section
Feldspar ($KAlSi_3O_8$) ($NaAl$ Si_3O_8), ($CaAl_2Si_2$ O_8)	colorless, white to gray, green	colorless	6	two cleavage planes meet at 90° angle	used in the manufacture of ceramics
Augite ((Ca,Na) (Mg,Fe,Al) $(Al,Si)_2 O_6$)	black	colorless	6	cleavage in two directions	square or 8-sided cross section
Olivine ($(Mg,Fe)_2$ SiO_4)	olive, green	none	6.5–7	conchoidal fracture	gemstones, refractory sand
Quartz (SiO_2)	colorless, various colors	none	7	conchoidal fracture	used in glass manufacture, electronic equipment, radios, computers, watches, gemstones

English Glossary

This glossary defines each key term that appears in bold type in the text. It also shows the chapter, section, and page number where you can find the word used.

A

abiotic (ay bi AH tihk): nonliving, physical features of the environment, including air, water, sunlight, soil, temperature, and climate. (Chap. 13, Sec. 1, p. 360)

accuracy: compares a measurement to the true value. (Chap. 2, Sec. 1, p. 41)

active transport: energy-requiring process in which transport proteins bind with particles and move them through a cell membrane. (Chap. 4, Sec. 2, p. 109)

aggression: forceful behavior, such as fighting, used by an animal to control or dominate another animal in order to protect their young, defend territory, or get food. (Chap. 7, Sec. 2, p. 188)

allele (uh LEEL): the different form of a trait that a gene may have. (Chap. 11, Sec. 1, p. 300)

alveoli (al VEE uh li): tiny, thin-walled, grapelike clusters at the end of each bronchiole that are surrounded by capillaries, where carbon dioxide and oxygen exchange takes place. (Chap. 6, Sec. 1, p. 157)

amniotic (am nee AH tihk) **sac:** thin, liquid-filled, protective membrane that forms around the embryo. (Chap. 10, Sec. 3, p. 283)

amplitude: distance a wave rises above or falls below its normal level, which is related to the energy that the wave carries; in a transverse wave, is one-half the distance between a crest and a trough. (Chap. 20, Sec. 2, p. 581)

asexual reproduction: a type of reproduction in which a new organism is produced from one parent and has hereditary material identical to the parent organism. (Chap. 8, Sec. 1, p. 215)

asteroid: small, rocky space object found in the asteroid belt between the orbits of Jupiter and Mars. (Chap. 17, Sec. 3, p. 502)

asthenosphere (as THE nuh sfihr): plasticlike layer of Earth on which the lithospheric plates float and move around. (Chap. 14, Sec. 3, p. 400)

asthma: lung disorder in which the bronchial tubes contract quickly and cause shortness of breath, wheezing, or coughing; may occur as an allergic reaction. (Chap. 6, Sec. 1, p. 162)

astronomical unit: unit of measure used to determine distances between objects in the solar system; 1 AU equals 150,000,000 km. (Chap. 17, Sec. 3, p. 496)

atmosphere: air surrounding Earth; is made up of gases, including 78 percent nitrogen, 21 percent oxygen, and 0.03 percent carbon dioxide. (Chap. 13, Sec. 1, p. 361)

atomic number: the number of protons in an atom. (Chap. 18, Sec. 1, p. 521)

atoms: tiny building blocks of matter, made up of protons, neutrons, and electrons. (Chap. 18, Sec. 1, p. 518)

auxin (AWK sun): plant hormone that causes plant leaves and stems to exhibit positive response to light. (Chap. 5, Sec. 2, p. 140)

axis: imaginary line around which Earth spins, causing day and night; drawn from the north geographic pole through Earth to the south geographic pole. (Chap. 17, Sec. 1, p. 482)

B

bar graph: a type of graph that uses bars of varying sizes to show relationships between variables. (Chap. 2, Sec. 3, p. 54)

basin: low area on Earth in which an ocean formed when the area filled with water from torrential rains. (Chap. 16, Sec. 1, p. 453)

behavior: the way in which an organism interacts with other organisms and its environment; can be innate or learned. (Chap. 7, Sec. 1, p. 180)

biosphere (BI uh sfihr): part of Earth that supports life, including the top portion of Earth's crust, the atmosphere, and all the water on Earth's surface. (Chap. 12, Sec. 1, p. 332)

biotic (bi AHT ik): features of the environment that are alive or were once alive. (Chap. 13, Sec. 1, p. 360)

bladder: elastic, muscular organ that holds urine until it leaves the body. (Chap. 6, Sec. 2, p. 166)

breaker: collapsing ocean wave that forms in shallow water and breaks onto the shore. (Chap. 16, Sec. 3, p. 463)

bronchi (BRAHN ki): two short tubes that branch off the lower end of the trachea and carry air into the lungs. (Chap. 6, Sec. 1, p. 157)

C

carbon cycle: model describing how carbon molecules move between the living and nonliving world. (Chap. 13, Sec. 2, p. 373)

carrier wave: particular transmission frequency assigned to a radio station. (Chap. 22, Sec. 3, p. 650)

carrying capacity: largest number of individuals of a particular species that an ecosystem can support over time. (Chap. 12, Sec. 2, p. 339)

cell membrane: protective outer covering of all cells that is made up of a double layer of fatlike molecules and regulates the interaction between the cell and the environment. (Chap. 3, Sec. 1, p. 70)

cell theory: states that all organisms are made up of one or more cells, the cell is the basic unit of life, and all cells come from other cells. (Chap. 3, Sec. 2, p. 83)

cell wall: rigid structure that encloses, supports, and protects the cells of plants. (Chap. 3, Sec. 1, p. 71)

chemical change: change in which the composition of a substance changes. (Chap. 19, Sec. 2, p. 554)

chemical property: a property of matter that cannot be observed without altering the substance. (Chap. 19, Sec. 1, p. 550)

chemosynthesis (kee moh SIN thuh sus): process in which producers make energy-rich nutrient molecules from chemicals. (Chap. 13, Sec. 3, p. 375)

chlorophyll (KLOR uh fihl): green, light-trapping pigment in plant chloroplasts. (Chap. 5, Sec. 1, p. 130)

chloroplast (KLOR uh plast): green, chlorophyll-containing, plant-cell organelle that converts sunlight, carbon dioxide, and water into sugar. (Chap. 3, Sec. 1, p. 74)

chromosome (KROH muh sohm): structure in a cell's nucleus that contains hereditary material. (Chap. 8, Sec. 1, p. 212)

cinder cone volcano: relatively small volcano formed by moderate to explosive eruptions of tephra. (Chap. 15, Sec. 2, p. 432)

circle graph: a type of graph that shows the parts of a whole; sometimes called a pie graph, each piece of which represents a percentage of the total. (Chap. 2, Sec. 3, p. 54)

climate: average weather conditions of an area over time, including wind, temperature, and rainfall or other types of precipitation. (Chap. 13, Sec. 1, p. 365)

comet: space object made of rocky particles and water ices; forms a tail when orbiting near the Sun and is found mostly in the Kuiper Belt and the Oort Cloud. (Chap. 17, Sec. 3, p. 502)

commensalism (kuh MEN suh lih zum): a type of symbiotic relationship in which one organism benefits and the other organism is not affected. (Chap. 12, Sec. 3, p. 346)

community: all the populations of different species that live in an ecosystem. (Chap. 12, Sec. 1, p. 334)

composite volcano: steep-sided volcano formed from alternating layers of violent eruptions of tephra and quieter eruptions of lava. (Chap. 15, Sec. 2, p. 433)

compound: matter that is made of two or more elements and has physical and chemical properties different from each of the elements that make it up. (Chap. 18, Sec. 2, p. 524)

compressional wave: a type of mechanical wave in which matter in the medium moves forward and backward in the same direction the wave travels. (Chap. 20, Sec. 1, p. 579)

concave lens: lens that is thicker at its edges than in the middle and causes light rays traveling parallel to the optical axis to diverge. (Chap. 23, Sec. 3, p. 679)

condensation: process that takes place when a gas changes to a liquid. (Chap. 13, Sec. 2, p. 369)

conditioning: occurs when the response to a stimulus becomes associated with another stimulus. (Chap. 7, Sec. 1, p. 184)

constant: variable that stays the same during an experiment. (Chap. 1, Sec. 2, p. 21)

consumer: organism that cannot create energy-rich molecules but obtains its food by eating other organisms. (Chap. 12, Sec. 3, p. 345)

continental drift: Wegener's hypothesis that all continents were once connected in a single large landmass that broke apart about 200 million years ago and drifted slowly to their current positions. (Chap. 14, Sec. 1, p. 392)

control: sample that is treated like other experimental groups except that the independent variable is not applied to it. (Chap. 1, Sec. 2, p. 22)

convection current: cycle of heating, rising, cooling, and sinking in Earth's mantle. (Chap. 14, Sec. 3, p. 405)

convex lens: lens that is thicker in the middle than at its edges. (Chap. 23, Sec. 3, p. 678)

Coriolis effect: shifting of winds and surface currents caused by Earth's rotation that turns currents north of the equator clockwise and south of the equator counter-clockwise. (Chap. 16, Sec. 2, p. 457)

courtship behavior: behavior that allows males and females of the same species to recognize each other and prepare to mate. (Chap. 7, Sec. 2, p. 189)

crater: depression formed by a large meteorite; the more craters in a region, the older the surface. (Chap. 17, Sec. 2, p. 487)

crest: highest point of a wave. (Chap. 16, Sec. 3, p. 462)

cyclic behavior: innate behavior that occurs in repeated patterns. (Chap. 7, Sec. 2, p. 192)

cytoplasm (SI toh plaz uhm): constantly moving, gel-like mixture inside the cell membrane that contains heredity material. (Chap. 3, Sec. 1, p. 70)

D

day-neutral plant: plant that doesn't require a specific photoperiod and can begin the flowering process over a range of night lengths. (Chap. 5, Sec. 2, p. 142)

density: a physical property of matter that can be determined by dividing the mass of an object by its volume. (Chap. 18, Sec. 3, p. 530)

density current: circulation pattern in the ocean that forms when a mass of more dense seawater sinks beneath less dense seawater. (Chap. 16, Sec. 2, p. 459)

dependent variable: factor that is being measured during an experiment. (Chap. 1, Sec. 2, p. 21)

descriptive research: answers scientific questions through observation. (Chap. 1, Sec. 2, p. 13)

diaphragm (DI uh fram): muscle beneath the lungs that contracts and relaxes to move gases in and out of the body. (Chap. 6, Sec. 1, p. 158)

diffraction: bending of waves around a barrier. (Chap. 20, Sec. 3, p. 589)

diffusion: a type of passive transport in cells in which molecules move from areas where there are more of them to areas where there are fewer of them. (Chap. 4, Sec. 2, p. 107)

diploid (DIH ploid): when a cell has chromosomes in pairs. (Chap. 8, Sec. 2, p. 218)

DNA: deoxyribonucleic acid, which is the genetic material of all organisms, made up of two twisted strands of sugar-phosphate molecules and nitrogen bases. (Chap. 8, Sec. 3, p. 224)

dominant (DAHM uh nunt): describes a trait that covers over, or dominates, another form of that trait. (Chap. 11, Sec. 1, p. 302)

Doppler effect: change in the frequency or pitch of a sound that occurs when the sound source and the listener are in motion relative to each other. (Chap. 21, Sec. 1, p. 610)

E

eardrum: membrane stretching across the ear canal that vibrates when sound waves reach the middle ear. (Chap. 21, Sec. 2, p. 622)

earthquake: movement of the ground that occurs when rocks inside Earth pass their elastic limit, break suddenly, and experience elastic rebound. (Chap. 15, Sec. 1, p. 420)

echo: a reflected sound wave. (Chap. 21, Sec. 1, p. 609)

ecology: study of the interactions that occur among organisms and their environment. (Chap. 12, Sec. 1, p. 333)

ecosystem: all the living organisms that live in an area and the nonliving features of their environment. (Chap. 12, Sec. 1, p. 333)

egg: haploid sex cell formed in the female reproductive organs. (Chap. 8, Sec. 2, p. 218)

electromagnetic spectrum: range of electromagnetic waves with different frequencies and wavelengths. (Chap. 22, Sec. 2, p. 639)

electromagnetic waves: waves that can travel through empty space, have a wide range of wavelengths and frequencies, and are produced by moving charged particles. (Chap. 20, Sec. 1, p. 580) (Chap. 22, Sec. 1, p. 634)

electrons: negatively-charged particles that move around the nucleus of an atom and form an electron cloud. (Chap. 18, Sec. 1, p. 520)

element: substance that contains only one type of atom and cannot be broken down by normal chemical or physical means— for example, oxygen, aluminum, and iron. (Chap. 18, Sec. 1, p. 519)

English Glossary

embryo: zygote that has attached to the wall of the uterus. (Chap. 10, Sec. 3, p. 283)

emphysema (em fuh SEE muh): lung disease in which the alveoli enlarge. (Chap. 6, Sec. 1, p. 161)

endocytosis (en duh si TOH sus): process by which a cell takes in a substance by surrounding it with the cell membrane. (Chap. 4, Sec. 2, p. 110)

endoplasmic reticulum (ER): cytoplasmic organelle that moves materials around in a cell and is made up of a complex series of folded membranes; can be rough (with attached ribosomes) or smooth (without attached ribosomes). (Chap. 3, Sec. 1, p. 75)

energy pyramid: model that shows the amount of energy available at each feeding level in an ecosystem. (Chap. 13, Sec. 3, p. 377)

enzyme: a type of protein that regulates nearly all chemical reactions in cells. (Chap. 4, Sec. 1, p. 103)

epicenter: point on Earth's surface directly above an earthquake's focus. (Chap. 15, Sec. 1, p. 422)

equilibrium: occurs when molecules of one substance are spread evenly throughout another substance. (Chap. 4, Sec. 2, p. 107)

equinox (EE kwuh nahks): twice-yearly time when the Sun is directly above Earth's equator and the length of day equals the length of night worldwide. (Chap. 17, Sec. 1, p. 485)

estimation: method of making an educated guess at a measurement. (Chap. 2, Sec. 1, p. 39)

evaporation: process that takes place when a liquid changes to a gas. (Chap. 13, Sec. 2, p. 368)

exocytosis (ek soh si TOH sus): process by which vesicles release their contents outside the cell. (Chap. 4, Sec. 2, p. 110)

experimental research design: used to answer scientific questions by testing a hypothesis through the use of a series of carefully controlled steps. (Chap. 1, Sec. 2, p. 13)

F

fault: fracture that occurs when rocks change their shape by breaking; can form as a result of compression (reverse fault), being pulled apart (normal fault), or shear (strike-slip fault). (Chap. 15, Sec. 1, p. 421)

fermentation: process by which oxygen-lacking cells and some one-celled organisms release small amounts of energy from glucose molecules and produce wastes such as alcohol, carbon dioxide, and lactic acid. (Chap. 4, Sec. 3, p. 116)

fertilization: in sexual reproduction, the joining of a sperm and egg. (Chap. 8, Sec. 2, p. 218)

fetal stress: can occur during the birth process or after birth as an infant adjusts from a watery, dark, constant-temperature environment to its new environment. (Chap. 10, Sec. 3, p. 286)

fetus: a developing baby after the first two months of pregnancy until birth. (Chap. 10, Sec. 3, p. 284)

focal length: distance along the optical axis from the center of a concave mirror to the focal point. (Chap. 23, Sec. 2, p. 672)

focal point: single point on the optical axis of a concave mirror where reflected light rays pass through. (Chap. 23, Sec. 2, p. 672)

focus: point deep inside Earth where energy is released, causing an earthquake. (Chap. 15, Sec. 1, p. 422)

food web: model that shows the complex feeding relationships among organisms in a community. (Chap. 13, Sec. 3, p. 376)

frequency: number of wavelengths that pass a given point in one second, measured in hertz (Hz). (Chap. 20, Sec. 2, p. 583)

frond: leaf of a fern that grows from the rhizome. (Chap. 9, Sec. 2, p. 246)

fundamental frequency: lowest natural frequency that is produced by a vibrating object. (Chap. 21, Sec. 2, p. 617)

G

gametophyte (guh MEE tuh fite) **stage:** plant life cycle stage that begins when cells in reproductive organs undergo meiosis and produce haploid cells (spores). (Chap. 9, Sec. 1, p. 243)

gamma ray: highest-frequency, most penetrating electromagnetic wave. (Chap. 22, Sec. 2, p. 644)

gene: section of DNA on a chromosome that contains instructions for making specific proteins. (Chap. 8, Sec. 3, p. 226)

genetic engineering: biological and chemical methods to change the arrangement of a gene's DNA to improve crop production, produce large volumes of medicine, and change how cells perform their normal functions. (Chap. 11, Sec. 3, p. 315)

genetics (juh NET ihks): the study of how traits are inherited through the actions of alleles. (Chap. 11, Sec. 1, p. 300)

genotype (JEE nuh tipe): an organism's genetic makeup. (Chap. 11, Sec. 1, p. 304)

germination: series of events that results in the growth of a plant from a seed. (Chap. 9, Sec. 3, p. 258)

Global Positioning System (GPS): uses satellites, ground-based stations, and portable units with receivers to locate objects on Earth. (Chap. 22, Sec. 3, p. 653)

Golgi (GAWL jee) **bodies:** organelles that package cellular materials and transport them within the cell or out of the cell. (Chap. 3, Sec. 1, p. 75)

graph: used to collect, organize, and summarize data in a visual way. (Chap. 2, Sec. 3, p. 53)

H

habitat: place where an organism lives and that provides the types of food, shelter, moisture, and temperature needed for survival. (Chap. 12, Sec. 1, p. 335)

haploid (HA ploid): when a cell has only half the number of chromosomes as body cells. (Chap. 8, Sec. 2, p. 219)

heredity (huh RED ut ee): the passing of traits from parent to offspring. (Chap. 11, Sec. 1, p. 300)

heterogeneous mixture: mixtures which are not mixed evenly and each component retains its own properties. (Chap. 18, Sec. 2, p. 527)

heterozygous (het uh roh ZI gus): describes an organism with two different alleles for a trait. (Chap. 11, Sec. 1, p. 304)

hibernation: cyclic response of inactivity and slowed metabolism that occurs during periods of cold temperatures and limited food supplies. (Chap. 7, Sec. 2, p. 193)

homogeneous mixture: mixtures which are evenly mixed throughout. (Chap. 18, Sec. 2, p. 527)

homozygous (hoh muh ZI gus): describes an organism with two alleles that are the same for a trait. (Chap. 11, Sec. 1, p. 304)

hormone (HOR mohn): chemical produced by the endocrine system and released directly into the bloodstream by ductless glands; affects specific target tissues, and regulate cellular activities. (Chap. 10, Sec. 1, p. 270)

hot cell: living cell in which a virus can actively reproduce or in which a virus can hide until activated by environmental stimuli. (Chap. 3, Sec. 3, p. 84)

English Glossary

hot spot: large, rising body of magma that can force its way through Earth's mantle and crust and may form volcanoes. (Chap. 15, Sec. 3, p. 438)

hybrid (HI brud): an offspring that was given different genetic information for a trait from each parent. (Chap. 11, Sec. 1, p. 302)

hypothesis (hi PAH thuh sus): prediction or statement that can be tested and may be formed by prior knowledge, any previous observations, and new information. (Chap. 1, Sec. 2, p. 21)

I

imprinting: occurs when an animal forms a social attachment to another organism during a specific period following birth or hatching. (Chap. 7, Sec. 1, p. 183)

incomplete dominance: production of a phenotype that is intermediate between the two homozygous parents. (Chap. 11, Sec. 2, p. 308)

independent variable: variable that can be changed during an experiment. (Chap. 1, Sec. 2, p. 21)

infrared wave: electromagnetic wave that is sensed as heat and is emitted by almost every object. (Chap. 22, Sec. 2, p. 641)

innate behavior: behavior that an organism is born with and does not have to be learned, such as a reflex or instinct. (Chap. 7, Sec. 1, p. 181)

inorganic compound: compound, such as H_2O, that is made from elements other than carbon and whose atoms can usually be arranged in only one structure. (Chap. 4, Sec. 1, p. 103)

insight: form of reasoning that allows animals to use past experiences to solve new problems. (Chap. 7, Sec. 1, p. 185)

instinct: complex pattern of innate behavior, such as spinning a web, that

can take weeks to complete. (Chap. 7, Sec. 1, p. 182)

interference: ability of two or more waves to combine and form a new wave when they overlap. (Chap. 20, Sec. 3, p. 591)

ion: electrically-charged atom whose charge results from an atom losing or gaining electrons. (Chap. 18, Sec. 2, p. 525)

isotopes: atoms of the same element that have different numbers of neutrons. (Chap. 18, Sec. 1, p. 521)

K

kelvin: SI unit for temperature. (Chap. 2, Sec. 2, p. 50)

kidney: bean-shaped urinary system organ that is made up of about 1 million nephrons and filters blood, producing urine. (Chap. 6, Sec. 2, p. 164)

kilogram (kg): SI unit for mass. (Chap. 2, Sec. 2, p. 49)

L

larynx (LER ingks): airway to which the vocal cords are attached. (Chap. 6, Sec. 1, p. 157)

lava: magma flowing onto Earth's surface. (Chap. 15, Sec. 2, p. 429)

law of conservation of mass: states that the total mass of matter is the same before and after a physical or chemical change. (Chap. 19, Sec. 2, p. 561)

law of reflection: states that the angle of incidence is equal to the angle of reflection. (Chap. 23, Sec. 2, p. 669)

lens: transparent object that has at least one curved surface that causes light to bend. (Chap. 23, Sec. 3, p. 677)

light ray: narrow beam of light traveling in a straight line. (Chap. 23, Sec. 1, p. 664)

limiting factor: anything that can restrict the size of a population, including living and nonliving fea-tures of an ecosystem, such as predators or drought. (Chap. 12, Sec. 2, p. 338)

line graph: a type of graph used to show the relationship between two variables that are numbers on an *x*-axis and a *y*-axis. (Chap. 2, Sec. 3, p. 53)

lithosphere (LIH thuh sfihr): rigid layer of Earth about 100 km thick, made of the crust and a part of the upper mantle. (Chap. 14, Sec. 3, p. 400)

long-day plant: plant that generally requires short nights—less than 10 to 12 hours of darkness—to begin the flowering process. (Chap. 5, Sec. 2, p. 142)

loudness: the human perception of how much energy a sound wave carries. (Chap. 21, Sec. 1, p. 606)

lunar eclipse: occurs during a full moon when the Sun, the Moon, and Earth line up in a specific way and the Moon moves into Earth's shadow. (Chap. 17, Sec. 2, p. 492)

M

magnitude: a measure of the energy released by an earthquake. (Chap. 15, Sec. 1, p. 423)

mass: amount of matter in an object, which is measured in kilograms. (Chap. 2, Sec. 2, p. 49)

mass number: the number of protons plus the number of neutrons in an atom. (Chap. 18, Sec. 1, p. 521)

matter: anything that has mass and takes up space; matter's properties are deter-mined by the structure of its atoms and how they are joined. (Chap. 18, Sec. 1, p. 518)

measurement: way to describe the world with numbers—for example, length, volume, mass, weight, and temperature. (Chap. 2, Sec. 1, p. 38)

mechanical wave: a type of wave that uses matter to transfer energy. (Chap. 20, Sec. 1, p. 577)

medium: material through which a wave can travel. (Chap. 23, Sec. 1, p. 665)

meiosis (mi OH sus): reproductive process that produces four haploid sex cells from one diploid cell and ensures offspring will have the same number of chromosomes as the parent organisms. (Chap. 8, Sec. 2, p. 219)

menstrual cycle: hormone-controlled monthly cycle of changes in the female reproductive system that includes the mat-uration of an egg and preparation of the uterus to receive a fertilized egg. (Chap. 10, Sec. 2, p. 278)

menstruation (men STRAY shun): monthly flow of blood and tissue cells that occurs when the lining of the uterus breaks down and is shed. (Chap. 10, Sec. 2, p. 278)

metabolism: the total of all chemical reactions in an organism. (Chap. 4, Sec. 3, p. 113)

meter (m): SI unit for length. (Chap. 2, Sec. 2, p. 47)

migration: instinctive seasonal movement of animals to find food or to reproduce in better conditions. (Chap. 7, Sec. 2, p. 194)

mitochondrion: cell organelle that breaks down lipids and carbohydrates and releases energy. (Chap. 3, Sec. 1, p. 74)

mitosis (mi TOH sus): cell process in which the nucleus divides to form two nuclei identical to each other, and identical to the original nucleus, in a series of steps (prophase, metaphase, anaphase, and telophase). (Chap. 8, Sec. 1, p. 212)

mixture: a combination of substances in which the individual substances do not change or combine chemically but instead retain their own individual properties; can be gases, solids, liquids, or any combination of them. (Chap. 4, Sec. 1, p. 101) (Chap. 18, Sec. 2, p. 527)

model: represents something that is too big, too small, too dangerous, too time consuming, too expensive, or happens too quickly or too slowly to observe directly. (Chap. 1, Sec. 2, p. 16)

moon phases: changing views of the Moon as seen from Earth, which are caused by the Moon's revolution around Earth. (Chap. 17, Sec. 2, p. 489)

mutation: any permanent change in a gene or chromosome of a cell. (Chap. 8, Sec. 3, p. 228)

mutualism: a type of symbiotic relationship in which both organisms benefit. (Chap. 12, Sec. 3, p. 346)

N

natural frequency: frequency at which a musical instrument or other object vibrates when it is struck or disturbed; relative to its size, shape, and the material it is made from. (Chap. 21, Sec. 2, p. 615)

nebula (NEB yuh luh): cloud of rotating gases and dust particles from which the solar system may have formed about 5 billion years ago. (Chap. 17, Sec. 3, p. 503)

nephron (NEF rahn): tiny filtering unit of the kidney. (Chap. 6, Sec. 2, p. 165)

neutron: particle without an electrical charge that is located in the nucleus of an atom. (Chap. 18, Sec. 1, p. 520)

niche (NIHCH): the unique ways an organism survives, obtains food and shelter, and avoids danger. (Chap. 12, Sec. 3, p. 347)

nitrogen cycle: model describing how nitrogen moves from the atmosphere to the soil, to living organisms, and then back to the atmosphere. (Chap. 13, Sec. 2, p. 370)

nitrogen fixation: process in which some types of bacteria can form the nitrogen compounds that plants need. (Chap. 13, Sec. 2, p. 370)

nucleus: organelle that controls all the activities of a cell and contains hereditary material made of proteins and DNA. (Chap. 3, Sec. 1, p. 72)

O

orbit: curved path followed by Earth as it moves around the Sun. (Chap. 17, Sec. 1, p. 483)

organ: structure, such as the heart, made up of different types of tissues that all work together. (Chap. 3, Sec. 1, p. 77)

organelle: structure in the cytoplasm of a eukaryotic cell that can act as a storage site, process energy, move materials, or manufacture substances. (Chap. 3, Sec. 1, p. 72)

organic compounds: compounds that always contain hydrogen and carbon; carbohydrates, lipids, proteins, and nucleic acids are organic compounds found in living things. (Chap. 4, Sec. 1, p. 102)

osmosis: a type of passive transport that occurs when water diffuses through a cell membrane. (Chap. 4, Sec. 2, p. 108)

ovary: female reproductive organ that produces eggs and is located in the lower part of the body. (Chap. 10, Sec. 2, p. 277)

ovary: swollen base of an angiosperm's pistil, where egg-producing ovules are found. (Chap. 9, Sec. 3, p. 253)

overtones: multiples of the fundamental frequency. (Chap. 21, Sec. 2, p. 617)

ovulation (ahv yuh LAY shun): monthly process in which an egg is released from an ovary and enters the oviduct, where it can become fertilized by sperm. (Chap. 10, Sec. 2, p. 277)

ovule: in gymnosperms, the female reproductive part that produces eggs. (Chap. 9, Sec. 3, p. 251)

P

Pangaea (pan JEE uh): large, ancient landmass that was composed of all the continents joined together. (Chap. 14, Sec. 1, p. 392)

parasitism: a type of symbiotic relationship in which one organism benefits but the other organism is harmed. (Chap. 12, Sec. 3, p. 346)

passive transport: movement of substances through a cell membrane without the use of cellular energy; includes diffusion, osmosis, and facilitated diffusion. (Chap. 4, Sec. 2, p. 106)

pharynx (FER ingks): tubelike passageway for food, liquid, and air. (Chap. 6, Sec. 1, p. 156)

phenotype (FEE nuh tipe): the way an organism looks and behaves as a result of its genotype. (Chap. 11, Sec. 1, p. 304)

pheromone (FER uh mohn): powerful chemical produced by an animal to influence the behavior of another animal of the same species. (Chap. 7, Sec. 2, p. 189)

photoperiodism (foh toh PIHR ee uh dih zum): a plant's response to the lengths of darkness each day. (Chap. 5, Sec. 2, p. 142)

photosynthesis: process by which plants and many other producers use light energy from the Sun to make sugars, which can be used as food. (Chap. 4, Sec. 3, p. 114) (Chap. 5, Sec. 1, p. 131)

physical change: change in which the form or appearance of matter changes, but not its composition. (Chap. 19, Sec. 2, p. 552)

physical property: characteristic that can be observed, using the five senses, without

changing or trying to change the composition of a substance. (Chap. 19, Sec. 1, p. 546)

pistil: female reproductive organ inside the flower of an angiosperm; consists of a sticky stigma, where pollen grains land, and an ovary. (Chap. 9, Sec. 3, p. 253)

pitch: how high or low a sound is. (Chap. 21, Sec. 1, p. 608)

plate: a large section of Earth's oceanic or continental crust and rigid upper mantle that moves around on the asthenosphere. (Chap. 14, Sec. 3, p. 400)

plate tectonics: theory that Earth's crust and upper mantle are broken into plates that float and move around on a plastic-like layer of the mantle. (Chap. 14, Sec. 3, p. 400)

pollen grain: small structure produced by the male reproductive organs of a seed plant; has a water-resistant coat, can develop from a spore, and contains gametophyte parts that will produce sperm. (Chap. 9, Sec. 3, p. 249)

pollination: transfer of pollen grains to the female part of a seed plant by agents such as gravity, water, wind, and animals. (Chap. 9, Sec. 3, p. 249)

polygenic (pahl ih JEHN ihk) **inheritance:** occurs when a group of gene pairs acts together and produces a specific trait, such as human eye color, skin color, or height. (Chap. 11, Sec. 2, p. 310)

population: all the organisms in an ecosystem that belong to the same species. (Chap. 12, Sec. 1, p. 334)

precision: describes how close measurements are to each other. (Chap. 2, Sec. 1, p. 40)

pregnancy: period of development—usually about 38 or 39 weeks in humans—from fertilized egg until birth. (Chap. 10, Sec. 3, p. 282)

producer: organism, such as a green plant or alga, that uses an outside source of energy like the Sun to create energy-rich food molecules. (Chap. 12, Sec. 3, p. 344)

prothallus (proh THA lus): small, green, heart-shaped gametophyte plant form of a fern that can make its own food and absorb water and nutrients from the soil. (Chap. 9, Sec. 2, p. 246)

proton: positively-charged particle that is located in the nucleus of an atom. (Chap. 18, Sec. 1, p. 520)

Punnett (PUN ut) **square:** a tool to predict the probability of certain traits in offspring that shows the different ways alleles can combine. (Chap. 11, Sec. 1, p. 304)

R

radiant energy: energy carried by an electromagnetic wave. (Chap. 22, Sec. 1, p. 638)

radio waves: lowest-frequency electromagnetic waves that carry the least amount of energy and are used in most forms of telecommunications technology—such as TVs, telephones, and radios. (Chap. 22, Sec. 2, p. 640)

rate: amount of change of one measurement in a given amount of time. (Chap. 2, Sec. 2, p. 50)

recessive (rih SES ihv): describes a trait that is covered over, or dominated, by another form of that trait and seems to disappear. (Chap. 11, Sec. 1, p. 302)

reflecting telescope: uses a concave mirror to gather light from distant objects. (Chap. 23, Sec. 4, p. 683)

reflection: occurs when a wave strikes an object or surface and bounces off. (Chap. 20, Sec. 3, p. 587) (Chap. 23, Sec. 1, p. 665)

reflex: simple innate behavior, such as yawning or blinking, that is an automatic response and does not involve a message to the brain. (Chap. 7, Sec. 1, p. 181)

refracting telescope: uses two convex lenses to gather light and form an image of a distant object. (Chap. 23, Sec. 4, p. 682)

refraction: bending of a wave as it moves from one medium into another medium. (Chap. 20, Sec. 3, p. 588) (Chap. 23, Sec. 3, p. 677)

resonance: sound amplification that occurs when an object is vibrated at its natural frequency by absorbing energy from a sound wave or other object vibrating at this frequency. (Chap. 21, Sec. 2, p. 616)

respiration: series of chemical reactions used to release energy stored in food molecules. (Chap. 4, Sec. 3, p. 115) (Chap. 5, Sec. 1, p. 133)

reverberation: repeated echoes of sounds. (Chap. 21, Sec. 2, p. 621)

revolution: the motion of Earth around the Sun, which takes about 365 1/4 days, or one year, to complete. (Chap. 17, Sec. 1, p. 483)

rhizome: underground stem of a fern. (Chap. 9, Sec. 2, p. 246)

ribosome: small structure on which cells make their own proteins. (Chap. 3, Sec. 1, p. 74)

rift: long crack that forms between tectonic plates moving apart at plate boundaries. (Chap. 15, Sec. 3, p. 437)

RNA: ribonucleic acid, which carries codes for making proteins from the nucleus to the ribosomes. (Chap. 8, Sec. 3, p. 226)

rotation: spinning of Earth on its axis, which causes day and night; it takes 24 hours for Earth to complete one rotation. (Chap. 17, Sec. 1, p. 482)

S

salinity (say LIHN ut ee): a measure of the amount of salts dissolved in seawater. (Chap. 16, Sec. 1, p. 454)

science: process used to investigate what is happening around us in order to solve problems or answer questions. (Chap. 1, Sec. 1, p. 6)

scientific methods: ways to solve problems that can include step-by-step plans, making models, and carefully thought-out experiments. (Chap. 1, Sec. 2, p. 13)

seafloor spreading: Hess's theory that new seafloor is formed when magma is forced upward toward the surface at a mid-ocean ridge. (Chap. 14, Sec. 2, p. 397)

seismic safe: describes the ability of structures to stand up against the vibrations caused by an earthquake. (Chap. 15, Sec. 1, p. 427)

seismic waves: earthquake waves, including primary waves, secondary waves, and surface waves. (Chap. 15, Sec. 1, p. 422)

seismograph: instrument used to record seismic waves. (Chap. 15, Sec. 1, p. 423)

semen (SEE mun): mixture of sperm and a fluid that helps sperm move and supplies them with an energy source. (Chap. 10, Sec. 2, p. 276)

sex-linked gene: an allele inherited on a sex chromosome and that can cause human genetic disorders such as color blindness and hemophilia. (Chap. 11, Sec. 2, p. 313)

sexual reproduction: a type of reproduction in which two sex cells, usually an egg and a sperm, join to form a zygote, which will develop into a new organism with a unique identity. (Chap. 8, Sec. 2, p. 218)

shield volcano: large, broad volcano with gently sloping sides that is formed by the buildup of basaltic layers. (Chap. 15, Sec. 2, p. 432)

short-day plant: plant that generally requires long nights—12 or more hours of darkness—to begin the flowering process. (Chap. 5, Sec. 2, p. 142)

SI: International System of Units, related by multiples of ten, that allows quantities to be measured in the exact same way throughout the world. (Chap. 2, Sec. 2, p. 46)

social behavior: interactions among members of the same species, including courtship and mating, getting food, caring for young, and protecting each other. (Chap. 7, Sec. 2, p. 186)

society: a group of animals of the same species that live and work together in an organized way, with each member doing a specific job. (Chap. 7, Sec. 2, p. 187)

soil: mixture of mineral and rock particles, the remains of dead organisms, air, and water that forms the topmost layer of Earth's crust and supports plant growth. (Chap. 13, Sec. 1, p. 362)

solar eclipse: occurs during a new moon, when the Sun, the Moon, and Earth are lined up in a specific way and Earth moves into the Moon's shadow. (Chap. 17, Sec. 2, p. 491)

solar system: extremely large system that includes the Sun, planets, comets, meteoroids and other objects that orbit the Sun. (Chap. 17, Sec. 3, p. 496)

solstice: time when the Sun reaches its greatest distance north or south of the equator, which occurs June 21 or 22 for the northern hemisphere (longest day of the year) and December 21 or 22 for the southern hemisphere (shortest day of the year). (Chap. 17, Sec. 1, p. 484)

solution: a kind of mixture in which one substance is completely and evenly mixed in another substance and is the same throughout. (Chap. 18, Sec. 2, p. 527)

English Glossary

sori: fern structures in which spores are produced. (Chap. 9, Sec. 2, p. 246)

sperm: haploid sex cells formed in the male reproductive organs. (Chap. 8, Sec. 2, p. 218) (Chap. 10, Sec. 2, p. 276)

spores: haploid cells produced in the gametophyte stage that can divide by mitosis and form plant structures or an entire new plant or can develop into sex cells. (Chap. 9, Sec. 1, p. 243)

sporophyte (SPOR uh fite) **stage:** plant life cycle stage that begins when an egg is fertilized by a sperm. (Chap. 9, Sec. 1, p. 243)

stamen: male reproductive organ inside the flower of an angiosperm where pollen grains form. (Chap. 9, Sec. 3, p. 253)

stomata (STOH mut uh): tiny openings in a plant's epidermis through which carbon dioxide and water vapor gases enter and leave a leaf. (Chap. 5, Sec, 1, p. 129)

surface current: wind-powered ocean current that moves water horizontally, parallel to Earth's surface, and moves only the upper few hundred meters of seawater. (Chap. 16, Sec. 2, p. 456)

symbiosis: any close relationship between species, including mutualism, commensalism, and parasitism. (Chap. 12, Sec. 3, p. 346)

T

table: displays information in rows and columns, making it easier to read and understand. (Chap. 2, Sec. 3, p. 53)

technology: application of science to make useful products and tools, such as computers. (Chap. 1, Sec. 1, p. 9)

testes: (TES teez) male organ that produces sperm and testosterone. (Chap. 10, Sec. 2, p. 276)

tidal range: the difference between the level of the ocean at high tide and the level at low tide. (Chap. 16, Sec. 3, p. 466)

tide: daily rise and fall in sea level caused, for the most part, by the interaction of gravity in the Earth-Moon system. (Chap. 16, Sec. 3, p. 465)

tissue: group of similar cells that work together to do one job. (Chap. 3, Sec. 1, p. 77)

trachea (TRAY kee uh): air-conducting tube that connects the larynx with the bronchi, is lined with mucous membranes and cilia, and contains strong cartilage rings. (Chap. 6, Sec. 1, p. 157)

transverse wave: a type of mechanical wave in which the wave energy causes matter in the medium to move up and down or back and forth at right angles to the direction the wave travels. (Chap. 20, Sec. 1, p. 578)

tropism: positive or negative plant response to an external stimulus such as touch, light, or gravity. (Chap. 5, Sec. 2, p. 138)

trough: lowest point of a wave. (Chap. 16, Sec. 3, p. 462)

tsunami: powerful seismic sea wave that begins over an ocean-floor earthquake, can reach 30 m in height when approaching land, and can cause destruction in coastal areas. (Chap. 15, Sec. 1, p. 425)

U

ultraviolet radiation: electromagnetic waves with higher frequencies and shorter wavelengths than visible light. (Chap. 22, Sec. 2, p. 643)

upwelling: circulation in the ocean that brings deep, cold water to the ocean surface. (Chap. 16, Sec. 2, p. 459)

ureter: tube that carries urine from each kidney to the bladder. (Chap. 6, Sec. 2, p. 166)

urethra (yoo REE thruh): tube that carries urine from the bladder to the outside of the body. (Chap. 6, Sec. 2, p. 166)

urinary system: system of excretory organs that rids the blood of wastes, controls blood volume by removing excess water, and balances concentrations of salts and water. (Chap. 6, Sec. 2, p. 163)

urine: wastewater that contains excess water, salts, and other wastes that are not reabsorbed by the body. (Chap. 6, Sec. 2, p. 164)

uterus: hollow, muscular, pear-shaped organ where a fertilized egg develops into a baby. (Chap. 10, Sec. 2, p. 277)

V

vagina (vuh JI nuh): muscular tube that connects the lower end of the uterus to the outside of the body; the birth canal through which a baby travels when being born. (Chap. 10, Sec. 2, p. 277)

virus: a strand of hereditary material surrounded by a protein coating. (Chap. 3, Sec. 3, p. 84)

visible light: electromagnetic waves with wavelengths between 0.7 and 0.4 millionths of a meter that can be seen with your eyes. (Chap. 22, Sec. 2, p. 642)

volcano: cone-shaped hill or mountain formed when hot magma, solids, and gas erupt onto Earth's surface through a vent. (Chap. 15, Sec. 2, p. 429)

W

water cycle: model describing how water moves from Earth's surface to the atmosphere and back to the surface again through evaporation, condensation, and precipitation. (Chap. 13, Sec. 2, p. 369)

wave: rhythmic movement that carries energy through matter or space. (Chap. 16, Sec. 3, p. 462) (Chap. 20, Sec. 1, p. 576)

wavelength: in transverse waves, the distance between the tops of two adjacent crests or the bottoms of two adjacent troughs; in compressional waves, the distance from the centers of adjacent rarefactions. (Chap. 20, Sec. 2, p. 582)

X

X ray: high-energy electromagnetic wave that is highly penetrating. (Chap. 22, Sec. 2, p. 644)

Z

zygote: new diploid cell formed when a sperm fertilizes an egg; will divide by mitosis and develop into a new organism. (Chap. 8, Sec. 2, p. 218)

English Glossary

Spanish Glossary

A

abiotic / abióticos: factores físicos inanimados del ambiente que incluyen el aire, el agua, la luz solar, el suelo, la temperatura y el clima. (Cap. 13, Sec. 1, pág. 360)

accuracy / exactitud: compara una medida con el verdadero valor. (Cap. 2, Sec. 1, pág. 41)

active transport / transporte activo: proceso que requiere energía en el cual las proteínas de transporte se enlazan con partículas y se mueven a través de la membrana celular. (Cap. 4, Sec. 2, pág. 109)

aggression / agresión: comportamiento enérgico, como las peleas, que usa un animal para controlar o dominar a otro animal con el propósito de proteger sus crías, defender su territorio u obtener alimento. (Cap. 7, Sec. 2, pág. 188)

allele / alelo: formas alternas que un gene puede tener para un sólo rasgo; puede ser dominante o recesivo. (Cap. 11, Sec. 1, pág. 300)

alveoli / alvéolos: racimos minúsculos de paredes finas que se hallan en el extremo de cada bronquiolo y que están rodeados de capilares, donde se lleva a cabo el intercambio de dióxido de carbono y oxígeno. (Cap. 6, Sec. 1, pág. 157)

amniotic sac / saco amniótico: membrana protectora, delgada y llena de líquido, que se forma alrededor del embrión. (Cap. 10, Sec. 3, pág. 283)

amplitude / amplitud: distancia a la cual una onda sube o baja de su nivel normal, la cual se relaciona con la energía que transporta la onda; en una onda transversal, es la mitad de la distancia entre una cresta y un seno. (Cap. 20, Sec. 2, pág. 581)

asexual reproduction / reproducción asexual: tipo de reproducción que comprende la fisión, gemación y regeneración, en el cual un progenitor produce un nuevo organismo que tiene DNA idéntico al organismo progenitor. (Cap. 8, Sec. 1, pág. 215)

asteroid / asteroide: pequeño cuerpo espacial rocoso que se encuentra en el cinturón de asteroides entre las órbitas de Júpiter y Marte. (Cap. 17, Sec. 3, pág. 502)

asthenosphere / astenosfera: capa viscosa de la Tierra en la cual las placas litosféricas flotan y se mueven. (Cap. 14, Sec. 3, pág. 400)

asthma / asma: trastorno pulmonar en el cual los tubos bronquiales se contraen rápidamente y dificultan la respiración y causan estornudo o tos; puede ocurrir como una reacción alérgica. (Cap. 6, Sec. 1, pág. 162)

astronomical unit / unidad astronómica: unidad de medida que se usa para medir distancias entre objetos en el sistema solar; 1 UA equivale a 150 000 000 km. (Cap. 17, Sec. 3, pág. 496)

atmosphere / atmósfera: comprende el aire que rodea la Tierra; la atmósfera está compuesta por gases, entre los cuales se incluye un 78 por ciento de nitrógeno, un 21 por ciento de oxígeno y 0.03 por ciento de dióxido de carbono. (Cap. 13, Sec. 1, pág. 361)

atomic number / número atómico: número de protones en un átomo. (Cap. 18, Sec. 1, pág. 521)

atoms / átomos: partículas diminutas de materia compuestas de protones, neutrones y electrones. (Cap. 18, Sec. 1, pág. 518)

auxin / auxina: hormona vegetal gracias a la cual las hojas y tallos de las plantas exhiben fototropismos positivos. (Cap. 5, Sec. 2, pág. 140)

axis / eje: línea imaginaria alrededor de la cual gira la Tierra, lo cual causa el día y la noche; se traza desde el polo geográfico norte a través de la Tierra hasta el polo geográfico sur. (Cap. 17, Sec. 1, pág. 482)

B

bar graph / gráfica de barras: tipo de gráfica que usa barras de distintos tamaños para mostrar las relaciones entre variables. (Cap. 2, Sec. 3, pág. 54)

basin / cuenca: depresión en la Tierra en donde se formó un océano cuando el área se llenó de agua debido a las lluvias torrenciales. (Cap. 16, Sec. 1, pág. 453)

behavior / comportamiento: la interacción de un organismo con otro organismo y con su ambiente; puede ser innato o adquirido. (Cap. 7, Sec. 1, pág. 180)

biosphere / biosfera: parte de la Tierra que sostiene la vida; incluye la parte superior de la corteza terrestre, la atmósfera y toda el agua sobre la superficie de la Tierra. (Cap. 12, Sec. 1, pág. 332)

biotic / bióticos: los factores del medio ambiente que son seres vivos o seres que una vez estuvieron vivos. (Cap. 13, Sec. 1, pág. 360)

bladder / vejiga: órgano elástico y muscular que retiene la orina hasta que ésta sale del cuerpo por la uretra. (Cap. 6, Sec. 2, pág. 166)

breaker / cachón: una ola oceánica que se forma en aguas poco profundas y la cual rompe en la playa. (Cap. 16, Sec. 3, pág. 463)

bronchi / bronquios: dos conductos cortos que se bifurcan del extremo inferior de la tráquea y por los cuales se introduce el aire en los pulmones. (Cap. 6, Sec. 1, pág. 157)

C

carbon cycle / ciclo del carbono: modelo que describe cómo las células del carbono se movilizan entre el mundo vivo y el inanimado. (Cap. 13, Sec. 2, pág. 373)

carrier wave / onda portadora: frecuencia de transmisión particular asignada a una estación radial. (Cap. 22, Sec. 3, pág. 650)

carrying capacity / capacidad de carga: el número mayor de individuos de una especie en particular que puede mantener un ecosistema de manera prolongada. (Cap. 12, Sec. 2, pág. 339)

cell membrane / membrana celular: cubierta externa protectora de todas las células; formada por una capa doble de moléculas adiposas y controla la interacción entre la célula y el medio ambiente. (Cap. 3, Sec. 1, pág. 70)

cell theory / teoría celular: establece que todos los organismos están formados por una o más células, la célula es la unidad básica de la vida y todas las células provienen de otras células. (Cap. 3, Sec. 2, pág. 83)

cell wall / pared celular: estructura rígida que encierra, sostiene y protege las células vegetales, las células de las algas, de los hongos y de la mayoría de las bacterias. (Cap. 3, Sec. 1, pág. 71)

chemical change / cambio químico: transformación que experimenta la composición de una sustancia. (Cap. 19, Sec. 2, pág. 554)

chemical property / propiedad química: propiedad de la materia que se puede observar cuando dos sustancias reaccionan o cuando una sustancia se convierte en otra sustancia. (Cap. 19, Sec. 1, pág. 550)

chemosynthesis / quimiosíntesis: proceso en el cual los productores elaboran moléculas nutritivas ricas en energía a partir de sustancias químicas. (Cap. 13, Sec. 3, pág. 375)

chlorophyll / clorofila: pigmento verde y absorbente de luz, fijado a los cloroplastos de las plantas y que es importante en el proceso de la fotosíntesis. (Cap. 5, Sec. 1, pág. 130)

chloroplast / cloroplasto: organelo de las células vegetales, de color verde y que contiene clorofila, que convierte la luz solar, el dióxido de carbono y el agua en azúcar. (Cap. 3, Sec. 1, pág. 74)

chromosome / cromosoma: estructura en el núcleo de una célula que contiene el material genético. (Cap. 8, Sec. 1, pág. 212)

cinder cone volcano / volcán de cono de carbonilla: volcán relativamente pequeño que se ha formado debido a erupciones violentas de tefra. (Cap. 15, Sec. 2, pág. 432)

circle graph / gráfica circular: tipo de gráfica que muestra partes de un todo; cada parte de la gráfica es un sector que representa un porcentaje del total. (Cap. 2, Sec. 3, pág. 54)

climate / clima: condiciones meteorológicas promedio de una región durante un período de tiempo, entre las cuales se incluyen el viento, la temperatura y la precipitación pluvial u otro tipo de precipitación como la nieve o la cellisca. (Cap. 13, Sec. 1, pág. 365)

comet / cometa: astro espacial compuesto de partículas rocosas y hielo; forma una cola cuando su órbita lo acerca al Sol y se encuentra principalmente en el cinturón Kuiper y en la Nube de Oort. (Cap. 17, Sec. 3, pág. 502)

commensalism / comensalismo: tipo de relación simbiótica en el cual un organismo se beneficia y el otro organismo no se ve afectado. (Cap. 12, Sec. 3, pág. 346)

community / comunidad: todas las poblaciones de diferentes especies que viven en un ecosistema. (Cap. 12, Sec. 1, pág. 334)

composite volcano / volcán compuesto: volcán de laderas abruptas que se ha formado por la alternación de erupciones violentas de tefra y erupciones más silenciosas de lava. (Cap. 15, Sec. 2, pág. 433)

compound / compuesto: materia que está hecha de dos o más elementos y que tiene propiedades físicas y químicas diferentes a las de los elementos que la formaron. (Cap. 18, Sec. 2, pág. 524)

compressional wave / onda de compresión: tipo de onda mecánica en la cual la materia del medio oscila en la misma dirección en que viaja la onda. (Cap. 20, Sec. 1, pág. 579)

concave lens / lente cóncava: lente que es más gruesa en los bordes que en el medio y que desvía los rayos luminosos que viajan paralelos al eje óptico. (Cap. 23, Sec. 3, pág. 679)

condensation / condensación: proceso que se efectúa cuando un gas se convierte en un líquido. (Cap. 13, Sec. 2, pág. 369)

conditioning / condicionamiento: ocurre cuando la respuesta a un estímulo se asocia con otro estímulo. (Cap. 7, Sec. 1, pág. 184)

constant / constante: variable que permanece igual durante un experimento. (Cap. 1, Sec. 2, pág. 21)

consumer / consumidor: organismo que no puede fabricar moléculas ricas en energía, sino que obtiene su alimento al alimentarse de otros organismos. (Cap. 12, Sec. 3, pág. 345)

continental drift / deriva continental: hipótesis de Wegener que afirmaba que todos los continentes estuvieron unidos en algún momento formando una sola masa continental, la cual se separó hace unos 200 millones de años, haciendo que los continentes derivaran lentamente a sus posiciones actuales. (Cap. 14, Sec. 1, pág. 392)

control / control: muestra que se trata como cualquier otro grupo experimental, excepto que no se le aplica la variable independiente. (Cap. 1, Sec. 2, pág. 22)

convection current / corriente de convección: corriente en el manto terrestre que transfiere energía en el interior de la Tierra y que provee la potencia de la tectónica de placas. (Cap. 14, Sec. 3, pág. 405)

convex lens / lente convexa: lente convergente que es más gruesa en el medio que en los bordes. (Cap. 23, Sec. 3, pág. 678)

Coriolis effect / efecto de Coriolis: cambio de vientos y corrientes superficiales provocados por la rotación de la Tierra; hace que las corrientes al norte del ecuador fluyan en dirección de las manecillas del reloj y las corrientes al sur del ecuador en dirección contraria. (Cap. 16, Sec. 2, pág. 457)

courtship behavior / comportamiento de cortejo: comportamiento que permite que machos y hembras de una especie se reconozcan mutuamente y se preparen para el apareo. (Cap. 7, Sec. 2, pág. 189)

crater / cráter: depresión formada por un meteorito grande; entre más cráteres presente una región, más data en antigüedad. (Cap. 17, Sec. 2, pág. 487)

crest / cresta: punto más alto de una onda. (Cap. 16, Sec. 3, pág. 462)

cyclic behavior / comportamiento cíclico: comportamiento que ocurre en forma de patrones repetidos. (Cap. 7, Sec. 2, pág. 192)

cytoplasm / citoplasma: mezcla gelatinosa en continuo movimiento dentro de la membrana celular que contiene material hereditario y en la cual se lleva a cabo la mayoría de los procesos de una célula. (Cap. 3, Sec. 1, pág. 70)

D

day-neutral plant / planta de día neutro: planta que no necesita un fotoperíodo específico y que puede comenzar el proceso de floración a lo largo de un rango de períodos nocturnos. (Cap. 5, Sec.2, pág. 142)

density / densidad: cambio físico de la materia que puede calcularse dividiendo la masa de un cuerpo entre su volumen. (Cap. 18, Sec. 3, pág. 530)

density current / corriente de densidad: patrón de circulación en el océano que se forma cuando una masa de agua salada más densa se hunde debajo de agua salada menos densa. (Cap. 16, Sec. 2, pág. 459)

dependent variable / variable dependiente: factor que se mide durante un experimento. (Cap. 1, Sec. 2, pág. 21)

descriptive research / investigación descriptiva: responde preguntas científicas a través de la observación. (Cap. 1, Sec. 2, pág. 13)

diaphragm / diafragma: músculo situado debajo de los pulmones que se contrae y se relaja permitiendo así la entrada y salida de gases del cuerpo. (Cap. 6, Sec. 1, pág. 158)

diffraction / difracción: desviación de las ondas alrededor de un obstáculo. (Cap. 20, Sec. 3, pág. 589)

diffusion / difusión: tipo de transporte pasivo celular en el que las moléculas se mueven desde áreas de mayor concentración a áreas de menor concentración. (Cap. 4, Sec. 2, pág. 107)

diploid / diploide: célula cuyos cromosomas se dan en pares. (Cap. 8, Sec. 2, pág. 218)

DNA / DNA: ácido desoxirribonucleico; material genético de todos los organismos y compuesto de dos hebras retorcidas de moléculas de fosfato de azúcar y bases nitrogenadas. (Cap. 8, Sec. 3, pág. 224)

dominant / dominante: describe un rasgo que cubre o domina otra forma de dicho rasgo. (Cap. 11, Sec. 1, pág. 302)

Doppler effect / efecto Doppler: cambio en la frecuencia o el tono de un sonido, el cual ocurre cuando la fuente sonora y el oyente están en movimiento relativo uno del otro. (Cap. 21, Sec. 1, pág. 610)

eardrum / tímpano: membrana que se extiende a través del canal auditivo y la cual vibra cuando las ondas sonoras llegan al oído medio. (Cap. 21, Sec. 2, pág. 622)

earthquake / terremoto: movimiento sísmico que ocurre cuando las rocas del interior de la Tierra exceden su límite elástico, se rompen repentinamente y experimentan un rebote elástico. (Cap. 15, Sec. 1, pág. 420)

echo / eco: onda sonora reflejada. (Cap. 21, Sec. 1, pág. 609)

ecology / ecología: estudio de las interacciones que se llevan a cabo entre los organismos y su ambiente. (Cap. 12, Sec. 1, pág. 333)

ecosystem / ecosistema: todos los organismos vivos que habitan en un área y las cosas inanimadas en su ambiente. (Cap. 12, Sec. 1, pág. 333)

egg / óvulo: célula haploide formada en los órganos reproductores femeninos. (Cap. 8, Sec. 2, pág. 218)

electromagnetic spectrum / espectro electromagnético: rango de ondas electromagnéticas, que incluyen las ondas radiales, la luz visible y los rayos X, las cuales poseen distintas frecuencias y longitudes de onda. (Cap. 22, Sec. 2, pág. 639)

electromagnetic waves / ondas electromagnéticas: ondas que pueden viajar a través del espacio vacío, poseen una amplia gama de longitudes de onda y frecuencias y las producen las partículas con carga eléctrica al moverse. (Cap. 20, Sec. 1, pág. 580; Cap. 22, Sec. 1, pág. 634)

electrons / electrones: partículas con carga negativa que se mueven alrededor del núcleo de un átomo y forman la nube de electrones. (Cap. 18, Sec. 1, pág. 520)

element / elemento: sustancia que sólo contiene un tipo de átomo; por ejemplo, el oxígeno, el aluminio y el hierro. (Cap. 18, Sec. 1, pág. 519)

embryo / embrión: óvulo fecundado adherido a la pared uterina. (Cap. 10, Sec. 3, pág. 283)

emphysema / enfisema: enfermedad pulmonar en la cual se produce una dilatación de los alvéolos. (Cap. 6, Sec. 1, pág. 161)

endocytosis / endocitosis: proceso que permite que una célula deje pasar una sustancia al rodearla con la membrana celular. (Cap. 4, Sec. 2, pág. 110)

endoplasmic reticulum (ER) / retículo endoplásmico: organelo citoplásmico que mueve materiales dentro de una célula y que está formado por una serie compleja de membranas plegadas; puede ser áspero (con ribosomas adheridos) o liso (sin ribosomas adheridos). (Cap. 3, Sec. 1, pág. 75)

energy pyramid / pirámide de energía: modelo que muestra la cantidad de energía disponible en cada nivel alimenticio de un ecosistema. (Cap. 13, Sec. 3, pág. 377)

enzyme / enzima: tipo de proteína que regula casi todas las reacciones químicas de las células. (Cap. 4, Sec. 1, pág. 103)

epicenter / epicentro: punto en la superficie terrestre que se halla directamente encima del foco de un terremoto. (Cap. 15, Sec. 1, pág. 422)

equilibrium / equilibrio: ocurre cuando las moléculas de una sustancia se esparcen uniformemente en otra sustancia. (Cap. 4, Sec. 2, pág. 107)

equinox / equinoccio: época que ocurre dos veces el año, cuando el Sol se encuentra directamente encima del ecuador y el número de horas diurnas y nocturnas son iguales en todo el mundo. (Cap. 17, Sec. 1, pág. 485)

estimation / estimación: método de hacer una conjetura razonada de una medida. (Cap. 2, Sec. 1, pág. 39)

evaporation / evaporación: proceso que se lleva a cabo cuando un líquido se convierte en un gas. (Cap. 13, Sec. 2, pág. 368)

exocytosis / exocitosis: proceso a través del cual las vesículas liberan sus contenidos fuera de la célula. (Cap. 4, Sec. 2, pág. 110)

experimental research design / diseño de investigación experimental: se usa para responder preguntas científicas mediante la prueba de una hipótesis usando una serie de pasos cuidadosamente controlados. (Cap. 1, Sec. 2, pág. 13)

F

fault / falla: fractura que ocurre cuando las rocas cambian de forma al fragmentarse; se puede formar debido a una compresión (falla invertida), a la separación (falla normal) o al cizallamiento (falla transformante). (Cap. 15, Sec. 1, pág. 421)

fermentation / fermentación: proceso en que las células carentes de oxígeno y algunos organismos unicelulares liberan pequeñas cantidades de energía de las moléculas de glucosa y producen desechos como el alcohol, el dióxido de carbono y el ácido láctico. (Cap. 4, Sec. 3, pág. 116)

fertilization / fecundación: en la reproducción sexual, la unión del espermatozoide y del óvulo. (Cap. 8, Sec. 2, pág. 218)

fetal stress / estrés fetal: puede presentarse durante el proceso de alumbramiento o después del nacimiento conforme el lactante se ajusta de un entorno acuoso, oscuro y de temperatura constante a su nuevo entorno. (Cap. 10, Sec. 3, pág. 286)

fetus / feto: bebé en desarrollo después de los primeros dos meses de embarazo hasta su nacimiento. (Cap. 10, Sec. 3, pág. 284)

focal length / longitud focal: distancia a lo largo del eje óptico desde el centro de un espejo cóncavo al punto focal. (Cap. 23, Sec. 2, pág. 672)

focal point / punto focal: punto único en el eje óptico de un espejo cóncavo a través del cual pasan los rayos luminosos reflejados. (Cap. 23, Sec. 2, pág. 672)

focus / foco: punto profundo en el interior de la Tierra donde se libera energía, lo cual provoca un terremoto. (Cap. 15, Sec. 1, pág. 422)

food web / red alimenticia: modelo que muestra las complejas relaciones alimenticias entre los organismos de una comunidad. (Cap. 13, Sec. 3, pág. 676)

frequency / frecuencia: número de longitudes de onda que pasan por un punto dado en un segundo; se miden en hertz (Hz). (Cap. 20, Sec. 2, pág. 583)

frond / fronda: hoja de helecho que crece desde el rizoma. (Cap. 9, Sec. 2, pág. 246)

fundamental frequency / frecuencia fundamental: frecuencia natural más baja que produce una cuerda o una columna de aire que vibra. (Cap. 21, Sec. 2, pág. 617)

G

gametophyte stage / etapa gametofita: etapa del ciclo de vida vegetal que comienza cuando las células de los órganos reproductores pasan por la meiosis y producen células haploides. (Cap. 9, Sec. 1, pág. 243)

gamma ray / rayo gama: la onda electromagnética más penetrante y de alta frecuencia. (Cap. 22, Sec. 2, pág. 644)

gene / gene: sección de DNA en un cromosoma que contiene las instrucciones para la elaboración de proteínas específicas. (Cap. 8, Sec. 3, pág. 226)

genetic engineering / ingeniería genética: métodos biológicos y químicos que se usan para cambiar el arreglo del DNA de un gene con el propósito de mejorar la producción de cosechas, producir grandes volúmenes de medicamentos y cambiar el funcionamiento normal de células. (Cap. 11, Sec. 3, pág. 315)

genetics / genética: estudia la manera en que se heredan los rasgos a través de las acciones de los alelos. (Cap. 11, Sec. 1, pág. 300)

genotype / genotipo: la composición genética de un organismo. (Cap. 11, Sec. 1, pág. 304)

germination / germinación: serie de eventos que dan como resultado el crecimiento de una planta a partir de una semilla. (Cap. 9, Sec. 3, pág. 258)

Global Positioning System / Sistema de Posición Global: usa satélites, estaciones terrestres y equipo portátil con receptores para ubicar objetos sobre la Tierra. (Cap. 22, Sec. 3, pág. 653)

Golgi bodies / cuerpos de Golgi: organelos que almacenan materiales celulares y los transportan dentro o fuera de la célula. (Cap. 3, Sec. 1, pág. 75)

graph / gráfica: se utiliza para recopilar, organizar y resumir datos de una manera visual, facilitando de esta manera su uso y comprensión. (Cap. 2, Sec. 3, pág. 53)

H

habitat / hábitat: lugar en donde vive un organismo y que le provee los tipos de alimento, refugio, humedad y temperaturas necesarias para la sobrevivencia. (Cap. 12, Sec. 1, pág. 335)

haploid / haploide: célula que sólo tiene uno de cada tipo de cromosoma. (Cap. 8, Sec. 2, pág. 219)

heredity / herencia: el traspaso de rasgos de los progenitores a la progenie. (Cap. 11, Sec. 1, pág. 300)

heterogeneous / heterogénea: mezclas que se no distribuyen igualmente y en las que cada componente retiene sus propias propiedades. (Cap. 18, Sec. 2, pág. 527)

heterozygous / heterocigoto: describe al organismo que presenta dos alelos distintos para un rasgo. (Cap. 11, Sec. 1, pág. 304)

hibernation / hibernación: respuesta cíclica de inactividad y disminución del metabolismo, la cual ocurre durante períodos de temperaturas frías y abastecimientos limitados de alimentos. (Cap. 7, Sec. 2, pág. 193)

homogeneous / homogénea: mezcla que se distribuyen igualmente en toda la extensión de la mezcla. (Cap. 18, Sec. 2, pág. 527)

homozygous / homocigoto: describe un organismo con dos alelos idénticos para el mismo rasgo. (Cap. 11, Sec. 1, pág. 304)

hormone / hormona: sustancia química que produce el sistema endocrino y la cual se libera directamente en el torrente sanguíneo a través de glándulas sin conductos; actúa en tejidos asignados y puede acelerar o aminorar las actividades celulares. (Cap. 10, Sec. 1, pág. 270)

host cell / célula huésped: célula viva en la cual un virus se puede reproducir activamente o en la cual un virus puede ocultarse hasta que los estímulos ambientales lo activen. (Cap. 3, Sec. 3, pág. 84)

hot spot / foco caliente: masa de magma extensa y ascendente que puede abrirse paso a través del manto y la corteza terrestres y que puede formar volcanes. (Cap. 15, Sec. 3, pág. 438)

hybrid / híbrido: progenie que ha obtenido información genética distinta para un rasgo de cada progenitor. (Cap. 11, Sec. 1, pág. 302)

hypothesis / hipótesis: predicción o enunciado que puede probarse y que se puede deducir del conocimiento previo, cualquier observación previa y de nueva información. (Cap. 1, Sec. 2, pág. 21)

I

imprinting / impronta: ocurre cuando un animal forma un vínculo social con otro organismo durante un período específico después del nacimiento o de salir del cascarón. (Cap. 7, Sec. 1, pág. 183)

incomplete dominance / dominancia incompleta: producción de un fenotipo intermedio al de los dos progenitores homocigotos. (Cap. 11, Sec. 2, pág. 308)

independent variable / variable independiente: variable que puede cambiarse durante un experimento. (Cap. 1, Sec. 2, pág. 21)

infrared wave / onda infrarroja: onda electromagnética que se siente como calor y la cual emiten casi todos los cuerpos. (Cap. 22, Sec. 2, pág. 641)

innate behavior / comportamiento innato: comportamiento con que nace un organismo y el cual no tiene que ser adquirido, como un reflejo o un instinto. (Cap. 7, Sec. 1, pág. 181)

inorganic compound / compuesto orgánico: compuesto cuyos constituyentes son otros elementos, en vez del carbono y cuyos átomos por lo general pueden arreglarse en sólo una estructura, como por ejemplo, el H_2O. (Cap. 4, Sec. 1, pág. 103)

insight / discernimiento: forma de razonamiento que permite a los animales usar las experiencias previas para resolver nuevos problemas. (Cap. 7, Sec. 1, pág. 185)

instinct / instinto: patrón complejo de comportamiento innato, como por ejemplo, tejer una telaraña y el que puede demorar semanas en completarse. (Cap. 7, Sec. 1, pág. 182)

interference / interferencia: capacidad de dos o más ondas de combinarse y formar una nueva onda cuando se traslapan. (Cap. 20, Sec. 3, pág. 591)

ion / ion: átomo con carga eléctrica cuya carga resulta cuando un átomo pierde o gana electrones. (Cap. 18, Sec. 2, pág. 525)

isotopes / isótopos: átomos del mismo elemento con diferentes números de neutrones. (Cap. 18, Sec. 1, pág. 521)

K

kelvin (K) / kelvin (K): unidad de temperatura del SI. (Cap. 2, Sec. 2, pág. 50)

kidney / riñón: órgano del sistema urinario en forma de frijol y que está formado por cerca de 1 millón de nefrones; filtra la sangre produciendo la orina. (Cap. 6, Sec. 2, pág. 164)

kilogram (kg) / kilogramo (kg): unidad de masa del SI. (Cap. 2, Sec. 2, pág. 49)

L

larynx / laringe: vía respiratoria a la cual se encuentran adheridas las cuerdas vocales. (Cap. 6, Sec. 1, pág. 157)

lava / lava: roca derretida que fluye a la superficie terrestre. (Cap. 15, Sec. 2, pág. 429)

law of conservation of mass / conservación de la masa: establece que la masa ni se crea ni se destruye. Como resultado, la masa de las sustancias antes de un cambio físico o químico es igual a la masa de las sustancias después del cambio. (Cap. 19, Sec. 2, pág. 561)

law of reflection / ley de la reflexión: establece que el ángulo de incidencia es igual al ángulo de reflexión. (Cap. 23, Sec. 2, pág. 669)

lens / lente: objeto transparente que tiene por lo menos una superficie que hace que la luz se doble. (Cap. 23, Sec. 3, pág. 677)

light ray / rayo luminoso: rayo angosto de luz que viaja en línea recta. (Cap. 23, Sec. 1, pág. 664)

limiting factor / factor limitativo: cualquier cosa que puede limitar el tamaño de una población, incluye los organismos vivos y los inanimados de un ecosistema, como los depredadores o la sequía. (Cap. 12, Sec. 2, pág. 338)

line graph / gráfica lineal: tipo de gráfica que se utiliza para mostrar la relación entre dos variables, en forma de números, en un eje *x* y un eje *y*. (Cap. 2, Sec. 3, pág. 53)

lithosphere / litosfera: capa rígida de la Tierra de unos 100 km de grosor formada por la corteza y parte del manto superior. (Cap. 14, Sec. 3, pág. 400)

long-day plant / planta de día largo: planta que necesita, por lo general, noches cortas (menos de diez a 12 horas de oscuridad) para comenzar el proceso de floración. (Cap. 5, Sec. 2, pág. 142)

loudness / volumen: de un sonido es el grado de percepción humana de la cantidad de energía que transporta la onda. (Cap. 21, Sec. 1, pág. 606)

lunar eclipse / eclipse lunar: ocurre durante la luna llena cuando el Sol, la Luna y la Tierra se alinean de una manera específica y la Luna se mueve dentro de la sombra de la Tierra. (Cap. 17, Sec. 2, pág. 492)

M

magnitude / magnitud: medida de la energía que libera un terremoto. (Cap. 15, Sec. 1, pág. 423)

mass / masa: cantidad de materia que posee un cuerpo, la cual se mide en kilogramos. (Cap. 2, Sec. 2, pág. 49)

mass number / número de masa: el número de protones más el número de neutrones en un átomo. (Cap. 18, Sec. 1, pág. 521)

matter / materia: cualquier cosa que tiene masa y ocupa espacio; las propiedades de la materia están determinadas según la estructura y enlace de sus átomos. (Cap. 18, Sec. 1, pág. 518)

measurement / medida: manera de describir objetos y eventos con números; por ejemplo: longitud, volumen, masa, peso y temperatura. (Cap. 2, Sec. 1, pág. 38)

mechanical wave / onda mecánica: tipo de onda que sólo puede viajar a través de la materia. (Cap. 20, Sec. 1, pág. 577)

medium / medio: material a través del cual puede viajar una onda. (Cap. 23, Sec. 1, pág. 665)

meiosis / meiosis: proceso reproductor que produce cuatro células sexuales haploides a partir de una célula diploide y asegura que la progenie tenga el mismo número de cromosomas que el organismo progenitor. (Cap. 8, Sec. 2, pág. 219)

menstrual cycle / ciclo menstrual: ciclo de cambios mensual controlado por hormonas del sistema reproductor femenino. Incluye la maduración de un óvulo y la preparación del útero para un posible embarazo. (Cap. 10, Sec. 2, pág. 278)

menstruation / menstruación: descarga mensual de sangre y células tisulares que ocurre cuando el revestimiento uterino se desintegra y se desprende. (Cap. 10, Sec. 2, pág. 278)

metabolism / metabolismo: el total de todas las reacciones químicas en un organismo. (Cap. 4, Sec. 3, pág. 113)

meter (m) / metro (m): unidad de longitud del SI. (Cap. 2, Sec. 2, pág. 47)

migration / migración: movimiento instintivo de ciertos animales de mudarse a lugares nuevos cuando cambian las estaciones, en busca de alimentos o para encontrar condiciones más propicias para el apareo. (Cap. 7, Sec. 2, pág. 194)

mitochondrion / mitocondria: organelo celular que descompone lípidos y carbohidratos y libera energía. (Cap. 3, Sec. 1, pág. 74)

mitosis / mitosis: proceso celular en que el núcleo se divide para formar dos núcleos idénticos uno al otro e idénticos al núcleo original, en una serie de pasos (profase, metafase, anafase y telofase). (Cap. 8, Sec. 1, pág. 212)

mixture / mezcla: combinación de sustancias en que las sustancias individuales no cambian ni se combinan químicamente, sino que retienen sus propiedades individuales; pueden ser gases, sólidos, líquidos o cualquier combinación de estos dos. (Cap. 4, Sec. 1, pág. 101; Cap. 18, Sec. 2, pág. 527)

model / modelo: representa algo que es muy grande, muy pequeño, muy peligroso, que consume mucho tiempo o que es muy costoso para ser observado directamente. (Cap. 1, Sec. 2, pág. 16)

molecules / moléculas: partículas constitutivas de los compuestos que se forman de la unión de átomos. (Cap. 18, Sec. 2, pág. 524)

moon phases / fases lunares: cambio en la apariencia de la Luna, vista desde la Tierra, debido a la revolución de la Luna alrededor de la Tierra. (Cap. 17, Sec. 2, pág. 489)

mutation / mutación: cualquier cambio permanente en un gene o cromosoma de una célula; puede ser beneficioso, perjudicial o puede tener un efecto mínimo en un organismo. (Cap. 8, Sec. 3, pág. 228)

mutualism / mutualismo: tipo de relación simbiótica en que ambos organismos se benefician. (Cap. 12, Sec. 3, pág. 346)

N

natural frequency / frecuencia natural: frecuencia a la cual vibra un instrumento musical u otro objeto cuando se puntea o se perturba, con relación a su tamaño, forma y el material del cual está hecho. (Cap. 21, Sec. 2, pág. 615)

nebula / nebulosa: nube de gases y partículas de polvo que rotan y de la cual puede haberse formado el sistema solar hace unos 5 billones de años. (Cap. 17, Sec. 3, pág. 503)

nephron / nefrón: una diminuta unidad filtradora del riñón. (Cap. 6, Sec. 2, pág. 165)

neutron / neutrón: partícula sin carga eléctrica ubicada en el núcleo del átomo. (Cap. 18, Sec. 1, pág. 520)

niche / nicho: en un ecosistema, se refiere a la manera en particular en que un organismo sobrevive, obtiene alimentos y refugio y evita peligros. (Cap. 12, Sec. 3, pág. 347)

nitrogen cycle / ciclo del nitrógeno: modelo que describe cómo se mueve el nitrógeno de la atmósfera al suelo, pasando luego a los organismos vivos y, finalmente, de regreso a la atmósfera. (Cap. 13, Sec. 2, pág. 370)

nitrogen fixation / fijación del nitrógeno: proceso en el cual algunos tipos de bacterias que se hallan en el suelo convierten el gas de nitrógeno en una forma de nitrógeno que pueden usar las plantas. (Cap. 13, Sec. 2, pág. 370)

nucleus / núcleo: organelo que controla todas las actividades de una célula y que contiene el material hereditario compuesto por proteínas y DNA. (Cap. 3, Sec. 1, pág. 72)

O

orbit / órbita: trayectoria curva que sigue la Tierra en su movimiento alrededor del Sol. (Cap. 17, Sec. 1, pág. 483)

organ / órgano: estructura, como el corazón, compuesta por tipos diferentes de tejidos que funcionan en conjunto. (Cap. 3, Sec. 1, pág. 77)

organelle / organelo: estructura en el citoplasma de una célula eucariota que puede actuar como lugar de almacenamiento, puede procesar energía, mover materiales o elaborar sustancias. (Cap. 3, Sec. 1, pág. 72)

organic compounds / compuestos orgánicos: los compuestos que siempre contienen hidrógeno y carbono; los carbohidratos, los lípidos, las proteínas y los ácidos nucleicos son compuestos orgánicos que se encuentran en los seres vivos. (Cap. 4, Sec. 1, pág. 102)

osmosis / ósmosis: tipo de transporte pasivo que se lleva a cabo cuando el agua se difunde a través de la membrana celular. (Cap. 4, Sec. 2, pág. 108)

ovary / ovario: base hinchada del pistilo de una angiosperma donde se hallan los óvulos productores de huevos. (Cap. 9, Sec. 3, pág. 253)

ovary / ovario: órgano reproductor femenino que produce óvulo; se encuentra ubicado en la parte inferior del cuerpo. (Cap. 10, Sec. 2, pág. 277)

overtones / sobretonos: múltiplos de la frecuencia fundamental. (Cap. 21, Sec. 2, pág. 617)

ovulation / ovulación: proceso mensual en que un ovario libera un óvulo que entra en el oviducto donde un espermatozoide puede fecundarlo. (Cap. 10, Sec. 2, pág. 277)

ovule / óvulo: en las plantas gimnospermas, la parte reproductora femenina, la cual produce huevos y tejidos almacenadores de alimento. (Cap. 9, Sec. 3, pág. 251)

P

Pangaea / Pangaea: masa de tierra extensa y antigua que una vez estuvo formada por el conjunto de todos los continentes. (Cap. 14, Sec. 1, pág. 392)

parasitism / parasitismo: tipo de relación simbiótica en que un organismo se beneficia y el otro organismo es perjudicado. (Cap. 12, Sec. 3, pág. 346)

passive transport / transporte pasivo: movimiento de sustancias a través de la membrana celular que no involucra el uso de energía celular; incluye la difusión, la ósmosis y la difusión facilitada. (Cap. 4, Sec. 2, pág. 106)

pharynx / faringe: región en forma de conducto por donde pasan los alimentos, los líquidos y el aire. (Cap. 6, Sec. 1, pág. 156)

phenotype / fenotipo: apariencia física externa y comportamiento de un organismo. (Cap. 11, Sec. 1, pág. 304)

pheromone / feromona: poderosa sustancia química producida por un animal para influir sobre el comportamiento de otro animal de la misma especie. (Cap. 7, Sec. 2, pág. 189)

photoperiodism / fotoperiodismo: reacción de una planta a la duración de horas de luz y oscuridad cada día. (Cap. 5, Sec. 2, pág. 142)

photosynthesis / fotosíntesis: proceso mediante el cual las plantas y muchos otros productores utilizan la energía luminosa del Sol para elaborar azúcares que pueden usar como alimento. (Cap. 4, Sec. 3, pág. 114; Cap. 5, Sec. 1, pág. 131)

physical change / cambio físico: cambio que experimenta la forma o apariencia de una sustancia pero sin alterar su composición. (Cap. 19, Sec. 2, pág. 552)

physical property / propiedad física: característica que se puede observar usando los cinco sentidos, sin alterar o tratar de alterar la composición de una sustancia. (Cap. 19, Sec. 1, pág. 546)

pistil / pistilo: órgano reproductor femenino que se encuentra dentro de la flor de las angiospermas; consta de un estigma pegajoso (donde aterrizan los granos de polen) y de un ovario. (Cap. 9, Sec. 3, pág. 253)

pitch / tono: el grado de agudeza o gravedad de un sonido. (Cap. 21, Sec. 1, pág. 608)

plate / placa: región extensa del manto superior rígido y de la corteza oceánica o continental de la Tierra que se mueve sobre la astenosfera. (Cap. 14, Sec. 3, pág. 400)

plate tectonics / tectónica de placas: teoría que afirma que la corteza y el manto superior terrestres se separan en placas que flotan y se mueven sobre una capa viscosa del manto. (Cap. 14, Sec. 3, pág. 400)

pollen grain / grano de polen: estructura pequeña producida por los órganos reproductores masculinos de una planta de semilla; posee un revestimiento resistente al agua, se puede desarrollar a partir de una espora y contiene partes gametofitas que producen espermatozoides. (Cap. 9, Sec. 3, pág. 249)

pollination / polinización: traspaso de los granos de polen a la parte femenina de una planta de semilla efectuado por agentes como la gravedad, el agua, el viento y los animales. (Cap. 9, Sec. 3, pág. 249)

polygenic inheritance / herencia poligénica: la que ocurre cuando un grupo de pares de genes actúan en conjunto y producen un rasgo específico; por ejemplo el color de los ojos, el color del cabello, el color de la piel o la estatura de los seres humanos. (Cap. 11, Sec. 2, pág. 310)

population / población: todos los organismos que pertenecen a la misma especie y que viven en una comunidad. (Cap. 12, Sec. 1, pág. 334)

precision / precisión: describe el grado de aproximación de las medidas entre sí y el grado de exactitud con que se tomaron tales medidas. (Cap. 2, Sec. 1, pág. 40)

pregnancy / embarazo: período de desarrollo, generalmente cerca de 38 ó 39 semanas en los seres humanos, a partir de un óvulo fecundado hasta el nacimiento. (Cap. 10, Sec. 3, pág. 282)

producer / productor: organismo que utiliza fuentes externas de energía como el Sol, para fabricar moléculas ricas en energía; por ejemplo, las plantas o algas verdes. (Cap. 12, Sec. 3, pág. 344)

prothallus / protalo: forma vegetal gametofita de un helecho, pequeña, verde y en forma de corazón, capaz de producir su propio alimento y absorber agua y nutrientes del suelo. (Cap. 9, Sec. 2, pág. 246)

proton / protón: partícula con carga positiva ubicada en el núcleo de un átomo. (Cap. 18, Sec. 1, pág. 520)

Punnett square / cuadrado de Punnett: instrumento que se usa para predecir ciertos rasgos en la progenie, que muestra las distintas maneras en que los alelos se pueden combinar. (Cap. 11, Sec. 1, pág. 304)

R

radiant energy / energía radiante: energía que transportan las ondas electromagnéticas. (Cap. 22, Sec. 1, pág. 638)

radio waves / ondas radiales: ondas electromagnéticas de la más baja frecuencia que transportan la menor cantidad de energía y las cuales se utilizan en casi todas las formas de telecomunicaciones, por ejemplo, en los televisores, en los teléfonos y en los radios. (Cap. 22, Sec. 2, pág. 640)

rate / tasa: razón de dos clases distintas de medidas. (Cap. 2, Sec. 2, pág. 50)

recessive / recesivo: describe un rasgo que es cubierto o dominado por otra forma de ese rasgo y, por lo tanto, parece desaparecer. (Cap. 11, Sec. 1, pág. 302)

reflecting telescope / telescopio reflector: usa un espejo cóncavo para recoger la luz de cuerpo distantes. (Cap. 23, Sec. 4, pág. 683)

reflection / reflexión: ocurre cuando una onda choca contra un cuerpo o una superficie y rebota. (Cap. 20, Sec. 3, pág. 587; Cap. 23, Sec. 1, pág. 665)

reflex / reflejo: comportamiento innato simple, como bostezar o parpadear, que es una respuesta automática y que no involucra el envío de un mensaje al encéfalo. (Cap. 7, Sec. 1, pág. 181)

refracting telescope / telescopio refractor: usa dos lentes convexas para recoger la luz y formar una imagen de un cuerpo distante. (Cap. 23, Sec. 4, pág. 682)

refraction / refracción: desviación de una onda a medida que se mueve de un medio a otro. (Cap. 20, Sec. 3, pág. 588; Cap. 23, Sec. 3, pág. 677)

resonance / resonancia: amplificación sonora que ocurre cuando un cuerpo vibra a su frecuencia natural al absorber energía de una onda sonora u otro cuerpo que vibra a esa misma frecuencia. (Cap. 21, Sec. 2, pág. 616)

respiration / respiración: serie de reacciones químicas utilizadas para liberar la energía almacenada en las moléculas de los alimentos. (Cap. 4, Sec. 3, pág. 115; Cap. 5, Sec. 1, pág. 133)

reverberation / reverberación: ecos de sonidos repetidos. (Cap. 21, Sec. 2, pág. 621)

revolution / revolución: movimiento de la Tierra alrededor del Sol, el cual toma unos 365 1/4 días, o sea, un año en completarse. (Cap. 17, Sec. 1, pág. 483)

rhizome / rizoma: tallo subterráneo de un helecho. (Cap. 9, Sec. 2, pág. 246)

ribosome / ribosoma: estructura pequeña en la cual las células producen sus propias proteínas. (Cap. 3, Sec. 1, pág. 74)

rift / dislocación: grieta larga que se forma entre placas tectónicas que se están separando en los límites de placas. (Cap. 15, Sec. 3, pág. 437)

RNA / RNA: ácido ribonucleico que lleva consigo los códigos para la elaboración de proteínas del núcleo a los ribosomas. (Cap. 8, Sec. 3, pág. 226)

rotation / rotación: movimiento giratorio de la Tierra sobre su eje que causa el día y la noche; la Tierra tarda 24 horas en completar una rotación completa. (Cap. 17, Sec. 1, pág. 482)

S

salinity / salinidad: medida de la cantidad de sales disueltas en el agua marina. (Cap. 16, Sec. 1, pág. 454)

science / ciencia: proceso que se usa para investigar lo que ocurre a nuestro alrededor, con el propósito de resolver problemas o responder preguntas; forma parte de la vida cotidiana. (Cap. 1, Sec. 1, pág. 6)

scientific methods / métodos científicos: maneras de resolver problemas que pueden incluir la planificación paso por paso, la confección de modelos y experimentos programados cuidadosamente. (Cap. 1, Sec. 2, pág. 13)

seafloor spreading / expansión del suelo marino: teoría de Hess que afirma que el nuevo suelo marino se forma cuando el magma es forzado a subir a la superficie en una dorsal medioceánica. (Cap. 14, Sec. 2, pág. 397)

seismic safe / seguridad sísmica: describe la capacidad de las estructuras de soportar las vibraciones que causa un terremoto. (Cap. 15, Sec. 1, pág. 427)

seismic waves / ondas sísmicas: ondas sísmicas, que incluyen las ondas primarias, las secundarias y las ondas de superficie. (Cap. 15, Sec. 1, pág. 422)

seismograph / sismógrafo: instrumento que se utiliza para registrar las ondas sísmicas. (Cap. 15, Sec. 1, pág. 423)

semen / semen: mezcla de espermatozoides y un líquido que ayuda a los espermatozoides a moverse y que les sirve como fuente de energía. (Cap. 10, Sec. 2, pág. 276)

sex-linked gene / gene ligado al sexo: un alelo heredado en un cromosoma del sexo y que puede causar trastornos genéticos, como por ejemplo, el daltonismo o la hemofilia. (Cap. 11, Sec. 2, pág. 313)

sexual reproduction / reproducción sexual: tipo de reproducción en que dos células sexuales, por lo general un óvulo y un espermatozoide, se unen formando un cigoto, el cual se desarrolla en un nuevo organismo con su propia identidad. (Cap. 8, Sec. 2, pág. 218)

shield volcano / volcán de escudo: volcán extenso y ancho y de laderas levemente inclinadas que se forma de la acumulación de capas basálticas. (Cap. 15, Sec. 2, pág. 432)

short-day plant / planta de día corto: planta que necesita, por lo general, noches largas (12 ó más horas de oscuridad) para comenzar el proceso de floración. (Cap. 5, Sec. 2, pág. 142)

SI / SI: Sistema internacional de unidades, relacionado por múltiplos de diez, que permite que las cantidades se midan de la misma manera exacta en todo el mundo. (Cap. 2, Sec. 2, pág. 46)

social behavior / comportamiento social: se dice de las interacciones entre los miembros de la misma especie; incluye el comportamiento de cortejo, el apareo, la obtención de alimentos, el cuidado de las crías y la protección mutua. (Cap. 7, Sec. 2, pág. 186)

society / sociedad: grupo de animales de la misma especie que viven y trabajan juntos de manera organizada en la que cada cual realiza una tarea específica. (Cap. 7, Sec. 2, pág. 187)

soil / suelo: mezcla de partículas minerales y rocosas, restos de organismos muertos, aire y agua que forma la capa superior de la corteza terrestre y que sostiene el crecimiento vegetal. (Cap. 13, Sec. 1, pág. 362)

solar eclipse / eclipse solar: ocurre durante la luna nueva, cuando el Sol, la Luna y la Tierra se encuentran alineados de una forma específica y la Tierra se mueve dentro de la sombra de la Luna. (Cap. 17, Sec. 2, pág. 491)

solar system / sistema solar: sistema extremadamente grande que incluye el Sol, los planetas, los cometas, los meteo roides y otros cuerpos que orbitan el Sol. (Cap. 17, Sec. 3, pág. 496)

solstice / solsticio: época cuando el Sol alcanza su mayor distancia al norte o al sur del ecuador; ocurre el 21 ó el 22 de junio en el hemisferio norte (el día más largo del año) y el 21 ó 22 de diciembre en el hemisferio sur (el día más corto del año en el hemisferio norte). (Cap. 17, Sec. 1, pág. 484)

solution / solución: tipo de mezcla en que una sustancia se mezcla completa y uniformemente con otra y que es idéntica en toda su extensión. (Cap. 18, Sec. 2, pág. 527)

sori / soros: estructuras de los helechos en los cuales se producen las esporas. (Cap. 9, Sec. 2, pág. 246)

sperm / espermatozoide: célula sexual haploide formada en los órganos reproductores masculinos. (Cap. 8, Sec. 2, pág. 218; Cap. 10, Sec. 2, pág. 276)

spores / esporas: células haploides producidas en la etapa gametofita que se puede dividir mediante la mitosis y pueden formar estructuras vegetales o una planta nueva completa o que se puede desarrollar en células sexuales. (Cap. 9, Sec. 1, pág. 243)

sporophyte stage / etapa esporofita: etapa del ciclo de vida vegetal que comienza cuando un espermatozoide fecunda un huevo. (Cap. 9, Sec. 1, pág. 243)

stamen / estambre: órgano reproductor masculino que se encuentra dentro de la flor de las angiospermas; consta de una antera (donde se forman los granos de polen) y de un filamento. (Cap. 9, Sec. 3, pág. 253)

stomata / estomas: aberturas microscópicas de la epidermis de las plantas a través de las cuales los gases de dióxido de carbono y vapor de agua entran y salen de una hoja. (Cap. 5, Sec. 1, pág. 129)

surface current / corriente de superficie: una corriente oceánica accionada por el viento; este tipo de corriente se mueve horizontalmente, paralela a la superficie de la Tierra y solamente mueve unos pocos cientos de los metros superiores del agua marina. (Cap. 16, Sec. 2, pág. 456)

symbiosis / simbiosis: cualquier relación estrecha entre especies, incluye el mutualismo, el comensalismo y el parasitismo. (Cap. 12, Sec. 3, pág. 346)

T

table / tabla: despliega información en hileras y columnas facilitando la lectura y comprensión de los datos. (Cap. 2, Sec. 3, pág. 53)

technology / tecnología: aplicación de la ciencia para fabricar productos y herramientas útiles, como por ejemplo, las computadoras. (Cap. 1, Sec. 1, pág. 9)

testes / testículos: órgano masculino productor de espermatozoides y testosterona. (Cap. 10, Sec. 2, pág. 276)

tidal range / amplitud de la marea: la diferencia entre el nivel del océano en pleamar y su nivel en bajamar. (Cap. 16, Sec. 3, pág. 466)

tide / marea: ascenso y descenso del nivel del mar provocado, en su mayor parte, por la interacción de la gravedad en el sistema Tierra-Luna. (Cap. 16, Sec. 3, pág. 465)

tissue / tejido: grupo de células semejantes que funcionan juntas para efectuar una tarea. (Cap. 3, Sec. 1, pág. 77)

trachea / tráquea: conducto transportador de aire que une la laringe con los bronquios; este conducto está forrado de membranas mucosas y cilios y contiene anillos cartilaginosos resistentes. (Cap. 6, Sec. 1, pág. 157)

transverse wave / onda transversal: tipo de onda mecánica en la cual la energía de la onda hace que la materia del medio suba o baje u oscile formando ángulos rectos con la dirección en que viaja la onda. (Cap. 20, Sec. 1, pág. 578)

tropism / tropismo: reacción positiva o negativa a un estímulo externo como el tacto, la luz o la gravedad. (Cap. 5, Sec. 2, pág. 138)

trough / seno: es el punto más bajo de una onda. (Cap. 16, Sec. 3, pág. 462)

tsunami / tsunami o maremoto: onda marina sísmica de gran intensidad que comienza sobre un terremoto del suelo oceánico; puede alcanzar 30 m de altura cuando se aproxima a tierra y puede causar destrucción en las zonas costeras. (Cap. 15, Sec. 1, pág. 425)

U

ultraviolet radiation / radiación ultravioleta: ondas electromagnéticas con frecuencias más altas y longitudes de onda más cortas que la luz visible. (Cap. 22, Sec. 2, pág. 643)

upwelling / corriente de aguas resurgentes: circulación del océano que lleva agua fría y profunda a la superficie oceánica. (Cap. 16, Sec. 2, pág. 459)

ureter / uréter: conducto que transporta la orina desde los riñones hasta la vejiga. (Cap. 6, Sec. 2, pág. 166)

urethra / uretra: conducto que transporta la orina desde la vejiga y la expulsa del cuerpo. (Cap. 6, Sec. 2, pág. 166)

urinary system / sistema urinario: sistema de órganos excretores que elimina los residuos de la sangre, controla el volumen sanguíneo al eliminar el exceso de agua y mantiene el equilibrio en las concentraciones de sal y agua. (Cap. 6, Sec. 2, pág. 163)

urine / orina: líquido residual que contiene el exceso de agua, sales y otros residuos que el cuerpo no reabsorbe. (Cap. 6, Sec. 2, pág. 164)

uterus / útero: órgano hueco, muscular y con forma de pera donde un óvulo fecundado se desarrolla hasta convertirse en un bebé. (Cap. 10, Sec. 2, pág. 277)

V

vagina / vagina: conducto muscular que conecta el extremo inferior del útero con la parte externa del cuerpo; el canal del nacimiento por el cual pasa el bebé cuando está naciendo. (Cap. 10, Sec. 2, pág. 277)

virus / virus: hebra de material hereditario rodeada por una capa proteíca. (Cap. 3, Sec. 3, pág. 84)

visible light / luz visible: ondas electromagnéticas con longitudes de onda entre 0.4 y 0.7 millonésimas de metro y las cuales se pueden ver a simple vista. (Cap. 22, Sec. 2, pág. 642)

volcano / volcán: montaña o colina cónica que se forma por la emisión de magma caliente, sólidos y gases a la superficie terrestre a través de una chimenea. (Cap. 15, Sec. 2, pág. 429)

W

water cycle / ciclo del agua: modelo que describe cómo se mueve el agua de la superficie de la Tierra a la atmósfera para regresar nuevamente a la superficie a través de la evaporación, condensación y precipitación. (Cap. 13, Sec. 2, pág. 369)

wave / onda: perturbación rítmica que transporta energía pero no materia. (Cap. 16, Sec. 3, pág. 462; Cap. 20, Sec. 1, pág. 576)

wavelength / longitud de onda: en las ondas transversales, es la distancia entre la parte superior de dos crestas adyacentes o la parte inferior de dos senos adyacentes; en las ondas de compresión, es la distancia desde los centros de rarefacciones adyacentes. (Cap. 20, Sec. 2, pág. 582)

X

X ray / rayo X: onda electromagnética de alta frecuencia que es muy penetrante y la cual se usa en el diagnóstico médico. (Cap. 22, Sec. 2, pág. 644)

Z

zygote / cigoto: nueva célula diploide que se forma cuando un espermatozoide fecunda un óvulo; se divide mediante mitosis y se desarrolla en un nuevo organismo. (Cap. 8, Sec. 2, pág. 218)

Index

The index for *Glencoe Science* will help you locate major topics in the book quickly and easily. Each entry in the index is followed by the number of the pages on which the entry is discussed. A page number given in boldfaced type indicates the page on which that entry is defined. A page number given in italic type indicates a page on which the entry is used in an illustration or photograph. The abbreviation *act.* indicates a page on which the entry is used in an activity.

A

Abdominal thrusts, 158–159, *159, act.* 170–171

Abiotic factors, 360–367, *360;* air, 361; climate, 365–366, *365, 366;* soil, 362, *act.* 367; sunlight, 362, *362;* temperature, 363–364, *363, 364;* water, 361, *361*

Abscisic acid, 140

Accuracy, 36, *39,* 40, **41**–43, *41, 42*

Active transport, 109, *109*

Active viruses, 85, *85*

Activities, 12, 28–29, 51, 56–57, 78, 88–89, 112, 118–119, 136, 144–145, 169, 170–171, 195, 196–197, 217, 230–231, 248, 260–261, 280, 290–291, 307, 318–319, 349, 350–351, 367, 378–379, 399, 410–411, 435, 442–443, 469, 470–471, 495, 504–505, 529, 536–537, 551, 562–563, 586, 594–595, 614, 624–625, 648, 654–655, 675, 686–687

Adenine, 225

Adolescence, 286, 288

Adulthood, 286, 288–289, *288, 289*

Aerobic respiration, 133, 134, *134,* 135

Aggression, 188

Agriculture: and nitrogen fixation, 370, *370*

Air: as abiotic factor in environment, 361; oxygen in, 154, *154*

Albumin, 167

Algae: mutualism and, 346, *346;* as producers, *344*

Alleles, 300, *301,* 304; multiple, 309

Alligators, *348*

Alveoli, *156,* **157,** *157*

Amino acids: in protein synthesis, 227, *227*

Amniotic sac, 283

Amplitude, 462, **581**–582, *581, 582,* 607, *607*

Amplitude modulation (AM), 650

Anaphase, 212, *213,* 220, *220, 221, 223*

Angiosperms, 252–256, *253, 254, 255, 256*

Animal(s): aggression in, 188; communication of, *act.* 179, 188–192, *188, 190, 191;* competition among, 336, *336;* conditioning of, 184, *184;* cooperation among, 348; courtship behavior of, 189, *189;* cyclic behavior of, 192–195, *192, 193, 194, act.* 195; food chain and, 375, *375;* habitats of, 335, *335,* 347, *347, act.* 196–197, *196, 197;* hibernation of, 193, *193;* imprinting of, 183, *183;* innate behavior of, 181–182, *181, 182;* instincts of, 182, *182,* 186; learned behavior of, 182–185, *182, 183, 184, 185;* migration of, 194, *194,* 341; reflexes of, 181; reproduction of, 210, *210,* 211, 212, *213,* 214, *214;* social behavior of, 186–187, *186, 187;*

submission in, 188, *188;* territorial behavior of, 187, *187*

Animal cell, *73*

Appendices. *see* Reference Handbook

Asexual reproduction, 215–216, *215, 216,* 240, *240,* 241, *241,* 246, *246*

Asteroid, *496,* **502,** 506–507

Asteroid belt, *496,* 502

Asthenosphere, 400

Asthma, 162

Astronauts, *494*

Astronomical unit (AU), 496

Astronomy Integration, 47, 557, 610, 650

Atmosphere, 361; as abiotic factor in environment, 361; oxygen in, 154, *154;* of planets, 498, 499, 500, 501, *501*

Atom(s), 98, **518,** *518;* interactions of, 523–524, *523, 524;* model(s) of, *98,* 520, *520;* nucleus of, 520, *520*

Atomic mass, 521

Atomic number, 521

Atomic theory of matter, 520

Auxin, 140, *140*

Axis, 482, *482, 483,* 484, *484, 485*

B

Bacteria: shapes of, *70*

Bacteriophage, 68, 86

Bar graph, 54, *54, 55*

Basin(s), 453, *453*

Index

Index

Index

Index

Index

Lodestone, 549, *549*
Long-day plants, 142
Loudness, 606, 607, *607*
Louse, *68*
Low tide, 465, 466, *466*, 467, 468
Lunar eclipse, 481, *481*, **492,** *492*
Lung(s), *156*, 157, 158, *158*; diseases of, 160–162, *161, 162*
Lung cancer, 160, 162, *162*

M

Magma, 431, 433; silica-rich, 431
Magnetic field(s), 635, *636*; of Earth, 397–398, *398*; seafloor spreading and, 397–398, *398*
Magnetic properties, 549, *549*
Magnetic time scale, 398
Magnetite, 398
Magnetometer, 398
Magnifying glass, *act.* 69, 82
Magnitude, 423, 425
Male reproductive system, 276, *276*
Mantle: of Earth, 405, *405*
Mantle: of the Moon, 487, *487*
Maria, 486
Mars, 333, 498, *498*
Mars: changing states of matter on, 535, *535*
Mass, 49, *49*; atomic, 521; conservation of, 561, *561*
Mass number, 521
Math Skill Handbook, 728–734
Math Skills Activities, 44, 76, 104, 139, 258, 271, 305, 364, 440, 460, 531, 558, 651
Matter, 516–537, **518;** appearance of, 547, *547*; atomic theory of, 520; atoms, 98, *98*, 521; chemical properties of, 524; classifying, 527; compounds, 100, *100*, 103–105; describing, 546–551, *act.* 551; elements. *see* Element(s); exploring, 528, *528*; inorganic compounds, 103–105; ions, 100–101, *101*;

light, 665–666, *665, 666*; mixtures, 101, *101*; molecules, 100, *100*; organic compounds, 102–103; physical properties of, *act.* 529, 530, *530*, 534, *534*; states of. *see* States of matter; structure of, 519
Measurement, 36–57, **38,** *act.* 5; accuracy of, 36, 39, *39*, 40–43, *41, 42*; of earthquakes, 423–424, *423, 424*, 425; estimation vs., 39–40, *40*; of length, *act.* 37, 43, 46, 47, *47*; of loudness, 607, *607*; of mass, 49, *49*; of movement along faults, 428, *428*; of physical properties, *act.* 529; as physical property, 548; precision of, 40–43, *41, 42*, 44; rounding, 43, 44; in SI, 46–50, *act.* 51; of small object, *act.* 69; of speed, 50, *act.* 56–57; of temperature, 50, *50*; of time, 36, *36*, *41*, 50; units of, 46, 47, 48, 49, 50, 496; of volume, 48, *48*; of weight, 49, *49*
Mechanical waves, 577–579, *578*, 585
Medicine: ultrasound in, 613, *613*; X rays in, 645, *645*
Medium, 665
Meiosis, 219–223, *219, 220–221, 223*, 243
Melting, 553, *553*
Melting point, 548
Mendel, Gregor, 301–303, 304, 306
Menopause, 279, *279*
Menstrual cycle, 278–279, *278*
Mercury, 333, 497, *497*
Messenger RNA (mRNA), 227
Metabolism, 113, *113*
Metallic bonds, 526, *526*
Metaphase, 212, *213*, 220, *220, 221*, *221, 223*
Meteorite, 502
Meteoroid, 502
Meter, 47
Methane, 501, *501*

Microscopes, 79–82, *79*, *80–81*, *act.* 88–89, 681, *681*
Microwaves, 640, *640*, *act.* 654–655
Mid-Atlantic Ridge, 401, 406
Middle ear, 622, *622*
Migration, 194, *194*, 341
Millipedes, *347*
Mini LABs, Inferring from Pictures, 9; Measuring Accurately, 40; Modeling Cytoplasm, 72; Determining How Enzymes Work, 103; Inferring What Plants Need to Produce Chlorophyll, 131; Modeling Kidney Function, 165; Observing Conditioning, 184; Modeling Mitosis, 215; Observing Asexual Reproduction, 241; Graphing Hormone Levels, 278; Interpreting Polygenic Inheritance, 310; Comparing Biotic Potential, 341; Comparing Fertilizers, 371; Modeling Convection Currents, 405; Observing Deformation, 421; Modeling Water Particle Movement, 463; Modeling the Moon's Rotation, 488; Classifying Forms of Matter, 527; Classifying Matter, 548; Comparing Sounds, 579; Modeling a Stringed Instrument, 618; Observing the Focusing of Infrared Rays, 641; Forming an Image with a Lens, 682
Mirror(s): concave, 672, *672*, *673*, 683, *683*; convex, *672*, 674, *674*; plane, 671, *671*, *act.* 675
Mitochondria, 74, *74*, 115, 116, 133, 134, *134*, 135
Mitosis, 212–214, *212, 213, 214*, 215, *act.* 217
Mixture, 101, *101*
Mixtures, 527, *527*, 528, *528*

Index

Index

Index

Index

Feature, 501; Searching for Elements, 519; Comparing Changes, 555; Observing How Light Refracts, 588; Comparing and Contrasting Sounds, 606; Observing Electric Fields, 637; Observing Colors in the Dark, 665

Tsunami, 425, *426,* 582

Twins, 282, *282*

U

Ultrasound, 613, *613*

Ultraviolet (UV) radiation, 643–644, *644*

Umbilical cord, 283, 285

Umbra, 492

Universe: viewing, 648, *646, 648*

Upwelling, 459, *459*

Uranus, 501, *501*

Urea, 167

Ureter, 166

Urethra, *165,* **166,** 276, *276*

Urinary system, 163–166, *163;* diseases and disorders of, 167–168, *168;* organs of, 164–166, *165;* regulation of fluid levels by, 164, *164,* 166

Urine, 164, *164*

Use the Internet, 28–29, 230–231, 410–411

Uterus, 277, *277,* 278, *278, 280,* 282, 283, *283*

V

Vaccines, 86, 87

Vacuoles, 75

Vagina (birth canal), 277, *277,* 285

Vaporization, 553, *553*

Variables: dependent and independent, **21**

Vascular plants: seedless, 246, *247, act.* 248

Venus, 333, 498, *498*

Venus's-flytrap plant, 137, *137*

Vesicles, 276

Virchow, Rudolf, 83

Virus(es), 84–87; active, 85, *85;* effects of, 86; fighting, 86–87; latent, 85; reproduction of, 84, *85;* shapes of, 84, *84*

Visible light, 642, *643, 644*

Vision: and lenses, 679–680, *679, 680*

Visualizing. *see* National Geographic

Vitamin(s), 129

Vocal cords, *156,* 157, *act.* 603, 608

Voice: pitch of, *act.* 603, 608

Volcanoes, *418,* **429**–435; Earth's plates and, 429, *429,* 436–438; eruptions of, 430, *430,* 431, 433, *433,* 434, *act.* 435; formation of, 429–431, *429,* 437–438, *438;* formation of oceans and, 453, *453;* on other planets, 500; plate tectonics and, 402, 404, 407; risks of, 431, *431;* types of, 431–433, *432, 433*

Volume: measuring, 48, *48*

W

Waning, *489,* 490

Water, *533;* as abiotic factor in environment, 361, *361;* as compound, 100, *100,* 524, *524;* diffusion of, 108–109, *108;* freezing point of, 460; from hydrothermal vents, 375; leaving plant cells, *act.* 97, 108, *108;* in living things, 103, 104–105, *105;* loss in plants, *act.* 127, 129; molecule of, 525, *525,* 526, *526;* molecules of, 100, *100,* 105; in oceans. *see* Ocean water; states of, *act.* 517, 534, *534*

Water cycle, 52, *52,* 368–**369,** *368, 369*

Water waves, 590, *590. see also* Ocean waves

Watson, James, 225

Wave(s), 462, 574–595, **576;** amplitude of, 462, 581, *581,* 582, 607, *607;* behavior of, *act.* 575, 587–593; breakers, 463, *464;* carrier, **650,** *650;* compressional, 604–605, *604, 605, 578,* **579,** *act.* 586; crest of, 462, *462, 578, 578;* diffraction of, 589–590, *590,* 612, *612;* electromagnetic. *see* Electromagnetic waves; energy and, 462, *462, 463, 463, 464,* 576, *576;* frequency of, 583–584, *583, 584,* 605, 608, *608,* 615–616, *615,* 617, *617,* 637; height of, 462, *462, 464;* infrared, **641**–642, *642;* interference and, 591–593, *592, 593;* of light, 664–665, *664, 665;* mechanical, **577**–579, *578,* 585; microwaves, 640, *640;* model for, 577, *577;* ocean. *see* Ocean waves; properties of, 581–585, *583, 584, act.* 586; radio, **640**–641, *640, 641,* 649–650, *649, 650,* 651, 652, *652;* refraction of, 588–589, *588, 589;* seismic, **422**–423, *422, 424,* 440, *440, act.* 442–443; sound, 604–605, *604, 605,* 608, *608,* 612–613, *612, 613,* 616, *616,* 579, *579,* 581; speed of, 585, *act.* 594–595; tides and, 465–468, *466, 467, 468;* transverse, **578,** *578,* 581, *act.* 586; trough of, 462, *462, 578, 578;* tsunami, 425, *426,* 582; ultraviolet, **643**–644, *643;* water, 590, *590*

Wavelength, 462, *464*, **582**, *582*, 605, *605*, 608, *608*, 612, *612*, 637, *637*; diffraction and, 590, *590*; frequency and, 584
Waxing, 489, *489*
Wegener, Alfred, 392, 393
Weight: measuring, 49, *49*
Wide-angle lens, 685
Wildebeests, *338*
Williams, Daniel Hale, *26*
Wind: and Coriolis effect, 457, *457*; 365, *365*
Winter solstice, 484, *484*, 485
Wolves, 187, *188*
Woodpeckers, 335, *335*, 336, *336*
Woodwind instruments, 619, *619*, 620, *620*

X chromosome, 312, *312*
X rays, **644**–646, *645*, *646*

Y chromosome, 312, *312*
Yeast, 116, *116*

Zebras, 186, *186*
Zoom lens, 685
Zygote, **218**, *219*, 223, 281, 282, 283, *283*

INDEX 791

Credits

Credits

(bl)Troy Mary Parlee/Index Stock/PQ, (br)Jeffery Myers/Southern Stock/PQ; **228** Stewart Cohen/Stone; **230** (t)Tom McHugh/PR, (b)file photo; **231** Monica Dalmasso/Stone; **232** Philip Lee Harvey/Stone; **233** Lester V. Bergman/CB; **234** (l)Camille Tokerud/PR, (tr)John Mitchell/PR, (br)David Scharf/Peter Arnold, Inc.; **235** (l)D. Yeske/VU, (r)GH; **238** Noble Proctor/PR; **238–239** Layne Kennedy/CB; **239** DM; **240** (l)Stephen Dalton/PR, (r)MM; **241** (l)Holt Studios/Nigel Cattlin/PR, (r)Inga Spence/VU; **242** (l)H. Reinhard/Okapia/PR, (c)John W. Bova/PR, (r)John D. Cunningham/VU; **244** (l)Biology Media/PR, (c)Andrew Syred/Science Photo Library/PR, (r)Runk/Schoenberger from GH; **246 247** Kathy Merrifield 2000/PR; **248** MM; **249** (l)John Kaprielian/PR, (r)Scott Camazine/Sue Trainor/PR; **250** Dr. Wm. H. Harlow/PR; **251** Christian Grzimek/OKAPIA/PR; **252** (l)M.J. Griffith/PR, (c)Stephen P. Parker/PR, (r)Dan Suzio/PR; **253** (t)Rob Simpson/VU, (c)Gustav Verderber/VU, (b)Alvin E. Staffan/PR; **254** (tl)C. Nuridsany & M. Perennou/Science Photo Library/PR, (tr)Merlin D. Tuttle/PR, (bl)Anthony Mercreca Photo/PR, (bc)Kjell B. Sandved/PR, (br)Holt Studios LTD/PR; **255** William J. Weber/VU; **257** (tl)Kevin Shafer/CB, (c)Darryl Torckler/Stone, (bc)Tom & Pat Leeson, (others)Dwight Kuhn, **258 260** DM; **261** MM; **262** Michael Black/BC; **263** (t)courtesy NIGMS OCPL, (b)Kevin Laubacher/FPG; **264** (tl)Zig Leszczynski/ES, (bl)MM/Peter Arnold, Inc., (r)Tim Davis/PR; **265** (l)Nils Reinhard/OKAPIA/PR, (c)Adrienne T. Gibson/ES, (r)Oliver Meckes/PR; **266** Marcia Griffen/ES; **268** Profs. P.M. Motta & J. Van Blerkom/Science Photo Library/PR; **268–269** Brownie Harris/TSM; **269** John Evans; **270** David Young-Wolff/PE; **272 273** Stephen R. Wagner; **279** Ariel Skelley/TSM; **281** David M. Phillips/PR; **282** (l)Tim Davis/PR, (r)Chris Sorensen/TSM; **283** Science Pictures Ltd./Science Photo Library/PR; **284** Petit Format/Nestle/Science Source/PR; **286** (l)Jeffery W. Myers/SB, (r)Ruth Dixon; **287** (tl b)MB, (tr)AH; **288** KS; **289** (l)NASA/Roger Ressmeyer/CB, (r)AFP/CB; **290** (t)Chris Carroll/CB, (b)Richard Hutchings; **291** MM; **292** (l)John Banagan/The Image Bank, (c)Ron Kimball Photography, (r)SuperStock; **293** (l)Martin B. Withers/Frank Lane Picture Agency/CB, (r)Joe McDonald/CB; **294** (tl)DM, (bl)David M. Phillips/PR, (r)David Woods/TSM; **295** (l)Bob Daemmrich, (r)Maria Taglienti/The Image Bank; **298** David Phillips/Science Source/PR; **298–299** MB; **299** Geoff Butler; **300** Stewart Cohen/Stone; **303** Special Collections, National Agriculture Library, (bkgd)Jane Grushow from GH; **304** Barry L. Runk from GH; **306** Richard Hutchings/PR; **308** (t)Robert Maier/AA, (b)Gemma Giannini from GH; **309** Raymond Gehman/**CORBIS; 310** Dan McCoy from Rainbow; **311** (l)Phil Roach/Ipol, Inc., (r)CNRI/Science Photo Library/PR; **312** Gopal Murti/PhotoTake NYC; **313** Tim Davis/PR; **314** (l)Alan & Sandy Carey/PR, (r)Renee Stockdale/AA; **317** Tom Meyers/PR; **318** (t)Runk/Schoenberger from GH, (b)MB; **319** Laura Sefferlin; **321** KS; **322** David R. Frazier Photolibrary; **326** CB; **328–329** Joseph Sohm/ChromoSohm Inc./CB; **329** Andrew A. Wagner; **330** David Cavagnaro/DRK; **330–331** Johnny Johnson/DRK; **331** John D. Cunningham/VU; **332** (tl)Adam Jones/PR, (tc)Tom Van Sant/Geosphere Project, Santa Monica/Science Photo Library/PR, (tr)G. Carleton Ray/PR, (b)Richard Kolar/AA; **333** (t)John W. Bova/PR, (b)David Young/TSA; **335** (t)Zig Leszczynski/AA, (b)Mitsuaki Iwago/Minden Pictures; **339** Joel Sartore from GH; **341** (t)Norm Thomas/PR, (b)Maresa Pryor/ES; **342** (tl)Wyman P. Meinzer, (bl)Wyman P. Meinzer, (r)Bud Neilson/Words & Pictures/PQ; **344** (tl)Michael Abbey/PR, (tr)OSF/AA, (b)Michael P. Gadomski/PR; **345** (tlc)Larry Kimball/VU, (tr)George D. Lepp/PR, (bl)Lynn M. Stone, (blc)Stephen J. Krasemann/Peter Arnold, Inc., (brc)AMP, (others)William J. Weber; **346** (t)Milton Rand/TSA, (c)Marian Bacon/AA, (b)Sinclair Stammers/Science Photo Library/PR; **347** (t)Raymond A. Mendez/AA, (bl)Donald Specker/AA, (br)Joe McDonald/AA; **348** Ted Levin/AA; **349** Richard L. Carlton/PR; **350** (t)Jean Claude Revy/PhotoTake NYC, (b)OSF/AA; **351** Runk/Schoenberger from GH; **353** (l)courtesy US Census, (r)Eric Larravadieu/Stone; **354** (tl)Tui De Roy/Minden Pictures, (bl)Stephen J. Krasemann/DRK, (r)Maslowski/PR; **355** (l)C.K. Lorenz/PR, (r)Hans Pfletschinger/Peter Arnold, Inc.; **356** Scott Camazine/PR; **358** (t)Dr. Jeremy Burgess/Science Photo

Library/PR, (b)Jeff Greenberg/VU; **358–359** Steve Bly/International Stock; **360** Kenneth Murray/PR; **361** (t)Jerry L. Ferrara/PR, (b)Art Wolfe/PR; **362** (t)Telegraph Colour Library/FPG, (b)Hal Beral/VU; **363** (l)Fritz Polking/VU, (r)R. Arndt/VU; **364** Tom Uhlman/VU; **368** (l)Jim Grattan, (r)Bruce S. Cushing/VU; **371** (t)Rob & Ann Simpson/VU, (c b)Runk/Schoenberger from GH; **372** Stephen R. Wagner; **374** (l)WHOI/VU, (r)Wolfgang Baumeister/Science Photo Library/PR; **378** (t)MM, (b)Gerald and Buff Corsi/VU; **379** Jeff J. Daly/VU; **380** Gordon Wiltsie/Peter Arnold, Inc.; **382** (tl)Dwight Kuhn, (tr)Stephen J. Krasemann/DRK, (bl)Gregory K. Scott/PR, (br)Simon Battensby/Stone; **383** (l)Soames Summerhay/PR, (r)Tom Uhlman/VU; **388** (t)Ken Lucas/TCL/Masterfile, (b)Patrice Ceisel/SB/PQ; **388–389** Robert Burrington/Index stock; **389** (t)Hal Beral/Photo Network/PQ, (b)Archive Photos/PQ; **390** Francois Gohier/PR; **390–391** Stone; **391** MB; **394** Martin Land/Science Source/PR; **397** Ralph White/CB; **403** Davis Meltzer; **404** Craig Aurness/CB; **406** Craig Brown/Index Stock; **407** Ric Ergenbright/CB; **408** Roger Ressmeyer/CB; **410** Burhan Ozbilici/AP/Wide World Photos; **412** L. Lauber/ES; **413** Courtesy Ed Klimasauskas; **414** (l)courtesy Takeo Suzuki, UCLA, (r)Galen Rowell/CB; **415** (l)Tim Barnwen/SB, (r)Bettmann/CB; **418** JPL/NASA; **418–419** Jim Sugar Photography/CB; **419** AH; **420** KS; **423** (t)Krafft/Explorer/PR, (b)Jean Miele/TSM; **426** (t b)NOAA, (c)Lisa Bigazoli, (bkgd)Galen Rowell/CB; **427** (t)KS, (b)Pacific Seismic Products, Inc.; **428** Roger Ressmeyer/CB; **430** (l)AP/Wide World Photos, (r)Kevin West/AP/Wide World Photos; **432** (t)Breck P. Kent/ES, (b)Dewitt Jones/CB; **433** (t)Lynn Gerig/TSA, (b)Milton Rand/TSA; **435** Otto Hahn/Peter Arnold, Inc.; **436** Spencer Grant/PE; **438** NASA/Peter Arnold, Inc.; **442** AH; **443** AH; **444** (l)Ted Streshinky/CB, (r)Underwood & Underwood/CB; **444–445** Bettmann/CB, (bkgd)Russell D. Curtis/PR; **445** (l)Bettmann/CB, (r)Robert Holmes/CB; **446** (t)Roger Ressmeyer/CB, (b)Tom Walker/Stone; **447** (l)James L. Amos/CB, (c)Michael Collier, (r)Phillip Wallick/TSM; **450** Judy Griesedieck/CB; **450–451** Warren Bolster/Stone; **451** Raven/Explorer/PR; **452** (l)Norbert Wu/Peter Arnold, Inc., (r)Darryl Torckler/Stone; **454** Cathy Church/Picturesque/PQ; **457** Bob Daemmrich; **458** (t)Darryl Torckler/Stone, (b)Raven/Explorer/PR; **462** Jack Fields/PR; **463** Tom & Therisa Stack; **464** (l)Spike Mafford/PD, (r)Douglas Peebles/CB, (bkgd)Stephen R. Wagner; **465** Arnulf Husmo/Stone; **466** (tl)Groenendyk/PR, (tr)Patrick Ingrand/Stone, (b)Kent Knudson/SB; **469** AH; **470** (t)Mark E. Gibson/VU, (b)Timothy Fuller; **471** Timothy Fuller; **473** Seth Resnick/SB/PQ; **474** (t)Worldsat Productions/NRSC/Science Photo Library, (cl)Phillippe Diederich/Contact Press Images/PQ, (cr)S.J. Krasemann/Peter Arnold, Inc., (b)Stephen J. Krasemann/Peter Arnold, Inc.; **475** (l)Carl R. Sams II/Peter Arnold, Inc., (r)Edna Douthat; **478** Johnathan Blair/CB; **478–479** Jerry Schad/PR; **479** MM; **480** NASA/JPL; **481** Jerry Schad/P; **486 489** Lick Observatory; **491** CB; **493** (bl)Stephen Frisch/SB/PQ, (br)Stephen R. Wagner, (bkgd)NASA, (others)David Meltzer; **494** NASA; **495** Timothy Fuller; **497** NASA/JPL/Northwestern University; **498** (t)NASA/JPL, (b)Dr. Timothy Parker, JPL; **500** (l)CB, (r)Erich Karkoschka, University of Arizona, and NASA; **501** NASA/JPL; **502** (t)Dr. R. Albrecht, ESA/ESO Space Telescope European Coordinating Facility/NASA, (b)Frank Zullo/PR; **506** Kauko Helavuo/The Image Bank; **507** Charles & Josette Lenars/CB; **508** CB; **509** Lick Observatory; **512** Tom Bean/DRK; **514** CB/PQ; **514–515** Stephen Frisch/SB/PQ; **516** IBMRL/VU; **516–517** Roine Magnusson/Stone; **517** MM; **519** (t)Mark Schneider/Peter Arnold, Inc., (tcl)Dane S. Johnson/VU, (tcr)Ken Lucas/VU, (tr)Mark A. Schneider/PR, (bl)AH, (bcl)AMP, (bcr)Charles D. Winters/PR, (br)AH; **520** John Evans; **523** (l)Herbert Kehrer/OKAPIA/PR, (c)DM, (r)Bruce Hands/Stone; **524** Kenji Kerins; **526** Ken Whitmore/Stone; **527** AMP; **528** Stuart Westmorland; **530** John S. Lough/VU; **532** CB; **533** (t)Storm Pirate Productions/Artville/PQ, (c)Breck P. Kent/ES, (b)CB/PQ; **534** (t)Paul Chesley/Stone, (b)David Muench/CB; **535** NASA/JPL/Malin Space Science Systems; **536** (t)StudiOhio, (b)MM; **537** (t)Tim Courlas, (b)AH; **538** (t)Geoff Butler, (br)StudiOhio, (bl)KS; **539** Geoffrey Wheeler/NIST; **540** (tl)MM, (tr)Keith Kent/Science Photo Library,

Acknowledgments

From the book, *The Everglades: A River of Grass* 50th Anniversary Edition copyright © 1997 by Marjory Stoneham Douglas. Used by permission of Pineapple Press, Inc. The Excerpt from "Sunkissed: An Indian Legend" is reprinted with permission from the publisher of *Tun-ta-ca-tun* (Houston: Arte Publico Press–University of Houston, 1986). "Listening In" by Gordon Judge. Reprinted by permission of the author. "The Jungle of Ceylon" by Pablo Neruda, from PASSIONS AND IMPRESSIONS by Pablo Neruda, translated by Margaret Sayers Peden. Translation copyright © 1983 by Farrar, Straus & Giroux. Reprinted by permission of Farrar, Straus & Giroux. Excerpt from "Tulip" from *Turtle Blessing*, by Penny Harter, published by La Alameda Press, copyright © 1996 by Penny Harter. Reprinted by permission of the author. Excerpt from "The Creatures on my Mind," by Ursula K. Le Guin, from *Harper's* (August 1990). Copyright © 1990 by Ursula K. Le Guin. Reprinted by permission of the author and the author's agent, Virginia Kidd.

PERIODIC TABLE OF THE ELEMENTS

Columns of elements are called groups. Elements in the same group have similar chemical properties.

Element — Hydrogen
Atomic number — 1
Symbol — H
Atomic mass — 1.008
State of matter

Gas
Liquid
Solid
Synthetic

The first three symbols tell you the state of matter of the element at room temperature. The fourth symbol identifies human-made, or synthetic, elements.

Group	1	2	3	4	5	6	7	8	9
1	Hydrogen 1 **H** 1.008								
2	Lithium 3 **Li** 6.941	Beryllium 4 **Be** 9.012							
3	Sodium 11 **Na** 22.990	Magnesium 12 **Mg** 24.305							
4	Potassium 19 **K** 39.098	Calcium 20 **Ca** 40.078	Scandium 21 **Sc** 44.956	Titanium 22 **Ti** 47.867	Vanadium 23 **V** 50.942	Chromium 24 **Cr** 51.996	Manganese 25 **Mn** 54.938	Iron 26 **Fe** 55.845	Cobalt 27 **Co** 58.933
5	Rubidium 37 **Rb** 85.468	Strontium 38 **Sr** 87.62	Yttrium 39 **Y** 88.906	Zirconium 40 **Zr** 91.224	Niobium 41 **Nb** 92.906	Molybdenum 42 **Mo** 95.94	Technetium 43 **Tc** (98)	Ruthenium 44 **Ru** 101.07	Rhodium 45 **Rh** 102.906
6	Cesium 55 **Cs** 132.905	Barium 56 **Ba** 137.327	Lanthanum 57 **La** 138.906	Hafnium 72 **Hf** 178.49	Tantalum 73 **Ta** 180.948	Tungsten 74 **W** 183.84	Rhenium 75 **Re** 186.207	Osmium 76 **Os** 190.23	Iridium 77 **Ir** 192.217
7	Francium 87 **Fr** (223)	Radium 88 **Ra** (226)	Actinium 89 **Ac** (227)	Rutherfordium 104 **Rf** (261)	Dubnium 105 **Db** (262)	Seaborgium 106 **Sg** (266)	Bohrium 107 **Bh** (264)	Hassium 108 **Hs** (277)	Meitnerium 109 **Mt** (268)

The number in parentheses is the mass number of the longest lived isotope for that element.

Rows of elements are called periods. Atomic number increases across a period.

The arrow shows where these elements would fit into the periodic table. They are moved to the bottom of the page to save space.

Lanthanide series	Cerium 58 **Ce** 140.116	Praseodymium 59 **Pr** 140.908	Neodymium 60 **Nd** 144.24	Promethium 61 **Pm** (145)	Samarium 62 **Sm** 150.36
Actinide series	Thorium 90 **Th** 232.038	Protactinium 91 **Pa** 231.036	Uranium 92 **U** 238.029	Neptunium 93 **Np** (237)	Plutonium 94 **Pu** (244)